Handbook of the Canadian Rockies

SHORT CONTENTS LIST

Full table of contents
follows the front matter

Introduction *1*

Physiography *11*

Geology *37*

Weather and climate *247*

Ecology *265*

Botany *289*

Invertebrates (insects, etc.) *465*

Fishes *536*

Amphibians and reptiles *558*

Birds *567*

Mammals *667*

Historical outline *745*

Recreation *767*

Safety *813*

Maps *831*

Index *851*

Handbook
of the Canadian Rockies

Ben Gadd

Corax Press

Canadian Cataloguing in Publication Data

Gadd, Ben, 1946-
  Handbook of the Canadian Rockies

Includes index.
Bibliography: p.
ISBN 0-9692631-0-4

1. Natural history - Rocky Mountains, Canadian -
Guidebooks.* 2. Rocky Mountains, Canadian -
Description and travel - Guidebooks.* I. Title.

FC219.G34 1986   508.711   C86-090264-1
F1090.G34 1986

Corax Press
Box 1557, Jasper, Alberta, Canada T0E 1E0

Printed and bound in Canada by Hignell, Winnipeg

Cover
Looking west from Pyramid Lake to Roche Noire
in Jasper National Park (photo by Ben Gadd)

Title page
Interpretive drawing of same view
(pen-and-ink by Gordon Ingraham, 1986)

This book is for my parents,
Sam and Mary B. Gadd,
who would have liked it.

Preface

Someone had to write this book.

It was either that or keep lugging all those other books around. Bird books, flower books, tree books, fish books, snake books, bug books, geology books—filling up my pack, poking me with their sharp corners.

It's rough, being a naturalist.

Well, *Handbook of the Canadian Rockies* should ease the load somewhat. It gathers a great deal of relevant information—things I need to know to do my job properly—into a single volume that goes into a pack pocket (a *large* pack pocket, admittedly) and can stand some abuse.

Important here is what has been discarded: everything that lives somewhere else, or doesn't outcrop here or didn't happen here. Not to belittle the creeping vole of western Washington or the woodland jumping mouse of Ontario, but it's better not to have to flip through entries about them when trying to look up the little gray thing that is licking up the spilled soup in the corner of the cabin and will be gone in about 15 seconds.

This book is more than a field guide, however. In leisurely circumstances you may wish to read entire sections. For example: what about the pika? Does it really eat its own droppings? See page 703 for the answer. What is it like to climb Mt. Robson? Who discovered Banff Hot Springs? Forget about the leak in the tent for a while and read about how British Columbia collided with North America back in the Mesozoic.

Further, *Handbook of the Canadian Rockies* has advice to offer. I have been exploring these mountains for nearly 20 years, discovering places to go and things to do. A recreational chapter passes along some of what I have learned about hiking, climbing, skiing and bicycling here. A short section on safety seemed advisable as well.

I had one other idea in mind when I began this project: people who know the value of something are inclined to cherish and protect it. The Canadian Rockies—beautiful, savage, delicate, unique—are worthy indeed. See the afterword (page 829) for some current concerns about the status of the region, particularly the northern half.

Maybe this book will be good for the Rockies. I hope so.

Ben Gadd
Jasper, Alberta
July 21, 1986

Acknowledgments

My thanks to the many academic, government and private-sector specialists who checked drafts of the text, giving freely of their time in correcting my errors and omissions. The remaining mistakes are strictly my own. Some of these people supplied copies of their recent technical publications. I am grateful for this up-to-date information.

Geology

Jim Aitken, Wayne Bamber, Helmut Geldsetzer, Jim Monger, Ray Price, Don Stott, Geological Survey of Canada; Norm Catto, Vic Levson, Nat Rutter and Mel Reasoner, University of Alberta; Eric Mountjoy, McGill University; Brian Luckman and Chris Smart, University of Western Ontario; Martin Teitz, Dome Petroleum, Calgary. Special thanks to Jim Aitken and Brian Luckman for providing some illustrations.

Weather and climate

Ben Janz, Alberta Forest Service.

Botany

Julie Hrapko, Alberta Provincial Museum; Job Kuijt, University of Lethbridge; Leni Shalkwyk, Edmonton; Dale Vitt, University of Alberta. Special thanks to Job Kuijt for permission to reprint his botanical drawings, and to Dale Vitt for allowing me to publish his photos of lichens.

Insects

Syd Cannings, Chris Guppy and Jens Roland, University of British Columbia; Charles Dondale, Agriculture Canada; Norbert Kondla, Alberta Environment; H.R. Wong, Canadian Forestry Service.

Fishes

Brenda Dixon, British Columbia Fish and Wildlife; Joe Nelson, University of Alberta.

Reptiles and amphibians

Wayne Roberts, University of Alberta.

Birds

Roy Richards, Jasper; Kevin Van Tighem, Parks Canada, Jasper.

Mammals

Allan Brooks, Parks Canada; Lu Carbyn, Canadian Wildlife Service; Eldon Bruns, John Gunson, Orval Pall and Arlen Todd, Alberta Fish and Wildlife; Val Geist, University of Calgary; Brian Horesji, Western Wildlife Consultants, Calgary; Jan Murie, University of Alberta; Hugh Smith, Alberta Provincial Museum.

History

Hugh Dempsey, Glenbow Museum; Jim MacGregor, Edmonton; Cyndi Smith, Jasper.

First aid

Peter Callegari, M.D., Jasper.

Picture credits

Most of the illustrations in this book have come from other publications, reprinted with permission. Where many drawings came from the same source, the author, publisher and illustrator (if known) have been credited by placing a set of initials next to each borrowed picture. See the block credits below for matching initials with sources. Where only one or two items were used, they have been credited individually. Uncredited illustrations are by the author.

The author and publisher gratefully acknowledge permission to reprint as follows.

Archives of the Canadian Rockies (Whyte Museum, Banff): permission to reproduce historical photos from the Mary Schäffer collection.

The British Columbia Provincial Museum and T.C. Brayshaw: permission to reprint Dr. Brayshaw's drawings of willows from *Catkin Bearing Plants of British Columbia.* Key: *BCPM*

Canadian Society of Petroleum Geologists: permission to reproduce geological sketches appearing in *Geological Guide for the CSPG 1977 Waterton-Glacier Field Conference,* by P.L. Gordy, F.R. Frey and D.K. Norris. Key: *CSPG*

Canadian Wildlife Service: permission to reprint drawings of aquatic invertebrates in *Limnological Studies in Jasper National Park,* by R.S. Anderson and D.B. Donald. Key: *CWS*

Doubleday & Company, New York: permission to reprint drawings from *The Illustrated Encyclopedia of American Birds,* by Leon A. Hausman. Copyright 1944, 1947 by Doubleday & Company, Inc. Key: *DD*

W.H. Easton, University of Southern California, Los Angeles: permission to reprint fossil drawings in his *Invertebrate Paleontology,* published by Harper and Row in 1960. Key: *WE*

Fitzhenry & Whiteside, Toronto: permission to reprint tree profiles from *Native Trees of Canada,* copyright Minister of Supply and Services Canada, published by Fitzhenry & Whiteside. Key: *FW*

Geological Society of America and University Press of Kansas: permission to reprint fossil drawings from *Treatise on Invertebrate Paleontology,* courtesy of The Geological Society of America and University of Kansas. Key: *GSA*

Geological Survey of Canada, Ottawa: permission to reprint illustrations from several of their publications, credited individually. Special thanks to S. Conway Morris of the University of Cambridge, UK, coauthor of *Fossils of the Burgess Shale,* GSC Miscellaneous Report 43, 1985. Credit to Minister of Supply and Services, Canada. Key: *GSC*

Glacier Natural History Association: permission to reprint illustrations by Max Wade Averitt in *Mammals of Glacier National Park* (1955) by R.R. Lechleitner. Key: *GNHA*

Government of Canada: illustrations from *Freshwater Fishes of Canada,* reproduced by permission of the Minister of Supply and Services Canada. Key: *CAN*

Paul Johnsgard, University of Nebraska: drawings from his *Waterfowl of North America* (1975) published by Indiana University Press. Key: *PJ*

Massachusetts Fisheries and Wildlife, Westboro: drawings by Edward Forbush from *Game Birds, Wild-fowl and Shore Birds of Massachusetts and adjacent States* (1912), reproduced courtesy the Commonwealth of Massachusetts. Key: *MASS*

McGraw Hill Book Company, New York: illustrations by Robert Stebbins from *Amphibians and Reptiles of Western North America* (1954). Key: *MH*

National Museum of Natural Sciences, National Museums of Canada: drawings of mammal skulls from *The Mammals of Canada* (1974 edition) by A.W.F. Banfield. Key: *NMC*

Oxford University Press of Canada: drawings from *Mammals of Eastern Canada* (1966) by Randolph Peterson. Key: *OUP*

Ray Price, Geological Survey of Canada, Ottawa: sketches by Dr. Price and E. Fernando of the geology at various viewpoints in the Rockies, as originally presented in field guidebooks of the 1972 International Geological Congress. (Key: *RP*) A few of these drawings are by other geologists, individually credited when known.

University of Alberta Press and Job Kuijt, University of Lethbridge: drawings by Dr. Kuijt from his *A Flora of Waterton Lakes National Park* (1982), published by The University of Alberta Press. I highly recommend this book to anyone interested in Canadian Rockies botany. Key: *UAP*

University of Washington Press, Seattle: drawings from *Flora of the Pacific Northwest* (1973) by C.L. Hitchcock and Arthur Cronquist. Key: *UWP*

Others who helped

National parks of Canada and the United States: the interpretive services of Waterton/Glacier International Peace Park, Banff, Kootenay, Yoho and Jasper national parks provided information and access to documents, as well as some of the photos. Thanks particularly to Jim Todgham and the park naturalists at Jasper National Park, who let me use their library and special equipment.

Other provincial and federal agencies: The British Columbia Ministry of Lands, Parks and Housing, and Alberta Parks and Recreation, provided information on natural features and wildlife in provincial parks in the Rockies. Travel Alberta supplied some of the photographs. Provincial and state agencies provided population data for the table on page 766. Entomologists Patrick Schofield (Alberta Environment, Calgary) and Diane Szlabey (Canadian Forestry Service, Edmonton), helped with a couple of insect identifications and provided some illustrations.

The difficult geology chapter could not have been written without the help of the Geological Survey of Canada. Besides the GSC reviewers listed on page *vi,* my thanks to Rudy Klassen, Margo McMechan, Neil Ollerenshaw, Willy Norris, Alan Pedder, Dave Proudfoot, Art Sweet and Gordon Taylor.

David Scollard copy-edited the text, solving editorial problems and tossing out the worst of my patronizing remarks. Jose Botelho checked all the Latin genus and species names, so that they would go into my word-processor correctly, never to emerge misspelled (maybe).

Gordon Ingraham, my stepfather, produced the drawing on the title page and the symbols for the various chapters. My son Toby and his cousin Dylan Gadd cut out the 150 pieces of halftone masking material needed during paste-up, thereby learning something about offset printing and earning the gratitude of the chief paste-up artist at Corax Press. Toby also prepared the map index and set my computer back on the straight and narrow when it went awry.

Cia Gadd, my wife, helped to support this project throughout its four-year length, offering advice, showing forbearance, helping with the editing and keeping things together no matter what.

To all these people, my sincere thanks.

How to use this book

There are three ways:

1. Read it from the beginning. There is a summary there, to whet your appetite. *Handbook* is a multidisciplinary work with some depth, and it proceeds from one topic to the next in a manner that I hope is logical. Technical concepts and terms are explained along the way, so the book can be used as a textbook if desired. Possible course applications: geography, geology, ecology, environmental studies, outdoor education . . .

2. Use it to look things up, which is what I imagine most readers will do. For that there is a complete contents listing following this section and a detailed index at the back. If you come across an unfamiliar term or idea, check the index. Go to the first page number listed for that item; there you will find either the definition or a cross-reference to the appropriate page number. Most places mentioned in the text are found on the topographic maps, which begin on page 834. There is a special map index on pages 832 and 833.

3. Or just go browsing. The cross-references will help those who like to skip around in the various sections.

A suggestion to readers who will be using this volume in the outdoors: rounding off the corners (on the opening side of the book, of course) will keep it from getting overly dog-eared in your pack. Trimming the corners off is easy to do. Get a single-edged razorblade at a hardware store. Lay the book flat and shave the corners away by working the blade straight down. (Rounding the corners during printing was prohibitively expensive.)

References

Professional users of this book will note few references to the technical literature—except in the geological section, where so many reviewers demanded references that I agreed to insert some.

My apologies to those who would like to see referencing throughout the book, but as in other summary publications of this kind it just wasn't feasible to document every statement or to provide long technical bibliographies (again, the geological section is a special case and does include a technical bibliography). Please be assured that the information is as accurate and current as I could make it, double-checked by one or more specialists in each field. For persons wishing more information, the reading lists at the ends of the chapters will help; many of the publications listed there contain technical bibliographies.

Errors? Please let me know

This is the first edition, and like most other first editions it is bound to have mistakes. These can be corrected in the next edition, with the help of readers.

If you see something that is incorrect, I would like to hear about it.

Please contact me, Ben Gadd, at Box 1557, Jasper, Alberta T0E 1E0.

CONTENTS

INTRODUCTION *1*

Geography and geology *3*
Weather and climate *4*
Biology *4*
Humanity *6*
General guidebooks *9*

BOUNDARIES *11*

Eastern *11*
Western *11*
Northern *12*
Southern *12*
Comparison with American Rockies *12*
Names *14*

DIVIDING UP THE MOUNTAINS *15*

Central Rockies *15*

Foothills *16*
Mountain front *16*
Structural control
    in the front ranges *19*
Coal mining *21*
Trellis drainage and flash floods *21*
Eastern main ranges *22*
Continental divide *22*
Western main ranges *24*
Western ranges *25*
Summary *26*

Southern Rockies *27*

Lewis Thrust *27*
Foothills *28*
Mountain front *28*
Flathead Fault *30*
Summary *30*

Northern Rockies *31*

Plains margin *31*
Foothills *32*
Mountain front *32*
Purcell-like rock *32*
Main/front ranges *34*
Western slope *34*
Summary *36*

ROCKS AND EVENTS *37*

The four great layers *37*
Geology picture-pages *41*

• Correlation charts *42*
   Block diagrams *45*
   Geological map *47*
   Cross-sections *50*
   Roadside views *51*
   Fossils *67*

Using the listings *70*
Purcell Supergroup *71*

Waterton Formation
    and origin of limestone *72*
Altyn Formation *73*
Greyson/Appekunny Formation *73*
Spokane/Grinnell Formation *74*
Siyeh/Helena
    and Empire formations *74*
Purcell Sill, Lava, dykes *75*
Missoula Group *76*
Muskwa assemblage *77*

Miette and Misinchinka groups *77*

Metamorphism
    in the Miette Group *78*
Lower Miette *81*
Old Fort Point Formation *81*
Middle-Miette grits *83*
Upper Miette *85*
Byng Formation *85*
Misinchinka Group *86*

Crowfoot dyke and other
    minor intrusives *86*
Gog and Atan groups *88*

Origin of clastic rock *88*
Cross-bedding *89*
Making quartzite *89*
Worm burrows and fool's gold *90*
Mural, McNaughton
    and Mahto formations *91*
Peyto Formation *91*
Atan Group *91*

Early Paleozoic 93

   Middle Cambrian sandwich 93
   Mt. Whyte and Naiset formations 95
   Cathedral Formation
      and making dolomite 95
   Stephen Formation
      and Burgess Shale 98
   Eldon Formation 100
   Kicking Horse Rim 101
   Pika Formation 104
   Arctomys Formation 105
   Waterfowl Formation 106
   Sullivan Formation 106
   Lyell/Ottertail Formation 106
   Bison Creek Formation 108
   Mistaya Formation 109
   Lynx Group 110
   Survey Peak Formation 110
   Outram Formation 111
   Monkman, Tipperary quartzites 112
   Skoki Formation 112
   Owen Creek Formation 113
   Mt. Wilson Quartzite 113
   Tegart Formation 115
   Kechika Group 115
   Nonda Formation 116
   Shale belt 116
   Chancellor Group 116
   McKay Group 117
   Glenogle Shales 117

Sub-Devonian unconformity 120

   Muncho-McConnell Formation 123
   Wokkpash Formation 123
   Devonian maps 124
   Stone Formation 127
   Golden Embayment rocks 127

Devonian reefs and the
   Fairholme Group 128

   Flume Formation 131
   Cairn and Southesk formations 132
   Besa River and
      Perdrix formations 134
   Mt. Hawk Formation 135
   Simla and Ronde formations 135
   Sassenach Formation 136

Miss Devonian's sandwich 136

   Palliser Formation 138
   Exshaw Formation 139
   Banff Formation 140
   Rundle Group and equivalents 142

Weirdest rock in the Rockies 146

   Spray Lakes and Ishbel groups 146
   Making chert 148
   Making phosphate 149
   Ice River Alkaline Complex 150

Muddy Mesozoic and Tertiary 152

   Episode I 153
   Episode II 155
   Episode III 155
   Cretaceous seaway 155
   Spray River Group 157
   Fernie Formation 158
   Kootenay, Nikanassin
      and Minnes groups 160
   Cadomin Formation
      (basal Blairmore Group) 162
   Blairmore Group and equivalents,
      Dunvegan Formation 162
   Alberta Group 165
   Brazeau, Paskapoo
      and equivalent formations 165

Orogenous zones 168

   Foreigners 170
   Running into the dock 170
   Columbian and
      Laramide orogenies 171
   Up-piling and down-sagging 174
   Stacking from west to east 176
   Big slips 176
   Block-faulting
      in the southern
      Rocky Mountain Trench 177
   Summary 178

Looking at rock structures
   in the Rockies 180

   Faults tend to follow layering 180
   Always older-over-younger 180
   Faults cut up-section to east 182
   Normal faults in main ranges 182
   Tear faults 182
   Thrust faults have
      folds at each end 182
   S-shaped folds in front ranges 184
   Deformation of shale
      vs. massive layers 184
   Slippage during folding 184

After mountain-building
and before Pleistocene
ice advances *186*

Kishenehn Formation 186
St. Eugene Formation 187
Pre-glacial gravels
on eastern slope 187

Ice in the Rockies *189*

- *Glacial dates table 189*
- *Glacial correlation chart 191*
Early Pleistocene glaciation 192
Great Illinoian glaciation 192
Ice-free corridor 193
Strange stones
on front-range summits 195
Wisconsinan glaciation 196
Glacial history
in northern Rockies 202
Western slope 202
Foothills Erratics Train 202
Holocene glaciation,
Little Ice Age 204
What's next? 207

MODERN LANDSCAPE:
FEATURES AND
PROCESSES *209*

- Erosion processes list *209*
Icefields and glaciers *210*

Glacial budget and flow 212
Sub-glacial streams 214
Ice-cored moraines
and glacier caves 214
Crevasses—a warning 214

Rock glaciers *216*
Rockslides *216*
Waterfalls and canyons *219*
Caves and karst *221*
Springs, hot and otherwise *225*

Odors 225
Tufa 227
Mineral springs 227
Life in a hot spring 227
- *Hot springs table 228*

Rivers *231*
- Rivers table *232*
Lakes and lake colors *234*
Sand dunes *236*
Geology reading list *237*
Geological maps available *244*

Topographic maps available *245*
Satellite photos available *245*

WEATHER AND CLIMATE *247*

- Climate table *248*
Latitude and slope angle *251*
Shading *251*
Pacific influence *251*
- Day-length table *252*
Prairie influence *253*
Orographic weather *253*
Mid-day clearing trend *254*
Effects of elevation *254*
Wind direction *255*
Glacial winds and frost hollows *255*
Effect of continental divide *257*
Chinooks *257*
Windiness at Waterton/Glacier *260*
Recent climatic change *260*
Annual weather pattern *260*
Predicting the weather *262*
Further reading *263*

WHAT IS GROWING ON HERE?
(ecology) *265*

Southern, central
and northern regions *267*
Alpine zone *268*
Subalpine zone *268*
Montane forest *269*

Eastern-slope montane 269
Southern foothills 269
Western-slope montane 269
Southern Rocky Mountain Trench 269
Columbian forest 269

Further reading *270*

Common and scientific names
of plant families *271*

Pictures of ecological communities *273*

PLANTS *289*

Using the listings *289*
Trees *292*

Evergreen conifers 292
Conifers that are not
evergreen (larches) 302
Leafy trees 303

Shrubs *307*

Willows *307*
Tall shrubs *312*
Short shrubs *318*

Wildflowers below timberline *329*

White *329*
Greenish *348*
Yellow or orange *352*
Red or pink *368*
Blue or purple *377*
Drab *389*

Alpine wildflowers *391*

White *391*
Yellowish-green, reddish-green,
    odd colors *397*
Yellow or orange *398*
Red or pink *402*
Blue or purple *404*

Water plants *409*

Algae *409*
Water mosses *409*
Higher water plants *410*

Grasses and grass-like plants *416*

Grasses *416*
Sedges *420*
Rushes *422*

Ferns, horsetails, clubmosses
    and spikemosses *423*

Ferns *423*
Horsetails *426*
Clubmosses and spikemosses *428*

Mosses and liverworts *429*

On forest floor (feather mosses) *429*
In swamps (peat mosses) *431*
Along streams and at seeps *432*
Alpine, on cliffs,
    in rocky places *432*
Liverworts *434*

Lichens *435*

On trees *435*
On the ground *437*
On rocks *439*

Mushrooms and other fungi *441*

Edibility, toxicity *441*
Identifying mushrooms *442*
Ordinary capped mushrooms *443*
Little brown mushrooms *451*
Chanterelles and
    chanterelle look-alikes *452*
True and false morels *453*
Club-like fungi *455*
Coral fungi *455*
Shelf fungi *456*
Cup fungi *458*
Jelly fungi *459*
Puffballs and earthstars *460*

Further reading *462*

INSECTS AND SPIDERS *465*

Bugs on land and in the air *466*

Mosquitoes *466*
Other kinds of flies *468*
Bees, wasps, hornets and mimics *471*
Stings of bees,
    wasps and hornets *475*
Ants *475*
Aphids *476*
Beetles *477*
Grasshoppers and crickets *479*
Cicadas *480*
Ticks *481*
Spiders and harvestmen *483*

Bugs in, on or over water *486*

Aquatic insect larvae *486*
Water bugs, water beetles *489*
Mayflies *492*
Dragonflies and damselflies *492*

Butterflies *494*

Boldly patterned butterflies *495*
Whites *497*
Sulphurs *499*
Swallowtails *502*
Anglewings *503*
Hairstreaks *504*
Elfins *504*
Blues *505*
Coppers *508*
Checkerspots *510*
Fritillaries and crescentspots *511*
Satyrs *516*

Skippers *520*

   Folded-wing skippers 520
   Spread-winged skippers 521

Butterflies and skippers rare list *524*
Moths *525*
Caterpillars *528*
Further reading *531*

LIFE IN THE SNOW and miscellany *532*

   Watermelon snow,
       snow worms, etc. *532*
   Snails, clams, leeches *535*

FISHES *536*

   Salmon, trout,
       grayling, whitefish *537*
   Pike and sturgeon *546*
   Codfish and lampreys *547*
   Suckers *548*
   Minnows *549*
   Sculpins *554*
   Miscellaneous *555*
   Tropical fish at Banff Hot Springs
       556
   Further reading *557*

AMPHIBIANS AND REPTILES *558*

   Salamanders, toads, frogs *558*
   Snakes, lizards, turtles *562*

BIRDS *567*

   Good birding localities *568*
   Using the listings *570*
   Ducks and duck-like water birds *572*
   Geese and swans *586*
   Swamp birds *587*
   Sandpipers and other shorebirds *589*
   Gulls *595*
   Birds that dive into water *597*
   Hawks and falcons *599*
   Eagles *605*
   Owls *606*
   Grouse and ptarmigan *609*
   Swallows, swifts, nighthawks *613*
   Woodpeckers *617*
   Ravens, crows, jays, magpies *622*
   Hummingbirds *626*
   Robins and other thrushes *627*
   Blue birds *630*
   Starlings, doves *631*
   Waxwings *633*
   Flycatchers and vireos *634*

Warblers that are yellow *638*
Warblers that are not
   mainly yellow *640*
Yellow birds that are not warblers *643*
Blackbirds, cowbirds *645*
Red/pink birds *647*
Little forest birds (chickadees,
   kinglets,
   nuthatches, wrens
   and creepers) *649*
Sparrows and sparrow-like birds
   with unstreaked breasts *654*
Sparrows with streaked breasts *659*
Rare list *663*
Bird families *664*
Reference literature *665*
Checklists available *665*

MAMMALS *667*

   Bats *675*
   Shrews *678*
   Mice and rats *680*
   Voles and lemmings *684*
   Chipmunks and striped
       ground squirrels *688*
   Unstriped ground squirrels,
       marmots and gophers *691*
   Tree-dwellers (squirrels,
       porcupines) *695*
   Water-dwellers (beavers,
       muskrats, otters) *698*
   Hares and pikas *702*
   Weasel family and the raccoon *704*
   Cats (lynx, bobcats, cougars) *712*
   Dogs (coyotes, wolves, foxes) *715*
   Bears *720*
   People vs. bears in the Rockies *723*

      What to do in an encounter
         with a bear 725
      To avoid bear trouble,
         avoid bears 727
      Making noise 728
      Repellents and guns 728
      Being realistic 729
      Why we need the grizzly 729

   Cloven-hoofed animals *730*

      Deer family (deer, elk,
         moose, caribou) 730
      Bovids (bison, sheep,
         mountain goats) 737

   Primates (humans) *742*
   Reference literature *744*

HISTORICAL OUTLINE *745*

• Current population table *766*

ENJOYING THE ROCKIES *767*

Must-see list *767*
Hiking *772*

*Recommended clothing
    and equipment 772*
Representative day-hikes 772

Backpacking *776*

*Suggested equipment,
    clothing and food 776*
*Representative
    backpacking trips 778*
*Long walks
    in the mountain parks 781*
The Great Divide Trail 782

Back-country accommodation *782*
Mountaineering *787*

Climbing season 787
Rockclimbing 789
Summer snow and ice 790
Frozen waterfalls 794

Ski-touring *796*

Equipment 796
Technique 799
Safety considerations 801
Places to ski 801
Popular day tours 802
*Overnight trips
    with hut accommodation 803*

Bicycling *805*

Season, weather 805
*How tough are the
    Canadian Rockies? 805*
Accommodations for cyclists 805
• *List of hostels and map 806*
Addresses of interest to cyclists 807
Cycling the Icefields Parkway 807
*Cycling the
    Going-to-the-Sun Road 809*
Cycling in Kananaskis Country 809
Trail bicycling 810

Recreational guidebooks *811*

KEEPING YOURSELF TOGETHER *813*

Avoiding trouble in the mountains *813*
If an accident should occur *814*
Storms and lightning *814*
Avalanches *816*
In case of avalanche *817*
Mouth-to-mouth resuscitation *818*
Stopping heavy bleeding *818*
Head injuries *819*
Mountain sickness *820*
Hypothermia *820*
Frostbite *822*
Giardiasis ("beaver fever") *824*
Treating minor injuries *824*
First-aid kit *825*
How to use a compass *826*
Further reading *828*

AFTERWORD *829*

TOPOGRAPHIC MAPS *831*

Guide map *831*
Map index *832*
Topos *834*

GENERAL INDEX *851*

CONVERSION TABLES
    Inside front cover

BASE MAP OF THE CANADIAN ROCKIES REGION

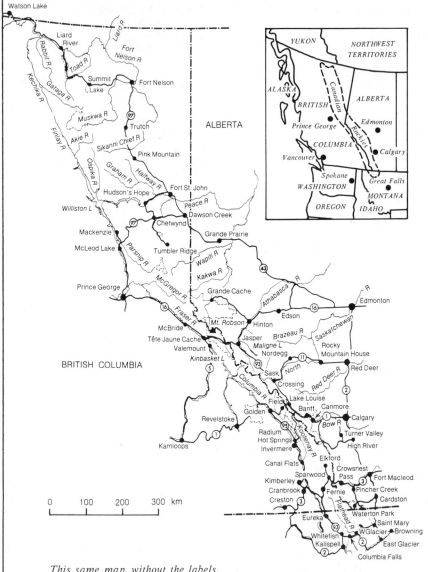

*This same map, without the labels,
is used as a base map elsewhere in the book.*

*Thin dashed lines enclose national parks
and major provincial parks. For these names
please refer to the map on page 850.*

Introducing the Canadian Rockies
Definitions, essential ideas and an invitation

The name "Canadian Rocky Mountains" is applied to a mountainous part of western Canada extending from the Interior Plains on the east to the Rocky Mountain Trench on the west, and from Liard River in northern British Columbia to the international boundary on the south.

For the purposes of this book the region is considered to extend south from Canada 100 km into Montana, to the southern boundary of Glacier National Park. The chapter on boundaries (page 11) presents the reasons for this; thinking of the Canadian Rockies as the Canadian-*style* Rockies takes care of the semantics problem. Here are the basic statistics:

> Length: 1450 km. Width: 150 km. Area: 180,000 km^2. Highest point: Mt. Robson, 3450 m above sea level. Lowest point: junction of Liard and Toad rivers, 305 m.

There are four east-west physiographic divisions (foothills, front ranges, main ranges and western ranges) and three north-south divisions (northern, central and southern regions).

Note that the Rockies do not include *all* of the mountains lying between the plains and the Pacific. A look at the physiographic map on page 10 shows that the Rocky Mountains are the easternmost of several ranges.

What is the "style" of the Canadian Rockies? It can be summarized in four points:

1. Geology

Predominantly marine sedimentary rock has been compressed into a long, narrow band fronting the Interior Plains of middle North America. Originally flat-lying, the sediments are now folded and faulted; they are inclined to the southwest overall.

2. Topography

Northwest/southeast-trending ridges are separated by parallel valleys. The largest valleys, deep and U-shaped, cut across the grain of the land. Glacial erosion has been heavy, and glaciers up to 325 km^2 in size still exist along the crest of the range.

3. Climate

The weather pattern is influenced strongly by the barrier-like nature of the Rockies. The eastern slope is noticeably cooler and drier than the western slope, and strong westerly winds (chinooks) warm the eastern slope suddenly in winter.

4. Ecology.

Plant and animal communities in the Rockies are controlled mainly by elevation. There are three easily recognizable life zones (montane, subalpine and alpine). Limestone-rich areas and quartzite-rich areas have distinctive biological features, as do a number of communities controlled by a surprising degree of geographic variety in climatic conditions at low elevations.

This style is consistent. One can cross these mountains anywhere and recognize them immediately as the Canadian Rockies. That such a long, narrow range could have this degree of integrity is remarkable.

Satellite view of the Canadian Rockies, prepared from Landsat photos taken between 1972 and 1974. White line encloses the Rockies.

Key to named points:

Larger letters: AB Alberta, BC British Columbia, MT Montana.

White dots: B Banff, Br Browning, C Calgary, Ch Chetwynd, CF Columbia Falls, Cr Cranbrook, CP Crowsnest Pass, E Edmonton, Ed Edson, F Fernie, FN Fort Nelson, FS Fort St. John, G Golden, GC Grande Cache, H Hinton, I Invermere, J Jasper, K Kamloops, L Lethbridge, LH Liard Hot Springs, LL Lake Louise, M Mackenzie, Mc McBride, ML Muncho Lake, PG Prince George, PM Pink Mountain, R Revelstoke, RM Rocky Mountain House, SL Summit Lake, TR Tumbler Ridge, V Vancouver, Vm Valemount, WL Williston Lake.

Geography and geology: old rock, middle-aged mountains, young landscape

In the satellite photo on the opposite page, the long ridges of the Canadian Rockies look rather like waves breaking against the Interior Plains—an oddly true analogy, for the shore of the Pacific Ocean (or of its older equivalents) moved east and west across this line throughout the region's long geological history.

Waves of stone are driven by the motions of the world's crustal plates, not by the wind. The impact that wrinkled the Rockies into existence came when the westward-moving continent of North America overran a collection of volcanic islands and other crustal fragments that now make up most of British Columbia.

Prior to the collision, continental-shelf-type seabed sediments—mostly sandstone, limestone and shale—had been collecting in the area for 1.5 billion years. That's a long time, even by geological standards, and there were few interruptions; continued slow subsidence allowed the pile to reach a thickness of 20 km in some places.

The strata now provide geologists with one of the better, more complete sedimentary records to be found anywhere in the world. The lower layers are Proterozoic, showing signs of simple forms of life—algae, jellyfish, worms—that evolved into the Cambrian trilobites so beautifully preserved in Yoho National Park's world-famous Burgess Shale. Higher in the sequence one finds corals, brachiopods, snails and cephalopods in Devonian and Carboniferous layers of the front ranges. The soft sandstone and shale beds of the foothills hold clams, oysters and plant fossils of the yet-younger Mesozoic and Cenozoic eras. (For a chart of the geological periods, see page 42.)

There are riches in these rocks: oil and natural gas from Devonian reefs; coal from the Cretaceous forests of 100 million years ago. But don't look for gold and silver in the Canadian Rockies. There's very little (although a lead/zinc deposit was mined in Yoho National Park, and there was a little copper mining in Glacier National Park).

Neither should you expect to find granite and high-grade metamorphic rocks such as gneiss, the core of many a mountain range, in the Canadian Rockies. There is granite and gneiss aplenty in the ancient North American Plate, which underlies the relatively thin sedimentary cover of the continent, and slices of the plate have been thrust upward to the surface at the western edge of the Rockies between Golden and Valemount (see page 81). But except for those exposures, and a bizarre intrusion in Yoho Park (page 150), there is little igneous or high-grade metamorphic rock at or near the surface in the Canadian section of the Rocky Mountains.

Thus, the building of the Canadian Rockies was not accompanied by much volcanic activity. During a 75-million-year period that began about 120 million years ago, the sediments of the west-coast continental shelf were pushed inland to the northeast, coming loose from the underlying plate and sliding along. Accordioned up to 300 km, the originally flat layers warped into folds and broke into moving sheets of rock (thrust sheets, page 17) that slid up and over one another, stacking skyward. These days the trilobites that once scuttled over the seabed weather out of the walls of peaks standing nearly 4000 m above the tides.

It is important to understand that the age of the rock and the age of the Rockies are different: the rock is much older than the events that built the mountains. As mountain ranges go, the Canadian Rockies are neither very old (like the Appalachians) nor very young (like the Himalayas). They can be thought of as middle-aged.

Having considered the age of the rock and the age of the uplift, there remains a third element in the picture: the age of the land surface. Erosion has whittled away at the Rockies ever since they poked above the waves, of course. Relatively recently—over the last two million years—glaciation has intensified in the region, carving it into big, rugged peaks separated by deep, wide valleys. This is a young landscape, freshly touched by ice. Along the continental divide hundreds of glaciers are still rasping away at the range, dumping fragments of it into milky-looking rivers that feed their rock flour into lakes of gem-like blues and greens.

A detailed look at the geology of the region begins on page 37.

Weather and climate: not bad, but ...

When Pacific storms roll in across the coast of British Columbia, they unload most of their rain and snow on the Coast Mountains and Columbia Mountains, which lie west of the Rockies, leaving much less moisture to fall over the Rockies. So our area is relatively dry. Typical annual precipitation figures for the Rockies are 400--500 mm, compared with 1113 mm for Vancouver or 1064 mm for Revelstoke. But although it may rain less here, there is still enough summer storminess to ruin many a vacation; enough winter snow to please the skiers. As in other mountainous regions, the daily weather is hard to predict.

The crest of the Rockies is a climatic divide. It is generally wetter and warmer (especially in winter) on the western slope; drier and cooler on the eastern side.

At Jasper, close to the divide and midway between the north and south ends of the range, the temperature touches -40°C in January. Hot spells in mid-July can reach 35°C. Neither of these extremes is as uncomfortable as it might seem, because the air is dry. The chapter on weather and climate starts on page 247.

Biology: still lots of wilderness, but ...

The Canadian Rockies are well wooded with pine, spruce, fir, aspen and poplar—with hemlock and cedar on the western slope. Travelers along the TransCanada Highway see mostly forest, perhaps coming to the conclusion that the Rockies are about nine-tenths trees. But that's a false impression. Anyone venturing up high, or getting a view from an airplane window, can see that much of the region is above timberline—about 40 percent of Jasper National Park, for example.

These mountains are famous for wildflowers. Pink moss-campion cushions and brilliant yellow-orange arctic poppies adorn the heights. Down in the valleys, sky-blue harebells stand out above green carpets of kinnikinnik. In late July every meadow at every elevation is full of color.

If you learn to identify a dozen common plants around Banff, then you will see most of them again at Waterton or along the Alaska Highway, 800 km north, for Canadian Rockies botany is surprisingly similar from one end to the other. The Waterton/Glacier area has the greatest diversity (about 1500 species). This book describes and illustrates 660 species of trees, shrubs, wildflowers, grasses, ferns, horsetails, lichens and fungi.

Despite the regional consistency, there are distinct differences in eastern-slope and western-slope floral checklists, and at low elevations there are strikingly different ecological regions. In the dry Rocky Mountain Trench south of Radium there is cactus; at the same latitude on the opposite side of the mountains there are peat bogs.

The Canadian Rockies are home to the sort of creatures one expects to find in a northern mountain wilderness: grizzly bears to keep you on your guard; wolves that watch you quietly from the forest edge; coyotes that wait patiently a few metres away from your picnic; cougars, lynx and wolverines to spot once or twice in a lifetime. There are beavers in the brooks and weasels in the willows.

Moose and caribou stand on the highway in winter, enjoying a respite from the deep subalpine snow. Mountain goats lick the salty shale at Disaster Point east of Jasper, their babies frisking about before the smiling, lucky onlookers.

Elk and deer nibble the shrubbery and the lawns in Jasper; bighorn sheep lie in the dust beside the TransCanada Highway west of Banff. Dall's sheep do the same near Summit Lake along the Alaska Highway. For more on our 69 species of mammals, turn to page 667.

Elk. Photo courtesy Jasper National Park.

There are 188 species of birds in the air and on the lakes, 40 species of fish in the water—but only one species of turtle, only one kind of lizard, only two kinds of toads and four sorts of snakes. Still, there are six species of frogs in the Canadian Rockies, including one that survives above timberline.

A hundred kinds of butterflies grace the flowery mountain meadows, some species appearing among the early-April snows. There are craneflies that walk the drifts in mid-winter, worms that eat the algae that grow on summer snowbanks, and primitive ice insects that live under rocks on glaciers. The mosquitoes here are just as fond of humans as they are anywhere; the ticks perhaps more so. The chapter on insects begins on page 465.

Tropical fish live in a warm marsh below the hot springs at Banff; mew gulls dive-bomb the bathers along the boardwalk to the hot springs beside Liard River. But we don't have everything. We have no black widows, no rattlesnakes, no scorpions.

Despite near-extirpation of elk before the turn of century, no mammal species has been driven to extinction here—although the wood bison lives only in paddocks at Waterton and Banff. A single wild bison, once part of a rancher's herd in the foothills, wanders the Rocky River area in eastern Jasper National Park at time of writing.

The wildlands of the Canadian Rockies are in decline proportionate to man's ascendancy, as elsewhere in the world, but fortunately some of the better landscapes are protected in spacious national and provincial parks.

Which brings us to:

Humanity in the Rockies: we love to visit, but most of us can't stay

People have been poking around in the western mountains for a very long time, as archeologists discovered in 1984. Test pits dug ahead of highway construction near Banff revealed a 10,500-year-old campsite. But few of those early campers lived year-round in the mountains proper, nor do very many people now. There are only seven towns between the mountain front and the Rocky Mountain Trench with over 1000 residents, and the total permanent population of the whole region, including the foothills and the trench, is under 150,000.

A lot of people come here seasonally, though, for mountain holidays. Jasper National Park, resident population 4000, swells to 20,000 on long weekends in July and August.

What do they do, all these visitors?

Parks Canada figures show that, by and large, they drive to the mountains, eat, sleep, excrete and go home. In quantity and over the long haul, this kind of visitation could rub away the wild character of the Rockies. But so far it hasn't proved to be nearly as damaging as industrial exploitation or agricultural land-clearing can be. Visitors provide jobs for the people who serve the meals, make the beds and clean up the mess. Those people need that work; tourism is the main source of cash here.

Of the ten percent of visitors who do more than stroll down Banff Avenue, the majority go for walks of a couple of hours. Although a person out of his car is arguably harder on the park than a person who stays in his car, the trail-walking visitor values that experience and thus resists efforts to urbanize the wilderness.

Day-hikers get good value for their small investment in time and energy. A walk past Lake Louise to the Plain of Six Glaciers fills the senses with mountain sights and sounds. There you are, among the great peaks of the continental divide. A blue-white glacier lies in its brown, bouldery bed. Ice breaks from Mt. Lefroy, booming down the cliffs. The clean fragrance of subalpine fir goes deep into the lungs when the trail gets steep. Turn to page 772 for a list of recommended day-hikes.

Smaller yet are the number of people who hike for two days or more in the back-country, getting the full course: sun and storms, bug-bites and fields of flowers, bears snuffing about in the night and eagles cruising the ridgelines by day. In Jasper park, especially, there are long trails that take only a few hundred

Banff's main street (Banff Avenue) in July. Banff National Park had 3.2 million visitors in 1985.

Back-country hiking in Castleguard Meadows, at the northern tip of Banff National Park. Watchman Peak (3009 m) in the background.

people each year into a landscape that still looks much as it did a thousand years ago. Advice for backpackers is given on page 776.

More people every summer are seeing the Canadian Rockies by bicycle. I have spoken with cyclists from all over the world who tell me that the Banff-Jasper ride is the best short tour on earth, offering good pavement, cheap hostel accommodation, camaraderie around the evening fire, splendid scenery and spicy weather. For information on how to do it, see page 805.

A new breed of machine has taken bicycle touring in another direction: into the back-country. Fat tires and low gears can send you over the trail at two or three times the speed of backpackers, whose generally negative reaction is understandable. Their paths are already muddied and polluted by horses; who needs tire tracks in the wilderness? I have mixed feelings about trail bicycling, too, but I own a mountain bike and appreciate its advantages.

You can't bicycle up Mt. Assiniboine (yet), or ride a horse up. Mountaineering is still the most personally demanding, most rewarding way to experience the heights. The east face of Mt. Robson, for example, presents a five-day climb on ice and snow—a mini-expedition. Rock-climbers in our area practice their craft mainly on limestone, which can be surprisingly solid if you know the right cliffs. In winter, ice-climbers enjoy frozen waterfalls that are unmatched in North America for their combined variety, size and easy access. See page 787 for mountaineering highlights.

We have fine skiing, of both the uphill and downhill varieties. There are several ski areas here, with the usual offerings, but for the cross-country skier there is much more. You can choose a gentle trail in the foothills or a crossing of the Columbia Icefield.

A few outdoorspeople are killed each year in these mountains, for the Canadian Rockies are unforgiving of errors in judgment. Safety considerations are presented on page 813, followed by ways of handling specific emergencies.

If you are not interested in careening down the slopes or hanging from your fingers over an abyss, the region has gentler avenues to explore. In Jasper park, for example, you might take the kids picnicking at Lake Annette. The water is wonderfully clear; warm enough for swimming on a hot afternoon in July or August.

After supper go for a walk up nearby Old Fort Point and listen for Swainson's thrush singing flute-like in the aspen. As night falls, head over to one of the campground amphitheatres for an interpretive program by a park naturalist.

This emphasis on recreation, and nondestructive forms of it, is in line with the history of our area (outlined beginning on page 745). A strong preservationist element in Canadian society has held the nation's favorite mountains dear for a hundred years; thus do we have the large national and provincial parks of Alberta and British Columbia. Explorers and settlers reached the Canadian Rockies so recently that government control preceded them. This lucky occurrence, and a paucity of easily exploitable natural resources, have helped the Canadian segment of the Rocky Mountains (and Glacier National Park, Montana) to avoid much of the environmental damage seen in the mountains of Colorado and New Mexico.

But human pressure is increasing, especially in provincially administered regions. Outside the national parks the perennial tamers of wildlands—industry, agriculture, human occupation and auto access—keep gnawing away at the 87 percent of the area that lacks federal protection.

Anyone seeing the Canadian Rockies for the first time is likely to feel an awestruck admiration for the place. It's a feeling that stays and grows. I hope you will join me in giving this incredible land the sensitive treatment it deserves—and in urging the governments that oversee it to do the same.

General naturalist's guidebooks to the Canadian Rockies

Hardy, W.G., ed. (1967) *Alberta: a Natural History* Hurtig, Edmonton. Covers the whole province, but includes material on the mountains. Section on human history at the end. Illustrated, indexed; 343 pages.

Patton, Brian (1975) *Parkways of the Canadian Rockies: an Interpretive Guide to Roads in the Mountain Parks* Summerthought, Banff. Descriptions of roadside features in Banff, Jasper, Yoho and Kootenay parks. Illustrated, 266 pages.

Pringle, Heather (1986) *Waterton Lakes National Park* Douglas & McIntyre, Vancouver. Handy guide, with better-than-average historical section. Illustrated, indexed, short reading list; 128 pages.

Root, John et al. (1981) *Rocky Mountain Landmarks* Hosford, Edmonton. Two-page descriptions of selected natural features and topics in the mountain-park block. Illustrated, 128 pages.

Spalding, A.E., Ed. (1980) *A Nature Guide to Alberta* Hurtig, Edmonton. Mapsheet-by-mapsheet guide to the province, with good introductory material and mountain coverage. Illustrated, indexed; 368 pages.

PHYSIOGRAPHIC REGIONS IN AND NEAR THE CANADIAN ROCKIES

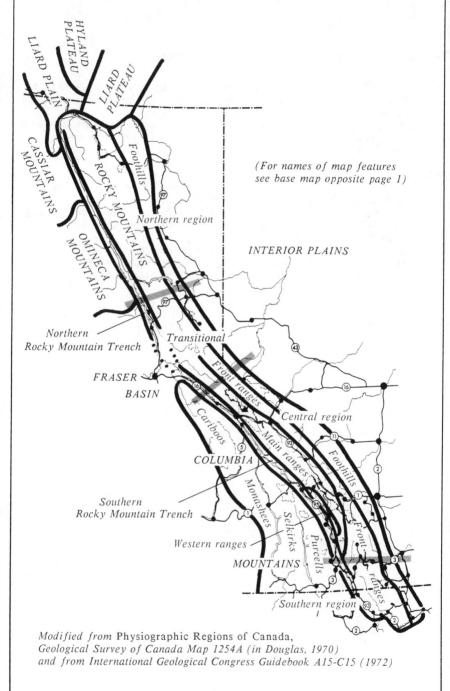

(For names of map features see base map opposite page 1)

LIARD PLAIN

HYLAND PLATEAU

LIARD PLATEAU

CASSIAR MOUNTAINS

Foothills

ROCKY MOUNTAINS

Northern region

OMINECA MOUNTAINS

INTERIOR PLAINS

Northern
Rocky Mountain Trench

Transitional

FRASER
BASIN

Front ranges

Cariboos

Central region

COLUMBIA

Main ranges

Foothills

Southern
Rocky Mountain Trench

Monashees

Selkirks

Western ranges

Purcells

Front ranges

MOUNTAINS

Southern region

Modified from Physiographic Regions of Canada,
*Geological Survey of Canada Map 1254A (in Douglas, 1970)
and from International Geological Congress Guidebook A15-C15 (1972)*

Boundaries
Drawing a line around the Rockies

Where are these mountains, what are the physical boundaries of the region and how is it divided up?

The Rockies are the easternmost part of the **Canadian Cordillera,*** the physiographic name for all the mountains of western Canada. When combined with the mountains of the western United States and those of Alaska, the whole region is called by geologists the **Western Cordillera** of North America.

Eastern boundary: the Interior Plains

In Canada, the **Interior Plains** (a gazetted name and thus capitalized) are the vast expanse of level land that lies between the granite hills of the Canadian Shield and the Rocky Mountains. In the United States the equivalent region is called the Great Plains.

Travelers approaching from the plains see the Rockies first as a blue line on the horizon. Later, face to face with the front ranges, they can see why the term "wall-like" is applied so frequently to the eastern aspect of these mountains.

The geological contrast is just as impressive as the topographic one: faults are few and folds are subtle under the prairies, but in the mountains it seems that everything is at an angle to everything else. You see that as soon as you pass from the Interior Plains into the foothills, which are part of the Rockies. At the plains/foothills boundary west of Calgary or Edmonton, the riverbanks and road-cuts show the sudden appearance of folds and faults—even though the topography is still plains-like. North of Peace River the plains/foothills boundary is different: the plains end abruptly at an impressive west-facing escarpment.

Western boundary: the Rocky Mountain Trench

The Rocky Mountain Trench is one of the great lines in the globe, a long valley that runs from the international boundary to Liard River, then resumes as the **Tintina** ("tin-TIN-uh") **Trench,** which continues to Alaska. Early Tertiary sediments in the Rocky Mountain Trench show that this valley has existed for at least 45 million years. The trench is visible in photos taken from the moon; it *has* to be some kind of major break in the earth's crust.

Indeed, it is. From Prince George north, the trench is a magnificent fault along which the Cassiar and Omineca mountains have ground their way northwest for about 400 km relative to the Rockies. South of Prince George the nature of faulting is different—primarily up and down rather than sideways—but except for a short section between Wood River and Skookumchuck the ditch-like character of the trench reflects an underlying down-dropped block of crust. (See page 177 for a more detailed discussion.)

At the international boundary the trench splits into two diverging valleys. The western valley holds Lake Koocanusa, a long reservoir that extends south into the USA. The eastern one is the route of Highway 93. East of that, along the western boundary of Glacier National Park, Montana, the Flathead River follows a third big valley, which would be a convenient place to put the western physiographic

---

*A note on pronunciation. "Cordillera" is Spanish for "mountain range." It should be pronounced "core-dee-YAIR-uh," a lovely sounding word that Canadians are inclined to pronounce "core-DILL-er-uh."

boundary of the Rockies—except that the Flathead Valley doesn't connect either geologically or topographically with the Rocky Mountain Trench in Canada. It's east of the trench, and therefore wholly in the Rockies.

However, the mountains west of Highway 93 are *not* part of the Canadian Rockies; they are southern extensions of Canada's Columbia Mountains, one of the ranges lying west of the Rockies. Thus, the valley of Highway 93 makes a good southwestern boundary.

The **Whitefish Range,** a minor collection of peaks found west of Glacier park and east of Highway 93, is the American name for mountains called the Galton and MacDonald ranges across the line in Canada, both of which are east of the Rocky Mountain Trench and thus unequivocally part of the Canadian Rockies. So it makes sense to include the Whitefish Range in the Rockies as well.

West of the Rocky Mountain Trench lie the **Columbia Mountains,** the **Omineca** ("oh-min-EEK-uh") **Mountains** and the **Cassiar** ("CASS-ee-yar") **Mountains.** They are differentiated geologically by age (they began to rise earlier than the Rockies) by rock types (mainly metamorphic and igneous rather than sedimentary), by geological history (they have been through at least two mountain-building episodes, compared with a single major one in the Rockies) and, of course, by the physical separation of the trench.

Topographically, the ranges west of the trench are not quite as high as the Rockies, although the valleys are deeper (they reach lower elevations). Climatically, the Columbias, Ominecas and Cassiars ranges are wetter and warmer than the Rockies, which gives them a different biological character.

Northern boundary: Liard River

Liard ("lee-YARD") River, in its deep canyon, separates the Rockies from Liard Plateau and Liard Plain to the north. Although there is more topographic relief here than the names suggest, the Liard plain and plateau are not mountainous on the scale of the Rockies. Geologically, too, there is a change at Liard River: a jump to younger rock on the north side. Further, the grain of the land bends 30° as the folds and faults run northeasterly into the Mackenzie Mountains.

Southern boundary: Marias Pass

This line is somewhat arbitrary, for the Rockies continue to the south. So does the Lewis Thrust (page 27), the plane along which the rock of the Waterton/Glacier region moved into the area. The Lewis Thrust carries on south for another 125 km, so one could make a case for carrying the name "Canadian-style Rockies" down there, too. But Marias Pass is low, a major gap in the range, and the peaks south of it are much less impressive than the peaks to the north. They are smaller, not as heavily glaciated, not as rugged. Further, the rock immediately south of Marias Pass is younger than that found to the north. This is as good a place as any to draw the line.

Comparison with the American Rockies

In southern Montana the character of the Rockies changes decisively, and the geological differences between the Canadian and American sections stand out plainly. There are three main ones:

1. While the Canadian Rockies represent a pile of sediments compressed between colliding crustal plates, the American Rockies were mainly uplifted in large blocks along a north/south line of weakness in the North American Plate. That uplift may have been related to compression farther west, part of the crustal collision that formed the Canadian Rockies, but the result in Wyoming, Colorado and New Mexico was primarily vertical uplift rather than horizontal compression (although there are overthrust belts here and there in the American Rockies that resemble those in the Canadian Rockies).

Comparing the Canadian and American Rockies

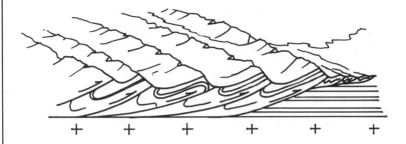

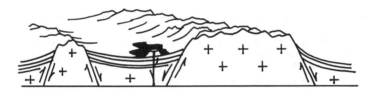

Canadian Rockies were formed by horizontal compression of sediments. Little uplift or volcanic activity; height caused mainly by stacking of overthrust sheets that slid along North American Plate.

American Rockies were formed mainly by uplifted blocks of North American Plate, accompanied by volcanic activity. Some overthrusting found as well (not shown in this diagram).

Arrows indicate motion along faults. Crosses: North American Plate.

2. The uplifted lands of the American Rockies are sections of the North American Plate itself—blocks of granite two billion years old. These oblong blocks rose under a cover of sedimentary rock typically 3000-4000 m thick, now stripped away by erosion and revealing the granitic cores of the various American Rockies ranges. The Canadian Rockies are not cored with granite, either from the plate or from more recent intrusions. The only known exposures of the plate in the Canadian Rockies are small; they occur at the western edge of the region, beside the Rocky Mountain Trench.

Driving from Denver to the mountain-front town of Boulder illustrates these differences. You move west through sediments bent upward by the rising American Rockies; at Boulder you see the Flatirons, steeply tilted sandstone flakes weathering off the granite beyond. Approaching the Canadian Rockies from Calgary, you see the beds dipping *downward* toward the west—just the opposite of the dip at Boulder. No granite is exposed in the peaks west of Calgary, for the basement granite was not involved in the deformation of the layers here. The sedimentary skin slid along the basement, piling up as it did so.

3. The timing of geological events in the two regions was quite different. While the American Rockies are younger than the Canadian Rockies, the American Rockies have older ancestors.

The north-south line of weakness in the plate mentioned in point one was active in the Late Carboniferous (325-280 Ma),* producing a range called the **Ancestral Rockies.** In contrast, the Canadian Rockies area was at or below sea level during this uplift. Canada has ancestral mountains, too, but they existed 500-800 million years ago (see page 77).

The Ancestral Rockies of the United States were worn down to low hills by the time the Laramide Orogeny pushed the same area up again in the Paleocene (66-57 Ma). That wasn't the end of it; the American Rockies received another 1500 m of uplift in the Miocene and Pliocene (28-5 Ma). This late phase of mountain-building is thought to have been caused by a hot spot under the crust, for it came with widespread volcanic eruptions.

By the time the Canadian Rockies appeared, the Ancestral American Rockies had been eroding for 180 million years. When the modern American Rockies rose, the main ranges of the Canadian Rockies had been standing for 55 million years and the front ranges for 20 million. But the Canadian foothills and the American continental divide seem to have appeared at about the same time. That was probably the end of mountain-building north of the 49th; the Canadian Rockies missed the Miocene fireworks south of the border.

A word about names

Americans call the mountains of Glacier National Park the "Northern Rockies," extending that term to include several ranges to the west—well west of the region Canadian physiographers think of as the Rocky Mountains. By all means, call the American section of the range whatever you like. But to be consistent throughout this book, "northern Rockies" refers to the northern part of the *Canadian* Rockies, not to mountains south of the international boundary.

---

*"Ma" is the metric abbreviation for "millions of years" (Mega-annums), often used informally by geologists in the sense of "millions of years ago." This book uses SI (metric) units of measure throughout. Persons unfamiliar with the SI system will find conversion tables inside the front cover.

Dividing up the mountains
A physiographic tour

The Canadian Rockies chain is long and narrow. But within the range there are even-narrower strips:

- The **foothills,** between the prairies and the mountains.

- The **front ranges,** which mark the mountain front.

- The **main ranges,** backbone of the Rockies between Crowsnest Pass and Peace River. These are subdivided into **eastern main ranges** and **western main ranges,** which have differing rock types (the western main ranges are shalier) and thus a different topographic style.

- The **western ranges,** a minor part of the Rockies bordering the Rocky Mountain Trench between Radium Hot Springs and Golden. In this area the strata are bent backward.*

These divisions are shown on the map on page 10. I am going to describe them as they appear on a trip from Calgary to Golden along the TransCanada Highway.

This is the classic transect of the **central** Canadian Rockies, which run from Crowsnest Pass on the south to about Jasper, where the geology starts to change. North of Peace River the rock and its structures are sufficiently different to call this region the **northern** Canadian Rockies. South of Crowsnest Pass lie the **southern** Canadian Rockies, which also differ in rock type and structure from the central Rockies.

After examining the character of the central Rockies, the other sections are described in trips from Saint Mary to West Glacier (the southern Rockies as seen along the Going-to-the-Sun road) and from Fort Nelson to Liard Hot springs (the northern Rockies as seen along the Alaska Highway).

To avoid duplication, I have emphasized the differences among these transects rather than the similarities. Reading the Calgary-to-Golden description first will help, for the central Rockies are the standard against which the other regions are compared.

The map on page 10 shows all the north-south and east-west physiographic regions of the Canadian Rockies. Note that not all four of the east-west divisions (foothills, front ranges, main ranges, western ranges) exist in each north-south region (southern, central, northern).

At this point it is worth mentioning that in the Canadian Rockies the biology follows the geology. There are typical plant communities for the foothills, front ranges, main ranges and Rocky Mountain Trench. There are also ecological differences between the southern, central and northern regions. See the ecology chapter (page 265) for the details.

---

*These informal physiographic names are frequently capitalized in the literature (e.g. "Main Ranges"), but they really shouldn't be: the regions to which they refer have not been strictly defined, the names are plural, and with the exception of the foothills they do not appear on the official physiographic map of Canada. (The foothills are shown separately from the Rockies on that map, where they are labeled "Rocky Mountain Foothills"). In this book I have left the divisions of the Rockies uncapitalized, choosing to capitalize such gazetted (officially recognized) terms as "Interior Plains" and "Rocky Mountain Trench."

The central Rockies: Calgary to Golden

In Calgary, sandstone outcrops along the shores of Glenmore Reservoir tell us that we are on the Interior Plains: the layers (part of the Paskapoo Formation, page 167) are essentially flat-lying.

Some 25 km out of the city we come to the first of the foothills: a low ridge that the highway goes straight over. The next ridge includes a road-cut that displays tilted bedding. The layers show curvature. Believe it or not, we are in the Rockies.

The ridges become taller and steeper to the west. At the crest of many there is an upturned edge of sandstone that is tougher to erode than the shaly rock on either side of it. On some of the hills the sandstone pokes through the soil, like the backbone of a skinny hog, and there you have the geologist's name for such ridges: **hogbacks.** They run from southeast to northwest, as does the grain of the Canadian Rockies generally.

Structure of the foothills

Under the parallel rows of foothills the geologic structure is more complicated than it looks: there is one fault after another. These are **thrust faults,** important elements in Canadian Rockies geology.

Thrust faults begin as folds, and folds are caused by horizontal compression. Squeezed from the sides, the rock starts to accordion, arching up and sagging down in gentle, wave-like folds that become tighter as the pressure increases. Eventually the rock reaches a point at which it just can't be pushed any farther without breaking. So it breaks. In the Canadian Rockies, where the pressure came from the southwest, the rock typically has broken on the northeast sides of fold. The southwesterly sides have ridden up and over.

Thrust faults in the foothills curve steeply at the top, then flatten downward (see the geological cross-sections through the central Rockies on page 50). These faults also join one another with increasing depth, and eventually all hook in to a nearly flat thrust along the buried surface of the continental plate some 5 km down. This is a general rule of Canadian Rockies geology, demonstrable wherever deep drilling has reached the plate. It applies throughout the range, except at the extreme western edge, where the plate itself may have been caught in the faulting.

The geological consequence of this configuration is that the entire Canadian Rockies must have been scraped northeastward along that big thrust fault at the base of the heap. It's as if you pushed the skin on the back of your hand along with your thumb, causing wrinkling ahead of the thumb. The skin slides on the ligament layer underneath, just as the sedimentary rock of the Canadian Rockies has slid on the North American Plate beneath.

Coming over the last foothills ridge on the TransCanada, we go down a long grade and out onto the grassy plain that lies along Bow River. This is **Morley Flats.**

Morley Flats is gravelly, windy, and often a cheerless place, but it is home to the Stoney Indians, who received the rights to it as a reserve. Thought to be worthless at the time of transfer, this land has proved valuable to the Stoney band, for Morley Flats is part of the foothills, under which lie enormous quantities of natural gas.

Mountain front

Next item of interest: the mountain front. At the west end of Morley Flats, just before the TransCanada Highway enters the mountains, it crosses Highway 1X at an overpass. At this point look north, toward a mountain with a long, flat, vertical face of gray-and-buff limestone. This is **Yamnuska Mountain,** which, besides being popular with climbers, shows where the **McConnell Thrust** runs along the bases of peaks at the mountain front.

Development of a typical thrust fault in the Canadian Rockies

As seen in a vertical rock face

If a single layer could be seen

 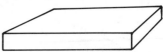

1. Flat-lying layers.

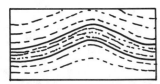 

2. Folding begins. Fold is symmetrical (left and right sides are even).

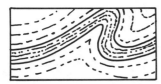 

3. Fold tightens and becomes asymmetrical. Right (northeast) side is steeper.

4. Fold breaks, becomes a thrust fault. Left (southwest) side moves up.

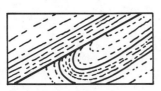 

5. Left side continues to move; overlying rock is now a thrust sheet.

Note on scale: thrust faults may be of any size, commonly from a few centimetres to several kilometres across.

A hogback ridge in the foothills west of Calgary. TransCanada Highway in the background.

Morley Flats in late winter, with Yamnuska Mountain (2545 m; named on maps as Mt. John Laurie) in the background. The McConnell Thrust runs along the base of the cliff.

The McConnell Thrust separates the foothills from the front ranges. This major fault brings Paleozoic rock up and over much-younger Cretaceous layers; it runs from just south of Bow River nearly to Athabasca River.

Even from the highway the fault is easily located in Yamnuska Mountain: it lies right at the base of the cliff. The Yamnuska Trail takes hikers to a good exposure of the fault plane, along which Eldon limestone (Middle Cambrian) has slid over coaly beds of Brazeau shale (Late Cretaceous) underneath.

Many geologists have walked beside that famous fault, marvelling at how thin the fault zone is (photo on page 181). The contact is not shattered and blurry, as you might expect along such a major rent. It is quite sharp. The limestone simply rests on the shale as if nothing had moved—yet the rock has slid at least 30 km. This is typical of Canadian Rockies thrusts.

It is important to understand that the mountain front is not simply the leading edge of the thrusted slab. The edge of the slab, along with a great deal of rock in the upper part of the slab, has been cut away by 80 million years of erosion. The tough limestone at the mountain front has weathered more slowly than the soft shales and sandstones of the foothills, so the mountain front stands high above the foothills. The mountain front is a product of **differential erosion**.

Peaks along the mountain front west of Calgary average around 2500 m in elevation;* the highest is Mt. Oliver, 3009 m. (The highest peak anywhere in the front ranges of the Canadian Rockies is Mt. Brazeau, 3470 m, near the south end of Maligne Lake in Jasper National Park.) Valley-floor elevations along the highway are around 1300 m, so the topographic relief—the difference between high and low points—is about 1200 m at the mountain front. At Banff, in the heart of the front ranges, the relief is greater, typically 1600 m.

The enormous amount of erosion in the Rockies should be kept in mind. Ever since the seabed poked above the waves here some 120 million years ago, it has been eroding. In that time a great deal of rock has been removed—a thickness of 10 km in places. We now see geologic structures that originally formed much deeper down, where the rock was warm and under enough pressure to deform it plastically. That explains how the great folds of the front ranges were produced in material as apparently brittle as rock.

Dip slopes and other kinds of structural control in the front ranges

At the Banff intersection on the TransCanada, Cascade Mountain to the north displays some exemplary folds. The kinked rock is quite obvious near the top of the peak, and there is a majestic curving fold near the base on the west side.

Looking south from the same spot, Mt. Rundle illustrates another front-range characteristic: the layers **dip** (geologese for "tilt downward") toward the southwest.

Mt. Rundle is a classic example of how the tilt of the bedrock controls the shape of many front-range mountains. Glaciers whittled away at the southwestern side of Mt. Rundle, cutting across the down-dip edges of the layers. This allowed entire beds to break loose from that side of the peak and slide into the valley. On the northeast side, where the up-dip edges of the beds are exposed, such massive slides could not occur. Erosion was slower, so the northeast cliffs stand tall.

What you see on the southwesterly slopes of a typical front-range peak such as Mt. Rundle is a slope angle determined largely by the angle of the rock itself: a **dip slope.** The northeasterly faces of such peaks are much steeper.

Thrust faults in the front ranges cause the same formations to repeat several times from east to west, just as they do in the foothills. Between the mountain front and Banff townsite, the unit of rock that makes up Mt. Rundle is crossed *four times* along the TransCanada Highway. And you cross it twice more before reaching the Sunshine turnoff only 10 km farther.

---

*All elevations in this book are given in metres above mean sea level.

Mt. Rundle from Vermilion Lakes Drive near Banff, showing the prominent dip slope on the southwest side of the mountain.

A typical front-range streamcourse, this one found along Highway 11 beside Abraham Lake. The main agent of erosion and deposition here is flash-flooding.

This explains another important feature of front-range physiography: the alternation of limestone peaks and shale valleys. In the geological sequence of bedding, which is much the same throughout the central-Rockies front ranges, a thick, soft unit of siltstone and shale overlies the tough limestone that makes up the peaks. When all the layers are tilted together to the southwest, the soft material lies like a ribbon on the landscape—a weak zone readily attacked by rivers and glaciers. It erodes more quickly than the bands of limestone on either side and becomes a valley.

Now, both these units—the tough limestone and the soft shale—repeat from east to west through thrust faulting, so their topographic expression—the peak and the valley—repeat as well. That is what produces the parallel ridges of the front ranges. The ridges of the foothills are similar, but on a smaller scale.

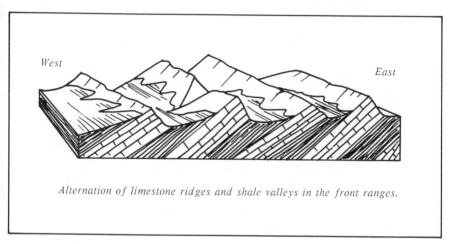

West *East*

Alternation of limestone ridges and shale valleys in the front ranges.

Coal mining

One of those repeating units is the Kootenay Group (page 160), which is rich in coal. Active on and off between 1898 and 1979, coal mines have reached in below the thrust fault that runs along the lower slopes of Mt. Rundle and Cascade Mountain. Parks Canada has prepared an exhibit on the subject at the abandoned mining town of **Bankhead**. Take the road to Lake Minnewanka from the Banff interchange; it passes right by the Bankhead site.

The geology of the Bankhead coal deposits and the method of extraction became a model for coal mining elsewhere in the Canadian Rockies during its heyday (from the 1900s to the early 1920s). See page 754 for more on the subject.

Trellis drainage and flash floods

Front-range streams reflect front-range geology. Consider any major river, such as the Bow. It follows a shale valley for a while, then cuts across a limestone ridge and bends into another shale valley, working its way out of the mountains in a series of steps. The smaller streams flow in the shale valleys only, while many little creeks drain the valley sides. The resulting pattern on a map is regular and angular; it is called **trellis drainage**, a hallmark of the front ranges. The topographic map on page 836 shows the trellis drainage in the Banff area.

Journey on foot up a front-range valley and you will discover that many of the smaller streambeds are dry. You have to hunt for water, perhaps finding it flowing far up the bed, near a melting snowbank. Yet the dry channel is often 10 m wide and over a metre deep. The vertical or overhung banks show that water has cut deeply into coarse gravel and angular rock fragments. In other places, trees are partly buried in these deposits.

Conclusion: this is flash-flood country. I have witnessed a couple of these events. They sometimes come in May or June, from rapid melting of snow, but most often in July or August from thunderstorms.

Such storms often drop a couple of centimetres of rain in less than an hour. The runoff quickly swells the creek. The velocity of the water increases to the point at which it can move head-size boulders with ease, and the little brook, now a muddy torrent, carries the top layer of its bed downstream. When the flow subsides the channel configuration will have changed noticeably. Thus are the front ranges washed to the sea.

And thus do we finish with the front ranges. A few kilometres before reaching the junction with Highway 93 (the turnoff for Radium), the TransCanada Highway crosses the Simpson Pass Thrust and enters the **main ranges**.

Eastern main ranges

"Main" is appropriate, for this strip of mountains is the backbone of the central Rockies. The stack of rock here is very thick, so the mountains are very high; the higher peaks in the eastern main ranges are about 500 m taller than those of the front ranges. These peaks pick up more rain and snow, so the climate is wetter than that of the front ranges. Glaciers are more common. At Lake Louise you can see several glaciers from the highway.

Castle Mountain, easily recognized northeast of the TransCanada/Highway 93 junction, is a classic example of an eastern-main-range peak. It is castle-like, all right, with steep walls and a tower at the south end.

Eastern-main-range rock is not steeply dipping or grandly folded, like that of the front ranges. Instead, the beds are nearly flat-lying. Folds are inclined to be broad and gentle. This produces topography strikingly different from that of the steeply dipping and more tightly folded front ranges next door. Main-range peaks are often castle-like, and dip slopes are not as pronounced here as in the front ranges. The drainage lacks the neat trellis configuration typical of dip-slope mountains; rather, it tends to spread irregularly from the higher peaks.

The rock in which the main ranges are carved can be thought of as a single sheet several kilometres thick. It was pushed in some 40 km from the southwest 110-120 million years ago along the **Simpson Pass Thrust,** a major fault like the McConnell.

The main-range thrust sheet moved far, yet it held together well. It slid along almost horizontally, which explains the low angle of dip in this part of Rockies. Regionally, the main ranges dip gently to the southwest.

Main-range rock is old; the oldest we have encountered so far on our east-to-west tour. The lowest layers in the thrust sheet are Precambrian, dating to 600-800 Ma, made of the purplish shale and brown-weathering gritstone of the Miette Group (page 77). Higher in the sequence comes the pinkish, cliff-forming Gog quartzite (page 88), then the dark limestone and pale dolomite of the Middle Cambrian formations, topped by the buffy Late Cambrian units. So eastern-main-range rock is more colorful than the subdued grays and tans of the front ranges.

Continental divide

West of Lake Louise the highway climbs moderately up to Kicking Horse Pass on the **continental divide.** A raindrop falling exactly on the divide theoretically could send its moisture to both the Atlantic and Pacific oceans—to the Atlantic by way of Hudson Bay; to the Pacific by way of the Columbia River.

Wapta Lake sits beside the highway near the summit of the pass. Major passes in the Rockies often have lakes and swamps at their crests. During some of the Pleistocene glacial advances, ice flowed over the divide from the west and through passes such as Kicking Horse, cutting deep gaps in the main ranges. Ice also flowed down to the pass from neighboring peaks, complicating the flow and causing the glacial floor to erode unevenly. As well, areas of melting stagnant

Castle Mountain (2728 m), about midway between Banff and Lake Louise along the TransCanada Highway.

Looking southwest along the gravelly streamcourse of the Kicking Horse River near Field. In the background are shaly peaks of the Van Horne Range, typical of the western main ranges.

Physiography

(non-moving) ice left till (page 189) and other glacial debris in irregular patches in the passes. The resulting hollows hold water.

Shortly after passing Wapta Lake the road starts to drop down the western side of the pass. The hill is long and the grade is steep, quite different from the eastern approach to the pass, which is gentle. Indeed, western-slope valleys are noticeably deeper than eastern-slope ones. The highway at Lake Louise is at an elevation of 1520 m. The pass is at 1630 m, for a climb of 110 m. But the elevation of Field, at the foot of Kicking Horse Pass on the western side, is only 1240 m, so the climb from that side is 390 m. The valley-bottom difference, then, is nearly 300 m.

Why this difference in valley depth? There are two possible factors, and both may be involved:

- Western-slope rivers have a shorter distance to go to the sea than eastern-slope rivers do. This produces a steeper streamcourse and hence more erosive power with which to deepen the valleys of the western slope.

- There were thicker ice buildups on the western slope during glacial advances. This resulted in heavier glaciation and thus deeper valleys.

Roadcuts along the descent to Field display some common eastern-main-range rock. At the top of the hill, the Cathedral and Eldon limestones sandwich a band of greenish Stephen shale; past the bridge there are exposures of the underlying Gog quartzite. See the individual descriptions of these formations for more detail (all formation names are keyed in the index.)

Field sits on an alluvial fan built out into gravelly outwash flats. These deposits probably date to the Little Ice Age (page 189), but upstream, in Yoho Valley, the Wapta and Waputik icefields still supply substantial quantities of gravel. The steep Yoho River carries it down to Field, where the valley gradient is gentler and the water speed slows. The stones drop out, adding to the fan year by year.

Western main ranges

Field is the site of a dramatic change in the bedrock: east of Field the peaks are made of tough quartzite, limestone and dolomite. West of Field the mountains are mostly of easily erodible shale. Thus, geologists divide the main ranges into eastern and western parts. Handily, the dividing line is generally just west of the continental divide. The eastern main ranges are tougher and hence higher than the shaly western main ranges, which are more rounded and less impressive.

At the turn of century, geologist J.A. Allan assumed that there was a major fault at Field, one that divided the eastern and western main ranges (Allan, 1914). Although he could not locate it precisely, he drew the fault onto the map. But Allan was wrong; there was no fault. Fifty years later, when the mistake was corrected, discovery of the true reason for the rock-type change had a major impact on Canadian Rockies geology. (See the Kicking Horse Rim, page 101.)

From Field to Golden the bedrock is generally soft and crumbly, with a preponderance of shale. There is one exceptional unit though: the Ottertail Formation (page 106). The Ottertail is a thick, tough limestone that supports the ramparts of Mt. Hurd and Mt. Vaux* about 10 km west of Field on the south side of the highway.

While the strong rock of the eastern main ranges lies in gentle folds, the weak rock of the western main ranges is quite deformed. Road cuts show wildly contorted beds, with tiny folds only a few centimetres across.

---

*"Vaux" is pronounced "VOX" in this case, according to the family of Mary Vaux, a Philadelphian for whom the mountain is named.

The shale here may not look like the sort of shale you are familiar with. Most shale is dark-colored, but roadcuts through the western main ranges display rock that is often greenish-silver. The reason: heat and pressure during mountain-building have altered the minerals in it slightly, creating silvery mica and greenish chlorite from what were originally clays. So this rock is mildly metamorphic. The proper term for it is **phyllite** ("FILL-ite"). Many geologists just call it "slate," which is shale in the first stage of metamorphosis (before it goes to phyllite). The rock here breaks as slate does: according to the direction of stress, not according to the original layering. (For more on metamorphism in the Rockies see page 78.)

Western ranges

Coming up: the head of Kicking Horse Canyon, which means we are crossing into the western ranges. Not western *main* ranges, but **western ranges,** which are subtly different.

Both mountain groups are made of weak, shaly rock that has been intensely folded and faulted. The topography is similar. But whereas the faults dip mainly to the southwest in the western main ranges, they dip to the *northeast* in the western ranges. The rock here has been **overturned**—bent upward and backward, beyond the vertical—and the faults within it also been overturned. Followed downward, the overturned rock curves back to the southwest as Rockies thrust sheets normally do.

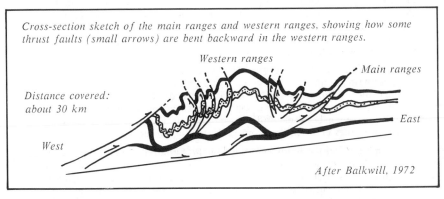

Cross-section sketch of the main ranges and western ranges, showing how some thrust faults (small arrows) are bent backward in the western ranges.

Western ranges

Main ranges

Distance covered:
about 30 km

East

West

After Balkwill, 1972

This overturned zone is narrow and not very long, found only between Radium Hot Springs and Golden, so it is not characteristic of the central Rockies generally. But the western ranges are significant to geologists because they show where a major thrust sheet from the neighboring Purcell Mountains literally rammed the shale of the western Rockies (Price and Gardner, 1979). Rather than riding smoothly up and over as most thrust sheets do, the Purcell sheet plowed into the malleable shale, collapsing it like a closing accordion and also squeezing it upward. This explains the overturned character of the western ranges.

The road descends steeply through Kicking Horse Canyon, which resembles the stream-cut John Stevens Canyon west of Marias Pass at the southern end of Glacier National Park, Montana. Other narrow, twisting valleys descend steeply into the southern section of the Rocky Mountain Trench, among them Sinclair Canyon, which winds down to Radium Hot Springs. Such valleys are more typical of the American Rockies than they are of the more heavily glaciated Canadian Rockies.

Speaking of the Rocky Mountain Trench, it is coming into view as we approach Golden. The trench is a deep, straight valley that marks the western edge of the Canadian Rockies, as discussed on page 11.

Summary of central-Rockies features

Boundaries: Crowsnest Pass on the south; transitional to the north, between Jasper and Peace River; Rocky Mountain Trench on the west; indistinct boundary on the east, marked by the most-easterly foothills folds.

Highest point: Mt. Robson (3954 m), northwest of Jasper in Mount Robson Provincial Park. Timberline drops from about 2300 m at Banff to 2100 m at Jasper.

Foothills: 40-50 km wide, underlain mostly by Cretaceous sandstone and shale that was folded and repetitively thrust-faulted at 45-50 Ma. The rock dips mainly to the southwest; harder beds form parallel hogback ridges aligned southeast-northwest.

Front ranges: 40-50 km wide, underlain mostly by Late Paleozoic limestone (forming peaks) and Mesozoic shale (forming valleys), with spectacular folds and repetitive thrust faults formed at about 80 Ma. The rock dips mainly to the southwest; ridges align southeast-northwest, with steep sides to the northeast. Trellis drainage.

Main ranges: 40-50 km wide (20-30 km wide beside the western ranges), underlain by Precambrian and lower Paleozoic rock. Mostly quartzite and limestone east of the continental divide (eastern main ranges) and shale west of it (western main ranges). The eastern main ranges have been carved from a single, tough thrust sheet that began to move at about 110-120 Ma. The mountains are castle-like, with steep sides all around. In contrast, the western main ranges are cut in tortuously folded and intricately faulted shale; they are irregular and more rounded. The drainage is not regular.

Western ranges: an arc 20 km across at the widest. Topographically similar to the western main ranges, with Cambrian and Ordovician rock that has been rammed by the Purcell Thrust Sheet and accordioned so tightly that faults in it dip to the northeast. The western ranges form the eastern wall of the Rocky Mountain Trench between Radium and Golden; they are about the same age as the main ranges (110-120 Ma) and really just a subset of them.

Note the sequence, which holds generally in the Canadian Rockies: main ranges created first, front ranges created next, foothills created last. Each of the major thrusts brings older rock up and over younger rock, so as you go west the rock gets older and older—until you reach the western ranges, which are no older than the main ranges. *Within* each southwest-dipping thrust sheet, the rock gets *younger* to the west.

The southern Rockies: Waterton/Glacier area

Viewed from west of Lethbridge, the mountains south of Crowsnest Pass look different from the ones north of the pass. The peaks to the south are those of the Waterton/Glacier area, colorful and castle-like, cut into the ancient red and green argillites of the Purcell Supergroup. In contrast, north of the pass one sees the long, gray ridge of the Livingstone Range, which is part of the central Canadian Rockies. So Crowsnest Pass is a convenient dividing line, even though the pass is actually about 20 km north of the Purcell outcrop area and thus you don't see Purcell rock through the pass itself. Further, a tongue of the Purcell exists north of the Crowsnest area. It forms the east wall of the Rocky Mountain Trench as far north as Skookumchuck.

West of Crowsnest Pass, around Fernie, Paleozoic central-Rockies-type rock swings south into the predominantly Purcell Waterton/Glacier region. This rock has been removed by erosion south of the international boundary (it reaches Trail Creek, a few kilometres into the USA west of Glacier park).

Lewis Thrust

The southern section of the Canadian Rockies is the land of the **Lewis Thrust**. Purcell rock has moved relatively northeastward in this area as a sheet perhaps 6.5 km thick, gliding along over slippery Cretaceous shale for a distance of 60-70 km. Through Glacier and Waterton parks the thrust sheet lies gently bowed down in the middle, with the centre of the fold running southeast-northwest.

The Lewis Thrust Sheet held together remarkably well as it moved along, even better than the main-range thrusts in the central Rockies. This is strange, considering that most Purcell rock is shaly and should deform rather easily. No one has fully explained the integrity of large thrust sheets such as this one; the explanation may lie in the mode of transport (possibly the sheet moved *downhill* from the west), in the large amount of water that was undoubtedly present in the shale, or simply in the strength the force of gravity gives when acting on masses this great.

The rock in these mountains is nearly flat-lying, like that of the main ranges farther north, yet the peaks of Waterton/Glacier are all in the front ranges. The Lewis Thrust, which underlies the region, runs north into the front ranges of the central Rockies. You can see the north end of the structure from Highway 40 just north of Fortress Mountain ski area in Kananaskis Country, where it has become a majestic fold in the south face of Mt. Kidd (photo on page 185).

This means that the Lewis Thrust was active during the building of the front ranges some 80 million years ago. Whether it was active earlier, during main-range construction at 110 Ma, is unknown. Main-range faults in the central Rockies run into a tangle of structures as they approach the Waterton/Glacier region; perhaps the Whitefish Range west of Glacier park is related to the main ranges farther north.

The Lewis Thrust Sheet is quite thick in the Waterton/Glacier area, and it has weathered into mountains that are correspondingly high. This is storm-spawning topography (the land to the west is lower), which helps to explain the intense glaciation that has occurred here. The result is a deeply dissected landscape of Matterhorn-like peaks standing 1300 m above classic U-shaped glacial valleys holding long lakes. At higher elevations there is very little flat land in the southern Rockies; on the trails it seems that one is either climbing steeply up or dropping steeply down.

On to our tour, which will be brief because most of the explaining has been done already.

Foothills

Saint Mary, Montana, is the eastern gate to Glacier National Park. The town sits in the foothills, which are geologically very much like those west of Calgary. But glacial outflow from the park has carved wide valleys right across the foothills belt here. There are deep glacial deposits as well. This combination has both eroded and masked the parallel southeast-northwest ridges typical of the foothills elsewhere in the Canadian Rockies. Drilling for oil and gas in the Waterton/Glacier area has shown that the faults and folds align southeast/northwest, and thus the underlying geological structure of the Waterton/Glacier foothills is like that of the foothills farther north.

Mountain front

Deep erosion along the mountain front has exposed the Lewis Thrust near the bases of most peaks. The plane of the thrust is practically horizontal here, dipping slightly eastward over slippery Cretaceous shales. This situation has proved to be geologically unstable: rock faces above the fault creep slowly forward, opening cracks behind and causing slides. These slides are plainly visible from the highway at many points along the mountain front.

Chief Mountain, a prominent peak at the mountain front west of the junction of highways 17 and 89, is a klippe ("CLIP-uh"): a chunk of the thrust sheet that has been eroded on all sides so deeply that the Lewis Thrust is exposed all the way around it. So Chief Mountain is like a cork of Purcell strata floating on the Cretaceous pond surrounding it.

Farther north, along Highway 3 in the Crowsnest Pass area, Crowsnest Mountain is also a klippe of the Lewis Thrust Sheet. Here the rock in the klippe is much younger: Devonian and Early Carboniferous (Palliser, Banff and Livingstone formations) resting on the Belly River Formation (Late Cretaceous). This shows how the Lewis Thrust cuts up into younger rock north of Waterton park.

The situation at Chief Mountain or Crowsnest Mountain is reversed at the headwaters of Ole Creek in southern Glacier park, where glaciation has cut a hole through the Lewis Thrust Sheet into the Cretaceous rock lying beneath. Geologists speak of this arrangement quite descriptively as a window (or more formally as a fenster, which is German for "window"). The Ole Creek Window is not accessible by road, but you see the same thing from Highway 2 along the eastern approach to Marias Pass, where the highway runs along the other side of the mountain from Ole Creek. Here the flat trace of the Lewis Thrust is visible in Summit Mountain on the north side of the road. It is marked by a light-gray band of Purcell shale above the gray-green Cretaceous rock beneath.

Peak elevations in eastern Glacier park reach 2600 m. Saint Mary Lake lies at 1363 m, so the topographic relief along the mountain front in the region is roughly 1300 m—some 100 m greater than that seen west of Calgary.

At Rising Sun Campground along Saint Mary Lake we cross the Lewis Thrust, and from there on the rock is Purcell strata. A detailed account of the formations begins on page 71. In cooperation with the United States Geological Survey, Glacier National Park has established a fine geology tour along the highway. The stops are marked with numbered signs that match a non-technical (but meaty) guidebook called *Geology along Going-to-the-Sun Road* (Raup et al., 1983) that you can pick up locally or from the USGS in Denver. Recommended.

The change from limestone to shale noted along the continental divide in the central Rockies doesn't occur here; the Purcell rocks are much older, deposited before the Kicking Horse Rim developed in western North America (page 101). But as usual in the Canadian Rockies, the western-slope descent is longer than the eastern-slope ascent because the western-slope valleys are deeper—400 m deeper—from more-active river erosion and/or heavier glaciation.

Peaks above St. Mary Lake along Going-to-the-Sun Road in Glacier National Park, Montana. Photo courtesy Glacier National Park.

Chief Mountain

Very old
Purcell rock

Lewis Thrust

*Relatively young
Cretaceous rock*

Chief Mountain, a klippe of the Lewis Thrust in eastern Glacier National Park.

Photo courtesy Glacier National Park

Flathead Fault

West Glacier sits in the half-graben (down-dropped fault block) that forms Flathead Valley. Going-to-the-Sun Road crosses the boundary fault **(Flathead Fault)** at the east end of Lake McDonald.

The Flathead Fault dips steeply to the west and forms the western wall of Glacier park. It became active at about 40 Ma. Total downward movement along it was on the order of 6100 m, which was enough to drop the whole Purcell sequence here below sea level and produce a depression deep enough to hold 2500 m of coarse material eroded from the surrounding heights (the Kishenehn Formation).

Summary of southern Canadian Rockies features

Boundaries: Marias Pass on the south, Crowsnest Pass on the north; the most-easterly foothills folds and faults (typical locations Pincher Creek, Cardston, Browning) on the east and Highway 93 on the west.

Highest point: Mt. Cleveland (3190 m), in Glacier National Park near the international boundary. Timberline is around 2400 m.

Foothills: 25-40 km wide, geologically similar to those of the central Rockies, but due to glacial erosion and deposition the northwest-southeast alignment of folds and faults is not expressed as well topographically.

Front ranges: 20-40 km wide and different both geologically and physiographically from the front ranges of the central Rockies. Instead, the Waterton/Glacier front ranges resemble the central-area main ranges: castle-like, cut into a single thrust sheet in an irregular drainage pattern.

Front-range rock in the Waterton/Glacier area is Middle Proterozoic in age (1300-1000 Ma), the oldest sedimentary rock in the Canadian Rockies. Mountain-building occurred here at 80 Ma or perhaps even later.

There is no limestone-to-shale change-over to the west, as there is in the central Rockies. Rather, a major down-dropping fault along the western edge of Glacier park juxtaposes the Purcell Supergroup and the second-*youngest* rock in our area: Kishenehn beds 35-40 million years old. (The youngest is the St. Eugene, a Miocene formation nearby in the Rocky Mountain Trench. See page 187).

Main ranges and western ranges: none, unless the Whitefish Range and its northerly extension, the Galton Range, are southerly continuations of these central-Rockies features.

Rocky Mountain Trench: not as well-defined as it is farther north. The trench splits near the international boundary into several down-faulted valleys that spread southward; the valley that Highway 93 follows is taken to be the western edge of the Canadian-style Rockies in this region.

The northern Rockies: Fort Nelson to Liard Hot Springs

This is the far northern end of the entire Rocky-Mountains chain (the southern end is in New Mexico, north of Sante Fe). The mountains here have little in common with the mountains of New Mexico; for a comparison of the Canadian and American Rockies, see page 13.

Even the central Canadian Rockies west of Calgary are far away from the northern-Rockies peaks west of Fort Nelson, so one must expect significant differences between the two areas. Indeed, the geologic history of the northern Rockies, while generally similar to that of the rest of the Canadian Rockies, has differed in the following ways:

1. Long before the creation of the modern Rockies there were several periods of fairly strong uplift in the northern region (in Precambrian, Cambrian and Ordovician times). These ancient hills were worn flat each time, leaving unconformities (buried erosion surfaces, page 121) in the rock sequence, some of them quite angular (i.e., with horizontal beds deposited on folded ones).

2. There is a greater proportion of shale in the northern Rockies than there is in the central Rockies. Shale is primarily a deep-water sediment, and its dominance in the northern Rockies follows from a general rule that whenever the sea was shallow in the central Rockies, or whenever the sea had withdrawn and the seabed was eroding, then the water was still deep in the northern Rockies, or at least covering the place.

   However, when the central region was gathering the Middle Cambrian limestone that now bulks thick in the main ranges, the northern region was above sea level and thus getting nothing at all. So in the northern Rockies there is a Middle Cambrian gap in the record.

3. Millions of years later, during the creation of the modern Rockies, the northern section seems to have been built about the same time as the central and southern sections, and by the same sort of northeastward motion, but in the northern region the predominantly shaly rock was inclined to fold rather than to break into thrust sheets like those of the central Rockies (where the sequence includes thick, tough layers of limestone and quartzite). So there are fewer thrust faults in the northern Rockies, especially in the foothills belt, and more folds.

4. While the central and southern Rockies were compressed about 200 km, the northern Rockies were accordioned only about 50 km. The foothills suffered the least; they weren't even overridden much by the front ranges, as happened farther south. Rather, the western edge of the foothills turned *up* against the front ranges rather than *down,* giving the foothills a general *easterly* tilt rather than the westerly one more common elsewhere in the Canadian Rockies.

5. Glaciation seems to have been lighter in the northern Rockies than it was in the central or southern Rockies. This seems odd (the northern Rockies are farther *north,* after all), but it is logical when you consider that much of the neighboring Yukon, which is even farther north, has not been glaciated at all.

Let us drive west from Fort Nelson on the Alaska Highway to see the northern Rockies.

Plains margin

The western edge of the Interior Plains is different here than it is in the central or southern Rockies. **Cuestas** (like hogback ridges, page 16, but with the ridge-forming rock layer dipping gently rather than steeply) mark the edge of the Interior Plains quite distinctly. South of Peace River the plains/foothills boundary is difficult to detect from the topography, but here it is obvious.

The plains margin is further accentuated by a long valley, 10-20 km wide, that follows the eastern edge of the northern foothills. This unnamed valley has no counterpart south of Peace River; it runs from just north of the Peace to the Liard and beyond, worn into soft Cretaceous shale. Hard sandstone and conglomerate layers of the Dunvegan Formation (page 164) form the cuestas along the eastern wall. The Prophet and Muskwa rivers follow the valley today; perhaps they cut it originally.

Occasional patches of till show that glacial ice has touched this area, but either a long time ago and/or not heavily, for beds of sandstone and conglomerate capping the cuestas overhang shaly slopes beneath, and the land is much-dissected with small streamcourses. These are relatively fragile landforms that are destroyed by glacial erosion. They are more typical of the plains margin around Denver than they are of the Canadian Rockies.

Foothills

Having noted differences in the plains margin, consider the foothills. In the central and southern Rockies the foothills belt is marked by thrust faults and tight folds. Here the rock is gently folded and there are no thrust faults at the surface, although geologists infer that they exist farther down.

The rock itself is rather like that found all along the foothills of the Canadian Rockies—Mesozoic shale and sandstone—but it lacks the coal content of the foothills south of Peace River.

The Alaska Highway enters the foothills along Tetsa River. These are large, rolling foothills, bringing to mind the Appalachians of eastern North America. The northern-Rockies foothills rise about 600 m above the river; summit elevations are typically 1350-1650 m. The hills are steep-sided and convex, following the underlying bedrock folds. This is interesting; it suggests a landscape that is more water-worn than glacier-worn. Could the northern foothills have escaped the most recent major ice advance? (The late-Wisconsinan, page 196.) Possibly, but no detailed glacial-history study has been done here.

Mountain front

Cross-cutting valleys like that of the Tetsa River are narrow, but flat-floored from a deep, gravelly fill. Could the gravel be outwash from glaciation upstream?

Yes. At the mountain front, the glacial character is abruptly restored, along with the familiar physiographic style of the central and southern Canadian Rockies. The valley broadens and becomes U-shaped. The peaks exhibit glacial cirques (page 213). The rock at the mountain front dips to the southwest, like it does in the central Canadian Rockies, producing steep eastern faces and gentler western ones—the dip slopes so typical of the whole range. At Summit Lake, high point on the Alaska Highway as it crosses the northern Rockies, the landscape bears a striking resemblance to that seen in Crowsnest Pass, over 1200 km away. This demonstrates the remarkable physiographic integrity of the Canadian Rockies.

Although familiar-looking, the mountains at Summit Lake are smaller. Topographic relief at the pass is 750 m, 400 m less than that seen in Crowsnest Pass, where the relief is 1150 m.

Purcell-like rock

Beyond Summit Lake comes something unexpected: colorful rock that looks very much like the Purcell Supergroup (page 71) of the Waterton/Glacier region at the other end of the Canadian Rockies. Called informally the **Muskwa assemblage,** (page 77) this unit is roughly the same age as the Purcell strata.

However, close examination has shown that the Muskwa assemblage does not correlate with the Purcell. Geologists doubt that Purcell-type rock ever extended from one end of the Canadian Rockies to the other. The striking resemblance shows mainly that environmental conditions in the Middle Proterozoic were much

A cuesta along the margin of the Interior Plains. View is from the Alaska Highway west of Fort Nelson.

The northern foothills along the Alaska Highway at Tetsa River.

the same at two distant locations on the barren coast of North America 1.5 billion years ago.

Lest one think that this ancient rock is characteristic of the northern Canadian Rockies, please be aware that the Muskwa assemblage occurs only from Prophet River north, and that it is patchy. Most northern Rockies sediments range from Late Proterozoic to Late Mesozoic in age, just as they do farther south. There are no through-going roads between Summit Lake and Pine Pass to provide easy views of what might be considered typical northern-Rockies scenery, but the views around Pine Pass are more typical of the region than the ones at Summit Lake.

Main/front ranges

Geologists do not divide the northern Rockies into front ranges and main ranges. The country west of Summit Lake *looks* like the main ranges: old rock, faulted here and there, gently dipping west until it runs into a shale belt like that of the western main ranges; there it becomes intensely deformed. This would make the main-range belt very thick here—over 100 km across—and the front ranges very thin—only about 5 km across.

But some researchers think that the main ranges gradually disappear between Jasper and Peace River, so in the northern Rockies there are only the foothills and front ranges, rather like the situation in the southern Rockies. Others think that the front ranges lie *under* the northern foothills, and that everything from the mountain front west is the main ranges. (Personal communication, Gordon Taylor, GSC Calgary.)

Western slope

Back to our tour. "Summit Lake" is just that: a lake lying close to the highest point along the Alaska Highway in the northern Rockies (1340 m). Summit Lake is yet another of the ponds so common in major Rockies passes. But the divide here (Summit Pass, a kilometre west of the lake), is not the continental divide. North of Peace River the continental divide swings west of the Rockies, so water flowing west from Summit Pass eventually hits the east-flowing Liard River and cuts back across the Rockies. Nothing winds up in the Pacific; it all goes to the Arctic Ocean via the Mackenzie River.

So the eastern slope of the northern Rockies is lower in elevation than the western slope—the opposite of the situation in the central and southern Rockies, where the eastern slope is higher.

Another important difference is that the Rocky Mountain Trench is a strike-slip feature (horizontal plate-motion, page 176) here rather than a half-graben (up-and-down motion along a normal fault, page 177) as it is in the southern section.

The downhill ride west from Summit Lake is steep, typical of the abrupt western-slope descents one finds throughout the Canadian Rockies. But the western slope is not lower than the eastern slope, as it is in the central and southern regions. Logically, the western slope of the far northern Rockies cannot be lower than the eastern slope, for both sides drain to the same river—the Liard. In the central and southern Rockies the western slope can be lower because it drains independently of the eastern slope (eastern to Hudson Bay or the Arctic Ocean, western to the Pacific).

West of Summit Lake, the *freshness* of glaciation strikes the eye. Cirques and valleys west of the pass have the rough look of late-Wisconsinan ice attack. In contrast, moraines in and east of the pass look older, as do east-facing cirques: they are rounded by weathering and incised by running water. Coupled with the lightly glaciated look of the foothills and plains margin, this suggests that eastern-slope glacial features in the northern Rockies (at least as displayed along the Alaska Highway) are older than late-Wisconsinan. I hope a detailed glacial study will soon be made here.

Typical topography in the northern Rockies, as seen along the Alaska Highway near Summit Lake. View is to the northwest, down the valley of MacDonald Creek.

Liard Hot Springs, along the Alaska Highway at the northern end of the Canadian Rockies. This is the main pool, which has its source at the far end.

Summit Pass is a good place to see Late Silurian and Early Devonian rocks not present in the central Rockies (see page 66 for a geological sketch of the pass area). Farther west comes the Purcell-like rock, which includes diabase dykes (igneous sheets cutting across the sedimentary layers; see page 75). Look for one of these dykes at the first bridge over Toad River.

At Muncho Lake one comes across something important in the geological history of the northern Rockies: the Atan Group (page 91). During the Cambrian Period, rifting stretched the continental margin in this area, causing blocks of the continental margin to slide down along normal faults. This tilting exposed the edges above sea level to create dry land—possibly mountains (see diagram 2 on page 45). As the mountains eroded, a layer of coarse conglomerate—the Atan Group—quickly accumulated just offshore. Next to the faults there are deposits 650 m thick.

Following Trout River down to the Liard, the Alaska Highway leaves the Canadian Rockies. The Liard seems to have maintained its course across the mountains during their creation. A rough road leads east to the **Grand Canyon of the Liard,** where this river, the biggest in or near the Rockies, is still busily cutting itself into the earth. Drilling along the canyon by crews from BC Hydro suggests that the government is thinking of subjecting the Liard to the indignity of a dam.

Liard Hot Springs marks the end of our journey. We ease into the clear, steamy, sulphurous water. Aaaah . . .

Summary of northern-Rockies features

Boundaries: Liard River (north), transitional between Jasper and Peace River (south), the Interior Plains escarpment (east) and northern Rocky Mountain Trench (west).

Highest point: there are few verified summit elevations in the northern Rockies and several candidates in the range of 2970-2990 m. Mt. Smythe, circa 2990 m in Kwadacha Lakes park, is probably the highest, although Mt. Ulysses, a peak at the headwaters of Besa River, is given the same elevation. Timberline is around 1700 m at Pine Pass/Peace River and 1500 m in the north end.

Foothills: 25-50 km wide, gently folded and turned up to the east rather than thrust-faulted and dipping to the west like the rest of the Canadian Rockies. Made of Mesozoic shale and sandstone like the central and southern foothills, but lacking the coal. Aligned in parallel rows and rather high, so there is trellis drainage, but without the hogback character of the central-Rockies foothills. Little obvious glacial character except for outwash along through-going streams. Eastern boundary is well defined by shale valley and erosional edge of the Interior Plains.

Front ranges/main ranges: difficult to differentiate, but up to 110 km across in total. Middle Proterozoic to Late Paleozoic rock, not as extensively folded and thrust-faulted as in the central Rockies, and shalier, but with the same gentle westerly dip to the beds. Old Purcell-like rock along the divide in the north end (Muskwa assemblage) produces Waterton-like color in the peaks, although most of the area is shaly and drab, with lower summits and less-rugged topography. The geological history here is slightly different and more complex than that of the central and southern Rockies. The drainage is less regular.

Rocky Mountain Trench: follows a major sideways-slip fault. This is sometimes called by geologists the "Northern Rocky Mountain Trench," to differentiate it from the southern section, which is a normal-fault feature, not a strike-slip one.

Rocks and events
Up through the layers, one by one

Welcome to the geological details. Readers with no geological background may find this chapter heavy going, but I have tried to keep the jargon to a minimum and to define terms the first time they are used—or to give the page number of the complete definition. When in doubt, use the index at the back of the book to get to the definition; it will usually be on the first page listed for that word.

To start, here is a way of conceptualizing the aggregate 30-km-thick sequence of sedimentary rock that makes up the Canadian Rockies. I think of it as *four great layers*, plus a skiff of soft, geologically recent glacial and post-glacial sediments. This is a grossly simplified scheme, but it fits the basic geological history of the region. Further, each of the four units has a characteristic geographic distribution.

No formal names are available for these super-layers, so for the purposes of this book I have given them informal names. Here they are, from oldest to youngest:

1. Purcell-type sediments

This is the ancient (1500-1300 Ma) 9-km-thick collection of colorful red-and-green mudstone and gray limestone found in the southern part of the region, mostly south of Crowsnest Pass in the Waterton/Glacier area. Near the north end of the Rockies there is similar rock that is about the same age.

The Purcell material and its northern equivalent (the Muskwa assemblage, page 77) represents a period of shallow-water deposition on what must have been a fairly wide continental shelf. I say "must have been" because after Purcell time a large chunk of that shelf broke off from the rest of the North American Plate, carried away by continental drift to parts unknown.

2. Old clastic unit

Next up the stack is roughly 10 km of conglomerate, gritstone, sandstone and shale with very little limestone: the Miette Group and Gog/Atan groups, which are **clastic** rock, meaning rock made of *eroded particles,* in this case weathered from land and deposited in seawater. The old clastic unit is characteristic of the main ranges of the Rockies; it is 770-550 Ma in age.

Through most of its thickness the old clastic unit is the result of rapid deposition along a new continental edge from granitic mountains eroding beside the sea—somewhat like the situation today along the coasts of California or British Columbia.

3. Middle carbonate unit

Above the old clastics lies a very different unit some 6.5 km thick. Much of it is limestone (or its close relative, dolomite), which has formed *in place,* in the sea, from crystals of lime generated by living things. For the details of this process, see page 72. Limestone and dolomite are called the **carbonate** rocks, for they contain mainly calcium and magnesium carbonate.

In the central Rockies the middle carbonate unit is characteristic of the front ranges and eastern main ranges (in the western main ranges and western ranges it is replaced by limy shales deposited at the same time). The shaly areas (western range main ranges) record deeper water at the edge of the continental

BASIC GEOLOGICAL COLUMN FOR THE CANADIAN ROCKIES
See map on page 10 for physiographic areas mentioned

Surficial deposits, up to 300 m thick
Till, river and lake deposits, slides and debris, windblown material
Age: Quaternary, 1.9 Ma to the present
Found in all three regions (northern, central, southern)

Young clastic unit, 5 km thick
Mostly sandstone and shale. Age: Mesozoic and Tertiary, 245–1.9 Ma
Exposed in foothills and front ranges, all three regions,
and in Rocky Mountain Trench, Flathead and Elk valleys

Middle carbonate unit, 6.5 km thick
Mostly limestone/dolomite and shale
Age: Paleozoic, 540–258 Ma
Exposed in front ranges and main ranges in all three regions

Old clastic unit, 10 km thick
Mostly gritstone, shale and quartzite
Age: Hadrynian and Early Cambrian, 770–540 Ma
Exposed in main ranges of the central and northern regions

Purcell-type unit, 8.8 km thick
Mostly mudstone and limestone
Age: Helikian, 1500–1300 Ma
Exposed in southern front ranges and northern front/main ranges

North American Plate, 30–50 km thick
Granite and gneiss
Age: Aphebian, averaging 1700 Ma
Underlies all three regions

shelf. North of Peace River this unit is shalier throughout than it is in the central Rockies, but it occupies the same time slot (Middle Cambrian through Permian; 540-245 Ma) and outcrops in the same place: from the mountain front west, not in the foothills.

When the ancient mountains that had supplied the sediments of the old clastic unit had been leveled, the sea crept inland over the low-lying continental plate and the middle carbonates were laid down in shallow water that was full of life. This is the time in which most of western Canada's oil and gas reserves accumulated.

4. Young clastic unit

Above the middle carbonates is the other big clastic sequence in our area: 5000 m of rather soft sandstone and shale encompassing many groups and formations. The young clastics are well exposed in the foothills, and to a lesser extent in the front ranges. They range in age from 245 Ma to the beginning of Pleistocene glaciation about 1.9 Ma. Much of this rock is **nonmarine**; i.e., deposited in fresh water or on land.

The young clastics record a major change in the geological history of North America at about 210 Ma. The continental plate changed its motion and plowed westward into material lying on oceanic crust. That material was added to the western edge of the continent. It was under great compression, so it formed new mountain ranges from west to east. The young clastic unit is the sediment worn from those mountains and spread along their eastern slope; it marks the progress of the disturbance. Toward the end came the Rockies themselves.

Usually too soft to be thought of as rock, geologically recent layers of glacial till, stream gravel, lake silt, volcanic ash, wind-blown silt, sand dunes and soils form a thin layer on the bedrock.

The regional extent of these four main units is shown on the geological map of the Canadian Rockies (page 47). The surficial-deposit unit is too thin to map at that scale.

Beyond this, the big picture, we are into the scenery layer-by-layer. A branch of geology known as **stratigraphy** (from **strata,** geologese for "layers") deals with such things; for readers unfamiliar with basic stratigraphic concepts the next few paragraphs should be helpful.

Stratigraphers think of a large area of sedimentary rock as something like a floor covered with pancakes. Each pancake is equivalent to one **formation:** the stratigrapher's name for a sequence of similar-looking layers. Some of the pancakes are thin and some are thick; some are large and some are small.

The various pancakes overlie and overlap one another; most are intergrown at the edges. For example, one pancake may comprise sand carried by a river into the sea at one point along an ancient coastline, while a hundred kilometres away along the same coastline another river was carrying in mud. Each deposit spread out just offshore, thickened and eventually hardened to rock as a separate formation, one of sandstone, the other of mudstone. They are the same age, and the edges of the formations feather into each other, but the rock is different.

Suppose that, as time went by, a third river appeared along the coast, halfway between the other two. This one was carrying coarse gravel, which accumulated as a conglomerate formation that overlay the sandstone and mudstone formations.

ESSENTIALS OF STRATIGRAPHY

1. Two rivers carry two different kinds of sediment into the sea.

2. Time passes and the sediments accumulate.
A third river begins to flow, producing a third kind of deposit.

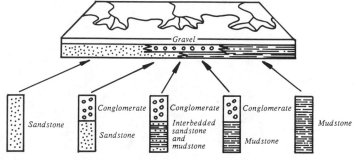

3. When the soft sediments harden to rock, here are the resulting formations as a geologist would see them at various locations.

Deposition from all rivers continued, so the conglomerate intergrew at the edges with the other units. The diagram shows the stratigraphy resulting from this geological history. The **geologic columns** in the diagram show what the stratigrapher would see of the stack at different locations.

By drawing geologic columns of the stratigraphy at several places in the region and linking the tops and bottoms of the various formations with lines, it is possible to figure out how the formations overlie and overlap. Figuring out such natural three-dimensional puzzles can become quite complicated—especially when the layering has been bent by folding and broken by faulting, as is the case in the Canadian Rockies.

Geologic columns for the region are given on pages 42-44. They show the formations of the Rockies as if they were not folded or faulted; that is, the columns display the original order before mountain-building made a mess of things. Don't expect to find the whole sequence in any particular outcrop; usually just part of a single formation is visible.

But there are some spots along the main highways that offer particularly good views of several formations in undisturbed order. Beginning on page 51, you will find *labelled sketches* of these views.

Fifty years ago those columns and sketches could not have been drawn. There was simply too little geological information available about the area. For the region north of Peace River there is barely enough data even now, as I write this in 1986. Researchers are still out there every summer, walking up and down the mountains with their hammers in their hands and their packs full of stones, filling in the gaps in the geologic maps. They are lucky enough to be getting first whack at what remains of a scientific frontier.

Those who preceded them in the 1950s and 1960s, which was probably the golden age of Canadian Rockies geology, can reflect with pride that fieldwork was perhaps more exciting and certainly much tougher then. Entire ranges had not been explored, and the field parties went in by horse rather than by helicopter.

We owe these hardy folks a thank-you for working out the general geological history of the Canadian Rockies. That history is presented in the block diagrams on pages 45-46. Following those diagrams, and the other graphic material in the geology picture pages, the rock record is examined in greater detail, formation by formation, from the bottom up. Be prepared for some surprises; the world was rather different 1.5 billion years ago.

A Geological Survey of Canada field party in the Canadian Rockies during the 1950s. Photo courtesy Geological Survey of Canada.

GEOLOGY PICTURE PAGES

Page

42 Formations and groups of the Canadian Rockies (correlation charts)

45 Block diagrams of key phases in the region's geological history

47 Geological maps

50 Cross-sections

51 Labeled sketches of roadside views

67 Illustrations of fossils

Key to symbols and abbreviations used on the charts that follow

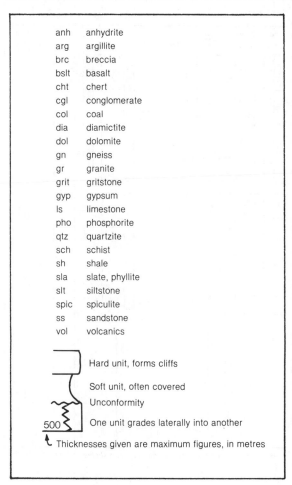

anh	anhydrite
arg	argillite
brc	breccia
bslt	basalt
cht	chert
cgl	conglomerate
col	coal
dia	diamictite
dol	dolomite
gn	gneiss
gr	granite
grit	gritstone
gyp	gypsum
ls	limestone
pho	phosphorite
qtz	quartzite
sch	schist
sh	shale
sla	slate, phyllite
slt	siltstone
spic	spiculite
ss	sandstone
vol	volcanics

Hard unit, forms cliffs

Soft unit, often covered

Unconformity

500 One unit grades laterally into another

Thicknesses given are maximum figures, in metres

Formations and groups of the Canadian Rockies (summary chart)

Part 1: Proterozoic and older Paleozoic

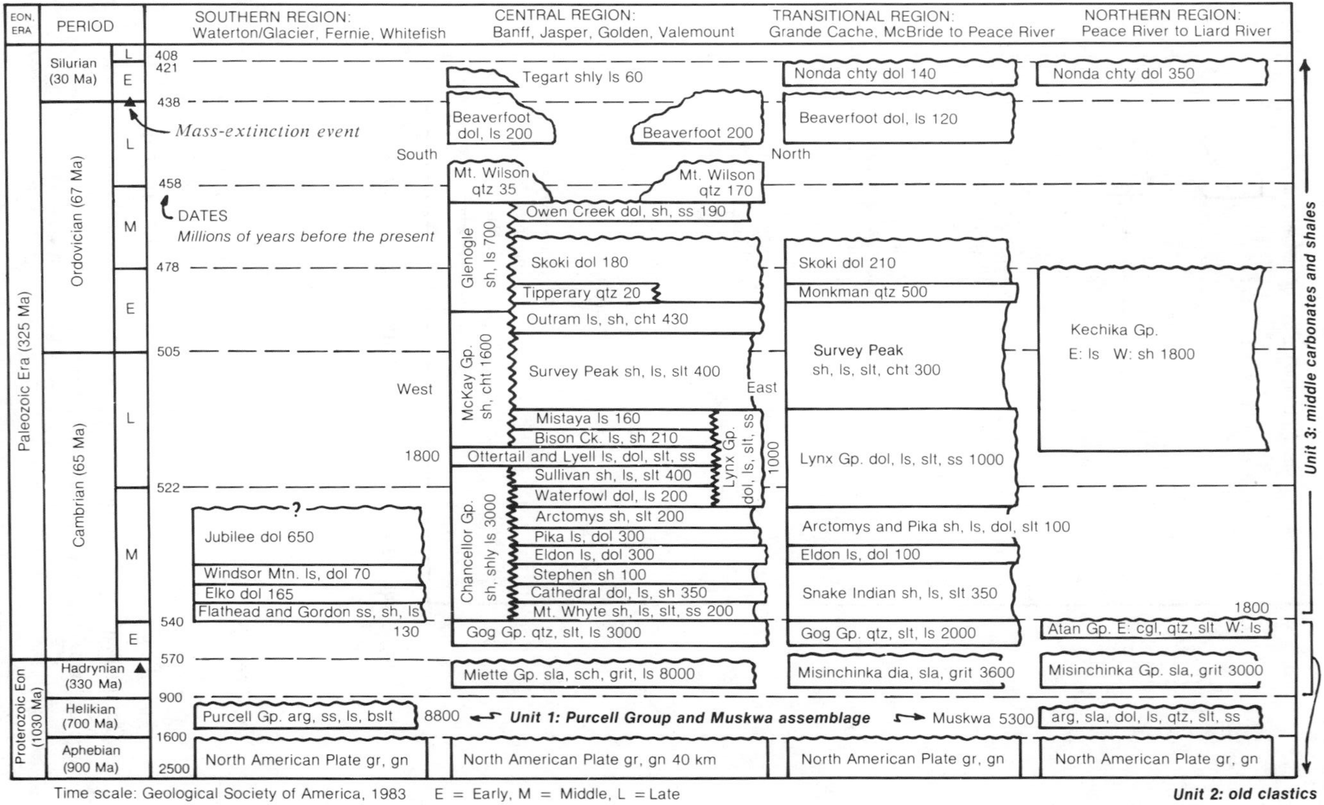

EON/ERA	Proterozoic Eon (1030 Ma)		Paleozoic Era (325 Ma)		
PERIOD	Helikian (700 Ma)	Hadrynian (330 Ma)	Cambrian (65 Ma)	Ordovician (67 Ma)	Silurian (30 Ma)

Aphebian (900 Ma)

Time scale: Geological Society of America, 1983   E = Early, M = Middle, L = Late

Dates / Millions of years before the present: 2500, 1600, 900, 570, 540, 522, 505, 478, 458, 438, 421, 408

Mass-extinction event

SOUTHERN REGION: Waterton/Glacier, Fernie, Whitefish
- Purcell Gp. arg, ss, ls, bslt
- Flathead and Gordon ss, sh, ls
- Elko dol 165
- Windsor Mtn. dol 70
- Jubilee dol 650
- Beaverfoot dol, ls 200
- Tegart shly ls 60

CENTRAL REGION: Banff, Jasper, Golden, Valemount
- Miette Gp. sla, sch, grit, ls 8000
- Gog Gp. qtz, slt, ls 3000
- Chancellor Gp. sh, shly ls 3000
- Mt. Whyte sh, ls, slt, ss 200
- Cathedral dol, ls, sh 350
- Stephen sh 100
- Eldon ls, dol 300
- Pika ls, dol 300
- Arctomys sh, slt 200
- Waterfowl dol, ls 200
- Sullivan sh, ls, slt 400
- Ottertail and Lyell ls, dol, slt, ss
- Lynx Gp. dol, ls, slt, ss
- McKay Gp. sh, cht 1600
- Bison Ck. ls, sh 210
- Mistaya ls 160
- Survey Peak sh, ls, slt 400
- Glenogle sh, ls 700
- Outram ls, sh, slt 430
- Tipperary qtz 20
- Skoki dol 180
- Owen Creek dol, sh, ss 190
- Mt. Wilson qtz 35
- Beaverfoot dol, ls 170

West 1800   South   East 1000

TRANSITIONAL REGION: Grande Cache, McBride to Peace River
- Misinchinka dia, sla, slt 3600
- Gog Gp. qtz, slt, ls 2000
- Snake Indian sh, ls, slt 350
- Eldon ls, dol 100
- Arctomys and Pika sh, ls, dol, slt 100
- Lynx Gp. dol, ls, slt, ss 1000
- Survey Peak sh, ls, slt, cht 300
- Monkman qtz 500
- Skoki dol 210
- Beaverfoot dol, ls 120

North

NORTHERN REGION: Peace River to Liard River
- Misinchinka Gp. sla, slt, ss
- Atan Gp. E: cgl, qtz, slt W: ls
- Kechika Gp. E: ls W: sh 1800
- Nonda chty dol 350
- Nonda chty dol 140

1800

North American Plate gr, gn   North American Plate gr, gn 40 km   North American Plate gr, gn   North American Plate gr, gn

← Unit 1: Purcell Group and Muskwa assemblage →
Muskwa 5300   arg, sla, dol, ls, qtz, slt, ss

Unit 2: old clastics

← Unit 3: middle carbonates and shales →

130   8800

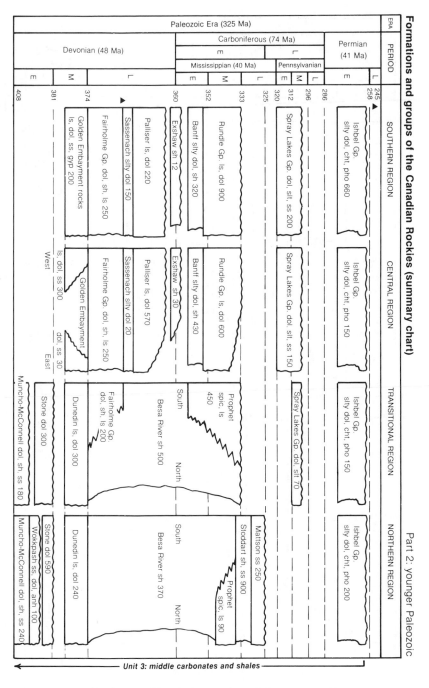

Formations and groups of the Canadian Rockies (summary chart)

Part 2: younger Paleozoic

For key to abbreviations and symbols, see page 41

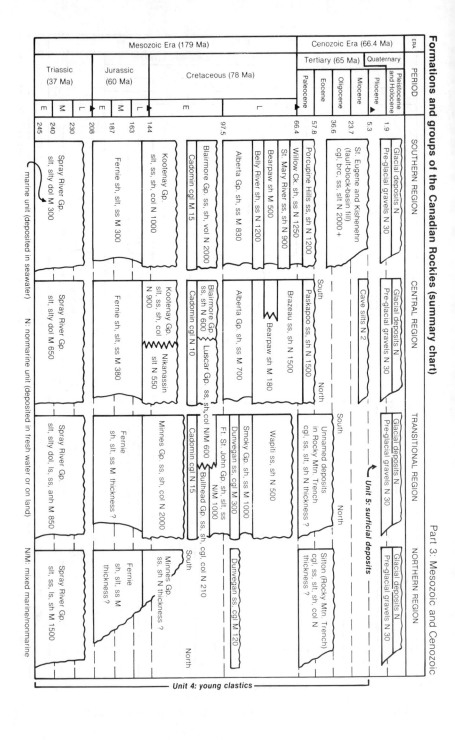

Formations and groups of the Canadian Rockies (summary chart)

Part 3: Mesozoic and Cenozoic

ERA	Mesozoic Era (179 Ma)			Cenozoic Era (66.4 Ma)	
PERIOD	Triassic (37 Ma)	Jurassic (60 Ma)	Cretaceous (78 Ma)	Tertiary (65 Ma)	Quaternary

SOUTHERN REGION

Spray River Gp. slt, slty dol M 300

Fernie sh, slt, ss M 300

Kootenay Gp. slt, ss, sh, col N 1000

Cadomin cgl M 15

Blairmore Gp. ss, sh, vol N 2000

Alberta Gp. sh, ss M 830

Belly River sh, ss N 1200

Bearpaw sh M 500

St. Mary River ss, sh N 900

Willow Ck. sh, ss N 1250

Porcupine Hills ss, sh N 1200

St. Eugene and Kishenehn (fault-block-basin fill) cgl, brc, ss, slt N 2000 +

Pre-glacial gravels N 30

Glacial deposits N

CENTRAL REGION

Spray River Gp. slt, slty dol M 650

Fernie sh, slt, ss M 380

Kootenay Gp. slt, ss, sh, col N 900

Nikanassin slt N 550

Cadomin cgl N 10

Blairmore Gp. ss, sh N 600

Luscar Gp. ss, sh, col N/M 600

Alberta Gp. sh, ss M 700

Bearpaw sh M 180

Brazeau ss, sh N 1500

Paskapoo ss, sh N 1500

South   North

Cave silts N 2

Pre-glacial gravels N 30

Glacial deposits N

TRANSITIONAL REGION

Spray River Gp. slt, slty dol, ls, ss, anh M 850

Fernie sh, slt, ss M thickness ?

Minnes Gp. ss, sh, col N 2000

Cadomin cgl N 15

Bullhead Gp. ss, sh, cgl, slt, ss N/M 600

Ft. St. John Gp. sh, slt, ss N/M 1000

Dunvegan ss, cgl M 300

Smoky Gp. sh, ss M 1000

Wapiti ss, sh N 500

Unnamed deposits in Rocky Mtn. Trench cgl, ss, slt, sh N thickness ?

South   North

South   North

Pre-glacial gravels N 30

Glacial deposits N

NORTHERN REGION

Spray River Gp. slt, ss, ls, sh M 1500

Fernie sh, slt, ss M thickness ?

Minnes Gp. ss, sh N thickness ?

Dunvegan ss, cgl N 120

Dunvegan ss, cgl, col N 210

Sitton (Rocky Mtn. Trench) cgl, ss, slt, sh, col N thickness ?

South   North

Pre-glacial gravels N 30

Glacial deposits N

Unit 5: surficial deposits

— **Unit 4: young clastics** —

M: marine unit (deposited in seawater)

N: nonmarine unit (deposited in fresh water or on land)

N/M: mixed marine/nonmarine

Block diagrams of key phases in the geological history of the Canadian Rockies

1. Earliest known sediments deposited (Helikian, 1500--1300 Ma)

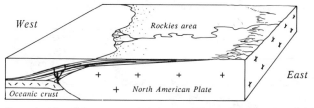

Fine-grained Purcell Supergroup and Muskwa Assemblage collect on continental shelf.

2. Old clastic unit deposited (Hadrynian, 730--570 Ma)

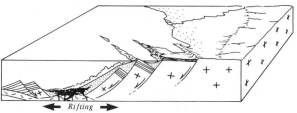

Some of continental shelf breaks away, taking with it most Purcell/Muskwa sediments. Coarse Miette/Misinchinka sediments pour over new continental edge, are spread far out to sea by turbidity currents.

3. Kicking Horse Rim appears (Early Cambrian to Early Silurian, (570--425 Ma)

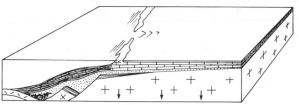

Continental edge cools, sinks deeper into mantle. Sea moves inland over new continental shelf. Kicking Horse Rim divides deep water to west (shaly zone) from shallow water to east (limy zone).

4. West Alberta Ridge rises (Early Silurian to Early Devonian, 425--390 Ma)

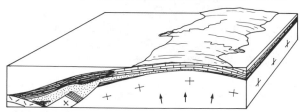

Mild uplift raises most of Rockies area above sea level. Some sediments are lost to erosion in central and southern region, creating major unconformity, but deposition continues in northern Rockies.

5. Reefs develop (Middle and Late Devonian, 385--367 Ma)

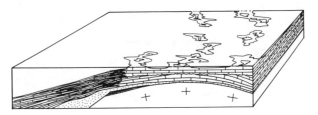

Warm, shallow seawater covers entire area, fostering growth of reef-building stromatoporoids. Mass-extinction event wipes out reef-builders, but many organisms survive and limestone/shale continues to accumulate to end of Paleozoic Era.

6. Mountain-building begins (Columbian Orogeny: Middle Jurassic to Early Cretaceous, 175--100 Ma)

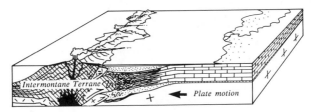

North American continent reverses direction of drift as Atlantic Ocean begins to open. Intermontane Terrane is run down, attaches to west coast, creating Columbia, Omineca and Cassiar Mountains. Rockies area receives coarse sediment from new highlands to west. Western ranges and main ranges appear at 120--100 Ma.

7. Mountain-building continues (Laramide Orogeny: Late Cretaceous to Middle Eocene, 85--45 Ma)

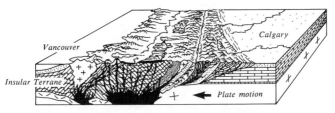

Insular Terrane attaches to North America, causing renewed mountain-building in western ranges and main ranges. Sea leaves the region. Front ranges and foothills appear. Compression ends at about 45 Ma; sideways plate motion creates Northern Rocky Mountain Trench Fault. Stretching across southern British Columbia causes block-faulting in Rocky Mountain Trench, Flathead and Elk valleys. Some faults are still active today.

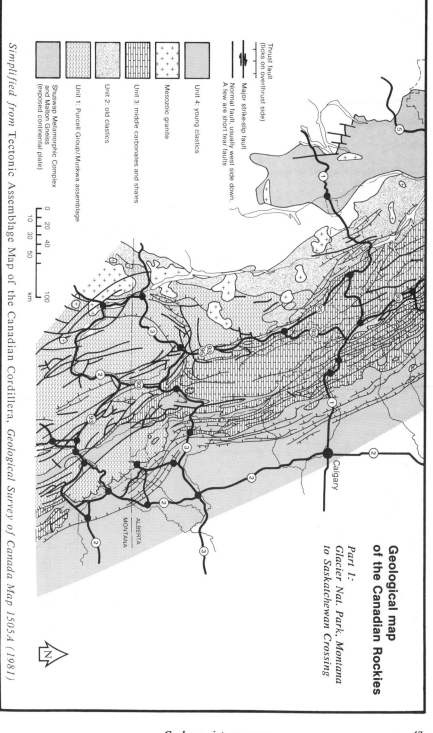

**Geological map
of the Canadian Rockies**

*Part 1:
Glacier Nat. Park, Montana
to Saskatchewan Crossing*

Thrust fault
(ticks on overthrust side)

Major strike-slip fault

Normal fault, usually west side down.
A few are short tear faults

Unit 4: young clastics

Mesozoic granite

Unit 3: middle carbonates and shales

Unit 2: old clastics

Unit 1: Purcell Group/Muskwa assemblage

Shuswap Metamorphic Complex
and Malton Gneiss
(exposed continental plate)

0   10   20   30   40   50   100
km

N

Calgary

ALBERTA
MONTANA

Simplified from Tectonic Assemblage Map of the Canadian Cordillera, *Geological Survey of Canada Map 1505A (1981)*

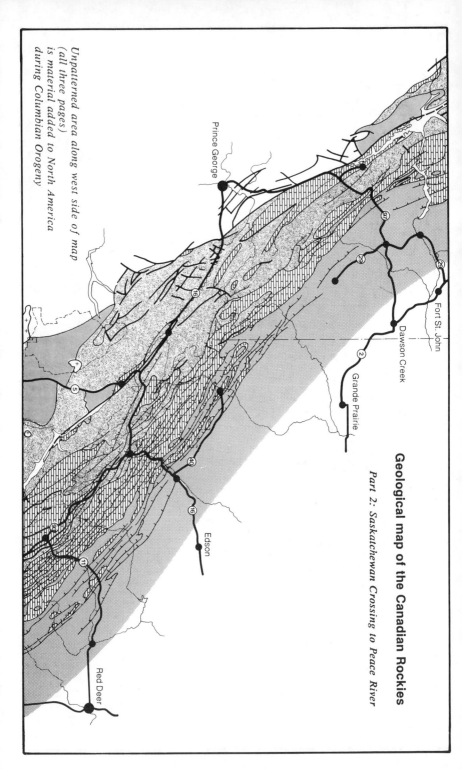

Geological map of the Canadian Rockies

Part 2: Saskatchewan Crossing to Peace River

Prince George

Fort St. John

Dawson Creek

Grande Prairie

Edson

Red Deer

Unpatterned area along west side of map (all three pages) is material added to North America during Columbian Orogeny

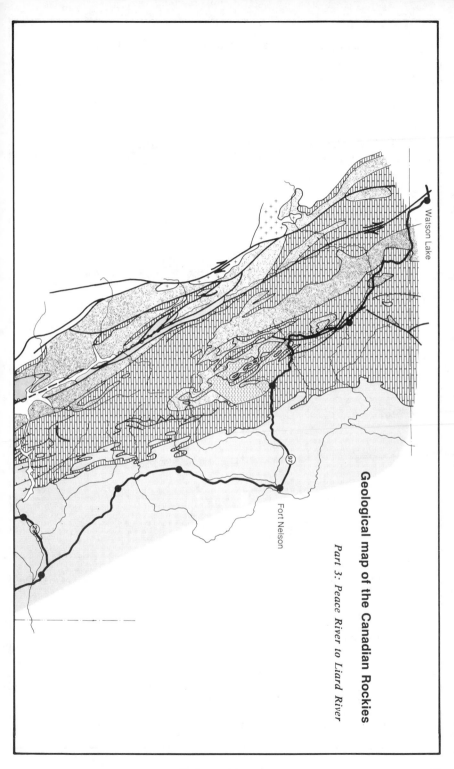

Geological map of the Canadian Rockies

Part 3: Peace River to Liard River

Watson Lake

Fort Nelson

Geologic cross-sections of the Canadian Rockies

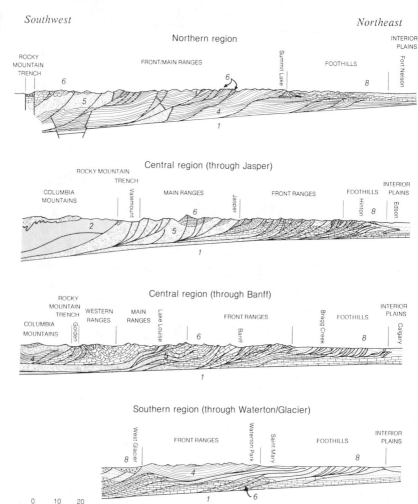

Southwest　　　　　　　　　　　　　　　　　　　　　　　*Northeast*

Northern region

Central region (through Jasper)

Central region (through Banff)

Southern region (through Waterton/Glacier)

```
0   10   20
km └──┴──┘
```
Horizontal and vertical scales are equal

Towns are shown in approximate geological positions
(not accurate topographic positions)

Key to rock units

1. *North American Plate (Aphebian gneiss and granite)*
2. *Shuswap Metamorphic Complex (upthrust Aphebian gneiss)*
3. *Oceanic crust (basalt and other mantle-derived rocks, age undetermined)*
4. *Purcell Supergroup/Muskwa Assemblage (Helikian argillite, slate, limestone)*
5. *Old clastic unit (Hadrynian and Early Cambrian gritstone, slate, quartzite)*
6. *Middle carbonate unit (Paleozoic limestone/dolomite, shale)*
7. *Mesozoic granite and gneiss (found west of the Rockies)*
8. *Young clastic unit (Mesozoic and Cenozoic sandstone, shale, conglomerate)*

SKETCHES OF GEOLOGY SEEN ALONG HIGHWAYS IN THE CANADIAN ROCKIES

Views along Going-to-the-Sun Road in Glacier National Park, Montana
Reproduced from Geological Guide for the CSPG 1977 Waterton - Glacier Park Field Conference
(Canadian Society of Petroleum Geologists, Calgary)

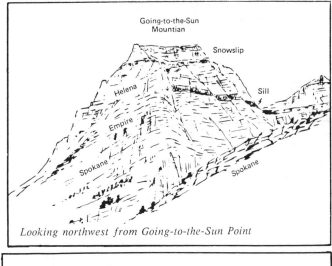

Looking northwest from Going-to-the-Sun Point

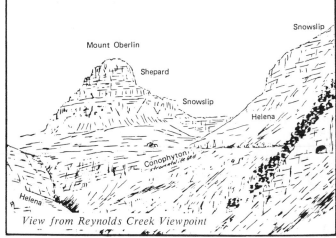

View from Reynolds Creek Viewpoint

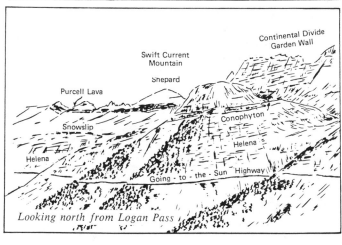

Looking north from Logan Pass

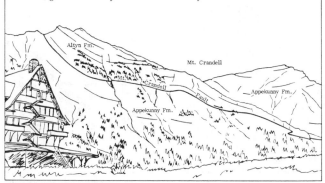

Looking southeast from near Waterton Park townsite

Looking northwest from the Prince of Wales Hotel

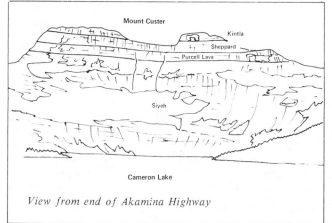

View from end of Akamina Highway

Looking west to the mountain front near Frank

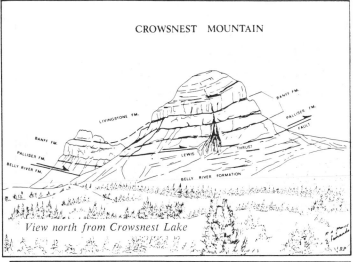

CROWSNEST MOUNTAIN

View north from Crowsnest Lake

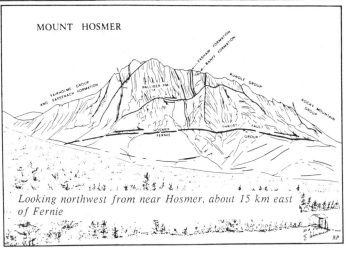

MOUNT HOSMER

Looking northwest from near Hosmer, about 15 km east of Fernie

*Geology seen along Highway 3 through Crowsnest Pass
Sketches from guidebooks of the 24th International Geological Congress, 1972*

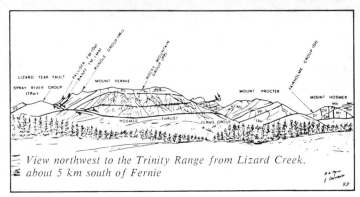

View northwest to the Trinity Range from Lizard Creek, about 5 km south of Fernie

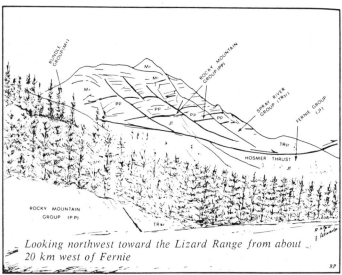

Looking northwest toward the Lizard Range from about 20 km west of Fernie

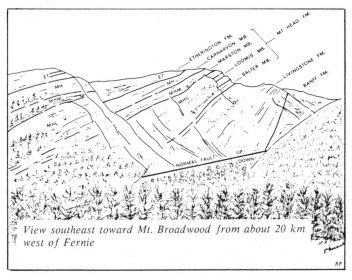

View southeast toward Mt. Broadwood from about 20 km west of Fernie

Looking northwest toward the south end of the Lizard
Range from about 5 km east of Elko

**Geology seen along Highway 93 between Elko and Radium Hot Springs
in the southern Rocky Mountain Trench**
Sketches from guidebooks of the 24th International Geological Congress, 1972

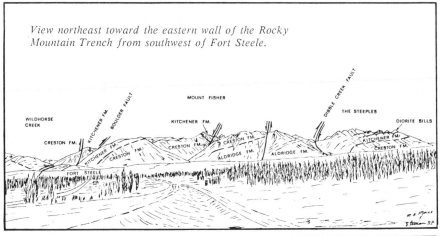

View northeast toward the eastern wall of the Rocky
Mountain Trench from southwest of Fort Steele.

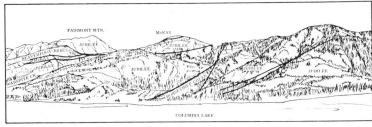

Looking northeast toward the Stanford Range from the
Columbia Lake Viewpoint, between Fairmont Hot Springs
and Canal Flats

Geology picture pages   55

ELPOCA MOUNTAIN

View north from Highwood Pass

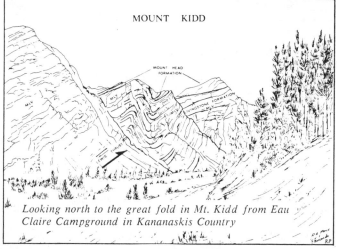

MOUNT KIDD

Looking north to the great fold in Mt. Kidd from Eau Claire Campground in Kananaskis Country

MOUNT LORETTE

View northwest toward Mt. Lorette from about 5 km north of Ribbon Creek

Geology seen along Alberta 40 between Crowsnest Pass and the TransCanada Highway junction (Kananaskis Country)
Sketches from guidebooks of the 24th International Geological Congress, 1972

Geology picture pages

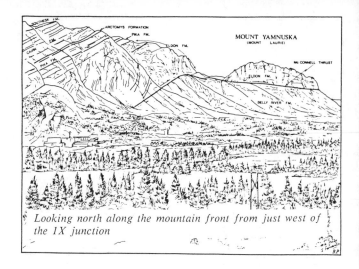

Looking north along the mountain front from just west of the 1X junction

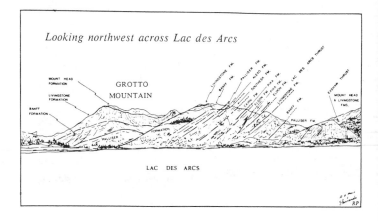

Looking northwest across Lac des Arcs

GROTTO MOUNTAIN

LAC DES ARCS

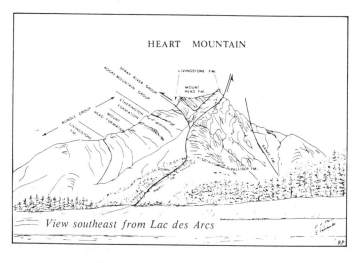

HEART MOUNTAIN

View southeast from Lac des Arcs

Geology seen along the TransCanada Highway east of Canmore
Sketches from guidebooks of the 24th International Geological Congress, 1972

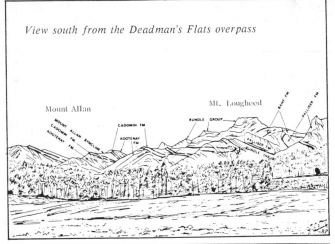

View south from the Deadman's Flats overpass

Mount Allan

Mt. Lougheed

MOUNT ALLAN SYNCLINE
CADOMIN FM.
KOOTENAY FM
CADOMIN FM.
KOOTENAY FM
RUNDLE GROUP
BANFF FM
PALLISER FM
PALLISER FM
RUNDLE THRUST

RP

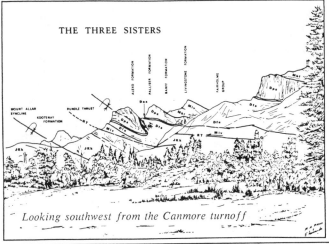

THE THREE SISTERS

MOUNT ALLAN SYNCLINE
KOOTENAY FORMATION
RUNDLE THRUST
ALEXO FORMATION
PALLISER FORMATION
BANFF FORMATION
LIVINGSTONE FORMATION
FAIRHOLME GROUP

Looking southwest from the Canmore turnoff

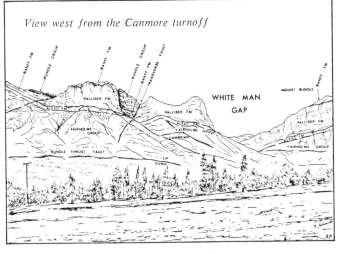

View west from the Canmore turnoff

BANFF FM
RUNDLE GROUP
BANFF FM
RUNDLE GROUP
BANFF FM
TRANSVERSE FAULT
MOUNT RUNDLE
BANFF FM
PALLISER FM
ALEXO FM
PALLISER FM
WHITE MAN GAP
PALLISER FM
FAIRHOLME GROUP
ALEXO FM
FAIRHOLME GROUP
CAMBRIAN
ALEXO FM
FAIRHOLME GROUP
RUNDLE THRUST FAULT
UP
DOWN

RP

*Geology seen along the TransCanada Highway near Canmore
Sketches from guidebooks of the 24th International Geological Congress, 1972*

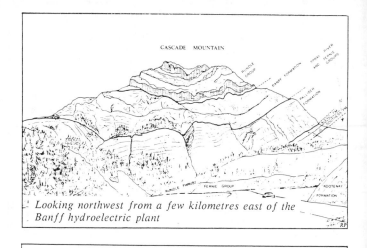

Looking northwest from a few kilometres east of the Banff hydroelectric plant

View southeast across Vermilion Lakes

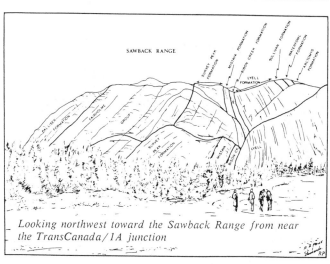

Looking northwest toward the Sawback Range from near the TransCanada/1A junction

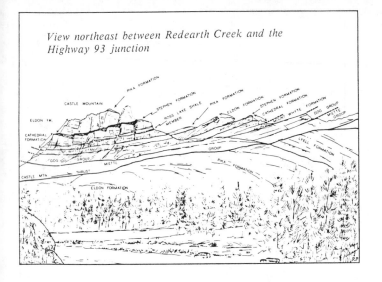

View northeast between Redearth Creek and the
Highway 93 junction

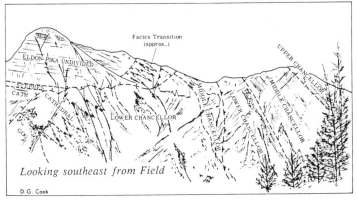

Looking southeast from Field

D.G. Cook

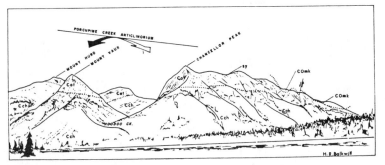

View east from Leanchoil in western Yoho National Park

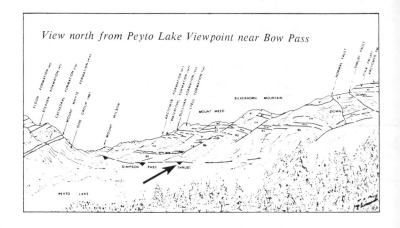

View north from Peyto Lake Viewpoint near Bow Pass

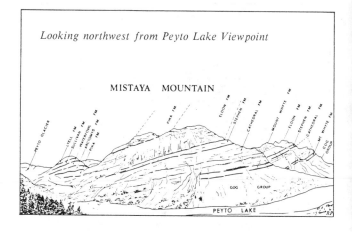

Looking northwest from Peyto Lake Viewpoint

MISTAYA MOUNTAIN

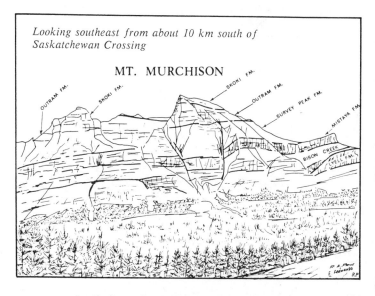

Looking southeast from about 10 km south of Saskatchewan Crossing

MT. MURCHISON

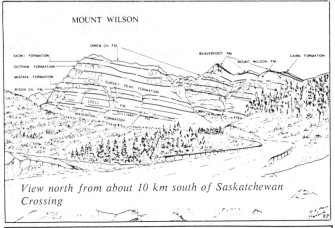

MOUNT WILSON

SKOKI FORMATION
OUTRAM FORMATION
MISTAYA FORMATION
BISON CK. FM.
SURVEY PEAK FORMATION
OWEN CK. FM.
LYELL FM.
SULLIVAN FM.
WATERFOWL FORMATION
BEAVERFOOT FM
MOUNT WILSON FM.
CAIRN FORMATION

View north from about 10 km south of Saskatchewan Crossing

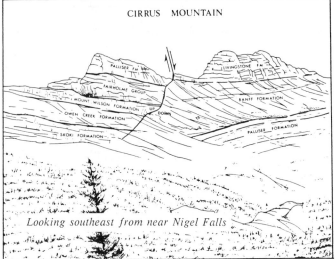

CIRRUS MOUNTAIN

PALLISER FM.
FAIRHOLME GROUP
MOUNT WILSON FORMATION
OWEN CREEK FORMATION
SKOKI FORMATION
UP
DOWN
LIVINGSTONE FM.
BANFF FORMATION
PALLISER FORMATION

Looking southeast from near Nigel Falls

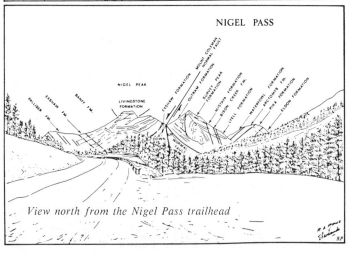

NIGEL PASS

PALLISER FM.
ESHAW FM.
BANFF FM.
NIGEL PEAK
LIVINGSTONE FORMATION
FLESHAW FORMATION
MOUNT COLEMAN NORMAL FAULT
OUTRAM FORMATION
SURVEY PEAK FORMATION
MISTAYA FORMATION
BISON CREEK FM.
LYELL FORMATION
WATERFOWL FORMATION
ARCTOMYS FM.
PIKA FORMATION
ELDON FORMATION
DOWN
NORMAL

View north from the Nigel Pass trailhead

Geology seen along the Icefields Parkway (Alberta 93) between Lake Louise and Jasper Sketches from guidebooks of the 24th International Geological Congress, 1972

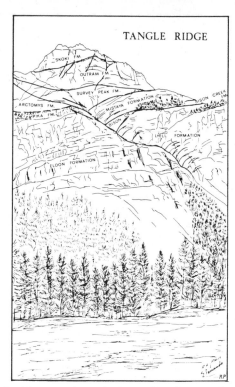

Looking east from the base of the long grade
north of the Columbia Icefield area

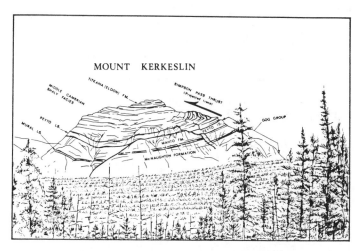

View east from Athabasca Falls

Geology seen along the Icefields Parkway (Alberta 93) in Jasper National Park
Sketches from guidebooks of the 24th International Geological Congress, 1972

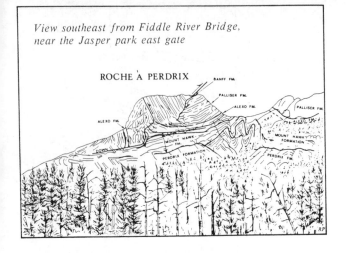

View southeast from Fiddle River Bridge,
near the Jasper park east gate

ROCHE À PERDRIX

Looking northwest along the mountain front from Fiddle
River Bridge

BOULE RANGE

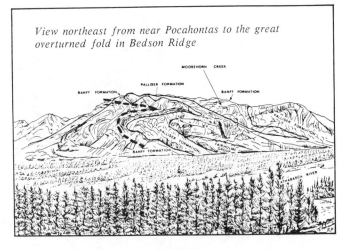

View northeast from near Pocahontas to the great
overturned fold in Bedson Ridge

Geology seen along Highway 16 in eastern Jasper National Park
Sketches from guidebooks of the 24th International Geological Congress, 1972

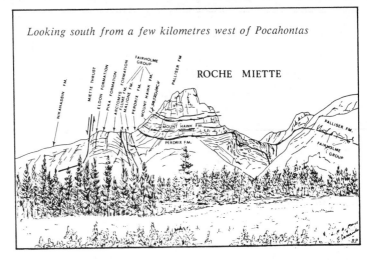

Looking south from a few kilometres west of Pocahontas

ROCHE MIETTE

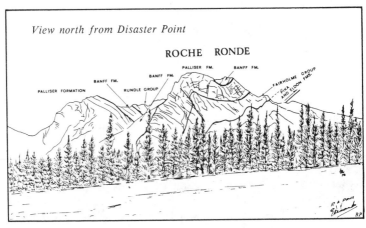

View north from Disaster Point

ROCHE RONDE

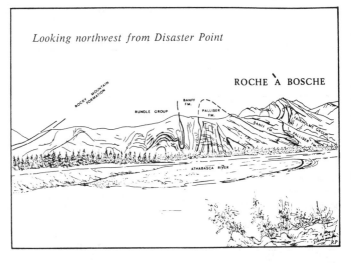

Looking northwest from Disaster Point

ROCHE À BOSCHE

Geology seen along Highway 16 in eastern Jasper National Park
Sketches from guidebooks of the 24th International Geological Congress, 1972

Geology picture pages 65

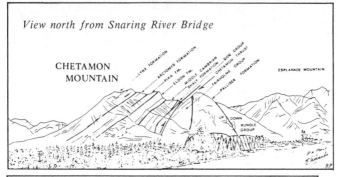

View north from Snaring River Bridge

CHETAMON MOUNTAIN

ESPLANADE MOUNTAIN

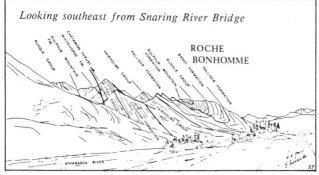

Looking southeast from Snaring River Bridge

ROCHE BONHOMME

ATHABASCA RIVER

MOUNT ROBSON

View east from near the west gate of Mt. Robson Provincial Park

*Geology seen along Highway 16 in Jasper and Mt. Robson parks
Sketches from guidebooks of the 24th International Geological Congress, 1972*

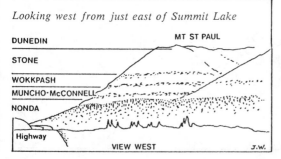

Looking west from just east of Summit Lake

MT ST PAUL

DUNEDIN

STONE

WOKKPASH

MUNCHO-McCONNELL

NONDA

Highway

VIEW WEST   J.W.

Geology seen along the Alaska Highway
Reproduced from The Northern Rocky Mountain Landscape, Muncho Lake and Stone Mountain Provincial Parks, *published by British Columbia Parks and Recreation, undated, author unknown*

COMMON FOSSILS OF THE CANADIAN ROCKIES

*Included in the caption with each fossil are the name and age
of the rock unit in which that fossil is most frequently found*

E = Early, M = Middle, L = Late

Trilobites

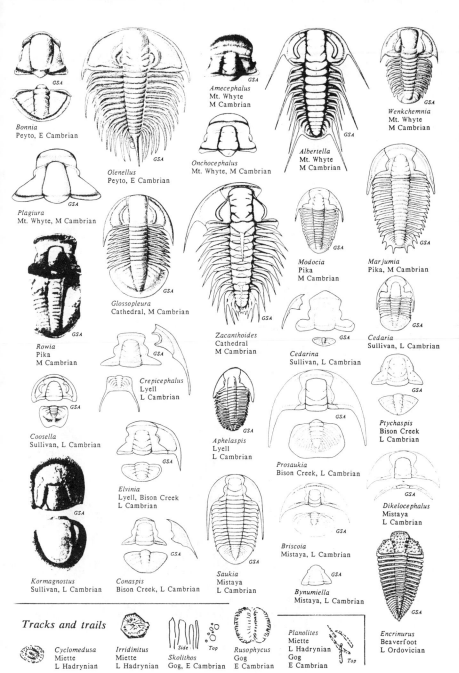

Bonnia
Peyto, E Cambrian

Olenellus
Peyto, E Cambrian

Plagiura
Mt. Whyte, M Cambrian

Amecephalus
Mt. Whyte
M Cambrian

Onchocephalus
Mt. Whyte, M Cambrian

Albertella
Mt. Whyte
M Cambrian

Wenkchemnia
Mt. Whyte
M Cambrian

Glossopleura
Cathedral, M Cambrian

Modocia
Pika
M Cambrian

Marjumia
Pika, M Cambrian

Rowia
Pika
M Cambrian

Zacanthoides
Cathedral
M Cambrian

Cedarina
Sullivan, L Cambrian

Cedaria
Sullivan, L Cambrian

Crepicephalus
Lyell
L Cambrian

Coosella
Sullivan, L Cambrian

Aphelaspis
Lyell
L Cambrian

Prosaukia
Bison Creek, L Cambrian

Ptychaspis
Bison Creek
L Cambrian

Elvinia
Lyell, Bison Creek
L Cambrian

Dikelocephalus
Mistaya
L Cambrian

Kormagnostus
Sullivan, L Cambrian

Conaspis
Bison Creek, L Cambrian

Saukia
Mistaya
L Cambrian

Briscoia
Mistaya, L Cambrian

Bynumiella
Mistaya, L Cambrian

Encrinurus
Beaverfoot
L Ordovician

Tracks and trails

Cyclomedusa
Miette
L Hadrynian

Irridinitus
Miette
L Hadrynian

Skolithos
Side   Top
Gog, E Cambrian

Rusophycus
Gog
E Cambrian

Planolites
Miette
L Hadrynian
Gog
E Cambrian
Top

Geology picture pages

67

Brachiopods

Dinorthis
Beaverfoot, L Ordovician

Rynchotrema
Beaverfoot, L Ordovician

Desquamatia
Harrogate, M Devonian

Atrypa
Flume, Mt. Hawk
L Devonian

Stringocephalus
Dunedin
M Devonian

Allanaria
Flume, L Devonian

Athyris
Flume, L Devonian

Devonoproductus
Mt. Hawk, L Devonian

Nudirostra
Mt. Hawk, L Devonian

Gypidula
Mt. Hawk, L Devonian

Cyrtospirifer
Mt. Hawk, L Devonian

Camarotechia
Palliser, L Devonian

Spirifer
Banff
E Carboniferous

Productid
Banff
E Carboniferous

Graptolites

Phyllograptus
Survey Peak, E Ordovician

Didymograptus
Survey Peak, L Cambrian

Bryozoans

Mt. Hawk, L Devonian

Crinoids

Crinoid fragments
Palliser, L Devonian
Rundle, E Carboniferous

Tentaculites

Tentaculites
Perdrix, Besa River
L Devonian

Typical stromatoporoid
Fairholme, L Devonian

Stromatoporoids

Amphipora
Fairholme, L Devonian

Ostracods

Typical ostracod swarm
Commonly Ordovician
to Cretaceous (X10)

Archaeocyathids

Archaeocyathus
Mural
E Cambrian

Corals

Bighornia
Beaverfoot
L Ordovician

Paleofavosites
Beaverfoot
L Ordovician

Thamnopora
Flume
Southesk
L Devonian

Acinophyllum
Southesk, L Devonian

Syringopora
Southesk
L Devonian

Alveolites
Flume, Southesk
L Devonian

Ekvasophyllum
Mt. Head
E Carboniferous

Canadiphyllum
Mt. Head
E Carboniferous

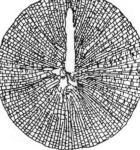
Faberophyllum
Mt. Head, E Carboniferous

Gastropods (snails)

Maclurites
Skoki, M Ordovician

Euomphalus
Palliser, L Devonian

Belemnites
(branch of cephalopods)

Fernie
Jurassic

Pelecypods
(clams and oysters)

Monotis
Pardonet, Triassic

Corbula
Fernie, Jurassic

Inoceramus
Many formations,
Jurassic and Cretaceous

Gryphaea
Fernie, Jurassic

Oxytoma cygnipes
Fernie, Jurassic

Cephalopods (squid-like molluscs)

   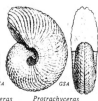

Prionolubus
Toad, Triassic

Wasatchites
Toad, Triassic

Anagymnotoceras
Toad, Triassic

Protrachyceras
Liard, Triassic

Meginoceras
Liard, Triassic

Discotropites
Pardonet, Triassic

Himavatites
Pardonet, Triassic

Malayites
Pardonet, Triassic

Titanites occidentalis
Fernie, Jurassic

Chondroceras
Fernie, Jurassic

Stemmatoceras
Fernie, Jurassic

Gastroplites
Ft. St. John, M Cretaceous

Watinoceras
Blackstone, L Cretaceous

Scaphites
Wapiabi, L Cretaceous

Placenticeras
Bearpaw, L Cretaceous

Buchia
Beattie Peaks, Monach
E Cretaceous

Posidonia
Ft. St. John
M Cretaceous

USING THE LISTINGS

In the catalogue of layers that follows, I have covered most of the rock-unit names currently in common use in the geological literature on our area. Sometimes one heading covers several related formations, which are named in the text under that heading. A few minor formations have been ignored.

Absolute ages are given in millions of years (abbreviated "Ma," which stands for the metric "Mega-annums"). Two dates appear with each entry. These bracket the true age of the unit, which in most cases cannot be determined directly because the rock is sedimentary. In a few cases just one date is given; these are for igneous units, which can be dated more accurately.

Here is a quick review of how geologists assign ages to rocks. Igneous rock (rock that was once molten) can be dated directly by measuring the products of radioactive decay in it, because the decay starts when the rock crystallizes from its magma. The atomic clock starts ticking, in effect. But sedimentary layers must be dated indirectly. Clastic sediments are mostly mineral grains worn from much-older igneous rock; the internal clocks in those grains began running long before the grains collected into the layer.

Carbonate (limy) sediments *do* crystallize, and the minute amounts of uranium and thorium present in some kinds of limestone have been used for dating, but the isotopes involved decay so quickly that if a limestone is older than about 350,000 years it is not possible to get good results with current techniques.

Lacking much directly datable rock, stratigraphers in the Canadian Rockies have had to rely mainly on **index fossils** in finding the ages of the formations.

A good index-fossil is any readily identifiable fossil species that appears and disappears in the geologic record within a rather short time, geologically speaking—meaning a few million years in the case of the older formations. If several locations can be found anywhere in the world in which igneous rock lies above or below sediments holding a particular index fossil, *and* if that igneous rock gives reliable dates, then it is possible to bracket the age of the fossil fairly accurately. In lucky cases, the fossil occurs in directly datable volcanic rock (such as a layer of volcanic ash that fell into the sea, covering the animals on the seabed).

It follows that any layer containing the same index fossil has to be more or less the same age, regardless of where it is found, provided that the organism was preserved in place. Thus the Sullivan Formation, with its Late Cambrian trilobites, is a Late Cambrian formation.

Of the thousands of different fossils appearing in Canadian Rockies strata, 87 are particularly characteristic and common. They are illustrated on pages 67, 68 and 69. If you wish to collect, do so outside the national and provincial parks. Collecting in these parks is illegal.

The names used to designate spans of geologic time haven't changed much in the last hundred years, but the absolute ages assigned to the geologic periods change slightly as the accuracy of the time scale improves. The scale given with the geologic columns (pages 42-44) is the best one currently available; the Geological Society of America published it in 1983.

Ordovician, Silurian, Carboniferous: those tongue-twisting names are hard to learn and to remember. Here is a clever sentence used by many generations of British geology students to memorize the names not only of the Paleozoic and Mesozoic periods but also of the Cenozoic epochs (and even the Holocene). It is a mnemonic: the first letter of each word is the first letter of the period or epoch name in its proper order. See the time charts (pages 42-44) for the names.

Camels Often Sit Down Carefully. Perhaps Their Joints Creak. Perhaps
Early Oiling Might Prevent Permanent Harm.

Substitute "Most Painfully" (Mississippian and Pennsylvanian) for "Carefully" (Carboniferous) if you prefer the American names for this period.

PURCELL SUPERGROUP/BELT SUPERGROUP AND MUSKWA ASSEMBLAGE
Middle Proterozoic (1600-900 Ma; probably 1500-1300 Ma)
Up to 8800 m (thicker west of the Rockies)

Composition of the Purcell Supergroup: mostly red-and-green mudstone and gray limestone, with sandstone and quartzite (hardened sandstone) at the top. The Muskwa assemblage (page 77) is rather similar.

"Purcell Supergroup" is a Canadian name derived from the Purcell Mountains west of the Rockies and pronounced "pur-CELL." Americans use the older term "Belt Supergroup," named for the Belt Mountains of Montana. In this discussion I will call it "Purcell."

A **supergroup** is made up of **groups**, which are in turn made up of **formations.** Formations themselves are often split into **members,** and the members are sometimes split into **lentils.** "Supergroup" is a mouthful, so I will just use "Group" in talking about the Purcell from this point on.

Purcell rock makes up the lowest, oldest of the four great layers in the Rockies stack (see page 37 for the others). Geologists know it as one of the older sedimentary sequences in North America; in the Rockies it has escaped the metamorphism (alteration through heat and pressure) that masks the features of most other Proterozoic formations. The only other place in the Rockies where you will find sedimentary rock this old is at the northern end of the range. Strangely, that rock looks very much like the Purcell sequence. See page 77 for a discussion.

Exposed most prominently south of Crowsnest Pass in the Waterton/Glacier area, Purcell beds also form the rolling Flathead and Whitefish ranges to the west. North of the Canada/US border, where the Rocky Mountain Trench becomes well-defined, Purcell strata are exposed along the eastern wall to a point about 10 km north of Skookumchuck. Purcell rock floors the trench itself from Radium South, but you don't see it under the gravelly valley fill.

West of the trench the Purcell is at the surface again, propping up the Purcell Range of the Columbia Mountains. It is thickest there, deposited largely as turbidites (page 84) on what was at that time oceanic crust under deep water off the edge of the continent. The Purcell extends south and southwest into southern Montana and central Idaho, where it disappears under volcanic cover or merges with areas of granite.

A couple of outcrops showing Purcell beds lying on the granitic continental crust have been found in Montana, but in the Canadian Rockies (meaning from Glacier park north), the base of the Purcell is the Lewis Thrust.

Most of the formations were laid down in shallow seawater, accumulating on what must have been a continental shelf that was gradually sinking. The subsidence was probably caused by cooling of the continental margin after it had pulled apart, accompanied by considerable heating (McMechan, 1981).

The Purcell thickens southwestward and the sediments grow coarser northeastward; this trend, coupled with what we know of the area the Purcell covers, shows that the coastline was located back then about where the Rocky Mountains are now.

To the east lay a pinkish landscape of low granite hills and sandy washes, without vegetation for at this time there was no life on land. Every day the tide would come sweeping in from the western horizon, gurgling across endless mudflats and feeding the primitive organisms growing there: primarily slimy mats of bluegreen algae. Vary that scenario with occasional storms tearing up the algal colonies and you have a pretty good picture of life in the area 1.5 billion years ago.

Sometimes the seabed sank a little quicker than the streams could supply sediments, so the shore moved inland and the water grew deeper. Sometimes a ripple of uplift brought the mudflats above sea level and erosion removed a few layers.

Further uplift came at about 1300 Ma. The plate tilted slightly down to the southwest and up to the northeast, bringing part of the region above sea level and allowing erosion to bevel off the beds at a gentle angle. Erosion continued for a very long time (half a billion years), after which additional rifting along the continental edge carried much of the Purcell Gp. sediments away.

The Waterton/Glacier area holds Purcell rock that did not rift away. This region lay above sea level until the middle of the Cambrian Period, when the sea moved back into the southern and central Rockies and the next round of sedimentation began. So the top of the Purcell is overlain in the Rockies by much-younger Middle Cambrian rock, a major unconformity (see page 120 for more on unconformities).

The word "argillite" is used often in describing Purcell units. This is a technical term usually applied to **mudstones,** which contain a mix of particle sizes ranging from clay-size to sand-size, and especially to very hard mudstones that are red and green—which the Waterton/Glacier area is famous for.

Waterton Formation, and the origin of limestone
Middle Proterozoic (1500-1350 Ma) 135 m

Pale gray or brownish dolomite and limestone. Cliff-maker. Lowest unit in the Purcell Gp., cut off at the base by faults associated with the Lewis Thrust. Rarely exposed, but well-displayed at Cameron Falls in Waterton Park townsite and along the opening stretch of the Cameron Lake Road. Not seen in Glacier park. Interesting for its primitive fossils: stromatolites and wavy structures formed by algae that grew in warm, shallow seawater (see illustration and discussion on page 75). Imagine a warm mudflat covered by sticky colonies of bluegreen algae, alternately covered by the tide and exposed to the air.

This is the oldest carbonate (limy) rock unit in the Rockies, so now is the time to discuss the origin of limestone.

Making limestone

Even though limestone is a very common rock type (10 percent of all sedimentary rock is limestone), geologists didn't really know how it formed until recently. The connection between limestone and life was well established—limestone is often richly fossiliferous—so it seemed likely that somehow sea life produced limestone by chemically removing dissolved lime ($CaCO_3$, calcium carbonate to a chemist; calcite to a geologist) from the water and using it to form shells and colonies. But the fossil content is a minor part of most limestone. Much of it is simply tiny, crystalline bits of calcite. Where did the crystals come from? Not from land, for calcium enters the sea dissolved in water, seldom as particles. So limestone has to be made in place, in the sea.

As it turned out, the source was obvious but overlooked. In the 1950s, geologists began to look closely at spots where lime mud, the forerunner of lime*stone,* was accumulating on the seabed. In the science of geology the present is often the key to the past, and so it was here: studies of lime deposition in the shallows of the Caribbean have shown that the vast proportion of lime mud begins as microscopically small, needle-like crystals of **aragonite** (a variety of calcite) produced inside the tissues of floating and suspended algae. The individual aragonite crystals are only a few micrometres* long. When the algae die and decompose, the aragonite needles drift to the bottom, building up deposits on the seabed. (See Blatt, Middleton and Murray, 1980, page 462)

Why these organisms produce aragonite crystals is still unknown. Even how they do so is uncertain. It may be by removing carbon dioxide from seawater, which makes it less acidic and causes aragonite to precipitate; it may be by changing the temperature of the water slightly (every form of life produces a

---

*A micrometre (symbol μm) is the SI/metric name for the older micron (μ), or 10^{-16} m.

little heat), which can cause dissolved aragonite to crystallize, for calcite and aragonite crystallize more easily in warm water than in cold water—the opposite of most minerals. Or it might have something to do with pressure, because under the right conditions lowering the pressure also produces aragonite. Maybe it is a combination of the above. To a much lesser extent, inorganic processes such as evaporation can also produce carbonate rocks.

Aragonite is not a stable form of calcium carbonate. It spontaneously recrystallizes to calcite, which has the same formula but a different arrangement of the calcium, carbon and oxygen ions in the crystal (calcite is trigonal, aragonite is orthorhombic). Most of the world's limestone is old enough for the aragonite to have converted itself to calcite; only modern rock contains much aragonite.

It is reasonable to assume that the biochemical processes at work today off the Bahamas are much the same as those that produced organic calcite 1.5 billion years ago: the same kinds of algae existed then and now, and when allowance for aging is made, the rock is chemically identical. So it seems plausible that algae have been the prime producers of limestone for as long a there has been limestone; that is, for at least 2.7 billion years.

Altyn Formation
Middle Proterozoic (1500-1350 Ma) 425 m

Pale-gray sandy limestone at the base, then black argillite, followed by gray limestone and dolomite with greenish/brownish argillite at the top. Tends to be erode easily, forming talus slopes and wooded areas. Lies at the base of peaks forming the mountain front from Lower Waterton Lake south. Lower contact is usually the Lewis Thrust, except where underlain by the Waterton Fm. There are good exposures along the first few kilometres of the Cameron Lake Road in Waterton park and at Geology Stop 2 along Going-to-the-Sun Road in eastern Glacier park. The rock is shallow-water marine, with ripple marks, cross-bedded sandy layers and algal structures.

Greyson Formation/Appekunny Formation
Middle Proterozoic (1500-1350 Ma) 820 m

Dark gray-green argillite, outcropping mostly in the lower slopes of peaks just inside the Waterton/Glacier area. Ledgy and loose. Two prominent bands of pale quartzite make good identifiers, as does the sharp contact between the sombre Greyson and the brilliantly red Spokane/Grinnell Fm. above.

Long known as the Appekunny Fm., this unit has been correlated recently with the more-widespread Greyson shale of Montana. American geologists have thus begun calling it "Greyson" because "Greyson" is the older name.

The cliffs on Singleshot Mountain along the north side of the Going-to-the-Sun Road in eastern Glacier park are made of Greyson argillite and provide a good distant view of the unit. See the formation up close at Geology Stop 4 beside St. Mary Lake.

During Greyson time the sea deepened and fine sediment rapidly accumulated, suffocating the algal colonies of the underlying Altyn Fm. Much of the bedding in the Greyson is thin and straight, but some layers are wrinkly and distorted. This occurs when a thick, heavy layer of sediment presses down irregularly into a soft layer underneath.

The greenish tint in the Greyson is from iron deposited in the oxygen-poor (reducing) conditions typical of rather deep water; mild heat and pressure from overlying rock have concentrated the iron in tiny green flakes of the mineral chlorite.

Spokane/Grinnell Formation
Middle Proterozoic (1500-1350 Ma) 100-335 m

Brick-red thin-bedded argillite in Montana, sandy in Canada. Iron-rich like the underlying Greyson/Appekunny but red rather than green because there was plenty of oxygen to rust the iron. Weathers into slopes rather than steep cliffs. Previously known as "Grinnell," these beds, like those of the underlying shales, have been matched with a more-widespread American formation that has an older name; in Canada, though, "Grinnell" is still more commonly used.

The Spokane/Grinnell is the easiest formation to pick out in the Waterton/Glacier region because of its bright red color, prominent in many peaks and beautifully exposed in Red Rock Canyon in Waterton park. Geology Stop 5 on the Going-to-the-Sun Road in Glacier park is another good place to examine it.

This is a shallow-water unit, displaying the ripple marks and sun-dried cracks of a typical warm-water tidal mudflat or of a wide, shallow riverbed near the coast. Storms ripped up the surface from time to time, leaving soft chips of red mud imbedded in layers of coarse white sand. A few greenish layers indicate periods of lower oxygen concentration, probably owing to deeper water. Despite the shallow water and warm climate, there was not enough algal growth in the area at this time to leave fossil evidence, possibly because the water was too muddy or because it was fresh (in the case of a river deposit) and thus would not support marine algae.

Siyeh Formation/Helena and Empire formations
Middle Proterozoic (1500-1350 Ma) 800-1000 m

In Canada, geologists still refer to this unit as the Siyeh Fm. But in 1967 American geologists began discarding the name "Siyeh" in favor of individual names for the lower part and the upper part (Empire and Helena).

The lower 250 m is known in the United States as the Empire Fm., which is siltier and sandier than the overlying Helena, with greenish beds similar to those found in the underlying Spokane Fm. Thus the Empire is transitional between the muddy-water Spokane and the clear-water Helena.

Americans call the upper part the Helena Fm. (for Helena, Montana); it is mostly black limestone and dolomite, frequently weathering tan or gray on exposed surfaces. Igneous rock is present in the Helena Fm., as a sill injected between layers in some places and capping the formation as a lava flow in other places. See the Purcell Sill/Lava, next page. (Technically speaking, the sill is not part of the formation, because it came later in time.)

The Empire and Helena often form one cliff together, so Canadians have been content to keep them together and call them the Siyeh Fm. The Siyeh resists erosion strongly; it is the most prominent cliff-former in the Waterton/Glacier region, buttressing the peaks along the continental divide. The best exposures occur along the Going-to-the-Sun Road in Glacier park, where geology stops 7 and 8 provide a close look.

Like the older Waterton and Altyn formations, the Siyeh Fm. was deposited in clear, very shallow seawater. Abundant colonies of bluegreen algae produced the rock. As it started to harden, it was enriched with magnesium ions from seawater, changing much of it to dolomite (dolomite discussion: page 96).

The rock is wavy-bedded and loaded with **stromatolites**. You can think of these as fossil algae, although strictly speaking they are not: the algal organisms themselves were too soft to remain as fossils. Rather, their effect on the sediments is what shows. Stromatolites are found in many formations of the Canadian Rockies, and they exist in tropical regions today; stromatolites in Shark Bay, Australia are identical to those found in the Siyeh Fm. Here is some general information about stromatolites.

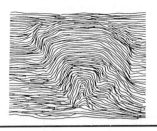

Cross-section view of a typical stromatolite

Domed-up layers preserve shape of algal mats that grew upward as sediments accumulated on a tidal flat. Scale: a few centimetres wide to a metre or more

A stromatolite is a succession of thickened, domed-up layers. Consider a single algal colony, a mat of algal filaments covering an area perhaps 10-20 cm across; one of many that are growing on tidal flats. When the tide is in, the mat is covered with perhaps a metre of water. The water is very clear, or the algae will not grow. In the geological record there have been types that could survive drying while the tide was out and other types, such as *Conophyton,* which forms a prominent bed in the Helena, that have needed deep-enough water to prevent drying.

These algae are producing their own residue of calcite (lime), and the algal threads are sticky, so calcite crystals catch among the filaments. If the mudflat is gradually sinking, this trapped material allows the stromatolite to grow upward, keeping pace with the rate of subsidence. Cutting away the mudflat to expose the layers reveals the domed stromatolite columns that have developed over thousands of years.

Purcell Sill, Purcell Lava and dykes
Middle Proterozoic (about 1350 Ma) 0-130 m

Occurs in the eastern parts of Waterton and Glacier parks as a diabase **sill** (magma injected between rock layers) near the top of the Siyeh formation. In the western half of the region the same magma reached the surface (in this case the sea bottom) and spilled out as basalt or andesite lava flow capping the Siyeh Fm.

Diabase is the coarse-grained equivalent of **basalt,** a common black volcanic rock with tiny crystals. The essential difference is that diabase cools slowly, deep underground, which gives the crystals time to grow large, while basalt cools quickly as it spreads out on the surface, so the crystals are small. The main minerals in either rock are grayish plagioclase feldspar (chemical formula $(Ca,Na)(Al,Si)AlSi_2O_8$) and greenish augite $(Ca(Mg,Fe,Al)(Al,Si)_2O_6)$.

Dykes (magma injected across layers) branch off from the Purcell Sill. Igneous rock is rare in the Canadian Rockies, and this batch is the most widespread (for information on the others, turn to page 86).

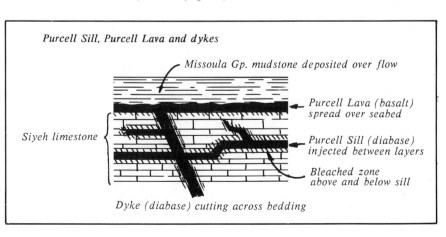

Purcell Sill, Purcell Lava and dykes

Missoula Gp. mudstone deposited over flow

Purcell Lava (basalt) spread over seabed

Siyeh limestone

Purcell Sill (diabase) injected between layers

Bleached zone above and below sill

Dyke (diabase) cutting across bedding

The Purcell Sill is easily approached on the Going-to-the-Sun Road, which crosses it at Geology Stop 9. It is also prominent along the road to Red Rock Canyon in Waterton park, seen high in the cliffs of Mount Blakiston. Look for a horizontal greenish-black band against the tan or gray cliffs.

The sill follows one layer for some distance, then cuts up or down to a different layer. Forced between layers under tremendous heat and pressure, the magma has baked the limestone above and below it, removing dark organic material and bleaching the limestone white. In some places the bordering limestone has recrystallized as a thin zone of white **marble**.

The Purcell Lava shows pillow-shaped structures characteristic of magma that oozed out under seawater. The rock is full of small cavities filled with white calcite. Look for dark, purplish boulders of this **amygdaloidal basalt** in any Waterton/Glacier stream; the white calcite speckles make it easy to spot. The lava-flow layer covers less area than the Purcell Sill and is not as easy to get to, although you can come close on an unimproved forestry road to North Kootenay Pass at the head of the Carbondale River. An outcrop of Purcell Lava lies a few kilometres south. Another approach is via trail to the Granite Park area in Glacier (there is no granite in Granite Park; the lava has been taken for granite, so to speak).

Unfortunately the Purcell magma has not proved amenable to radiometric dating, but the magma is the type that comes from melted oceanic crust, showing that the continental plate was thin and weak in this area late in Purcell time. If the plate were thick and strong, then the basalt coming up would have mixed with melted continental-crust granite to produce other kinds of magmas.

Turn-of-the-century prospectors found copper mineralization associated with the Purcell Sill: small bodies of ore in Siyeh limestone. Mines were opened in what would soon become Glacier National Park. Locations: Grinnell Point and Mt. Siyeh, in the Manyglacier area. The mines soon failed, but not before the boom camp of **Altyn**, long since abandoned, was built on Cracker Flats, an alluvial fan about 2 km downstream from the modern location of the Manyglacier Hotel.

Missoula Group
Middle Proterozoic (1500-1350 Ma) Up to 2500 m

Thin layers a few centimetres thick of pale red, green, yellowish and purplish argillite and sandstone with a few stromatolite beds, capped by quartzite. Found mostly west of Flathead River, but also in the northern part of Glacier park, in the western part of Waterton park and in the ranges west of Flathead River. Recessive and often tree-covered at lower elevations; best viewed around Logan Pass, where it forms the upper part of the peaks.

"Missoula Gp." is a new name (see Mudge, 1977) applied by American geologists to unify several formations with a confusing history of study. The Americans now recognize the **Snowslip, Sheppard, Mount Shields, Bonner** and **McNamara** formations within the group; Canadians use the older names **Sheppard, Kintla, Gateway, Phillips, Roosville** and **Nelson** for units that match the American formations in some cases and don't in others. Until the nomenclature is straightened out I am just going to think of all this as the Missoula Gp.

The lowest formation, Snowslip/Sheppard, is fairly typical of the whole group: shallow-water sediments deposited on seashore mudflats cut by rivers—a **delta**, in other words. At times, algal colonies formed stromatolites in spots on the delta where the water wasn't too muddy. These stromatolites are uniquely colorful; they incorporate the reddish argillite that was choking them as mud at that time. See them at Geology Stop 13 along the Going-to-the-Sun Road in Glacier park.

Coarse, sandy layers in the Missoula Gp. show that river water was reaching this part of the seabed. The shoreline was creeping seaward because the land surface was starting to rise. Eventually the shoreline passed through this area, exposing the upper Purcell layers to erosion. The next subsidence recorded here occurred in the Middle Cambrian, when the erosion surface was buried beneath new sediments.

Muskwa assemblage: Purcell-like rocks at the northern end of the Rockies
Middle Proterozoic (1600-900 Ma) 5300 m

Ancient sediments that are about the same age as the Purcell Gp., and look very similar, form the crest of the northern Canadian Rockies between Toad River and the Tuchodi Lakes area. So the oldest layered rocks in the Canadian Rockies occur at opposite ends of the area.

The northern Middle Proterozoic sequence is called informally the **Muskwa assemblage**. (It was first studied along the Muskwa River). The unit is well-exposed in the peaks just southwest of Summit Lake along the Alaska Highway. Walk 3 km up the gravel flats of MacDonald Creek to reach the formations. The oldest (**Chischa Formation**, 760 m) is a light-colored dolomite with algal structures and some quartzite; it resembles the Waterton and Altyn formations of the Purcell. Next younger is the **Tetsa Formation** (210 m), a dark argillite. Above that, the **George Formation** (425 m) is a tan carbonate (limestone/dolomite) unit rather similar to the Empire/Helena/Siyeh. Above that, the **Henry Creek Formation** (210 m) is a limy argillite resembling the Snowslip Fm. (lowest Missoula Gp. member).

Higher still, the formations are thick and varied in rock type, with less limestone/dolomite and many shaly beds. The **Tuchodi Formation** (1200 m) includes quartzite, dolomite, siltstone and red shale like that of the Missoula Gp. But above the Tuchodi the similarities with the Purcell (or with any other rock in the Rockies) end. The **Aida Formation** (1200 m) is mostly deep-water argillite, while the overlying **Gataga Formation** (also 1200 m max) is argillite, siltstone and sandstone, much of it quite slaty. Thus, the Muskwa assemblage of the northern Rockies record deeper-water conditions in their upper layers, while the Purcell Gp. of the southern Rockies records shallowing conditions.

Like the Purcell, the Muskwa assemblage has been intruded by igneous rock: dykes of diabase that crystallized from the same sort of ocean-crust magma that provided the Purcell Sill/Lava/dykes in the Waterton/Glacier area. As in the Purcell proper, no radiometric dates have been obtained from these northerly dykes.

If you are wondering where the rest of the Purcell Gp. is—that is, the part that should cover a lot of kilometres between the northern and southern patches of Middle Proterozoic rock in the Rockies—current thinking allows three possibilities: (a) it was never deposited there, (b) it was deposited but was eroded away later or (c) it was lost during the pulling-apart episode described on page 71.

UNDERSEA LANDSLIDES, AND A HINT OF PRECAMBRIAN GLACIATION: MIETTE AND MISINCHINKA GROUPS
Late Proterozoic (730-570 Ma). Top of Misinchinka is Early Cambrian (550 Ma) 550 m to 8-9 km

The Miette is easily identified by alternating layers of buff-colored **gritstone** (very coarse sandstone, with a fair proportion of minerals other than quartz), conglomerate, and brown or purplish shale that have been metamorphosed to slate and phyllite. Stronger metamorphism has produced Miette schist in the Selwyn Mountains southwest of Jasper. These metamorphic rock types are described shortly.

The grits are just one of several units in the Miette, but they are distinctive-looking and prominent, especially surrounding Jasper townsite. The full Miette sequence is described in the pages that follow.

The Miette outcrops mostly on the western slope, sometimes a bit east of the continental divide as at Jasper. If you include the Misinchinka Gp. of the northern Rockies, then Miette-type rock runs north almost continuously from the south end of Banff park to Liard River—and beyond, on north through the Mackenzie

Mountains, across the Yukon and into Alaska. This is the lower part of the old clastic unit introduced on page 37. (The upper part is the Gog Gp., page 88.)

Miette strata are part of the **Windermere Supergroup,** which includes similar beds in both the Rockies and ranges to the west (Columbias, Ominecas, Cassiars). Miette strata were studied first along the Miette River west of Jasper; "Windermere" is from a creek running into Windermere Lake, which is between Fairmont and Radium Hot Springs.

Miette-style rock overlies the older Purcell Gp. (previous entry) at several locations west of the Rocky Mountain Trench, and in central Montana, but in the Canadian Rockies proper the lower contact is seldom seen. At the northern end of the Rockies, the Miette-like Misinchinka Gp. lies on Purcell-like rock (Taylor, 1982), and at Hugh Allan Creek near Valemount it is known to lie on gneiss that is probably the continental crust (Oke and Simony, 1981).

The Miette lies on a continental margin that was undergoing **rifting.** The western edge of the ancient North American Plate was breaking up into tilted blocks (see diagram 2 on page 45). In tilting, some of these blocks probably stood partly above sea level as mountains that were rapidly eroding into the sea. The Miette represents the eroded debris; it is very coarse in the Rockies area, which lay near the old shoreline. From 500 m the group thickens to 15 km in the adjacent Purcell Mountains, where it is somewhat finer-grained. Within the Rockies the Miette is thickest in the Selwyn Range southwest of Jasper, where it may reach 9 km (making it the thickest of all Rockies units).

Mild uplift and a drop in sea level at the end of Miette time exposed the group to erosion. At least a few hundred metres of the upper part were removed before the sea moved back in and began a new round of deposition. Slight tilting accompanied the uplift, and thus the overlying Gog Gp. lies at a slight angle to the top of the Miette. The best place to see this is from the Icefields Parkway at Bow Peak, 26 km north of Lake Louise. If you sweep your eye back and forth along the cliffs of Bow Peak, you can see that the rusty layers of the upper half (Gog) meet the dark-brown layers of the lower half (Miette) at a very slight angle that opens to the north. This is an angular unconformity at this site; at most other localities the contact is flat. (See page 120 for more on unconformities.)

Mountains carved in Miette and Misinchinka strata tend to be rounded and lumpy rather than pointed and cliffy, because overall the group is rather easy to erode. The hard gritstone layers are not very thick (about 100 m at most), and they are interbedded with very crumbly shale.

From Castle Junction north, there are many good places to view Miette rock. Along the TransCanada Highway at the point where the Icefields Parkway splits off just north of Lake Louise, look for curving slaty slabs of Miette rock beside the road. A couple of kilometres north, on the road to Jasper, the low cliffs on the west side of the highway look like granite, but they are not; they are very coarse, mica-rich Miette gritstone, crisscrossed with veins of white quartz.

The trails surrounding Jasper townsite wind through a landscape cut in this kind of rock. Roadcuts west of Jasper along Highway 16 display the group exceptionally well. The western approach to Pine Pass on Highway 97 crosses Miette strata for many kilometres between the Mackenzie turnoff and the pass itself.

Metamorphism in the Miette Gp.

There was originally a lot of shale in the Miette Gp., now changed by pressure and heat into **slate.** Rather than splitting along the bedding planes as sedimentary rock normally does, slate splits at an angle to the bedding. This is **slaty cleavage.** In Miette Gp. slate, the original bedding is often obscured by the cleavage, which can cut across it at any angle. You must look carefully at an outcrop to find the true bedding, which often is represented by wavy bands that vary subtly in color and texture.

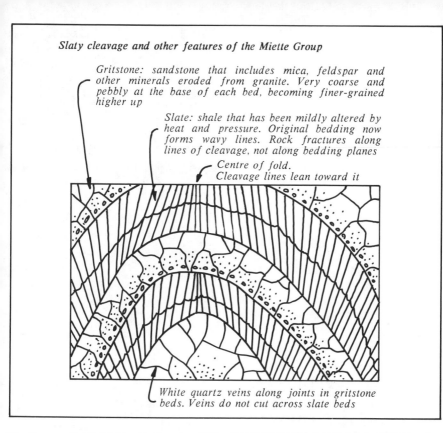

Slaty cleavage and other features of the Miette Group

Gritstone: *sandstone that includes mica, feldspar and other minerals eroded from granite. Very coarse and pebbly at the base of each bed, becoming finer-grained higher up*

Slate: *shale that has been mildly altered by heat and pressure. Original bedding now forms wavy lines. Rock fractures along lines of cleavage, not along bedding planes*

Centre of fold. *Cleavage lines lean toward it*

White quartz veins along joints in gritstone beds. Veins do not cut across slate beds

It is pressure that causes cleavage in slate; the illustration shows the pattern of cleavage planes that commonly develop around a fold. This is directly applicable in the Jasper area, where the middle Miette Gp. is folded like an accordion.

At Jasper townsite the Miette is slaty. As you follow the Miette west from Jasper it shows evidence of higher temperatures and greater pressures. Individual flakes of muscovite (white mica) are visible, and the rock is called **phyllite** ("FILL-ite").

At Yellowhead Lake the next stage of metamorphism is reached: outcrops on the Yellowhead Mountain trail are silvery **schist** (rhymes with "list"). Schist is mostly mica, in flaky, wavy bands that do not follow the original bedding. Roadcuts at the junction of Highway 16 and Highway 5 (Tête Jaune Cache) are in Miette schist; look for little reddish garnets in it. People familiar with the garnet schist of the Appalachians will recognize this rock immediately.

Making schist requires a good bit of heat and pressure, the sort of conditions one finds 20 km deep in the crust. Thus, the Miette Gp. was deeply buried in this area, probably by over-thrusting of Intermontane Terrane during the Columbian Orogeny (page 171). The Miette also suffered strong horizontal compression during the creation of the Rockies.

Yet-higher temperatures and pressures produce wavy black-and-white bands of **gneiss** ("nice"), which indicate that the rock came close to melting. Gneiss is common in the Columbia and Omineca mountains, just west of the Rocky Mountain Trench, but in the Rockies proper it is known only in patches found between Valemount and Golden (at Bulldog, Hugh Allan and Blackman creeks along the eastern wall of the trench).

Slabs of Miette Group slate along the TransCanada Highway near Lake Louise, at the junction with the Icefields Parkway.

Close-up of silvery, mica-rich Miette schist from the junction of Highway 5 and Highway 16 west of Jasper.

Gneiss exposed along Highway 5 southwest of Valemount in the Malton Range.

These gneisses are not part of the Miette Gp. The Miette Gp. overlies them. They seem to be slivers of the North American Plate—the continental crust underlying the sedimentary rock of the Rockies—that have been thrust eastward and upward (Oke and Simony, 1981). Immediately west of them, across the Rocky Mountain Trench, lies the **Malton Gneiss,** a larger region of gneiss that makes up a range of peaks (the Malton Range) south of Highway 5. Farther south and west lies the **Shuswap Metamorphic Complex,** a major gneissic area in western Canada that includes the Monashee Mountains and part of the Selkirks (ranges of the Columbia Mountains).

All this gneiss is significant: it shows that the continental plate itself was caught in the mountain-building that created the Rockies, Columbias, Ominecas and Cassiars between 120-60 Ma.

The gneiss was also disturbed much earlier, when the continental margin rifted during Miette time (page 78). This happened at high temperatures, with the rock behaving like taffy, and some of the minerals in it melted. Radiometric dating provides the time in years since recrystallization. Applied to the gneiss, it shows that rifting began between 800-730 Ma. This also gives a maximum age for the Miette Gp., for it is known to rest on the gneiss.

Chunks of Miette schist and Malton-like gneiss have been found in glacial deposits well east of Jasper, in the Athabasca valley as far away as Edson. This shows that in the last major glacial advance the ice must have been deep enough on the western slope to flow over Yellowhead Pass and into Alberta. For more on that, turn to page 200.

To end our discussion of metamorphism: heating rock beyond the gneiss stage produces magma. Allowed to crystallize slowly under a thick blanket of insulating rock, a magma derived from sediments such as the Miette Gp. becomes **granite**—a common igneous rock. There is granite in the mountains west of the Rocky Mountain Trench, but none is known from the Canadian Rockies.

Perhaps the reader will forgive the following string of famous geological puns, for they recall the basic metamorphic series:

> *Slately like phyllite, schist is a gneiss rock,*
> *but don't take it for granite.*

On to a discussion of the various members of the Miette Gp.

Lower Miette
Late Proterozoic (730-570 Ma) About 3000-4500 m

Recent field work in the Selwyn Mountains southwest of Jasper (Mountjoy, 1985) may have found the bottom part of the Miette Gp. A formal name for the new material has not been established yet; for now the name is just "lower Miette." There are two parts: an upper unit of mostly dark-gray shale metamorphosed to schist (possibly 2500 m thick, although the thickness is indeterminate because of complex folding) and a lower unit of gritstone and shale beds (maximum 2000 m) like those of the middle Miette, but limy/dolomitic, which the middle-Miette grits are not. The lower-Miette grits are very similar to the **Horsethief Creek** and **Kaza** groups, which lie on the west side of the Rocky Mountain Trench in the Columbia Mountains.

Old Fort Point Formation
Late Proterozoic (730-570 Ma) 360 m

Pinkish/purplish limestone and gray-green shale or siltstone; likely either the remains of a tidal mudflat or a deeper-water deposit built up from material carried in by strong bottom currents (limy turbidites; see page 84).

Old Fort Point rock may or may not be found only in the Jasper area. J.D. Aitken (GSC Calgary, personal communication) claims to have found Old Fort Point rock as far south as Lake Louise, among middle-Miette strata. Thus, there is some controversy about the distribution and age of the unit.

Breccia of the Old Fort Point Formation at Old Fort Point near Jasper. The rectangular pieces are pink limestone, embedded at angles in gray-green siltstone.

Middle Miette gritstone and slate along Highway 16 about 10 km west of Jasper. The gritstone bed is the wavy band above the car.

The formation looks rather like parts of the Purcell Gp. (page 71) found 450 km to the south, in the Waterton/Glacier area. Along Highway 16, 14 km west of Jasper, the unit is smoothly laminated, looking very Purcell-like. But on Old Fort Point itself, a hill opposite Athabasca River from Jasper townsite (a road leads right to it), the bedding is quite strange. In some layers, angular, thumb-size to platter-size pieces of limestone are imbedded at crazy angles in a fine, silty matrix. This type of rock is called **breccia** ("BRETCH-yuh"). In the Old Fort Point breccia, the angular pieces weather more quickly than the surrounding matrix, forming indentations in exposed surfaces.

How did this odd-looking rock form? Evidently the angular pieces have broken loose from laminar beds, have swirled around in mud, then become locked in the surrounding sediment at random angles. This happened while the rock was still soft, for the pieces are often bent and curved. Study has shown that portions of the formation slid in masses down into deeper water, breaking up the bedding.

Middle-Miette grits
Late Proterozoic (730-570 Ma) Maximum about 2500 m

Beds up to 100 m thick (but typically 5-50 m) of massive gray-green, tan-weathering gritstone, alternating with dark gray shale/slate/phyllite (see page 78), rusty-weathering from the presence of iron. Fresh exposures of the gritstone beds are tinted gray-green by tiny flakes of chlorite, a low-grade metamorphic mineral.

In the Athabasca valley around Jasper townsite the gritstone layers are often steeply dipping; they have been ground down by heavy glaciation to form low ridges, while the shale beds have been eroded slightly deeper to form the intervening small valleys. The trail to Valley of the Five Lakes beautifully illustrates this interesting hard-and-soft topography.

Creamy white quartz veins cut across the gritstone layers. Very hot water, under so much pressure from overlying rock that it would not boil even at temperatures high enough to carry quartz in solution, has dissolved quartz from grains in the rock and redeposited the mineral in cracks and joints. The slate layers are seldom cut by quartz veins; this is because shale, forerunner of slate, compacts under pressure, closing any fissures that might otherwise carry mineral-laden water.

Rock-type names applied to the middle Miette over the years show how the science of geology has advanced. "Gritstone" is an old British term for coarse sandstone. Around the turn of the century, geologists began to look at gritstone in detail. They found that it is made mainly of bits of quartz, feldspar and mica. These are the major components of granite. Further study showed that gritstone does indeed come from eroding granite, carried away in fragments by rivers and dumped into a nearby ocean. Here was a step forward in understanding.

But what could explain the alternation of coarse gritstone and fine-grained shale in such deposits? In the 1930s it became clear that sediments like this are **turbidites**: a special kind of deposit that has resulted from huge underwater landslides down the long continental slopes and out into the ocean basins. These are common today, especially so where the continental shelf is narrow and mountains are eroding into the sea—as is the case off the coast of California, for example.

With the rapid accumulation of sediments, the edge of the shelf collapses and underwater slides occur. These slides set up strong currents that carry muddy slurries of rock fragments far out to sea. Such currents are termed **turbidity currents** because they are loaded with rock particles ("turbid" means "muddy"). The debris carried in the current makes it denser than the surrounding water, so a turbidity current flows along the bottom, whether it is a lakebed or a seabed. (See Blatt, Middleton and Murray, 1980, for more)

A look at the middle-Miette grits shows that they are indeed turbidites. Each layer is very coarse near the bottom—a conglomerate, really—with marble-sized pebbles in it (the size ranges up to boulders in some outcrops) and chunks of shale ripped up from the underlying layer. The grains become smaller toward the top of the layer until they are microscopic, the right size to form a layer of shale. This is typical of turbidites: the heavy, coarse, mudflow-like part drops to the bottom first, followed by finer particles as the speed of the current slows. So the resulting sedimentary layer is **graded**: it gets finer upward, from conglomerate to very coarse sandstone to medium sandstone and fine sandstone, then to silt and finally to shale. The Miette grits along Highway 16 just west of Jasper display this grading quite well.

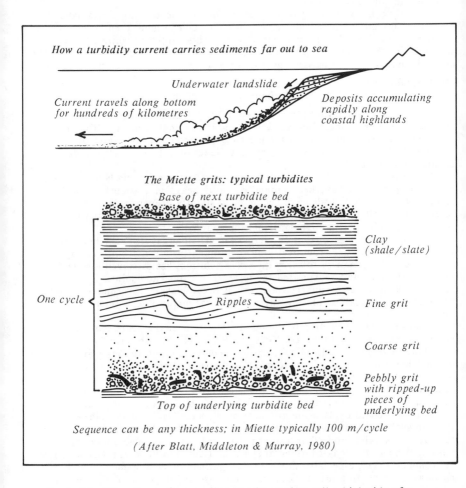

How a turbidity current carries sediments far out to sea

Underwater landslide

Current travels along bottom for hundreds of kilometres

Deposits accumulating rapidly along coastal highlands

The Miette grits: typical turbidites

Base of next turbidite bed

One cycle

Ripples

Clay (shale/slate)

Fine grit

Coarse grit

Pebbly grit with ripped-up pieces of underlying bed

Top of underlying turbidite bed

Sequence can be any thickness; in Miette typically 100 m/cycle

(After Blatt, Middleton & Murray, 1980)

Graded bedding is one feature that can be used to tell which side of a disturbed bed was originally facing up. If the sequence seems wrong—fine stuff at the bottom of a layer, coarse stuff on top—then you are looking at rock that has been turned upside down during mountain-building.

Science now knows rather a lot about turbidites such as the Miette grits: what they are made of, where they came from, where they ended up and how they got there. As usual in sedimentary geology, knowledge was gained by finding modern examples of events that happened long ago.

Well, *how* long ago? The Miette grits don't contain fossils to use in correlating them with other formations of known age. Also, there is no point in trying radiometric dating techniques. Applied to the grits, this would tell us when the individual grains crystallized in the igneous granite, but that happened long before those grains were eroded from the Canadian Shield and spread over the seabed.

However, the imprints of jellyfish found in the *upper* Miette (see next entry) occur only in Late Proterozoic rock and we note that the Malton Gneiss (page 81), which underlies the Miette southwest of Jasper, has been radiometrically dated to about 800 Ma. This narrows the age range of the Miette to 800-570 Ma, which is pretty good accuracy for a Precambrian sedimentary unit.

Upper Miette
Late Proterozoic (730-570 Ma) Up to 1500 m

Greenish-gray or brown slate, phyllite and shale that weather rusty and purplish. The rock is variously soft, brittle and splitty, so it weathers back into slopes covered with vegetation.

There are very good exposures of upper-Miette slate beside Highway 16 20-30 km west of Jasper. In some roadcuts the cleaved rock spalls off in thin, rusty-looking sheets that stack like pieces of paper at the base of the cliff.

The earliest known animal fossils in the Rockies have been found in upper-Miette shale (Hofmann, Mountjoy and Teitz, 1985). Impressions of the Late Proterozoic jellyfish *Cyclomedusa* and *Irridinitus* have been found recently in greenish siltstone beds about 330 m below the top of the upper Miette on Mt. Fitzwilliam (Yellowhead Pass area). Tracks and trails identified as *Planolites*, which may have been made by marine worms, have been found in the upper Miette near Mt. Robson.

To the south, around Lake Louise, micro-fossils have been identified as that of the bluegreen alga *Spaerocongregus variabilis*. They come from fine-grained upper-Miette shale that is probably slightly older than the exposures in the Mt. Robson area, which would make these tiny clusters of cells the oldest preserved organisms known in the Rocky Mountains. (The stromatolites of the Purcell Gp., although older, do not preserve their algal builders. See page 75.)

Byng Formation, and other upper-Miette dolomite
Late Proterozoic (730-570 Ma) 0-180 m

Orange-weathering gray or bluish dolomite, with wavy bedding, stromatolites (algal mounds, page 75) **pisoliths** (concentrically layered, pea-sized algal balls) and zones of fragmented rock caused by underwater landslides.

The Byng is *not* named for Mt. Byng, west of Banff near Mount Assiniboine (the formation is not found that far south) but for Byng Pass at the head of the Snake Indian River in northern Jasper park. The unit outcrops sporadically atop Miette Gp. exposures in the main ranges from Monte Cristo Mountain in northwestern Jasper park to The Colonel, a peak northwest of Yellowhead Pass.

Byng rock, or another dolomite of about the same age, is found south of Yellowhead Pass in the Ramparts area. Mt. Fitzwilliam, the south buttress of Yellowhead Pass, has a thick, highly visible band of this dolomite, easily seen from the Fitzwilliam Viewpoint along Highway 16. Look for an orangish layer running from timberline to about halfway up the peak. To see the unit up close, go to Jasper and follow Trail 7 for about 5 km from Old Fort Point to a large outcrop of steeply tilted, pale-orange Byng-like dolomite in the hillside south of the trail.

Farther north, in the Miette-equivalent Misinchinka Gp. of the northern Rockies (next page), an unnamed unit of Byng-like rock is found in the upper part of the group.

Recent study in the Yellowhead Pass area has turned up a steep slope or escarpment in the Byng-like dolomite there—the edge of the oldest known reef in the Canadian Rockies (Teitz and Mountjoy, 1985). This underwater structure was built by algal colonies long before corals, the usual reef-builders these days, had evolved. From time to time pieces of the reef as big as boulders would crumble, perhaps under the onslaught of heavy storms, and spill down the underwater slope.

There they would be buried under the steady rain of algae-generated lime mud and thus be reincorporated into the reef. The outcrop at Jasper doesn't seem to show these imbedded chunks, but it does show the wavy bedding characteristic of limestone layers formed in and around algal colonies. Like other occurrences of dolomite, this one began as limestone and changed to dolomite through chemical interchange with magnesium-rich seawater (see page 96).

The dolomite in the upper part of the Miette Gp. is patchy in the Rockies, occurring at slightly different stratigraphic levels with intervening areas of shale. A simple interpretation would be that it represents reef-building on a shallow, muddy seabed in different places and at slightly different times. The unit may have been much more extensive before the Miette Gp. was raised above sea level at the end of the Proterozoic Era. The Byng proper, deposited near the top of the group, was probably largely eroded away, although it almost certainly existed in the eastern part of Jasper park and in the Monkman Pass area.

Misinchinka Group
Late Proterozoic to Early Cambrian (730-540 Ma) Up to 3000 m

The **Misinchinka Group** is found north of Peace River. It is roughly similar to the Miette Gp. in age and rock type, and thus part of the Windermere Supergroup (page 78), but inclined to be even shalier. In the upper part there is a limestone that looks a great deal like the Byng Fm. dolomite of the central Rockies (previous entry) but is probably older and thus may not be the same unit. The Misinchinka is generally limier than the Miette, and the discovery of archaeocyathid fossils (page 91) shows that the Misinchinka is Early Cambrian near the top.

Parts of the Misinchinka are **diamictite:** rock that looks like hardened glacial deposits. Proterozoic glaciation is known from Africa and Australia; it may have happened here as well. There are also diamictites of about this age in the Columbia Mountains west of the Rockies and in the Mackenzie Mountains to the north.

Highway 97 runs through topography cut in Misinchinka rock for many kilometres between the turn-off for the town of Mackenzie and the summit of Pine Pass. The Alaska Highway crosses Misinchinka beds from west of Coal River to west of Fireside at the north end of the Rockies.

The Misinchinka Gp. has not been studied in the detail accorded recently to the Miette Gp., but like the Miette, the Misinchinka seems to have been dumped quickly into deep water from eroding granite mountains along the coast. From the north end of Williston Lake south, there is a gritstone-and-shale unit low in the Misinchinka that resembles the Miette grits. Above that lie diamictite beds which grade westerly into more gritstones and shales.

Differences between the Miette and the Misinchinka may relate to the presence of a recently discovered, as yet unnamed westerly bulge in the Precambrian shoreline between Grande Cache and Peace River. This would have tended to separate the sediments into a northern lobe (Misinchinka) and a southern lobe (Miette).

CROWFOOT DYKE AND OTHER MINOR INTRUSIVES IN THE ROCKIES
Late Proterozoic (730-570 Ma) About 50 m

West of the Rockies, in the Columbia, Omineca and Cassiar mountains, igneous (once-molten) rock is common. It includes many dykes (cross-cutting igneous veins). But in the Rockies themselves, any kind of igneous rock is rare. Such is the Crowfoot Dyke, a sheet of greenish-brown diabase crossed by the Icefields Parkway just south of Bow Lake, 1 km south of the interpretive display at the Crowfoot Glacier viewpoint. Diabase is essentially basalt (a common type of lava) that cooled slowly underground and thus became more coarsely crystalline (see page 75).

The Crowfoot Dyke has been traced from Bow River northeast across the highway, through a ridge and into the next valley, where it ends just short of Helen Creek (total length 2.8 km). The dyke cuts through upper Miette beds but does not cut into the overlying Gog quartzite, indicating (a) that it is younger than the Miette, (b) that it is older than the Gog and (c) that a good deal of Miette rock has been removed by erosion, because the rock exposed in the dyke must have cooled under a blanket of rock at least a few hundred metres thick.

Other minor intrusives in the Rockies include diabase dykes along Icefall Brook (north tributary of Valenciennes Creek, west of the Lyell Icefield), in the Freshfield Icefield area, and a diabase sill in the Mt. Assiniboine area. A highly deformed diabase dyke cuts through the Old Fort Point Fm. west of Jasper (location: 1 km northwest of Geikie siding along the old road to Decoigne).

There are orange-weathering greenish dykes of unknown igneous composition just off the Columbia Icefield near Castleguard Mountain. Nearby I have seen boulders of **pegmatite** (any igneous rock with very coarse grains) lying on the west side of Castleguard Meadows, near the north end. Thumb-size crystals of white mica make these blocks very distinctive; their source is unknown.

Diatremes (small volcanic pipes containing pieces of the surrounding rock—and sometimes diamonds) have been discovered recently at several locations in the western Rockies: some 40 pipes between Mt. Joffre and Cranbrook, and a few farther north (Columbia Icefield area and near the Peace River effluent of Williston Lake, where there is also a body of **carbonatite**: igneous rock with the same constituents as limestone or dolomite.

Elsewhere in this book there are descriptions of the Purcell Sill and dykes (page 75), similar dykes in the Muskwa assemblage of the northern Rockies and dykes in Ordovician rock in that area (page 77), the Ice River Alkaline Complex (page 150) and the Crowsnest volcanics (page 162).

One of several dykes exposed after recent glacial melt-back on the southwestern slopes of Castleguard Mountain in northern Banff National Park. These dykes were once thought to be "neptunian" (sheets of sand squeezed into soft sediments soon after deposition) but analysis by the Geological Survey of Canada has shown them to be igneous.

THE HARDEST ROCK IN THE ROCKIES:
QUARTZITE OF THE GOG AND ATAN GROUPS
Early Cambrian (570-540 Ma) 700-4000 m

The Gog Group is fine-grained white, buff, pink or purple quartzite beds, mostly 1-10 m thick, separated by thin layers of brown, reddish or purplish siltstone. There are layers of pebble conglomerate near the base. Bedding planes and fractures are often stained red or orange with iron oxide. Some iron-rich zones weather into brilliantly red-orange patches on mountainsides. Lichens (mostly greenish *Rhizocarpon geographicum,* black *Umbilicaria* species and many gray encrusting types) grow thickly on talus slopes and boulderfields of Gog rock, giving them an overall gray look from a distance.

From central Jasper park north a layer of gray/pinkish limestone/dolomite occurs in the upper third of the Gog: the Mural Fm., up to 380 m thick. Between Lake Louise and Mt. Chown (northwestern tip of Jasper park) the interesting Peyto limestone occurs at the top of the group.

Gog rock is present from Mt. Assiniboine to Peace River. North of there the Gog contains more conglomerate, including imbedded boulders up to 3 m across; the name changes to Atan Group. There are also a few patches of Gog-like rock south of Crowsnest Pass, lying on the Purcell Gp. But these patches are younger (Middle Cambrian) and much thinner, hence given a different name: **Flathead Formation.**

Gog quartzite is easy to identify and interesting; it should be on any naturalist's short-list of formations to know. The name is from Gog Lake, near Mt. Assiniboine, where the unit was first studied. Gog rock is exposed mostly in the main ranges, sometimes in the western part of the front ranges, but seldom at the eastern mountain front. The rock is very resistant to erosion and thick enough to form enormous cliffs.

If you want to see the Gog at its best, go to Jasper, where Pyramid Mountain and the other peaks of the Victoria Cross Range are made of it. So is Mt. Edith Cavell, and the road to the north face of the peak is the best place to appreciate the character of this important Rockies building block (photo on page 92).

There are many other good Gog outcrops along the Icefields Parkway. Gog rock makes up all the reddish peaks along the west side of the Icefields Parkway between Jasper and Poboktan ("po-BOCK-tun") Creek. Endless Chain Ridge, on the east side of the road from Sunwapta Falls south to Poboktan, is a classic dip-slope ridge (page 19) made of tilted Gog quartzite.

Farther south, around Lake Louise, there are good Gog outcrops beside the trail at the west end of the lake. The Ten Peaks looming above Moraine Lake are Gog quartzite from base to middle, and the big slide damming the lake provides a terrific collection of Gog boulders that visitors enjoy exploring. Forestry roads into the Rockies between Tête Jaune Cache and Prince George pass through the thick Gog sequence there.

North of Prince George the Gog is less spectacular, but ten kilometres east of Pine Pass, Highway 97 crosses an area of Gog rock between Mt. Murray and Mt. Garbitt.

Origin of most clastic rock

The group is mostly **quartzite:** extremely hard sandstone. This is the hardest rock in the Rockies, for much of it is nearly pure quartz, the hardest common mineral in the world (7 on Moh's scale; harder than steel). But with that hardness comes brittleness, and while the Gog stands up in great reddish cliffs, climbers on those cliffs discover that the handholds are inclined to be portable, for every layer is cracked and broken.

Gog quartzite began as quartz grains eroded from granite and carried to the sea. River transport quickly ground up to powder or dissolved most other minerals, but quartz is hard stuff—and practically insoluble at normal temperatures—so it arrived at the ocean in fragments up to the size of pebbles. There, the waves sorted the sediments out by size. The pebbles wound up where the surf was heavy, the sand-size grains collected in a belt from the shoreline out a few hundred metres into deeper water, and the fines (silt-size and clay-size particles) settled out in another belt farther offshore. Hardened to rock, the pebbles became conglomerate, the sand became sandstone, the silt became siltstone and the clay became shale.

This is a common geological process, accounting for most of the world's clastic (particulate) sedimentary rock.

Cross-bedding

Cross-bedding is often found in sandstone, and it is prominent in the Gog. Look for lines that are at an angle to the bedding surfaces above and below a layer. Cross-beds show that the sand grains were carried by currents to the growing edge of a layer, then dumped over. In this way the edge grew forward, just as a delta grows out into a lake. Another kind of Gog cross-bed occurred when a current cut a channel through a layer and then filled the channel with sand.

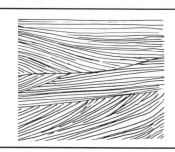

Cross-bedding

Lies at an angle to the overall bedding. Marks the forward growth of sand layers as grains are carried to the sloping edge and dumped over.

Also occurs where shifting currents cut channels into the soft sand and then fill them.

Same principles apply to dune deposits.

Much of the Gog was laid down in shallow water on a sea bed that was gradually sinking. So the sand layer became very thick—so thick (and so pure) that geologists think the Gog sand was probably redeposited, that is, washed in from some preexisting eroding sandstone. There are much-older sandstone remnants (Middle Proterozoic, 1600-900 Ma) to the northeast on the Canadian Shield. This area was above sea level and thus eroding during Gog time; the hard quartz grains would easily have withstood the long river journey to the sea, where they were redeposited as the Gog. More evidence: the Gog thins and coarsens to the northeast, and the alignment of cross-beds also indicates a northeasterly source area.

Making quartzite

Regardless of where it comes from, how does soft sand become hard quartzite? As a sand layer is covered with younger beds, the sand grains compact to become sandstone, a soft rock. But if the sedimentary stack thickens to about 10 km, then superheated water (water under so much pressure that it won't boil) can dissolve a little quartz from around each sand grain. Should the overburden be removed, as it is when uplift raises the stack above sea level and erosion goes to work, the rock cools, the pressure is diminished and the dissolved quartz crystallizes between the grains, sticking them together with quartz cement. So the rock becomes nearly solid quartz, so tough that it breaks across the sand grains rather than around them, the main difference between sandstone and quartzite.

This process is remarkable: it changes the rock, yet it leaves the original layering and fossil structures intact. Higher temperatures turn the rock pasty, destroying the layering and fossils—which is what often happens in quartzites that are more strongly metamorphic—while lower temperatures do not allow the quartz to dissolve, leaving the sandstone soft and gritty. So the Gog quartzite of the Canadian Rockies is something special.

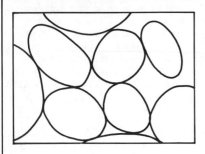

Making quartzite from sandstone

1.
Pure sandstones such as the Gog are over 90 percent quartz particles. The grains are loosely packed at first, with spaces between them. The rock breaks around the grains, not across them.

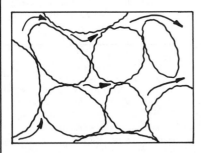

2.
When covered with younger layers to a depth of several kilometres, sandstone is saturated with superheated water (water well above the boiling point but still liquid because of the great pressure). Water moves among the grains, dissolving quartz from the grain surfaces and carrying it in solution. Further heating can turn the rock pasty, for quartz melts at a lower temperature (about 1100°C at such depths) than most minerals. The Gog does not reach this point, so the fine sedimentary structures and fossils are preserved.

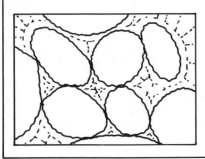

3.
*Erosion or uplift eventually bring the rock closer to the surface. The pressure falls and the temperature drops. The quartz in solution precipitates among the grains as microscopic crystals, cementing the sandstone together. It now breaks **across** the grains; is quartzite.*

Worm burrows and fool's gold (iron pyrite)

You can see **worm burrows** half a billion years old in the Gog. Look for vertical rods 1-20 cm long and up to 2 cm across at the tops of thick buff-colored layers. On the surface of a burrowed layer the rods show up as clusters of various-sized circles. For convenience paleontologists have named these burrows *Skolithos* and *Monocraterion,* as if they were fossils of the animals themselves, which they are not. Sinuous trails *(Planolites),* decorate some bedding planes. Small raised spots that look like impressions of coffee beans can be seen on the surface of siltstone layers. These are called *Rusophycus*; they indicate places where small trilobites are thought to have dug themselves into the mud.

Also interesting is the large amount of **iron pyrite** (FeS_2) in the Gog. Most buff-colored layers are speckled with black, brown or reddish dots of pyrite; bedding-plane surfaces are often coated with paint-thin deposits that have an iridescent sheen. Pyrite deteriorates when wetted; the iron portion goes black or purplish, then turns to iron oxide (rust, in other words), which stains the formation yellowy-orange if the iron oxide is **goethite** ("GUR-tite," $HFeO_2$, also called **limonite**) or crimson-red if it is **hematite** (Fe_2O_3). These minerals often intermix on the same rock surface, staining it streaky red-orange. In many Gog beds hematite among the grains colors the rock pink.

Mural Formation, McNaughton and Mahto formations

A word about the **Mural Formation**. This is mostly gray-weathering limestone, although some beds have been altered to reddish dolomite. In Mural time sand was not being laid down, so organisms dependent on clear water could survive. The Mural contains the trilobite *Olenellus*, which has been used to date the Gog Gp. as Early Cambrian. **Archaeocyathids** are also common. They look rather like horn corals, but they became extinct after the Early Cambrian and thus the nature of their soft parts is unknown. See the drawing on page 68.

The Mural is found in the main ranges and western front ranges from Brazeau River (southeastern boundary of Jasper park) to Mt. Sir Alexander (just north of Willmore park). It reaches thicknesses of up to 380 m in the area north of Jasper, but thins quickly to the south. You won't see it in roadcuts along major highways, but from the Icefields Parkway at Athabasca Falls the Mural is fairly obvious as a gray line running through Mt. Kerkeslin near timberline. The rough road up Small River, branching off Highway 16 about 20 km northwest of Tête Jaune Cache, crosses the formation at kilometre 18. The Mural is becoming known as a cave-forming unit (see page 223).

Limestone deposition ended when the choking sand returned, covering the Mural with more Gog-type deposits. Where the Mural exists, the underlying part of the Gog is called **McNaughton Formation** and the overlying part, which is like the McNaughton but thinner, is called the **Mahto Formation.**

Peyto Formation

At the top of the Gog there is a peculiar limestone unit called the **Peyto Formation**. The best highway view of the Peyto limestone is in Mt. Kerkeslin south of Jasper, which is marked by a couple of thin but prominent red bands in the cliffs about halfway up the mountain. The layer is loaded with red **oolites** ("OH-uh-lights"): BB-sized to pea-sized round bits of limestone that form when concentric rinds of calcite (the main mineral in limestone) grow around a nucleus of some kind, often a speck of sand. In the Bahamas, oolites are forming today; they roll about in shallow water that is rich in dissolved minerals and agitated by currents. Such conditions favor sand deposition, too, and thus the Peyto is sandy. Farther east the unit thins and becomes a sandstone layer.

The Peyto limestone is found capping the Gog in the main ranges and western front ranges from Mt. Chown to Lake Louise. A road-cut exposes it at Whirlpool Point on the David Thompson Highway, 21 km east of Saskatchewan Crossing near the Banff park boundary. Thickest around Mt. Robson (128 m), the Peyto Fm. thins southward to only 6 m at Lake Louise. Trilobites such as *Bonnia* and *Olenellus* fix the Peyto as late Early Cambrian in age.

Not long after the unit was deposited, the seabed rose slightly, exposing the top of the Gog to erosion and probably removing most of the Peyto beds. So there is an unconformity on top of the Gog Gp.

The top of the Gog is a conspicuous geological boundary in the central Canadian Rockies: it marks the top of the old clastic unit (page 37), a thick succession of sandstone and shale. From that time on, many thick carbonate layers (limestones and dolomites) were deposited until the end of the Paleozoic Era.

Atan Group
Early and possibly Middle Cambrian (570-540 Ma or 523 Ma) 0-1500 m+

A northern Rockies unit, pronounced "at-TAN." Very coarse gray conglomerate near Cambrian faults, changing to reddish quartzite and siltstone a few kilometres away, then to marine limestone still farther away.

Mt. Edith Cavell (3033 m), typical of main-range peaks carved in Gog quartzite. The base of the Gog Group is at the base of the 1400-m cliff. View from Cavell Lake, near the end of the Cavell Road south of Jasper.

Horizontal (left) and vertical (right) burrows of marine worms, common in silty layers of the Gog quartzite. Dime for scale on left; penny on right.

Found from Peace River to the Liard and beyond, the Atan Gp. is a classic example of what happens when the edge of a continental plate is breaking up. This was happening throughout the Canadian Rockies region during Miette time, but rifting in the northern Rockies continued into the Cambrian, after it had stopped to the south. The faulting reached farther eastward, deeper into the plate.

In the process some of the seabed was tilted above sea level, much like the tilted blocks in Miette time (see page 45). The effect was to create islands, which shed very coarse material—the Atan Gp.—into the nearest basin (in this case, the sea). The ancient faults have been located in the Tuchodi Lakes area (Taylor, 1973), and next to them the conglomerate contains boulders up to 3 m in diameter. Along the Alaska Highway in the last few kilometres south of Muncho Lake, you can see some of this coarse material. Farther away from the fault, the Atan is a red quartzite with siltstone beds, roughly resembling the Gog Gp.

West of the faulted area the water was deeper and clearer. There, the Atan Gp. is limestone. The limestone ends along what must have been a slope into even deeper water farther west. And here some unusual geology occurred: pieces of the limestone layer up to the size of a city block broke off the edge and slid, intact, partway down the slope. There they were buried in mud that became shale. At first these big limestone blocks were thought to be reefs, but the water was too deep here for reef growth and the inclined beds show how the blocks tilted as they moved. To see these **alistostromes,** hike 15 km up the West Toad River, where the white limestone blocks contrast with dark shale in the peaks.

The Atan Gp. was uplifted late in the Cambrian, and folded as well, for it lies at various angles below Ordovician rock (see the drawing of an angular unconformity, page 121).

ROCK SANDWICH, REEF, CYCLIC SEDIMENTS AND SHALE BELT
The fascinating Early Paleozoic of the central Rockies

We are now into the third great layer of the Rockies: the Middle Cambrian to Permian layer, which is mostly limestone and shale. Within that huge unit, the Early Paleozoic formations (Cambrian, Ordovician and Silurian) have a theme in common, which is the topic of this section: the rise and fall of the sea over the outer edge of an ancient continental shelf.

That edge was also the western edge of the North American Plate, a location in which science has come to expect interesting discoveries and difficult problems. Entire geological careers have been spent trying to figure out the meaning of only a few layers in the rock sequence here.

Research over the last 20 years has put the main points in focus. They include:

- the **Middle Cambrian sandwich,** which led to discovery of
- the **Kicking Horse Rim** along the continental divide,
- and the meaning of the **shale belt** found to the west.

The Middle Cambrian sandwich
Mt. Whyte, Cathedral, Stephen and Eldon formations

There are two geologic sandwiches in the central Rockies: this one and Miss Devonian's sandwich, which is described on page 136. Each consists of two thick layers of limestone (or dolomite) with a layer of shale between.

A classic view of the Middle Cambrian sandwich may be had at Castle Mountain, between Banff and Lake Louise at the junction of the TransCanada Highway and the road to Radium. The peak has two cliffs: an upper one and a lower one, divided by a ledge. The lower cliff is Cathedral dolomite, the ledge is Stephen shale, and the upper cliff is Eldon limestone. A sandwich.

Another fine view is along the west side of the Icefields Parkway between Bow Summit and Saskatchewan Crossing, in the Kaufmann Peaks and Mt. Sarbach. Again, the Cathedral Stephen Eldon sandwich is well displayed. The cliffs below the glaciers are Cathedral limestone (cut with two shale layers); the glaciers sit on a bench carved from Stephen shale, and the cliffs above the glaciers are Eldon limestone.

Between Bow River and Brazeau River the unit makes up the cliffs at the mountain front—but the formations are much thinner there than in the main ranges, for the sandwich thickens quickly to the west. The maximum is reached in the peaks west of Saskatchewan Crossing, where the sandwich is about 1000 m thick; at the mountain front the total thickness is only 250 m.

These figures include the Mt. Whyte Fm. (page 95), a thin but interesting shale-and-limestone unit found just below the Cathedral.

North of Athabasca River the sandwich analogy breaks down, for the Cathedral Fm. gets shaly and doesn't weather into cliffs. The same thing happens west of Field in the main ranges, where all the Middle Cambrian limestones change abruptly to shale over a short distance. (See page 101 for the interesting story on this.) North of Peace River there was mild uplift in the Middle Cambrian, which prevented deposition in the north end of the Rockies until the Early Ordovician. And south of Mt. Assiniboine the Middle Cambrian sandwich dips down under the cover of younger rocks. But Middle Cambrian rock reappears farther south, just east of the continental divide and just north of Waterton park, where the **Windsor Mountain Formation** lies on ancient Purcell Gp. sediments (page 71).

South of Elko, the southern sequence includes four formations that total about 900 m in thickness. These include the Gog-like Flathead sandstone (page 88), Mt. Whyte equivalent Gordon Fm. (page 95), Stephen-equivalent Windsor Mountain Fm., Cathedral-equivalent Elko Fm. (page 96), and a younger, poorly understood dolomite called the **Jubilee Formation** that seems to take the place of the Stephen, Eldon and possibly even younger formations. South of there, all Middle Cambrian rock in our area has been eroded away.

The Middle Cambrian sandwich in Castle Mountain (2728 m), along the TransCanada Highway near Castle Junction. Lower cliff is Cathedral dolomite, snowy ledge halfway up is Stephen Shale, and upper cliff is Eldon Limestone. Photo courtesy Banff National Park.

Mount Whyte and Naiset formations
Middle Cambrian (540-523 Ma) 0-200 m

The Mt. Whyte is not very thick but is quite varied: green shale, thin-bedded limestone with oolites and oncolites (oolites discussed on page 91; oncolites in this entry), limy siltstone and the odd thin sandstone layer. There are stromatolites in the Mt. Whyte, their first appearance in our area after a long absence (last seen in the Middle Proterozoic Purcell Gp.).

"Mt. Whyte" is one of the peaks above Lake Louise. The formation is thickest around Sunwapta Pass (140 m). At Kicking Horse Pass the Mt. Whyte is only 43 m thick; south of Mt. Assiniboine it is not exposed, except in the Middle Cambrian patches mentioned in the previous entry; there, it is called the **Gordon Formation.** The Mt. Whyte gets muddier to the east; under the foothills and prairies the rock is mostly red-and-green shale, siltstone and sandstone. The unit also goes shaly north of the Columbia Icefield, where it forms the lower part of the Snake Indian Fm. (next entry).

After the Gog Gp. lost some layers to erosion, the sea moved back in and deposited the Mt. Whyte. The water was shallow, often muddy, and the shore was not far away to the northeast. During clear-water periods, **oncolites** ("ONK-oh-lights") appeared in hollows where wave motion above could wash them gently back and forth.

Oncolites still form today, so we know something about them. The typical oncolite begins when algae grow on a particle—a grain of sand, for example—that is being moved gently back and forth in a pool by wave action. Because of the constant motion, the algae grow all the way around the particle, coating it with sticky green slime. The slime picks up other particles and the algal colony grows over them. Soon there is a BB-sized green ball rolling to and fro. It continues to grow as particles continue to stick to it; when it gets to be marble-sized it becomes oval rather than round, and it may grow to 8 cm across.

Oolites, which are BB-sized inorganic pellets of calcite, also occur in the Mt. Whyte, but not usually in the same layer as oncolites.

There are trilobite fossils in the Mt. Whyte Fm. Many species have been found, but the more common ones are *Plagiura* (which fixes the age of the unit as earliest Middle Cambrian in western exposures), *Amecephalus, Onchocephalus, Wenkchemnia* and *Albertella*. This last one is found only in easterly outcrops, and it shows that the formation is millions of years younger there. Thus, the shoreline moved steadily inland over a long period, leaving a trail of Mt. Whyte deposits to mark its progress.

The **Naiset Formation** (up to about 100 m thick, named for a peak in the Assiniboine area) is a minor unit lying in a narrow band that runs from the south end of Banff park through the Kicking Horse Pass area. Equivalent in time to the Mt. Whyte, the Naiset is the thin-bedded siltstone and mudstone that accumulated in somewhat deeper water west of the shallow-water, limy Mt. Whyte. It may merge to the west with the deep-water limy shales of the Chancellor Fm. (page 116).

Cathedral, Snake Indian, Chetang-Tatei and Elko formations
Middle Cambrian (540-523 Ma) 0-350 m

The Cathedral is composed of massive, cliff-forming dark-and-pale-gray banded limestone and/or buff-to-pink dolomite, with beds up to 100 m thick. Usually there are two shale layers 10-20 m thick that break up what would otherwise be a single cliff. The name comes from Cathedral Mountain, a prominent peak along the TransCanada Highway just west of Kicking Horse Pass.

This is the lower slice of bread in the Middle Cambrian sandwich (page 93). The Cathedral Fm. outcrops in many locations between Mt. Assiniboine (south end of Banff Park) and the Columbia Icefield area. Most prominent in the eastern main ranges, where it forms big cliffs, the Cathedral is thickest along the continental divide west of Saskatchewan Crossing in the Mt. Forbes area.

North of Tangle Ridge the Cathedral thins and becomes shaly; rock of that age is assigned to the Mt. Whyte Fm., which is also shaly there, and the Stephen Fm. (next entry), shaly everywhere. The three cannot be differentiated, so from that point north they are known as the **Snake Indian Formation** (Mountjoy and Aitken, 1978) which carries on nearly to Peace River, north of which Middle Cambrian rock was not deposited in the Rockies.

In the Mt. Robson area the Snake Indian is thicker and limier; it has been known for many years there as the **Chetang-Tatei** ("tat-EH-ee") **Formation**. In the patch of Middle Cambrian rock north of Waterton and Glacier parks the Cathedral equivalent is the **Elko Formation**.

West of the continental divide, in the western main ranges, the whole Middle Cambrian sandwich (Cathedral, Stephen and Eldon formations) abruptly changes to shale, as detailed beginning on page 101.

East of the Rockies the Cathedral (or similar rock) exists under the prairies. From Prince George south the ocean moved inland in a great bay that reached nearly to central Saskatchewan; the area it invaded is delineated by Middle Cambrian units such as the Cathedral. This invasion left the Rockies region well out to sea, although the ocean was shallow and the Cathedral was laid down in water only 100-200 m deep. The water was clear, favoring an increase in algal growth and other organic activity. Slow subsidence resulted in a thick accumulation of lime mud, which later hardened to limestone.

In some outcrops the Cathedral is limestone and in others it is dolomite. In the Columbia Icefield area the formation is beautifully banded and blotched with dolomite, apricot-on-gray. In our area there is perhaps no better example of **dolomitization** than the Cathedral Fm., so now is the time to summarize the process. (For more detail see Blatt, Middleton and Murray, 1980)

Making dolomite

In limestone the alteration of aragonite to calcite (page 72) is one kind of spontaneous chemical change; dolomitization is another. Some of the calcium ions (electrically charged atoms) in the $CaCO_3$ crystal give up their positions to ions of magnesium. The amount of exchange varies, from just a few Ca-Mg interchanges to nearly complete replacement of calcium with magnesium.

Dolomitization changes the texture of the rock, often making it coarsely crystalline. Often there are gaps between the crystals. (When aragonite goes to calcite just the opposite occurs: the rock becomes denser.) Dolomitization is such a complete transformation that it normally (but not always) obliterates any fossils that were present. The color the rock weathers also changes, from the drab gray of limestone to dolomite's brighter buffs and oranges/pinks. Breaking open a piece of colorfully weathered dolomite leads to a surprise: the true, unweathered color of this rock is usually white or pale blue.

Why does dolomitization occur? When does it happen? As the rock is laid down? A bit later, when it is soft? Or much later, when it is quite hard?

Geochemists struggled with dolomitization, getting nowhere until the 1970s, when the basics of the process were worked out. Ordinary seawater is full of dissolved magnesium—saturated, in chemical terms—but dolomite won't form directly from seawater because the magnesium ion does not readily give up the water molecules attached to it and enter a crystal structure. For this reason no one has observed dolomite crystals forming in seawater at normal temperatures. Dolomite will form quite easily in hot water, so you find dolomite around hot springs and in rock veins that once carried superheated water.

However, when *calcite* (the main mineral in limestone) is available, or its organically produced equivalent, **aragonite,** *and* water is evaporating from seawater that can't easily circulate with the rest of the ocean (in a lagoon, for example, or in a bay with a narrow entrance) then the magnesium ion loses its water molecules and slips into the calcite crystal lattice, bumping calcium ions out. In fact, once the process gets going, magnesium continues to replace calcium until the rock is either all dolomite, or there are no more magnesium ions in the vicinity, or evaporation stops.

Evaporation causes water to become denser, because the amount of dissolved minerals increases, and the mineral-laden water permeates the bottom mud, carrying dissolved magnesium among the calcite grains. The calcium/magnesium exchange occurs. The water keeps going, down and through the sediments until it passes out of the basin and mixes with normal seawater. This carries away the salt that would otherwise form if the basin were enclosed, as it is at Great Salt Lake, Utah, for example.

The thermodynamics of this process are complicated, but that is essentially what happens. The technical term for it is **evaporative reflux.**

Dolomite can also form when fresh water mixes with old, very salty seawater trapped in limestone, a process called **Dorag dolomitization.**. This mechanism is not thoroughly understood, but it helps to explain how dolomite appears in places where evaporation was never abnormally strong.

Concerning the "when" aspect of dolomitization, the answer is "at any time." Under the conditions described above, dolomitization occurs whenever calcite or aragonite are available, either as existing limestone or as lime mud produced by microorganisms (as explained on page 72).

Then there is the "where" business of dolomitization, to me the most interesting part. You can find dolomite nearly anywhere in affected rock: from tiny crystals or small infillings of joints and cracks to entire formations that are solidly dolomite. Sometimes the mineral is in thin, wavy sheets that follow bedding planes. Sometimes it follows the burrows of marine worms, preserving them as a network called **dolomite mottling** (very common in the Palliser and Eldon formations). Sometimes there will be alternating layers of limestone and dolomite, such as those in the Lynx Gp. Sometimes dolomite occurs in blobby masses that cut randomly across the bedding. These blobs may be fist-sized to mountain-sized; the Cathedral and Eldon formations are well known for them.

Irregularly banded Eldon dolomite in a roadcut along the Icefields Parkway south of Saskatchewan Crossing.

Middle Cambrian sandwich

In all these cases it is usually easy to tell the dolomite from the limestone in the Canadian Rockies because the dolomite typically weathers buff or pink (often apricot-colored) while the limestone weathers gray. The next time you see a gray cliff with a big pinky-buffy spot on it, you may be looking at a dolomite patch. Be aware, though, that limestone protected under overhangs weathers light buff and looks rather like dolomite.

To be sure whether a specimen is limestone or dolomite, you will have to be carrying a bottle of dilute acid (7-10 percent hydrochloric recommended). Acid of this strength bubbles and fizzes actively on limestone as it releases carbon dioxide from the rock, but it reacts only a little on dolomite—until you scratch the acid-bathed surface, at which point the scraped-off bits will fizz noticeably.

Fossils in the Cathedral are found only in the two shale beds. Look for *Albertella* in the **Ross Lake Member** (lower of the two shales) and *Glossopleura* and *Zacanthoides* in the **Trinity Lakes Member** (upper shale). The Snake Indian Fm. is shalier throughout and trilobites are common in it (except in the Mt. Robson area). When looking for trilobites keep in mind that they are seldom found whole; one usually finds a hash of spines, heads, tails and other parts.

Stephen Formation and the Burgess Shale
Middle Cambrian (540-523 Ma) 20-150 m

Mostly green shale, often appearing olive-drab or leathery brown at a distance. It is limy, with minor thin limestone/dolomite beds that contain oolites (page 91), oncolites (page 95) and limestone-pebble conglomerate. Brilliant green and yellow lichens often adorn the formation.

Like the other Middle Cambrian formations, the Stephen shale runs east under the prairies as a thin tongue; to the west it merges with the limy shales of the middle Chancellor Fm. Because it is shale, the Stephen provides evidence of deepening water caused by movement of the ocean shoreline eastward. Wave-action caused erosion as the shore advanced, and the finer eroded particles were carried out to sea by currents, accumulating as the shale layer.

The Stephen dips out of sight south of Mt. Assiniboine. North of Brazeau River the formation loses its identity and is included in the Snake Indian Fm. (page 96), which can be traced to Peace River.

Recessive, the Stephen weathers back into ledges and undermines cliffs. It is the filling in the Middle Cambrian sandwich (Cathedral-Stephen-Eldon), often covered with debris from the Eldon cliffs above. For this reason the Stephen is seldom well displayed except at high elevations in the faces of peaks in the main ranges. A road-cut exposes it, though, with some of the underlying Cathedral and overlying Eldon formations, along the TransCanada Highway between Lake Louise and Field. Watch for olive-drab shales at the first highway bridge west of Wapta Lake in Kicking Horse Pass.

The Stephen shale is named for Mt. Stephen, which hulks over the little community of Field in Yoho park. This mountain has made the Stephen Fm. world-famous for its fossil quarry in the **Burgess Shale,** an older name for the Stephen Fm. that denotes a peak across the valley from Mt. Stephen.

In the 1870s a railway surveyor/engineer named Otto Klotz discovered a sensational horde of fossils in this area, but word didn't reach the scientific community until Charles Walcott, a paleontologist with the Smithsonian Museum in Washington, DC, happened to notice the fossils while on a geological expedition in the area in 1909. What he found kept him busy on Mt. Stephen for many years.

Embedded in fine black shale, the organisms were extremely well preserved. Most were trilobites or their close relatives, but some were creatures new to science—and still known only from this locality. The place is important; in 1980 it was declared a World Heritage Site.

Finding a whole trilobite anywhere is unusual—the various parts were normally scattered after death by scavengers (probably other trilobites)—yet in the Burgess Shale most of the specimens are complete. Soft-bodied creatures such as worms, which lack hard parts, practically never leave any other trace than tracks

Restoration of some of the Burgess Shale species living on, above, and in the muddy sediments being deposited at the foot of the submarine cliff (in background). The animals have been numbered from left to right in successive rows across the drawing, beginning with the vertical section in the foreground. The animals shown comprise: branching and globular sponges (*Vauxia*, 22, *Choia*, 25, *Pirania*, 20); the monoplacophoran mollusc *Scenella* (16); *Hyolithes* (4); two priapulid (*Ottoia*, 1, *Louisella*, 3) and one polychaete (*Burgessochaeta*, 2) worms; various arthropods, [the trilobite *Olenoides*, 18; the non-trilobites *Sidneyia*, 17, *Leanchoilia*, 6, *Marrella*, 15, *Canadaspis*, 12, *Molaria*, 13, *Burgessia*, 19, *Yohoia*, 11, *Waptia*, 10, and *Aysheaia*, 5 (crawling on the sponge *Vauxia*, 22)]; the echinoderm *Echmatocrinus* (21); and the chordate *Pikaia* (14). Miscellaneous animals shown are *Opabinia* (8), *Dinomischus* (9), *Wiwaxia* (23), and the giant *Anomalocaris* (24). The animals are drawn to show their approximate relative size.

Drawing reproduced from Morris and Whittington (1985) courtesy Geological Survey of Canada.

in the mud, yet in the Burgess Shale they were preserved. Why this lucky occurrence?

That question remains unanswered, although some clues exist. The Burgess Shale accumulated in water perhaps 200 m deep at the foot of an undersea cliff: the Cathedral Escarpment (next page). From the cliff base the dark, muddy sea bottom sloped downward. Occasionally a piece of the bottom would slide gently down the slope, stirring up a cloud of fine particles and carrying the organisms into even deeper water. When the muddy cloud settled, it covered the creatures, preserving even the most delicate of them whole, for there seem to have been no burrowing scavengers down there to disturb the remains. The oxygen content of the water was probably low, explaining not only the absence of life but the lack of decay before fossilization occurred.

Should you wish to go collecting, don't. The fossil beds are in Yoho National Park, and taking specimens requires federal-government permission that is rarely given. Trails to the beds are regularly patrolled by wardens, who search hikers suspected of fossil-thievery. The fines are large.

To satisfy public curiosity about the fossils, a large display of specimens is being prepared for public viewing. Currently there are small displays at information centres in the park. The Geological Survey of Canada has recently brought out a beautifully illustrated non-technical publication called *Fossils of the Burgess Shale: a National Treasure in Yoho National Park, British Columbia* (Morris and Whittington, 1985). Recommended and inexpensive.

Eldon Formation
Middle Cambrian (540-523 Ma) 300-430 m

Massive dark-gray limestone mottled with intersecting worm burrows, or white/bluish dolomite. Fresh surfaces look very much like the Cathedral Fm. (page 95), although in weathered surfaces the Cathedral is more inclined to wavy orange banding than the Eldon, which tends to weather uniformly very light gray. Eldon is a rail siding near Banff.

Like the Cathedral, the Eldon Fm. is common throughout the eastern main ranges from Mt. Assiniboine north. But while the Cathedral goes to shale in the Columbia Icefield area, the Eldon remains a carbonate rock (limestone/dolomite) all the way to Jackpine River in Willmore park. Farther north, rock of that age was not deposited because the region was above sea level.

In the western main ranges the Eldon is replaced by its shale counterpart, the middle part of the Chancellor Fm. (page 116). South of Mt. Assiniboine it goes under cover of younger layers; it may pop up again as the Windsor Mountain Fm. (page 94), which overlies the Purcell Gp. north of Waterton park.

Thickest around Lake Louise (490 m), Eldon rock tends to form the upper parts of high peaks such as Mt. Victoria. East of there, it is thick even at the mountain front (240 m), and that is perhaps the best place to look at it. The TransCanada Highway punches through a glacially smoothed Eldon outcrop exactly at the mountain front west of Calgary. The west-facing slabs are so white that from a distance they look snowy in midsummer. Great cliffs of Eldon limestone rear up on either side of the Bow River here; the impressive one facing the highway to the north is Yamnuska Mountain.

The same situation occurs at Windy Point on the David Thompson Highway (Alberta 11) west of Rocky Mountain House: you cross the Eldon at the mountain front, and it is quite pale. But if an Eldon road-cut is fresh, or if chunks have fallen off recently, note how dark the unweathered rock is: practically black from embedded organic material. It closely resembles the Palliser Fm. (page 138) in both weathered and fresh exposures, as I learned the hard way by confusing the two on a university field project. A quick method for telling these look-alikes apart is given on page 138) it relies on the notable absence of fossils in the Eldon.

In the main ranges the rock is not only dark on the inside; weathered surfaces are usually dark, too, because the rock's composition is slightly different here. In some main-range locations the unit is quite pale from patchy dolomitization. A quarried outcrop beside the road near the entrance to Waterfowl Lakes Campground along the Icefields Parkway is in gray-weathering massive black limestone; a kilometre north the same unit is dolomitic and cliffs above the highway are brownish and loose. Frequently just the worm burrows of this formation will be dolomitized; they erode more slowly than the limestone around them and stand out beautifully on weathered surfaces.

Eldon limestone often forms the summits of the bigger peaks along the continental divide in Banff National Park. Although it stands in great cliffs, the rock is surprisingly rotten. The dolomite patches look solid but aren't, and pieces are inclined to fall off—as I discovered to my horror halfway up Mt. Hungabee above Lake O'Hara. A block of dolomite came loose while I was hanging onto it, unroped, just above a steep ice slope that would have led, after a 200-m unstoppable slide, over a cliff about twice that high. Thanks to a lucky jump, I didn't make the trip down that day.

But in the front ranges the Eldon is much more solid. Yamnuska Mountain (location and photo on page 18) is a block of Eldon limestone that is very popular with climbers.

The Kicking Horse Rim and its sedimentary cycles
Or, losing facies in the Rockies

When is a fault not a fault? When it doesn't exist, of course, and for many years there was a nonexistent fault in Yoho National Park. Geologist J.A. Allan was the first to describe it (Allan, 1914). He had been walking back and forth across Mt. Stephen, trying to figure something out: how could 885 m of limestone change so abruptly to shale? There just *had* to be a fault here, although it was proving difficult to find. Mind you, this was the Canadian Rockies, new geologic territory; if things seemed a bit odd, then so be it. Allan marked the approximate location of the limestone-shale boundary on the map—it passed between Mt. Stephen and Mt. Dennis, he decided—and the "Stephen-Dennis Fault" was invented.

Generations of geologists marched up Mt. Stephen to look at the fossil beds there (see page 98), no doubt with Allan's fault marked in their field notes. It wasn't until a student named Don Cook published his Ph.D. thesis in 1967 that the world learned of Allan's mistake. There was, it turned out, no fault at all. Instead, the geology of the Canadian Rockies was turning out to be even odder than Allan had thought, for, indeed, 885 m of limestone *did* change, quite abruptly, to shale.*

This kind of thing is called a **facies change.** If the particular layer of rock you are following becomes another kind of rock, then it has changed facies.

Gradual facies changes are common in sedimentary rock, because different kinds of sediments are laid down in different places at the same time. For example, a river might carry mud into an otherwise-clear bay with lots of lime-producing plankton in it, which would result in a shaly facies around the river's mouth and a limestone facies elsewhere in the bay. But the facies change between Mt. Stephen and Mt. Dennis is a special type: it marks an underwater cliff, long buried under younger sediment. This is the **Cathedral Escarpment,** the edge of a reef-like platform of limestone that had built up 215 m above the seabed to the west.

The Cathedral Escarpment was a true reef, but it was not built by corals. Corals didn't exist in the Middle Cambrian (they evolved in the next period, the Ordovician). Instead, the Cathedral reef-builders were mainly lime-producing colonial algae, especially one called *Epiphyton*. Trilobites and other animals lived on and near the reef, but their remains did little to build it.

The western edge of the Cathedral Fm. (page 95) includes the reef; the Chancellor Fm. (page 116) was the limy shale that collected in deeper water seaward of the escarpment. The shale of the overlying Stephen Fm. (page 98)

---

*In fairness to Allan, it should be pointed out that there *are* faults in the zone in which he placed the Stephen-Dennis Fault. But they are minor.

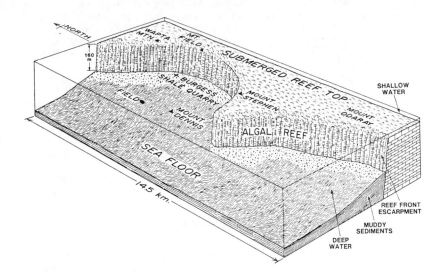

What the Cathedral Escarpment may have looked like when the reef was active. Drawing reproduced from Morris and Whittington (1985) courtesy Geological Survey of Canada.

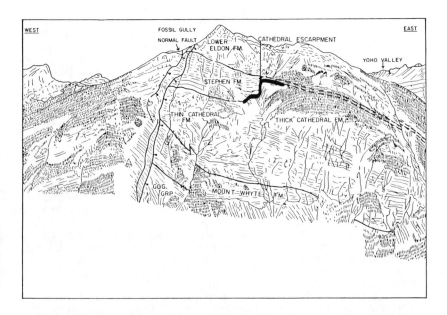

The buried Cathedral Escarpment as seen in Mt. Field in Yoho National Park. View is from the TransCanada Highway near the exit for Takakkaw Falls, looking north. Drawing reproduced from Aitken (1981) courtesy Geological Survey of Canada.

represents a time when the reef was buried under an influx of muddy water; it runs over the top of the reef and out into the shale basin, merging with the Chancellor. The Eldon Fm. (page 100), which lies above the Stephen, was reef-like, too, in this location, but by the time the Eldon was deposited the cliff had become a gentle slope.

The Cathedral Escarpment had actually been discovered (although not named) in the 1940s by a mining geologist named Charles Ney. But his findings were not published until 1954, and they were tucked away in an obscure guidebook to some old lead-zinc workings nearby (see page 755 for more on the mines).

While studying fossils in the area, amateur paleontologist Franco Rasetti (who is better known as a nuclear physicist who managed to co-patent the atom bomb) had noticed huge boulders of limestone that were embedded in shale. Rasetti mentioned the boulders in a 1951 paper on his fossil finds, and suggested that they had rolled down a slope, but he hadn't realized that the slope was so close by, and that it was a steep-sided reef. This isn't surprising; at that time reefs in Cambrian rock were unknown in the Canadian Rockies.

Twice, now, the reef had eluded the wider geological establishment. But not three times: in 1966 Jim Aitken and Bill Fritz of the Geological Survey of Canada rediscovered it on their own. Don Cook was also working in the area; he was having trouble finding the Stephen-Dennis Fault, and the find was good news to him. Paleontologists quickly realized that the Burgess Shale fossil troves lay along the base of the Cathedral Escarpment, helping to explain their origin (see page 98).

As so often happens in science, Aitken made his discovery while working on a different problem altogether: the **cyclic sediments** of the Canadian Rockies. But the escarpment tied in perfectly, as it turned out, and had important ramifications.

Climbing up through the stack of formations that spanned the Middle Cambrian through the Ordovician periods in this area, Aitken found that they were cyclic. A shale formation was followed by a limestone/dolomite formation, then more shale, then limestone/dolomite again, shale again and so on. What was causing this?

The layers were not only repetitive, they were all laid down in shallow water. And the limestone beds were complicated, full of strange textures that were difficult to explain. What was going on here?

One thing, at least, was certain: there had to be ongoing slow subsidence to allow such a thick stack of shallow-water sediments to accumulate.

When Aitken discovered the underwater escarpment and noted the facies change, the explanation for the unusual limestones was at hand, if not the key to the cycles. Aitken followed the facies change upward through the Late Cambrian and Ordovician formations, and found that it existed on and off for about 70 million years. In a 1971 paper he named this feature the **Kicking Horse Rim** and set off a wave of interest in it.

To date, research has shown that the strange sediments had been laid down between the rim and the shoreline, a region very sensitive to changes in water depth, tidal effects and currents. These conditions exist in and around modern-day reefs, producing fascinating rock.

Further, the Kicking Horse Rim has turned out to be just one small segment in an enormous, continent-fringing limestone reef complex about 1900 km long. It built well out into the sea and reached far south—into Nevada, where there is a region of similar sediments in the Basin and Range geological province. At this time the north pole was where the western Pacific Ocean is now, so the continental edge ran east-west, with the sea to the north.

But back to Aitken's problem: the *cyclic* character of the sediments. What accounted for that? Sudden rises in sea level would explain this nicely, he decided.

When the depth was stable and the water was clear, abundant sea life would produce a layer of limestone. It would thicken quickly, reaching nearly to the surface and spreading over vast areas of the continental shelf. The water was so shallow that the larger waves would be damped and thus kept from reaching the coast.

Then a rapid increase in water depth—meaning an increase that the reef-builders could not keep up with—would disrupt things. Given deeper water, large waves would roll eastward over the reef and on across the limy flats beyond. They would reach the coast, battering the shoreline and causing rapid erosion along it. The rise in sea level would have sent the shoreline advancing inland, further aiding erosion.

Return currents moving along the bottom, especially strong during storms, would carry eroded material (mostly fine mud) out to sea over the limestone flats and the reef, smothering the sensitive organisms living there. Limestone deposition would stop, and a layer of shale—the fine material—would be laid down.

Later, when sea level stopped rising (or, alternatively, when subsidence of the seabed slowed), then erosion along the shore would taper off, clear-water conditions would return, and the lime-producing organisms would establish themselves again, completing the cycle.

A final question remains: what caused the jumps in sea level? Answer: this is still unknown. There are several possibilities. The weight of accumulating sediments on the continental shelf was causing subsidence that may have come irregularly, in sudden episodes of deepening water. The swelling and shrinking of the mid-oceanic ridges as they discharged new material from the mantle could also have affected the level of the sea. Worldwide glaciation occurred in the Ordovician (although apparently not in the Cambrian), which probably caused changes in sea levels then, just as it did more recently in the Pleistocene Epoch. But at this point it is not possible to say which process was at work. Maybe *all* were. Watch this space in the next edition.

Formations of the Middle Cambrian sandwich (Mt. Whyte, Cathedral, Stephen and Eldon, discussed previously) are included in the group of cyclic sediments. Here are the others.

Pika Formation
Middle Cambrian (540-523 Ma) 90-275 m

Dark-weathering brown limestone and dolomite, mostly thinner-bedded than the underlying Eldon Fm. and shalier, with fossils (the Eldon is barren). The rock is moderately resistant to erosion but is not the outstanding cliff-former the Eldon is. There is a recessive zone at the base, which helps to separate Pika beds from the underlying massive Eldon. Named for Pika ("PIE-kuh") Peak, east of Lake Louise.

The Pika thickens southwestward. It is thinnest at the mountain front and thickest around Kicking Horse Pass. West of there the formation loses its identity as it merges with rock of the middle Chancellor Fm. (page 116). To the south it dips under cover of younger rock at Mt. Assiniboine. North of Jasper the Pika becomes shaly, resembling the overlying Arctomys Fm. (described next); the two can be traced as a single unit called the **Titkana Formation** as far as Jackpine River in central Willmore park.

A good place to see the Pika up close is in outcrops of glacially smoothed rock 100 m west of the glacier-ride concession building near the Icefield Chalet, along the Icefields Parkway. Here the white-veined Pika lies beside red and green bands of Arctomys shale. There is a road-cut through the Pika just west of extensive Eldon outcrops at the mountain front along the TransCanada Highway, and another in a similar geological setting at Windy Point on Highway 11, 55 km east of Saskatchewan Crossing.

Fossils: the trilobites *Modocia, Marjumia* and *Rowia*.

Arctomys Formation
Middle Cambrian (540-523 Ma) 30-340 m

Red and green shales, interbedded with orange or buff dolomitic siltstones. The Arctomys (properly pronounced "ARK-toe-miss") is a formation to know in the Rockies; it is found throughout the front ranges and eastern main ranges between Bow River and Peace River, readily identifiable as a colorful unit between the sombre gray and brown formations above and below. Even though Arctomys shale is soft and thus recessive, you can still often see the formation above timberline as a deep-red, orange or yellowish stripe in the mountainside.

Named for Arctomys Peak, west of Saskatchewan Crossing, the unit is thinnest at the mountain front and thickest west of Jasper in the Mt. Robson area. In the western main ranges it merges with shales of the upper Chancellor Fm. (page 116), but in the eastern main ranges and front ranges it can be followed to at least Jackpine River. North of Peace River rock of that age is missing due to uplift.

Not only is it colorful; the Arctomys is interesting for its **salt-crystal casts.** These casts are up to 3 cm across (although usually less than a centimetre wide) and often hopper-like: weathering as boxes-within-boxes. The water here was not only very shallow, as verified by ripple marks and mud cracks; it was also extremely salty, for salt was crystallizing in the mud.

Salt is an **evaporite.** Evaporites usually form in an ocean basin that becomes cut off from the rest of the sea—or nearly so, allowing only a weak flow in and out of the basin—in climates that are sunny and warm. Evaporation removes water but leaves dissolved minerals behind. Eventually the water becomes chemically saturated and the minerals start to precipitate as crystals of salt, gypsum, calcite and dolomite. Don't expect to find fossils in the Arctomys; they are quite rare.

Salt-crystal casts in Arctomys shale. Penny for scale.

Waterfowl Formation
Middle Cambrian (540-523 Ma) 12-200 m

Mostly buff-weathering dolomite at the mountain front, where the formation is thinnest. Thickens westward in the main ranges, where it is usually gray limestone, often with interesting wavy or mottled bedding, between thin yellow or white dolomite bands.

There are thick Waterfowl sections around Glacier Lake (west of Saskatchewan Crossing) and at Kicking Horse Pass. West of the continental divide, the shaly time-equivalent is part of the upper Chancellor Fm. The Waterfowl runs south to Mt. Assiniboine; north of Jasper it merges with the Lynx Gp. (page 110).

Waterfowl Lakes are along the Icefields Parkway south of Saskatchewan Crossing. The formation outcrops high on the eastern valley slope, but there are handier exposures an hour away along Highway 11 at the mountain front (the second cliff down from the top in the small peak north of the highway at Windy Point is Waterfowl dolomite). Farther south, you can get your hands on Waterfowl outcrops a few minutes' walk above the Bow Valley Parkway 2 km west of its junction with the TransCanada Highway some 5 km west of Banff. The section here runs from Eldon Fm. on the east to Survey Peak Fm. on the west, before hitting the sub-Devonian unconformity (page 120) and Cairn Fm. beds above.

The Waterfowl is a limestone-student's formation, full of interesting layers: massive ones, in which the bedding was destroyed by burrowing organisms when the sediment was still soft; crinkly layers and stromatolites from algal growth (see page 75); oolites (page 91); dolomite mottling in the form of buff squiggles against featureless massive limestone—all quite interesting to examine layer by layer. North of Athabasca River there are also sandstone beds with limestone pebbles in them. But there don't seem to be any fossils.

Sullivan Formation
Late Cambrian (523-505 Ma) 12-200 m

Mostly soft olive-drab shale with occasional thin limestone and siltstone beds (siltstone at base in main ranges; also higher elsewhere). The Sullivan is thin at the mountain front and nearly always covered by soil or talus, but thicker to the west, especially between Saskatchewan Crossing and Sunwapta Pass, where it is well exposed at higher elevations. Named for Sullivan Peak, west of Saskatchewan Crossing. Distribution: Mt. Assiniboine to the Columbia Icefield area, north of which it becomes limy and loses its identity in the Lynx Gp. It is present (but thin) at Maligne Lake.

Sullivan shale occurs in a road-cut 1 km west of Windy Point along Highway 11 near the mountain front. In the main ranges you can see the upper part in the slope behind the Columbia Icefield Chalet. The formation outcrops along the Icefields Parkway some 15 km farther north, in low hills beside the highway.

Among the shale beds of the Sullivan are layers of gray limestone containing trilobites (mostly bits and pieces, as usual). Species include *Cedaria,* a marker fossil that places the Sullivan Fm. at the beginning of the Late Cambrian; other common ones are *Coosella, Cedarina* and a small but interesting, eyeless trilobite called *Kormagnostus.* It looks the same at both ends.

Lyell Formation/Ottertail Formation
Late Cambrian (523-505 Ma) 100-600 m

Banded limestone and dolomite, commonly gray at a distance with dull yellow or buff stripes. Up close many of the gray beds are seen to be silty or sandy limestone, with shallow-water features such as algal structures. The buff beds are dolomitic. "Lyell" is from Mt. Lyell ("lie-ELL"), near Glacier Lake in the north end of Banff park. Under that name it is found in the eastern main ranges and front ranges from White Man Mountain in the south end of Banff park to Tangle Ridge in the Columbia Icefield area. To the north it becomes an anonymous part of the

The Rockwall above Floe Lake in Kootenay National Park. The Rockwall is a continous cliff of Ottertail limestone; here it is about 900 m high.

Bands of pale dolomite and dark sandy limestone in the Lyell Formation near Icefield Centre. Two sets of joints (cracks) have developed in the formation at this outcrop, so that the rock breaks across the banding into angular oblong chunks. Penny for scale.

Lynx Gp. (page 110), but westward it continues as the Ottertail Fm. in the western main ranges and runs south through Yoho and Kootenay parks.

The Lyell and Ottertail are the odd men out in the Middle Cambrian to Ordovician carbonate sequence hereabouts. All the others are limestone/dolomite east of the continental divide and shale to the west except these, which are carbonate throughout. The Ottertail lies between the Chancellor and McKay shales (page 117), keeping its identity all the way to the Rocky Mountain Trench.

The Lyell is interesting rock, too: banded yellowy buff and gray from dolomitization of alternating layers. In the lower part the beds are full of oolites (page 91). In the middle part the bedding is much thinner and so is the banding. This is the weak part of an otherwise erosion-resistant formation; in the main ranges the Lyell produces two very steep (often vertical or overhanging) cliffs with a slope in between that marks the weaker middle section. In the slopes of Wilcox Peak across from the Athabasca Glacier, these middle-section layers are buff dolomite and gray limestone on the order of a few centimetres thick. The pieces lying about look as if a zebra had shattered. This is one of the better places to look at the Lyell Fm.; just wander up the slope between the Icefield Chalet and Icefield Campground. But don't collect; it is illegal in the parks.

"Ottertail" is from the Ottertail River in Yoho Park. The Ottertail limestone is similar to the Lyell in both age and rock type, but separated geographically from the Lyell and thicker (up to 600 m, compared to a maximum of 345 m for the Lyell). The two units were studied independently and at time of writing still maintain separate names, even though they are really the same formation.

Ottertail rock appears just north of Blaeberry River (north of Golden) and runs south into western Yoho park, through the twin peaks of Mt. Goodsir (the enormous faces are made of McKay shale, not Ottertail limestone) and then on into Kootenay park, where the unit forms the spectacular **Rockwall**. South of Vermilion River the Ottertail dips down out of sight, having formed a seldom-broken 53-km cliff that is the epitome of what geologists call **structural control**: a landscape dominated by the underlying geology.

The Lyell/Ottertail represents a time when the seabed west of the Kicking Horse Rim, normally deeper than the rim, had collected so much shale that the water was shallow. This encouraged rim-dwelling organisms to advance westward, laying down telltale limestone as they went. The Ottertail records that advance.

Few fossils appear in Lyell/Ottertail rock, although the trilobite *Crepicephalus* appears at the base of the Lyell and *Elvinia* can be found at the top, placing the Lyell/Ottertail in the middle of the Late Cambrian. *Aphelaspis* occurs in the middle and upper parts.

Bison Creek Formation
Late Cambrian (523-505 Ma) 10-210 m

Interbedded limestone and shale, reminiscent of the Sullivan Fm. (page 106) but less easily eroded. Bison Creek is a small stream on the south side of Mt. Murchison, which is the big peak beside (east of) the Icefields Parkway just south of Saskatchewan Crossing. But the best place to see this unit at a distance is in Mt. Wilson, just north of the crossing. The Bison Creek and all the other Late Cambrian and Ordovician formations are beautifully exposed there, right up to the sub-Devonian unconformity (see page 120).

Like the underlying Lyell Fm., the Bison Creek falls mostly within Banff and Yoho parks, changing laterally to shale in the western main ranges (where rock of that age is part of the McKay Gp., page 117) and blending into the limestone/dolomite Lynx Gp. (page 110) elsewhere. Bison Creek rock is recessive and seldom well exposed right beside a highway, but a walk up the creek running through Icefield Campground (along the Icefields Parkway near Athabasca Glacier) takes you up to outcrops at timberline in about 30 minutes.

The more resistant beds are full of interesting structures called **thrombolites**: gray, rough-weathering blobs averaging a metre tall and perhaps half as wide. "Thrombo-," meaning "clot," is a perfect description. Like stromatolites (page 75), thrombolites are algal mounds; they simply lack the curved laminations found in stromatolites, perhaps because the laminations have been destroyed by seabed burrowers.

Limestone Bison Creek strata are rich in fossils, mostly broken-up trilobites of the genera *Elvinia, Conaspis, Ptychaspis* and *Prosaukia.* The crinoids (sea-lily branch of the echinoderm phylum) had appeared on the scene by then, and some beds are loaded with snowflake-shaped pieces from the platy columns of these animals. The Rundle Gp. (page 142) is the only other crinoid-rich unit in our area, and it is much younger (Early Carboniferous).

Mistaya Formation
Late Cambrian (523-505 Ma) 45-160 m

Massive limestone beds, often a metre thick or more and weathering pale gray. Looks obviously different from the underlying thinner-bedded Lyell and Bison Creek formations (see previous entries). Named for the Mistaya River, which parallels the Icefields Parkway from Mistaya Lake to Saskatchewan Crossing.*

This resistant limestone stands out between the shaly formations above and below; often it forms a cliff. The formation is entirely a shallow-water deposit, and it contains the biggest stromatolites in our area: they are frequently 1.5 m tall, found side-by-side in the massive limestone layers. Above the Mistaya, stromatolites are less common (for more on stromatolites, turn to page 75).

The Mistaya follows the same geographic distribution as the underlying Bison Creek beds, (previous entry). It is well-exposed at the **type section** (place where originally studied): a gully cutting through the cliffs of Mt. Murchison, south of Saskatchewan Crossing. Like the Bison Creek, the Mistaya can be approached quickly from Icefield Campground. It is also accessible in gullies on Mt. Wilson, across the North Saskatchewan River from Mt. Murchison. Fossils: the trilobites *Saukia, Bynumiella, Dikelocephalus* and *Briscoia,* dating the formation as latest Late Cambrian.

---

*Mistaya, pronounced "miss-TIE-yah," is the Stony Indian word for the grizzly bear.

Lynx Group
Late Cambrian (523-505 Ma) Up to 1060 m

Interbedded gray limestone and dolomite, often silty or sandy, with algal laminations. Weathers in gray and buff bands. Resistant, forming ledgy cliffs.

The Lynx Gp. is simply the Waterfowl, Sullivan, Lyell, Bison Creek and Mistaya formations all lumped into one unit. Reason: traced east from the main ranges, the Sullivan and Bison Creek shales change to limestone/dolomite. This makes it impractical to separate them from the other formations, which are themselves limestones and dolomites. So where this happens the whole works is called Lynx Gp. The formations the Lynx Gp. replaces lie mostly in Banff and Yoho national parks; the Lynx group surrounds this area, except on the west side, where rocks of that age are shaly (except for the Lyell/Ottertail, page 106).

"Lynx" is from Lynx Mountain, a peak near Mt. Robson. C.D. Walcott first studied the unit there around 1913. Since then, most of Walcott's names for Cambrian and Ordovician formations have been abandoned, but this one has stuck. Further, the Lynx Gp. has turned up in other places in the Canadian Rockies. To the north it can be traced to Pine Pass. To the south it has been found as far as Ghost River east of Banff. There are no Lynx exposures along the TransCanada Highway or the Icefields Parkway; the handiest outcrop is at Cold Sulphur Spring, 20 km east of Jasper along Highway 16. The first break in the cliff east of the spring occurs in Lynx rock. (See page 132 for a description of the sub-Devonian unconformity at this site.)

Fossils have not been found in the Lynx, although the formation preserves many wavy algal structures.

Survey Peak Formation
Late Cambrian and Early Ordovician (500-515 Ma) 345-400 m

Mostly gray-green shale, but in three distinct parts: silty at the base, shaly higher, then limy in the top third, where there are limestone flat-pebble conglomerates, thrombolites (previous page) and oolites (page 91). Not resistant to erosion except at the top, but thick and thus well-exposed at higher elevations. Named for Survey Peak, west of Saskatchewan Crossing near Glacier Lake.

The Survey Peak Fm. is easy to recognize at a distance by the putty-like color of the shale in it. Geologists refer to the **putty shales** of the Survey Peak. Survey Peak itself, the rounded mountain west of the Icefields Parkway just north of Saskatchewan Crossing, gives a good distant impression of the color. Access to exposed Survey Peak beds usually requires a trip well above timberline; perhaps the shortest approach (one-half hour) is to follow the creek running from Wilcox Pass through Icefield Campground, along the Icefields Parkway near Sunwapta Pass.

This unit has by far the widest distribution of any Ordovician or Silurian formation in our area; Survey Peak rock can be found under one name or another from just north of Fernie to the north end of the Rockies, and from the front ranges to the Rocky Mountain Trench. Other Ordovician/Silurian formations occur only between Sunwapta Falls (south of Jasper) and Fernie.

North of Sunwapta Falls the Survey Peak is sometimes identified by an older name: **Chushina Formation** (which also includes the northern equivalent of the Outram Fm., next entry.) Between Pine Pass and the Alaska Highway the rock becomes limy again and is placed in the Kechika Gp. (page 115). On the western slope the unit makes up part of the McKay Gp. shales (page 117).

The Survey Peak is not very fossiliferous, but the graptolites *Didymograptus* and *Phyllograptus* have been found in it, pegging the age of the formation as Late Cambrian in its lower layers and Early Ordovician in its upper layers. See page 119 for more on graptolites.

Outram Formation
Early Ordovician (505-478 Ma) 170-440 m

Peculiar nodular, cherty limestone beds and brown shale with limestone nodules that have chert blobs in their centres. Good exposures are banded sombre brown and dark gray. "Outram" is from Mt. Outram, a prominent peak west of Saskatchewan Crossing that many people take to be Mt. Forbes (Forbes is higher but is mostly hidden behind Outram). Sir James Outram was a Scottish climber who made the first ascent of Mt. Assiniboine; he pronounced his name "OOT-rum," and so should we.

The Outram limestone stands up to erosion a bit better than the underlying Survey Peak shale but is still recessive. Not widespread, the formation is most prominent in the eastern main ranges from Copper Mountain (northwest of Banff) to Tangle Ridge (along the Icefields Parkway just north of the Columbia Icefield area). North of there Outram-type rock is included in the Survey Peak Fm. (previous entry); to the west it merges with the McKay Gp. and the Glenogle Shales (page 117). To the east, Outram rock interfingers with the Skoki (page 112) and Owen Creek (page 113) formations. It was also being laid down at the same time as the Tipperary Quartzite (page 112) farther south. So the relationship of the Outram to neighboring rock units is complex.

Outram rock also includes lacy black silica (micro-crystalline quartz) and chert (blobs of silica) in the limestone beds. The chert weathers away more slowly than the lime and so stands out in bold relief. This formation seems to have been laid down in water that was poorly oxygenated and subject to the sort of alternating acidic/basic chemistry that produces chert deposits (see page 146 for more on this). Fossils are present, but they tend to be in very small pieces.

The Outram Fm. is visible in the cliffs of Mt. Wilson above Saskatchewan Crossing. Perhaps the best exposures near a highway are in gullies on the southeastern slope of the mountain, about two hours' walk from the road.

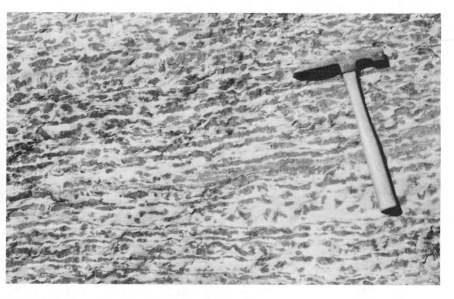

Nodular limestone from the Outram Formation. Photo by Jim Aitken, reproduced courtesy Geological Survey of Canada.

Monkman Quartzite and Tipperary Quartzite
Early Ordovician (505-478 Ma) 0-300 m

The Monkman and Tipperary quartzites resemble the other two quartzite units in our area (the Gog Gp., page 88, and Mt. Wilson Qtz., page 113). They are all very hard, cross-bedded sandstone in shades of white, gray or buff (sometimes yellowish or pink), weathering buff, orange or pink. See page 89 for a discussion of quartzite, cross-beds, etc. "Monkman" is from the Monkman Pass area northeast of Prince George; "Tipperary" is from Tipperary Lake, near the head of the Palliser River just west of Kananaskis Lakes. Both formations grade into shale to the west and wedge out to the east against the sub-Devonian unconformity (page 120).

Monkman rock is widespread, found in the eastern main ranges from Kakwa Lake, just northwest of Willmore Park, to Peace River. The most accessible outcrops are right in Pine Pass, in cliffs below the highway. Tipperary rock is harder to get to; outcrops at the western end of Spray Lake (west of Canmore) can be approached via the rough Calgary Power road on the northwest shore of the lake, and there are outcrops at Upper Kananaskis Lake. The formation is thin here and difficult to locate; thicker exposures on the western side of the divide require a rough trip by here-today, gone-tomorrow logging roads.

One might think that these two isolated patches of Early Ordovician quartzite (Monkman and Tipperary), so similar in rock type and age, had been deposited as part of a larger sheet of sand. But such is not the case; each thins out toward the other. The intervening space is occupied by the Skoki Fm. (next entry), which partly interfingers with the Tipperary. This shows that Skoki dolomite was being deposited at the same time as the Tipperary quartzite, so the Monkman and Tipperary units were never connected. They look so much alike that they may have had the same source: possibly ancient Middle Proterozoic sandstones uplifted on the Canadian shield to the northeast and eroding into the sea at both places. Could uplifted Gog Gp. sands have been the source? This is unlikely: they would have had to have been washed in from the west, where the sea lay.

No fossils have been found in Tipperary or Monkman rock, which is typical of quartzite, but the underlying and overlying beds contain fossils that date both units as Early Ordovician.

Skoki Formation
Early and Middle Ordovician (488-458 Ma) 0-230 m

Light-gray dolomite, medium-bedded to massive, weathering buff to yellowish or pale orange, with one excellent identifier: a single bed filled with large fossil snails (*Palliseria* and *Maclurites*) near the top of the formation. Oncolites (page 95) are also common in the upper layers.

"Skoki" (pronounced "SKO-key") is from Skoki Mountain, in the front ranges east of Lake Louise. Skoki dolomite is widespread, found in the eastern main ranges and western front ranges from Sunwapta Falls south to about Mt. Peck along the Elk River north of Fernie. The formation is thickest around Mt. Sir Douglas in the Kananaskis area. To the west, Skoki beds interfinger with Outram limestone (page 111) and Glenogle shale (page 117). The Outram underlies the Skoki as well, a neat geological trick that happened because Outram sediments were laid down first, then continued to accumulate just west of the region in which the Skoki material was being laid down. The eastern edge of the Skoki is the sub-Devonian unconformity (page 120).

Getting your hands on good Skoki outcrops isn't easy, despite the wide distribution. The best exposures are probably at Skoki Mountain and nearby Fossil Mountain, a hike of 20 km from Lake Louise. Skoki dolomite runs through Mt. Wilson, quite high up on the huge west face above the Icefields Parkway at Saskatchewan Crossing, but it gets closer to the highway as you drive north. Just south of Cirrus Mountain Campground, which is found a few kilometres south of the viewpoint at the Weeping Wall, the formation crosses the road and outcrops are fairly close by on the east side. Walking up from Wilcox Campground to Wilcox Pass will take you to Skoki outcrops there.

Soon after the Skoki was deposited, some parts of it were raised above sea level and caves formed in it. The small passages were later filled with sand, which has hardened to veins of white quartzite. West of Saskatchewan Crossing near the Lyell and Mons glaciers, the filled passages are up to 10 m wide. Smaller cave remnants can also be seen in Wilcox Pass.

Owen Creek Formation
Middle Ordovician (478-458 Ma) 45-190 m

Mostly gray- or buff-weathering dolomite, darker than the underlying Skoki, with reddish or greenish shale in the lower part and sandstone in the upper part. Most easily identified by its position under the distinctive pale cliffs of the Mt. Wilson Quartzite (next entry). Owen Creek is the first drainage east of Mt. Wilson, the big peak seen to the north from Saskatchewan Crossing along the Icefields Parkway. It is fed by the Wilson Icefield.

This formation occurs in two patches in the eastern main ranges and front ranges. The northern one runs from about Poboktan Creek (Sunwapta Warden Station on the Icefields Parkway) to just north of Kicking Horse Pass. The southern patch is small and narrow, a band running along the continental divide from Spray Lake west of Canmore to the upper reaches of the White River some 60 km farther south. A stiff climb up Owen Creek gets you to the type section, but you can see this rock more easily north of Mt. Wilson, where the Icefields Parkway runs steadily up through the Ordovician section. Owen Creek strata outcrop in the hillside south of Cirrus Mountain Campground, along with the Skoki and Mt. Wilson formations.

The Owen Creek is not fossiliferous. Westward, it becomes part of the Glenogle Shales (page 117).

Mount Wilson Quartzite
Middle or Late Ordovician (478-438 Ma)

White quartzite, weathering gray on gentle surfaces and yellowish on steep or overhanging surfaces, sometimes dazzlingly white, with dark stains where water runs down. Named for Mt. Wilson, where it forms a spectacular yellowish fin on the skyline above Saskatchewan Crossing.

Note that the name is Mt. Wilson *Quartzite,* not Mt. Wilson *Formation.* To use the rock type in the formation name is British geologic practice; the Americans are inclined to use "Formation." In Canada you will see both.

The Mount Wilson Qtz. occurs in two separate patches in our area. They were originally connected, but uplift not long after deposition allowed erosion to remove most of the formation. Only the two isolated patches remain. The Owen Creek dolomite underlying the Mt. Wilson Qtz. was eroded along with it; the two occur together.

The northern patch is centred at Mt. Wilson. It is found north from there in the eastern main ranges and western front ranges to about Tangle Ridge, and south nearly to Hector Lake. Outcrops close to the highway are in the hillside one-half kilometre south of Cirrus Mountain Campground, along the Icefields Parkway 25 km north of Saskatchewan Crossing.

The other portion of this formation runs through the western ranges from Golden south to Radium Hot Springs, then into the western main ranges to a point south of Top of the World Provincial Park, then hooking back north in the eastern main ranges to Mt. Sir Douglas. It crosses Highway 93 about 2 km east of the aquacourt at Radium Hot Springs, where the canyon is narrow.

It took 30 years for geologists to realize that the quartzite at Mt. Wilson and the quartzite near Radium were the same formation. Charles Walcott had described the Radium beds in 1924 and named them "Wonah Formation." Even though he had named the Mount Wilson Qtz. a year earlier, he didn't realize that the Wonah was actually the Mt. Wilson. This was an easy mistake to make: until

Mt. Wilson Quartzite, as seen high in Mt. Wilson from Saskatchewan Crossing. The massive quartzite is 165 m thick and extremely resistant to erosion; it forms the pale cliff, which is overhanging in places. Dark streaks are lichens growing on places where water runs down the face. Summit is in Beaverfoot limestone/dolomite; dark layers at the base of the Mt. Wilson are Owen Creek dolomite.

the Lyell/Ottertail equivalence was worked out, no other Cambrian or Ordovician formation in this part of the Rockies was known to go all the way across from the front ranges to the western ranges. So it seemed unlikely to him that the two quartzites were the same, even though they looked similar. F.K. North and G.G. Henderson corrected the mistake in 1954, using "Mount Wilson" for both.

The Mount Wilson Quartzite is significant:

1. This is the most quartz-rich sandstone in our area: 99 percent quartz grains in most outcrops. Sandstone this pure is so rare that one wonders what the source of the Mount Wilson was. It could have been derived from eroding Proterozoic sandstone on the Canadian Shield to the northeast, just as the Gog was a hundred million years earlier (see page 89).

2. The big pulse of sand covered a lot of the seabed lying west of the Kicking Horse Rim (page 101), a place that had accumulated nothing but shale (with the exception of the Ottertail limestone) since at least the beginning of the Middle Cambrian. The sand layer marks the end of the cyclic sedimentation that had been going on along the Kicking Horse Rim in the central Rockies since Middle Cambrian times.

3. The Mount Wilson is the last sandstone in our area to get its material from the northeast, off the main part of the continent. Younger ones received theirs from the west, during the mountain-building phase of western Canada's geological history.

Beaverfoot Formation
Late Ordovician and Early Silurian (458-421 Ma) 0-540 m

Brown-weathering dolomite and limestone in medium and thick beds, resistant and cliff-forming. Named for the Beaverfoot Range (east wall of the Rocky Mountain Trench for a 50-km stretch south of Golden).

There was patchy uplift and erosion after the Mt. Wilson Qtz. (previous entry) was laid down. When the sea covered the region again after a few million years, Beaverfoot beds were deposited on rock that had been worn down to Late Cambrian layers in some places and not worn down at all (left below sea level, in other words) elsewhere.

The current distribution of the Beaverfoot Fm. roughly follows the two-part arrangement of the Mt. Wilson, reaching Peace River in the northern segment and Top of the World park in the southern segment. But that isn't the original extent of the formation. The sea covered most of western Canada during Beaverfoot time; patches of the formation can be found under various names farther north, through the Mackenzie Mountains to the arctic islands and as far east as Hudson Bay. It is a remarkably widespread unit.

Silicified fossils are common in Beaverfoot dolomite, and the limestone layers can be richly fossiliferous. Look in the lower part of the formation for some of interesting things: the warty trilobite *Encrinurus,* the corals *Bighornia* and *Paleofavosites,* the brachiopods *Dinorthis* and *Rynchotrema,* echinoderms, cephalopods, snails, graptolites—a paleontological smorgasbord that shows the great variety of life that had evolved by this time.

The type Beaverfoot exposure is in the Beaverfoot Range southeast of Golden. Beaverfoot rock caps the great cliffs of Mt. Wilson and comes close to the Icefields Parkway in the hillside just south of Cirrus Mountain Campground.

Tegart Formation
Early Silurian (428-421 Ma) 0-75 m

Dark-gray and brownish shaly limestone, thin-bedded and aphanitic ("aphanitic" means "without much texture"). Named for Mt. Tegart, bordering the Rocky Mountain Trench east of Windermere Lake.

The Tegart beds are thin and the area covered is small (Radium to Top of the World park). Further, there are no outcrops along highways; you have to hike up Windermere Creek to Pedley Pass to see it. But this is the only strictly Silurian rock in the southern part of the Canadian Rockies. Above the Tegart lies the sub-Devonian unconformity, discussed on page 120. Fossils in the Tegart are mostly graptolites.

Kechika Group
Late Cambrian and Early Ordovician (523-478 Ma) About 1800 m

A northern-Rockies unit, merging southward with the Survey Peak Fm. (page 110) of the central Rockies but somewhat younger at the top. The Kechika also includes rock of the same age as the upper part of the Lynx Gp. (page 110). The formation is limy in the east and shaly in the west, like the Middle and Late Cambrian and Ordovician formations to the south. It lies on an erosion surface atop uplifted and bevelled Atan Gp. beds (page 91), so it shows that the ocean moved back into the north end of the Rockies area after mid-Cambrian uplift pushed it away for a while.

Renewed uplift and tilting in the Middle Ordovician caused another retreat, which lasted until the sea returned in the early Silurian. The intervening period of erosion bevelled off the tilt, so the Kechika underlies the next unit (Nonda Fm., next entry) at an angle. The area probably lay close to the western continental edge at this time, for there are particles of volcanic rock in the Kechika south of Tuchodi Lakes (volcanism is common along the boundaries of crustal plates). Dykes of diabase (see page 75) cut through the Kechika south of Redfern Lake.

The Alaska Highway just touches a large area of Kechika rock in the Terminal Range, which lies west of the road when it turns north to Muncho Lake after Kilometre 710.

Nonda Formation
Early Silurian (428-421 Ma) 210-305 m

Mostly dark-gray cherty dolomite, weathering buff, with sandstone at the base and the earliest appearance in the Canadian Rockies of stromatoporoids (page 128), which became common in the Devonian Period.

The Nonda is found from about halfway between Pine Pass and Peace River north to at least Liard River. It outcrops at Summit Lake along the Alaska Highway. The highway crosses it again farther west, along Toad River, and also at the south end of Muncho Lake.

Nonda rock is sparsely fossiliferous and rather uninteresting, but in some places it rests above the greatest unconformity (not counting Pleistocene or Holocene deposits) exposed in the Canadian Rockies: below is the Chischa Fm. (page 77), a Middle Proterozoic unit dating to about 1400 Ma. So the gap in the record here spans over a billion years.

Another interesting thing about the Nonda is that it goes rather abruptly from dolomite in the east to shale in the west, like the change-over from limestone to shale off the Kicking Horse Rim in the central Rockies.

The Nonda is just a little younger than the Tegart (page 115), which makes it the youngest pre-Devonian rock exposed in the Canadian Rockies. Above the Nonda there is another gap: the sub-Devonian unconformity, an important, widespread buried erosion surface that is discussed on page 120. But before dealing with that we should backtrack in time somewhat and present the western shaly equivalents of the Early Paleozoic formations discussed so far.

The shale belt

While organisms were busily producing limestone during the Cambrian, Ordovician and Silurian periods on the shallower portion of the continental shelf, deeper water next door to the west was collecting shale. This is the **shale belt** of the Canadian Rockies, found west of the continental divide. The formations there are the same age as the neighboring limestones and dolomites—just a different facies, meaning a different rock type. The shale facies is also much thicker.

If you have struggled through the description of the welter of Cambrian to Silurian formations discussed thus far, you may be pleased to hear that their shale-belt equivalents can be handled by only three names for the central and southern Rockies: Chancellor, McKay and Glenogle. For the northern Rockies there is only one: Kechika. Together, these units represent the mud that accumulated in the deeper-water area off the Kicking Horse Rim (page 101), and with minor exceptions they tongue into the whole packet of limestones and dolomites in the eastern main ranges, from the Mt. Whyte Fm. all the way up through the Cambrian and Ordovician to the Owen Creek Fm. A major exception is the Ottertail Fm. (page 106), a thick Late Cambrian limestone that lies between two of the shales: the McKay and the Glenogle.

The shale belt begins near Fernie, reaches its best development east of Golden, then angles out into the Rocky Mountain Trench where it dips under the Purcell Thrust Sheet. The belt picks up again farther north at Pine Pass, which is the southern limit of the Late Cambrian and Early Ordovician Kechika Gp. (page 115) of the northern Rockies. The limestone-to-shale facies change seen in the central Rockies is also found in the northern Rockies, although there is no Middle Cambrian rock here because of uplift and erosion at this time.

Chancellor Group
Middle and Late Cambrian (540-505 Ma) 2500-3000 m

A thick sequence of brown or gray shales and thin shaly limestones found west of the continental divide in the western main ranges between Fernie and Peace River. The Chancellor is the western equivalent of the Mt. Whyte, Cathedral, Stephen, Eldon, Pika, Arctomys, Waterfowl and Sullivan formations, as described in previously. The name comes from Chancellor Peak in southern Yoho park.

The Chancellor accumulated in water more than 200 m deep next to the Kicking Horse Rim, where occasional underwater flows carried fine-grained material off the rim and out into the deep-water basin. Such flows are called turbidity currents (see page 83 for details); in the Chancellor they are responsible for great thicknesses of alternating shale and shaly limestone beds.

There are three units in the Chancellor, all of them cleaved (page 78) and often gone to slate or silvery phyllite (page 79). The lower part (1000 m of shaly limestone/dolomite, no fossils) is equivalent to the interval from the Mt. Whyte Fm. to the Pika Fm. next door. The middle part (600 m, shaly low and limy higher), matches up with the Arctomys and Waterfowl formations, and the upper part (1000-1400 m of greenish shale with a few *Cedaria* trilobites) corresponds only to the Sullivan Fm. Picking out the three units takes some experience, because overall the Chancellor is fossil-poor and monotonous.

Thick and wildly contorted from folding, this great wad of shale is on display for 15 km along the TransCanada Highway west of Field. It is also exposed in roadcuts west of Marble Canyon on Highway 93 to Radium. Structural geologists have worked hard to understand the amazingly tortured strata. Go and see for yourself; any road-cut demonstrates what pressure will do to material that we ordinarily think of as rigid. Some of the outcrops show that the sediments slumped into chaotic masses while it was still soft, long before folding distorted it further during the uplift of the Rockies.

The Chancellor Gp. forms dark-colored, irregularly shaped mountains that are not as high as peaks just to the east, where the tougher limestone equivalents are. But the group is often cliffy nonetheless.

McKay Group
Late Cambrian and Early Ordovician (523-478 Ma) 400-1600 m

Mostly gray-green shale reminiscent of the Survey Peak Fm. (page 110), with cherty beds like those of the Outram Fm. (page 111) appearing near the top. "McKay" ("Muck-EYE") is from John McKay Creek, water supply for the town of Radium Hot Springs.

The TransCanada Highway runs through good McKay exposures in the canyon of the Kicking Horse River. Look for the shale along the 15-km stretch east from Golden. Like the other western-slope shales, this one is smashed up beyond belief; from the highway you can see a couple of contorted limestone beds in the slaty-looking shale that show just how deformed these rocks are. For this reason, no one has ever been able to measure the thickness of the McKay Gp. precisely.

The beds are not very fossiliferous, either, but they do contain graptolites (see next entry) and trilobites that date the McKay as Late Cambrian and Early Ordovician, making it the shaly equivalent of the Bison Creek, Mistaya, Survey Peak and lower Outram formations of the eastern main ranges. At this time there were periods of clear, shallow water east of the shale belt that allowed reef-like algal limestone to accumulate (see the Kicking Horse Rim, page 101), but in the area covered by the McKay Gp. the water was deeper and bottom-dwelling life sparser. Still, there are limestone beds in the McKay, particularly evident near the head of Kicking Horse Canyon.

Glenogle Shales
Early and Middle Ordovician (505-458 Ma) 140-700 m

Mostly black or dark-gray shales with lots of graptolite fossils (described in this entry) and thin limestone layers. The upper quarter is silty, sandy and dolomitic, weathering brownish and fossil-poor. The whole formation is soft, weathering back into slopes.

This formation name uses the rock type rather than "Formation," so it is properly Glenogle *Shales,* not Glenogle *Formation.*

The Glenogle is the third division in the great stack of beaten-up shale that makes up the western part of the Canadian Rockies. It is the western equivalent of several formations found in the eastern main ranges: upper Outram, Tipperary,

Skoki, and Owen Creek. The Glenogle is thick for the amount of time represented. It seems to have filled a rapidly deepening trough in the seabed, topped off by the sands of the Mt. Wilson Qtz., which overlie the Glenogle Shales.

Where you find the McKay Gp. (previous entry), then you will often find Glenogle rock overlying it. But the two formations are so tightly folded and intricately thrust-faulted that it can be hard to tell which is which when looking at a particular bed. Color is a helpful criterion: Glenogle shale is always darker than that of the McKay Gp., and never greenish.

Both units are well exposed in roadcuts along the TransCanada Highway east of Golden, in the eastern 10 km of Kicking Horse Canyon. "Glenogle" comes from Glenogle Creek, near the head of the canyon.

The Glenogle is loaded with **graptolites**: peculiar fossils that are common in Ordovician and Silurian black shales but scarce at other times and in other rock types (range: Cambrian to Mississippian). The only living things resembling graptolites are the pterobranchs, a class of the phylum Protochordata, whose members have a primitive notochord and thus bridge the evolutionary gap between the chordates and the invertebrates.

Under a magnifying glass, graptolite fossils look like little pieces of hacksaw blades. They are the broken remains of linear colonies, preserved as flattened films of carbon. Each organism grew in a tiny tube made of **chitin**; the material of which the exoskeletons of modern insects and crustaceans are made. Each colony member beat the water around it with a couple of fleshy plumes that it used to snag microscopic swimmers, which it would then draw toward its mouth as the corals do. When something wanted to eat *it*, a graptolite could pull itself inside the tube and hide.

The bits and pieces of graptolite colonies found in rock are flattened; the teeth of the hacksaw blade are the individual cups of the organisms. Entire colonies are seldom found, but occasional whole specimens demonstrate that hundreds of these little animals were attached in strings to gas-filled floats of the kind that jellyfish use. The colonies drifted about the oceans, often over deeper water than that preferred by other creatures; hence their preservation in black shale, a deep-water rock type.

Graptolites spread rapidly around the world and evolved quickly. This makes them good index fossils: each species spans only a short period of time (meaning a couple of million years to a geologist) and is often found worldwide.

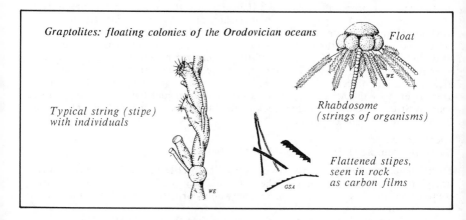

Graptolites: floating colonies of the Orodovician oceans *Float*

Typical string (stipe) with individuals

Rhabdosome (strings of organisms)

Flattened stipes, seen in rock as carbon films

Kinky Chancellor beds along the TransCanada Highway west of Field. Dark bands are limestone; light bands are shale.

Slaty beds of black Glenogle shale in Kicking Horse Canyon, about 10 km east of Golden along the TransCanada Highway.

Shale belt

NOTES ON THE SUB-DEVONIAN UNCONFORMITY
AND OTHER MISSING THINGS

In the eastern front ranges of the central Rockies, Devonian rock rests on Middle Cambrian rock. There is a gap in the record here of about 150 million years. Gaps this large are not common in the Canadian Rockies, but the really peculiar thing is that some 20-30 km west of the mountain front the Devonian beds rest on Ordovician rock, which means that the gap is 60 Ma *less* than at the mountain front. Farther west the Devonian formations rest on Silurian beds, closing the gap even more—to about 50 Ma.

The illustration on the opposite page displays the situation: the older units underlie the Devonian layers at a slight angle.

Here is how this came to be. For a very long time the Canadian Rockies region had been underwater collecting sediments. But at about 425 Ma, in the middle of the Silurian Period, sea level *dropped* in our area, exposing the whole region to erosion. Most of the Silurian sediments were washed back into the sea. (Referring to the maps that begin on page 124 will aid in following this discussion.)

In the Early Devonian (at about 390 Ma) the sea began making its way back, advancing from the north and leaving sediments in the northern Rockies to mark its path.

Meanwhile, two regions of western Canada were experiencing mild uplift. One of these highlands lay west of the Rockies area (the **Purcell Landmass**) and the other to the east (the **West Alberta Ridge**). See the map on page 125.

The nature of the Purcell Landmass is not well-understood; it underwent deformation and dislocation during mountain-building later, which obscured the evidence. But the West Alberta Ridge lay farther east, beyond the disturbance, and its history is clear.

The West Alberta Ridge rose perhaps a thousand metres above sea level. It was an arch-shaped affair that produced a gentle bend in the layers running across it. As it rose it was attacked by the sea, of course, and the sea eventually won—abetted perhaps by some subsidence of the ridge.

When the sea marches inland it knocks down everything in its path, battering down the headlands with waves and carrying the debris offshore with currents. This is a slow process, but what the ocean has accomplished over the course of geologic time is startling. Grinding away a large item such as the West Alberta Ridge took only a few million years. (The northern end of the West Alberta Ridge resisted the waves for a while longer, remaining an island called the **Peace River Arch** until about 375 Ma.)

Eventually everything was beaten board-flat and covered with a shallow sea in which the famous Late Devonian reefs of western Canada grew, as discussed on page 130.

Consider those slightly arched formations dipping gently off either side of the ridge. Consider the western side of the arch, where the central and southern Canadian Rockies are now. Everything was planed at a low angle by the advancing sea; first the younger layers, then older and older ones as the waves chewed their way eastward into the ridge. Once underwater, the flat erosion surface was soon blanketed with Devonian sediments, producing the configuration seen today.

The buried erosion surface is an **unconformity**: a wonderfully abstract geological idea. The one I have been describing has been known among geologists for many years as simply the **sub-Devonian unconformity.**

An unconformity doesn't exist. It is a place in the rock record where something is missing. Almost always this is because rock has been exposed to the elements of erosion, either by uplift above sea level or by a drop in sea level.

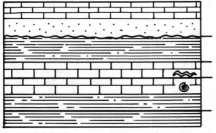

Types of unconformities found in the Canadian Rockies

Disconformity

Obvious buried erosion surface

Abrupt change in rock type

Fossil-indicated disconformity

Hard-to-detect disconformity

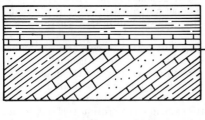

Angular unconformity

Flat beds lying on angled ones
(or any beds that meet at an angle
and not along a fault)

When angle is very low,
resembles disconformity

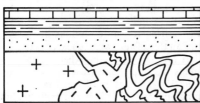

Nonconformity

Sedimentary beds resting
on igneous or metamorphic rock
(e.g. sandstone lying on granite)

Nature of the sub-Devonian unconformity in the central Canadian Rockies

Western
front ranges

Eastern
front ranges

Devonian

Sub-Devonian unconformity

Ordovician

Late Cambrian

Middle Cambrian

20--30 km

There are several kinds of unconformities, and each appears at least once in this book, so I will describe them briefly here.

The simplest to imagine is the **disconformity,** in which layers are missing from a stack of sediments. This cannot happen unless (a) the seabed is high and dry, eroding, or (b) there are strong currents that either cause undersea erosion or keep the seabed swept clean. As a rule, whenever there is water covering something there is sedimentation, no matter how slow. So a disconformity, like any other kind of unconformity, is nearly always an erosion surface.

Shallow-water formations, of which there are many in our area, are punctuated with frequent minor disconformities. They often mark times when sea level was just a few centimetres lower than it had been. A little erosion would occur, as is usual when land pokes up above the sea, then a rise in sea level would bring with it the next layer of sediments. In some formations the breaks between layers are all small disconformities; they represent short periods of sediment loss, perhaps on the order of a hundred years.

But if erosion continued for a longer period, say several million years, then the fossils that would ordinarily mark that interval of time would be missing and the disconformity would be detectable by their absence, even if the layering had no obvious break. In the Canadian Rockies some notable disconformities occur atop the Gog Gp., Skoki Fm., Glenogle Shales and Mt. Wilson Qtz. There are many others, especially in the northern region.

An **angular unconformity** is easier to pick out than a disconformity: the beds below meet the beds above at an angle. There had to be some tilting of the beds, then erosion, then the deposition of younger sediments. The sub-Devonian unconformity is an angular unconformity, but the angle is very small and you have to follow the unconformity from east to west over a distance of several kilometres, checking the age of the formations below the erosion surface, to detect it. The same sort of examination has turned up angular unconformities atop the Purcell Gp., the Miette Gp. and the Rundle Gp.

In the northern Rockies angular unconformities are more obvious because crustal movement was greater and so are the angles. There are at least five angular unconformities in the Tuchodi Lakes region, where the Alaska Highway passes through the mountains. The known ones lie atop the Muskwa Assemblage, the Atan Gp., the Kechika Gp., the Fantasque Fm. and the Pardonet Fm.

Another type of unconformity is the **nonconformity.** This is the easiest kind to identify. Water-borne or wind-borne sediments have been deposited directly on rock that formed deep in the earth. A bed of sandstone lying on granite, for example, is nonconformable. So is a sedimentary layer resting on metamorphic rock.

Granite cannot form close to the surface; it must crystallize slowly from magma under an insulating cover many kilometres thick. Likewise, the sort of metamorphism one finds below a nonconformity occurs at depth. It should come as no surprise, then, that nonconformities often span large gaps in time, for it takes a long while to remove the overlying rock.

To answer an obvious question: volcanic rocks are igneous, too, but they spread out on the earth's surface—including the seabed. So a situation in which volcanic beds cover sediments is not a nonconformity.

There is a widespread nonconformity in the Rockies, although it is visible at the surface in only one place. This is the nonconformity at the base of the entire sedimentary pile, where the lowest layer lies on the igneous and high-grade metamorphic rock of the Canadian Shield, the crust of the continent—in geo-slang, "the basement."

We know the basement nonconformity exists, because many oil and gas wells have been drilled down to it east of the Rockies, where the sedimentary cover is much thinner than it is in the mountains. The basement can be followed deeper, as it dips westward under the mountains, by seismic (shock-wave) methods. At the Rocky Mountain Trench the trace of the smooth basement surface, by now deeply buried, is lost. Paradoxically, basement rock appears at the surface here, hugging the eastern wall of the trench between Bulldog Creek and Hugh Allan Creek south of Valemount. The Miette Gp. lies on this metamorphic rock, creating a nonconformity that represents a billion-year gap: the base of the Miette is at about 730 Ma; the plate dates to about 1700-1800 Ma. (See page 81 for more on this area.)

One last, whimsical note on unconformities. Glacial deposits lying on bedrock are unconformable, as are stream gravels, sand dunes and the contents of the Jasper dump. Would you like to generate an unconformity? Find some bare bedrock and slop a bit of mud on it. There, under the mud, is your unconformity. Depending on the age of the rock, you could be creating an impressively large gap in the record—*if you could only make it last.*

Back to the catalogue of Rockies rock.

Muncho-McConnell Formation
Latest Silurian or Early Devonian (414-401 Ma) 100-565 m

Light gray fine-grained dolomite, with some shaly and sandy beds. Fairly resistant; weathers into cliffy slopes. This is the oldest Devonian rock in the Canadian Rockies. The unit occurs from the north end of the Rockies to about 25 km south of Peace River. It is named partly for Muncho Lake, where there are good exposures along the Alaska Highway a kilometre from the south end; other outcrops occur near Summit Lake. The Alaska Highway crosses it a few kilometres east of the lake and again a few kilometres west.

The area covered by the Muncho-McConnell lay north of the West Alberta Ridge and just to the northwest of the Peace River Arch. Following the Late Silurian emergence of the whole Canadian Rockies region, the northern section was again covered by the sea, so sediments built up here while they were still eroding farther south. Farther north the water was deeper. This has led geologists to think of the area as a "platform": a region of shallow seawater next to a region of deeper water (a "basin"). Thus, the northern Rockies are known to geologists specializing in Devonian stratigraphy as the region of the **MacDonald Platform.**

The shoreline here was not far to the south, and occasionally mild uplift would push the sea northward, out of the area, and some erosion would occur. Then slight subsidence would allow the sea back in, and with it would come more sediment. So in the northern Rockies there are several minor Early Devonian unconformities instead of the single, major sub-Devonian unconformity that one finds in the central Rockies.

The Muncho-McConnell is not very fossiliferous, but the bluish phosphatic plates of Early Devonian fish have been found in it, as has the brachiopod *Kirkidium,* a Late Silurian fossil.

Wokkpash Formation
Early Devonian (about 405-401 Ma)

Yellowish sandstone and dolomite, with **anhydrite**: a sulphur-rich mineral $(CaSO_4)$ similar to gypsum but lacking gypsum's water content. Both minerals are evaporites: substances produced, as salt is, when seawater evaporates. So the Wokkpash indicates that the sea was drying up in the area it covers.

The Wokkpash is thin and rather easily eroded, with a disconformity at the top. The formation occurs along the mountain front and through the main ranges from the north end of the Rockies to about Halfway River; south of there it is included in the Stone Fm. (next entry). You can see Wokkpash rock with the other Early Devonian units of the northern Rockies around Summit Lake on the Alaska Highway. "Wokkpash" is from Wokkpash Creek, the second big valley southwest of Summit Lake. No fossils are known from the formation.

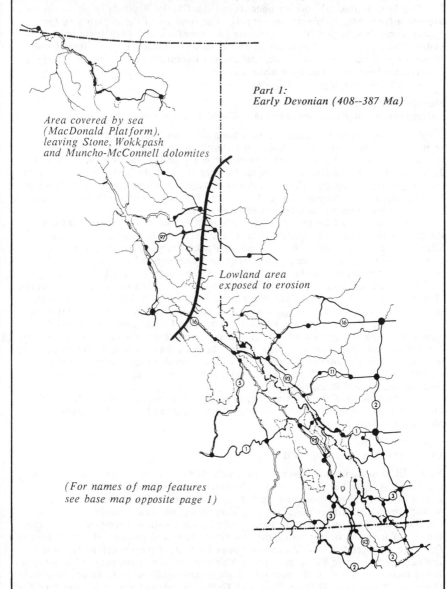

LAND AND SEA IN THE CANADIAN ROCKIES AREA DURING THE DEVONIAN PERIOD (408--360 Ma)

Part 1:
Early Devonian (408--387 Ma)

Area covered by sea
(MacDonald Platform),
leaving Stone, Wokkpash
and Muncho-McConnell dolomites

Lowland area
exposed to erosion

(For names of map features
see base map opposite page 1)

Maps simplified from Morrow and Geldsetzer, in press

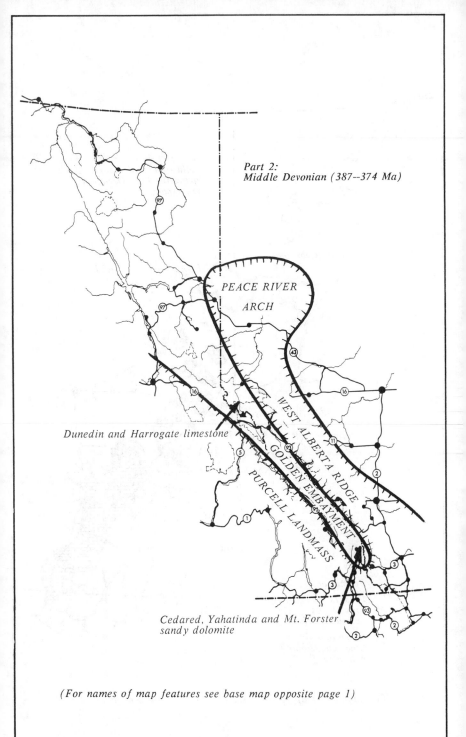

Part 2:
Middle Devonian (387--374 Ma)

PEACE RIVER
ARCH

WEST ALBERTA RIDGE

GOLDEN EMBAYMENT

PURCELL LANDMASS

Dunedin and Harrogate limestone

Cedared, Yahatinda and Mt. Forster
sandy dolomite

(For names of map features see base map opposite page 1)

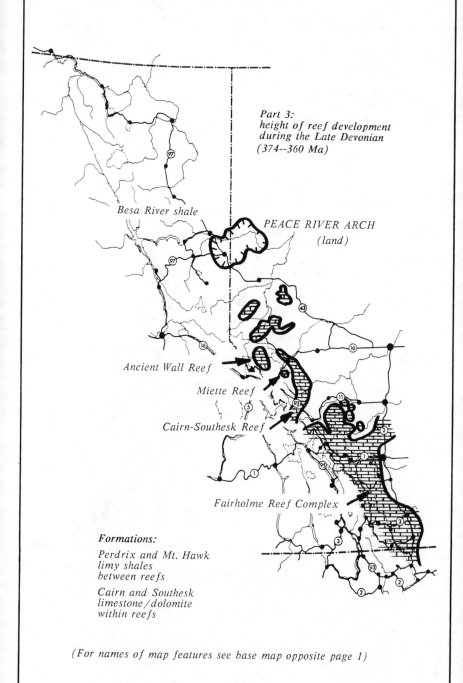

Part 3:
height of reef development
during the Late Devonian
(374--360 Ma)

Besa River shale

PEACE RIVER ARCH
(land)

Ancient Wall Reef

Miette Reef

Cairn-Southesk Reef

Fairholme Reef Complex

Formations:

Perdrix and Mt. Hawk
limy shales
between reefs

Cairn and Southesk
limestone/dolomite
within reefs

(For names of map features see base map opposite page 1)

Stone Formation
Early Devonian (394-387 Ma) 450-590 m

Banded gray dolomite, resistant and cliff-forming. Contains **barite**, a heavy mineral left occasionally by evaporation of seawater. South of Pine Pass a sandstone layer at the base of the Stone marks an unconformity atop Ordovician rocks.

The Stone Fm. runs from north of the Rockies to Monkman Pass. The middle slopes of Mt. St. Paul, the peak just north of Summit Lake along the Alaska Highway, display the formation well. The name comes from Stone Mtn., a peak 15 km north of Summit Lake.*

Stone stone contains **conodonts** (tiny fossils that are the remains of tooth-like chewing structures in marine worms) and the coral *Roemeripora spelaeana.*

Dunedin Formation and other rocks of the Golden Embayment:
Harrogate, Cedared, Burnais, Yahatinda and Mount Forster formations
Middle Devonian (385-378 Ma) 0-300 m

The Dunedin ("dun-EE-den")is the most widespread of the Middle Devonian formations in the Rockies. The Dunedin is a pale sandstone and siltstone in the lower quarter, with a disconformity at the base. The rest is largely yellowish-gray limestone. The upper part is fairly resistant to erosion and often forms cliffs. The name comes from a river in the northern Rockies.

Like the underlying Early Devonian formations, the Dunedin extends north beyond the Canadian Rockies. It thins southeasterly to an erosional edge at Mt. Buchanan in Willmore park. The formation outcrops along the Alaska Highway near Summit Lake; accessible exposures are 5-6 km west of the lake, just west of the point at which MacDonald Creek intersects the road. Fossils to look for: stringocephalid brachiopods, abundant in some beds.

Dunedin beds were laid down on the seaward side of a long barrier reef that ran north from the Peace River Arch. Called the Presqu'ile ("press-KEEL") Barrier Reef, this feature prevented ocean currents from circulating freely across it. The water between the reef and the shore became very salty, leaving evaporite deposits (mostly salt and gypsum) under northern Alberta.

Dunedin-type sediments extended south along **Golden Embayment,** an arm of the sea reaching through what is now the central Rockies between the West Alberta Ridge and the Purcell Landmass (see map on page 125). Later erosion has removed much of this rock, but near the south end of the bay the **Harrogate Formation** remains, with its Dunedin-like rock. You see it in the western main ranges between Golden and Fernie; it is named for a small community there.

South of Radium one finds the **Cedared** ("see-der-RED") **Formation,** shallow-water, light-gray or brown sandy dolomite and limestone that help to delimit the southern shore of the bay. On the other side of the Rockies the similar **Yahatinda** ("yah-ha-TIN-duh") **Formation** marks the eastern shore, while a very sandy deposit marks the western shore: the **Mount Forster Formation,** named for a peak on the west side of the Rocky Mountain Trench. Although probably part of the same deposit, the Cedared and Yahatinda segments occur on opposite sides of the Rockies, were studied independently and have kept different names.

"Cedared" is from Cedared Creek, on the eastern side of the Rocky Mountain Trench south of Golden. There are good exposures in the ridge behind Fairmont Hot Springs, where you can also see the Harrogate and Mt. Forster. "Yahatinda" is from the Yahatinda Ranch, along the mountain front north of the TransCanada Highway; Yahatinda rock can be viewed above Canmore under the hydro penstocks (large pipes) accessible from the Spray Lakes Road.

---

*This name has an amusing aspect: the stone of the Stone Fm. is named for Stone Mountain, which is not named for its stone but rather for a biologist named Stone, for whom Stone's sheep (page 740) is named.

The Cedared grades into a bed of gypsum known as the **Burnais Formation,** named for Burnais Creek near Windermere—a good place to see the unit. It shows that the sea was very shallow here and cut off at times from the rest of the ocean, so that evaporation concentrated the gypsum until it started to crystallize in the water.

Harrogate fossils include conodonts (page 127), corals and the brachiopod *Desquamatia;* the Cedared holds fish fragments, as does the Yahatinda, which also includes fossil marine plants. No fossils have been reported from the Burnais.

STROMATOPOROIDS
Devonian reefs in the Rocky Mountains

Gentle uplift of western Canada occurred near the end of the Middle Devonian, probably linked to mountain-building to the north and south.* This exposed the seabed for 2-3 Ma and caused a widespread unconformity between Devonian layers called the **Watt Mountain Break,** not to be confused with the sub-Devonian unconformity (page 120), which underlies all the Late Devonian rocks in the Canadian Rockies.

By the time the sea came back, the West Alberta Ridge (page 120) was almost gone, leaving only the Peace River Arch—a northern remnant of the ridge—as an island east of the Rockies. The Purcell Landmass (page 120) persisted to the west, although it, too, suffered some erosion.

In the northern Rockies the water deepened quickly and stayed deep, as shown by the great thickness of shale that accumulated there: the Besa River Fm. But farther south the water was shallower. The climate was warm (western Canada was down in the tropics) and the clear, sunlit seabed was swarming with life. These conditions produced reefs, and the rock therein has kept Alberta geologists busy for several generations. Their labors have made some of them rich, because they have turned up a lot of oil and gas.

From Berland River in Willmore park, where the northernmost of the major reefs grew, on south to Crowsnest Pass, the Late Devonian outcrops of the Rockies have become world-famous among geologists as places to study the reef rock, collectively called the **Fairholme Group.** The name comes from the Fairholme Range, part of the front ranges east of Banff.

Formation details begin on page 131, but here is an outline to help make sense of some complicated stratigraphy.

In the beginning, these were not coral reefs. Corals had evolved in the Ordovician, but their heyday was still to come. In the Devonian the main reef-builders were their coarse relatives the **stromatoporoids** (pronounced "strome-uh-TOP-or-roids" or "strome-at-oh-PORE-oids," as you prefer).

Hollywood should make a film called *Attack of the Stromatoporoids.* These things were bizarre, they took over everything, and then they died in a cataclysm.

It has taken many years to figure out exactly what the stromatoporoids were. Nature had a fondness for turning them into dolomite, which destroyed the fine detail; what remains are fist-sized gray blobs with hollow centres. Lucky fossil finds have enabled paleontologists to learn that the blobs were, in fact, colonies of coral-like organisms. They were inclined to grow in crusts and layers, thus the "stromato-" (scientific Greek for "bed," or anything spread out) and "poroid" ("with pores") in "stromatoporoid."

There were tough, encrusting stromatoporoids that preferred the zesty ocean side of a reef; blobby-looking stromatoporoids that liked the side away from the big waves, and fragile, spaghetti-like stromatoporoids that sheltered in the protected central lagoon.

---

*Geologists know these episodes as the Antler Orogeny (affected the southwestern United States) and Ellesmerian Orogeny (affected the arctic).

Life and death of a typical Devonian reef

Drawings prepared in consultation with H. Geldsetzer and E. Mountjoy

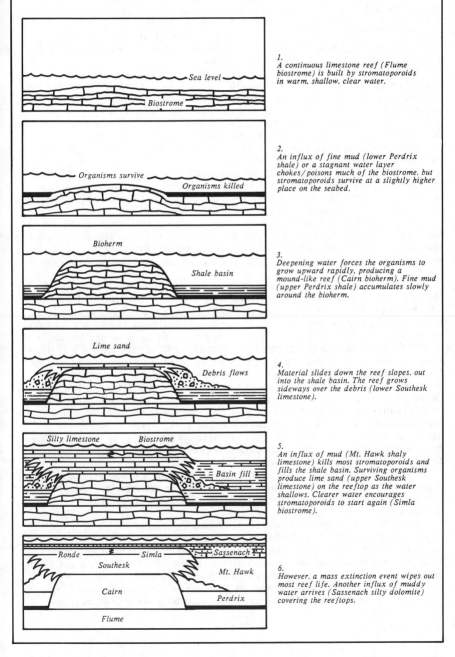

1.
A continuous limestone reef (Flume biostrome) is built by stromatoporoids in warm, shallow, clear water.

2.
An influx of fine mud (lower Perdrix shale) or a stagnant water layer chokes/poisons much of the biostrome, but stromatoporoids survive at a slightly higher place on the seabed.

3.
Deepening water forces the organisms to grow upward rapidly, producing a mound-like reef (Cairn bioherm). Fine mud (upper Perdrix shale) accumulates slowly around the bioherm.

4.
Material slides down the reef slopes, out into the shale basin. The reef grows sideways over the debris (lower Southesk limestone).

5.
An influx of mud (Mt. Hawk shaly limestone) kills most stromatoporoids and fills the shale basin. Surviving organisms produce lime sand (upper Southesk limestone) on the reeftop as the water shallows. Clearer water encourages stromatoporoids to start again (Simla biostrome).

6.
However, a mass extinction event wipes out most reef life. Another influx of muddy water arrives (Sassenach silty dolomite) covering the reeftops.

Here is how the reefs got started, lived and died, based on the latest research (Morrow and Geldsetzer, in press).

As usual in the tropics, bluegreen algae were living in the sunlit water and producing a goodly supply of lime crystals that settled on the seabed as soft, oozy lime mud. As the tide moved in and out, currents channeled the mud, carving into it here, piling it up there—and it was on the piles that the reefs began to grow. First a few brachiopods and calcareous algae would set up shop, then some stromatoporoids and corals would move in with the brachiopods, then some bryozoans would move in with the corals, then the clams would arrive, and the crinoids and the fish and . . . you know how it is. Another unspoiled spot discovered by the masses—especially by the stromatoporoids, which comprised about 90 percent of reef life in the Devonian.

Sea levels fluctuated, but the water was never very deep at this time—often just a few metres under the tides—so the reefs had little space in which to grow upward. They spread *outward* instead, and pretty soon the seabed was virtually covered with intergrown reefs, home to innumerable creatures all eating one another, dying and leaving their hard parts to be incorporated into the layer. That layer remains as a **biostrome** (the technical term for such a widespread accumulation) called the Flume Fm. in the central Rockies and the Hollebeke Fm. in a geographically separated exposure in the southern Rockies.

But then this lively scene was threatened. Lime mud carrying fine silt and clay particles (Maligne and lower Perdrix formations) spread thinly across the seabed from the north and east, covering the Flume biostrome and killing many of the stromatoporoids, which could live only in very clear water.

An alternative explanation for cessation of growth in most of the Flume biostrome is that currents in the western Canadian sea became sluggish, allowing a thin zone of stagnant water to develop near the bottom. Oxygen-poor and bearing poisonous hydrogen sulphide gas, this zone was so hostile that few organisms could live in it.

However, some spots on the seabed were havens for bottom-dwellers. Parts of the biostrome had enough surface irregularity to *channel* the flow of Perdrix mud, which can be thought of as a thin sheet moving along the bottom, so that the higher-standing spots remained free of the deadly sediment. (These low humps would also have stood above a stagnant zone.) Here the stromatoporoids survived.

The sea was on the rise at this time, probably because the seabed was slowly sinking, so the reef-builders had room in which to grow upward, producing the **bioherms** (mound-like reefs) of the Cairn Fm. Fine mud (the rest of the Perdrix Fm.) continued to accumulate around the reef bases, but the rate of deposition was even slower than the rate of subsidence, so the water between the reefs gradually deepened. The reefs grew tall, especially northern ones such as the **Miette** and **Ancient Wall** reefs in eastern Jasper park, which stood 100-200 m above the seabed. Few life forms could survive off the reefs, on the intervening bottom where the water was deep, dark and chemically unfit for most forms of life. Geologists refer to such areas as "shale basins."

Jarred by earthquakes or exposed to the weather by a drop in sea level, portions of the reefs broke up and slid down into the shale basins. These **debris flows** were soon covered with stromatoporoids, widening the reefs (lower Southesk Fm.).

A further rise in sea level was accompanied by another influx of muddy water that gradually filled the basins between the reefs with limy shale and siltstone (the Mt. Hawk Fm.). Only scattered brachiopods, crinoids and other creatures able to tolerate the muddy water survived; they lived on the shallowing ocean floor as the reefs were surrounded nearly to the top with Mt. Hawk sediments. Few stromatoporoids grew on the reefs in these muddy conditions; the reef-tops became collectors of lime sand produced by other organisms (upper Southesk Fm).

The mud influx ended with a temporary drop in sea level, exposing the reef-tops to a short period of erosion. Higher water brought in the Ronde Fm., a silty limestone, with no further biostrome or bioherm development south of the Ancient Wall Reef in Jasper park. North of there, however, the Ronde is replaced by a silt-free limestone (the Simla Fm.) which in places is a stromatoporoid biostrome rather like the Flume Fm. This might have been the beginning of a comeback by the stromatoporoids, but for them the end was near.

Something hit the earth about 367 million years ago—a very large meteorite, perhaps, or a comet—with ensuing darkness and cold. Most of the light-dependent, temperature-sensitive plankton that make up the base of the oceanic food chain were killed, and many higher organisms died out as a consequence.

This disaster is known as the **Late Devonian mass-extinction event**. It occurred at the boundary between the Frasnian and Fammenian divisions of the Devonian Period. Such mass-extinction events are well-known in the fossil record (see black triangles on the geological time charts, pages 42-44). Some of these events are very impressive, such as the Late Cretaceous mass extinction that wiped out the dinosaurs, while others are less important. Now that the Late Cretaceous event has been linked to the impact of a foreign body, geologists are looking for evidence of similar impacts associated with the other mass extinctions. That evidence is now coming in. A thin bed of pyrite-rich silt atop the Ronde Fm. records the Late Devonian event in the Canadian Rockies area, after which stromatoporoids ceased to be important in the fossil record, here or anywhere else.

Three hundred and sixty million years later, oil trapped in a Devonian reef gushed out of an exploratory well drilled through the thick accumulation of younger sediments at Leduc, Alberta. Humans suddenly took a keen interest in the hollow centres of stromatoporoids.

Glaciers have carved cross-sections through the Late Devonian reefs at several spots in the Rockies. Each reef is a little different, but the one near Miette Hot Springs, in Jasper park, is perhaps the most-studied and the easiest one to approach on foot—although none are just a short walk from the car. However, small patches of exposed reef rock can be seen beside the highway at several locations in the southern and central Rockies. See the Cairn Fm. entry (page 132).

On to details of the Fairholme Group.

Flume, Maligne and Hollebeke formations (base of Fairholme Group)
Late Devonian (375-373 Ma) 30-250 m

Massive limestone/dolomite in the lower part, often with rice-like *Amphipora* fossils and bits of brachiopods. A thin sandstone lies at the base, marking the sub-Devonian unconformity there. (Sand is often a near-shore deposit, laid down as the sea moves back into a region that had been above the waves and thus eroding.) Higher up the rock is dolomite, with lots of chert (page 148) in irregular masses, lenses and even beds. There are blobby stromatoporoids in this layer, as well as the brachiopods *Atrypa, Allanaria, Athyris* and corals such as *Thamnopora* and *Alveolites*.

The Flume Fm. is a good one to know, even though it's not very thick. The unit is a classic biostrome: a layer of limestone actively built by organisms. It is the base upon which the Devonian reefs grew.

At some locations the upper part of the Flume is silty and known as the **Maligne Formation** (pronounced "muh-LEEN," not "muh-LINE"), the name coming from Maligne River in Jasper park. The Maligne marks the first arrival of the fine mud that may have choked much of the Flume biostrome. "Flume" is from a creek near Roche Miette, along the Athabasca River east of Jasper.

Flume rock is found from northern Willmore park to Crowsnest Pass. Roadside outcrops occur along Highway 16 near Disaster Point in eastern Jasper park and in the northern tip of Banff park (northbound past Nigel Falls, look for a two-sided road cut. Just past it, the North Saskatchewan River has eroded a very narrow gorge in Flume dolomite under a bridge over the old road). Another location in this area is one kilometre south of the Weeping Wall viewpoint.

South of Crowsnest Pass, Flume-like rock is known as the **Hollebeke Formation,** from Mt. Hollebeke. This formation is siltier and less fossiliferous in the lower part than the Flume is; not cherty in the upper part. The best and most accessible Hollebeke exposures are at North Kootenay Pass, head of the Carbondale River. This is also a renowned place to look at the western margin of the **Fairholme Reef Complex,** the largest Devonian reef mass in Alberta.

Throughout the front ranges of the central Rockies, Flume and Hollebeke beds rest directly on the sub-Devonian unconformity (page 120). The gap is marked by the sudden appearance of fossils, for the underlying beds are often Late Cambrian or Ordovician and often unfossiliferous. The classic place to see this is at Cold Sulphur Spring, 20 km east of Jasper along Highway 16. Walk east from the spring along the base of the glacially-smoothed cliff, which at this point is in steeply dipping Flume rock bearing *Amphipora* stromatoporoids (see description in next entry). You cross the unconformity at the spot where the fossils end. The rock in the next bed looks similar at first, but close inspection shows that it is fossil-free dolomite of the Late Cambrian Lynx Gp.

Cairn, Borsato and Southesk formations (upper Fairholme Group, reef facies)
Late Devonian (373-370 Ma) Up to 400 m

The Cairn and Southesk formations go together; where you find one you will usually find the other. They outcrop in the front ranges from Peace River south to Waterton park, where a unit similar to the Cairn/Southesk is called **Borsato Formation** (from Mt. Borsato, near Kootenay Pass).

The **Cairn** is distinctive: poorly bedded black or dark-brown dolomite up to 300 m thick and full of blobby gray stromatoporoids, often with hollow centres. Little white rods, like grains of rice in the dark rock, are the oddball stromatoporoid *Amphipora*—definitely a fossil to learn, for it is easy to recognize and it instantly labels the rock as Late Devonian (although *Amphipora* also occurs in the Middle Devonian Dunedin Fm. of the northern Rockies (page 127). The organisms were actually long and stringy, like spaghetti, but they usually look rice-like in the rock.

This is reef rock. It is black with dried hydrocarbons (oil) and loaded with organic compounds. When you break a piece of the Cairn Fm. it smells like a refinery.

"Cairn" comes from the Cairn River in eastern Jasper park. There are two massive and well-studied reefs in the park, one in the Ancient Wall and the other just west of Miette Hot Springs. At the springs the creek bed is studded with beautifully stream-worn boulders that have come from the slopes of Utopia Mountain upstream, where the reef is exposed.

The **Southesk Formation** is mostly light-gray dolomite and limestone, resistant to erosion and 150-200 m thick. Often it can be identified at a distance by a dark-colored band 5-25 m thick (Grotto Member, see below) that runs through about halfway up. Southesk rock forms the upper part of the Devonian reefs in our area; thus, it overlies the Cairn Fm., which makes up the lower part.

"Southesk" is from the Southesk River in eastern Jasper park. Distribution follows that of the Cairn. Heavily studied by petroleum geologists, the Southesk Fm. has been divided into three members: a lower light-gray limestone/dolomite with stromatoporoids (**Peechee Member**), a middle limestone coral bed (**Grotto Member**) and an upper pale-gray limestone made of lime sand (**Arcs Member**). "Grotto" and "Peechee" are from peaks in the Fairholme Range; "Arcs" is from Lac des Arcs ("lack-days-ARK") in the same area. The Grotto bed is usually about 15 m thick and richly fossiliferous; common corals include *Alveolites, Syringopora, Thamnopora* and *Acinophyllum.* The other members of the Southesk are not as obviously fossiliferous, mainly because the fossils are sand-size **foraminifera:** tiny chambered animals. This group has been evolutionarily successful, with many descendant species living today. Fossil algae colonies are also found in the Southesk.

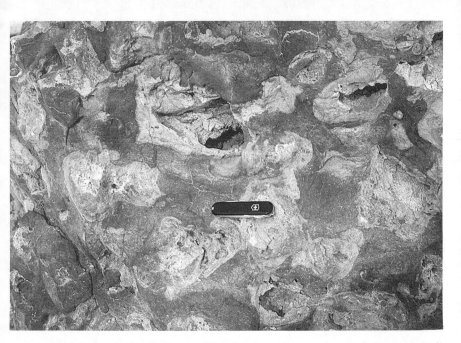

Reef rock: dark Cairn dolomite with pale stromatoporoids. Photo of specimen in front of Geological Survey of Canada centre in Calgary.

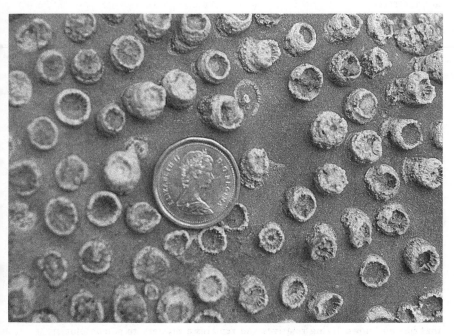

A coral colony preserved in black limestone of the Grotto Member, Southesk Formation. Penny gives scale.

The TransCanada Highway passes by an excellent Cairn-and-Southesk road-cut at the mountain front, just west of the white-weathering Eldon Fm. outcrops. A little farther west, where the road curves north around the west end of Lac des Arcs, there is more Cairn. Another good place to examine Cairn and Southesk rock is along the Icefields Parkway at Cirrus Mountain, where a tongue of the Cairn-Southesk Reef (see map on page 126) has been discovered. Park at Cirrus Mountain Campground and scramble up the hillside to the southwest.

Farther north, just past the high bridge over Nigel Falls, a two-sided road-cut displays very dark Southesk strata, showing the Peechee-Grotto-Arcs sequence. The trail up Parker Ridge, a few kilometres toward Jasper, displays the flashy white-on-black coral beds very well. Thanks to the honesty of park visitors (it is illegal to collect in the parks), the outcrops have not been spoiled. For legal collecting, take Alberta 11 east from Saskatchewan Crossing to the Cline River Bridge. The coral beds are a short walk upstream.

If you can't get to the mountains for a look at this interesting rock, just drop by the Institute of Sedimentary and Petroleum Geology in Calgary (3303 33rd Street NW), where the Geological Survey of Canada has a goodly chunk of Cairn dolomite on display outside the entrance. The vugs (hollows) in the stromatoporoids of this specimen are impressively large. I once found a bat sleeping in one—a little flying mammal curled up inside a sea creature that lived 300 million years before bats appeared on the earth.

Besa River and Perdrix formations

Late Devonian to Early Carboniferous for Besa River (370-330 Ma) 0-500 m
Late Devonian for Perdrix (373-370 Ma) 0-200

Both formations are black to grayish-green limy shale, the darker beds with embedded marble-sized blobs of gold-colored pyrite (page 90) that weather into rusty streaks. These are recessive units, eroding back into slopes and hidden under soil and scree.

The **Besa River Formation** spans the time from the Late Devonian through the Early Carboniferous (Mississippian) periods. It is the deeper-water shale laid down in the north at the same time that the shallower-water limestones of the Fairholme Gp. (Flume, Cairn and Southesk formations, previous entries) and the Rundle Gp. (page 142) formed to the south. Besa River shale is up to 500 m thick at Liard River; 245 m at Peace River. Besa River is a tributary of the Prophet River.

The **Perdrix Formation** is named for Roche à Perdrix, the type section near the eastern boundary of Jasper National Park. Although included in the Fairholme Group, the Perdrix can be thought of as a thin tongue of the lower Besa River shale that extends south into Fairholme Gp. country. The unit is found in the front ranges between Pine Pass and the international boundary. South of Crowsnest Pass it is mainly western-slope, lying above the Borsato Fm. (page 132). The Perdrix shale looks a lot like the Exshaw Fm. (page 139), but Perdrix rock smells of sulphur when broken and Exshaw shale does not.

In the Late Devonian the central and southern Rockies area lay in shallow water spotted with reefs. The Perdrix represents the limy clay and silt deposited between the reefs. During Perdrix time, the northern Rockies lay in deeper water where there were no reefs, so just Besa River shale accumulated. The water there stayed deep during the Early Carboniferous, so Besa River rock continued to accumulate, while to the south the Early Carboniferous formations are mainly limestones.

Large fossils are scarce in Perdrix and Besa River beds, probably because of the low oxygen levels associated with black shales. Spores and conodonts occur, though, and an organism called *Tentaculites*: a small phosphatic cone-like fossil that has no known living relatives and remains a mystery to paleontologists. Possibly the cone held a worm of some kind.

A good exposure of Perdrix shale along Fiddle River, south of Highway 16 in eastern Jasper National Park.

Good exposures of Perdrix or Besa River shale are difficult to find because the stuff is so recessive. There is a small Perdrix outcrop just east of Jasper townsite, a half-kilometre east of the Maligne Road turnoff on Highway 16, but the site is close to a major fault (the Pyramid Thrust) and badly torn up. Better exposures are found in eastern Jasper park, a short distance south of Highway 16 along the west bank of Fiddle River. The Alaska Highway crosses Besa River shale at One Ten Creek, which is the first drainage coming in from the south after the road descends from Summit Lake into the valley of McDonald Creek.

Mount Hawk formation (off-reef limestone)
Late Devonian (370-369 Ma) 0-220 m

Shaly black limestone that weathers gray; upper part nodular. Usually occurs with the Perdrix Fm. (previous entry) as the off-reef facies of the Fairholme Gp.

The Mt. Hawk is limier and tougher than the Perdrix shale that underlies it, so the Mt. Hawk is inclined to form steep slopes and rotten cliffs. Distribution: in the front ranges from Pine Pass south to the Kananaskis Lakes, then somewhat farther west from there south to the international boundary.

"Mount Hawk" is technically a misnomer; the peak for which the formation is named is Hawk Mountain, along the Athabasca River east of Jasper (so the name should really be "Hawk Mountain Formation," not "Mount Hawk"). There are good exposures there, on the slopes above Highway 16 east of the bridge 20 km east of Jasper. Alberta 11 crosses the Mt. Hawk about 3 km west of Windy Point, near the mountain front. The shaly Mt. Hawk beds there are richly fossiliferous. Typical fossils for this formation are the brachiopods *(Atrypa, Devonoproductus, Nudirostra, Gypidula, Cyrtospirifer)* and **bryozoans:** tiny coral-like animals in colonies that resemble bits of window screen. See the drawing on page 68.

Simla and Ronde formations (top of Fairholme Group)
Late Devonian (369-367 Ma) 0-100 m

Two very different units that grade into each other. Together, they mark the top of the Fairholme Group. Simla is light-gray massive limestone, often a biostrome (page 130) of stromatoporoids and other fossils; it weathers into a pale cliff that is rather easily identified among the other Devonian formations. The Ronde is thin-bedded silty and sandy limestone, not biostromal.

Simla beds are found from the Ancient Wall Reef in northern Jasper park (Mt. Simla is nearby) north to Monkman Pass, where they pinch out from erosion that occurred before the Banff Fm. (page 140) was laid down. To the south, the Simla merges with the Ronde Fm. (named for Roche Ronde in eastern Jasper), which represents fine mud spread across the Devonian reef-tops as far south as Kananaskis Country. The Simla records a clear-water interval during which colonies of stromatoporoids (page 128) began a new cycle of reef-building. Perhaps the Simla colonies might have continued to grow, but the Late Devonian extinction event (page 131) snuffed nearly all of them out.

No roadside outcrops of Simla rock are known, but Ronde beds are visible 43 km east of Saskatchewan Crossing along Cline River (access via Alberta 11), west of the highway downstream from the gorge.

Sassenach Formation
Late Devonian (367-366 Ma) 0-200 m

Mostly fine-grained, thin-bedded, buff-weathering silty dolomite, found from the Ancient Wall in Jasper park south to Elko, in the southern Rockies near the international boundary. The Sassenach is patchy. It filled rather deep local depressions in the otherwise shallow seabed of the time. Those depressions are interesting; they lie along the west side of the Devonian reefs, the side away from the source of the Mt. Hawk muds. Up to 150 m deep beside the Miette Reef, these depressions may have existed because Mt. Hawk sediment did not accumulate on the far side of the reefs. The Sassenach, however, came from that direction, probably filling the depressions rather quickly. The westerly source demonstrates that the Purcell Landmass (page 120) existed throughout the Devonian Period in western Canada. This was the first layer to be laid down after the Late Devonian extinction event, marked by a pyrite-laden zone at the base (where the formation overlies shale basins, not reefs).

There are good Sassenach exposures at the southern tip of the Colin Range in Jasper park, along the ridge separating Medicine Lake from the valley of Beaver Lake. The low gray cliff 3 km east of Jasper along Highway 16 (spring at the base) is Sassenach rock, and the formation also outcrops along Cline River at the Highway 11 bridge.

MISS DEVONIAN'S SANDWICH
Palliser, Exshaw and Banff formations, and the Rundle Group

There are two geological sandwiches in the Canadian Rockies: the Cathedral-Stephen-Eldon sandwich of the Middle Cambrian (page 93), and this one. It's a limestone-shale-limestone combination, just like the Middle Cambrian sandwich, and as such is easy to spot all over the front ranges between Crowsnest Pass and Jasper. The silly name "Miss Devonian's sandwich" recalls the age of the rock: Mississippian (Early Carboniferous to British-trained Canadian geologists) and Devonian.

The classic place to admire Miss Devonian's sandwich is on the approach to Banff, after turning off the TransCanada Highway. Look straight south to the large sloping peak, Mt. Rundle. The two big gray cliffs are made of limestone. The brownish slope between them (the filling in the sandwich) is made of limy shale. The sequence is Palliser Fm. (lower), Banff Fm. (middle) and Rundle Gp. (upper). Hidden between the Palliser and Banff is the apple butter on the lower piece of bread: the thin, dark Exshaw Fm.

Infantile as this analogy sounds, it is useful. The three main units in Miss Devonian's sandwich are readily identifiable, and recognition tells you immediately where you are in the overall stratigraphic pile of the Canadian Rockies: near the top of the limestone-and-shale sequence (the middle carbonates, third great unit of the four introduced on page 37).

The Weeping Wall, a great cliff of Palliser limestone. View is along the Icefields Parkway between Saskatchewan Crossing and the Columbia Icefield.

The northeast face of Mt. Rundle, a classic place to see Miss Devonian's sandwich. Lower cliff is Palliser limestone, middle weathered zone is Banff shale, and upper cliff is Rundle Group limestone/dolomite. View is from the Banff exit on the TransCanada Highway.

Miss Devonian's sandwich   137

Palliser Formation
Late Devonian (366-363 Ma) 0-620 m

Gray-weathering, very massive limestone that is surprisingly dark inside (often jet black), mottled with buff-weathering dolomite. Very resistant to erosion; forms big cliffs. Named for the Palliser Range of southern Banff park.

In the front ranges the Palliser is easily confused with the Eldon Fm. (page 100), which is also massive, gray-weathering and about the same thickness. The two also look alike on fresh surfaces: jet black with white calcite veins. If you know the overlying and underlying formations (and can get to them) you can quickly figure out whether it is Palliser or Eldon you are looking at, but a quick way to differentiate the two is to look around the outcrop for fossils. If you find some you have the Palliser; if you don't you have the Eldon. The Palliser is not richly fossiliferous, but a few minutes' hunt will usually turn up some brachiopods, coiled snails or crinoid plates. The Eldon, on the other hand, is barren.

Palliser limestone makes its southernmost appearance at Trail Creek in the Whitefish Range west of Glacier park, a few kilometres south of the international boundary. It becomes more widespread on the western slope around Fernie. East of Fernie at North Kootenay Pass (head of the Carbondale River), the Palliser appears right along the divide, expanding east and west to outcrop throughout the front ranges and main ranges north to Kananaskis Lakes, where it then sticks to the front ranges all the way to Jasper. North of Jasper it becomes rather crumbly, even though the rock is still limestone and not shale, and it thins through erosion (there is an unconformity on top) to a zero edge near Hook Lake, between Monkman Pass and Pine Pass.

The Palliser also thins away from two thick spots that represent depressions in the seabed: one at Phillips Peak, northwest of Fernie (620 m) and the other at Jarvis Lakes, northwest of Willmore Park (530 m).

The eroded northern part of the Palliser would soon have merged with the Besa River Fm. anyway, for in the northern Rockies the black Besa River shales (page 134) were accumulating in deep water there at the same time the shallow-water Palliser limestone was forming to the southeast. The unconformity atop the Palliser shows that there was uplift at the end of the Devonian Period throughout our area. The sea drained off to the north during the uplift and returned from that direction as well.

No one knows what happens to the Palliser to the west, where thrust plates of older rock cover the evidence. Probably the Palliser becomes silty and sandy, for the Purcell Landmass lay in that direction.

The Palliser is perhaps our most massively layered, most homogeneous limestone (runners-up: Eldon and Cathedral.) It was laid down as lime mud on a shallow seabed densely populated with worms and other burrowing organisms. They constantly displaced the soft sediment, churning it so much that in many layers neither the natural bedding nor the burrows can be seen. The buzzword for this is **bioturbation**. Particularly intense burrowing from Jasper park north accounts for the crumbly nature of the formation there. In other places, the burrows are beautifully displayed as a lacework of buff-weathering dolomite against the gray-weathering calcite (the "mottling" mentioned earlier).

How is it possible to get 620 m of limestone that looks so much the same throughout? *Stability* is the key concept, here: not much changed for three million years. Steady subsidence, coupled with continuously clear water and a stable climate, produced the striking uniformity of this formation. The lower part (**Morro Member**, from Morro Peak northeast of Jasper, up to 300 m thick) is quite monotonous, fine-grained black limestone with scattered fossils. But there is an upper part (**Costigan Member**, from Mt. Costigan in eastern Banff park, at the east end of Lake Minnewanka, 0-130 m) that is thinner-bedded and siltier, with layers of breccia (angular fragments) and far more fossils. It is found from Jasper south; north of there it was not deposited.

Common Palliser fossils include snails (mostly *Euomphalus*), the brachiopod *Camarotechia* and crinoid debris in upper layers. Interestingly, a few labechid (columnar) stromatoporoids have been found here and there near the base—survivors of the Late Devonian extinction event.

Palliser cliffs are both common and spectacular; anyone seeing the Rockies between Crowsnest Pass and Jasper cannot help but be impressed. Palliser classics visible along the TransCanada Highway include Wind Tower, which sits in front of Mt. Lougheed as you pass the Deadman Flats turnoff 10 km east of Canmore; all the peaks on the west side of the highway between Wind Mountain and Cascade Mountain, including the Three Sisters and the lower cliff on Mt. Rundle, and the dog-tooth spire of Mt. Louis, visible to the northwest from the Banff interchange. There is a road-cut in Palliser rock along the TransCanada at the west end of Lac Des Arcs.

Along Highway 11 there are impressive Palliser cliffs in the vicinity of Cline River, which has cut through the formation in a spectacular gorge. (Such Palliser gorges are common in the Rockies; Maligne Canyon is another one.) The Weeping Wall, beside the Icefields Parkway in the north end of Banff park, is a huge cliff of Palliser limestone striped with ribbon-like waterfalls that freeze into wide curtains of ice in winter.

Along Highway 16, between Jasper park's east gate and the townsite, the Palliser is prominent and wonderfully folded. Bedson Ridge (north side of Athabasca River at the mountain front) has a particularly amazing fold in it that looks like a squashed Z when viewed from the turnoff to Miette Hot Springs (see geological sketch on page 64). The big cliff on Roche Miette, just a bit farther west on the south side of the highway, is also Palliser limestone. At the bridge over the Athabasca 20 km east of Jasper, a glacially rounded Palliser hump (locally called "River Rock") offers excellent exposures, both fresh and weathered, and a few fossils. The great gray slabs of the Colin Range lie east of the highway between River Rock and Jasper; they are classic Palliser, as is the Palisade on the other side of the valley—where the rock is starting to show the crumbliness of the unit from that point north. North of Jasper park the rock erodes more easily and the cliffs are less impressive.

The Palliser Fm. is well-known for caves (see page 223).

Exshaw Formation
Latest Devonian and Early Carboniferous/Mississippian (363-358 Ma) 0-10 m

A thin unit of jet-black shale, often with marble-sized blobs of gold-colored pyrite (page 90) in it that weather as rusty streaks. Similar in most respects to the Perdrix Fm. (page 134), but not limy like the Perdrix (not limy on freshly broken surfaces; existing cracks in the Exshaw may be limy from calcite-carrying groundwater). Nor does the Exshaw smell of sulphur when split as the Perdrix does. Very recessive and normally covered with soil or debris, but often exposed in stream gullies and bare slopes at high elevations. Has the same distribution as the underlying Palliser Fm. but is missing in the Jasper area. "Exshaw" is a small community along Highway 1A near the eastern mountain front.

This unit is remarkably widespread, found throughout western Canada and even in the American midwest and south, where it is called the Chatanooga Fm. How could such a thin formation cover so much area?

One might think that the Exshaw Fm. marks a mass-extinction event, but current wisdom is that it represents a rapid invasion by the sea. The formation lies over a low-relief erosion surface (the top of the Palliser Fm. is worn billiard-table flat), so the ocean may have been able to move quickly inland over a huge, featureless region.

Banff Formation
Lower Carboniferous/Mississippian (360-320 Ma) 0-820 m

Mostly interbedded gray silty, cherty dolomite in the lower part, with a dark-gray or black shale at the base that looks a lot like the Exshaw shale (previous entry). The Banff shale is limy, though, while the Exshaw is not; test with acid. In the middle of the formation there is a gray-weathering limestone member up to 100 m thick. Above the middle band the Banff is shaly interbedded dolomite and limestone. The formation weathers brown from a distance but is strikingly banded gray and brown close up. It is easily eroded and thus recessive except for the cliffy middle band, which helps to differentiate the Banff from other shales.

Distribution: from Trail Creek in the Whitefish Range west of Glacier park to Sukunka River (south of Pine Pass), where it merges with shales of the Besa River Fm. (page 134). The Banff Fm. is mostly front-range rock, but it reaches the surface in the western foothills at Moose Mountain (southwest of Calgary) and at Folding Mountain (west of Hinton). It can be found in the main ranges south of Kananaskis Lakes, and farther north in the Weeping Wall along the Icefields Parkway in the Columbia Icefield area. South of Kootenay Pass (just north of Waterton) the Banff Fm. is west of the divide only. "Banff" is from Banff townsite.

Banff shale is the filling in Miss Devonian's sandwich (page 136). The formation appears as a light-brown band running through the peaks of the front ranges, very conspicuous along the TransCanada Highway between Canmore and Banff (Mt. Rundle, Cascade Mountain). The road to Spray Lakes west from Canmore displays the whole Banff shale sequence, starting about 5.5 km out of Canmore.

Highway 16 passes by a good exposure of crumbly Banff beds about 23 km east of Jasper. Unfortunately the rock is on the other side of a water-filled ditch. But a little farther west, at Cold Sulphur Spring, the Overlander Trail takes you west above fine outcrops along the Athabasca River after a 20-minute walk (descend to the river where the trail begins to head south).

Banff beds begin at an unconformity. They show a gradual return of life to the dead sea of Exshaw time. The water was getting shallower, with limy shoals developing in the middle of the formation. The upper Banff is quite fossiliferous, loaded with brachiopods, discussed next, and crinoid fragments (page 142).

Brachiopods look like clams but aren't; clams are in a different group altogether (the pelecypods), while brachiopods have a whole phylum to themselves. The upper and lower shells ("valves") of pelecypods match each other, for they are symmetrical along the hinge line, while those of brachiopods don't because they are symmetrical at 90° to the hinge line. The two valves were held slightly open, and a "lophophore," a coiled feeding aid, would create incoming currents to snag small organisms swimming/drifting by. If you find a complete specimen, note the little hole at the back of the beast. A fleshy stalk came out that hole in most species, an anchor to stick into the sea-bottom muck or onto something more substantial. Some brachiopod species spent most of their time hiding in the mud, while others kept themselves elevated slightly above the bottom on the ends of their stalks.

This way of life has been quite successful; brachiopods have been with us for 600 million years. In fact, the genus *Lingula* does just as well in modern muddy shoals as it did in the Early Cambrian—an amazing evolutionary success that shows the value of simplicity and nonspecialization.

If you find yourself out on a steep, rubbly slope of Banff rock (the usual way you meet this formation), then you may see large, well-preserved specimens of the brachiopod *Spirifer rowleyi*. (No collecting in the parks, remember.) There are other spiriferid brachiopods in the Banff shale, too, including some rare ones, and also **productid** types that had spines on them. The spines are usually broken off, but the spine bases show up as dots on the shells. Nut-like **rynchonellid** brachiopods are abundant in some beds; they are smooth and quite round.

Typical buff-and-gray banding in the Banff Formation.

Brachiopods

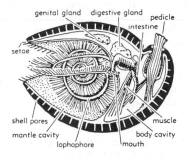

Anatomy of a typical brachiopod

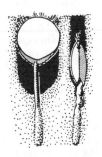

How a mud-dwelling brachiopod uses its pedicle (stalk) to withdraw

How the shell opens and closes

Drawings from Invertebrate Fossils, *by R.C. Moore, C.G. Lalicker and A.G. Fischer (1952) reproduced courtesy McGraw-Hill Book Company*

Rundle Group and related rocks
Lower Carboniferous/Mississippian (360-320 Ma) 0-900 m

Mostly gray limestone made of fossil fragments, with porous dolomite layers in the upper parts. A thick and resistant unit, forming big gray cliffs rather like those of the Palliser Fm. (page 138), but dark-banded at a distance and ledgier. Named for Mt. Rundle, the much-photographed peak south of Banff.

The Rundle Gp. is easy to pick out: it's the upper slice of bread in Miss Devonian's sandwich. The group generally follows the distribution of underlying Palliser and Banff beds, appearing west of Waterton/Glacier, running through the main ranges north to Kananaskis Lakes, then staying in the front ranges north to Peace River. Rundle rock also reaches the surface here and there in the western foothills, as in Moose Mountain west of Calgary or Folding Mountain west of Hinton.

Rundle-type rock is widespread in western North America. Under one name or another the unit is found all the way to the north end of the Rockies and beyond, through the Mackenzie Mountains into the arctic. The Madison Fm. of Montana and Wyoming is essentially Rundle rock, as is the Redwall Limestone of the Grand Canyon in Arizona.

Alberta 40 (the forestry trunk road) provides access to classic Rundle exposures south of the TransCanada Highway in Kananaskis Country and on south to Crowsnest Pass. Much of what you see along this road is Miss Devonian's sandwich, with the Rundle Gp. forming the jagged upper parts of many rugged peaks.

Rundle rock is a stratigrapher's delight: full of varied beds that can be followed for long distances, the result of waxing and waning seas. Natural gas comes from Rundle strata in the foothills and eastern prairies, prompting geologists to study the group intensively. It has been divided into several formations, themselves subdivided into many members. The stack is difficult for anybody but an expert to sort out, so I have simplified things as follows. Referring to the diagram on the opposite page may help.

The central-Rockies Rundle has two main parts: the **Livingstone Formation** (300 m) below and the **Mount Head Formation** above. South of Waiparous River (east of Lake Minnewanka), the **Etherington Formation** caps the group; north of there it has been largely removed by erosion, although Etherington beds can be found as far north as Brazeau River. The top of the Rundle is a major unconformity.

"Livingstone" is from the Livingstone Range, a continuous high ridge at the mountain front between Crowsnest Pass and Highwood River. The formation consists mostly of grainy limestone made of the remains of crinoids (discussed next) and bryozoans (page 135).

Crinoids are echinoderms, in the same group that includes the starfish. There are lots of living crinoid species today; people know them as **sea lilies,** although they are animals, not plants. Crinoids evolved in the Cambrian but were not common in the Rockies region until the Early Carboniferous, when they seem to have taken over the seabed.

Crinoids

*A typical crinoid, showing the main part of the animal (the cup-shaped **calyx** and arms). A long stem supports the calyx.*

Crinoid fragments as they appear in limestone. Most are plates from the stem.

The Opal Range, viewed from the road to Fortress Mountain Ski Area in Kananaskis Country. Steeply dipping beds of Rundle limestone have been eroded into spectacularly ragged ridges.

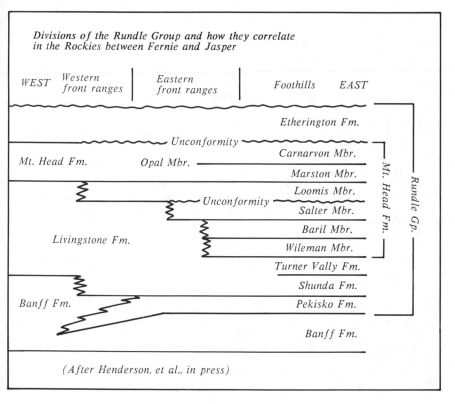

Divisions of the Rundle Group and how they correlate
in the Rockies between Fernie and Jasper

WEST	Western front ranges	Eastern front ranges	Foothills	EAST

Etherington Fm.

~ Unconformity ~

Mt. Head Fm. — Opal Mbr. — Carnarvon Mbr.

Marston Mbr.

Loomis Mbr.

~ Unconformity ~ Salter Mbr.

Baril Mbr.

Livingstone Fm. — Wileman Mbr.

Mt. Head Fm.

Turner Vally Fm.

Shunda Fm.

Banff Fm. — Pekisko Fm.

Rundle Gp.

Banff Fm.

(After Henderson, et al., in press)

A typical crinoid anchors to a suitable spot in fairly agitated, shallow seawater and grows by producing small disks and plates of lime. A stalk of stacked disks leads upward to a cup that holds the main part of the animal. Platy tentacles extend from the cup; they wave about in the water and sweep passing small organisms down into the cup, toward the mouth. It's a living.

When a crinoid dies it falls apart, all the myriad little pieces scattering about the sea floor. In Rundle time there were such enormous numbers of crinoids that with the addition of some lime mud to hold the debris together the resulting limestone consisted mostly of crinoid parts. The plates that formed the stalks and tentacles are easy to identify: they are round, up to 3 cm across (usually a centimetre or so), with a white star in the middle, five-sided in classic echinoderm fashion. Only rarely is the diagnostic cup-like part preserved, which means that identifying crinoid fossils is quite difficult, even though the rock is literally made of them.

But one needn't know the species to conclude that any outcrop full of crinoid hash is probably part of the Rundle Gp. I say "probably" because the middle unit of the Banff shale (previous entry) can also be very crinoid-rich. There are crinoid plates in the Palliser, too, especially at the top, but crinoidal rock is usually Rundle rock.

At the mountain front and in the foothills, the part of the Rundle that would otherwise be the Livingstone Fm. formed in very shallow water that kept drying up. The distinctive rock resulting comprises the **Shunda** and **Turner Valley** formations, eastern equivalents of the Livingstone. They contain fewer crinoids but more oolites (BB-like lime pellets, page 91), more dolomite and evaporites (minerals formed when seawater evaporates). This rock is made of sugary-looking dolomite crystals that are loosely intergrown, leaving pores and tiny cavities from which the evaporites have been removed by solution—making room for the hydrocarbons found in foothills oil and gas fields.

The **Pekisko Formation** is also shallow-water dolomite and was once thought to correlate with the Livingstone, but the Pekisko has recently been traced southwestward into the underlying middle and upper Banff Fm., as shown in the up-to-date correlation chart on page 143. So the Pekisko is older than the Livingstone. Where it can be identified separately from the Banff, though, the Pekisko is still considered to be part of the Rundle Gp.

Above the Livingstone Fm. lies the **Mount Head Formation**, 150-300 m thick. Mt. Head is at the mountain front just north of Highwood River. The formation is all shallow-water rock, finer-textured than the coarse Livingstone beds under it, with much less crinoid debris and more corals, more oolites and more dolomite. There is **bird's-eye** texture in this rock: the limestone or dolomite is peppered with little white marks. Bird's-eye texture is thought to form in very shallow water, from gas bubbles that produce cavities later filled with calcite or dolomite.

The Mt. Head has been subdivided into six members: lowest to highest, **Wileman, Baril, Salter, Loomis, Marston** and **Carnarvon.** Some of these are shaly, so the Mt. Head is ledgier than the Livingstone, as is the overlying unit, the Etherington Fm. The Rundle Gp. frequently makes up the top of mountains (softer units above the Rundle have been eroded away), and the beds are often tilted steeply. The hard-and-soft alternation produces spectacular sawtooth ridges—an easy way to pick out the Mt. Head and Etherington formations from a distance.

Further explanation of the Mt. Head requires that we go back to the Livingstone for a moment. Livingstone rock gets thicker to the west and shows signs of deposition in deeper water. The edge of the continental shelf seems to have been here in Rundle time, along what is now the crest of the Rockies. Livingstone rock formed the shelf for a while, then changed character upward to become the Mt. Head as the shelf shallowed and built itself outward (westward) into the sea. At the advancing edge of the shelf, Livingstone-style sediments continued to accumulate as the Mt. Head did the same to the east, so the Mt. Head grades into the Livingstone in the western front ranges and main ranges. In these places the six members of the Mt. Head are difficult to pick out, except for the upper two (the dark-weathering Marston and Carnarvon), which are known together as the **Opal Member** in that area.

Massive Mt. Head beds are often sprinkled with beautifully preserved **horn corals**. The fossils do look like small horns; the fine radiating structures of the coral cup are often strikingly displayed against the dark-gray limestone. Common species include *Faberophyllum, Ekvasophyllum* and *Canadiphyllum.* The fossils seldom weather out of the rock surrounding them; one must either enjoy them where found or lug a slab home. A line of corals is usually interspersed with blobs of chert, the hard, insoluble chert sticking out of the rock because it weathers much more slowly than the limestone surrounding it. For more on chert see page 148.

Corals in the Mt. Head Formation. Photo courtesy Jasper National Park.

The **Etherington Formation** is named for a creek and mountain in the Highwood Range, east of Alberta 40 in Kananaskis Country. It occurs from Brazeau River south, gradually thickening southward and westward to about 300 m in the Kananaskis area, where it is best exposed. The formation is mostly dolomite and limestone, often sandy and rather easily eroded compared to the rest of the Rundle Gp. There are red and green shale beds in the Etherington—signs of shallow, muddy water that was sometimes well-oxygenated and sometimes not.

The Etherington is the last major carbonate (limestone or dolomite) to be laid down in the central and southern Rockies (but not in the northern Rockies, where there are some thick Triassic limestones). After the end of the Carboniferous, which is what the Etherington records, there was a period of uplift and erosion more marked in the central Rockies than any since the Silurian (see the sub-Devonian unconformity, page 120). Near the top the Etherington is quite sandy, showing that the shoreline was close. By the time the sea returned, its chemistry in our area had changed markedly, producing the unusual sediments of the Spray Lakes and Ishbel groups (next page).

In the northern Rockies, Carboniferous rocks are not as well-studied as the Banff and Rundle strata of the central Rockies. But it is known that the geography of the time caused some interesting differences in the kinds of sediments laid down.

From about Monkman Pass to Halfway River, the Rockies region lay just offshore from the entrance of the **Peace River Embayment,** a lobe of the sea that reached well east, into an area that had been land for much of the Devonian Period (see the Peace River Arch, page 120). Now, in the Carboniferous, the plate here had sagged down. That sag crossed the Rockies area between about Monkman Pass and Halfway River, and the water was deep enough in the middle of the trough to collect black shale—a lobe of the Besa River Fm. (page 134), which had been accumulating to the north and west for a long time.

The shallower portions of the trough, north and south of the centre, are preserved as the **Prophet Formation,** which is up to 1000 m thick. There were so many marine sponges growing here, and preservation of their remains was so good, that the Prophet can be called **spiculite:** rock made mostly of sponge spicules, with limestone nodules and layers in it. Prophet rock is about the same age as the Banff and Livingstone formations; it grades northwestward into the Besa River shale, then resumes its identity north of the region affected by the embayment.

So: if you follow the Rundle Gp. north from Jasper, you pass into Prophet beds around Monkman Pass, then into deeper-water Besa River shale around Peace River and then back to shallower-water Prophet beds at about Halfway River.

Buildups of sediment along the underwater slopes of the bay would occasionally slide into deeper water—a process that left turbidites (sediments moved along the bottom by slide-generated currents; see page 83) in the Prophet and Besa River formations. Tidal currents moved in and out of the bay's mouth as well, cutting channels in Prophet-type sediment there.

Eventually the trough quit deepening and filled with sediments, as shown by the **Stoddart Group,** (60-120 m) which overlies the Prophet and the Besa River in this area. Stoddart rock is mostly shale, but sandiness toward the top shows that the sea was getting shallower and muddier—a sign of retreat. Indeed, next up in the pile is the **Mattson Formation,** 200 m of sandstone laid down in river deltas that were carrying material eroded from land nearby.

As you might expect, the top of the Mattson is an unconformity. The shoreline moved through our area from northeast to southwest, exposing the whole region. During the long period of erosion that followed, a great deal of rock that once lay on top of the Rundle Gp. and its northern equivalents was lost.

When the sea returned, it brought with it some very strange deposits. They are described next.

THE WEIRDEST ROCK IN THE ROCKIES

Spray Lakes and Ishbel groups (Late Carboniferous/Pennsylvanian and Permian; 320-245 Ma) 0-300 m, and the Ice River Alkaline Complex

Along the Maligne Road in Jasper park, between Medicine Lake and Maligne Lake, there lies a cabin-sized boulder of dark-brown rock. I had driven by that boulder many times on my way to Maligne Lake, where Parks Canada used to send me once a week, but it wasn't until two years ago that I stopped to look at it. I was astounded: it was made entirely of chert.

Chert occurs in blobs and lumps (proper term: nodules) scattered through many Rockies limestones, but seldom in the massive quantity required to produce a huge block of it. Where did that boulder come from?

It came from the mountain east of the road, as part of a huge rockslide (see page 218 for more on the Maligne slides). The boulder was originally part of a layer of chert about 50 m thick that is present, although often much thinner, all over the front ranges of the central and northern Rockies.

Chert is a form of quartz, so it is very hard. But chert is not a product of high temperatures and pressures like the Gog quartzite (page 88) or the quartz veins one finds in the middle Miette grits (page 83). This is *microcrystalline* quartz: clots of tiny quartz crystals that grew in seawater. But quartz doesn't

Boulder of massive Ranger Canyon chert along the Maligne Road in Jasper National Park.

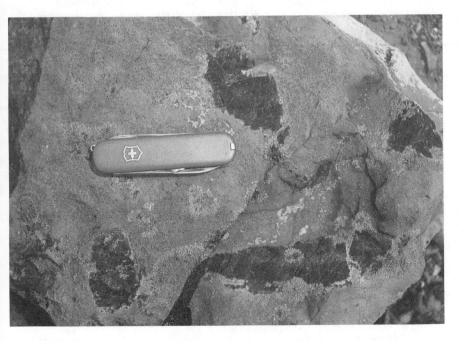

Dark chert nodules against lighter Rundle limestone at the Rock Gardens beside the Banff golf course. Rock is encrusted with Xanthoria lichen.

Weirdest rock in the Rockies

usually dissolve or crystallize in water at normal temperatures. How could it do that?

It had some organic help. The quartz in Rockies chert has come from radiolaria and sponges, sea creatures that sidestep such problems.

Radiolaria are one-celled animals that float about the oceans as members of the plankton layer. They make tiny symmetrical skeletons of **silica,** the biologist's word for quartz. These skeletons fall to the seabed when the animals die. Many species of sponges grow needle-like rods of silica called **spicules** throughout their tissues; these litter the floor when the animals decompose. (Bathtub-type sea sponges don't grow spicules, so they are soft, not crunchy like most sponge species.) Diatoms are also siliceous, but they are relatively recent life forms (Mesozoic) and not found in the rock we're discussing here.

Sponges and radiolaria extract silica from seawater by turning it into **opal,** a form of quartz that contains water. The sea hungers to get its silica back, but the organisms protect their opal by covering it with living tissue and thus keeping it from re-dissolving. Once a siliceous organism dies, the opal usually disappears in a few years. Occasionally it is preserved, though, in opal deposits that are mined for gem-grade stones.

There are no known opal deposits in the Canadian Rockies.* However, we have plenty of chert here, which is opal minus the water, i.e. mostly silica with various impurities. Another name for this material is **flint,** the stuff of Indian arrowheads and sandpaper.

Making chert

To get accumulations of chert, one must have alkaline (the opposite of acidic) seawater, which favors silica precipitation. This kind of chemistry is common on the floors of the basins between the continents, where the water is very deep and the temperature is just above freezing, with little dissolved oxygen or carbon dioxide present. Sediment gathered from the deep-sea floor is loaded with radiolarian and diatom remains; given time, the nearly pure silica in these deposits recrystallizes to form layers of massive chert.

So massive chert beds have been thought to mean that there was deep water in the area at the time they formed.

However, all other clues in our chert beds point to *shallow* water, not deep water. How so?

No one knows. The problem of shallow-water chert beds still plagues geologists. The most likely possibility is that rising ocean currents bring alkaline water up from the depths, allowing layers of siliceous remains to accumulate until they are well-covered with other sediments and thus protected.

Chert **nodules**—lumps and irregular masses in limestone—are a little easier to explain, although the mechanism of formation is still speculative. Such nodules are commonly found in the deeper-water types of limestones, in places where currents could have concentrated sponge spicules and then covered them with lime mud. The silica in the spicules has largely dissolved anyway, but it has recrystallized again nearby to produce the nodule. So it seems that chert, like dolomite, is a mineral produced *after* deposition, when chemical changes can occur in the hardening rock.

Back to our story. In the Canadian Rockies the rock gets more and more cherty in the Early and Late Carboniferous (known among American geologists as the Mississippian and Pennsylvanian periods), reaching a peak in the Permian. Massive beds of dark-brown chert appear in the **Ranger Canyon Formation,** from whence fell that boulder along the Maligne Road.

---

*The Opal Range in Kananaskis Country was named by G.M. Dawson (page 754) for the chert there; the Opal Hills above Maligne Lake were named by Mary Schäffer (page 769) for their contrasting colors (green patches of tundra against reddish/yellowish rock).

The Ranger Canyon chert, and its northern equivalent the **Fantasque Formation,** are Early Permian in age (268-258 Ma). They are easy to identify and widespread, although not present everywhere and quite variable in thickness (maximum 100 m). The two formations would have the same name were it not for a gap in their distribution: between Wapiti Lake and Pine Pass you won't find either of them.

The other Late Carboniferous/Pennsylvanian and Permian formations are inclined to be look-alikes; they are thin and discontinuous, present here and absent there. Just picking them out from the underlying Rundle beds is tricky, let alone identifying the various formations. For many years the whole works were just lumped together as the "Rocky Mountain Group" and given a general Late Carboniferous and Permian age. In the last ten years, though, new techniques for extracting and identifying microscopic fossils have allowed the various layers to be dated and correlated with one another so that the sequence of events could be worked out.

The sequence begins at the erosion surface atop the Rundle Gp., where dolomite, dolomitic sandstone, dolomite and cherty beds of the Late Carboniferous **Spray Lakes Group** (70-200 m) mark the return of a shallow sea. The group includes several thin formations—**Misty, Kananaskis, Tyrwhitt, Storelk, Tobermory** and **Hanington.** Their distributions and intertonguings are very complex, beyond the scope of this book.

Above the Spray Lakes Gp. there is another unconformity, then the Permian **Ishbel Group** (150-660 m), which includes that good marker, the Ranger Canyon chert, at the top. The Ishbel Gp. is irregularly distributed and usually thin (under 200 m in most locations), but in spite of this it correlates in time and rock types with the widespread Phosphoria Fm. of the USA. "Phosphoria" brings to mind "phosphate," and indeed there is phosphate-bearing rock in the Ishbel Gp. The major deposits occur in the **Johnston Canyon Formation,** the lower member of the Ishbel Gp. in the southern and central regions.*

Making phosphate

Phosphate (PO_4) occurs in nature mainly as the mineral **apatite,** which combines calcium (as Ca_5), with varying proportions of phosphate and (usually) some fluorine. Apatite forms today in shallow seawater as nodules on the bottom. The source of the phosphate is thought to be the bones, scales and teeth of fishes, all rich in phosphorus, and the shells of ostracods (small crustaceans). But again, as in the case of chert, the exact mechanism for creating phosphate nodules is unknown. They seem to occur only in water that is 30-300 m deep and fairly warm, on a continental shelf close by a source of upwelling currents—such as the marine environment off the coast of southern California.

Rock rich in phosphate nodules is termed **phosphorite,** and it is eagerly sought by prospectors, for phosphates are the main ingredients in fertilizers, always in demand. Thus far that demand hasn't resulted in strip-mining of the Johnston Canyon Fm.

Much of the formation is silty dolomite, with black phosphatic blobs up to 5 cm across in the upper layers. The unit is thick in the southern part of the central Rockies (215 m southwest of Fernie), thinning northward (30 m at Banff). The formation is named for Johnston Canyon, near the junction of Highway 1A and Highway 93 between Banff and Lake Louise; north of there it quickly tapers by later erosion to a thin edge. In a small area along the Elk River north of Fernie, the erosion didn't go as deep, and it failed to remove another couple of

---

*Aside to anyone trying to learn all these formation names: the nomenclature is unfortunate. In the central Rockies we have the Spray Lakes Gp. and the Spray River Gp.; the Ranger Canyon Fm. and the Johnston Canyon Fm.—all fairly close together stratigraphically and all occurring in the same area.

formations on top of the Johnston Canyon: the **Telford Formation** (215 m of silty limestone) and the **Ross Creek Formation** (150 m of siltstone).

North of Jasper, between Willmore park and Pine Pass, the Johnston Canyon is replaced by the **Belcourt Formation,** up to 135 m thick. The Belcourt is limestone/dolomite, with pebbles of chert at the base and not much phosphorite. North of Pine Pass the unit becomes silty and shaly; there it is known as the **Kindle Formation** (150 m).

Next up is our chert-bed marker, the Ranger Canyon Fm. Both it and the Fantasque are easy to spot by their dark color against the pale limestones of the front ranges. An amazing unconformity is found at the base of both units. It represents an erosion surface that can be traced over an area of 155,000 km^2 in Canada and the western United States.

Above the Ranger Canyon there is yet another unconformity, which represents the top of the Permian sequence—except between Monkman Pass and the Athabasca River, where there is a thin sandstone lying above the Ranger Canyon: the **Mowitch Formation,** 3-22 m, which escaped erosion in this area. You can see the Mowitch at Mt. Greenock, along the Celestine Lakes Road in Jasper park.

Counting the ones at the base and the top, there are *four* unconformities in the Spray Lakes and Ishbel Groups, which helps to explain why the collection is so thin and varied: erosion was the norm in western Canada during the 60-million-year span of the Late Carboniferous and Permian periods. Thick, easy-to-sort-out sediments were laid down elsewhere in North America at this time. We shouldn't complain; the Canadian Rockies already have one of the more complete geological records in the world.

And that's the top of the Paleozoic stack in our area, including the great middle carbonate unit introduced early in this book (see page 37). Above lie the siltstone, sandstone, shale and coal of the last great sequence of rocks in the Rockies: the young clastics of the muddy Mesozoic.

Before wading in, however, consider the only known sizable patch of igneous rock in our area. It is about the same age as the sediments we have been discussing, and in keeping with the theme of this section it is the strangest stuff of all.

Ice River Alkaline Complex
Late Permian (about 245 Ma) igneous intrusion

The only true pluton (mass of once-molten rock) exposed in our area, the Ice River Complex covers 29 km^2 in the southern end of Yoho National Park. It makes up the peaks immediately south and east of Mt. Goodsir; they have names such as Zinc Mountain and Manganese Mountain, hinting at the geology there. Access is by trail up Beaverfoot River and Ice River about 30 km to Sodalite Creek, in the heart of the intrusion. The Beaverfoot River section is a fire road, currently open to mountain bicycles.

The Ice River intrusion is famous among geologists as one of the better exposures in the world of some rare rock types with appropriately alien names: jacupirangite, ijolite, urtite and carbonatite. These are all varieties of **nepheline syenite:** a grainy igneous rock that is mostly augite (chemical formula $Ca(Mg,Fe,Al)(Al,Si)_2O_6$) and nepheline ($NaAlSiO_4$), usually with a good percentage of orthoclase feldspar ($KAlSi_3O_8$). In the Ice River complex the augite is a peculiar variety called "titanaugite"; as the name indicates, the mineral contains the element titanium. There is also a fair proportion of magnetite (the magnetic iron mineral) in this rock. "Zinc Mountain" is misnamed (zinc is not significant in the complex), although Manganese Mountain does contain some manganese. But there isn't enough to be worth mining, and mining isn't allowed in Canadian national parks in any case.

The "alkaline" in "Ice River Alkaline Complex" is a geochemistry term referring not to alkali (mineral salts left after evaporation of water) but to rock that is rich in orthoclase feldspar yet lacking in quartz. This is an unusual combination, for normally orthoclase and quartz go together. Granite, for example, is about 90 percent orthoclase and quartz. But the nepheline syenite in the Ice River complex is very low in quartz. This hints that the Ice River magma probably came up from beneath the underlying North American plate, where many a strange rock type is born through intermelting with the very different minerals of the mantle.

K.L. Currie (1975) did a definitive study of the Ice River complex. He concluded that a blob of magma worked its way up from great depths into the overlying sedimentary strata here, where it spread out between the layers to form a sill (lens-shaped horizontal mass). It cooled slowly, so the minerals grew into large grains. Minerals crystallizing out of the molten pool floated upward or sank downward according to their densities, resulting in zones of differing rock types. The weathered zones look layered from a distance, yet the rock is not sedimentary.

After this first intrusion there was another, the second one a spreading vertical column that cut through the ceiling of the first. The second magma may have reached the surface, but if it did, then Permian beds in the front ranges nearby ought to contain bits of material blown out of the resulting volcano (alkaline volcanoes are usually explosive, like Mt. St. Helens). However, no evidence has been found; if there was a volcano, the evidence may have been lost to erosion, for Permian units in the Canadian Rockies are marked by several unconformities.

Nepheline is a greenish mineral reminiscent of jade and closely related. Blue **sodalite**, $Na_8(AlSiO_4)_6Cl_2$, is found in the area, too. But take heed, rockhounds: you risk a heavy fine if you are caught removing specimens from the national park.

During uplift of the Rockies, the Ice River complex behaved like a hard nut imbedded in soft clay. The sediments surrounding the complex crumpled under the stress, but the complex itself, which was made of stronger rock, survived with moderate folding and faulting.

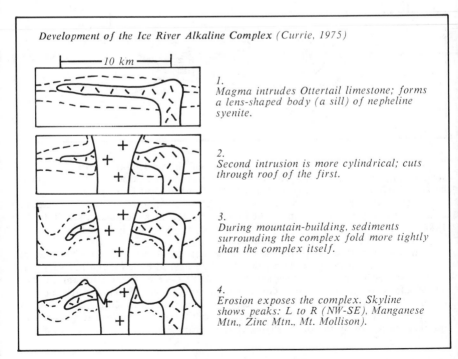

Development of the Ice River Alkaline Complex (Currie, 1975)

*1.
Magma intrudes Ottertail limestone; forms a lens-shaped body (a sill) of nepheline syenite.*

*2.
Second intrusion is more cylindrical; cuts through roof of the first.*

*3.
During mountain-building, sediments surrounding the complex fold more tightly than the complex itself.*

*4.
Erosion exposes the complex. Skyline shows peaks: L to R (NW-SE), Manganese Mtn., Zinc Mtn., Mt. Mollison).*

THE MUDDY MESOZOIC (and a touch of the Tertiary)
Triassic, Jurassic, Cretaceous and Paleocene (245-45 Ma)

We are now dealing with the young clastic sequence, the uppermost of the four great rock units of the Canadian Rockies (see page 39). Most of the rock in this collection is made of particles worn from nearby landmasses; limestone and other made-in-place rock is uncommon. The young clastics are found mostly in the foothills and front ranges, although in the southern Rockies some of the formations are also found west of the divide, in a region of coal-bearing rock that geologists call the **Fernie Basin.**

Mesozoic sediments in our area record interesting features and exciting events: an inland seaway linking the Gulf of Mexico with the Canadian arctic; a lost volcano in the southern Rockies, and the collision of far-traveled groups of islands with North America, creating the mountains of western Canada.

Mesozoic geological history around the world has been worked out in fine-tooth detail, thanks to excellent index fossils. Among these are the **ammonites,** a distinctive group of Cretaceous cephalopods (squid-like animals in shells). The ammonites evolved so quickly, and they can be identified to the species level so easily (by experts of course) that ammonite-containing beds are routinely dated to within half a million years. Some units have been pegged to within 10,000 years—which is astonishing accuracy in dealing with sedimentary rocks 66-144 million years old.

Typical coiled cephalopod

Essentially a squid in a shell. There were straight-shelled types as well.

Inside, the shell is divided into chambers.
The ammonite group had complexly folded
septae (bulkheads) between the chambers.
These are used by specialists to make
precise identifications.

Simple septae

Ammonite septae

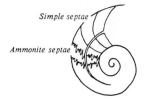
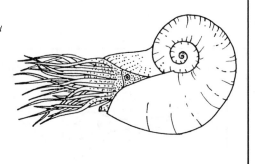

Geologists have good reason to apply state-of-the-art techniques to Mesozoic stratigraphy in and about the Rockies, for there is a lot of coal and natural gas to be found in the Cretaceous formations of the foothills and front ranges.

Despite all this detailed study, the big picture of Mesozoic events in western Canada has only recently been worked out (for a technical summary, see Stott, 1984). Before describing the various formations, an overview is in order.

Widespread gentle uplift in the Late Permian or Early Triassic (250-245 Ma) left an erosion surface atop the Paleozoic formations of the Rockies. When the sea returned a few million years later, the shoreline pushed east, though not very far, so Triassic sediments in our area are mostly shallow-water types, silty and sandy. They belong to the Spray River Gp. and its northern equivalents. Toward the end of the Triassic the shoreline moved westward, exposing those sediments to erosion.

The sea came back late in the Early Jurassic (at about 190 Ma) and deepened quickly, as shown by the black shales of the Fernie Fm.

The upper Fernie is silty/sandy, and for the first time since the Devonian the source of the particles is from the *west*. That is significant: it marks the impact of Intermontane Terrane (page 170) at about 175 Ma. This was the first of the two mini-plates run down by North America in the Mesozoic; with it came the accordioning of the continental margin into mountain ranges west of the Rockies region (Columbias, Ominecas and Cassiars). These new ranges started shedding sediment as soon as they poked up above the sea, and some of the material spread far eastward across our area, which was still underwater and undisturbed by the mountain-building.

Paradoxically, the same forces producing mountains west of us were causing subsidence here. The growing stack of folded, overthrust rock was heavy, and it pushed the continental margin down into the mantle. The crust of the margin was stiff enough to include our area in the downward bend. The resulting trough-like feature, which lay along the eastern front of the mountains, is called the **Rocky Mountain Trough.** Note that this is different from the Rocky Mountain *Trench,* which is a valley in the modern landscape bordering the Rockies on the west. (For more on the Rocky Mountain Trough see pages 154 and 155.)

Thanks to the sediments accumulated in the Rocky Mountain Trough, we have a record of the whole mountain-building sequence.

As the floor of the trough sagged down, erosion kept it filled with bits and pieces of the eroding highlands in British Columbia. The Rocky Mountain Trough received sediment at rates of up to 300 cm per thousand years—torrential compared with the 5 cm per thousand years of, say, the Devonian Palliser Fm.

The Rocky Mountain Trough filled throughout the rest of the Mesozoic and into the Paleocene Epoch of the Tertiary Period. It did so in three episodes, discussed here informally as episodes I, II and III. Each ended in a period of erosion. Thus, there are three layers of sediments in the trough, each separated from the others by an unconformity. The deepest point in the basin holds nearly 7 km of rock.

Episode I

Counting the upper Fernie as the beginning of deposition, episode I continued with the Kootenay Gp. of the southern region (Late Jurassic to Early Cretaceous), and its northerly equivalents-in-time, the Nikanassin Fm. and the Minnes Gp.

The Kootenay contains detritus from older formations seen in the Rockies, such as chert from the Banff Fm. This shows that the Rockies appeared in Kootenay time, about 120 million years ago, for the main ranges must have been standing above sea level, eroding and thus producing sediments. The mountains need not have been very high at this point; I think of them beginning as lines of hills on the seabed, growing taller and forcing the sea away to the northeast.

The soft upper layers of sediment must have eroded quickly at first. In the northern-Rockies area, which was still under the waves but close to the rising Cassiars and Ominecas, sand and mud went quickly into the sea. Farther south the sea retreated earlier and much of the sediment wound up in immense alluvial fans on heavily vegetated, swampy coastal plains. Remains of this vegetation formed the coal seams for which the Kootenay Fm. is noted.

Kootenay sediments didn't have to accumulate in the sea, for the material was deposited faster than the trough deepened and faster than erosion could carry it away. Conditions favoring the preservation of terrestrial sediments such as these are not common in the earth's history; the young clastics include the only **nonmarine rock**—rock not deposited in seawater—of much thickness or extent in our area (all previous nonmarine deposition had been thin and patchy). Reversing the earlier trend, *most* of the rock in the Rocky Mountain Trough is nonmarine.

At about 135 Ma there was a lull in mountain-building activity to the west. Erosion overtook upward growth and the mountains of BC began to wear down. Over the next 10 Ma this relieved the western margin of some of its burden and the crust sprang back up, raising with it the Rocky Mountain Trough. The result

THE ROCKY MOUNTAIN TROUGH:
A MOVING FOREDEEP IN FRONT OF THE CANADIAN ROCKIES

Episode I: Late Jurassic and Early Cretaceous

Thrust sheets begin to pile up on the continental margin, pushing the plate down to the southwest. Fernie and Kootenay sediments are washed from the Columbia Mountains and westernmost Rocky Mountains into the developing foredeep.

Rocky Mountain Trough (foredeep) catches eroded sediments

Southwesterly dipping North American Plate

Southwest   *Distance across the region sketched: about 100 km*   **Northeast**

Episode II: mid-Cretaceous

Rocky Mountain main ranges are shedding sediment into the trough, which has moved northeastward.

Thrusting and folding have moved along, too; Fernie and Kootenay beds are now involved in mountain-building. Blairmore sediments are accumulating in the trough, so eroding Kootenay and Fernie wind up in Blairmore beds.

Episode III: Late Cretaceous and Early Tertiary

Front ranges are up and the foredeep has moved farther northeastward, receiving sediments of the Alberta Group, Brazeau and Paskapoo formations. The Blairmore is now disturbed; some winds up in these younger beds.

Near the end of mountain-building, Alberta and Brazeau beds are folded and thrusted, perhaps recycling into the Paskapoo, which is little disturbed.

was uplift of our area above sea level, the end of infilling episode I and the first major erosion surface on the batch of sediments in the trough.

Episode II

The plates took another crunch at about 120 Ma. Mountain-building resumed in British Columbia, and the pile on the western continental margin began to grow again. As before, the crust responded, the Rocky Mountain Trough sagged and a second round of deposition began in our area. In episode II the Blairmore/Bullhead/Fort St. John groups poured into the trough.

Like the Kootenay Gp., material in these units includes fragments from older formations in the Rockies. The presence of Gog Gp. quartzite (page 88), which is main-range rock, suggests that the main ranges were well above sea level by 100 Ma. Volcanic eruptions farther west loaded rivers flowing into the southern and central parts of the basin with volcanic particles, giving the Blairmore Gp. its characteristic greenish color. Late in episode II some fireworks went off in the southern end of our area, where the Crowsnest Fm. records flows of volcanic mud from a vent that must have been nearby but hasn't been located (page 162).

Another period of crustal quiet followed, with erosional loss in the western mountains and an accompanying upward adjustment in the continental plate. The second batch of sediments in the Rocky Mountain Trough suffered minor erosion, leaving 2100 m of rock within the trough, which by this time was holding nearly 5 km of Mesozoic sediments. (The thickness of these deposits varies from place to place; these are maximum figures.)

Episode III

At this point another terrane (Insular Terrane, page 170) was run down by the continent and smeared onto the western edge, rejuvenating mountain growth across British Columbia in the Late Cretaceous and Early Tertiary (85 Ma to 45 Ma). The force was additional to that already being applied by Intermontane Terrane, and the old continental margin collapsed some more, producing the front ranges and foothills of the Canadian Rockies. As described in the section that follows, the main-range thrust sheets kept moving and stacking as younger ones developed eastward; it was during this period that the Rockies probably reached their greatest height.

In response to this new load, the crust sagged a third time and the Rocky Mountain Trough sagged with it, receiving a third (and last) batch of sediments: the shaly Alberta/Smoky Gp., followed by the Brazeau/Belly River/Wapiti formations, which are sandy and coaly. These rocks include detritus from the front ranges, which means that the front ranges were up by about 80 Ma. Atop a minor unconformity lies the youngest unit in the Rocky Mountain Trough: the freshwater sandstone and shale of the Paskapoo/Porcupine Hills Fm.

There is an interesting angle here. As the Rockies developed eastward, the sediments they shed were themselves caught in the eastward-moving disturbance. The deepest part of the Rocky Mountain Trough basin moved along, too, jumping eastward about 20-30 km during each of the three episodes of infilling.

Thus, sediments were recycled eastward. Recalling that Kootenay Gp. rock includes fragments of older Rockies-area formations, it is interesting to think of the Kootenay itself eroding in the front ranges and feeding sediment to the Brazeau, which was later exposed in the foothills and perhaps shed fragments into the Paskapoo.

The Cretaceous seaway

An important part of the Mesozoic story is the waxing and waning of shallow Cretaceous seas in the Rocky Mountain Trough and out on the Interior Plains.

Sea level was generally higher during the Cretaceous Period than it had been earlier in the Mesozoic, and it fluctuated markedly at least three times. The cause of these rises and falls is unknown; they may relate to expansion and contraction along the mid-oceanic ridges. Couple with this the subsidence along the front of

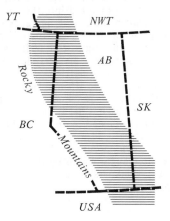

The Cretaceous seaway in western Canada

There were many advances and retreats through this corridor. The Kiowa/Skull Creek Sea was perhaps the largest, shown at its maximum extent (reached at about 98 Ma, near the end of the Early Cretaceous).

Map after Stott, 1984

Bow Falls, where Bow River has cut into Sulphur Mountain siltstone (lower part of the Spray River Group) near the Banff Springs Hotel.

Mesozoic summary

growing mountain ranges in western Canada and the United States, which kept the western Interior Plains low-lying from the Gulf of Mexico to the arctic, and the result was widespread inundation of the region.

Following a couple of advances and retreats during basin-infilling episode I, the greatest of these marine invasions occurred about 98 Ma, toward the end of episode II. The sea crept into western Canada from the north and joined a tongue lapping up from the south—the **Kiowa/Skull Creek Sea**—to produce a shallow seaway through the centre of North America. This was an inland ocean far larger than any inland sea currently existing on earth.

Size notwithstanding, this and the other Cretaceous floodings were ephemeral, coming and going in spans of a few million years. The rock record in the Rocky Mountain Trough documents no fewer that *11 cycles* of deepening and shallowing.

It was during one of these retreats, at about 93 Ma, that deposition in most of the basin decreased dramatically (although in some parts it probably continued). Some 2100 m of sediment in the Rocky Mountain Trough attributed to episode II still remain.

Episode III led off with another deep marine advance that laid down the shaly Alberta/Smoky Gp. By about 80 Ma the sea had left our area again, but it made one last advance some 75 Ma, when the **Bearpaw Sea** reached up from the south as far as Edmonton.

The Rockies were here by then, the front ranges standing well above the waves. But the foothills belt was still submerged, and one finds in the southern foothills the marine shale from that event: the Bearpaw Fm. Later, it too was caught in the folding and thrust-faulting.

Nonmarine sediments of the Paskapoo Fm. and its equivalents fill out the record on the eastern slope. On the western slope, though, the youngest formations in the Rockies accumulated in down-dropped fault valleys that developed after the main crustal collisions were over (for more on that, see page 177).

Herewith the details, formation-by-formation, from the beginning of the muddy Mesozoic.

Spray River Group
Triassic (245-208 Ma) 90-740 m

Erroneously (and often) called the "Spray River *shale*," much of this rock is actually siltstone and fine sandstone.

Shale is made of clay-sized particles; **siltstone** of silt-sized particles, which are intermediate in size between clay and sand. The grains in sandstone are large enough to see easily, but to tell the difference between shale and siltstone, look at a piece of the rock through a magnifying glass. If it sparkles as you tilt it, then it is siltstone. The tiny grains of quartz—the main component in sandstone and siltstone—flash tiny reflections. A piece of shale, on the other hand, doesn't sparkle because the grains are just too small—and they are often of clay minerals, which aren't as shiny as quartz.

The Spray River Gp. includes two formations in the southern and central Rockies: a lower reddish-brown-weathering dark-gray siltstone (**Sulphur Mountain Formation,** 100-500 m) and an upper buff-colored silty dolomite (**Whitehorse Formation,** up to 420 m) with gypsum beds in it. Both are marine.

These two formations are found from the upper Flathead drainage south of Crowsnest Pass to Monkman Pass, where the Triassic sequence thickens to about 1500 m and changes somewhat, taking on new formation names. But the group name (Spray River) continues north to the end of the Rockies, eroded away (and the erosion surface covered with other sediments) north of Liard River.

"Spray River" and "Sulphur Mountain" are familiar names to Banffites. Spray River joins Bow River just east of the Banff Springs Hotel, which sits at the base of Sulphur Mountain. The road to Bow Falls passes by outcrops of Sulphur Mountain siltstone, and the falls themselves are cut into the formation. Sulphur Mountain rock is thin-bedded and laminar; it makes excellent building stone and has been used extensively in Banff townsite. Both the park administration building and the Banff Springs Hotel are faced with it. The Whitehorse Fm. is named for Whitehorse Creek, in the front ranges south of Hinton.

The Spray River Gp. often lies along the southwestern sides of tilted front-range ridges, where it is easily identifiable above timberline as a softly contoured reddish-brown zone that supports lush, brilliantly green vegetation.

Whitehorse Fm. beds are easily eroded and thus seldom exposed. They usually occur with the very soft Fernie Fm. (next entry) in tree-covered front-range valley bottoms.

Interpreting the Spray River Gp. is straightforward: a shallow, muddy sea advanced inland from the west (Sulphur Mtn. Fm.). During Whitehorse Fm. time this sea became restricted, meaning the water in it didn't mix much with the rest of the ocean. Evaporation at a few locations produced gypsum and other evaporites (page 105): the **Starlight Member** of the Whitehorse Fm. One of those spots is at Helmet Mountain in eastern Jasper park, where there is a bed of gypsum 44 m thick. Few life forms can survive in water that is this heavily charged with minerals, so there aren't many fossils in Whitehorse rock. Nor are there many in the Sulphur Mountain, probably because the seabed was so muddy at that time.

North of Pine Pass the Triassic sequence acquires different formation names, but the geological history is fairly similar and the group name still applies. An eastward movement of the shoreline left mud (**Grayling Formation**, 500-900 m) and silt (**Toad Formation**, 275-600 m). Then an influx of sand (**Liard Formation**, 150 m) was followed by shallow, evaporating seas (**Charlie Lake Formation** dolomite and evaporites, up to 300 m). Limestone in the northern succession (**Baldonnel Formation**, 60 m) provides evidence of deepening water. This was followed by possible shallowing (**Pardonet Formation** shale and siltstone, 60 m), and then by the emergence of the seabed. Losses to erosion were small in the west, greater to the east; the sea soon returned, laying down the widespread Fernie shale (next entry).

Fossils in the northern formations are more common than in the Spray River Gp. They include the coiled shells of **ammonoid cephalopods** (squid-like animals) such as *Prionolubus, Wasatchites* and *Anagymnotoceras* (Toad Fm.); *Protrachyceras* and *Paratrachyceras* (Liard Fm); *Discotropites, Himavatites* and *Malayites* (Pardonet Fm.). The Pardonet is also well-known for the pelecypod *Monotis*.

And so into the Jurassic Period, near the end of which the Rocky Mountain Trough appeared (page 153), with its episodes of infilling.

Fernie Formation (start of episode I)
Jurassic (208-144 Ma) 300-600 m

Mostly dark, very soft shale in the lower half, with thin gray beds of orange-weathering siltstone; gray or brown silty shale, siltstone and sandstone in the upper part, with ripple marks. Fernie shale is recessive (easily eroded) and thus seldom exposed in mountain slopes. Places to find outcrops are in gullies and along streams that have cut down to bedrock.

Fernie strata are found from just north of the international boundary to Prophet River in the northern Rockies. Despite this long north-south distribution, the Fernie doesn't go very far east; it thins out quickly under the Interior Plains, barely reaching Edmonton and Calgary. The formation is best-developed west of Crowsnest Pass; look for outcrops of it along Highway 3, especially where the road crosses Alexander Creek and Hartley Creek. North of Crowsnest Pass Fernie shale commonly makes up the bottoms of front-range valleys and is sometimes exposed along streams. Good outcrops occur just east of the Banff interchange on the TransCanada Highway, and about midway along the road to Miette Hot Springs east of Jasper.

Fernie exposures are fascinating to look at: thin, orange-weathering siltstone beds follow the contorted folding in the dark shale. The underlying and overlying siltstone and sandstone formations are usually much less disturbed, showing how

The Fernie Formation, as seen along the TransCanada Highway between the eastern park gate and Banff. Light-toned beds are siltstone; dark beds are soft shale.

Kootenay formation exposure just east of the Fernie beds in the upper photo. Ragged dark line is a coal seam.

Apparently monotonous, there is more to the Fernie shale than meets the eye. There are four unconformities (gaps in the record from erosion). The formation coarsens upward, with silt and sand common in the upper part. These are the **Passage Beds,** which indicate from their westerly source that land in that direction was shedding sediments into a narrowing seaway. The Rockies area lay in that seaway. On the western side, Intermontane Terrane (page 170) was closing with the rest of Canada. So the Passage Beds of the Fernie Fm. are the first evidence for the mountain-building phase in western Canada.

Fernie shale is not very fossiliferous in the darker layers, although some contain abundant **belemnites:** the cuttlebone-like remains of a group of cephalopods. The silty/sandy layers are richer. One of these is known for its small clams as the "*Corbula munda* bed." Also present are ammonoid cephalopods, oysters and snails.

A good location to look at Fernie fossils is along Ribbon Creek at the base of Mt. Allan in Kananaskis Country, where the Fernie Fm. is exposed in a small quarry for Spray River flagstone. The Fernie here is loaded with snails and clams; some 38 different species have been collected at this site over the years. But collection is illegal now, for the site is within the provincial recreation area. Near Crowsnest Pass a giant ammonite species *(Titanites occidentalis)* was found in Fernie rock; it had a shell a metre in diameter.

Common Fernie Fm. fossils include the ammonites *Chondroceras* and *Stemmatoceras* and the clams *Inoceramus ferniensis, Gryphaea* and *Oxytoma.*

The upper Fernie Fm. represents the start of infilling in the Rocky Mountain Trough (page 153). This first round included also the overlying Kootenay Gp. and more northerly formations of Late Jurassic and Early Cretaceous age, described next.

Kootenay Group, Nikanassin Formation and Minnes Group (episode I, cont'd)
Late Jurassic to Early Cretaceous (165-97.5 Ma) 600-1200 m

These three units are all the same age, but they vary in rock type from south to north.

The **Kootenay Group** (100-1000 m) is mostly reddish-brown-weathering siltstone and sandstone, with shale and coal beds. It was named by G.M. Dawson (see the history section, page 754) in 1886 for the "east Kootenays," meaning in those days the coal-bearing region around Fernie. The name is still in use, applied mainly to towns in the southern Rocky Mountain Trench such as Cranbrook and Kimberley. The Kootenay Gp. runs north through the front ranges and foothills to Brazeau River (the southern boundary of Jasper park). A classic place to study Kootenay rock is on Mt. Allan in Kananaskis Country, where the entire unit is exposed. Other good outcrops occur along the TransCanada Highway between the eastern park gate and the Banff interchange, where the Kootenay Gp. and the Fernie Fm. are exposed together.

Kootenay strata include the **Morrissey Formation** (fine- to medium-grained gray marine sandstone, 20-80 m) at its base; the **Mist Mountain Formation** (25-665 m of interbedded nonmarine gray siltstone, sandstone and coal), and the **Elk Formation** in the upper part (up to 590 m thick and similar to the Mist Mtn. but with little coal). The Elk includes chert-pebble conglomerate. The names come from the Kananaskis area, except for "Morrissey," which is a rail siding south of Fernie.

Except for plant fragments impressed in the coal, large fossils are not common in the Kootenay Gp. Those that exist consist mostly of worm burrows in the Elk Fm. The group has been dated mainly from fossil pollen and spores in the Mist Mtn. Fm.

Significant in the Kootenay are pebbles and grains of chert that could only have come from older chert-bearing rock in the Canadian Rockies, such as the Banff Fm. (page 140). Sands and limestone/dolomite fragments in the group have likewise been traced to older units of the Rockies. Thus, those units had to be eroding from highlands to the west, which shows that the Canadian Rockies were on the rise in the Early Cretaceous.

More important to geologists over the years has been Kootenay *coal.*

Coal is made of plant remains that have not rotted. This occurred because (1) the water they fell into was too acidic to support much bacterial life and (2) they were buried rather quickly under other sediments (in the case of our coal, under influxes of river-borne sand).

Plant fibers are mostly cellulose, which is essentially carbon dioxide (CO_2) and water (H_2O). As time passed, the oxygen was removed by chemical reactions. But much of the carbon remained, gradually concentrating to become coal. The Kootenay Fm. is famous as a coal producer between Canmore and the Crowsnest Pass region, including mines near Banff.

What? Coal-mining in Banff National Park? Yes! Go and see the exhibits at Bankhead, along the road to Lake Minnewanka from the Banff interchange.

Like most of the coal in the Rockies, the deposits at Bankhead were of semi-anthracite, which is about 95 percent carbon. This kind of coal gave off very little smoke, so it was used in huge quantities in World War One for fueling troop-ships, which didn't want to give their positions away over the horizon. After the war a depression in the Canadian coal market resulted in the permanent closing of the mine at Bankhead, along with most other mines in the Rockies region. A few, though, continued to operate until quite recently, including the large underground mine at Canmore (closed in 1979).

Strip mining, which is cheaper, took over in the 1950s and 1960s. Open pits in the Crowsnest area, Hinton area and at Grande Cache are still being deepened today. As recently as 1980 a strip-mining venture backed by the British Columbia government, complete with the brand-new town of Tumbler Ridge, started up in the foothills.

But all these mines are having trouble surviving in the current depressed economy, showing that the term "boom-and-bust" is just as descriptive of this industry now as it was at the turn of the century. Environmentalists decry the damage that strip-mining causes in the Canadian Rockies, where the revegetation process is slow and reclamation is very expensive.

Between the North Saskatchewan and Brazeau rivers the Kootenay Gp. interfingers with the **Nikanassin Formation** (300-600 m), named for the Nikanassin Range just east of Jasper National Park. Nikanassin beds are mostly gray marine siltstone, with a few thin coal seams in the upper part. At Miette Hot Springs in eastern Jasper park there are easily accessible Nikanassin outcrops along the access road to the old pool.

North of Jasper park the Nikanassin grades into the **Minnes Group**, named for Mt. Minnes (northeast of Kakwa Lake). The Minnes Gp. thickens to the north (maximum about 2000 m) and carries on to Sikanni ("sick-KAHN-ee") Chief River, north of which it has been eroded.

Lowest in the Minnes is the **Monteith Formation**, which is mostly fine-grained marine sandstone, with turbidites (material carried in bottom currents, page 83). Both sides of the Rocky Mountain Trough are preserved in the formation, showing that the trough was narrow at this stage.

Above the Monteith lies the **Gorman Creek Formation**, about 1300 m thick in the Kakwa/Smoky River area. This formation is coarse and coaly, a river-bed and delta deposit. North of Pine Pass the Gorman Creek breaks into three smaller units. The mudstone of the **Beattie Peaks Formation** (500 m) indicates deepening; above that, sandstones of the **Monach Formation** (300 m) indicate shallowing, followed by a short period of fluctuating water levels represented in the marine-and-nonmarine **Bickford Formation** (400 m), which is coaly sandstone and shale. Look for the clam *Buchia* in the Beattie Peaks and Monach.

Above that there is an unconformity, marking the end of deposition in this first infilling of the Rocky Mountain Trough.

Cadomin Formation (basal Blairmore Group, start of infilling-episode II)
Early Cretaceous (144-97.5 Ma) 0-200 m, usually 10-20 m

Cadomin is a small community at the mountain front southwest of Hinton. The name comes from "Canadian Dominion Mining," which built the coal-company town in the early part of the century.

The Cadomin Fm. is a tough, erosion-resistant conglomerate. It looks like concrete, with pebbles, cobbles and even head-sized boulders in it.

Found from south of Fernie to just north of Peace River, Cadomin rock often caps ridges in the western foothills of the central Rockies. There are no outcrops along the TransCanada Highway, but the Lusk Creek Road in northern Kananaskis Country takes you through excellent exposures. Punchbowl Falls in Jasper park, not far off Highway 16 along the road to Miette Hot Springs, pours over the Cadomin at a spot where the formation is steeply tilted. Cadomin conglomerate is also prominent around Grande Cache, where you can see it twisting through the folded Mesozoic beds there.

Beyond its ability to make hogback ridges, the Cadomin conglomerate is significant for its pebbles and cobbles, which are derived from the Paleozoic formations of the Canadian Rockies—especially the Gog quartzite (page 88)—which means that the main-range thrust sheets were present and the peaks weren't very far away in Cadomin time, close to the end of the Early Cretaceous.

The Cadomin is strangely thin for a formation covering this much area, a fact that has led geologists to think it may be a **pediment**: a thin veneer of gravel over bedrock that forms at the foot of a mountain range. Rivers create pediments in dry climates, when storms move massive amounts of material in flash floods. Thickest around Peace River, the Cadomin becomes finer and grades northward into the sandstone of the Gething Fm. (next entry).

The rest of the Blairmore Group, the Bullhead and Fort St. John groups, and the Dunvegan Fm. (episode II, cont'd)
Mid-Early Cretaceous to early Late Cretaceous (124-93 Ma) 400-2000 m

The **Blairmore Group** outcrops from southwest of Fernie through the foothills and front ranges north to Highwood River, beyond which it is found in the foothills only. It includes the Cadomin conglomerate at its base (previous entry), then alluvial sand and shale of the **Gladstone Formation** (75 m, named for Mt. Gladstone north of Waterton park), overlain by soft salt-and-pepper sandstone with a greenish cast (**Beaver Mines Formation**, 300 m, named for a small community in the same area), which also contains red and green shales. These are all freshwater deposits.

South of Burnt Timber Creek the Blairmore is topped by the **Mill Creek Formation** (about 100 m thick from Sheep River south), composed of sandstone, red-and-green shale beds and interesting plant fossils.

In and about Crowsnest Pass, lying atop the Mill Creek and occurring nowhere else, you will find one of only two units of volcanic rock known in the Canadian Rockies (the other is the lava flow capping the Siyeh Fm. in Waterton/Glacier, page 75). The **Crowsnest Formation** is about 160 m thick, made up of pinkish fragments of **trachyte**: a kind of lava rich in feldspar and mica.

Trachyte is typical of violent eruptions; it emerges with the consistency of toothpaste, then quickly stiffens and tends to block the vent from which it issued. This causes a buildup of pressure underneath and an explosion—like the one that blew the top off Mt. St. Helens in 1980.

The vent for the Crowsnest volcanics has not been found. It may lie under the Lewis Thrust Sheet (page 27), which overrode the region after the eruption. The Crowsnest Fm. has been dated by its radioactive mineral content to 93 Ma.

Blairmore strata are common in the southern and central foothills. The group is perhaps best viewed along Highway 3 on the eastern approach to Crowsnest Pass. The town of Blairmore itself (now part of the larger municipality of

Cadomin conglomerate at Punchbowl Falls, 1.5 km up the road to Miette Hot Springs in Jasper National Park. The Cadomin Formation is resistant to erosion, producing the falls.
Photo courtesy Jasper National Park.

The Blairmore Group (here called Luscar Formation) at a large open-pit coal mine along Alberta 40 south of Hinton. Two coal seams are visible in the wall of the excavation, which shows a small fault at the left side (as well as the larger fold), and a third seam lies exposed farther left.

Crowsnest Pass) sits mostly on Fernie shale, but some outcrops show the pale greenish color of Blairmore strata. This is from the mineral chlorite, originating as volcanic material, that cements the sand grains.

There is a limy zone in the Gladstone Fm. with abundant freshwater snails, clams and little nut-like **ostracods:** freshwater crustaceans still plentiful today.

The Blairmore Gp. contains more and more coal as you follow it north through the foothills. Beyond the North Saskatchewan River it is so coal-rich that it acquires a different name: **Luscar Group** (maximum thickness about 1000 m). North of Grande Cache the Blairmore/Luscar thins considerably as the overlying units thicken; it is known here as the **Bullhead Group** (210 m).

Within the Blairmore/Luscar, the Gladstone continues to Grande Cache, where it becomes coal-bearing and is known as the **Gething Formation** (100-550 m); the Beaver Mines merges northward with the **Gates Formation** (400 m). The Gladstone/Gething and Gates are separated by a shale: the **Moosebar Formation** (100 m), which appears south of the main Bullhead region at Burnt Timber Creek.

Both the Gething and the Gates have been mined for coal; the Gates at Nordegg, Cadomin, Luscar (where the formation is exposed in a large pit along the road between Hinton and Cadomin) and at Pocahontas in eastern Jasper park. A convenient place to see a bit of the Gething Fm. is near Pocahontas, at Punchbowl Falls on the way to Miette Hot Springs. There are thin seams of coal in basal Gething beds at the lower viewpoint. Both the Gething and the Gates are currently mined at Grande Cache. Farther north, in northeastern British Columbia, the Gething is mined at Tumbler Ridge and from there to Peace River. Beyond Peace River the coal peters out (there are only thin seams at Sikanni Chief River) and the strata go to marine sandstone and shale of the **Fort St. John Group** (1000-1500 m).

"Gething" and "Bullhead" are from mountains that overlook the Bennett dam on Peace River. "Fort St. John" is from the British Columbia town to the east.

Stratigraphic relations among the Blairmore, Bullhead and Fort St. John groups are complicated, beyond the scope of this book. For a summary consult Stott, 1984. But their geological significance is fairly straightforward. These rocks document another invasion of the Rocky Mountain Trough by the sea. It moved in from the north, in several phases of deepening and shallowing. The shaly Fort St. John Gp. represents the deepest water, which is logical because it is the most northerly. In it are found the molluscs *Gastroplites* and *Posidonia.* Bullhead beds are mostly those of swampy, heavily vegetated deltas built out into the sea from the west. The strata carry plant fossils. Meanwhile the Blairmore Gp. accumulated above sea level, on land that was west of the sea's southward advance. To the east, though, on the Interior Plains, the sea reached south into Montana.

Withdrawal came early in the Late Cretaceous (at about 93 Ma), when the Rocky Mountain Trough rose slightly. At the same time, sea level dropped worldwide. As the inland sea shallowed, a vast delta/alluvial plain built eastward along the front of the northern Rockies. This is the **Dunvegan Formation,** up to 120 m of cliff-forming sandstone and conglomerate, which can be seen capping the foothills around Chetwynd and Hudson's Hope. Dunvegan rock lies atop the escarpment at the western edge of the Interior Plains farther north, where you see it from the Alaska Highway. Fossils include the ubiquitous clam *Inoceramus.*

The Dunvegan delta divided the seaway as the arms pulled back to north and south. Deposition could not keep up with erosion in much of our area, so there is an unconformity atop the Blairmore Gp. and the Dunvegan Fm. That unconformity marks the top of the second great packet of sediments in the Rocky Mountain Trough and thus points out the end of infilling-episode II.

Alberta Group (start of episode III)
Late Cretaceous (93-80 Ma) Up to 750 m

The **Alberta Group** includes two thick units of dark, soft marine shale (**Blackstone Formation** below, 250-500 m, and **Wapiabi Formation** above, 300-500 m) with a marine sandstone bed (the **Cardium Formation**, 10-75 m) sandwiched between. These units range from south of the Waterton/Glacier are to about Athabasca River, where rock similar to the Alberta Gp. continues north as the **Smoky Group**. The name changes because the Dunvegan sandstone (previous entry) replaces the lower part of the Blackstone. The Smoky Gp. is found mainly in the foothills, as is the Alberta Gp., but Alberta Gp. beds also appear in the front ranges south of Bow River and in the Mesozoic exposures southwest of Fernie.

Recessive and usually covered, Alberta/Smoky rock is best seen in the bedrock gorges along foothills streams. Two good places to look at the Alberta Gp. are at the front of the Kananaskis Dam along the Bow River west of Cochrane (accessible along Alberta 1A) and below Bighorn Dam, near the mountain front west of Rocky Mountain House (access via Alberta 11). These sites expose the interesting, lumpily-bedded Cardium sandstone.

Blackstone beds outcrop where the TransCanada highway crosses Jumping Pound Creek west of Calgary, and also at the Oldman River bridge along Alberta 22 north of the Crowsnest area. Look for black Wapiabi strata beside the TransCanada Highway where it crosses Kananaskis River, just east of the Highway 1X turnoff near the mountain front. There is a sizable quarry in Wapiabi rock beside 1X, and a sandstone bed in the Wapiabi (the **Chungo Member**) is being quarried nearby, at the foot of Yamnuska Mountain (quarry accessible by taking 1X to 1A and turning north off 1A about one kilometre east).

The Alberta Gp. is marine—not quite the last marine rock in our area (that's the Bearpaw shale), but the last major unit. The Blackstone Fm. holds fossils of lovely Upper Cretaceous mother-of-pearl ammonites that swam the sea where prairie wheat grows now. The Cardium sandstone resulted from a shallowing phase (a complete withdrawal for about 4 Ma north of Peace River); the unit is oil-bearing west of Edmonton, having sopped up from the surrounding shale the hydrocarbons of countless planktonic organisms. Atop the Cardium, the Wapiabi shale records a re-advance in which the shoreline moved westward, followed by yet another retreat a few million years later.

Fossils in this group include *Inoceramus* and *Watinoceras* in the Blackstone, tracks and trails in the Cardium, *Scaphites* and *Inoceramus* in the Wapiabi.

Brazeau and Paskapoo formations and equivalents (infilling-episode III, continued)
Late Cretaceous to Paleocene (80-60 Ma) Up to 4000 m

The **Brazeau Formation** (1600 m) is a central-Rockies unit of nonmarine sandstone and river-carried shale, the sandstone beds full of dark and light grains that give them a salt-and-pepper look like that of the Blairmore Gp. Also like the Blairmore, the Brazeau has a greenish cast from volcanic dust and rock particles in it. North of Grande Cache the unit is called the **Wapiti Formation**, which is similar in thickness and rock type.

There are roadcuts through tilted Brazeau strata along Highway 16 from Obed Summit to west of Hinton, and an excellent natural Brazeau outcrop occurs at the turnoff to the Jasper-Hinton Airport. Fossils in all these units are mainly those of plants.

Swampy conditions near the end of Brazeau time were right for coal formation. Seams of the **Coalspur Formation** are the youngest commercial deposits in the Canadian Rockies; the soft-coal seams were extensively mined in the foothills east of Hinton in the first half of this century. Strip-mining of the Coalspur Fm. continues at Sterco (along Alberta 40 near the Pembina River) and at a new mine opening closer to Hinton.

Greenish Brazeau sandstone and shale in a road cut along Highway 16 west of Hinton.

Typical weathered outcrop of Paskapoo sandstone along the TransCanada Highway west of Calgary. Such outcrops are often encrusted with brilliantly colored lichens.

Late Cretaceous and Early Tertiary

South of Bow River, Brazeau-equivalent sediments are more complicated. The nonmarine **Belly River** (600 m) and **St. Mary River** (250 m) formations resemble the Brazeau, but they are split by the marine **Bearpaw Formation** shale (180-490 m), left from the last advance of the sea into our area. You can see the Bearpaw shale in the eastern foothills southwest of Calgary; it holds the ammonite *Placenticeras*.

Above the St. Mary River comes the soft **Willow Creek Formation**, 1200 m of buffy, pink or greenish sandstone and shale. The Willow Creek is the western equivalent of the upper Edmonton Gp., which is famous for dinosaur fossils in the Drumheller area of south-central Alberta. The big reptiles did very well in the thickly vegetated swamps fringing the last of the Cretaceous sea, but for some reason the finds are few in the Rockies foothills. Perhaps the area was too close to the mountains (both the main ranges and front ranges were up by this time). Still, you can see the same sort of pastel-hued beds that hold the big bones farther east if you travel Highway 22 north of Crowsnest Pass, where the road runs along the west side of the Porcupine Hills.

The end of the Cretaceous Period at 66.4 Ma has long been known for the sudden disappearance of the dinosaurs. However, the *cause* wasn't identified until recently, when the discovery of a worldwide iridium-rich zone at the Cretaceous/Paleocene boundary led geologists to speculate about a catastrophe: the impact of an asteroid-sized object with the earth, producing a pall of dust that blocked the sun's warmth for many years. Confirming evidence is accumulating rapidly.

I should add that in western Canada the dinosaurs were already losing ground when the extinction event occurred. Climatic change and other factors had reduced Alberta dinosaur populations considerably in the Late Cretaceous; the astrophysical disaster seems to have been the capper.

Discovery of the Cretaceous/Tertiary event has prompted the search for iridium layers at other mass-extinction points in geological history. Eight major extinctions are known: late in the Proterozoic (650 Ma), at the end of the Ordovician (438 Ma), in the Late Devonian (367 Ma), in the Late Permian (253 Ma), at the end of the Triassic (208 Ma), Jurassic (144 Ma) and Cretaceous (66.4 Ma), and early in the Pliocene (4 Ma). In our area the Late Devonian extinction of reef-building stromatoporoids is perhaps the most striking (see page 131). All these mass-extinctions are noted on the geologic charts that begin on page 42.

Topping the stack in the Rocky Mountain Trough is the Paleocene **Paskapoo Formation** and its southern equivalent the **Porcupine Hills Formation**: up to 1500 m of buffy sandstone and gray shale. The shale is rich in plant fragments and contains many freshwater snails. A good place to see this unit is in the Porcupine Hills (north of Crowsnest Pass), in the Calgary area and along Highway 16 west of Edson. From Hinton north, the Paskapoo is out on the Interior Plains, lying east of the road to Grande Cache (Alberta 40). So there is no Paleocene rock in the northern Rockies.

Is this the top of the whole collection of layers in the Canadian Rockies? Not quite.

There are some formations on the western slope, in and around the Rocky Mountain Trench, that are younger than the youngest material in the Rocky Mountain Trough (again, keep in mind that the *trench* and the *trough* are two different things). Most of these trench deposits came after the mountain-building period in western Canada, and they exist because of events late in the disturbance. So they are best described *after* going into the mechanics of the upheaval.

OROGENOUS ZONES
Columbian and Laramide Orogenies: Middle Jurassic to Middle Eocene (170-45 Ma)

Preface: the earth's mountain ranges have been built by nuclear energy. I know how strange that sounds, but it is true. The slow decay of radioactive elements throughout our planet releases heat, which is why the temperature climbs as the miners descend. At depths of 100 km the crust is so hot that rock will melt.

Consider what is going on in the **mantle,** that nuclear furnace under the crust. Hot rock is less dense than cold rock, so it rises toward the surface. Along the way it cools, in so doing becoming denser and thus sinking again. A stovetop analogy is a pot of boiling water.

This circulation produces slow but enormously powerful currents in the mantle. These currents are the driving forces of **plate tectonics,** the scholarly name for continental drift.

Considered revolutionary twenty years ago, plate tectonics is now a well-established branch of geological science, supported by a vast body of research. Here is a short review of the plate-tectonics principles essential to understanding the rest of this chapter.

Plate tectonics: a crash course

The crust flooring the ocean basins is only about 10 km thick. It is created continuously, mainly by hot upwellings from the mantle at the mid-oceanic ridges. From these ridges new oceanic crust spreads sideways, toward the continents.

Not only is oceanic crust steadily created; it is also steadily destroyed. Currents in the mantle suck it down under the continents, where it remelts—a process called **subduction.**

The continents are thicker (30-50 km) than the oceanic plates. Continental crust is mostly granite and high-grade metamorphic rock with a layer of sediments on the surface. These rock types are less dense than oceanic crust; they are too light to be pulled down by descending currents, so the continental plates drift around, tugged here and there by the restless mantle underneath.

While oceanic crust may exist for perhaps 100-200 Ma between its creation at a mid-oceanic ridge and its demise by subduction, continental crust is practically indestructible. If a spot is melted, which often happens when a continent drifts over a hot spot in the mantle, the hot blob simply rises and recrystallizes as another patch of granite in the plate. The **Canadian Shield**—the large region of granite and metamorphic rock exposed over much of eastern Canada—is a naked patch of the North American Plate. The time-worn surface of the shield dips westward under the prairies and provides the Canadian Rockies with a floor about 1.7 billion years old.

This isn't to say that the continental plates aren't changed in their long, slow journeys about the globe. Occasionally they get pulled apart by diverging mantle currents, a process called **rifting** (see illustration 2 on page 45). For example, the Americas and Europe/Africa rifted some 175 million years ago in the middle of the Jurassic Period. Not only did this open the basin of the Atlantic Ocean, it indirectly created the Rocky Mountains.

Before rifting, the motion of North America had been relatively eastward ("relatively" because the turning of the continent has changed its orientation with respect to the poles). This left western Canada on the trailing edge of the plate, a geologically stable place for sediment to accumulate. It accumulated, all right: the sedimentary pile here is up to 20 km thick and goes back 1.5 billion years.

But with rifting came a major change in the direction of continental drift. North America now began to move relatively *westward*. Our area was now near the *leading* edge of the continent—a geologically active place, for it is along such leading edges that nearly all the world's mountain ranges have formed—including the **Canadian Cordillera,** the formal name for the mountains of western Canada. (See page 11 for a note on pronunciation of "cordillera.")

FUNDAMENTALS OF PLATE TECTONICS

Oceanic crust pulls apart along the mid-oceanic ridges, marked by active undersea volcanoes (sometimes reaching above sea level, e.g. Iceland). New crust is created here from upwelling mantle. Oceanic plates are dense and thin, thus they ride low in the mantle and are covered by the sea to form the ocean basins.

Continental crust (e.g. the Canadian Shield) is much older than oceanic crust; is seldom destroyed by subduction. Continental plates drift about on the mantle, riding high because they are thicker and less dense than oceanic plates.

Terranes being peeled from oceanic crust and accreting to the western edge of the North American Plate. This is the main force that built the Rockies.

Hot spots of upwelling mantle rock form volcanic islands (e.g. Hawaii) and can penetrate continental crust to produce inland volcanoes (e.g. Yellowstone).

Heat of radioactive decay produces currents in the mantle

Collision between continental plates (e.g. India and Asia) produces folded mountains such as the Himalayas.

Subduction zone where oceanic crust slips under the edge of a continent. Ocean plates remelt here to become part of the mantle again.

Deep subduction causes melting of continental crust, which creates Andean-style mountains.

Some of the world's mountain ranges have developed where continents collide, crumpling the edges. The Himalayas are an example of this. And mountain chains can be raised by subduction alone, because the down-going slab of oceanic crust melts and sends hot rock upward, melting the overlying continental crust and producing granitic and volcanic ranges. The Andes are classic examples of mountains raised by subduction. But how can ranges such as the Rockies, lying 1000 km east of the place where oceanic crust is going under the edge of the continent, be formed?

The answer lies in the chains of islands that ride the oceanic crust.

Most of these islands have volcanic roots, with sedimentary accumulations spread about the sea floor surrounding them. As oceanic crust slides beneath a continent, these **island arcs** collide with the continental plate and stick themselves onto it.

A case in point is the western edge of North America. Canada and the United States have *grown wider* by the addition of island arcs and other foreign material. The impact of these crustal slivers has wrinkled up mountains from the old edge of the continent right across the added-on material.

Among that added-on material is most of the province of British Columbia, a fact established by Ray Price and Jim Monger of the Geological Survey of Canada and other plate-tectonics specialists (for a recent summary that is only moderately technical see Monger, 1984). Their findings have revolutionized the geology of the Canadian Cordillera, which is becoming known as a textbook example of the **accretion** (adding-on) of **terranes**: the technical term for parts of a landmass that have come from somewhere else. "Terrane" is pronounced like "terrain" but spelled differently.

Foreigners

There are some 50 terranes that make up the western part of the Canadian Cordillera, much of Alaska and most of the American states bordering the Pacific. Where did these terranes come from?

Possibly from very far away, for fossils in one of the terranes are like those seen in Japan, while others are of tropical species. By looking at magnetic minerals, which orient themselves with the dip of the compass needle during deposition, it has been demonstrated that many of the terranes have moved 3000-5000 km northward. Where they started from is unknown, a problem under intensive study by geologists.[*]

Another interesting aspect: examining the connections between the terranes shows that they were bumping into one another and joining together *as the continent approached*. They seem to have formed two long, skinny super-terranes—named **Intermontane Terrane** and **Insular Terrane**—that were then struck by the west coast one after the other. Some of the material in these terranes is sediment from the continent, dumped along the coast by rivers, then caught in the squeeze and pushed back up on land.

Running into the dock

The story of mountain-building in western Canada opens as the North American Plate begins to move relatively west, gobbling up oceanic crust that was moving relatively north. So the *apparent* direction of closure was oblique, along a northwest-southeast line. A time-lapse film would have shown large islands (or shoals, if the terranes didn't quite stick up above the waves) approaching the Pacific coast from the southwest, from the point of view of a camera riding on

---

[*]Perhaps you know that the north end of a compass needle dips downward as well as pointing at the magnetic pole. That dip is least at the equator and greatest near the poles, so the dip of magnetic minerals in rock gives a rough indication of the latitude during time of formation.

the continental plate. The islands moved in rather quickly, geologically speaking; a recent estimate is five centimetres per year.

(One dinosaur to another: "Walter, that island over there—I could swear it's closer today!")

Docking happened next. This is a mild term for a savage event. Intermontane Terrane hit the continent edge to edge, for its rock was too light—too buoyant—to slide down under the continental edge along with the denser ocean crust. Thus, the super-terrane crumpled as plate motion kept up the squeeze. When it had crumpled as much as it could, Intermontane Terrane moved up and over the continental edge as an enormous sheet thousands of square kilometres in size and perhaps 25 km thick. This is a process known as **obduction**; it is the opposite of *sub*-duction, where rock goes down under a continent.

During obduction the continent acted as a wedge, literally peeling Intermontane Terrane from the underlying oceanic plate. Creeping inland for many kilometres, the terrane's leading edge shoved the sedimentary cover of the continental plate eastward, creating ranges of folded mountains ahead of the zone of overlap. The terrane also did some peeling of its own, wedging between sedimentary layers on the continent.

Eventually no more of the terrane could be obducted onto the continent; the friction of movement was too great. The rest of the terrane broke loose from the underlying oceanic crust, which now began to slip beneath the terrane just as it had slipped beneath the continental plate during normal subduction. Intermontane Terrane had become a part of North America, adding a broad band of land onto the western edge of the continent.

By this time the added overburden of the terrane had pushed the old continental edge—the zone of overlap—down into the mantle, to depths at which rock becomes pasty and viscous. In some spots the depth of burial was so great that the crust melted. Some of this heated rock worked its way up to the surface, causing volcanic eruptions. Most of it, though, recrystallized underground as gneiss (page 79) and granite, forming a weld between Intermontane Terrane and the old continental edge.

Meanwhile the continent, now with Intermontane Terrane attached, was slowly closing with Insular Terrane. At contact the story was repeated, except that this time the west coast of Intermontane Terrane took the impact as Insular Terrane accreted to North America.

Making mountains: the Columbian and Laramide orogenies

Sheared off at the basement, each colliding super-terrane was still being dragged forward by the rock moving beneath it. So it continued to press hard against the continent. This enormous, steady compression produced mountain ranges made of accordioned rock, both in the terranes and along the continental margin.

The one-word description for this is **orogeny** ("oh-RAH-jen-ee"): the creation of mountains by horizontal compression.

Orogenies need not involve enough heat and pressure to create metamorphic rocks, regions of granite and volcanoes, but they often do. When rock melts and then cools, the minerals in it recrystallize. This resets the atomic clock—the steady change from one element to another by radioactive decay—and thus it is possible to tell how long ago an orogeny occurred.

Intermontane Terrane docked with the continent about 175 million years ago, in the middle of the Jurassic Period. That event kicked off the **Columbian Orogeny,** which is named for one of its products, the Columbia Mountains.* The Columbia Mountains are one of the ranges immediately west of the Rockies. The Columbian Orogeny also built the others: the **Ominecas** and the **Cassiars.**

---

*"Columbia Mountains" is a newer term for what some readers will recognize as the "Interior Ranges" of British Columbia, including the Purcells, Selkirks, Monashees and Cariboos.

THE MAKING OF CANADA'S WESTERN MOUNTAIN RANGES

(Maps and schematic cross-sections made in consultation with J. Monger, E. Mountjoy and R. Price)

1.
Before the arrival of Intermontane Terrane

(Early Jurassic, about 200 Ma)

North America begins to move westward.

Islands of Intermontane Terrane (true sizes and shapes unknown) are approaching.

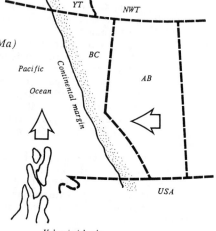

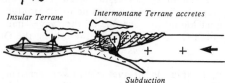

2.
Intermontane Terrane accretes to North America

(Middle Jurassic, 175 Ma)

Intermontane Terrane smears onto the old continental edge, which crumples to form the Columbia, Omineca and Cassiar mountains during Columbian Orogeny. Western parts of the Rockies are created near the end of this phase. The continent has been extended westward.

Insular Terrane closes with the new continental edge.

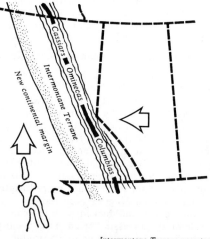

3.
Insular Terrane accretes
(Late Cretaceous, 85 Ma)

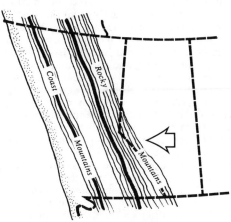

*Docking of Insular Terrane
causes renewed
mountain-building (the
Laramide Orogeny), which
creates the Coast Mountains.
Front ranges and foothills of
the Rockies form.*

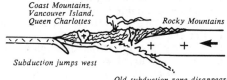

4.
**Compression phase ends,
but sideways motion
and stretching continue**
*(Early Tertiary, 66 Ma,
to the present)*

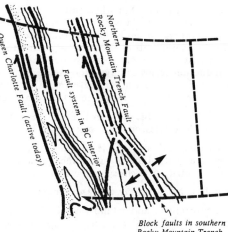

*Strike-slip faults move the
terranes (and a strip of the
continental plate)
northwestward.*

*Crustal stretching across
southern British Columbia
causes normal faulting along
the southern Rocky Mountain
Trench, Flathead and Elk
valleys. Streams fill the
down-dropped trenches with
debris eroded from
surrounding mountains.*

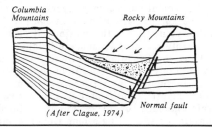

(After Clague, 1974)

But the Rockies were not created immediately after this first collision. The Rockies area lay perhaps a hundred kilometres to the east, safely out of range on the continental shelf. The rock layers were still intact.

However, the tectonic activity to the west did register in our region, in the form of an influx of sand eroded from the land rising in that direction. This sand appears in the mid-Jurassic Fernie Fm. as the Passage Beds (see page 160).

Compression continued into the Early Cretaceous. The mountains of British Columbia kept growing and spreading eastward, shedding sediment into our area. Formations overlying the Fernie contain coarser sediment, showing that it was being carried a shorter distance as time went by. They also contain a significant amount of volcanic dust borne eastward by the wind into the Rockies region, attesting to the violent events happening not far away.

By 120 Ma the disturbance had reached our area, as the western ranges of the central Rockies began to pile up, then the main ranges.

Insular Terrane docked with North America at about 85 Ma, producing another strong orogenic pulse: the **Laramide Orogeny.** Vancouver Island and the Queen Charlottes are part of this second super-terrane, much of which is under water and forms the modern western continental shelf. The granitic Coast Mountains mark the approximate suture line between Intermontane Terrane and Insular Terrane, although the Coast Mountains may have been part of Insular Terrane before it contacted Intermontane Terrane.

During the Laramide Orogeny the pressure of Insular Terrane thrust the sedimentary skin of the continent farther inland, creating the front ranges and foothills of the Canadian Rockies. Farther south it created the American Rockies.

That calls to mind the same question asked earlier: how could this second collision, which occurred well west of the Rockies, bulldoze up the mountains in our area? After all, they formed *after* the continental margin had been widened by the addition of Intermontane Terrane.

We are at the frontier of knowledge on this, so the answer is not certain, but it seems most likely that when Intermontane Terrane and Insular Terrane joined, the pressure on the old continental margin—which was close to the Rockies—increased. Both those terranes were being held tightly against the continent by the pull of the oceanic crust slipping beneath them; more terrane to pull against meant more force applied to the continental edge. Further, the speed of subduction seems to have increased during the Laramide Orogeny from about 5 cm per year to 15 cm per year—in plate tectonics, a gallop.

As a result, two things seem to have happened:

1. The eastern edge of Intermontane Terrane was forced farther inland—far enough to telescope the rock of the Rockies.

2. The original edge of the continental plate, now pushed down into the mantle by the overlap of Intermontane Terrane, grew softer. It buckled and contracted, wrinkling up the sedimentary skin covering it.

Not uplift, but up-*piling* and an accompanying down-sag

It is important to understand that the Rockies grew taller from a buildup of folded and overthrust rock, not by uplift from below (which had a lot to do with the creation of the American Rockies; see page 12). Geologists estimate that the once-horizontal sedimentary layers in the central Canadian Rockies telescoped at least 200 km; perhaps as much as 300 km. That rock had to go somewhere, and it couldn't go down, for the continental plate underlay the sediments. So it stacked up, possibly reaching Himalayan heights.

Thus, the Canadian Cordillera stands tall not through uplift but through up-piling. In fact, the opposite of uplift occurred: the growing pile of heavy rock pushed the underlying western margin of the continental plate about 20 km down into the mantle. Continental crust is not very flexible, and the bend in the western margin extended for several hundred kilometres beyond the eastern edge of the mountain mass, creating a long trough along the mountain front called a **foredeep**

Up-piling built the Canadian Rockies, not uplift

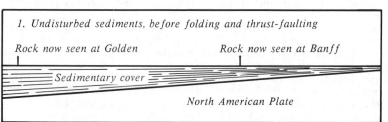

1. Undisturbed sediments, before folding and thrust-faulting

Rock now seen at Golden   Rock now seen at Banff

Sedimentary cover

North American Plate

West   East

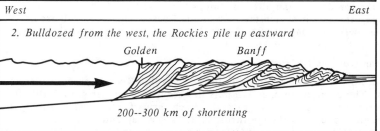

2. Bulldozed from the west, the Rockies pile up eastward

Golden   Banff

200--300 km of shortening

How Rockies thrust sheets propagated eastward

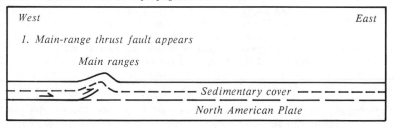

West   East

1. Main-range thrust fault appears

Main ranges

Sedimentary cover

North American Plate

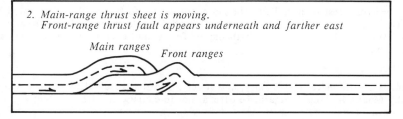

2. Main-range thrust sheet is moving.
Front-range thrust fault appears underneath and farther east

Main ranges   Front ranges

3. Both main-range and front-range thrust sheets are moving.
Foothills thrust fault appears underneath and farther east

Main ranges   Front ranges

Foothills

(literally, a deep place in front of a mountain range). Foredeeps are common beside growing mountain chains; they subside gradually, filling with sediments as they deepen. As the mountains advance inland, the foredeep moves along in front of them (it **migrates**).

Western Alberta and northeastern British Columbia form one segment of a migrating foredeep east of the Canadian Cordillera. Long known to geologists as a region of thick sedimentary deposits, this feature is named the **Rocky Mountain Trough,** as introduced previously (page 153).

Because the Columbian and Laramide orogenies were responsible for the creation and infilling of the Rocky Mountain Trough, the Cretaceous and Tertiary conglomerate, sandstone and shale in the foredeep document the rise of the Rockies. Long before this was known, geologists looking for coal, natural gas and oil in the foredeep found all these things there—and in abundance.

Next: the way in which the rock of the Rockies moved. If you are not familiar with the concept of thrust-faulting, you may want to review page 17 before continuing.

Stacking from west to east

The record is clear: thrust faulting in the Canadian Rockies proceeded from west to east. The diagram on page 175 puts this sequence together graphically. It shows a concept that is difficult to grasp: that each thrust formed *under and ahead of* the previous one, even though thrust-faulting is an up-and-over action.

Since deformation proceeded from west to east, and because the thrust faults of the Rockies were known to flatten out westward as they were traced deeper, geologists theorized that the faults of the front ranges had formed *under* the main ranges. Likewise, it seemed impossible to escape the conclusion that the faults of the foothills had developed under the front ranges. Fieldwork and drilling have shown this idea to be true. The thing to keep in mind is that as the thrusted zone expanded to the east, *the whole works kept moving.* This maintained the up-and-over motion as new thrusts originated below and east of old ones.

Amazingly, you can model this process in the nearest sandbox. Smooth out a patch of damp sand about a metre square. Now step firmly into it, with a forward motion of your foot. The sand will form rings ahead of your footprint. These rings are actually thrust faults. Cutting a cross-section in the sand will show the same upward-curved fault planes you find in Rockies thrusts. The heavier you step, the more faults you get—and they spread from the toe of your foot outward, just as the thrust faults of the Rockies spread outward from the zone of the crunch—from west to east. Thus, the main ranges should be the oldest, followed by the front ranges and finally the foothills. The sedimentary record in the Rocky Mountain Trough agrees with this theory perfectly, and even provides the timing of the events.

Big slips

There is a little more to this story, and it relates to that fascinating feature, the **Rocky Mountain Trench.** Again, be careful not to confuse it with the Rocky Mountain Trough.

Because Intermontane and Insular terrane were drifting northward when west-moving North America ran them down, the convergence was oblique and the effect was to smear the terranes northwestward along the edge of the continent. For this reason, the super-terranes are stretched-out, long and narrow, probably quite distorted in comparison with their shapes and orientations before docking.

After docking, when the terranes had come loose from the underlying oceanic crust, they continued to be dragged from beneath by that crust. Thin and easily fractured, the terranes split lengthwise and were tugged northward in strips. Those lengthwise breaks are **strike-slip faults,** similar to the San Andreas Fault in California.

Two slabs of crust move horizontally along such a fault, sliding past each other. The plates move smoothly at depth, where the rock deforms plastically, but nearer the surface, where the rock is cool and brittle, the motion is jerky—causing the earthquakes for which the San Andreas and other strike-slip faults are famous.

There are many long southeast/northwest strike-slip faults in British Columbia, and one of them follows the Northern Rocky Mountain Trench. West of the **Northern Rocky Mountain Trench Fault,** British Columbia has moved northwestward a distance of about 400 km relative to the rest of the continent.

Given the maximum 50-million-year period of motion (Late Cretaceous to Eocene), the annual slippage along the Northern Rocky Mountain Trench Fault must have been nearly a centimetre per year on the average. This would have produced strong and frequent earthquakes. One imagines the little fox-like horses that lived in western Canada getting knocked off their feet from time to time. The big slips of the Canadian Cordillera still move today, as evidenced by earthquakes in western British Columbia and Alaska.

A final note on these faults. It is important to realize that the Northern Rocky Mountain Trench Fault *does not* follow the suture between Intermontane Terrane and the North American Plate. The terrane boundary lies 50-100 km west of the fault. Slivers of the continental margin have been dislocated far to the north along the west side of the northern Rocky Mountain Trench. That rock might otherwise be part of the central Canadian Rockies; instead, it is found 400 km north in the Cassiars.

Block-faulting in the southern Rocky Mountain Trench

The northern section of the Rocky Mountain Trench runs straight as a die from the Yukon boundary to the south end of Williston Lake, where it begins to lose its clean lines. Just south of there, in the Prince George area, there is no trench. Reason: the main fault breaks up here into a number of smaller faults that angle southwesterly in a wide zone of weakness.

But southwest of Prince George the southern portion of the trench begins. In this section it is in most places a **graben** ("GRAH-ben"): a strip of rock that has dropped down relative to the rock on either side. Along the eastern wall of the trench there is a major **normal fault:** a type in which one slab moves up or down relative to the other. Layers seen low in the trench around McBride match up with the edges of layers exposed a thousand metres higher on the northeastern wall. "Trench" is an appropriate name for the valley here; the Rockies overlook a natural ditch in the crust.

Things aren't so clear-cut on the western wall of the trench. If there is no normal fault there, then the proper term for the trench is **half-graben,** indicating that the slab has dropped downward on one side only. See the diagram on page 173.

This kind of faulting is called **block faulting.** It is caused by *crustal stretching,* the opposite of the compression that built the Rockies. After the compression phase (the Columbian and Laramide orogenies) came the strike-slip phase introduced above; depending on how the terranes and the continent fitted together, and whether plate-motion changed, the stretching could have occurred along with the horizontal slippage, or it may have occurred afterward. Either way, normal faults had opened across much of the southern cordillera by about 35 Ma in the Late Eocene.

The Rocky Mountain Trench from Prince George south seems to reflect only block-faulting, not strike-slipping. The rocks on either side match fairly well, indicating little or no sideways motion along this segment.

Between Wood River (opposite the place where the Columbia River exits Kinbasket Lake) and Skookumchuck (a hamlet between Canal Flats and Wasa) the trench cuts across thrust sheets, as if there were no normal fault controlling its location. Erosion by rivers and glaciers in the soft, shaly rock here gives the trench its topographic expression.

South of Skookumchuck the trench is definitely a half-graben. The eastern side has dropped down at least 2100 m along a major fault forming the western wall of the Rockies. Near the international boundary the trench breaks into several half-graben valleys and loses its linear character.

Coarse Tertiary sediments eroded from the surrounding mountains (the Kishenehn and St. Eugene formations) filled these half-grabens as they formed, which is why there are no gigantic holes along the southern section of the trench. There are also Tertiary sediments in the northern Rocky Mountain Trench (the Sifton Fm.) suggesting that some block faulting occurred here, too—although this section shows predominantly strike slippage.

To the east, within the Rockies, the trench-like Flathead Valley is a half-graben 6 km deep (!) bordered by the **Flathead Fault.** This major fault forms the western edge of Glacier National Park, Montana and continues north into Canada, across Highway 3 and up the Elk River valley to about the confluence with Forsyth Creek. Followed westward by seismic exploration, the Flathead Fault flattens at depth and merges with the Lewis Thrust.

Interestingly, the mountains forming the eastern wall of the Rocky Mountain Trench at its southern end (the Galton Range) seem to have been *uplifted* at least 600 m in the past five million years, well after the compression of the Laramide Orogeny ended. The entry on the St. Eugene Fm. (page 187) describes how this conclusion was reached. Uplift along block faults in this part of the Canadian Rockies is not surprising, for Late Tertiary uplift is common not far to the south in the American Rockies. Minor block faulting has continued in the southern Rocky Mountain Trench until the geological present, as shown by faulted gravels in the southern trench less than 11,000 years old (John Clague, GSC Vancouver, personal communication).

Summing up the sequence

To recap: the whole of the Canadian Cordillera, from the Rockies to the Pacific, was created by compression over a period of about 125 million years, from about 170 Ma until about 45 Ma, followed by crustal stretching and some minor uplift that may still be occurring. The main features developed in five steps:

1. After a long period of drifting relatively eastward, North America begins to move westward, splitting off (rifting) from Europe and Africa. The Atlantic Ocean begins to open. Intermontane Terrane and Insular Terrane are lying offshore. Each is a super-terrane, an amalgamation of smaller terranes (mostly volcanic islands) that are foreign to North America, having been carried as much as 3000-5000 km north on moving oceanic crust.

2. In the Early and Middle Jurassic (175-165 Ma), soon after westward drift begins, Intermontane Terrane is run down by the continent. The super-terrane smears on, elongating as it crumples. This is the Columbian Orogeny; enormous compression wrinkles up the continental margin to produce the Columbia, Omineca and Cassiar mountains. High-grade metamorphic rock and granite forms along the suture between the terrane and the continent. Compression continues, creating the western ranges of the Rockies at about 120 Ma; the main ranges are up by 100 Ma. Thrust sheets in the Rockies stack from west to east, and sediments are shed into a foredeep called the Rocky Mountain Trough.

3. Insular Terrane is run down in the Early Cretaceous, starting about 85 Ma. This is the Laramide Orogeny. Increased pressure on the continental margin creates the front ranges and foothills of the Rockies by about 60 Ma.

4. The Laramide Orogeny begins to taper off in the Paleocene (about 60 Ma) and by 45 Ma strike-slip faulting, which has been occurring since at least the Late Cretaceous, becomes dominant. Strips of the Canadian Cordillera west of the Rockies move northwestward along major faults such as the one underlying the Northern Rocky Mountain Trench, which offsets the western edge of the old

continental margin by about 400 km. Motion along the more westerly of these faults continues to the present.

5. Either at the same time or beginning somewhat later, crustal stretching occurs across southern British Columbia. Normal faults form the southern Rocky Mountain Trench, Flathead Valley and Elk Valley. These half-grabens fill with material eroded from the surrounding ranges. Late in the Tertiary Period at least 600 m of uplift occurs on the Canadian-Rockies side of the fault forming the eastern wall of the Rocky Mountain Trench at its southern end. Minor normal faulting continues to the present in this area.

Timing of events in building the Canadian Rockies

175 Ma (Mid-Jurassic): Intermontane Terrane docks. Columbian Orogeny begins.

175-120 Ma (Mid-Jurassic to Early Cretaceous): Columbia, Omineca and Cassiar mountains form west of Rockies.

120 Ma (Early Cretaceous): main ranges are above sea level; thrust sheets of the western ranges of the central Rockies are moving.

85 Ma (Late Cretaceous): Insular Terrane docks. Laramide Orogeny begins. Front ranges begin to form.

60 Ma (Late Paleocene): thrusting has reached the foothills belt.

45 Ma (Mid-Eocene): compression phase ends. Crustal stretching begins, with normal faulting across southern British Columbia. Southern Rocky Mountain Trench, Flathead Valley and Elk Valley form as half-grabens. Strike-slip faulting (with some normal faulting) produces northern Rocky Mountain Trench. Rock that would otherwise be in the Rockies is carried northwestward 400 km on far side. Volcanic activity continues west of the Rockies.

5 Ma and later (post-Miocene): uplift occurs at the southern end of the Rocky Mountain Trench. Minor normal faulting occurs there until the present.

". . . for utterly impossible as are all these events
they are probably as like those which may have taken place
as any others which never took person at all
are ever likely to be."

—*James Joyce, in* Finnegan's Wake

LOOKING AT ROCK STRUCTURES IN THE ROCKIES

So far, this discussion of the building of the Canadian Rockies has concerned itself with the sort of thing you see in satellite photos and geologic maps of western North America. But now it is time to consider the smaller-scale results of mountain-building. After all, this book is supposed to be useful in the *field*.

Here are a few rules and general observations about faults and folds in the Canadian Rockies that geologists find useful when they are trying to figure out the structure of a particular mountain-sized batch of rock. Despite the technical mystique surrounding this kind of activity, the specialists know that it's more a matter of practice than anything else, akin to learning the birds or the botany of a particular region. Here, then, is some field geology, for fun (if not for profit) in your spare time.

Faults in the Rockies tend to follow the layering.

Most Rockies faults are low-angle thrust faults, the kind that result when one large sheet of rock is shoved over another for many kilometres (up to 50 km in some Rockies thrusts). Low-angle thrust faults tend to follow bedding planes, so that the beds above lie more or less parallel to the ones below and nothing looks disturbed—until you check the sequence of beds and realize that something is wrong.

You might be strolling up a slope, crossing a familiar formation—say the Spray River siltstone, which is an easy one to know—and then you step up over a ledge of . . . what's this? Palliser limestone? But the Palliser is 120 million years *older* than the Spray River. How can it be lying *on top* of the Spray River?

Not to worry. Say to yourself: "Aha! I've crossed a fault!" even though you didn't see the actual trace because it runs parallel to the bedding. The Palliser is above the fault; the Spray River below. The fact that *formations are out of order* marks the fault, not an obvious offset in the beds.

If you hunt around the outcrop sometimes you can find the fault itself. But you will seldom see the sort of crumbly fault zone pictured in geology textbooks. The upper surface will have slid smoothly over the lower surface. The reason for this smoothness is unknown; it must have something to do with the same principle that kept the thrust sheet in one piece as it moved along.

A classic place to view a major Rockies thrust is at Yamnuska Mountain, west of Calgary at the mountain front. From the parking area, follow the dirt road up past the quarry and take the trail (keep left at the boulder) up to the base of the huge cliff (about one hour). Follow the left branch of the trail; it leads in a couple of minutes to an exposure of the McConnell Thrust, one of the great faults of the Canadian Rockies. Eldon limestone (Middle Cambrian) overlies coaly Belly River shale (Late Cretaceous) along a smooth, polished plane.

It's always older-over-younger in the Canadian Rockies.

The mechanics of producing thrust faults makes it very unlikely that you will see a thrust fault in which younger rock is thrust over older. I made this mistake as an undergraduate, trying to draw a geological map. I thought that the Palliser Fm. had been thrust over the Lynx Gp., which is older than the Palliser. My professor corrected the error, saying "It's always older-over-younger with thrust faults, kid."

He was right; what I had taken to be the Palliser Fm. was the look-alike Eldon Fm., which is, yes, older than the Lynx.

However, sometimes one finds younger rock *apparently* thrust over older, as shown in the diagram. This situation is not unusual in the Canadian Rockies—especially near the mountain front and in the foothills. Here, many thrusts are **imbricated** (stacked), a process that tends to bend the more westerly ones beyond the vertical. The faults become steeper with each additional slice.

Close-up of the McConnell Thrust at Yamnuska Mountain. Knifeblade marks the fault exactly. Pale rock above the blade is Middle Cambrian limestone (Eldon Formation). Dark rock below is Late Cretaceous shale (Belly River Formation). Horizontal movement of the limestone over the shale has been 30-50 km.

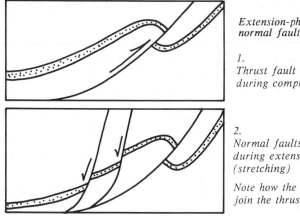

Extension-phase normal faulting

1.
Thrust fault forms during compression

2.
Normal faults form later, during extension (stretching)

Note how the normal faults join the thrust fault

How a thrust fault can appear to place younger rock over older rock

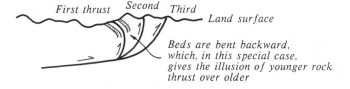

First thrust Second Third

Land surface

Beds are bent backward, which, in this special case, gives the illusion of younger rock thrust over older

Faults cut up-section to the east.

As each thrust fault propagated eastward, it tended to follow the bedding in soft, shaly formations—the plane of least resistance. But every now and again it would cut upward at a steeper angle, usually through a tougher formation (a thick limestone, for example). Overall, this produced the **listric** (concave-upward) shape of thrust faults that you see in geological cross-sections through the Canadian Rockies. But note that the shape is actually a series of steps: the shales are the treads and the more resistant units are the risers.

It is usually not possible to see this stepping-up in a single outcrop, but looking at a sequence of outcrops cut by the same fault will show the thrust cutting steeply across massive beds of limestone or quartzite, then following the bedding in softer formations.

Normal faults in the Rockies are found mostly in the main ranges, are steeply dipping and of small displacement. Except . . .

In a normal fault the rock above the fault plane moves down, not up as it does in a thrust fault. Normal faults are caused by stretching, not by compression. Since the Rockies were built by compression, there are few normal faults, especially in the front ranges and foothills—but they do exist in the main ranges, where there was some backsliding after the compressional phase of the Laramide Orogeny ended. (There are also normal faults that trend northeast/southwest, across the grain of the mountains, in some thrust sheets. These are thought to have formed *before* the Columbian or Laramide orogenies.)

Normal faults bordering sections of the Rocky Mountain Trench from Prince George south have much larger vertical displacements—some are measured in kilometres. Unlike Rockies thrust faults, these big normal faults fringing the trench have textbook-style pulverized walls. A good example of this is the brecciated (extensively fractured) zone along the **Redwall Fault,** which Highway 93 crosses near Radium Hot Springs. It separates limy shales of the McKay Gp. on the east from Beaverfoot dolomite on the west. The reddish cliffs near the hot springs are Beaverfoot rock. (For info on the springs themselves, see page 228.)

Tear faults occur in the Rockies, but they are not common.

One might think that when a thrust sheet moves, one section would start sliding faster than another and thus break loose, resulting in a *tear fault* between the two (see diagram).

This happens, all right, but surprisingly seldom. In the Rockies, irregularities in thrust sheet motion were mostly evened out by flexing of the rock. The entire sheet kept together quite well as it moved northeastward. That's why there aren't very many tear faults in the Rockies with displacements of a kilometre or more. Small offsets (1-100 m) are fairly common.

The enormous strike-slip fault that underlies the northern Rocky Mountain Trench (page 175) is like a tear fault in that one slab of rock has moved beside another one, but the term "tear fault" is reserved for a strike-slip fault formed in a moving thrust sheet.

Thrust faults usually have folds at each end.

No single thrust runs the full length of the Rockies, and each begins and ends at a fold (some disappear under another thrust sheet, which itself begins/ends at a fold). You can sometimes see a fault in one mountain that dies out as a fold in a neighboring mountain. So theoretically it is possible to walk around either end of each thrust fault in the Rockies.

Suppose you started at the eastern edge of the foothills. When you came up against the first fault, you would just follow it northwest or southeast until it died out into a fold. Then you would walk west across the fold, gaining a few kilometres, until you came to the next fault, which you could end-run like the

Thrust fault cutting up-section

*A thrust fault always cuts up
through the rock, never down*

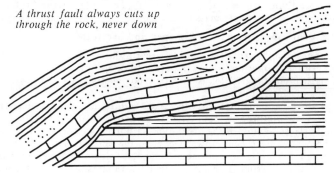

*Note how it cuts upward steeply in tough limestone,
but angles more gently through soft shale*

How a tear fault forms

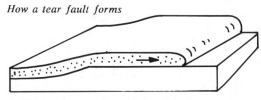

1. Thrust sheet moving northeastward

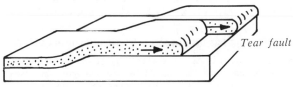

Tear fault

2. Part of the sheet starts moving faster

Crossing the Rockies without crossing a thrust fault

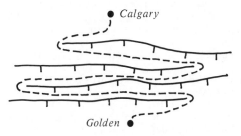

● *Calgary*

Golden ●

*Nearly all thrusts have folds at each end
(a few disappear under other thrust sheets)*

first one, etc.. Eventually you would reach the Rocky Mountain Trench without ever crossing a fault.

This is more than just an amusing notion. It shows that as the faults propagated eastward the whole mass of the Canadian Rockies moved together.

Folds in the front ranges tend to be S-shaped and overturned.

The front ranges display wonderful folds, great arching things that attest to the flexibility of stone in motion. Following from the point above, the reason for the S-shape of most front-range folds is that they commonly mark the northwest and southeast ends of thrust faults.

A well-known example of this is the great fold on Mt. Kidd in Kananaskis Country. The view pictured is from Alberta 40 between Wedge Lake and the turnoff for Fortress Mountain ski area, looking north. Note how the beds in the centre of the *S* have been been upward beyond the vertical, i.e. overturned.

Even more amazing is the enormous Z-shaped fold in Bedson Ridge in eastern Jasper park, best seen from Highway 16 near Pocahontas. Look north across the valley; the fold stands out nicely in pale-gray Palliser limestone.

Travelers on the TransCanada Highway should look south from the Dead Man's Flats overpass between the mountain front and Canmore for a view of the overturned syncline in Mt. Allan. The reddish-brown Kootenay Gp. rock there is folded over like a taco shell.

Shaly rock is often highly folded, while massive beds in the same mountain are usually much less disturbed.

Shale deforms differently than massive limestone, sandstone or conglomerate. Outcrops that show a hard layer next to a soft layer often demonstrate this well. In the front ranges, exposures of the Fernie shale along Snake Indian River are wildly contorted, even though the sandstone units above and below are essentially planar. On Highway 16 west of Jasper, the tough Miette gritstone beds show folding on a larger scale than the minutely kinked slates lying between them.

On a larger scale, contrast the tough formations of the eastern main ranges around Lake Louise, which are gently folded, with the intensely folded shales west of Field.

Slippage during folding has produced faults along bedding planes.

You can demonstrate this interesting effect by bending a stack of paper. As it bends, note how the edges of the stack (the edges in your hands) don't stay parallel to each other. If you have bent the centre of the stack downward, into a **syncline,** then the angle between the two edges closes upward. If you have bent the stack upward, into an **anticline,** then the angle closes downward. The more you bend the stack, the more obvious that angle becomes.

This is because the sheets are all the same size, but the distance around the curve is greater on the outside than it is on the inside. Thus, every sheet of paper in the stack must *slide slightly* against its neighbors during the bending.

The same thing happens in the bending of a stack of rock. The layers make up some of the distance around the curve by stretching on the outside of a fold and compressing on the inside, but there will also be sliding—i.e. faulting—between beds. This is called **flexural-slip folding:** the beds slip slightly as they flex around the fold.

When two beds of rock slide even a few centimetres, the two surfaces along which they move are easy to recognize by the **slickensides** on them: smooth rock surfaces with scratches that all run the same way.

Massive limestone beds in the front ranges are particularly prone to flexural-slip faulting. The slickensides are much whiter than the rock, and they are amazingly smooth. Along the Maligne Road in Jasper park, where the highway runs beside Medicine Lake, blasting has exposed classic slickensides with vertically aligned scratches. In a couple of outcrops the slickensides occur right beside glacially polished exposures, in which the scratches are aligned horizontally.

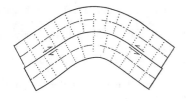

Folding produces faults along bedding planes. The diagram shows the theoretical basis for the slippage. Reproduced from Price (1964) courtesy Geological Survey of Canada.

The great S-shaped fold in Mt. Kidd (2972 m), seen along Alberta 40 in Kananaskis Country. This is the northern end of the Lewis Thrust, a major fault that runs south to the Waterton/Glacier area. See also the geological sketch of Mt. Kidd on page 56.

Blasting along the Maligne Road at Medicine Lake, in Jasper National Park, has exposed typical bedding-plane faults. This one is in Palliser limestone. The fault-plane surface is much smoother and whiter than normal bedding planes in this outcrop.

AFTER MOUNTAIN-BUILDING AND BEFORE THE PLEISTOCENE ICE ADVANCES

The entire Rockies region has been above sea level since the Laramide Orogeny, which means that erosion rather then deposition has been the rule here for about 60 Ma. An exception occurs on the western slope, in the Rocky Mountain Trench and other deep valleys. Sediment worn from the mountains has accumulated here, in grabens (down-dropped crustal blocks) along faults that became active at about 45 Ma in the Middle Eocene.

The **Sifton Formation** occurs in the northern Rocky Mountain Trench between Ingenika River (near the north end of Williston Lake) and somewhat north of Sifton Pass (a slight rise in the trench floor that divides Kechika River drainage from Finlay River drainage). There is also a patch of Sifton sediment farther south on the west shore of the Williston Lake opposite the Peace River outflow. An outcrop of similar (but unstudied) rock occurs yet farther south along Reynolds Creek east of McLeod Lake, and Sifton-like deposits dated as Oligocene occur nearby along Highway 97 at the bridge over Parsnip River.

The Sifton is a little-studied nonmarine sequence of limestone-pebble conglomerate with beds of finer clastic rock and coal; the thickness is undetermined, but some of the sediments are known from plant fossils to be Paleocene and Eocene. They were derived in part from the *east*; thus, Sifton sediments probably came in as detritus eroded from the Rockies near the end of the Laramide Orogeny. They are also mildly tilted, showing that earth movements were still occurring in the northern Rocky Mountain Trench at this time.

Two better-known Cenozoic units in the south end of our area mark the tapering-off of mountain-building more closely: the Kishenehn Fm. (next entry) and the St. Eugene Fm. (page 187). Both occur on the western slope, in and about the trench. They are little deformed, showing that the main event was over, although tilts and minor faults in them show that tectonic activity was still going on in this area *after* the end of the last big glacial advance 11,000 years ago. So perhaps the Rockies are still moving a little—although the moderate earthquakes that should accompany these twitches are not being felt.

Kishenehn Formation
Late Eocene to Oligocene (40-24 Ma) 300-2500 m

Pronounced "KISH-en-en." Mostly very coarse conglomerate, with boulders up to 2 m across, overlain by Oligocene lake silt. The Kishenehn is found along the Flathead Fault from the southern end of our area north to Packhorse Peak along the continental divide northwest of Waterton Park. There are good exposures beside Flathead River, reached via the Flathead Road along the western border of Glacier National Park.

Following the main uplift of the Canadian Rockies, the **Flathead Fault** formed as a result of stretching. This is a big normal fault running from the Elk River valley north of Fernie to beyond the southern end of Glacier park. Followed westward by seismic exploration, the fault flattens and merges with the Lewis Thrust.

Land west of the fault dropped some 6000 m, and the resulting deep depression picked up a great deal of material eroded from the young Rockies beside it. In the Flathead Valley that material is the Kishenehn Fm., which is essentially a collection of alluvial fans. Following Kishenehn beds upward illustrates the erosional stripping of the Rockies. The lower layers are full of pebbles that could only have come from the cherty Rundle limestones. The upper ones contain Palliser pebbles, equally easy to identify, that were washed in after the Rundle Gp. (and the underlying shaly Banff Fm.) had been eroded away, exposing Palliser rock beneath. Atop the coarse conglomerate beds, fine-grained lake deposits show that erosion proceeded more slowly.

Kishenehn beds are tilted, indicating that the rock of the Rockies was still somewhat restless during the Oligocene, although mountain-building seems to have finished.

St. Eugene Formation
Middle and Late Miocene (16.6-5.3 Ma) Up to 1500 m

A Rocky Mountain Trench deposit of **colluvium** (coarse, angular, unconsolidated material that has moved downhill only a short distance), **fanglomerate** (hardened mudflows and alluvial-fan material), silt, sand and coarse gravel. Overlain by Pleistocene glacial deposits. Best seen on the western side of the southern Rocky Mountain Trench between Kimberley and Cranbrook along Highway 95A. A good exposure is located just off the highway on the north bank of the St. Mary River, 1.5 km northwest of the highway bridge over it, below a fenced picnic site. The unit is also found along Gold Creek (north of Newgate) and on the east side of the trench along the Elk River south of Elko.

St. Eugene sediments are the youngest pre-glacial deposits known in the trench; they, and perhaps other, unexposed sediments filled the half-grabens of the extreme southern section.

The St. Eugene came in as the faults moved, so the sediments themselves are faulted, showing Late tertiary tectonic activity in the region. Detritus derived from a distinctive layer of volcanic rock in the neighboring Galton Range should be present in the St. Eugene but isn't—suggesting that the volcanic layers were *uplifted* 600 m after the St. Eugene was laid down. That's interesting; block uplift is rare in the Canadian Rockies, where mountain-building has been accomplished through the stacking of thrust sheets. But block uplift in the Miocene was common in the American Rockies to the south; maybe it was felt here, too. Minor faults noted in Holocene glacial deposits above the St. Eugene show that some motion has occurred since the end of the Wisconsinan ice advance only 11,000 years ago.

Plant fossils and pollen of ferns, alders, birch, spruce and pine preserved in the St. Eugene suggest a warmer, wetter climate in the area during the Miocene than at present.

Pre-glacial gravels on the eastern slope
Pleistocene or older (1.9 Ma or more) 0-30 m

River gravel lying on bedrock in pre-glacial river valleys through the foothills and on the eastern prairies. Stones are all from Canadian Rockies formations; none are from the Canadian Shield.

Rivers have been carrying the Rockies bit-by-bit to the sea for ages, of course. Here and there in the foothills, and quite commonly on the prairies, one can find gravel deposits from these rivers. The older ones represent the only sediments on the eastern slope that assuredly postdate the uplift of the Rockies (they cross folds and faults with no sign of disturbance) and they predate the arrival of ice from the Canadian Shield (because there are no Shield-type stones included).

Possible pre-glacial gravel deposits may also be found on flat upland surfaces in the southern foothills and along the eastern prairie margin. Typical of these are the deposits found on Broadcast Hill and Nose Hill above Calgary. These features resemble the partly eroded **pediments** found along the mountain front in the American Rockies. Veneers of gravel lie on bedrock surfaces that slope eastward, out onto the plains. To differentiate such deposits from glacially derived gravels, one must check them thoroughly for the absence of Shield-type stones.

Heavy glacial erosion seems to have removed all pre-glacial gravel from the mountains (but see page 195).

The St. Eugene Formation along Highway 95A near Wycliffe, in the southern Rocky Mountain Trench.

Pre-glacial gravels atop Broadcast Hill in Calgary, exposed in a gravel pit.

After mountain-building, before ice advances

ICE IN THE ROCKIES
The Quaternary Period (Pleistocene and Holocene epochs)

In reading this section you may see some glacial-geology terms that are not familiar. Or you may want a more general introduction to the topic. If so, turn to the section on modern glaciers, which begins on page 210; the diagrams and photos in that section explain many glacial features.

Whenever there has been glacial ice at the poles, there has probably been glacial ice in high-latitude (northerly or southerly) mountain ranges such as the Canadian Rockies. That bald statement should be true, but it is difficult to prove: a highly erosive glacial buildup during the Pleistocene ("PLICE-tuh-seen") Epoch seems to have removed whatever earlier evidence there was in our mountains.

That evidence is in the form of **till**, the essential glacial product. Glaciers move; they pick up rock, carry it, grind it up and dump it out as an unlayered mixture of mud and scratched-up stones—that is, as till. Nothing else seems to make till except glaciers; other processes—landslides, mudflows, even turbidity currents—can produce deposits that have some characteristics of till but not all of them (some are subtle, involving alignment of stones, scratch patterns and proportions of constituents). So till is undeniable evidence of glaciation. It is often in the form of **moraines**: landforms made of till.

Till is found sporadically throughout the geological record as **tillite** (till gone to rock) as old as 2.3 billion years. There is good evidence for glaciation near the end of the Proterozoic Era; in our area the Late Proterozoic Misinchinka Gp. (page 86) has strikingly till-like units.

Evidence of more recent glaciation (but still pre-Pleistocene) in western North America has come from moraines in southern Alaska that are 8 million years old. Till 2.7 million years old is known from the Sierra Nevada mountains of California. By chance, both these tills were covered by lava flows and thus protected from erosion.

The table below presents key dates in the glacial history of the Canadian Rockies. The other important element in this story is the sequence of named glacial deposits. Nat Rutter, of the University Alberta, has prepared a summary chart of major tills in western Canada, including those for the Rockies area. The relevant portion is presented on page 191.

Glacial periods in the Canadian Rockies

Event	Began	Ended
Cavell advance ("Little Ice Age")	1200 A.D. (730 BP*)	1900 A.D. (50 BP)
Hypsithermal (warm period)**	8700 BP	4000-5000 BP
Crowfoot advance	After 11,000 BP	Before 6600 BP
Late Wisconsinan advance	20,000 BP	11,000 BP
Early Wisconsinan advance	75,000 BP	64,000 BP
Illinoian (Great Glaciation)	240,000 BP	128,000 BP

Early Pleistocene advances began worldwide at about 1.87 Ma
Misinchinka tillite (?) may show glaciation around 730 Ma

*"BP" is the Quaternary geologist's abbreviation for "Before the Present," defined as the year 1950.
**Two peaks in temperature: 8100 BP and 5900 BP.

1.
How the Rockies may have looked before the Pleistocene glacial advances (before two million years ago.) There were probably small glaciers at high elevations, but note the generally rounded, water-worn topography. Slopes are convex, with broad summits and long, gentle ridges. Rivers run in winding, V-shaped valleys; there are few lakes or waterfalls.

2.
At the height of glaciation (the Illinoian interval, 240,000--128,000 years ago) the ice buildup is several kilometres thick. The Rockies are ice-capped: so deeply covered that only the higher summits stick through as **nunataks**. During later Pleistocene glacial advances (early and late Wisconsinan, 75,000–64,000 and 20,000–11,000) the ice is not as thick).

3.
Climatic warming melts most of the ice, revealing the newly glaciated landscape. The peaks have been whittled into rugged **horns**; the ridges connecting them are sharp-edged **aretes** ("ah-RETS"). The valleys are now straight and U-shaped. Side valleys meet the main valley at a higher level; they are **hanging valleys**. There are many waterfalls and lakes.

Till exposed in a recessional moraine near the toe of the Athabasca Glacier. Raven gives the scale.

Glacial deposits in and near the Canadian Rockies (Based on a chart by Rutter, in press)

Area and main reference(s)	Glacier National Park (Karlstrom)	Waterton and Crowsnest (Stalker, Harrison, Alley)	Bow Valley and Kananaskis area (Rutter, Jackson)	Red Deer Valley, Rocky Mtn. House (Boydell)	Lower Athabasca Valley (Roed)	Williston Lake, Peace River (Rutter, Mathews)	Liard Plain, just north of Rockies (Klassen)
Distance*	1 10 100	1 10 100	1 10 100	1 10 100	1 10 100	1 10 100**	—
Holocene 11,000 to the present	Cavell; Crowfoot	Cavell; Crowfoot	Cavell; Crowfoot; Mazama tephra (6600 BP)	(Holocene by Luckman & Osborne)	Cavell; Crowfoot		
Late Wisconsinan 20,000—11,000	Unnamed	Hidden Peak, Waterton IV	Eisenhower Jct <18,300; Canmore <26,600	Sylvan Lake; Unnamed	Drystone Creek; Obed	Deserter's Canyon; Late Portage Mtn; Early Portage Mtn; Upper Laurentide; Ft. St. John	Till D <23,900
Early Wisconsinan 75,000—64,000	Unnamed	Episode III, Waterton III; Waterton II ?	Bow Valley; Banff; Calgary	Jackfish, Elkton, Lamora; Sylvan Lake, Sundre; Rocky Mountain House	Obed, Marlboro, Raven Creek; Edson, Mayberne; Edson	Lower Laurentide; Early Glaciation	Till C
Illinoian 240,000—128,000	Unnamed	Great Glaciation; Maunsell; Labuma	Pre-Bow Valley; Labuma	Baseline, Hummingbird; Unnamed	Marsh Creek; Early Cordilleran	Early Glaciation	Unnamed; Till B >232,000
Early Pleistocene (up to 1.9 million)	Four advances	Waterton II, Maycroft; Waterton I, Albertan					Till A >765,000

*Distance from continental divide

**Distance from Rocky Mountain Trench

Given with Rutter's chart are references to the researchers who have worked in various parts of the Rockies. Their reports are the basis for the discussion that follows; to save space and avoid repetition, no further references to this literature will be made. Refer to the bibliography that begins on page 237 for each author's relevant major paper(s).

Early Pleistocene glaciations: no firm evidence in the mountains

If the Rockies followed the worldwide pattern, there were many glacial advances and retreats here during the early and middle parts of the Pleistocene. The climate cooled overall, but did so by cooling a little, then warming a bit, then cooling further and so on, in two-steps-forward, one-step-back fashion. In this scenario the glaciers of the Rockies would advance down the valleys, then retreat, then advance again, gradually gaining ground.

The main ice centre for the mountains of western Canada was in central British Columbia, well west of the Rockies. An ice cap over a kilometre thick built up there during each glacial episode. From it glaciers flowed in all directions. The Rocky Mountain Trench collected ice from both the Columbia Mountains, under the icecap, and from the Rockies, where there was another buildup. The two ends of the trench were very far apart, so ice in the trench also escaped by overtopping the continental divide and flowing across the Rockies. It may have taken the same routes during each major glacial advance, deepening the gaps more and more.

Today those gaps remain as the major Rockies passes—Crowsnest, Kicking Horse, Howse, Yellowhead, Pine and so on—including the largest and deepest of them all, which doesn't even have a name. It is the gap through which Peace River flows.

It is unlikely that ice reached east beyond the mountain front during the early Pleistocene glaciations, because no tills from mountain glaciers of this age are found on the prairie. Mountain tills are found there, but they are younger.

Far to the east, another centre of glaciation was on the Canadian Shield west of Hudson Bay. Ice would spread out from this centre during glacial intervals, deepening enough to overcome the gentle uphill grade southwest across the prairies. Eastern glaciers reached the Rockies during several of the Pleistocene ice build-ups, although probably not during the early ones (at least not in southern Alberta; eastern ice may have reached the mountains farther north in the early Pleistocene).

By the time eastern glaciers reached the foothills they were at their western limits. They had lost much of their erosive power and were dumping their burdens of till, leaving especially thick deposits in low spots such as river valleys in the eastern foothills and on the prairies. It is in those valleys, now reoccupied by modern streams, that the record is best exposed. Each early Pleistocene advance of eastern ice overrode the till of the previous one. These multiple glaciations are clearly shown by multiple till layers.

Mountains are the givers of glaciers, not the receivers, and glaciation has been mainly an erosional process west of the mountain front, not a depositional one. So as each mountain glacial advance overrode the previous till the older evidence was scraped away. Thus, no tills from early Pleistocene glaciations are known west of the mountain front.

However, it is only reasonable to expect that one glacial advance outdid all the others in ice depth and glacier length, and this seems to have been the case. Of this we have some evidence.

The Great Glaciation: good evidence on the eastern slope

Preliminaries over, the main event got underway. It was now the waning quarter of the Pleistocene, during the next-to-last major glacial period recorded worldwide: the **Illinoian** glaciation (called in Europe the **Riss** glaciation). It began about 240,000 BP and ended circa 128,000 BP in a return to climatic conditions not much different from those of today.*

During the Illinoian, which some geologists are calling the **Great Glaciation** in the Rockies, mountain ice flowed east through the foothills and onto the Interior Plains. At the mountain front, each valley poured forth its stream of slow-moving glacial ice as a spreading lobe that mingled with others. The scene might have looked like air views of the arctic islands today, where glaciers now empty from the mountain valleys and spread out on the flats beyond.

River valleys of the foothills and eastern prairies were overrun by ice that unloaded till into them, just as they had earlier received prairie till.

This was fortunate, for it preserved evidence of the Great Glaciation along the eastern margin of the Rockies. In southern Alberta, the Oldman, Castle and St. Mary rivers have since cut down into these deposits. If you visit Lethbridge, look at the record of multiple glaciation exposed so strikingly there. The tall banks of the Oldman are banded in buff and gray, showing several layers of till separated by river and lakebed sediments.

The strata tell the tale, although glacial stratigraphers are forever arguing about times and events. There seem to have been at least two Illinoian advances, about equally strong, each one involving mountain ice from the west, out of the Rockies, and prairie ice from the east, carrying stones from the Canadian Shield.

Did the eastern and western ice sheets meet? Yes. At the prairie margin from Calgary north, mountain ice was deflected southward against the prairie ice front. South of Calgary, though, the two lobes seem never to have touched, although they crossed overlapping territory. Mountain ice would flow out first, maintain itself there for a while, then retreat to the mountain front before the far-travelled prairie ice would arrive. During the first Illinoian advance, prairie ice reached the mountain front throughout our area; during the second it barely reached the foothills in the southern area but probably made it to the mountain front north of Bow River.

The crest of the Porcupine Hills was not touched by ice from either direction. That makes the upper slopes and summits of the hills, and a few spots about 15 km west near the continental divide, the only places known in the Canadian Rockies that definitely have never been glaciated.

The ice-free corridor

Interfingering eastern and western tills along the prairie/foothills boundary mark what is known as the **ice-free corridor**. This provided a convenient northwest-southeast pathway between eastern and western ice that may have remained open for most of the Pleistocene, closed only during the maximum extent of eastern and mountain ice.

The ice-free corridor was walked by many animals—possibly including man, who may have used it to get from unglaciated but very cold parts of the north (western Yukon and northern Alaska) to the more hospitable country south of the ice sheets. Archeological sites in the corridor go back 11,000 years, which is a long time in North American anthropology; perhaps even older ones will turn up.

But travelers in the ice-free corridor during glacial periods may have had to use it in winter, for in the summer there was often lots of open water there. Ice on the prairies would block the normal northward and eastward drainage in our area; all water would have had to flow south to the edge of the ice sheet in Montana. This formed a string of short-lived but deep **proglacial lakes** along the corridor ("proglacial" meaning "in front of the ice"). Still-water layers of sand and

---

*To answer a question you may be asking: classical names for the earlier glaciations—Kansan and Nebraskan in North America, Mindel and Gunz in Europe—are no longer being used. A new scheme based on sea-core studies is in preparation that should correct errors in dating and stratigraphy that have rendered the classical sequence largely useless. The Illinoian/Riss and Wisconsinan/Würm glaciations are on firmer ground, though, and are still current.

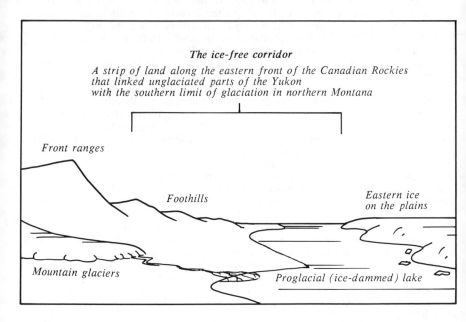

The ice-free corridor

A strip of land along the eastern front of the Canadian Rockies that linked unglaciated parts of the Yukon with the southern limit of glaciation in northern Montana

Front ranges

Foothills

Eastern ice on the plains

Mountain glaciers

Proglacial (ice-dammed) lake

Pleistocene deposits exposed along Oldman River near Brocket, east of Crowsnest Pass in southern Alberta. Till sheets from mountain ice and prairie ice overlie one another here. Photo by Jerry Osborn.

silt lie between the tills of the buried valleys, showing that proglacial lakes appeared with each prairie-ice advance.

Illinoian advances are recorded in the Rockies proper just east of Crowsnest Pass, where two Illinoian tills from mountain ice (called **Albertan** and **Maycroft**) interfinger with two Illinoian tills from the prairies (called **Labuma** and **Maunsell**. In the lightly glaciated far-northern end of the Rockies west of Fort Nelson, glacial features along the eastern prairie margin and in the foothills look old (photo on page 201); they may be Illinoian, but they have not been studied.

In the central Rockies, Illinoian till has not been identified with certainty west of the mountain front. Illinoian till *does* occur in the foothills and on the eastern prairies, where Illinoian ice from the mountains met Illinoian ice from the Canadian Shield.

So it is certain that Illinoian mountain ice flowed well out of the valleys. This means that the buildup in the central Rockies must have been very thick, possibly ice-capping the area. If that is the case, then why haven't we found any Illinoian till in the mountains?

It had been thought that the Wisconsinan glaciation (the next round) was also strong, and that Wisconsinan ice was thick enough to remove the Illinoian till. But recent research is showing that the Wisconsinan was less severe in the Rockies than previously thought, so there should be pockets of Illinoian till at high elevations in the front ranges, untouched by the thinner valley glaciers of the Wisconsinan. None has been found with certainty at time of writing—but there is a good chance that pre-Wisconsinan deposits have been reported, yet not recognized as such. Read on.

Strange stones on front-range summits

While working on a geologic map in the eastern front ranges along the North Saskatchewan River in 1970, I noticed that the mountain summits were sprinkled with pebbles, cobbles and even boulders of pink and buff quartzite that were unmistakably from the Gog Gp (page 88). These stones were lying 1500 m above the valley floors and on rock that was decidedly un-Gog (front-range limestone and shale). The sites were many kilometres away from the nearest Gog outcrops. Later I found that these stones had been reported occasionally in the geological literature of the Canadian Rockies since the 1930s, but never studied.

Lacking a detailed investigation, the simplest explanation is that they are all **erratics**: chunks of rock carried by thick, valley-filling glaciers to places where they would not otherwise be found. The source area is to the west, in the Gog peaks of the western front ranges and main ranges.

Gog erratics of this sort are found from east of Banff north to at least Sentinel Mountain (between Jasper and Pine Pass), where they have been reported on the summit at an elevation of 2515 m. I have seen similar erratics of Atan Gp. quartzite on the peaks above the Alaska Highway in the north end of our area, so probably they occur anywhere in the Rockies with a source of quartzite to the west. A typical deposit is on Roche Miette, where there are many pebbles and boulders scattered over the summit uplands (maximum elevation 2377 m). Looking for these erratics is good mountain-top entertainment; there always seem to be a few.

Many of the erratics are blocky, but others are well-rounded, indicating that they have been moved by water. This suggests several possible origins: (a) they may be the remains of preglacial rivers (unlikely, for they lie on glaciated terrain), (b) they have been carried by water flowing on and beside glaciers thick enough to reach such elevations (reasonable), or (c) that they are all that remains of till deposits (also possible, if the till included water-worn stones).

Two lines of evidence suggest that the quartzite erratics are at least early Wisconsinan in age and probably older.

The first is their high elevation. It is unlikely that the late Wisconsinan produced ice thick enough at the mountain front to reach the summits there,

An erratic of Gog quartzite (boulder between person and camera) resting on Palliser limestone high on Roche Miette in eastern Jasper National Park. Note the weathered character of the bedrock in the foreground; nodules of chert stand 5-10 cm above the more readily dissolved limestone surface. This surface was scraped smooth by glaciation that may have been Illinoian.

which lie 1300 m above the valley bottoms. Wisconsinan moraines a few kilometres away show that ice levels were hundreds of metres lower.

The other line of evidence is the erratics themselves. Amazingly, they are nearly all quartzite. I have found a few that are siltstone or dolomite, but I have never found a *limestone* erratic at such elevations in the eastern front ranges, even though there are plenty of limestone boulders in obvious glacial deposits lower down. It is unlikely that any till or outwash deposit as widespread as the Gog erratics would include only quartzite; there must have been limestone pieces mixed in when the erratics arrived. Where has the limestone fraction gone?

Taking the simplest explanation again, maybe the limestone portion has weathered away, leaving the practically insoluble, slow-weathering quartzite behind. Dolomite in our area weathers more slowly than limestone, which may explain why there is a little dolomite left; the few dolomite fragments I have found among the quartzite erratics have been small and deeply weathered.

If the degree of weathering is any indication, then the quartzite erratics must be old—older than either early or late Wisconsinan deposits lower down, which show plenty of limestone chunks at the surface. I suspect that these intriguing stones may be evidence of one or more earlier glaciations, such as the Great Glaciation.

This is all speculation, of course. Is there a geology student out there who would like to prepare a thesis on the high-elevation erratics of the Canadian Rockies? The fieldwork will certainly get you into shape.

Wisconsinan glaciation: lots of evidence, but many problems

This was the last major glacial period in the Canadian Rockies, as elsewhere in the world. It seems to have occurred in two parts: an early phase, with two advances that came close together in time and extent between 75,000 BP and 64,000 BP, and a later, weaker advance that lasted from 20,000 BP to about 11,000 BP.

Deposits of that later advance suffered no further glacial erosion in the mountains, so they are plentiful. Because the later advance didn't entirely overrun the earlier advances, the earlier deposits are still around, at least from the mountain front east, and exposed. That's handy for study. Further, carbon-isotope dating can reach back into Wisconsinan time to give the number of years that have passed since a living thing produced such carbon-bearing materials as wood, bone, horn or a calcium carbonate shell. Burned material can also be carbon-dated.

So you would think that the sequence of Wisconsinan glacial events would be easy to work out. Not so; the Wisconsinan is giving science a lot of trouble, because the deposits are complex and little datable material has been found. Further, only a handful of glacial studies have been done in our area.

Keeping all these disclaimers in mind, I am still going to pass on current ideas about Wisconsinan glaciation in the Canadian Rockies, even though they haven't been proved and may turn out to be wrong. Besides the published literature, the information that follows comes from recent interviews with Canadian glacial-history specialists.

Waterton/Glacier area

Let's start in the Waterton/Glacier area, where the Wisconsinan sequence is better understood than it is elsewhere. The early Wisconsinan seems to have provided two advances here, about equally strong. They occurred close together in the 11,000-year interval between 75,000 BP and 64,000 BP. Perhaps the ice thinned and retreated only a little, then re-advanced. Or there may have been a retreat right to the valley heads. Whatever happened, two tills have been left, complete with nicely developed moraines at the mountain front and a set of interesting melt-back features around Lower Waterton Lake: **kames, kettles, kame terraces** and **eskers.** See the diagrams for explanations of these terms.

As is usual with glaciation in our area, deposits farther west in the upper mountain valleys are patchy and confusing, but a weak late-Wisconsinan advance seems to have reached only a few kilometres down the valleys.

Bow Valley

In the mountains west of Calgary the pattern is not so clear. There were at least two Wisconsinan glaciations (possibly three), but it is hard to say which of the two obvious ones is early-Wisconsinan and which one is late.

Two advances reached out into the foothills, leaving moraines at the mountain front—and **drumlins,** too. Drumlins are hills made of soft material (till or gravel) that has been molded by glacial flow. They are egg-shaped in outline, with the smaller, tapered end pointing down-glacier and the larger, blunter end pointing up-glacier into the ice stream. Near the mountain front there are eskers as well.

Along the TransCanada Highway you can see a couple of classic drumlins on Morley Flats. Look for them between the long hill that descends to the flats from the east and the turnoff for Morley about 10 km to the west. There are many other drumlins in the area, but these are wooded and clustered over one another, thus not as easy to pick out. The ones at higher elevations on the south rim of the flats point off to the southeast, showing that ice flowing from the mountains in the early Wisconsinan was either deflected south, probably by prairie ice to the east, or that it simply spread to the north and south as a widening lobe that did not come into contact with eastern ice.

There are also extensive glacial deposits upstream in the mountain section of the Bow Valley. See them along Highway 1A between Canmore and Banff. These landforms look like low lateral moraines or kame terraces, but actually they are neither, strictly speaking. Work on such deposits has shown that they are mostly the remains of till left on the valley floor: **ground moraine,** since eroded back by Bow River almost to the valley walls. (There are also kame terraces here; the diagram shows their relationship to the ground moraine.)

The Prince of Wales Hotel in Waterton Lakes National Park, showing the kame terrace the hotel sits on. The terrace formed about 65,000 years ago, when there was glacial ice to the left, in the area now occupied by Middle Waterton Lake and Upper Waterton Lake. Photo courtesy Travel Alberta.

Drumlin on Morley Flats along the TransCanada Highway west of Calgary, near the Morley exit. The blunt end faced upstream in the flow of eastward-moving glacial ice.

Drawings on the opposite page reproduced from Harrison (1976) courtesy Geological Survey of Canada.

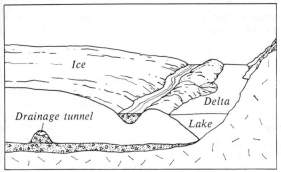

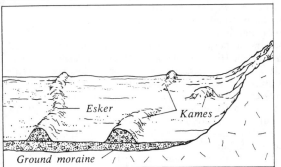

1.
Streams flowing on top of the glacier carry gravel, as do streams flowing under the glacier in drainage tunnels.

2.
When the ice melts, the gravel is left behind as **kames** (piles of gravel from atop the glacier) and eskers (sinuous lines of gravel marking the drainage tunnnels under the glacier).

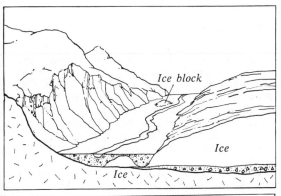

1.
Streams flowing beside the glacier deposit gravel between the ice and the edge of the valley. Here and there, ice blocks (fragments of the glacier) become buried in these deposits.

2.
When the ice melts, the gravel deposit beside the glacier is left as a **kame terrace.** Such terraces are often pocked with **kettles:** depressions created when the ice blocks melt and the overlying gravel collapses into the voids below. When filled with water, a kettle is a **kettle pond.**

Water has washed through much of this till, removing fine-grained clay from the mud but leaving the particles that are silt-sized and larger. Geologists call the material **washed till**.

Hoodoos

Lime in some Wisconsinan till deposits in our area has hardened somewhat, strengthening the deposits. In the first 5 km of the trail up Forty-mile Creek near Banff, there are scattered till blobs along the trail that are cemented so well with calcite that they have become rock (tillite). Between Carrot Creek and the Banff hydroelectric plant along the TransCanada Highway you can see vertical walls 20 m high of material that is similar but softer. It is easy to recognize: pale-buff and studded with cobbles and boulders.

There are **hoodoos** here: pillars of till capped by boulders that have protected the underlying material from eroding away in the rain. For a close look at hoodoos, follow the Tunnel Mountain Road from Banff townsite to a marked viewpoint overlooking a group of classic hoodoos.

There are scattered hoodoos in the major valleys throughout our area. A small group is visible from the TransCanada Highway near the Canmore turnoff (look northeast, toward Grotto Mountain). An impressive set of hoodoos lies right beside Highway 93 in the Rocky Mountain Trench, a few kilometres south of Fairmont Hot Springs, where the road crosses Dutch Creek. These hoodoos are cut in till that resembles the washed Wisconsinan till of the eastern slope.

Up-valley from Banff, a younger till enters the picture around Castle Mountain (midway between Banff and Lake Louise). This may correspond to the weak late-Wisconsinan advance established in Waterton. Or if one of the more extensive advances is already late Wisconsinan, then it may be evidence for a second late-Wisconsinan glaciation, one unknown farther south. Or this till may simply represent a period of stability during the last ice retreat, during which moraines would build up at the stationary glacial front.

Jasper area, and the Athabasca Valley Erratics Train

There was little research done in the Jasper area until quite recently, when a thesis on glacial sedimentation made use of some till deposits here (Levson, 1986). This has prompted a thorough glacial stratigraphy study in the upper Athabasca Valley by the same student (field work in progress).

Older work has concerned the area from the mountain front east. These older studies conclude that Wisconsinan glaciers reached out beyond the mountains in the Athabasca drainage. An early advance spread east across the foothills, ran up against prairie ice and was deflected south. A later, somewhat weaker advance seems to have made it well beyond the mountain front (to east of Obed Summit), but was not deflected.

A possible third advance, weaker yet, seems limited to front-range cirques. It has not been studied farther west, where it ought to have been more extensive. This till may represent a minor advance or period of stability during late-Wisconsinan time. If not, we may be looking at evidence for three glacial episodes, which in light of what is known of glacial periods elsewhere would make the two major Athabasca tills Illinoian and early Wisconsinan, the minor one late Wisconsinan.

One or both of the main advances down the Athabasca Valley carried rocks from west of the continental divide, perhaps as from as far west as the Cariboo Mountains, across the divide and into the Rockies. This is the **Athabasca Valley Erratics Train** (not to be confused with the Foothills Erratics Train, page 202).

The erratics are easy to identify: they are metamorphic, not the usual sedimentary types you find in the Rockies. The commonest type is silvery, wavily textured schist with small red garnets in it (the Miette schist, page 79). Occasionally one finds high-grade metamorphic and igneous erratics from the western side of the Rocky Mountain Trench. Most of the pieces are cobble-sized or smaller, but a few are desk-sized boulders. There is one that size beside the trail

Hoodoos near Banff, as seen from a marked viewpoint along the road that passes by Tunnel Mountain campground. Figures at the base of the hoodoos give the scale.

Subdued glacial topography on Mt. St. George (2261 m), south of the Alaska Highway near Summit Lake. The terraced deposits in the centre of the photo have been rather deeply eroded, suggesting that they are older than late Wisconsinan.

up Roche Miette, and another big one south of the Celestine Lakes Road along Jasper Lake.

The Athabasca Erratics Train has been followed east into the foothills, then south along the prairie-foothills margin. There the erratics are mixed with eastern till, which carried metamorphics from the Canadian Shield. The presence of these eastern metamorphic stones makes the Athabasca metamorphic erratics difficult to pick out south of Edson. The mixing shows that the Athabasca Valley glacier was deflected south by the eastern ice front at this time.

Glacial history north of the Athabasca

North of Athabasca River there have been reconnaissance studies of landforms and surficial deposits, but they tell little about the glacial history of the area. At the mountain front along Peace River one of these studies shows evidence of three glaciations, the last of which has been carbon-dated as late Wisconsinan. Melt-back of the late-Wisconsinan ice has also been studied here; there was a large proglacial lake in the region, dammed by prairie ice. It extended west through the Peace River gap and into the Rocky Mountain Trench.

The big moraine that provided material for the Bennett Dam on Peace River at the mountain front also dates to the late-Wisconsinan advance, so ice moved west to east across the Rockies here. This isn't surprising, for the Peace River gap is the deepest, widest pass in the range.

Glacial landforms along the Alaska Highway west of Fort Nelson have not been studied in enough detail to say much about them. As described on page 34, the landscape traversed by the highway between the prairie margin and Summit Lake (on the crest of the Rockies) is subdued by weathering. It may have missed the late Wisconsinan ice advance. West of Summit Lake the valley of MacDonald Creek looks more recently glaciated.

The western slope: too little and too late

On the western slope, glacial studies have been limited to the Rocky Mountain Trench, and there haven't been many. A study of deposits in the trench between Skookumchuck (south of Radium) and the international boundary produced evidence for three advances; a carbon-isotope date under what seems to be the oldest till shows that all three are late Wisconsinan. Between Golden and Valemount, BC Hydro's damming of the Columbia River at Mica Dam has placed unstudied glacial deposits out of reach beneath Kinbasket Lake.

In the northern trench, a hurried effort to gather evidence from excellent deposits in the region before they were flooded by Williston Lake (another hydroelectric project) turned up four glacial events, the latter three all carbon-dated to late in the Wisconsinan. One presumes that the older one is early Wisconsinan, but its age is uncertain. We will probably never know, because the lake has covered all.

The Foothills Erratics Train: a classic part of the geology of our area

The Foothills Erratics Train is a collection of boulders strung out in a line from the Athabasca Valley south along the western prairie margin all the way into northern Montana. The boulders are angular and sharp-edged; they look like they were quarried yesterday. The rock in all of them is strikingly similar: coarse pink-and-white quartzite, with thin layers of greenish siltstone. Beyond a doubt, this is Gog quartzite from the main ranges of the central Canadian Rockies.

Their consistent similarity, their apparent freshness and their distribution have led to speculation that all these erratics came from one or more large rockslides that fell onto the Athabasca valley glacier, perhaps from the big quartzite peaks west of Jasper. (Mt. Edith Cavell is in this area, as are the Ramparts.) It is possible that glaciers from other Gog-rich valleys farther south (those of the Brazeau and North Saskatchewan, for example) could have contributed some of the rock. Whatever its source(s), the debris rode along on top

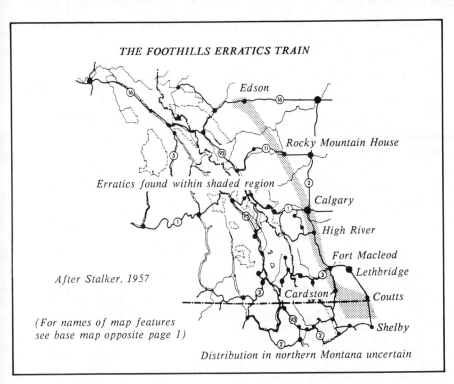

THE FOOTHILLS ERRATICS TRAIN

Edson

Rocky Mountain House

Erratics found within shaded region

Calgary

High River

Fort Macleod

Lethbridge

After Stalker, 1957

Coutts

Cardston

*(For names of map features
see base map opposite page 1)*

Shelby

Distribution in northern Montana uncertain

The Big Rock near Okotoks, in the eastern foothills south of Calgary. This is the largest block known of the Foothills Erratics Train.

of the glacier (or near the surface), thus escaping the rough treatment accorded materials carried deeper in the ice.

Once out of the mountains, the erratic-bearing ice seems to have been deflected south against the edge of the eastern ice sheet. Erratic blocks up to the size of houses dropped out in a zone about 10 km wide that passes a few kilometres west of Edson and Rocky Mountain House, and right through Sundre, Calgary and Okotoks. South of Crowsnest Pass the erratics are spread eastward as far as Coutts on the international boundary. They are also found in northern Montana, where the southern edge of the prairie ice sheet lay. By this time the deflected mountain ice had mixed with eastern ice, so the erratics sit in eastern-type till.

Much of the Foothills Erratics Train came to rest in lake silt—a situation that seems unlikely at first glance. However, there is a way in which the rocks could have been transported on the large ice-dammed lakes (page 193) that existed at this time along the foothills. The erratics could have been rafted about on or in icebergs that had calved from the ice front. Or the boulders may have dropped onto thick lake ice in winter and then been transported on floes in the spring as the ice broke up. The evidence for ice-rafting is good: many of the boulders are concentrated along known glacial-lake shorelines such as the ones on the western outskirts of Calgary.

What ice advance was responsible for the erratics? Illinoian? Early Wisconsinan? Late Wisconsinan? The age of the ice that brought the erratics has not been established, but it is probably not late Wisconsinan, for current thinking is that mountain ice and prairie ice did not meet in the late Wisconsinan. This leaves the early-Wisconsin and the Illinoian advances as possibilities.

The **Big Rock** at Okotoks, south of Calgary, is the biggest and best-known member of the Foothills Erratics Train. You can see the Big Rock sitting in a field 8 km west of Okotoks ("OH-kuh-tokes") on Highway 7. Now split into three parts, the block originally measured 9 m tall, 18 m wide and 41 m long. Its mass is about 16,300 t.

The Blackfoot Indians have a folk tale about the Big Rock. In the story the rock is rolling around, chasing people and squashing them (which shows that the notion of the deadly rolling boulder is not limited to Hollywood culture). Naapi ("NAH-pee"), the Blackfoot mythical hero, shoots an arrow up into the sky; it comes down on the Big Rock, splitting it into the three pieces and thus bringing it to a halt.

Holocene glaciation and the Little Ice Age

It has been about 11,000 years since the withdrawal of the late-Wisconsinan glaciers to their present limits—a period known as the **Holocene Epoch**—and no major glaciation has occurred since. This is a short length of time for any geological time division, let alone an entire epoch, and there is nothing fundamentally different about the Holocene to separate it from the Pleistocene. Climatic indicators suggest that major glaciations, worldwide hallmark of the Pleistocene Epoch, are not finished, so in that sense the Holocene is like one of the Pleistocene interglacial periods. For this reason geologists place the Pleistocene and Holocene epochs together in the **Quaternary Period.**

The last 5000-year period is called by Quaternary geologists the **Neoglacial.** There have been seen several minor Neoglacial advances during this time, the most recent of which corresponds to the **Little Ice Age** of Europe.

All these terms create a cumbersome lexicon, but thick words for thin layers are just as much a part of geology as long words for short bones are a part of medicine. After all, the closer we get to the present, the more geological evidence there is. So time divisions get finer and finer.

The world's climate has been warm during the Holocene, warmer at times than it is now. Logs preserved in alpine swamps show that between 8700 and 5200 BP timberline was up to 100 m higher than at present. This corresponds to a worldwide warm period known as the **Hypsithermal.** Pollen in lakebed cores shows that in the central Canadian Rockies there were two temperature peaks during the Hypsithermal, during which plants made advances into places too cold for them now. These climatic heat waves came at 8100 BP and 5900 BP.

No on knows how far back the ice melted in the Hypsithermal, but it probably didn't melt away entirely from major icefields such as the Columbia.

Tephra

Holocene researchers in our area have a couple of very good tools to use in their studies: carbon-isotope dating and layers of **tephra**. Tephra is dust ejected in great quantities from erupting volcanoes. Another term for tephra is "volcanic ash" (although it is not ash in the usual sense).

Tephra is common in the Canadian Rockies from Grande Cache south. To find some, locate a river cut-bank exposing fine-grained material (silt) and check the top metre or so. You may see a whitish band a couple of centimetres thick. Dig a bit out with the end of your finger; if it is uniformly white or pinkish in color and texture—a *layer* in other words, not just a concentration of white calcite in the soil—then probably it is tephra.

A good place to see tephra is in the Sunwapta Pass area (boundary between Banff and Jasper parks), where road cuts between Icefield Campground and the Parks Canada information centre show obvious tephra layers. An excellent exposure is along the Maligne Road in Jasper park, 8.5 km south of Maligne Canyon. Look for a thick pinkish tephra layer on the east side of the road near the top of a slumped area.

Prevailing winds from the big volcanic eruptions in the Cascades and Coast Mountains carried tephra into our area several times during the last 12,000 years. The exact age of each eruption has been determined by isotopic dating techniques, and each tephra has a distinctive chemical composition that can be determined in the laboratory. Tephra collects over a period of only a few days or weeks, so a better time-marker could hardly be found.

There are four tephra layers in the Canadian Rockies. The thickest, easiest to recognize and most widely distributed is that from two closely spaced eruptions of **Mt. Mazama** (now Crater Lake, Oregon) 6600 years ago. Between Jasper and Saskatchewan Crossing there are two others as well: **Mt. St. Helens** (3400 BP) and **Bridge River** (2400 BP). South of Crowsnest Pass the region did not receive the Mt. St. Helens or Bridge River tephra, but it did get Mazama and also **Glacier Peak** tephra, the oldest one in the area (12,000 BP). It is a pity that older tephras don't occur here (they do on the prairies and closer to the west coast), for they would help to sort out the problems in understanding Wisconsinan and older glacial events.

But the Holocene is becoming reasonably clear. There have been at least two Holocene advances documented in the Canadian Rockies.

Holocene advances in the Canadian Rockies

One of these occurred sometime between 9000-12,000 BP: the **Crowfoot Advance,** named for Crowfoot Glacier near Bow Lake. It occurred so soon after the end of the big late Wisconsinan advance that it may represent the last gasp of that major glaciation.

The other advance began 600-700 years ago, in the 13th century A.D. It was on the wane by the beginning of the 20th century. This was the **Cavell Advance,** named for Mt. Edith Cavell, where it was first documented. This is the Rockies equivalent to Europe's Little Ice Age, when old records show that the summers there became cooler and wetter.

Both these advances were minor. On average, ice reached only a kilometre or two down-valley from where it is now. Of the two advances, the later one (Cavell) got a bit farther, so moraines from the earlier one (Crowfoot) were mostly overridden and thus difficult to detect. They were discovered in the late 1970s.

Pair of photos taken from approximately the same point showing recession of the Angel Glacier at Mt. Edith Cavell. Left photo shows the glacier as it appeared in about 1922, not long after the Cavell advance (Little Ice Age) had reached its maximum. Right photo shows the glacier in 1971. Much of the glacier in the valley (Cavell Glacier) had disappeared by 1971. Historical photo by F.M. Slark, courtesy Mrs. D. Guild. 1971 photo courtesy Parks Canada and Brian Luckman.

A layer of Mazama tephra (volcanic dust) found between Maligne Canyon and Medicine Lake along the Maligne Road in Jasper National Park.

Photos taken of Rockies glaciers at the turn of the century show them nearly at their maximum Cavell extent. In the years that followed, a general warming and drying trend caused the loss of about a third of the glacial ice in the region. In 1898 the Athabasca Glacier reached almost to the site of today's Parks Canada information centre. Now it is almost 2 km away.

Another place to appreciate Holocene glaciation is on the Path of the Glacier Trail at Mt. Edith Cavell. You step out of your car at the edge of a heavy, dark subalpine forest that has been growing there since the end of the late Wisconsinan 10,000 years ago. Then you climb up a few metres onto a low ridge running across the valley—the outermost moraine of the Cavell advance—and get a sudden, shocking view of the wasteland on the other side. Most of it was covered with ice less than a century ago.

Ever date a lichen?

The slow, steady growth of long-lived lichens on the rocky moraines here has made it possible to date the melt-back of the Cavell Glacier. The **map lichen** (*Rhizocarpon geographicum*, page 440) is a green-and-black lichen common on quartzite boulders; it grows at a known rate and colonizes such boulders soon after they are exposed by glacial withdrawal. One can see large patches of map lichen on the moraine near the parking lot, where the Edith Cavell Memorial is; as you walk south, toward the north face of the peak, the patches become smaller and smaller. By taking hundreds of lichen measurements—enough to get statistically significant results—geologist Brian Luckman worked out the melt-back sequence here, showing where the ice front had been at different dates (Luckman, 1977).

What's next: glacial advance or glacial retreat?

Considering the recent rapid retreat, one wonders whether the glaciers will melt entirely. In the 1970s a visitor to the Columbia Icefield area was so concerned about this that he wrote to Parks Canada in Jasper and suggested that the Athabasca Glacier be refrigerated to prevent further loss! (His company, he wrote, could supply the necessary equipment, tastefully hidden behind the moraines.)

The retreat may be over, for the world's climate has cooled perceptibly (about 0.5 °C) since 1940. Glacial melt has slowed generally over the past ten years, and some Rockies glaciers are now advancing. The Columbia Glacier, which drains the northwest side of the icefield, has advanced over a kilometre since 1950.

Should the residents of Jasper and Banff pack their bags, then? Nay; glaciers are slow to rouse. Further, mankind has increased the proportion of carbon dioxide in the atmosphere from burning coal and oil. The CO_2 concentration is now high enough to be causing a mild greenhouse effect—holding in more of the sun's radiation than normal—and thus possibly delaying the onset of the next glaciation. If the warming is as much as recent predictions indicate (up to 1 °C in the next hundred years), then the current advance will almost certainly end, followed by a major retreat. In fact, that retreat may have already begun. A study of glacial fluctuations in the Cariboo Mountains, a range immediately west of the Rockies, shows that an advance between 1950 and the late 1970s is over and that the glaciers there are currently in retreat (Luckman, in press).

On that note we will conclude this geological history of the Canadian Rockies. Coming up: notes on some interesting features of the *modern* Rockies landscape.

This rockslide occurred along the Icefields Parkway just after a snowfall in November of 1982. View is to the southwest from near Nigel Falls.

Modern landscape

Looking at the landscape
Features and processes at work in the Rockies today

A complete discussion of current geological processes in the Canadian Rockies is beyond the scope of this chapter, but here is a quick review of the ways in which erosion is turning the peaks into prairies.

- **Chemical weathering:** breakdown on the molecular scale, as one mineral changes to another or dissolves.

- **Mechanical weathering:** expansion and contraction of rock as it heats and cools. Most active on south-facing slopes in summer.

- **Spalling and exfoliation:** rock splitting away in sheets to release internal pressure. Common in massive limestone and quartzite cliffs.

- **Freeze-and-thaw.** Water expands nine percent in freezing, which wedges bits of rock loose (another name for this is **frost-wedging**). Also causes a slow churning of the soil. Freeze-and-thaw processes are most active in spring and fall, on north-facing slopes and at high elevations.

- **Glaciation** scrapes away rock particles, which are carried to the glacial toe. Glaciers undercut cliffs, causing slides.

- **Avalanches** bring down rock and soil torn loose by the sliding snow.

- **Raindrops, snowflakes, hail and sleet** loosen soil and mineral grains, especially when hurled against surfaces by wind.

- **Running water** washes across rock and soil surfaces, removing particles and soluble minerals.

- **Streams and rivers** remove materials in gullies, streambeds and along river banks. The **bed load** of a stream includes sand, gravel, cobbles and boulders that grind together, wearing away as they move down the streambed. This and the **suspended load** (silt and clay) and **dissolved load** (minerals in solution) are all carried out of the Rockies.

- **Wave-lapping** gradually washes the finer particles from the shoreline into a lake or stream. Sand and gravel near the shore grind together as they are washed back and forth.

- **Soil creep:** constant near the surface in soft materials.

- **Impacts:** one falling rock shattering or dislodging another.

- **Rockslides** move masses of bedrock down-slope, breaking up the rock and aiding disintegration.

- **Slides of soft material (soil slumps, mudflows)** move downhill when unconsolidated sediments are saturated with water. Common along moraines and in stream-cuts/road-cuts through lakebed sediments and glacial till.

- **Solifluction** occurs in sloping alpine meadows underlain by **permafrost:** ground that does not thaw completely every year. Partial thawing in summer saturates an upper layer of soil with water, but the soil doesn't slump or flow because the roots of plants hold it together. Rather, lobes typically the size of a city lot move a metre or two downhill.

- **Wind** transports silt-size particles (especially out of front-range valleys); moves sand grains in hops of a metre or two. Flings precipitation and rock particles at surfaces.

- **Earthquakes:** rare around here, but with cumulative effects over time. In the late 1970s the north face of Mt. Clemenceau lost a great deal of its glacial cover in a massive ice avalanche that may have been earthquake-triggered.

- **Biological action:** very important; everything from root expansion and biochemical breakdown of minerals to the work of burrowing animals, goat-hooves and human machines.

This long list of erosive agents suggests an interesting question:

How long will the Rockies last?

By measuring the amount of sediment in a sample of river water and doing some outrageous extrapolations, it is possible to figure that out. One must also assume that the rate of erosion is going to remain the same—a dubious assumption, what with a glacial advance or retreat possibly on the way. Still, let's give it a try.

The watershed of the North Saskatchewan River is typical of others in the Rockies: a mix of sedimentary rock types, about 5-10 percent covered with glaciers. In a regional summary paper on geomorphic processes, Luckman (1981) notes that the North Saskatchewan River carries off its portion of the Rockies at the rate of 60 Bubnoffs.*

This means that the North Saskatchewan basin is getting worn down about 6 cm every thousand years, or 6 mm in a hundred years, or 0.06 mm each year. That turns out to be the average for the whole area. Calculating our Bubnoffs forward, we find that the summit of Mt. Robson, highest point in the Canadian Rockies, will lie at the elevation of Edmonton in exactly 54,766,666 years and eight months.

ICEFIELDS AND GLACIERS

In the eastern front ranges, and in the southern and northern ends of the Rockies, the glacial cirques, aretes and horns are fossil features: the ice that carved them is now largely gone. There is too little ice here to be doing much work on the landscape. Glacial erosion is still going strong, though, in the central Rockies along the continental divide, where there are **icefields**: large glaciers covering upland areas at high elevations. There is a string of icefields along the divide between Kicking Horse Pass and the northwest corner of Jasper park; the **Columbia Icefield** is the largest at 325 km^2. Fewer glaciers are found north of Peace River, but in the northern Rockies the **Lloyd George Icefield** is the centrepiece of Kwadacha Lakes Provincial Park, and there is a large unnamed upland glacier around **Great Snowy Mountain** near the headwaters of Akie River.

Some of the Alberta icefields are visible from the aptly named Icefields Parkway. But views from the road don't do them justice; like a toddler looking up to the dinner table, one sees the edges, not the surfaces of the ice-covered plateaus. Still, peering up the valleys of the glaciers draining the icefields gives the odd glimpse. Look for the **Waputik** ("WAH-poo-tick") **Icefield** at the head of Hector Lake and the **Wapta** ("WAHP-ta") **Icefield** above Bow Lake. From the north side of Bow Summit there is a grand view up the valley of Peyto Lake to Peyto Glacier and the north end of the Wapta Icefield. A small icefield covers the gentle eastern slope of **Mt. Wilson,** the big peak just north of Saskatchewan Crossing.

The Columbia Icefield is the most accessible; the Icefields Parkway runs right by the toe of the Athabasca Glacier, one of six named glaciers (there are many unnamed ones) that carry the flow from the central ice mass down to lower

---

*The "Bubnoff" should be nominated for Funniest-sounding Unit of Measure Ever Invented. It represents 1 mm of land-surface reduction per thousand years.

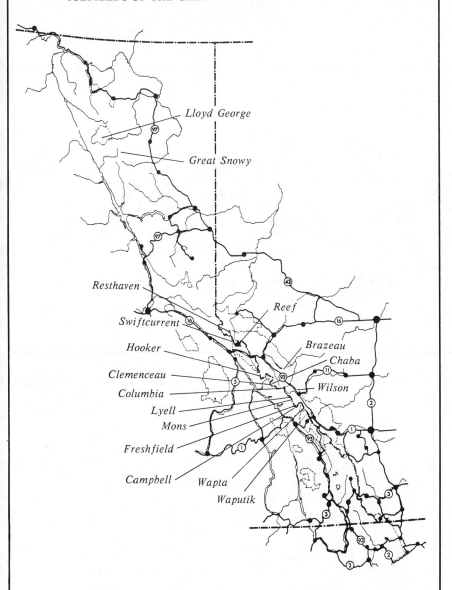

ICEFIELDS OF THE CANADIAN ROCKIES

Lloyd George

Great Snowy

Resthaven

Reef

Swiftcurrent

Hooker

Brazeau

Chaba

Clemenceau

Wilson

Columbia

Lyell

Mons

Freshfield

Campbell

Wapta

Waputik

An icefield is a large glacier covering an upland area that is flat or gently sloping

(For names of map features see base map opposite page 1)

Icefields and glaciers 211

elevations. The icefield itself is mostly out of view at the head of Athabasca Glacier, but the edge can be seen atop the cliffs of nearby peaks such as the Snow Dome and Mt. Kitchener.

The other main-range icefields—**Freshfield, Mons, Lyell** ("lie-ELL"), **Clemenceau** ("klem-AWN-so"), **Chaba** ("CHAH-ba"), **Hooker, Reef, Swiftcurrent** and **Resthaven**—are well off the highway, although you can get distant views of them here and there. There is also an icefield in the front ranges: the **Brazeau** ("brah-ZOE") Icefield, at the head of Maligne Lake.

Hundreds of other glaciers dot the Rockies. If you venture into the great cirques along the continental divide, or under the larger peaks of the front ranges, you can find modern glaciers surviving under the present temperate climatic conditions.

Glacial budget and flow

A key concept in understanding glaciers is the **glacial budget.** At higher elevations on the Columbia Icefield, 5-10 m of snow may fall each winter. Some of it **sublimates** (evaporates directly from ice crystals to water vapor, bypassing the liquid stage), but much remains for the sun to devour between May and October. As you might expect, melting is slow on the icefield, and more snow falls than melts. This, then, is the **zone of accumulation,** where each annual layer of snow is buried under the next, the accumulated layers gradually turning into ice by compaction and aging. Essentially, the air is squeezed out and the crystals intergrow, becoming larger and larger as the years pass. If you start digging in the centre of the Columbia Icefield you will have to fetch the jackhammer after 10-20 m, because everything from there on down is ice. This is, truly, a *field of ice.*

Ice is brittle stuff in the refrigerator tray, but stack up 30-40 m of cubes (if that is possible) and the lower layers will start to squeeze out to the sides, toothpaste-like. So ice flows—albeit slower than molasses in January—when pressure is put on it. It flows downhill, of course, from the heights of the icefield into the valley below.

At lower elevations, down in the valley, the glacier starts to meet its end. Summer temperatures are warmer down there, and the snowfall season is shorter. The annual snow layers melt off the glacier, exposing deeper (and thus older) layers the farther down-valley you go. This is the **zone of ablation,** where deposits made on the icefield are withdrawn. Only the flow of the glacier maintains the ice here. On the lower reaches of the Athabasca Glacier bare ice is exposed in July, August and into September.

Inevitably an elevation is reached at which the forward flow cannot supply enough ice to overcome the rate of melt, and here you have the front of the glacier. If the rate of melting and the rate of supply exactly balance, then the toe stays in the same place. Although the speed of glacial flow is fairly constant (a little faster in summer than in winter), the melting rate changes hour by hour, day by day and season by season, so the glacial front is seldom stationary—although the position changes so slowly that it *looks* stationary.

Glaciers in the central Rockies move forward at an average rate of about 15 m per year. In the winter, when there is hardly any surface melt, the front forges ahead a few metres, pushing up a line of bouldery muck called an **annual moraine.** In the July heat, the glacier cannot supply ice fast enough and the front melts back, leaving the annual moraine to show how much loss is occurring as the days go by.

Now: given a number of snowy winters and cool, cloudy, rainy summers, the rate of supply can exceed the rate of melt. In this case the front moves forward to a lower elevation, one at which summer melt and forward motion are again in balance. Conversely, a series of dry winters and hot, clear summers can force the front back to a higher elevation. These are the main factors in glacial advances and retreats.

Part of the Columbia Icefield. View southwest from Snow Dome (3520 m) to Mt. Columbia (3747 m, highest peak in Alberta). Photo courtesy Jasper National Park.

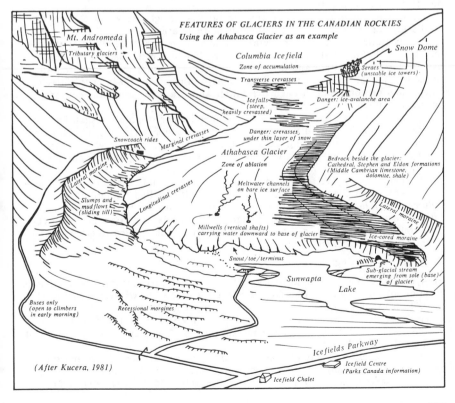

FEATURES OF GLACIERS IN THE CANADIAN ROCKIES
Using the Athabasca Glacier as an example

Mt. Andromeda
Tributary glaciers

Columbia Icefield
Zone of accumulation

Snow Dome

Seracs
(unstable ice towers)

Transverse crevasses

Icefalls
(steep,
heavily crevassed)

Danger: ice-avalanche area

Danger: crevasses
under thin layer of snow

Snowcoach rides

Marginal crevasses

Athabasca Glacier
Zone of ablation

Bedrock beside the glacier:
Cathedral, Stephen and Eldon formations
(Middle Cambrian limestone,
dolomite, shale)

Lateral moraine

Slumps and
mudflows
(sliding till)

Longitudinal crevasses

Meltwater channels
on bare ice surface

Lateral moraine

Millwells (vertical shafts)
carrying water downward to base of glacier

Ice-cored moraine

Snout/toe/terminus

Sub-glacial stream
emerging from sole (base)
of glacier

Sunwapta

Lake

Buses only
(open to climbers
in early morning)

Recessional moraines

Icefields Parkway

Icefield Centre
(Parks Canada information)

Icefield Chalet

(After Kucera, 1981)

Icefields and glaciers

Sub-glacial streams

It may surprise some readers to learn that the rock under Canadian Rockies glaciers is not below the freezing point. At this latitude, earth heat at the glacial sole keeps the temperature slightly above freezing, so there is always a thin film of water there. The film is also sustained by pressure-melting, as under a skater's blade. That water has to go somewhere, and it does, moving steadily downhill as a sheet.

Meanwhile, surface meltwater in the ablation zone also finds its way under the ice, moving down through crevasses wherever the ice is thin enough (usually less than 40 m, although sometimes 50-60 m) to maintain vertical conduits and horizontal tunnels. The sub-glacial film of water finds its way into this system, swelling the flow through the network.

That is why you often see a sizable stream of meltwater pouring out from *under* the toe of a glacier. The water is gray with tiny particles of rock—rock flour—scraped away by glacial flow. Surface meltwater on a glacier is surprisingly clean.

Ice-cored moraines and glacier caves

Scrambling over the moraines besides Rockies glaciers, one often comes across **ice-cored** patches. A thin veneer of till or other rock debris covers the ice, which dates back several hundred years to the Cavell advance (page 205). Often you can't tell when you are on an ice-cored moraine, until suddenly your footing fails and away you go, slipping down into a mucky mess of glacial glop or perhaps getting injured on the rocks.

Ice-cored moraine is nasty stuff to travel over, but I've had some beautiful hours *under* ice-cored moraines: in winter, venturing into **glacier caves** hollowed out by summer meltwater.

If you ski along the snout of any central-Rockies glacier you are likely to find a glacier cave. In winter the innards of these are frozen, so they are not wet or muddy (unless there is strong winter flow of water, as there is out of the big ice cave at the toe of the Athabasca Glacier), but in summer such caves are usually too wet to enter—and dangerous besides. The water level can rise quite suddenly and the roof is more prone to collapse than it is in winter (although glacial motion continues through the winter and can bring down the ceiling anytime, I suppose).

Glacier caves are especially common under ice-cored moraine. Such ice is stagnant—not moving—and thus the cave passage does not close up as readily as it does in clean, actively moving ice. Nonetheless, the location of a glacier cave entrance changes from year to year due to collapses, melting and channeling by meltwater.

Glacial features are fascinating, so let me recommend an excellent little book on the Athabasca Glacier that gives more detail. It is called *Exploring the Columbia Icefield,* by Richard Kucera. Pick it up in many shops in Banff or Jasper, or order from the publisher: High Country, Box 5000, Canmore, Alberta T0L 0M0. The principles in Kucera's description can be applied to other glaciers in the Canadian Rockies.

Crevasses—a warning

Flow in a glacier is smooth at depth, but near the surface (meaning within the top 40 m or so) the ice is brittle. At spots where the glacier flows over a convex slope in its bed, the upper zone is stretched. That upper ice is too brittle to stretch much, so cracks form. These are **crevasses** ("kreh-VASS-es"; not "crevices"). Crevasses on the Athabasca Glacier measure up to 32 m deep; they may reach 40 m in some Rockies glaciers.

Hence this advice: stay off a glacier unless you have mountaineering training and equipment. Falling into a crevasse unroped is quite likely to kill you. Crevasses narrow gradually and they are miserably cold, so it is possible to

Glacier cave in the toe of the Vulture Glacier, near Balfour Pass north of Lake Louise.

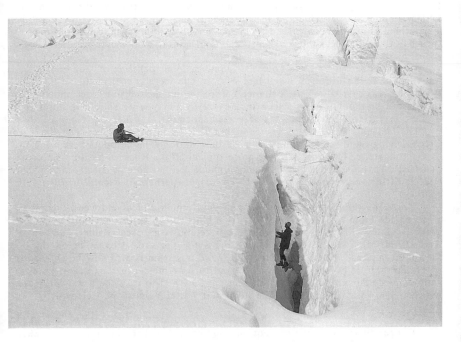

A crevasse on the snow-covered upper Robson Glacier in Mt. Robson Provincial Park. The roped mountaineering party is practicing crevasse-rescue techniques. The crevasse is perhaps 30 m deep; anyone falling in unroped is unlikely to be rescued alive.

simultaneously suffocate and die of hypothermia, never mind the broken bones. See page 787 for a list of organizations offering proper instruction in glacier travel.

Crevasses are obvious on the lower part of a glacier, where last winter's snow has melted down to the ice and exposed them, but higher up, where the glacier is still covered, they lurk under a thin layer of snow that may support your weight in the morning, when the surface is hard, and break through in the afternoon, when the snow is slushy. The entire glacial surface is dangerous in winter, when snow covers all,* and especially in the fall, when the snow-cover is thin.

ROCK GLACIERS

Rock glaciers are lobe-like masses of boulders that have crept downhill. There must be thousands of these in the Canadian Rockies; they are common at and above timberline, especially where the bedrock is Gog quartzite (page 88). Perhaps the most easily approachable rock glacier in the region is in Kananaskis Country, just north of Highwood Pass beside Highway 40. There are interpretive signs here that explain the landform.

Heavy lichen cover and lack of fresh surfaces on our rock glaciers show that they are moving very slowly these days, if at all. Some were simply ice-cored Wisconsinan or Holocene moraines that continued to slip downhill for a while before the cores melted out. Others started out as rockslide heaps that collected ice between the boulders during Holocene glacial advances and moved a few hundred metres before they dried out.

ROCKSLIDES

The Canadian Rockies are rockslide country. In 1903 a good-sized chunk of Turtle Mountain landed on the town of Frank, along the eastern approach to Crowsnest Pass. At least 75 people were killed. Highway 3 goes right through the slide heap, which is about 1.5 km wide and includes about 36,500,000 m^3 of Rundle limestone. Turtle Mountain has been carved from rock involved in a large, tight fold over a thrust fault, which left the peak unstable. Coal mining at the base may have led to the disaster.

Moraine Lake, near Lake Louise, is dammed by a rockslide of Gog quartzite, not till. But if the slide fell when late-Wisconsinan ice was still in the valley, and the debris was carried a little distance before the ice melted out from under it, then it can be thought of as a moraine anyway. Or maybe we should think of it as a pile of erratics. The distinctions here are academic.

The Icefields Parkway passes through a slide in Jasper park between Jonas Creek Campground and the Sunwapta Warden Station. The boulders here are also of Gog quartzite. This rockfall was quite typical of the Rockies: a tilted slab, quarried away at its base by Wisconsinan glaciation, let go and coasted down. The slide is little overgrown and may be fairly recent (perhaps it occurred in the 19th century).

Also along the parkway, the first viewpoint north of Icefield Centre displays a large slide from Mt. Kitchener. This slide blocked the valley, accounting for the gravelly valley fill upstream between the slide and Athabasca Glacier. Sunwapta River is cutting a ragged gorge through the Kitchener slide directly below the viewpoint, and as a consequence the valley fill upstream is also now being eroded.

Impassable to horses, the gorge deterred turn-of-the-century explorers from following the Sunwapta through this section; they had to take the next valley east, which is known as **Wilcox Pass**. The story that Walter Wilcox, the Coleman

---

*Dangerous for someone on foot, but less hazardous for someone on skis. Skis distribute the weight, and thus icefield skiers seldom rope up in winter—although they do in spring, when near the firn line. The main danger is skiing into an open crevasse, which is reason enough for going roped at any time of year.

The Frank Slide, east of Crowsnest Pass along Highway 3. The highway goes right through the slide heap. Photo courtesy Travel Alberta.

brothers and other early travelers (see page 755) used Wilcox Pass mainly to avoid the Athabasca glacial snout is untrue; the gorge was more of an obstacle.

Jasper's Maligne Valley displays textbook rockslides. From the huge heap damming Medicine Lake on south to Maligne Lake, the road runs largely through rockslide debris from the eastern valley wall. The bedrock there is tilted at 30-40°, which is just right for maximum activity. Maligne Lake itself is dammed by slides from the Opal Hills and from a peak just to the south called locally (and aptly) "The Sinking Ship." The lake is not dammed by moraines, as previously thought; perhaps by the time you read this the Parks Canada interpretive signs there will be corrected.* The heap from the Sinking Ship slide totals 498,000,000 m^3, which makes it by far the largest measured rockslide in the Canadian Rockies. There may be larger unmeasured ones, of course. The Medicine Lake slide is next-largest at 89,000,000 m^3. (Estimates by Cruden, 1976.)

Organic deposits in a depression on the Opal Hills slide are at least 5500 years old (personal communication, Brian Luckman, University of Western Ontario) but whether this is close to the actual age of the slide is unknown. The other Maligne Valley slides are undated. They are old enough to support mature subalpine forest, meaning at least several hundred years.

It is likely that most of these slides came down not long after the last major ice advance ended some 11,000 years ago. The glaciers had cut into the valley sides, sawing away at the down-dip ends of the tilted slabs here. When they melted away, there was no ice left to support the undercut slabs and down they came.**

Many of the limestone slide boulders in the valley are marked with **rillenkarren** ("RILL-en-car-en"): tiny gullies dissolved in the rock by rain and snowmelt. The rillenkarren here are up to several centimetres deep and intergrown; they look like miniature mountain ranges.

Rillenkarren. Photo courtesy Jasper National Park.

---

*Also in need of correction: the sign at the small depression near the start of the trail to Opal Hills. This and many other depressions around the north end of Maligne Lake are not kettles (glacial ice-melt features) as stated. But neither are they merely hollows in the slide heap. Air photo interpretation and ground-checking have shown that these depressions occur in parallel lines. They also seem still to be deepening, as if water moving underneath the slide is removing debris. Thus, they are karst features (see page 221)—although not necessarily linked to limestone caves beneath.

**In light of this principle, consider the quarrying operation at the base of Grotto Mountain, along the Bow River near the town of Canmore. A cement company is stripping away limestone from the down-dip edge of the tilted slabs there, doing exactly what the glaciers did. I hope the engineers handling this operation have done their homework. If they destabilize the mountain, some of it could come crashing down into Bow River. It wouldn't take much of a slide to block the river and flood the valley upstream—wherein lies Canmore, built right on the floodplain.

WATERFALLS AND CANYONS

In the Canadian Rockies the valleys are nearly all U-shaped from glaciation, not V-shaped from millions of years of erosion by running water. Side valleys are often **hanging,** meaning that they join main valleys at a higher level—another glacial hallmark. Followed upstream, our valley floors often rise in a series of cliffy steps rather than smoothly.

Streams flowing from hanging valleys and down valley steps often form lovely waterfalls, the highest and best-known of which is **Takakkaw Falls** in Yoho National Park (380 m).

In the Canadian Rockies the term "canyon" does not mean the same thing that it does in the western United States. There, a canyon is a steep-walled valley (such as the Grand Canyon) with a V-shaped profile. In Canada the glaciers left the valleys of the central Rockies only about 11,000-15,000 years ago, which hasn't allowed enough time for stream erosion to have cut very deeply into the valley floors. But the process has begun, resulting in spectacularly narrow-walled limestone gorges at many valley steps and hanging-valley edges. These are the "canyons" of the Canadian Rockies.

Maligne Canyon, near Jasper, is a classic example of a Canadian-style canyon. This one is up to 55 m deep and only a couple of metres across in places—so narrow that boulders have rolled in from the sides and jammed across the top. The upper section, near the teahouse, displays well-developed **potholes**: places where water has swirled gravel around and around, causing it to drill downward into the rock, which is Palliser limestone.*

Such canyons are common in the Canadian Rockies. Full of impassable waterfalls, they seem to materialize whenever I'm trying to follow a creek down through a limestone step in the valley, thereby complicating that day's explorations considerably.

Besides Maligne, here are some other deep canyons with easy access. From north to south:

- The canyon at **Athabasca Falls,** the only major one I know of to be cut in Gog quartzite, not limestone.

- The canyon at **Sunwapta Falls,** south of Jasper on the Icefields Parkway. Not as deep or narrow as Maligne, but with wonderful torrents pounding through on hot summer days when the Sunwapta River is swollen with glacial meltwater. The rock is Cathedral limestone.

- **North Saskatchewan Canyon,** beside the parkway and spectacular, but unnoticed by travelers because there is no marked viewpoint. In the north end of Banff park, go 1.5 km toward Jasper from the new bridge over Nigel Creek, which is about 3 km north of the Weeping Wall viewpoint. Just before you cross the gravel flats ahead at a big loop in the road, spot the old highway bridge down the bank. The canyon is under it, cut in Flume dolomite. Warning: there are no railings (which is probably why Parks Canada has not publicized the place).

- **Mistaya Canyon,** a short walk down a marked trail from a widened pull-off on the parkway a few kilometres south of Saskatchewan Crossing. Cut in Eldon limestone, the canyon features a small natural bridge (bedrock arch, not the jammed blocks common in other canyons) and some wonderful potholes on the east side.

---

*In winter the flow of water in Maligne Canyon slackens, then stops; the canyon floor freezes and one can enter on foot—although an experienced guide is recommended, because the dropping water level under the ice presents hazards from ice collapse.

Waterfalls on the Weeping Wall, along the Icefields Parkway in northern Banff National Park. Some of the falls here are present all summer, but most of the ones in this picture were short-lived and muddy, fed by rapid snowmelt during a hot spell in June of 1986.

Aerial view of Maligne Canyon near Jasper, the deepest and most spectacular of the limestone gorges accessible by car in the Canadian Rockies. Photo courtesy Jasper National Park.

- **Johnston Canyon,** between Castle Junction and Banff on the Bow Valley Parkway (Highway 1A). Wider than most; Parks Canada has installed a steel walkway on one wall. The rock through the developed portion is the Rundle Gp.

- **Marble Canyon,** 17 km west of Castle Junction on the road to Radium (Highway 93). The gorge is carved in Cathedral dolomite, not marble.

- **Sinclair Canyon,** just east of Radium Hot Springs. Highway 93 passes right through Sinclair Canyon, so it has been blasted out and spoiled, but the reddish color of the rock (Beaverfoot dolomite) is striking.

It is interesting to speculate on the ages of these gorges and on their origins. Evidence at Maligne Canyon suggests that it may have existed under the ice of the most recent glaciation (late Wisconsinan). Small gorges can be seen emerging from the fronts of modern glaciers and moraines in the Rockies, so it is possible that larger ones carried sub-glacial meltwater during the major glaciations of the past. Also interesting is the intimate connection of Maligne Canyon with the Maligne Valley cave system. This suggests that parts of the canyon may be cave passages that have been laid bare by glacial erosion, as is the case just upstream, where a smaller canyon can be followed into a sizable passage. Geologists wanting to pursue this subject may contact me for more information.

CAVES AND KARST

There are countless shallow shelter caves in our area, most of them **frost pockets**: niches formed by freeze-and-thaw (page 209) at seeps. The caves I will discuss here are proper caverns dissolved out of limestone by groundwater. They may be many kilometres long.

Of these there are surprisingly few in the Canadian Rockies, considering the large amount of limestone here. Perhaps this is due to severe glacial erosion in the area. If erosion by running water were primarily responsible for the rock removal, then there should be more caves, not fewer, because water is the prime agent of cave formation. So it seems likely that the glaciers have eroded away most caves in the region, leaving only those that were well-protected under thick layers of rock or found in places where glaciation was not heavy. Further, glacial deposits undoubtedly cover entrances to many unknown caves.

In deference to the caving community I am not providing cave locations. Caves are easily damaged, even by people not intent on vandalism, and Canadian cavers are understandably protective. All the caves in the region are cool (temperatures in most are just a few degrees above freezing, with little seasonal variation; some retain year-round ice deposits just inside near their entrances) and most are dangerous as well, with slippery slopes and deep holes to fall into, so it is just as well that inexperienced people stay out. If you are an experienced caver, or want to become one, contact me at the address given at the front of this book. I will put you in touch with the Alberta Speleological Society.

Our caves have formed in limestone, as most caves do. Groundwater is slightly acidic, for it picks up carbon dioxide present in the soil and in the atmosphere to form weak carbonic acid. The acid reacts chemically with the limestone, dissolving it. Isotopic uranium-to-thorium dating of calcite deposits in Rockies caves has shown that most were fully formed 350,000 years ago. This may be a gross underestimate; discovery of late-Miocene pollen in **Castleguard Cave** (northern Banff park) shows that the upper level is at least 10-13 million years old (Gale, Hunt and Smart, in press).

Cavern entrances in the Rockies are often perched 500-1000 m above the valley floors. Yet those caves formed below the water table, at a time when they were *beneath* the valley floors. The difference in elevation between perched cave passages and the present valley bottoms provides a rough measure of how much rock has been lost to erosion of all kinds since the caves formed. By doing some clever arithmetic and making some educated assumptions, geographers have

Looking out from Cliffside Cave in the Snaring River back-country of Jasper National Park.

Deep in Castleguard Cave. This is Canada's longest known cave (20 km of explored passages). It is located in the Columbia Icefield area. Various dangers make it inadvisable (and illegal) to enter except for experienced caving parties, who must apply to Parks Canada for permission.

Caves and karst

estimated that the ridgelines we see now were at the level of the valley floors some 6-12 million years ago (Ford et al., 1981).

The longest known cavern in our area is Castleguard Cave, with 20 km of explored passages in Middle Cambrian limestones. The limits of exploration lie several kilometres out *under the Columbia Icefield* and about 300 m below the base of the glaciers. Several passages end in plugs of glacial ice, a feature known in the world only from Castleguard. If you plan to visit the cave, be aware that the first kilometre of passage is subject to sudden flooding. Castleguard is dangerous for other reasons, too, and Parks Canada has made entry illegal except to caving groups receiving advance permission.

The deepest cave known in North America outside Mexico is not far away, in the Mt. Robson area. Arctomys ("ARK-toe-miss") Cave follows steeply tilted Mural limestone into the earth in a seemingly endless series of short steps, some requiring technical gear. Only 2.4 km long, it reaches a total depth of 522 m below the entrance. (Recent discoveries in the Rockies and on Vancouver Island may soon eclipse this record.)

What may be the longest cave system in Canada lies unexplored below the Maligne Valley in Jasper National Park, running through Palliser limestone (page 138). It certainly carries the most water: the entire Maligne River goes underground at Medicine Lake. The system has been traced by pouring special dye into sinks at Medicine Lake and detecting the dye at the many springs in and about Maligne Canyon, 15 km away. This dye-trace work has shown that if only one passage were involved, it would have to be 16 m in diameter to carry all the water known to enter the system. Flow-through times in the summer are on the order of 12-24 hours; in winter on the order of 5-9 days.

Medicine Lake has a pronounced seasonal cycle because of the cave connection. The lake has no outlet stream; all water flowing into the lake drains into the cave system. The lake level rises and falls according to the amount of water flowing into it from Maligne River. In late summer, when the river is low, the cave can carry away all the water, so the lake-level drops. By mid-October there is little water left in the basin and the river braids its way across mudflats to sinkholes located along the east side and at the north end. In June, snowmelt increases the inlet flow and the sinks can't handle it all; they back up and the lake starts to fill. About one year in five Medicine Lake overflows, usually in July (it did so in July of 1986).

Water flow through the cave is greatly reduced in winter, probably rendering it at least partially air-filled and thus potentially explorable. Although several entrances to the system have been found in the canyon area and entered, all are blocked by rubble after a short distance; the water can move between the blocks but humans are too large. Attempts to enter the cave by drilling and digging have failed.

This is terribly frustrating to cavers, of course. However, the usual history of these things engenders hope: long after the experts have given up, someone will blunder onto the entrance. I just hope that person stops by the park information centre in Jasper to pass news of the discovery on.

Any place in which the landscape is being altered markedly by solution, with or without caves, is called **karst**. The rillenkarren mentioned on page 218 are karst features of a sort, but more impressive are the deep cracks and/or shafts sometimes found in the Canadian Rockies in flat expanses of limestone above timberline. These surface features often connect with extensive caves below.

Thus far, karst has been found to develop in six Rockies limestones, roughly in order of prevalence the Palliser Fm., Rundle Gp., Cathedral and Eldon formations, Mural Fm., and Triassic limestones just south of Peace River. At least one karst area occurs in the mixed limestone/dolomite sequence of the Lynx Gp.

The *oldest* known karst in the Rockies is found in the Ordovician Skoki Formation, (page 112), in which caves developed not long after deposition of the limestone 488-458 million years ago. The passages have since been filled with sand, which has hardened to quartzite, so exploration is not possible.

Medicine Lake in Jasper National Park, showing the annual cycle of filling (spring) and draining (fall). Photos courtesy Jasper National Park.

An example of karst in the Canadian Rockies. This deeply fissured limestone surface is found on Snaring Mountain in Jasper National Park. Water has dissolved the cracks, working its way down into caverns beneath.

I have an interest in cave geology and would like to be informed of any karst discoveries you may make; please contact me if you find something interesting.

SPRINGS, HOT AND OTHERWISE

The largest spring known in our area is probably **Big Springs** below Castleguard Meadows. This spring drains the lower levels of Castleguard Cave; the typical summer discharge is 300,000 l/min (5 m^3/sec). The springs in Maligne Canyon, which drain the Maligne karst system (page 223), undoubtedly have a combined discharge greater than that of Big Springs, but the total discharge at Maligne is unmeasured. Another very large spring emerges near Watridge Lake in Kananaskis Country. **Karst Spring** can be reached by trail (4.7 km) from the Smith-Dorrien Road.

Smaller but more interesting to most people are the **hot springs** and **mineral springs** of the Canadian Rockies. These do not seem to tie into cave systems and may be found in rock other than limestone; information on the known ones is given in the table.

In the Rockies, hot springs and mineral springs seem to work the same way: as natural pumps.

Water can move through solid rock that is **permeable,** meaning that it contains interconnected pores or fractures. Since most rock in our area is at least slightly permeable, surface water seeping into the ground can be pulled by gravity down to great depths.

The temperature underground in the Rockies increases about 1 °C for every 30 m in depth. Near-surface valley-floor temperatures in the central Canadian Rockies are about 3-5 °C (annual average), so at depths of three kilometres or more the rock temperature is at or above the boiling point of water.

Hot water is less dense than cold water, and expanding gases in it also decrease its overall density. If given the chance, hot water will rise over cold water. But normally the hot water at depth cannot force its way up through the rock fast enough to retain the heat, which is lost as it moves up into cooler layers, so it stops rising before it reaches the surface.

However, scattered through the earth's crust are long upward conduits to the surface—the hot-spring systems—that allow the hot water to rise rapidly. As it rises, replacement water is drawn in from the surrounding rock, keeping the hot-springs pump running. In the Canadian Rockies the water seems to move up along fault planes, for many of the springs are found at or close to faults.

The hot water cools on its way up, often mixing with normal groundwater near the surface. But it retains enough heat to provide warm soaks for eager humans who would much rather squeeze into crowded pools with dozens of strangers than have a hot bath at home.

An interesting point about hot springs is that they are essentially nuclear-fueled. The earth's heat is generated mainly by the slow decay of radioactive minerals throughout the planet—a fact that surprises many people. (See page 168 for how radioactive decay powers continental drift.) Our hot springs reach deep enough to tap a little of that heat. The returning water is no more radioactive than normal groundwater (the decay process is too slow to emit much radiation), so there is no radiation hazard in a Canadian Rockies hot-springs soak.

Odors

The rotten-egg odor of hydrogen sulphide gas (H_2S) wafts from most of these pools. Where does it come from?

Gypsum (calcium sulphate, $CaSO_4 2H_2O$) is a common sulphur-bearing mineral that dissolves rather easily in warm water. Another is **pyrite** (iron sulphide, FeS_2), which is broken down and dissolved by sulphate-oxidizing bacteria. One or both of these minerals are present in much of the bedrock in the Canadian Rockies region, so the dissolved sulphates are brought to the surface in our hot-springs systems. On the way up, further bacterial action often turns some of the dissolved sulphate into hydrogen sulphide.

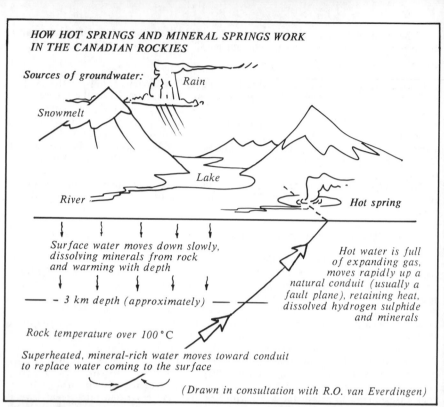

HOW HOT SPRINGS AND MINERAL SPRINGS WORK IN THE CANADIAN ROCKIES

Sources of groundwater:

Rain

Snowmelt

Lake

River

Hot spring

Surface water moves down slowly, dissolving minerals from rock and warming with depth

– 3 km depth (approximately) –

Rock temperature over 100°C

Superheated, mineral-rich water moves toward conduit to replace water coming to the surface

Hot water is full of expanding gas, moves rapidly up a natural conduit (usually a fault plane), retaining heat, dissolved hydrogen sulphide and minerals

(Drawn in consultation with R.O. van Everdingen)

Cold Sulphur Spring, beside Highway 16 in eastern Jasper National Park. The milky-looking water is cloudy with particles of sulphur, and the spring emits the rotten-egg odor of hydrogen sulphide gas.

Some of the gas remains dissolved in the water, which explains why rings made of silver tarnish if worn in a sulphurous hot pool. H_2S also oxidizes to form microscopic particles of elemental sulphur (S) that give the water flowing from most of our springs its characteristic milky look.

Springs that *don't* smell like rotten eggs are those in which oxygen has mixed with the water on the way up (e.g. Radium and Fairmont). Odorless hot springs are not nearly as common as stinky ones.

Heavy rainfalls sometimes dilute and thus cool the flow from hot springs. Such downpours also wash foreign material (plant matter, soil particles) into the systems. Earthquakes can dirty the water of Rockies springs by shock disturbance to the systems (the great Alaska Earthquake did this from a distance of 2300 km in 1964). However, the notable water-dirtying and cooling at Miette Hot Springs in Jasper park after the big eruption of Mt. St. Helens in 1980 was caused by a thunderstorm, not directly by the eruption—although the sudden onset of rainy weather throughout western North America that summer may have been related to the event. Water droplets condense around airborne particles of dust, and the volcano ejected great quantities of tephra (volcanic dust) into the atmosphere.

Tufa

Surrounding most springs are deposits of **tufa** ("TOO-fuh," not to be confused with tuff, a kind of volcanic rock). The tufa deposits in our area are lumpy, spongy-looking masses of crumbly calcite (with a little gypsum) that build up in layers as the hot water dribbles out. Dissolved carbon dioxide escapes, reducing the water's capacity to hold calcium and magnesium compounds in solution, so tiny crystals form. These accumulate as the tufa deposit. Evaporation also causes some precipitation of calcite and gypsum, especially when the water flow is slow and the hot-spring stream doesn't join another water body for some distance.

Mineral springs

A **mineral spring** in the Canadian Rockies is simply a hot spring that flows cool at the surface. The hot water either cools a great deal on the return trip to the surface (perhaps by traveling farther or slower), or it becomes diluted with enough cool groundwater to lose its heat. Such springs tend to produce little tufa, but they often carry dissolved iron that precipitates as the iron-oxide mineral **goethite** ("GUR-tite," $HFeO_2$) which colors the surface around many of our mineral springs brilliantly red, orange and ochre.

The **Paint Pots** near Marble Canyon in Kootenay park are the most famous of these springs. The oxides there were used as pigments by the Stoney and Kootenay Indians. A geological study of the Paint Pots concludes that they probably lie over a deposit of lead and zinc sulphides, similar to the ones near Field (see page 755 for a description of the mines there).

Life in a hot spring

Colonies of highly specialized algae and bacteria are present in our sulphurous hot springs and mineral springs. Much of the soft, gray, pasty-looking material surrounding such springs is actually alive! Bright-yellow or purple coloring is from sulphur-dependent bacteria; stripes of white or brilliant green are usually algae.

Deprived of a spring's queer water chemistry and/or heat, these sensitive organisms die, as happens at the Banff springs due to influxes of normal water from heavy rain or rapid snowmelt.

Tropical fish are present in marshes warmed by one of the Banff springs. See page 556 for the details.

HOT SPRINGS AND MINERAL SPRINGS OF THE CANADIAN ROCKIES

Name (see numbered notes for location)	Temp °C	Flow l/min	TDS* ppm	pH	Remarks
1. Turtle Mountain	9.1	450	748	7.1	Sulphur odor
2. Fording Mountain	25.9	325	2647	7.1	Sulphur odor
3. Wildhorse River	28.5	440	-	6.6	Odorless
4. Ram Creek	36.6	225	225	7.6	Beware poison ivy
5. Lussier Canyon	43.4	225	2708	7.1	Sulphur odor, log pool
6. Red Rock	-	-	-	-	Emerges in river bottom
7. Fairmont	48.9	2200	2069	6.8	Odorless, developed
8. Radium	47.7	1817	706	6.8	Odorless, developed
9. The Paint Pots	10.7	330	3086	3.7	Iron pigment; tasteless
10. Canmore Creek	6.1	5	1135	7.2	Slight sulphur odor
11. Banff (Upper)	47.3	545	1029	7.2	Sulphur odor, developed
12. Banff (Kidney)	39.2	91	1060	7.1	Sulphur odor
13. Banff (Middle)	34.8	225	1100	7.1	Sulphur odor
14. Banff (Cave)	32.8	500	963	7.2	Sulphur odor, developed
15. Banff (Basin)	34.5	680	1677	7.1	Sulphur odor, developed
16. Banff (Pool)	32.0	550	974	7.2	Sulphur odor
17. Vermilion Lake	19.7	750	411	7.4	Sulphur odor
18. Stoney Squaw**	6.5	1	584	7.4	Slight sulphur odor
19. Mt. Fortune	14.0	-	1697	7.7	Strong sulphur odor
20. Panther River	3.0	45	1146	7.4	Slight odor, no tufa
21. Forty-Mile Creek	-	-	-	-	Small, lukewarm, odor
22. Ink Pots	4.8	1800	253	7.5	Odorless karst springs
23. Canoe River	60.0	15	1540	-	Odorless
24. Miette	53.9	800	1865	6.9	Strong odor, developed
25. Cold Sulphur	9.0	>500	724	7.4	Strong odor
26. Overlander	-	-	-	-	Flooded in summer, odor
27. Shale Banks	-	-	-	-	Cool, iron pigment
28. Mud Creek	-	-	-	-	Cool, mineral mounds
29. Prophet River	-	-	-	-	No information
30. Racing River	-	-	-	-	Sulphur odor
31. Liard River	54.0	2400	-	-	Sulphur odor, developed
32. Deer River	32.0	4400	-	-	Sulphur odor
33. Portage Brule	48.0	40	814	7.1	Odorless

Hyphens indicate data not available.

*"TDS" is abbreviation for "total dissolved solids," a measure of how mineral-rich the water is. "ppm" = parts per million. Normal drinking water usually has less than 400 ppm TDS.

**No longer evident. See note 18.

Sources: van Everdingen (1972); McDonald, Pollock and McDermot (1978); Kevin Van Tighem (Parks Canada, Jasper).

Location notes

1. Just west of Frank, Alberta. Follow Highway 3 across the Crowsnest River bridge, then note two gas stations a little farther on. Slow down and start looking for a trail south of the railway tracks with an old cabin beside it. Follow a short distance between rock outcrops and across a creek to the spring.
2. From Natal, take the Elk River Road 26.6 km north to springs and pools in a large meadow.
3. From Ft. Steele, follow the road up Wildhorse River for 27 km, where a dirt track branches right; follow it down to the river. The springs (one warm, two cold) are on the other side.
4. Approach from Skookumchuck, via Lussier River Road (14.5 km), or as per Lussier Canyon springs (see note 5), continuing another 18.5 km past the Lussier springs and turning off on Hobonoff Road. Follow over a pass and down to the springs.
5. 6.5 km south of Canal Flats, follow White Swan Lake Road 18.5 km to a widened parking lot and short path to the river. Two springs, one with a bathhouse.
6. Follow the Kootenay River Road from Canal Flats 15.2 km northeast to the Red Rock site and tufa deposits.
7. Between Radium and Canal Flats along Highway 93. Resort.
8. A few kilometres east of Radium along Highway 93. Operated by Kootenay National Park; open year-round.
9. 3 km south of Marble Canyon on Highway 93, in Kootenay park. Interpretive signs.
10. From Canmore, take the Spray Lakes Road a few kilometres to Canmore Creek and follow a trail 800 m to a spring on the north side of the creek.
11. Follow Banff Avenue south across the river; follow signs 4.5 km up Sulphur Mountain to the aquacourt.
12. From upper Banff springs, follow Mountain Avenue back toward Banff for about 200 m; springs lie beside the road.
13. As per upper Banff springs, but park at the curve where the road turns south and follow a trail west 400 m to springs.
14. At the east end of the Cave-and-Basin Aquacourt, reached through a short tunnel.
15. At the west end of the Cave-and-Basin Aquacourt, in an artificial pool.
16. From the southeast corner of the Cave-and-Basin Aquacourt, take stairs to a trail and follow it past the hole in the top of the cave to the Pool Springs.
17. Follow Vermilion Lakes Drive from Banff west to Third Vermilion Lake, where there are springs beside the road.
18. Along the TransCanada Highway, on the northeast side of the Mt. Norquay interchange (western entry to Banff). During recent highway construction here the spring has been covered with earth and forced to drain away underground, so there is no sign of it at the surface.
19. Follow Spray River Fire Road about 35 km to a warden cabin (or approach the same cabin more quickly if the Calgary Power road along the north side of Spray Lake is open). The springs are 360 m north of the cabin, on a trail.
20. Follow Cascade Fire Road 48 km to springs on both sides of Panther River.
21. From upper Mt. Norquay ski area parking lot (near Banff), follow the Cascade Amphitheatre trail north 3.1 km to a crossing of Forty-Mile Creek (keep right at the junction with the trail to Mystic Pass). Leave the main trail at the creek and follow the north bank of the creek, crossing a tributary. The spring is about half a kilometre farther, in the woods.
22. From Johnston Canyon, along Highway 1A between Banff and Castle Junction, follow a marked trail 6.4 km to several pools.
23. Jeep 15 km south of Valemount along the west bank of Kinbasket Lake. The springs are close to the shore.
24. From Pocahontas, 41 km east of Jasper, follow Fiddle Valley Road south to the springs at the end.
25. 20 km east of Jasper along Highway 16, just east of the first bridge over Athabasca River. Marked by an interpretive sign.
26. From Cold Sulphur Spring (#25), find a trailhead 100 m west at the same parking area and follow Overlander Trail for about 6 km. Look for a faint path branching west down to the river. A small mineral spring flows out at the base of a short cliff at river level; it's covered by the river from June through August.
27. From Shale Banks warden cabin along Snake Indian Fire Road in eastern Jasper park, follow the east bank of Snake Indian River about 1 km to a small orange-pigmented cold spring.
28. Just west of Mud Creek in northern Jasper park, on both sides of the North Boundary Trail. Marshy area of 1-2 ha (4-5 acres) with several flowing pools up to 5 m across, some in mounds of soft tufa (?). No odor, but strong mineral taste. Apparently unstudied.
29. Near the Prophet River headwaters, but no other information.
30. Near the junction of Toad and Racing rivers, northwest of the Alaska Highway. No other data.
31. After crossing Liard River on Alaska Highway, continue to Liard Hot Springs Provincial Park. The springs are developed, but no admission fee is charged. Interesting boardwalk approach across warm marshes.
32. Follow a trail 16 km east along the north bank of Liard River from the Alaska Highway crossing at Kilometre 800, turning north up Deer River. It's 13 km farther to the springs, involving six river fords.
33. Eight springs and seeps in a 30-mm strip along north bank of Liard River about 3 km east of mouth of Coal River. Approach unknown, but the Alaska Highway passes within a few kilometres of the site.

The Sunwapta River, a typical braided stream.

RIVERS

Rivers are the main exporters of the substance of the Rocky Mountains, but a fair bit also departs dissolved in groundwater, and a little leaves by air in the form of dust.

The **Liard** is the biggest river in the region, with an average discharge of 1350 m³/sec, measured near the northern tip of the Rockies. The Peace is next largest at 1050 m³/sec, measured at the mountain front. The others are much smaller; check the table on the next page.

River flow (properly termed **discharge**) varies greatly with the seasons in the Canadian Rockies. The lowest rate of discharge generally comes in March, although for a few rivers low water comes in February or even as early as January. Annual greatest discharge is reached at the peak of snowmelt, which usually comes in late June or early July. The average crest can be up to 100 times the average minimum flow, although a figure between 15 and 30 times the minimum flow is typical. The champion trickle/flood river is the Kootenay, measured at Kootenay Crossing in Kootenay park. This is the one with the hundred-fold increase. The most well-adjusted river is the Cascade (which is otherwise rather odd; check the stats), at 4.3 times minimum.

Note how the glacially fed main-range rivers of the central Rockies tend to peak in July while most of the others peak in June. Meltwater from the high-elevation uplands, with their glaciers, seems to contribute the most to the annual swelling of major central-Rockies rivers; discharge rises dramatically when summer hits the icefields along the continental divide.

Streams fed by meltwater also have a pronounced *daily* cycle. Hikers in the Rockies often learn about this the hard way. They cross a stream easily in the morning, hopping from rock to rock. But when they return in the late afternoon, the brook has turned into a roaring monster and crossing is quite out of the question. It may take hours to find a safe crossing point—or a long wait until the daily surge has gone by. The farther downstream you are, the longer it takes for the crest to pass; at Jasper, the Athabasca doesn't quit rising until the wee hours of the morning.

The Canadian Rockies are famous for **braided streams**: gravelly streams with multiple channels. The Sunwapta River at Beauty Creek (45 km south of Jasper on the Icefields Parkway) is a classic example. The valley is wide and filled wall-to-wall with gravel. The river, which carries mostly meltwater from the Columbia Icefield, splits up and wanders about the stony flats in many shallow separate channels that rejoin and diverge. "Braided" describes the river perfectly.

Braided streams and glaciers go together. Glacial meltwater is loaded with mud and stones that cannot be carried far unless the streambed is steep. In the case of the Sunwapta, the bed is steep enough for a while, but not across the flats at Beauty Creek. The speed of the river slows and thus its load-carrying ability diminishes. So the load gets dumped and the valley clogs with debris. The Sunwapta sneaks through Beauty Flats, spreading out and finding its way at low speed among the gravel bars. The number of channels that are used changes hour by hour, as the river level rises and falls; the positions of the channels change day by day, as the river cuts and fills.

Consider also the character of the water in that river. Like the Athabasca, or any glacial stream near its source, the Sunwapta is dishwater gray with glacial muck. Much of this is **rock flour**: tiny bits ground from the glacier's bed. Included in the suspended load are pollen that landed on the glacial surface, particles of forest-fire smoke and atmospheric dust that once formed the nuclei of the snowflakes that became the glaciers. See page 234 for the effect this material has on lakes downstream.

Amazingly, fish thrive in the milky Athabasca. Fisherfolk at Jasper catch rainbow trout, brook trout and whitefish—but can't tell what is on the line until it comes flapping out of the murk.

DISCHARGE DATA FOR RIVERS IN THE CANADIAN ROCKIES (m^3/sec)

Name and station site	Watershed area (km^2)	Mean flow	March min	June max	Record maximum and date	
Athabasca near Jasper	3880	89	10.1	272*	637	11 Jun 72
Athabasca at Hinton	9780	175	30	508	1270	13 Jun 72
Belly near Mountain View	319	8.8	1.9J	31	464	8 Jun 64
Blaeberry near Golden	738	20	3.1	63	125	3 Jun 67
Bow River at Lake Louise	421	11	1.4	32*	123	14 Jun 18
Bow River at Banff	2210	40	7.6	128	399	14 Jun 23
Bow River at Calgary	7860	92	43F	237	2270	18 Jun 97
Brazeau below Cardinal R	2590	56	-	96	668	4 Jun 80
Brewster Ck near Banff	109	2.3	0.1	5.5	20	17 Jun 74
Bull River near mouth	1530	34	7.4F	112	428	17 Jun 74
Cardinal near the mouth	495	7.4	-	14	278	4 Jun 80
Cascade near Banff	664	8.0	3.7M	16*	74	28 Jun 15
Castle near Beaver Mines	826	17	2.7F	65	736	20 Jun 75
Clearwater above Limestone Ck	1340	23	0.6F	39	510	18 Jun 65
Columbia near Fairmont	891	11	3.6	36	99	11 Jun 72
Columbia at Donald	9710	175	31F	528	1320	12 Jun 72
Columbia at Nicholson	6660	109	23F	325*	770	11 Jun 72
Crowsnest near Frank	402	5.1	1.3F	16	74	9 Jun 53
Elbow above Elbow Falls	437	7.4	1.8	20	159	30 May 67
Elbow at Bragg Ck	792	7.7	2.5F	26	283	31 May 67
Elk River at Fernie	3110	50	12F	178	620	18 Jun 74
Finlay at Ware	11000	190	30	722	1720	12 Jun 64
Finlay at Finlay Forks	43300	680	128	2360	6140	29 May 48
Flathead at Flathead	1110	27	4.9F	102[1]	462	8 Jun 64
Forty-Mile Ck near Banff	133	3.5	0.5	7.2	21	17 Jun 74
Fraser at Red Pass	1700	47	5.6	149	402	12 June 72
Fraser at McBride	6890	201	32	579	1390	12 Jun 72
Ghost near Black Rock Mtn	211	3.3	0.5	8.8	126	13 Jun 53
Halfway above Graham R	3780	28	4.4F	85	289	3 Jul 79
Highwood near Eden Vly IR	776	13	-	41	283	9 Jun 53
James near Sundre	821	6.2	0.6J	11	215	25 Jun 72
Johnston Ck near mouth	124	3.3	-	6.5	36	26 May 81
Jumpingpound Ck near mouth	571	1.5	0.1J	6.4	138	29 Jun 69
Kananaskis near Seebe	933	15	7.2A[2]	41	337	2 Jun 32
Kechika at mouth	22700	243	46	407	1980	12 Jun 64
Kicking Horse near Field	344	11	1.2	50[3]	124	26 Jun 12
Kicking Horse at Golden	1850	41	5.4	129	402	19 Jun 16
Kootenay near Kootenay Crossing	420	4.5	0.2	20	53	6 Jun 61
Kootenay at Canal Flats	5390	89	18	302	841	24 May 48
Kootenay at Newgate	20000	298	72F	1050	2780	28 May 48
Kwadacha near Ware	2720	49.3	6.3	161	391	14 Jun 72
Liard above Beaver R	119000	1150	251	4300	9510	16 Jul 74
Maligne near mouth	908	16	2.2	47*	92	8 Jul 82
McGregor above Woodall Ck	4770	235	40F	671	2090	12 Jun 72
McLeod above Embarras	5540	21	2.4F	61	1260	5 Jun 80
Miette near Jasper	651	11	0.9F	40	121	23 Jun 74

Name and station site	Watershed area (km^2)	Mean flow	March min	June max	Record maximum and date	
Mistaya at Sask Crossing	249	6.5	0.6	21*	64	15 Jul 53
Moose near Red Pass	458	15	1.3	51	189	18 Jun 67
Murray above Wolverine R	2410	53	7.9	198	395	4 Jun 79
Muskeg near Grande Cache	706	6.0	1.1	18	286	12 Jun 72
Muskwa near Ft. Nelson	20300	207	16F	596*	4620	28 Jun 75
North Saskatchewan at Sask Crossing	1290	45	3.0	134*	314	15 Jul 53
N Sask at Whirlpool Point	1920	53	4.9F	169*	377	11 Jun 72
N Sask at Saunders	5160	99	12	254*	1240	27 Jun 15
N Sask near Rocky Mtn House	11000	141	24F	349*	4110	27 Jun 15
Oldman near Brocket	4400	41	7.8J	157	1560	20 Jun 75
Parsnip above Misinchinka R	4900	148	26F	491	1380	13 Jun 72
Parsnip below Misinchinka	5520	212	48F	718	1190	3 Jun 67
Parsnip near Finlay Forks	20300	390	87	1280	2830	4 Jun 64
Peace at Hudson's Hope	70200	1050	558	3070	8810	14 Jun 64
Pipestone near Lk Louise	306	10	0.7	18	81	14 Jun 18
Ram near mouth	1860	16	3.0	49	951	27 Jun 15
Red Deer above Panther R	943	17	-	34	154	16 Jun 70
Redearth Ck near mouth	147	6.0	-	12	43	24 Jun 74
" below Burnt Timber Ck	2250	20	4.9J	63	311	17 Jun 74
Rocky near mouth	1140	15	1.7F	51*	168	27 Jun 15
Sheep at Black Diamond	554	4.9	0.9	21	200	28 Jun 16
Siffleur near mouth	510	16	-	27	62	14 Jun 81
Smoky near Grande Cache	3840	80	9.1	262	1380	12 Jun 72
Snake Indian near mouth	1580	47	-	97	564	12 Jun 72
Spray at Banff	749	9.3	2.7F	28	156	17 Jun 33
Sukunka above Burnt R	927	21	1.8F	86	280	27 May 79
Sukunka near mouth	2510	47	5.1F	186	507	27 May 79
Sunwapta at Athabasca Gl	48	2.4	-	4.7	15	17 Jul 55
Toad above Nonda R	2570	43	7.2	130	762	17 Jul 74
Trout near Muncho Lk	1190	15.7	5.5	43	411	16 Jul 74
Vermilion at Mt Verendrye	951	22	3.0	73	191	5 Jun 56
Waiparous near mouth	334	1.8	0.3J	5.4	110	31 May 67
Wapiti above Mistanusk Ck	2400	77	7.4	138	328	4 Jun 79
Waterton below L Wat Lk	614	19	3.6	80	728	9 Jun 64
Whirlpool at mouth	598	29	-	48*	121	23 Jun 74
Wood at Kinbasket Lk	956	41	4.2F	119*	343	27 Jun 68

Letter following minimum figure: minimum reached in month other than March (J = January, F = February, A = April, M = May)

*Maximum comes in July instead of June
[1] Flathead crests in May
[2] Kananaskis minimum came in March before damming
[3] Kicking Horse crests in August

Data source: Environment Canada (1981, 1983)

LAKES: HOW *DO* THEY GET THOSE COLORS?

Before answering that question, a couple of statistics. The longest lake in the Canadian Rockies is Maligne, in Jasper park (22.3 km). The deepest with a verifiable sounding is Upper Waterton, at 148 m. However, the depth of Muncho Lake, along the Alaska Highway, is quoted in tourist literature as 223 m, even though the official depth, taken by the BC government in 1972, is 109 m. A new official depth is expected soon. In the meantime, Maligne is third-deepest at 97 m.

On to the question I get asked by visitors a hundred times every summer: what accounts for the brilliant hues of the lakes in our area?

It is *not* because the surface is simply reflecting the sky, although sky color can have a minor effect, and the amount of sun reaching the surface certainly makes a difference. Nor is it because the bottoms are coated with copper sulphate (misinformation regularly passed off on tourists in our area).

Digging through two university libraries has failed to turn up a definitive study of mountain lake colors. Nonetheless, based on some straightforward physics and educated guesses from a hydrologist friend (who wishes to remain unnamed in case he's wrong), here is what *I* have been telling the tourists.

Water is highly transparent, but it tends to absorb the longer wavelengths of light (yellow, red) more than it does the shorter wavelengths (blue, green). These blue and green hues are reflected back to our eyes, and that is why water is blue or bluegreen. It is the same for the blueness seen in ice, although trapped air bubbles scatter the light, making ice look white. (The whiteness of snow is also due to light-scattering.) Contaminants in glacial ice often give glaciers a dirty gray look.

Liquid water can give a deep blue tone—*if* the water is very clear, relatively free of algae and other microscopic dwellers (which are inclined to turn it murky brown), and also not carrying much in the way of dissolved minerals.

When free of rock flour, Canadian Rockies river water meets all these criteria for clarity. It hasn't traveled very far from its source and it is quite cold, so there isn't much organic matter or dissolved material in it. That is why many Rockies streams are wonderfully clear (the ones that aren't glacier-fed).

Suppose this clear water flows into a lake. When the depth reaches a couple of metres, then the beautiful blue color starts to show. Viewed from the upper tramway terminal on The Whistlers, Lac Beauvert and the other lakes across the river from Jasper townsite look brilliantly blue. The ones west of town lie in iron-rich rock, contain more dissolved minerals and more organic matter than the others, so they are darker.

Light is gradually absorbed with increasing depth, so deep water that is pure looks practically black—the midnight blue color one sees in many of the deeper lakes in the Rockies that are not glacially fed.

Consider now the water that comes from a glacier. The meltwater stream carries boulders, rocks, sand, silt, pollen, atmospheric dust, soot from forest fires and rock flour. All this turns the water mucky gray or brown as it departs the glacial snout.

Let's follow that glacial stream along until it enters a lake. The boulders, gravel and sand drop out as the water slows, gradually building a delta out from shore. The silt gets somewhat farther into the lake, but soon it, too, sinks to the bottom. This leaves the rock flour and the other colloidal-sized particles (those less than about 1 micron in size), which are so small that they can stay in suspension in the water for months. The colloidal fraction diffuses—spreads out in all directions—and thus distributes itself as evenly as possible through the whole lake.

And that is when some magic occurs. A particle of any kind reflects most strongly the wavelength of light closest to its size. A mix of sizes gives a whitish look to lake water because the particles are reflecting all the wavelengths. But as the larger particles settle out the smaller ones remain in suspension. These reflect strongly in the blue and green parts of the spectrum. Fluorescence (emission of light by certain minerals) is a minor factor.

Lakes and lake colors

Maligne Lake in Jasper National Park, Spirit Island in the foreground. The oft-heard statement that Maligne is the "second-largest glacier-fed lake in the world" is untrue; there are many lakes larger than Maligne supplied by glacial meltwater, including several in British Columbia. Photo courtesy Jasper National Park.

Dunes and blowing sand along Highway 16 beside Jasper Lake. Photo taken in winter, when the lakebed is dry and the wind picks up sand and dust from it. Photo courtesy Jasper National Park.

Thus, a lake loaded with particles is gray (like the meltwater pond at the toe of the Athabasca Glacier). A lake in which some of the particles have settled is pastel green (as Lake Louise often is) and a lake in which only the finer particles remain is bluegreen (Maligne Lake is a good example).

The other part of the glacial-lake-color magic is the *uniformity* of the color. The whole lake is often the same shade. Why?

This is harder to explain, but here is a working hypothesis. Diffusion of the colloidal rock particles accounts for some of the uniformity. The tiny particles also reflect light upward, scatter it and absorb it; scuba divers find that such lakes darken quickly with depth. When you look down into Lake Louise, for example, it may be that you are seeing the upper, optically active layer of water, which masks the deeper, optically inactive dark water beneath. But no one seems to have the definitive answer to this question.

Perhaps the best place to explore (and appreciate) the nature of glacial lake color is at Maligne Lake, and the best time is early in the summer. Take the commercial boat trip. Cruising toward the inlet end in June takes you over the dark depths for awhile, then suddenly the boat crosses a line into that colorful water the Rockies are famous for. This is the diffusion front of the rock flour spreading northward through the lake as the melting season proceeds. By late July it has reached the outlet, and the Maligne River runs a little milky until freeze-up reduces the glacial flow and allows the water to clear over the winter. The milky water also travels through the Maligne cave system (page 223), causing the springs at Maligne Canyon to run milky and bringing an uncharacteristic opalescence to Lac Beauvert, which is also fed from springs carrying Maligne water.

SAND DUNES IN THE CANADIAN ROCKIES?

Yes, there are dunes here. Perhaps the best-developed set is at **Jasper Lake**, 20 km east of Jasper townsite along Highway 16. Jasper Lake is the first large water body along the Athabasca River, so it receives a great deal of glacial sand and silt each year. It also has an interesting annual cycle, and the cycle produces the dunes.

In the fall and winter Jasper Lake is a barren sand flat 8 km long and 2 km wide. Every spring, usually in late May, it fills—although to a depth of less than a metre in most places (except along the Athabasca main channel, which lies near the north shore and is several metres deep). Thus, it is possible to wade far out into the lake before it gets even knee-deep. In late summer the lake shrinks again, exposing the silty, sandy floor to the westerly wind—constant and strong in this valley—which picks up the grains and carries them down the lake in dust storms.

The silt stays aloft for many kilometres, dusting the foothills to the east,* but the sand grains are too heavy to rise more than about a metre above the surface; they proceed in short hops until they reach places where the wind speed drops. There they form dunes up to 30 m in height.

You can see some of these dunes along Highway 16. The ones beside the road are small and mostly overgrown, but across the lake and farther west they are fresher and larger. The wind howls through the Jasper Lake dunes. Stones lying among them have been eroded and polished on their upwind sides by sandblasting—like the faceted stones one finds in windy deserts.

---

*Deposits of windblown silt are called **loess,** a German word pronounced somewhere between "loose" and "lurse." At the end of the last major ice advance (late-Wisconsinan), the glaciers retreated very quickly, leaving most of the major valley bottoms in the Canadian Rockies bare of trees. Huge quantities of silt picked up by the wind in these valleys now lie in loess deposits throughout the eastern front ranges and foothills; the greatest proportion, though, was spread over the prairies.

REFERENCES CITED AND GEOLOGY READING LIST

Deciding to cite a few references in the geology chapters has led me to include a bibliography of selected technical publications. This is because there are not many authoritative and up-to-date nontechnical items on the geology of the Canadian Rockies. The few available are marked with an asterisk.

At the end there is a list of geological maps of the region published by the Geological Survey of Canada (abbreviated here as "GSC") and available at the GSC's Institute of Sedimentary and Petroleum Geology in Calgary (3303 33rd St. NW, Calgary T2L 2A7; 403-284-0110). Many of the GSC reports in the reference list are available here, as are topographic maps. See pages 244 and 245 for lists of geological and topographic maps.

Aitken, J.D. (1966) "Middle Cambrian to Middle Ordovician cyclic sedimentation, southern Rocky Mountains of Alberta" *Bull. Can. Petrol. Geol.* 14, 405-441
—— (1967A) "Lower Ordovician Survey Peak and Outram Formations, Southern Rocky Mountains of Alberta" *Bull. Can. Petrol. Geol.* 15, 150-207
—— (1967B) *Upper Cambrian Formations, Southern Rocky Mountains of Alberta: an Interim Report* GSC Paper 66-49
—— (1968) *Cambrian Sections in the Easternmost Southern Rocky Mountains and the Adjacent Subsurface, Alberta* GSC Paper 66-23
—— (1971) "Control of Lower Paleozoic sedimentary facies by the Kicking Horse Rim, southern Rocky Mountains, Canada" *Bull. Can. Petrol. Geol.* 19, 557-569
—— (1978) "Revised models for depositional grand cycles, Cambrian of the southern Rocky Mountains, Canada" *Bull. Can. Petrol. Geol.* 26, 515-542
—— et al. (1981) *The Cambrian System in the Southern Canadian Rocky Mountains* Second International Symposium on the Cambrian System, Guidebook for Field Trip 1, available from GSC
*—— (undated) *The Building of the Rocky Mountains of Canada - a Brief Account for Laymen* Unpublished paper for Parks Canada, Calgary
*—— and McIlreath (1984) "The Cathedral Reef Escarpment, a Cambrian great wall with humble origins" *Geos* 13/1, 17-19
Allen, J.A. (1914) *Geology of the Field Map-area* GSC Memoir 55.
Alley, N.F. (1973) "Glacial stratigraphy and the limits of the Rocky Mountain and Laurentide ice sheets in southwestern Alberta, Canada" *Bull. Can. Petrol. Geol.* 21, 153-177
—— and S.A. Harris (1974) "Pleistocene glacial lake sequences in the foothills, southwestern Alberta, Canada" *Can. J. Earth Sci.* 11, 1220-1235
*Alt, D.D. and D.W. Hyndman (1973) *Rocks, Ice and Water: the Geology of Waterton-Glacier Park* Mountain Press, Missoula, Montana
*Baird, D.M. (1963A) *Yoho National Park: the Mountains, the Rocks, the Scenery* GSC Miscellaneous Report 4 (some of the geology in this series is outdated, but the books are worth having for their road logs)
*—— (1963B) *Jasper National Park: behind the Mountains and Glaciers* GSC Miscellaneous Report 6
*—— (1964A) *Kootenay National Park: Wild Mountains and Great Valleys* GSC Miscellaneous Report 9
*—— (1964B) *Waterton Lakes National Park: Lakes amid the Mountains* GSC Miscellaneous Report 10
*—— (1965) *Glacier and Mount Revelstoke National Parks: Where Rivers Are Born* GSC Miscellaneous Report 11
*—— (1967) *Banff National Park: How Nature Carved Its Splendour* GSC Miscellaneous Report 13
Balkwill, H.R. (1972) "Structural geology, lower Kicking Horse River region, Rocky Mountain, British Columbia" *Bull. Can. Petrol. Geol.* 20, 608-633.

Bamber, E.W. and R.W. Macqueen (1979) *Upper Carboniferous and Permian Stratigraphy of the Monkman Pass and Southern Pine Pass Areas, Northeastern British Columbia* GSC Bulletin 301

*Beaty, C.B. (1975) *The Landscapes of Southern Alberta: a Regional Geomorphology* University of Lethbridge Production Services

Bell, R.T. (1968) *Proterozoic Stratigraphy of Northeastern British Columbia* GSC Paper 67-68

*Belyea, H.R. (1960) *The Story of the Mountains in Banff National Park* GSC Miscellaneous Report 1

Blatt, H.; G. Middleton and R. Murray (1980) *Origin of Sedimentary Rocks, 2nd Edition* Prentice-Hall, Englewood Cliffs, NJ

Boydell, A.N. (1978) *Multiple Glaciations in the Foothills, Rocky Mountain House, Alberta* Alberta Research Council Bulletin 36

*British Columbia Provincial Parks (undated) *The Northern Rocky Mountain Landscape: Muncho Lake and Stone Mountain Provincial Parks* BC Provincial Parks, Prince George

Campbell, R.B.; E.W. Mountjoy and F.G. Young (1973) *Geology of McBride Map-area, British Columbia* GSC Paper 72-35

Chamberlain, V.E. and R. St J. Lamberta (1985) "Cordilleria, a newly defined Canadian microcontinent" *Nature* 314, 707-713

Charlesworth, H.A. et al. (1967) *Precambrian Geology of the Jasper Region, Alberta* Research Council of Alberta Bulletin 23

Clague, J.J. (1974) "The St. Eugene Formation and development of the southern Rocky Mountain Trench" *Can. J. Earth Sci.* 11/7, 916-938

—— J.J. (1975) "Late Quaternary sediments and geomorphic history of the southern Rocky Mountain Trench" *Can. J. Earth Sci.* 12, 595-605

—— (1981) *Late-Quaternary Geology and Geochronology of British Columbia* GSC Paper 80-35

Cook, D.G. (1975) *Structural Style Influenced by Lithofacies, Rocky Mountain Main Ranges, Alberta-British Columbia* GSC Bulletin 233

Currie, K.L. (1975) *The Geology and Petrology of the Ice River Alkaline Complex, British Columbia* GSC Bulletin 245

Cruden, D.M. (1976) "Major rock slides in the Rockies" *Canadian Geotechnical Journal* 13/1, pp. 8-20

Dahlstrom, C.D. (1970) "Structural geology in the eastern margin of the Canadian Rocky Mountains" *Bull. Can. Petrol. Geol.* 18, 332-406

Davis, G.A., J.W. Monger and B.C. Burchfiel (1978) "Mesozoic construction of the Cordilleran 'collage,' central British Columbia to central California" in *Mesozoic Symposium* vol. 2, 1-32

Douglas, R.J., ed. (1970) *Geology and Economic Minerals of Canada* GSC Economic Geology Report No. 1

Dumanski, J. et al. (1980) "Pedogenesis and tephrochronology of loess-derived soils, Hinton, Alberta" *Can. J. Earth Sci.* 17, 52-59

Edmonton Geological Society (1964) *Sixth Annual Field Trip Guidebook, Medicine and Maligne Lakes* Edmonton Geological Society

Ettensohn, F.R. and L. Barron (1981) *Depositional Model for the Devonian-Mississippian Black Shale Sequence of North America: a Tectono-climatic Approach* United States Dept. of Energy DOE/METC/12040-2

Ford, D.C., ed. (1983) "Castleguard Cave and karst, Columbia Icefields area, Rocky Mountains of Canada: a symposium" *Arctic and Alpine Research* 15, 425-554

—— et al. (1981) "Estimates of the age of the existing relief within the southern Rocky Mountains of Canada" *Arctic and Alpine Research* 13, 1-10

Frebold, H. (1963) *Illustrations of Canadian Fossils: Ammonite Faunas of the Upper Middle Jurassic Beds of the Fernie Group in Western Canada* GSC Bulletin 93

—— (1964) *Illustrations of Canadian Fossils: Jurassic of Western and Arctic Canada* GSC Paper 63-4

Fulton, R.J., M.M. Fenton and N.W. Rutter (1984) "Summary of Quaternary stratigraphy and history, Western Canada" in *Quaternary Stratigraphy of Canada—a Canadian Contribution to IGCP Project 24* GSC Paper 84-10, 69-83

Gabrielse, H. (1975) *Geology of the Fort Grahame East Half Map-area, British Columbia (94C E1/2)* GSC Paper 75-33

Gale, S.J.; C.O. Hunt and C.C. Smart (in press) *The Castleguard Formation and its implications for Cenozoic Landscape Evolution in the Canadian Rockies*

Geldsetzer, H.H. (1982) "Depositional history of the Devonian succession in the Rocky Mountains southwest of the Peace River Arch" in GSC Paper 82-1C, 55-64

—— and N.C. Meijer Drees (1984) "Upper Devonian surface and subsurface lithostratigraphic units, west central Alberta and east central British Columbia" in *Carbonates in Subsurface and Outcrop* Canadian Society of Petroleum Geologists, Calgary

Gibson, D.W. (1974) *Triassic Rocks of the Southern Canadian Rocky Mountains* GSC Bulletin 230

Gordy, P.L.; F.R. Frey and D.K. Norris (1977) *Geological Guide for the CSPG 1977 Waterton-Glacier Park Field Conference* Canadian Society of Petroleum Geologists, Calgary

Harmon, R.S.; D.C. Ford and H.P. Schwarcz (1977) "Interglacial chronology of the Rocky and Mackenzie Mountains based upon Th-230 - U-234 dating of calcite speleothems" *Can. J. Earth Sci.* 14, 2543-2552

Harris, A.G. and E. Tuttle (1983) "Glacier National Park" in *Geology of National Parks* Kendall/Hunt, Dubuque, Iowa

Harris, S.A. and J. Howell (1977) "Chateau Lake Louise moraines—evidence for a new Holocene glacial event in southwest Alberta" *Bull. Can. Petrol. Geol.* 25, 441-455

*Harrison, J.E. (1976) *Evolution of a Landscape: the Quaternary Period in Waterton Lakes National Park* GSC Miscellaneous Report 26

Henderson, C.M. et al. (in press for 1987) "Carboniferous and Permian Stratigraphy and Depositional History, Eastern Cordillera" in *The Cordilleran Orogen: Canada* GSC Special Publication G-2

Hockley, G.D. (1973) *Stratigraphy and Paleoenvironmental Patterns on the Peyto-Mt. Whyte Sediments (Lower-Middle Cambrian) of the Southwestern Canadian Rocky Mountains* MSc thesis, University of Calgary

Hofmann, H.J., E.W. Mountjoy and M.W. Teitz (1985) "Ediacaran fossils from the Miette Group, Rocky Mountains, British Columbia, Canada" *Geology* 13, 819-821

Holland, S.S. (1976) *Landforms of British Columbia: a Physiographic Outline* BC Dept. of Mines and Petroleum Resources Bulletin 48

Hopkins, W.S. Jr. and N.W. Rutter (1972) "Geology, paleoecology and palynology of some Oligocene rocks in the Rocky Mountain Trench of British Columbia" *Can. J. Earth Sci.* 9, 460-470

Hunt, C.B. (1974) *Natural Regions of the United States and Canada* W.H. Freeman, San Francisco

International Geological Congress (1972) Field excursion guidebooks, available from GSC:

    A15-C15, *The Canadian Rockies and Tectonic Evolution of the Southeastern Canadian Cordillera*

    A03-C03 *Geology of the Southern Canadian Cordillera*

    X01-A01 *Structural Style of the Southern Canadian Cordillera*

    A10 *Stratigraphy and Structure Rocky Mountains and Foothills of West Central Alberta and Northeastern British Columbia*

A19 *Cambrian and Ordovician Biostratigraphy of the Southern Canadian Rocky Mountains*

C18 *Devonian Stratigraphy and Facies of the Southern Rocky Mountains of Canada and the Adjacent Plains*

C17 *Lower Carboniferous Stratigraphy and Sedimentology of the Southern Canadian Rocky Mountains*

A16 *The Permian of the Southeastern Cordillera*

A20 *The Cretaceous and Jurassic of the Foothills of the Rocky Mountains of Alberta*

A21 *Vertebrate Paleontology, Cretaceous to Recent, Interior Plains, Canada*

A02 *Quaternary Geology of the Southern Canadian Cordillera*

C22 *Quaternary Geology and Geomorphology between Winnipeg and the Rocky Mountains*

A26 *Hydrogeology of the Rocky Mountains and Interior Plains*

A25 - C25 *Coal, Oil, Gas and Industrial Mineral Deposits of the Interior Plains, Foothills and Rocky Mountains of Alberta and British Columbia*

Irish, E.J. (1968) *Structure of the Northern Foothills and Eastern Front Ranges, Alberta and British Columbia, between Latitudes 53°15' and 57°20'* GSC Bulletin 168

Jackson, L.E. Jr. (1980) "Glacial history and stratigraphy of the Alberta portion of the Kananaskis Lakes map area" *Can. J. Earth Sci.* 17, 459-477

Javor, B.J. and E.W. Mountjoy (1976) "Late Proterozoic microbiota of the Miette Group, southern British Columbia" *Geology* 4, 111-119

Jeletzky, J.A. (1964) *Illustrations of Canadian Fossils: Lower Cretaceous Index Fossils of the Sedimentary Basins of Western and Arctic Canada* GSC Paper 64-11

Jones, P.B. (1969) "The Tertiary Kishenehn Formation, British Columbia" *Bull. Can. Petrol. Geol.* 17, 234-246

Kearney, M.S. and B.H. Luckman (1981) "Evidence for late Wisconsin-early Holocene climatic/vegetational change in Jasper National Park, Alberta" in *Quaternary Paleoclimate*, Geoabstracts Ltd, Norwich, U.K.

Kerr, R.A. (1983) "An early glacial two-step?" *Science*, 221, 143-144

*Kucera, R.E. (1974) *Lake Louise-Moraine Lake: Interpreting the Mountain Landscape* Published by the author, Vancouver

*—— (1981) *Exploring the Columbia Icefield* High Country, Canmore

Kukla, G.J. (1977) "Pleistocene land-sea correlations, I: Europe" *Earth-Science Review* 13, 307-374

Lang, A.H. (1947) *Brûlé and Entrance Map-areas, Alberta* GSC Memoir 244

Levson, V. (1986) *Quaternary Sedimentation and Stratigraphy of Montane Glacial Deposits in Parts of Jasper National Park, Canada* MSc thesis, University of Alberta

Luck, S. (1979) "Quaternary ash layers as marker beds in sediments in Alberta" *Albertan Geographer* 15, 37-47

Luckman, B.H. (1977) "Lichenometric dating of Holocene moraines at Mount Edith Cavell, Jasper, Alberta" *Can. J. Earth Sci.* 14, 1809-1822

—— (1981) "The geomorphology of the Alberta Rocky Mountains: a review and commentary" *Zeitschrift für Geomorphologie*, Feb. 1981, 91-119

—— (in press) "Reconstructing Little Ice Age events in the Canadian Rockies" *Geographic Physique et Quaternarie*

—— (in press) "Reconstruction of Holocene changes in alpine vegetation and climate in the Maligne Range, Jasper National Park, Alberta" *Quaternary Research*

—— L.A. Jozsa and P.H. Murphy (1984) "Living seven-hundred-year-old **Picca engelmannii** and **Pinus albicaulis** in the Canadian Rockies" *Arctic and Alpine Research* 16, 419-422

—— and G.D. Osborn (1979) "Holocene glacier fluctuations in the middle Canadian Rocky Mountains" *Quaternary Research* 11, 52-77

——, —— and R.H. King (1978) "Chateau Lake Louise moraines—evidence for a new Holocene glacial event in southwest Alberta: a discussion" *Bull. Can. Petrol. Geol.* 26, 398-402

Mathews, W.H. (1978) *Quaternary Stratigraphy and Geomorphology of Charlie Lake (94A) Map-area, British Columbia* GSC Paper 76-20

—— (1980) *Retreat of the Last Ice Sheets in Northeastern British Columbia and Adjacent Alberta* GSC Bulletin 331

McCrossan, R.G. and R.P. Glaister, eds. (1964) *Geological History of Western Canada* Canadian Society of Petroleum Geologists, Calgary

*McDonald, J., D. Pollock and B. McDermot (1978) *Hotsprings of Western Canada: a Complete Guide* Labrador Tea Company, Vancouver

McLaren, D.J. (1955) *Devonian Formations in the Alberta Rocky Mountains between Bow and Athabasca Rivers* GSC Bulletin 35

—— (1958) "Common Devonian fossils from the Alberta Rocky Mountains" in *Alberta Society of Petroleum Geologists Eighth Annual Field Conference Guidebook* Canadian Society of Petroleum Geologists, Calgary

——, A.W. Norris and D.C. McGregor (1962) *Illustrations of Canadian Fossils: Devonian of Western Canada* GSC Paper 62-4

McLearn, F.H. and E.D. Kindle (1950) *Geology of Northeastern British Columbia* GSC Memoir 259

—— and E.W. Mountjoy (1962) *Alexo Equivalents in the Jasper Area* GSC Paper 62-23

McMechan, M.E. (1981) "The Middle Proterozoic Purcell Supergroup in the southwestern Rocky and southeastern Purcell mountains, British Columbia, and the initiation of the Cordilleran Miogeocline, southern Canada and adjacent United States" *Bull. Can. Petrol. Geol.* 29, 583-621

Monger, J.W. (1984) "Cordilleran tectonics: a Canadian perspective" *Bull. Soc. geol. France* 26/2, 255-278

—— R.A. Price and D.J. Tempelman Kluit (1982) "Tectonic accretion and the origin of the two major metamorphic and plutonic welts in the Canadian Cordillera" *Geology* 10, 70-75

*Morris, S.C. and H.B. Whittington (1985) *Fossils of the Burgess Shale: a National Treasure in Yoho National Park, British Columbia* GSC Miscellaneous Report 43

Morrow, D.W. and H. Geldsetzer (in press for 1987) "The Devonian of the Western Cordillera" in *The Cordilleran Orogen: Canada* GSC Special Publication G-2

Mountjoy, E.W. (1958) "Jasper area, Alberta, a source of the Foothills Erratics Train" *Journal of the Alberta Society of Petroleum Geologists* 6, 218-226

—— (1961) "Rocky Mountain front ranges along the Athabasca Valley, Jasper National Park, Alberta" in *Edmonton Geological Society 1961 Guidebook, 3rd Annual Field Trip*

—— (1962) "Mount Robson (Southeast) Map-area, Rocky Mountains of Alberta and British Columbia" GSC Paper 61-31

—— (undated) "Factors governing the development of the Frasnian Miette and Ancient Wall reef complexes (banks and biostromes), Alberta" in *International Symposium on the Devonian System* (No publisher given)

*—— (1979) *Overview and Origin of the Structures of the Rocky and Columbia Mountains* Unpublished report for Parks Canada

—— (1985) "Structure and stratigraphy of the Miette Group, Selwyn Range, between Ptarmigan and Hugh Allan creeks, British Columbia" GSC Paper 85-1A, 485-490

—— and J. Aitken (1978) "Middle Cambrian Snake Indian formation (new), Jasper Region, Alberta" *Bull. Can. Petrol. Geol.* 26, 343-361

—— and W.S. Mackenzie (1973) *Stratigraphy of the Southern Part of the Devonian Ancient Wall Carbonate Complex, Jasper National Park, Alberta* GSC Paper 72-20

Mudge, M.R. (1977) "General Geology of Glacier National Park and adjacent areas, Montana" *Bull. Can. Petrol. Geol.* 25, 736-751

Nelson, S.J. (1965) "Field Methods in Paleontology" *Bull. Can. Petrol. Geol.* 13/1 (common fossils in western Canada)

*—— (1970) *The Face of Time: the Geological History of Western Canada* Canadian Society of Petroleum Geologists, Calgary

Ney, C.S. (1954) "Monarch and Kicking Horse mines, Field, British Columbia" in *Guidebook, Fourth Annual Field Conference* Alta. Soc. Petrol. Geol. (now Can. Soc. Petrol. Geol., Calgary)

Norford, B.S. (1969) *Ordovician and Silurian Stratigraphy of the Southern Rocky Mountains* GSC Bulletin 176

North, F.K. and G. Henderson (1954) "Summary of the geology of the southern Rocky Mountains of Canada" in *Fourth Annual Field Conference, Guide Book* Alberta Society of Petroleum Geologists (now Canadian Soc. Petrol. Geol., Calgary)

Østrem, G. and K. Arnold (1970) "Ice-cored moraines in southern British Columbia and Alberta, Canada" *Geografiska Annaler* 52, 120-128

Price, R.A. (1965) *Flathead Map-area, British Columbia and Alberta* GSC Memoir 336

—— and Gardner, D.A. (1979) "Porcupine Creek Fan Structure: tectonic significance of a reversal in regional structural vergence in the southern Canadian Rockies" Geol. Soc. America *Abstracts with Programs* 11, 499

Poulton, T.P. (1984) "The Jurassic of the Canadian western interior, from 49°N latitude to the Beaufort Sea" in *The Mesozoic of Middle North America* Canadian Society of Petroleum Geologists, Calgary.

Pugh D.C. (1974) *Cambrian Stratigraphy from Western Alberta to Northeastern British Columbia* GSC Paper 74-37

Rasetti, F. (1951) *Middle Cambrian Stratigraphy and Faunas of the Canadian Rocky Mountains* Smithsonian Miscellaneous Collection, vol. 116 no. 5

*Raup, O.B. et al. (1983) *Geology along Going-to-the-Sun Road, Glacier National Park, Montana: a Self-guided Tour for Motorists* Glacier Natural History Assoc., West Glacier, Montana

Roed, M.A. (1975) "Cordilleran and Laurentide multiple glaciation, west-central Alberta, Canada" *Can. J. Earth Sci.* 12, 1493-1515

—— E.W. Mountjoy and N.W. Rutter (1967) "The Athabasca Valley Erratics Train, Alberta, and Pleistocene ice movements across the continental divide" *Can. J. Earth Sci.* 4, 625-632

Rubin, C.M. (1980) *Carbonate Petrology across the Top of the Ptychaspid Biomere, Survey Peak formation, Alberta, Canada* MSc Thesis, University of Montana

Rutter, N.W. (1971) *Quaternary Geology Road Logs, Banff Area, Alberta* GSC Paper 70-67

—— (1972) *Geomorphology and Multiple Glaciation in the Area of Banff, Alberta* GSC Bulletin 206

—— (1977) *Multiple Glaciation in the Area of Williston Lake, British Columbia* GSC Bulletin 273

—— (1984) "Pleistocene history of the western Canadian ice-free corridor" in *Quaternary Stratigraphy of Canada—a Canadian Contribution to IGCP Project 24* GSC Paper 84-10, 49-56

—— (1985) *Quaternary Glacial Events in the Rocky and Mackenzie Mountains (and Adjacent Interior Plains), Bluefish Basin, Yukon Cordillera and Brooks Range, Alaska* Unpublished correlation chart, University of Alberta

Sargent, M.W. (1975) *Depositional Patterns in the Upper Cambrian Lyell formation, Southern Canadian Rocky Mountains* PhD thesis, University of Calgary

Sedgwick, J.K. and W.E. Henoch (1975) *Peyto Glacier: General Information* Inland
    Waters Branch, Environment Canada
Smart, C.C. (1985) *The Maligne Karst System: Winter and Spring Dye Tracing
    (Interim Report)* Report submitted to Parks Canada, Jasper National Park.
Smith, N.D., M.A. Venol and S.K. Kennedy (1982) "Comparison of sedimentation
    regimes in four glacier-fed lakes in western Alberta" in *Research in
    Glacial, Glaciofluvial and Glaciolacustrine Systems*, A.R. Davidson, ed.
Stalker, A. MacS. (1956) *The Erratics Train, Foothills of Alberta* GSC Bulletin 37
—— (1961) *Buried Valleys in central and southern Alberta* GSC Paper 60-32
—— (1963) *Quaternary Stratigraphy in Southern Alberta* GSC Paper 62-34
—— (1968) "Geology of the terraces at Cochrane, Alberta" *Can. J. Earth Sci.* 5,
    1455-1466
—— and J.E. Harrison (1977) "Quaternary geology of the Waterton-Castle River
    region of Alberta" *Bull. Can. Petrol. Geol.* 25, 882-906
Stearn, C.W. (1961) "Devonian stromatoporoids from the Canadian Rocky
    Mountains" *J. of Paleontology* 35/5, 932-948
Stott, D.F. (1984) "Cretaceous Sequences of the Foothills of the Canadian Rocky
    Mountains" in *The Mesozoic of Middle North America* Canadian Society of
    Petroleum Geologists, Calgary.
Stronach, N.J. (1984) "Depositional environments and cycles in the Jurassic Fernie
    Formation, southern Canadian Rocky Mountains" in *The Mesozoic of
    Middle North America* Canadian Society of Petroleum Geologists, Calgary.
Taylor, G.C. (1973) *Tuchodi Lakes Map-area, British Columbia* GSC Memoir 373
—— (1982) *Geological Guide to the Central and Southern Rocky Mountains of
    Alberta and British Columbia* Field guidebook, Trip No. 4, CSPG-AAPG
    Joint Annual Meeting, Calgary, 1982; available from Canadian Society of
    Petroleum Geologists, Calgary
Teitz, M. and E. Mountjoy (1985) *The Yellowhead and Astoria carbonate platforms
    in Late Proterozoic Upper Miette Group, Jasper, Alberta* GSC Paper 85-1A,
    341-348
Thompson, P. (1970) "A method for absolute age determinations of speleothems"
    Canadian Caver 3, 8-18
van Everdingen, R.O. (1972) *Thermal and Mineral Springs in the Southern Rocky
    Mountains of Canada* Environment Canada, Ottawa
Varley, C.J. (1984) "The Cadomin Formation: a model for deep basin type gas
    trapping mechanisms" in *The Mesozoic of Middle North America* Canadian
    Society of Petroleum Geologists, Calgary.
Walcott, C.D. (1923) *Nomenclature of Some Post-Cambrian and Cambrian
    Cordilleran Formations* Smithsonian Miscellaneous Collection, vol. 67, no. 8
—— (1924) *Geological Formations of the Beaverfoot-Brisco-Stanford Range, British
    Columbia* Smithsonian Miscellaneous Collection, vol. 75, no. 1
Walker, M.J. (1973) "The nature and origin of a series of elongated ridges in the
    Morley Flats area of the Bow Valley, Alberta" *Canadian Journal of Earth
    Science* 10, 1340-1346
Water Survey of Canada (1980) *Historical Streamflow Summary, British Columbia,
    to 1979* Inland Waters Branch, Environment Canada
—— (1983) *Historical Streamflow Summary, Alberta, to 1982* Inland Waters
    Branch, Environment Canada
Young, F.G. (1979) *The Lowermost Paleozoic McNaughton Formation and
    Equivalent Cariboo Group of Eastern British Columbia: Piedmont and Tidal
    Complex* GSC Bulletin 288
Ziegler, P.A. (1969) *The Development of Sedimentary Basins in Western and Arctic
    Canada* Canadian Society of Petroleum Geologists, Calgary

Geologic maps of the Canadian Rockies
available as of 1986 from the Geological Survey of Canada

GSC address: 3303 33 St. NW, Calgary T2L 2A7 (403-284-0110)

Those called "open-file" are still in press, but one-color prints of the roughs are available from **Riley's Datashare International,**
1223 31 Avenue NE, Calgary T2E 7W1 (403-230-5942).

Canadian Cordillera (1505) 1981
Southeastern Cordillera (IGC map) 1972
Kootenay River (GSC open-file 481)
Cross-sections: Rocky Mountains to Fraser Plateau (GSC open-file 844)
Structure Section of the Cordilleran Foreland Thrust and Fold Belt West of Calgary, Alberta (GSC Paper 84-14, by Price and Fermor)

82 G/7	Flathead E (1154) 1965
	Cardston (49-3) 1949
82 G/W	Fernie (11-1960) 1960
82 G/9	Blairmore (55-18) 1955
	Beaver Mines (739) 1943
	Carbondale River (RCA 22) 1951
	Cowley (816) 1945
	Callum Creek (982) 1949
	Pekisko Creek (698) 1942
	Gap (978) 1949
82 J/7	Mount Head E (1958)
	Upper Elk & Upper Highwood Rivers (1980) 1924
	Bragg Creek (654) 1942
	Turner Valley (257) 1931
82 K/E	Lardeau (12-1957) 1957
82 M/E	Big Bend (12-1964) 1971
82 M/W	Adams Lake (48-1963) 1963
82 N	Rogers Pass (4-1961) 1961
82 N/1	Mount Goodsir E/W (1476, 1477) 197
82 N/7	Golden E/W (1496, 1497) 1980
82 N/8	Lake Louise E/W (1482, 1483) 1980
82 N/9	Hector Lake E/W (1463, 1464) 1978
82 N/16	Siffleur River E/W (1465, 1466) 1978

82 O	Calgary (1457) 1978
	Ribbon Creek (RCA 21) 1949
	Canmore E/W (1265, 1266) 1970
	Banff Geomorphology (Rutter, 1972)
82 O/4	Banff E/W (1294) 1972
82 O/5	Mount Eisenhower E/W (1296, 1297)
82 O/6	Lake Minnewanka, E/W (1271) 1970
82 O/12	Barrier Mountain E/W (1273, 1274) 1971
33 O/13	Scalp Creek E/W (1275, 1276) 1971
	Main Ranges, Vermilion Pass to Blaeberry R/Bow L (1368) 1974
83	Athabasca River (1339) 1977
83 C/1	Whiterabbit Creek (1388, 1389) 1974
83 C/13	Medicine Lake (GSC open-file 372)
83 D	Canoe River (15-1967) 1967
83 D/16	Jasper (1611A) 1985
83 D/9	Amethyst Lakes (GSC open-file 1075)
83 E	Mount Robson (1499) 1980
83 F/4	Miette E/E (40-1959) 1959
83 E/14	Grande Cache E/W (1049) 1957
93	Parsnip River (1424) 1979
93 A/E	Quesnel Lake (1-1963) 1963
	Fort Nelson (Taylor, not released)
93 I	Monkman Pass (GSC open-file 630)
93 O	MacKenzie (GSC open-file 925)
94 B	Halfway River (1232) 1968
94 F,G	Trutch (GSC open-file 606)
94 K	Tuchodi Lakes (1343) 1972
94 L	Kechika (42-1962) 1962
94 M	Rabbit River (46-1962) 1962
94 N	Toad River (GSC open-file 673)

Topographic maps of the Canadian Rockies
Scale 1:250,000 (also available at 1:50,000,
but the list would be too long to include here)

82 G	Fernie		93 I	Monkman
82 H	Lethbridge		93 J	McLeod Lake
82 I	Gleichen		93 N	Manson River
82 J	Kananaskis		93 O	Pine Pass
82 K	Lardeau		93 P	Dawson Creek
82 M	Seymour Arm		94 A	Charlie Lake
82 N	Golden		94 B	Halfway River
82 O	Calgary		94 C	Mesilinka River
83 B	Rocky Mountain House		94 E	Toodoggone River
83 C	Brazeau		94 F	Ware
83 D	Canoe River		94 G	Trutch
83 E	Mount Robson		94 J	Fort Nelson
83 F	Edson		94 K	Tuchodi Lakes
83 L	Wapiti		94 L	Kechika
93 A	Quesnel Lake		94 M	Rabbit River
93 G	Prince George		94 N	Toad River
93 H	McBride			

Scale 1:500,000

82 SE	Cranbrook Lethbridge		93 NW	Smithers - Fort St. James
82 NW	Vernon - Golden		93 NE	Prince George - Dawson Creek
82 NE	Banff - Bassano			
83 SE	Red Deer - Edmonton		94 SE	Hudson Hope
83 SW	Tête Jaune - Edson		94 SW	Finlay River
83 NW	Grande Prairie		94 NE	Fort Nelson - Kotcho Lake
93 SE	Williams Lake - Prince George		94 NW	Liard River

Scale 1:1,000,000
The maps below have been reproduced in this book (pages 834-849).

NM-11	Kootenay Lake		NN-11	Lesser Slave Lake
NM-12	Lethbridge		NO-9	Dease Lake
NN-10	Prince George		NO-10	Fort Nelson

Satellite photo-mosaics (Landsat false color, about 20 x 20 cm)
Order from National Air Photo Library,
2464 Sheffield Road, Ottawa, ON K1A 0E9

Single-frame Landsat prints and slides also available, as are standard aerial
photographs too numerous to list here.

1608	Kootenay River, NTS 82		1647	Beatton River, NTS 94
1609	Athabasca River, NTS 83		1649	Parsnip River, NTS 93
1610	Hay River, NTS 84		1651	Fraser River, NTS 92

Large satellite photo-mosaics (color or black-and-white, about 60 x 60 cm)

Map sheet 11 (Alberta-Saskatchewan)
Map sheet 12 (British Columbia)

These two have been spliced and reproduced on page 2.

Sailing on Maligne Lake; thunderhead growing in the background.

Weather and climate

Weather and climate
Could be worse, could be better, but not bad

Like the biology and the geology, the climate* of the Canadian Rockies has an overall style. Here it is, in a one-paragraph summary:

The Rockies are hottest in July, with a typical daily maximum of 20°-25°C in the valleys from one end of the region to the other. The coldest days come in January, when the average overnight low is around -15°C in the south end and -30°C in the north end. The higher the elevation, the lower the temperature generally (except during inversions, page 254) and the greater the precipitation. At subalpine and alpine levels more moisture arrives in winter than in summer, while on the montane valley floors it is the other way around. The subalpine zone on the western slope receives the most snow; the montane valleys in the eastern-slope front ranges get the least.

This is what climatologists call a "continental" climate, which means simply "inland." Such climates are marked by a great range in temperature over the year (39°C between daily summer highs and winter lows at Banff, for example), coupled with a moderate amount of precipitation (471 mm at Banff). This contrasts with the "maritime" climate of Vancouver, for example, in which the annual temperature variation is less (24°C) and the precipitation is much more (1113 mm).

Under the Koeppen classification system, which is the climatologist's standard, our climate is "Dfc": a "cold, snowy forest climate with no distinct dry season and short, cool summers."

The table on the next two pages provides essential data for all weather stations in the area that operate year-round, with figures from Denver, Colorado for comparison with the American Rockies. The map on page 250 shows the pattern of temperature (a companion precipitation map could not be drawn confidently due to great local variation and too few data points).

These are long-term figures, averaged over many years. But we are speaking of the mountains, which are notorious for climatic instability. The kind of weather we have, summer or winter, can vary considerably from year to year: warm and dry one summer, cool and wet the next; snowy and mild one winter, bare and bone-chilling cold the next. Further, the rough topography makes the climate of any particular hillside a little different from that of its neighbors.

The daily weather also varies from valley to valley, and it changes quickly. As mountain residents are fond of telling visitors, "If you don't like the weather, just wait a minute." Corollary: "It may get worse." Even on a fine summer day, there is always a jacket in my pack to repel a sudden cold mountain shower or the chilly high-country wind.

Consider the factors that influence the atmosphere in the Canadian Rockies:

---

*Climate** is defined as the long-term averages of temperature, hours of sunshine, amount of precipitation (rain and snow), humidity, wind speed and wind direction at a particular place. **Weather** is the status of these things at any given time at that location.

CLIMATIC DATA FOR THE CANADIAN ROCKIES, 1951-1980

LOCATION	Elev (m ASL)	Mean temp (°C)	Days of frost	Daily July high	Daily Jan low	All-time high	All-time low	Annual precip (mm)	Snow-fall (cm)	Days rain/ snow
BRITISH COLUMBIA										
Canal Flats RS	817	5.7	-	27.2	-13.9	38.0	-41.7	369	140	64/36
Chetwynd	660	2.0	-	22.0	-19.2	34.4	-42.8	467	189	63/46
Cranbrook	918	5.0	181	26.8	-14.4	38.9	-41.1	451	193	72/54
Dome Creek	648	3.1	-	22.3	-16.7	34.4	-46.1	840	307	107/57
Elko	939	6.1	-	26.7	-10.7	38.9	-35.0	605	170	97/46
Fernie	1003	4.7	185	24.6	-12.3	36.1	-41.7	1128	397	100/62
Fording River	1702	1.5	-	22.0	-14.2	37.5	-49.0	726	425	49/72
Fort Nelson	382	-1.4	219	22.8	-28.2	36.7	-51.7	452	187	66/75
Fort St. John	695	1.3	193	21.3	-21.9	33.3	-47.2	493	222	62/74
Fort Steele	856	5.4	-	26.9	-12.2	37.0	-46.7	450	121	29/104
Golden	787	4.6	196	26.1	-15.3	40.0	-46.1	477	206	56/37
Grasmere	869	7.0	-	28.3	-9.2	39.4	-42.8	494	109	62/22
Hudson's Hope	678	1.9	-	21.3	-19.7	33.3	-46.1	551	194	55/50
Ingenika Point	680	0.5	-	20.8	-22.7	30.5	-47.0	503	184	91/73
Kootenay Crossing	1170	1.7	-	24.1	-18.1	36.1	-42.8	505	193	64/48
Radium	1088	3.8	208	24.0	-14.1	36.7	-32.8	547	190	66/37
Lower Post	583	-2.9	-	22.3	-31.4	35.0	-52.8	461	189	60/57
Mackenzie	700	1.9	-	21.7	-18.7	35.0	-44.4	692	337	89/81
McBride	722	4.2	191	23.8	-14.7	37.8	-46.7	626	219	92/45
McGregor	610	3.5	-	22.5	-16.1	36.1	-46.1	964	328	104/55
McLeod Lake	704	2.1	-	21.5	-18.7	33.9	-44.4	802	321	79/62
Mount Robson Ranch	869	2.8	-	22.7	-12.6	34.0	-36.0	630	235	91/54
Muncho Lake	835	-0.7	-	20.2	-24.4	33.3	-46.1	459	144	62/61
Natal Harmer Ridge	1890	0.3	-	17.9	-13.7	30.0	-35.5	841	662	40/117
Natal Kaiser	1128	4.1	-	24.4	-13.6	34.4	-40.0	637	247	87/53
Pine Pass	945	0.8	-	19.7	-17.9	31.1	-40.0	1916	1076	83/93
Pink Mountain	1202	-0.5	-	18.4	-20.1	28.5	-40.0	533	211	41/33
Prince George	676	3.3	203	22.0	-16.6	34.4	-50.0	628	242	104/78
Red Pass	1059	1.7	230	21.7	-18.4	32.8	-39.4	743	405	86/69
Sinclair Pass*	1486	1.6	243	21.6	-15.1	36.1	-42.2	608	262	58/40
Smith River	673	-2.9	247	20.8	-29.9	33.3	-58.9	481	203	68/84
Spillimacheen	818	4.4	190	25.1	-14.2	36.7	-40.0	452	163	74/40
Valemount	797	3.7	205	24.0	-15.2	40.6	-51.1	503	180	80/44
Ware	777	-0.6	-	21.0	-24.4	33.3	-48.3	493	187	60/47
Wonowon	914	0.4	-	20.3	-21.2	28.9	-40.0	565	232	54/5
Yoho Boulder Creek	1219	2.9	-	23.7	-14.5	33.0	-35.0	557	323	54/47
ALBERTA										
Anthracite	1387	2.9	215	22.8	-15.9	37.2	-43.9	454	196	62/36
Banff	1397	2.5	221	22.3	-16.4	34.4	-51.1	471	251	74/75
Beaver Mines	1286	4.0	201	23.1	-14.2	35.6	-45.6	645	305	50/44
Bighorn Dam	1326	2.2	-	21.2	-18.5	33.3	-43.3	486	168	59/47
Bow Valley park	1298	3.5	-	23.3	-16.3	33.9	-42.8	539	233	58/47
Caldwell	1311	4.2	187	23.3	-14.3	36.7	-41.1	723	367	42/47
Cardston	1154	4.8	210	25.0	-14.5	38.9	-41.7	550	229	47/44
Carway	1359	3.8	197	23.0	-14.4	36.7	-43.9	515	244	40/41
Castle RS	1364	3.0	217	23.3	-15.3	34.4	-43.9	852	500	64/66

LOCATION	Elev (m ASL)	Mean temp (°C)	Days of frost	Daily July high	Daily Jan low	All-time high	All-time low	Annual precip (mm)	Snow-fall (cm)	Days rain/snow
Chedderville	1036	2.7	-	21.7	-18.2	33.3	-40.6	581	164	60/40
Clearwater RS	1280	1.8	250	20.9	-18.7	32.8	-41.7	656	213	69/52
Coleman	1341	3.2	198	23.0	-14.1	33.9	-41.1	569	218	64/33
Columbia Icefield	1981	-2.1	-	15.2	-19.0	26.1	-41.1	930	643	57/102
Cowley Airport	1182	3.8	200	24.3	-16.7	37.2	-43.9	497	240	57/61
Edson Airport	922	0.9	232	21.7	-21.7	33.3	-46.1	533	205	80/64
Elbow RS	1433	1.4	270	21.5	-19.8	32.8	-45.6	611	244	60/52
Entrance	1006	2.0	226	22.1	-20.4	37.8	-51.1	513	164	50/38
Fort Macleod	950	5.4	169	25.8	-15.3	43.3	-45.0	434	146	49/37
Ghost RS	1434	2.6	220	20.9	-16.7	32.8	-40.6	553	216	57/58
Grande Cache	1250	2.1	-	20.5	-17.5	31.0	-40.0	602	278	79/71
Grande Prairie	669	1.2	204	22.1	-23.0	34.4	-52.2	453	180	74/65
Highwood RS	1493	1.9	-	21.3	-16.9	34.4	-45.6	623	296	56/47
Hinton	1013	2.5	218	22.1	-17.9	33.3	-41.1	502	119	50/27
Jasper	1061	2.8	213	22.5	-17.8	36.7	-46.7	409	152	83/59
Jasper East Gate	1003	3.1	-	24.2	-17.2	36.1	-48.3	541	226	65/31
Kananaskis	1390	2.8	220	21.8	-16.3	33.9	-45.6	657	292	58/52
Kananaskis RS	1463	1.4	-	22.7	-18.7	32.8	-41.1	599	264	53/44
Lake Louise	1524	-0.4	271	21.0	-22.0	34.4	-52.8	684	418	60/69
Nordegg RS	1326	0.7	-	20.9	-21.6	35.0	-47.2	555	181	63/48
Gap RS*	-	1.2	266	22.8	-17.9	34.4	-46.1	647	317	54/58
Pekisko	1439	2.8	233	21.4	-17.8	36.1	-46.7	696	326	48/56
Pincher Creek	1155	4.4	190	24.5	-14.9	35.6	-41.7	543	316	54/64
Prairie Creek RS	1173	0.4	20.5	20.5	-23.0	32.8	-46.7	606	154	58/44
Robb RS	1130	1.5	-	21.3	-19.5	32.2	-42.2	626	208	69/45
Rocky Mtn House	1015	2.6	211	22.0	-18.5	33.3	-43.9	556	188	69/63
Sheep RS	1494	2.1	-	21.4	-18.0	32.8	-42.8	644	279	52/56
South Wapiti RS	762	1.3	-	21.8	-22.6	33.3	-47.2	582	197	83/54
Turner Valley	1237	2.1	224	21.4	-19.2	32.8	-45.6	574	232	51/46
Whiskey Gap	1311	3.8	-	23.8	-15.2	37.2	-41.1	453	175	34/43
MONTANA										
Kalispell	904	5.8	191	27.8	-11.6	40.6	-38.9	405	124	132/22
Marias Pass	1589	2.1	245	23.2	-13.8	34.4	-48.3	936	651	102**
Polebridge	1072	4.0	238	27.3	-14.5	38.3	-43.3	570	314	68**
West Glacier	961	5.4	191	27.0	-9.9	38.3	-40.0	713	339	81**
COMPARE WITH:										
Calgary, AB	1084	3.4	201	23.3	-17.6	36.1	-45.0	424	153	58/62
Edmonton, AB	715	1.6	212	22.4	-22.0	35.0	-48.3	467	138	74/61
Lethbridge, AB	929	5.3	175	26.1	-16.0	39.4	-42.8	423	176	51/53
Revelstoke, BC	456	6.9	150	27.2	-9.2	40.6	-34.4	1064	423	139/70
Vancouver, BC	3	9.8	57	21.9	-0.2	33.3	-17.8	1113	60	156/15
Denver, Colorado	1609	10.1	60	30.5	5.0	40.0	-34.4	394	50	98/8

RS = Ranger Station
*1941-1970 data
**Rain & snow combined

Sources: Dightman, undated; Janz and Storr, 1977;
United States Dept. of Commerce, undated;
Atmospheric Environment Service, 1982;
Denver data from the 1985 *World Almanac*

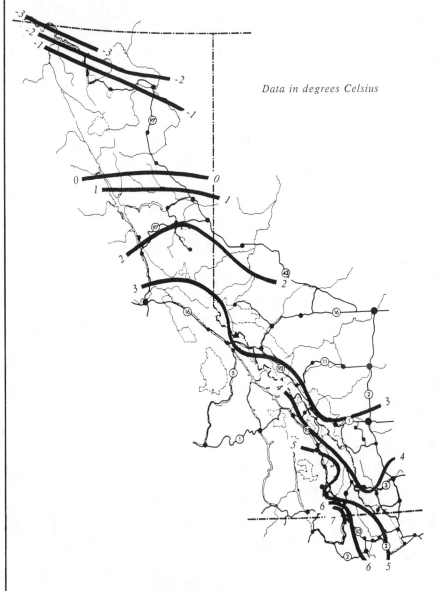

MEAN ANNUAL VALLEY-BOTTOM TEMPERATURE
IN THE CANADIAN ROCKIES

Data in degrees Celsius

Data source: see table on page 248

(For names of map features see base map opposite page 1)

LATITUDE AND SLOPE ANGLE

This is a northerly mountain range, so the angle of the sun to the ground is more oblique over the course of the year than it is farther south. That means lower temperatures generally, because low-angle sunlight heats the ground less than high-angle sunlight.

Another effect of our high latitude is that the length of the day changes a great deal through the seasons. At the north end of the Rockies there are only six hours of sunlight each day in December and January. This is precisely the same time that the sun provides the least warmth. In June and July, the long days there (18 hours) can become quite hot. Thus the temperature along Liard River can range from -50 °C in the dark days of January to 35 °C in the long, hot days of July—a yearly temperature range of 85 °C. Fortunately the dry mountain air cools quickly after sundown (moist air holds heat longer), so hot nights are rare throughout the region. That same dryness makes the winter cold feel more bearable than it would in a damp climate.

South-facing slopes in the Canadian Rockies are heated more strongly than north-facing slopes, because the sun lies at a fairly low angle throughout the year. The rays hit a north-facing slope obliquely, even at noon in summer, when the sun is highest in the sky, but they hit a south-facing slope at a nearly perpendicular angle. So south-facing slopes are warmer (and thus drier) than north-facing ones, an important factor in the ecology of northerly mountain ranges.

SHADING

Mountains create shade, locally delaying sunrise and hastening sunset. This reduces the number of hours of sunlight reaching shaded points, especially in winter when the sun's angle is low.

Regardless of the season, though, the east-facing wall of a valley feels the sun's touch sooner in the day than the west-facing wall, and the sun goes down later on the west-facing side. Given a perfectly symmetrical valley, one would think that these two factors balance, but they don't: the later sundown on west-facing slopes means that the sun is still shining there when the day has warmed. In contrast, the east-facing slopes receive their sun earlier, when the day is new and the air is cool. This tends to keep east-facing slopes cooler overall than west-facing ones.

THE PACIFIC INFLUENCE

The western coast of Canada is one of the wetter places in North America, and the Rocky Mountains are close enough to it to receive a goodly dose of moisture each year from the prevailing westerly winds—were it not for the many mountain ranges west of the Rockies, which grab much of the rain and snow that would otherwise fall here. Typical annual valley-floor precipitation in the Rockies is 400-600 mm, compared with Vancouver's 1113 mm or Revelstoke's 1064 mm. The western slope of the Rockies is somewhat wetter than the eastern slope, receiving about 100 mm more precipitation at equivalent elevations—except for the southern Rocky Mountain Trench, the dry corner of the whole region (only 369 mm annual precipitation at Canal Flats).

A special case here is the region south of Crowsnest Pass. Here the western slope is wetter than one would expect, especially on the western side of Glacier park. Perhaps this is because the ranges west of the Rockies are lower here than they are farther north. This would leave more moisture in easterly moving airmasses to be precipitated upon reaching the Rockies. A view of Glacier park from the southwest shows how wall-like it is, sopping up moisture moving in from that direction.

SEASONAL VARIATION IN SUN ANGLE AND DAY LENGTH IN AND NEAR THE CANADIAN ROCKIES

Values computed for a flat horizon; actual values somewhat less
Locations listed from north to south

LOCATION	Latitude (degrees & min)	Maximum angle Jun 21	Equinox angle Mar 21	Minimum angle Dec 21	Max day (hrs) Jun 21	Min day (hrs) Dec 21
Yukon/BC border	60 00	53 27	30 00	6 33	18.9	5.9
Liard River	59 25	54 02	30 35	7 08	18.6	6.2
Fort Nelson	58 48	54 39	31 12	7 45	18.3	6.4
Summit Lake	58 39	54 48	31 21	7 54	18.3	6.4
Trutch	57 44	55 43	32 16	8 49	18.1	6.7
Hudson's Hope	56 02	57 25	33 58	10 31	17.6	7.1
Pine Pass	55 24	58 03	34 36	11 09	17.5	7.2
Mackenzie	55 20	58 07	34 40	11 13	17.4	7.2
Prince George	53 55	59 32	36 05	12 38	17.1	7.4
Hinton	53 23	60 04	36 37	13 10	16.9	7.6
McBride	53 18	60 09	36 42	13 15	16.9	7.6
Jasper	52 52	60 35	37 08	13 41	16.9	7.6
Valemount	52 50	60 37	37 10	13 43	16.8	7.7
Nordegg	52 28	60 59	37 32	14 05	16.8	7.7
Columbia Icefield	52 10	61 17	37 50	14 23	16.7	7.8
Sask. Crossing	51 59	61 28	38 01	14 34	16.7	7.8
Lake Louise	51 26	62 01	38 34	15 07	16.6	7.9
Field	51 24	62 03	38 36	15 09	16.6	7.9
Golden	51 18	62 09	38 42	15 15	16.6	7.9
Banff	51 11	62 16	38 49	15 22	16.5	7.9
Calgary	51 00	62 27	39 00	15 33	16.5	7.9
Turner Valley	50 40	62 47	39 20	15 53	16.4	8.0
Radium	50 38	62 49	39 22	15 55	16.4	8.0
Fort Macleod	49 43	63 44	40 17	16 50	16.3	8.1
Crowsnest Pass	49 38	63 49	40 22	16 55	16.3	8.1
Cranbrook	49 31	63 56	40 29	17 02	16.3	8.2
Fernie	49 30	63 57	40 30	17 02	16.3	8.2
Pincher Creek	49 29	63 58	40 31	17 04	16.3	8.2
Cardston	49 12	64 15	40 48	17 21	16.2	8.2
Canada/US border	49 00	64 27	41 00	17 33	16.2	8.3
St. Mary	48 45	64 42	41 15	17 48	16.1	8.3
Browning	48 34	64 53	41 26	17 59	16.1	8.3
West Glacier	48 30	64 57	41 30	18 03	16.1	8.3
East Glacier	48 27	65 00	41 33	18 06	16.1	8.3
Whitefish	48 25	65 02	41 35	18 08	16.1	8.3
Columbia Falls	48 23	65 04	41 37	18 10	16.1	8.4
Marias Pass	48 19	65 08	41 41	18 14	16.0	8.4
Compare with:						
Denver, Colorado	39 45	73 42	50 15	26 48	15.0	9.3

Source: interpolated from figures in *World Almanac*, 1985

THE PRAIRIE INFLUENCE

Although winds in the Canadian Rockies are mostly from the west, they tend to come from the east in early summer and during mid-winter cold snaps.

Summer easterlies often push moist air into the mountains from the prairies. The increasing elevation forces the air upward, where it expands and cools. Water droplets condense and rain starts to fall in the foothills and front ranges. This is **upslope weather.** It can go on for a week at a time. To beat it, head west, for the effect diminishes rapidly as you approach the continental divide. If Banff is cool and drizzly due to upslope conditions, look for better weather at Lake Louise.

During winter upslope episodes, the airmass moving in is usually quite cold—part of the huge arctic high-pressure cell that keeps the Canadian north frigid all winter. Air this cold is also dry, so there is little snow associated with winter upslope. However, the increase in elevation often induces a constant precipitation of tiny ice crystals in the atmosphere. The mountains get overnight snow-dustings during winter upslope weather and ice-crystal haziness during the day.

The crystals often create **sundogs:** two small bright patches in the sky, flanking the sun. Sundogs are blurry images of the sun, sometimes with pale rainbow-like colors. They appear about 22° right and left of it, which is the angle of refraction (light-bending angle) in the ice crystals. The crystals drift slowly to the ground, keeping a more-or-less flat orientation, like that of falling leaves, because of their platiness. The uniformity in orientation keeps the sundogs in their apparent position.

OROGRAPHIC WEATHER

Upslope activity occurs at a smaller scale throughout any mountain range, regardless of wind direction. As long as air is moving at all, it will rise over ridges and fall over valleys. The rising motion produces clouds from cooling and condensation, which explains why a single mountain in the middle of a desert can have the only cloud in the area hanging doggedly over its summit. Every geography student has to learn the buzzword for this effect: **orographic lifting**.

In most mountain ranges there is a daily cycle operating on this principle. It is called **orographic weather,** is mainly a summer phenomenon and operates as follows. The day begins clear. Clouds start to form around the summits in mid-morning, building up in the afternoon to bring on local thunderstorms. In the early evening the rain stops, the clouds disappear and the night is starry.

Such is the pattern in the Colorado Rockies to the south of us, where in summer one can confidently predict a thunderstorm at 3 p.m. if there are clouds in the sky by 9 a.m. We have orographic weather in the Canadian Rockies, too, but fast-moving airmasses and fronts influence the weather more. So the rule about morning clouds and afternoon showers is not as reliable here.

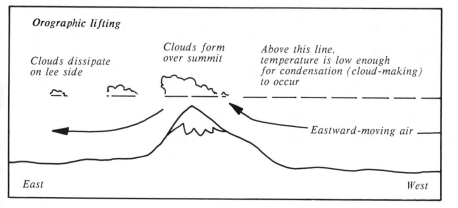

Orographic lifting

Clouds dissipate on lee side

Clouds form over summit

Above this line, temperature is low enough for condensation (cloud-making) to occur

Eastward-moving air

East   West

THE MID-DAY CLEARING TREND

One element in our weather picture seems to occur daily, winter and summer: a clearing trend at mid-day. I have not found this phenomenon written up anywhere, but experience has shown its validity. No matter how bad the weather is, for some reason the cloud cover in our area tends to diminish noticeably for an hour or so around noon. Perhaps Thor is having his lunch.

EFFECTS OF ELEVATION

The air temperature drops about half a degree Celsius for every 100 m of elevation gain, just from thinning of the atmosphere (any gas cools as it expands). This is why the temperature at the upper tramway terminal on The Whistlers is usually about 5-10 °C cooler than it is at Jasper, 1400 m below. Valley-bottom elevations are 300-500 m lower on the western slope than on the eastern slope, so valley-bottom temperatures are normally a little higher west of the divide, other conditions being equal.

At times it can be *warmer* at higher elevations than at lower elevations. This can occur in any season, but most noticeably in winter, when the valleys are filled with very cold air from an arctic high-pressure system that has crept in from the prairies. The cold air is not very deep (often only 200-300 m). Overlying it is air that is perhaps 10-15 °C warmer—a **temperature inversion.**

Skiers are familiar with this phenomenon. During cold snaps they can practically count on more-pleasant conditions up on the mountain than down in the valley.

Not only is the air warmer above the inversion, it is often clearer as well. Below the inversion ceiling the cold, dense air is murky with ice crystals and trapped air pollution. Above the ceiling the sun shines brightly through drier, cleaner air. Of course, sometimes the cold air is so deep that it covers even the summits. The farther north you go, the deeper these inversions are.

In the mountains, elevation has a great effect on precipitation as well as on temperature. This is especially obvious in checking the snow accumulation at different elevations. At 1850 m, not far below timberline on the slopes of Marmot Basin ski area above Jasper, the average snow depth on April first is 120 cm. Down in the townsite there is often less than a tenth of that. Summer or winter, there is more precipitation at higher elevations than there is down on the valley floors, mainly because the temperature is lower at higher elevations and thus more rain and snow condense up there.

A characteristic of the mountain climate is that the valleys get the bulk of their annual precipitation in the warm months, while the peaks get theirs mainly in the winter. A little thought turns up the reason for this. In winter, clouds are usually made of snow rather than mist. Thus, any spot swathed in winter clouds is usually receiving snow. Summits and upper mountain slopes are frequently cloud-covered during the cold months, so they get far more snow than the valleys, which lie below the cloud bases (except during storms). Both the uplands and the valleys get watered in summer, when storms are the main moisture suppliers.

In the eastern-slope valley bottoms and foothills, the maximum snow depth usually occurs in early March, while in the Rocky Mountain Trench it is reached in mid-February. The snow lies deepest in the subalpine zone (roughly the last 300-500 m below timberline) and reaches its greatest thickness there in late March or early April. Measurements are traditionally taken by governments on April 1; from these the amount of spring runoff can be projected.

Although more snow falls higher up, in the alpine zone, the unbroken wind there blows the snow over ridges and down into leeward valleys. Drifts fill the gullies and extend downwind behind rocks. The alpine zone in winter is a mosaic of drifts and bare patches, impossible to measure accurately for snow accumulation.

The region of heaviest accumulation in the Canadian Rockies is along the continental divide between Lake Louise and Jasper, where the mountain wall is continuously high and thus very effective in snagging moisture moving across it. Several large valleys cut across the Columbia Mountains west of this region, feeding in storms. The result is the chain of icefields one sees along Highway 93, the Icefields Parkway. Although Lake Louise is only 150 m higher than Banff, Lake Louise lies close to the heavy-snow section of the divide and gets considerably more snow (85 cm on the ground at Lake Louise; only 30 cm at Banff).

East of the icefield chain, the front ranges lie in a **rain shadow**: a dry area downwind of a wet one. Having dumped moisture over the main-range glaciers, the descending air has little left for the front ranges. At lower elevations there is often bare ground in mid-winter along affected valleys such as that of the Athabasca valley between Jasper and the eastern park gate, or the North Saskatchewan valley at Kootenay Plains. In most winters the light and infrequent snowfalls in these valleys are blasted by strong westerly winds, keeping windward slopes bare. Those slopes are essential winter range for bighorn sheep. In other places the snow is too deep for them to scrape down to the grasses they depend on.

South of Calgary, elevations along the divide are generally lower and the snowpack is correspondingly thinner. Further, chinooks (page 257) are frequent here. In the foothills south of Crowsnest Pass, west-facing slopes are usually snow-free. The windblown snow piles up in huge drifts on the lee sides of hills.

WIND DIRECTION

The predominant wind direction in the Canadian Rockies is southwesterly, perpendicular to the northwest-southeast alignment of ridges and valleys. This has two effects. The first is that winds in most valleys are light and shift frequently in direction, while winds in the few cross-cutting, southwest/northeast-aligned valleys are steadier and stronger. The second effect is that snow blows off the southwest-facing windward slopes and accumulates on the northeast-facing leeward slopes.

Because northeast-facing slopes receive little sun in winter, snow accumulating there tends to stay a long time. That is one reason glaciation has been more severe on northeast-facing slopes. (The other reason is geological: the bedding here dips generally to the southwest, which favors steeper slopes on the northeastern sides of ridges. See page 19.)

GLACIAL WINDS AND FROST HOLLOWS

In summer, large glaciers such as the icefields cool a layer of air over their surfaces. This makes the air denser. It flows downhill, producing a breeze that is noticeably chilly. People walking up to the toe of the Athabasca Glacier often run back to their cars for jackets when they get within 50-100 m of the ice and feel the glacier's frigid breath. It is frequently 10°cooler at the snout than at the Icefield Centre nearby, where the air may be warm and still. Meteorologists call such winds **catabatic.** On days with a westerly breeze, the whole area between the toe and the Icefield Chalet is kept refrigerated by catabatic wind. Glacial winds can be particularly strong at night—a point forcibly impressed upon climbers who have pitched their tents near a glacial front.

Another kind of catabatic wind is felt more generally in the mountains in the evening, when cool air moves down the slopes. At the same time, the regional wind flow slackens, so the cool descending air collects in glacial cirques and valley bottoms, forming small temperature inversions. Such inversions occur at all elevations and during all seasons, but they are most noticeable in the winter and in the upper subalpine zone, just below timberline. The effect is so pronounced in this zone that ecologists credit catabatic winds with producing subalpine meadows. A classic example is the subalpine meadow that stretches from Sunwapta Pass (Banff/Jasper park boundary) to Icefield Centre (photo on page 281).

Snow-laden clouds moving across Mt. Rundle, near Banff. Pushed by westerly winds, snow that falls on the southwestern slope of the mountain (in the sun in this picture) tends to blow up the slope and over the ridge crest, producing a deeper accumulation on the northeastern side. This process favors glacier development on northeast-facing slopes.

Weather and climate

Low temperatures through much of the winter in these **frost hollows** combine with a high water table to restrict the species of plants that can grow there. Trees do poorly, while shrub-size willows, grasses and sedges can withstand the severe microclimate. In this sense, subalpine frost hollows are little alpine patches among the forest.

Skiing down into a frost hollow can be a brutal experience. The temperature suddenly drops as you enter one, and your forward motion adds wind chill. The result is sometimes frostbite. Bow Lake and the gravel flats east of Saskatchewan Glacier are notorious for this; both are large frost hollows.

Winter campers suffer if they've selected a frost hollow in which to bed down on a cold night. Moving only 10-20 m up the slope, where the overnight low may be several degrees higher, can mean the difference between shivering the hours away or sleeping soundly.

EFFECT OF THE CONTINENTAL DIVIDE

The Canadian Rockies present a long, tall barrier to airmasses moving across them. This is most noticeable in winter, when a pool of cold air on the eastern slope is keeping valley temperatures in the -30°C to -40°C range while on the western slope the thermometer might be reading -10°C. Elevations on the western slope are also lower, so the air tends to be a little warmer on that side at all times.

Low spots in the divide funnel Pacific air through the mountains, making the eastern approaches to major passes such as Kicking Horse and Yellowhead wetter than they would otherwise be. The Peace River gap is the biggest of these holes; moist air moving through it spreads into the foothills to the east, supporting anomalous stands of devil's club around Chetwynd and Hudson's Hope. (Note that the continental divide actually lies west of the Rockies at this point, but the eastern-slope/western-slope concept still applies.)

The flip side of the coin is that cold prairie air also drains west through these low spots a few times every winter. The town of Field, some 20 km west of Kicking Horse Pass, is famous for this. The wind suddenly comes in from the east at about 30 km/h and -25°C—invigorating, to say the least. Residents of Field call this the **Yoho Blow**. Kalispell, Montana, reports similar cold winds funneling through Marias Pass.

CHINOOKS

A chinook is a warm westerly wind encountered in winter along the eastern edge of the entire North American cordillera, from Alaska to New Mexico, but perhaps most frequently in the eastern-slope foothills of the Canadian Rockies. Chinooks usually occur here 5-10 times between mid-December and mid-March, more often than that in the Waterton/Glacier region, heart of the chinook belt, where chinook winds blow for 30 days out of 120 in an average winter. Chinook conditions can also arise during summer, but the warm wind feels like any other summer breeze and goes unnoticed.

A similar wind is felt in western Europe, where it is called a **foehn** wind ("Foehn" is German, pronounced about halfway between "phone" and "fern.")

A typical chinook occurs when the eastern slope is very cold, submerged under an arctic high-pressure cell. To the west and northwest, in the Gulf of Alaska, a low-pressure system develops; its counter-clockwise spin sends winds eastward across the mountain ranges of British Columbia. At first this weak flow of warm Pacific air skips across the dense, frigid air below, offering no relief. However, when a chinook is about to begin the Pacific flow strengthens. It floods across the mountains, producing standing waves downwind of the easternmost range—the Rockies—much as a stone in a river produces standing waves on its downstream side.

The most westerly of these waves is large: the crest can reach 10,000 m in elevation. Moisture in the air riding the crest condenses, forming a cloud—the **chinook arch** familiar to foothills residents—that forms a sharp westerly edge up to 1000 km long, paralleling the Rockies. People in Calgary see the edge of the

Lenticular clouds over Jasper, March, 1985, announcing a chinook in the foothills. Like other places in the main ranges, Jasper is seldom very windy during a chinook, but standing water in the picture shows that the rising temperature has caused a late-winter thaw.

Chinook arch over the Rockies as seen from just west of Calgary, February 1986.

cloud band to the west, stretching from horizon to horizon in a gentle, arch-like curve; thus the name. Narrow at first, the cloud band can spread eastward for hundreds of kilometres as the chinook strengthens.

A wave has a trough as well as a crest, and it is the trough of this great standing wave, where air is rushing downward, that causes the surface wind felt as a chinook. The air descends the eastern slope, touching down at high speed in the foothills and pushing the cold air back across the prairies for 100-200 km. Typical wind speeds during a chinook are 30-50 km/hr; they can reach 100 km/hr.

The effect on the ground is sensational: the temperature rises 20-40 °C in only a few hours.

"Chinook" is an Indian word meaning "snow-eater," and the name is certainly appropriate: the wind is warm and quite dry (from gas compression as the air descends the eastern slope), so it laps up the snow very quickly. Given a strong chinook lasting several days, the front ranges as well as the foothills are affected. Unseasonably warm conditions can continue for a week or more, the ending often accompanied by a storm as the low pressure system moves in. Clear, cold weather then follows the storm, completing the cycle.

But while the foothills are basking in the sun, in the main ranges along the continental divide the weather during a typical chinook is usually anything but pleasant. Although the temperature will have risen somewhat, the residents of places such as Lake Louise and Field experience variable gusty winds and twenty-minute blizzards that alternate with patches of blue sky. The clouds roil about uncertainly. This is the "rotor" effect of chinooks: the smooth westerly flow of air at higher elevations induces turbulent flow near the ground in the rough topography of the mountains. You can see this turbulence from Calgary on a chinook day as a line of swirling storminess at the mountain front. Pilots of light planes avoid it; weathermen refer to it as the **foehn wall**.

Predicting a chinook a day or two in advance requires a weather map to see the configuration of high and low pressure areas. The chinook arch often appears a few hours ahead. In the mountains proper the arch is not usually visible; however, the appearance of **lenticular clouds** (see photo on facing page) indicates a strong westerly flow of air—and suggests that chinook conditions are developing in the foothills.

Another way of predicting a chinook is to note how you are feeling, for many people become irritable or restless a few hours before the wind hits. This may be caused by sensitivity to the positive-ion concentrations found in fast-moving dry air. The chinook flow moves overhead for some hours, gradually working its way down into the pool of cold air it is displacing. Studies have documented mood changes among ground-dwellers just before a chinook. A jump in the number of auto accidents, crimes and suicides is associated with chinook weather.

There may be a sound physical reason for this: absorption of positive ions causes the body to release **serotonin,** a known mood-affecting hormone that also raises the blood pressure. In Europe, surgeons have found that people bleed more readily during foehns. When possible, operations are rescheduled.

One hears stories of cattle dying in the fields when powerful chinooks strike the southern foothills. I have my doubts about this, but other effects on the biota of the Rockies are well-demonstrated.

For example, the warm chinook wind can dry lodgepole-pine needles to the point of killing them, for in winter the flow of resin is too slow to replace the lost moisture quickly enough. As a result, west-facing slopes in the foothills often show stands of brown-needled trees the following summer, a condition known as **red-belt.** (See also the entry on lodgepole pine, page 294.)

The chinook zone is the winter home of most of the elk in the Rockies, for the wind removes snow from west-facing slopes, exposing the grassy feed the elk prefer. The floors of major valleys that cut through the front ranges and foothills are swept practically free of snow most of the winter; here the herds are largest.

THE WINDINESS AT WATERTON/GLACIER

The southern region of the Canadian Rockies is famous for wind—and not just in winter, when chinooks there are frequent and strong. Winter or summer, there is often a strong **pressure gradient** over the mountains south of Calgary: a band of high pressure lying just west of the Rockies, next to a band of low pressure over the southern Alberta foothills. This is independent of the regional eastward-high/westward-low configuration associated with chinooks (see previous section). Wind blows from zones of high pressure to zones of low pressure, which explains why the Waterton/Glacier area so often feels a westerly breeze. But the underlying cause—the reason the strong pressure gradient develops—is unknown.

Helping the wind along in Waterton and eastern-slope Glacier are the large cross-cutting valleys there, which tend to funnel air through the mountains. Missing in this area are the wind-slowing parallel northwest-southeast ridges of the foothills, so typical of the Rockies farther north. Check the satellite photo on page 2; it shows clearly that the lay of the land in the Waterton/Glacier area is much less strongly northwest-southeast than it is in the central and northern regions.

RECENT CLIMATIC CHANGE

Long-time residents in Jasper and Banff will tell you that the weather has changed over the years, from warmer and drier before the 1970s to cooler and wetter these days. The data support their recollections; in comparing climatic normals for the thirty-year period 1941-1970 with the 1951-1980 data used in the climate table (page 248), most stations show a small drop in temperature and an increase in precipitation, with more days of rain and snow. This change has been most noticeable in the last 15 summers, which have been generally cooler than the previous 70, with cloudier, rainier days. The summers of the fifties and sixties, with their long hot spells, are rare these days. The winters have become slightly warmer and wetter.

Glaciers have long memories for weather, and their behavior also suggests a climatic turnaround. In the Rockies the general glacial retreat that has gone on since the end of the Cavell Advance about 100 years ago has slowed or stopped, and many glacial fronts have shown advances in the last ten years.

However, during that 100 years the burning of fossil fuels has approximately doubled the amount of carbon dioxide in the atmosphere. This is now causing a detectable **greenhouse effect,** in which worldwide atmospheric temperatures are increasing due to trapping of infrared radiation. If the effect develops as predicted, the increase will more than offset the current climatic cooling trend. Forty years hence, a substantial melt could be underway that would shrink the glaciers considerably. Glaciers around Mt. Sir Wilfrid Laurier, just west of the Rockies, are now in retreat after the recent minor advance (Brian Luckman, personal communication, 1986).

ANNUAL WEATHER PATTERN

In comparing one year's weather records with the next, it seems that in the Canadian Rockies each year is different from the rest. But an average seasonal weather pattern does exist. You just can't rely on it. With that in mind, here is the weather pattern during a typical year.

Spring comes in early April to the Rocky Mountain Trench, in mid-April to the eastern-slope montane valleys. Sunny days reaching highs of 10-15 °C trade off with blustery days mixing rain and snow. This is frustrating weather, pretty unpleasant, really, and not at all as the once-popular song *Springtime in the Rockies* extols. However, between flurries the skiers can enjoy their sport in teeshirts.

By late May the snow has gone from the valleys, although snow falls and sticks at lower elevations in every month except July. As I write this, it is June 24 and there is snow on the ground from an overnight cold front. But this is unusual; normally the last hard frost at Jasper occurs in early June.

In the central Rockies there is often a week of warm, clear weather during May. The snowline moves quickly up the slopes and the rivers rise suddenly; the valleys become instantly green and the temperature soars. Out come the short pants.

Then, when it seems that summer has arrived prematurely, the clouds roll in, the temperature drops, the rain falls and so do the spirits of people wasting their holidays here in June. You see them huddling in picnic shelters at the campgrounds, watching wet flakes of snow covering their tent-trailers. Much of their discomfort comes from the upslope weather prevalent in the Rockies in early summer (see page 253).

But there is often a spectacular improvement in the first week of July. I have seen this many times. The sun comes out and stays out for several days—sometimes for over a week. The temperature climbs to summer normals and the rivers rise again, reaching their highest levels of the year and flooding low spots. The days are long. The sunburn season is on.

The rest of July is inclined to be warm, with afternoon showers. The wildflower season is at its height and the mountains are full of tourists. And bugs.

Late summer is less predictable. In some years August has provided weeks of wonderfully clear, warm weather, but in others a succession of Pacific low-pressure systems has kept the Rockies soggy and cool. You take your chances coming to the Canadian Rockies in August (whereas in July you have a good chance of getting at least a few good days, and in June you are practically assured of rain). Foul weather in August is more common from Jasper north than it is to the south.

Throughout the North American cordillera, fall seems to enter with a week of bad weather. This frequently happens in late August in the northern Rockies, in the first week of September between Jasper and Waterton/Glacier, and in late September or early October in Colorado. As the rain falls, so does the temperature, until one morning there is snow on the ground.

Then the weather often clears. Indian summer arrives, bringing fairly warm days (highs of 15-20 °C) and cool nights that drop below freezing. The Rockies are famous for long, beautiful falls, both in Canada and in the United States. During a good one the sky is deeply blue for weeks on end, the aspen are golden and the bugs are gone. This weather pattern can last from mid-September to the end of October; it has the spooky habit of finishing right at Halloween, when the kids often go door-to-door in falling snow.

In November the temperature drops steadily and so does the snowline. In many years a windy arctic front blasts through late in the month, leaving little snow but freezing everything up for the winter.

The first half of December is a prime time for one or two major Pacific storms that lay down 50 cm of powder in the high country and 10-20 cm in the valley bottoms. This is an important period in the central Rockies, where most of the skiing in the Canadian Rockies occurs. It sets the pattern for the rest of the winter, for there is seldom another big snowfall until February or March. If the snow comes early, say in mid-November, then it falls on ground that is still warm from the summer. There is a fair bit of melting, leaving thin snow-cover for the rest of the winter. That's bad news for skiers, not only because there is less snow to ski on, but because the avalanche hazard can become extreme. A contradiction? Not at all; turn to the section on avalanches of depth-hoar (page 817).

Following the Pacific-storm period, frigid arctic air moves in, bringing cold, clear weather to the eastern slope in late December and January. Valley-bottom temperatures dip to -40 °C, sometimes reaching -45 °C along major valleys in the front ranges (the cold spots in the area). The western slope suffers less, for the heavy air has difficulty crossing the continental divide (but it does, on occasion. See the Yoho Blow, page 257).

Then the unexpected sometimes occurs: warm, moist air wafts through the mountains from British Columbia. The deeply frozen eastern slope gets rain in January, which coats everything with ice.

Jasper townsite is famous for this. When I was new in Jasper I wondered why so many of the locals walked in the street, winter and summer, instead of on the sidewalks. After my first ice storm, which left the sidewalks unbelievably treacherous for a month, I knew the reason: the streets, at least, are sanded.

Merely inconvenient for humans, mid-winter ice-ups can be the undoing of ungulates such as sheep, deer and elk. Freezing rain forms a tough crust on the snow, making winter feed more difficult for these animals to reach. Their predators, on the other hand—especially wolves—can often travel atop the crust, giving them an advantage at a time when the prey are weakened.

In December of 1981 a flock of 120 bighorns in Jasper National Park lost 17 of its members to a bizarre accident caused by iced ground. The sheep tried to escape a pack of wolves by running to ledges just below the top of Cinquefoil Bluff, a hill that overlooks Talbot Lake. This would ordinarily have foiled the wolves, for dog-family members are notable acrophobes, but in this case the steep slope was glazed with ice and many of the sheep lost their footing. They fell over a cliff onto the ice of the lake, where the wolves found a banquet waiting.

North of Peace River the Rockies often lie under arctic air for the rest of the winter, gathering little snow until March or even April. The snow is often only 20-30 cm deep for most of the winter. The temperature hovers between -20°C and -40°C; the days are very short, with little solar heating, and the snow is generally nothing but sugary depth hoar (page 817).

South of Peace River in the central Rockies, temperatures are more moderate (highs in January average -10°C to -20°C; lows -25°C to -35°C) and there are more frequent snowfalls, especially from mid-February through April.

Chinooks can come at any time in the Canadian Rockies, disrupting this pattern, but by February the region is almost certain to have one. The first chinook after a cold December and January provides a welcome thaw on the eastern slope. The ice fog disappears; the sun shines warmly; the air feels good on one's face and everything that has survived the desperate days of the post-Christmas cold snap gets a touch of spring giddiness.

A storm follows the chinook and winter returns. But there is another chinook a couple of weeks later, a shorter cold snap, yet another chinook—longer this time—and no cold snap, then ... it is April and maybe spring has arrived. "Boy; it's early this year," I think. Look: the grass is turning green and the birds have returned! Ah, such short-memoried fools we are. Mother Nature produces one last blizzard in May, just to show us who is really in charge.

On the western slope the winters are milder and shorter, although the snow accumulation is up to 50 percent greater at any given elevation. The temperature difference is particularly evident in late March or early April, when a trip over the continental divide from Banff to Golden is a trip into spring. The grass greens and the flowers bloom a couple of weeks earlier in the Rocky Mountain Trench than on the eastern slope, where arctic air keeps the lid on spring awhile longer.

PREDICTING THE WEATHER

In summer the regional forecasts are accurate for the mountains only when large airmasses are involved. If you hear that British Columbia has washed away, then prepare for some wet days at Banff, with low clouds and shivery temperatures. If BC is basking, then probably the Rockies will be, too. But smaller systems do unexpected things here. I recall climbing Mt. Forbes in murk that arrived black and nasty the evening before, despite a fair-weather prediction on the radio. As the wind came up and the tent shook us awake, my friend took a peek outdoors, sighed and said, "Another unknown, uncharted storm system hits the Canadian Rockies."

Few of us carry a barometer around, but any Compleat Climber has an altimeter, which is essentially the same thing. If you are going to be at the same elevation for a while, keep an eye on the instrument. If the reading rises overnight, so that you seem to have gained a few metres, then the pressure is falling and the weather will probably deteriorate. If you seem to lose elevation, the pressure is rising and the weather should improve. But the pressure remains high during rainy upslope conditions (page 253). Further, normal summer-afternoon storminess can arrive without much change in pressure.

Not owning an altimeter, I go by the clouds. Most of our rough weather comes from the west, and it usually announces itself in the form of cirrus (high, wispy clouds) fingering in from that direction. If the cirrus wisps go to a solid overcast within an hour or two, the rain/snow will probably start only a few hours later—sooner than expected, if you are used to the weather on the prairies. Out there, one can see the edge of a moist airmass when the mares' tails are still hundreds of kilometres away. In the mountains one doesn't see them until they are practically overhead, because the alignment of ridges in most places blocks westerly views.

Clearing trends are indicated by cloud-lifting and thinning (obviously). The sky looks to be drying out, which is exactly what is happening. Lenticular clouds indicate a strong westerly flow at high elevations; they often precede a chinook.

Readers inclined to reach high points in the mountains (climbers, especially) may want to turn to the section on storms and lightning, which begins on page 814. Skiers should take to heart the section about avalanches, page 816.

FURTHER READING

Atmospheric Environment Service (1975a) *Canadian Climate Normals, 1941-1970: Temperature* Atmospheric Environment Service, Environment Canada
—— (1975b) *Canadian Climate Normals, 1941-1970: Precipitation* Atmospheric Environment Service, Environment Canada
—— (1982a) *Canadian Climate Normals, 1951-1980: Temperature and Precipitation, Alberta* Atmospheric Environment Service, Environment Canada
—— (1982b) *Canadian Climate Normals, 1951-1980: Temperature and Precipitation, British Columbia* Atmospheric Environment Service, Environment Canada
—— (1982c) *Canadian Climate Normals, 1951-1980: Volume 5: Wind* Atmospheric Environment Service, Environment Canada
Christison, Tim (1986) "Snow-eater: the chinook turns winter into sprig in an hour" *Nature Canada* Spring, 16-22. The most readable discussion of chinooks I have seen.
Dightman, R. (undated) *Climate of Glacier National Park, Montana* National Weather Service, Great Falls, Montana
Janz, B. and D. Storr (1977) *The Climate of the Contiguous Mountain Parks* Atmospheric Environment Service Project Report No. 30, Environment Canada. Technical, but still fairly accessible to lay readers.
United States Dept. of Commerce (undated) *Climatography of the United States, No. 20-24* National Weather Service, Great Falls, Montana

> *On a day when the sky was uniformly overcast and rain was pelting down, climber Peter Zvengrowski turned to his partner and said, hopefully, "I think I see a cloud."*

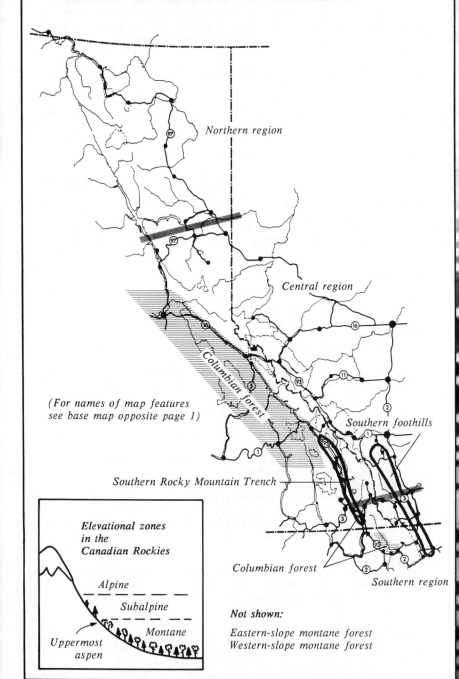

ECOLOGICAL REGIONS REFERRED TO IN THIS BOOK

Northern region

Central region

Columbian forest

(For names of map features see base map opposite page 1)

Southern foothills

Southern Rocky Mountain Trench

Columbian forest

Southern region

Elevational zones
in the
Canadian Rockies

Alpine

Subalpine

Montane

Uppermost
aspen

Not shown:

Eastern-slope montane forest
Western-slope montane forest

What is growing on here?
The pattern of vegetation in the Canadian Rockies

Many plant species occur from one end of our area to the other, and on both sides of the continental divide. That kind of ecological integrity is a lucky thing for those of us with an interest in botany; if one learns the wildflowers in the Waterton/Glacier area, then one will also know many of them at Banff, at Jasper, and even along the Alaska Highway in the far northern end of the Rockies.

However, if you spend some time in the region, traveling east and west, north and south, then the differences begin to emerge. The alpine meadows in Waterton park begin to look different from those above Lake Louise. The forests around Golden acquire a different character from the forests around Banff. To the practiced eye, the botany of Summit Lake along the Alaska Highway looks very different from the botany of the Summit Lake one finds in Waterton park.

As you travel north from the south end of our area you pass through three rough divisions: **southern** (from Marias Pass to Crowsnest Pass), **central** (from there all the way to Pine Pass/Peace River) and **northern** (to Liard River). As you go through the plant and animal listings in later chapters, you can see how some species are southern, some are northern, some are central and so on.

These biological divisions parallel the geological ones, which is handy—but not surprising, for the ecology of a region has a great deal to do with what the plants are growing on (their **substrate**).

The map on the opposite page shows the three divisions. The southern-central boundary is fairly clear, because Crowsnest Pass forms a sort of botanical divide (more on that later). The central-northern transition is more gradual, noticeable more easily in the animal species and geology than in the botany.

Going east to west there are more abrupt differences. Along the TransCanada Highway west from Calgary, for example, one passes from the grassy prairies into the wooded but meadowy foothills and front ranges, then into the thick forests of the continental divide. These differences are based mostly on elevation, for you are climbing higher and higher into the mountains. The forests don't thin much as you descend the western slope, though—if anything, they are thicker—until you reach the rim of the Rocky Mountain Trench near Golden and the landscape seems suddenly drier.

If you were to take the same trip west from Edmonton, you might get a different impression. The land between the city and the mountains is not grassy; in its natural state it is a mixture of heavy woods and wetlands. The foothills are solidly forested, broken only by logged-off patches. The front ranges seem rather bare and dry in comparison (there are even sand dunes along the Athabasca River). The continental-divide forests are familiar—thick and dark—but in descending the western slope, one finds groves of cedar trees around the base of Mt. Robson.

Obviously, there is more at work here than just elevation.

Now take a final ride west, this time from Fort Nelson at the north end of the range. For the first 50 km the country looks very much like the aspen parklands west of Edmonton. But in the foothills proper the plant community is a low-elevation type on one side of the road and a higher-elevation type on the other, a function of the low angle of the sun at this latitude (see page 251 for more on slope-angle effects). Still, most of the species are typical of the Canadian Rockies farther south. However, where are the Douglas-firs so common on the western slope?

Answer: they thin out north of Prince George and are absent beyond McLeod Lake.

How does one describe this ecological variety? There are various approaches.

Naturalists discovered long ago that different kinds of plants grew at different elevations in any mountain range. They thought of mountain ecology in terms of elevational zones. Perhaps the simplest of these systems comes from Colorado, where one finds the "plains" zone (for plants growing on the flats surrounding the mountains), the "foothills" zone (self-descriptive), the "montane" zone (lower mountain slopes), "subalpine zone" (upper mountain slopes to timberline) and "alpine" zone (above timberline).

As an ecological overview this idea works pretty well in the American Rockies, so it has been carried north to the Canadian Rockies. The alpine and subalpine designations match reasonably well throughout our area, and on the eastern slope south of Crowsnest Pass one can recognize a northern version of the grassy plant communities of the American plains zone lapping against the mountains.

But the foothills and montane zones blur here, as they do in other parts of the Canadian Rockies. Below the subalpine zone in our area, it is not how high up you are, it is *where* you are that counts. A variety of plant communities spread out over the lower slopes and foothills of the Canadian Rockies like a patchwork quilt.

Let's go in for a closer look. There is an open, grassy forest in the Alberta foothills south of Bow River and a dense, heavy forest to the north. Same elevation, different vegetation. On the western slope there are no foothills at all: tall peaks rise right out of the Rocky Mountain Trench.

The trench is a strange place botanically. The dry section from Golden south to the international boundary supports grassy woods of ponderosa pine and Douglas-fir, while to the north there is an abrupt change to dense forests of cedar and hemlock—an extension of the wetter Columbia Mountains to the west. Again: same elevation, different vegetation.

What we are seeing here are the effects of *differences in climate*. The table on pages 248-249 shows the variation in temperature and precipitation throughout the region; reading the discussion of the annual weather pattern (page 260) will also help to explain.

Also noted in the chapter on weather and climate is how the low angle of the sun in our area keeps north-facing slopes much shadier—and thus cooler and damper—than south-facing slopes. So different vegetation grows on either side of any particular mountain.

Is it any wonder that ecologists working in this part of the world have always had trouble stating that such-and-such a plant grows in one elevational zone or another? Elevation is important, yes, but other factors come strongly into play.

Thus, some Alberta ecologists have recently scrapped the zone designations, erecting a new system based on what they call "ecoregions." Getting beyond the buzzword reveals a sensible idea based on differences in plant communities, climates and soils. The entire province has been divided into seven ecological regions, and the results are available in a provincial government publication (Strong & Leggat, 1981) that comes with a detailed map.

For most of Alberta the ecoregion system applies nicely, but in the mountains the system has its shortcomings. The term "montane," for example, has been restricted to apply only to the Douglas-fir woods lying mainly along the floors of certain major valleys, while the rest of the lodgepole/spruce/aspen woods that characterize much of the Rockies have been lumped in with the very different forest of the subalpine zone. The BC side of the Rockies is not dealt with at all in the Alberta ecoregion map, and unfortunately there is no equivalent ecoregion map available at time of writing for the western slope with which to compare.

If you are trying to identify a flower by checking whether it is growing in the right sort of place, none of this is very helpful.

Rather than setting forth an alternative system, which would be even more confusing (and I am not qualified to do it), I have borrowed from both the older zone system and the newer ecoregion system to present a practical view of the gross ecology of the Canadian Rockies. The various zones and regions are used in the plant listings to match species with their usual environments, and the same terms appear later in the book to describe animal habitats as well.

SOUTHERN, CENTRAL AND NORTHERN REGIONS,
within each of which one finds the

ALPINE ZONE, SUBALPINE ZONE and MONTANE FOREST
The montane forest divides into the

eastern-slope montane forest, which contains a special area

the **southern foothills**

and the **western-slope montane forest,** which contains two special areas:

the **southern Rocky Mountain Trench** and the **Columbian forest**

COMPARISON OF SOUTHERN, CENTRAL AND NORTHERN REGIONS

The three very general north/south divisions reflect differences in soil, elevation and climate. Here is a comparison.

- **Southern region (Marias Pass to Crowsnest Pass)**

  Purcell Group bedrock (page 71), inclined to be shaly overall, is predominant. There is much less limestone than in the central Rockies, and thus the soils are inclined to be acidic. The climate is warmer and somewhat drier than in the other areas, with strong and frequent chinook winds in winter. Sun angle is higher than in more northerly areas.
  Eastern-slope lands in the southern region (Waterton park and eastern Glacier park) are perhaps the most botanically interesting part of the Canadian Rockies. Some plants make their only eastern-slope appearance in this area (beargrass and ninebark, for example). Yet others are strangely rare or absent (crowberry, twinflower and monkshood among them).

- **Central region (Crowsnest Pass to approximately Pine Pass/Peace River)**

  Bedrock mostly calcareous and dolomitic, so soils are not as acidic. Temperature, precipitation, weather pattern, chinook influence and sun angle are typical of the Canadian Rockies as a whole. Elevations, though, are higher than in the other sections, with icefield development along the continental divide and rain-shadowing (dry areas downwind from the divide) in the front ranges.

- **Northern region (Pine Pass/Peace River to Liard River)**

  Elevations are lower and glaciers are fewer here than in the central region. The climate is cooler and wetter in summer than it is in the other areas, colder and drier in winter. Chinook influence is similar to that of the central Rockies. Low sun angle has a strong effect on local ecology (north-facing slopes much colder than south-facing slopes).

Having considered the main differences in the three main ecological regions, let us move on to defining and describing the subdivisions in more detail. It is easier to walk downhill than up, so let us start at the top of the mountains.

ALPINE ZONE

The alpine *zone* of past days and the alpine *ecoregion* of the present are the same thing, which is handy. But the term "ecoregion" seems poorly applied to alpine areas, which are scattered over the mountains rather than forming a single "region." So in this book I am retaining the older term "alpine **zone**," which means, simply, the land above timberline, whether it is meadow, bare rock or glacier.

Note that timberline has nothing to do with absolute elevation; it depends on elevation and latitude combined. Timberline is at 3600 m in New Mexico at the south end of the Rockies, where the climate is considerably warmer that it is at Liard River at the north end of the Rockies. Timberline there is down to 1300 m.

On any particular mountain, the treeline is a transitional thing. As you approach it from below, the trees become shorter and the forest more open, the conifers packed together in clumps that look like islands of trees among the meadows. Farther upslope, the tree-islands flatten. The trees are shrub-like, growing only waist-high and often on the leeward (eastern) side of rocks and ridges. In so doing, they hide under the snow and thus escape the terrible winds of winter storms. These patches of **krummholz** (pronounced "KRUM-holts," meaning "crooked wood" in German) get smaller and more scattered as you climb higher, until the highest-growing trees are reached: rare, tiny and stunted, barely surviving on this botanical frontier. The transition from forest to highest-growing krummholz takes a couple of hundred metres vertically. You get there sooner on a north-facing mountainside than on a south-facing one, for timberline is a little lower on the colder north exposure.

So exactly where on the slope is the treeline? It is, after all, supposed to be a *line*, right?

Well, it is a rather *thick* line. I have heard botanists arguing heatedly about the exact location of timberline, using tree heights, tree spacing, climatic data and other esoteric stuff to tighten up an annoyingly imprecise element in their science. This may be the ultimate purpose of timberline: to give the academics something to talk about while strolling uphill.

One thing is certain, though. True to the biological rule that pleasant environments have more species than nasty ones, there is more botanical variety in the gentle mountain valleys than at the hostile summits. So fewer kinds of plants grow in the alpine zone than lower down. Further, the alpine plant list is surprisingly consistent all over our area. At any given latitude, you will find nearly all the same alpine species on either side of the continental divide, and many of the species growing above timberline in Waterton/Glacier are also found in alpine meadows above the Alaska Highway in the northern Rockies.

SUBALPINE ZONE

In these pages the **subalpine zone** is considered to extend from timberline (wherever that is) downslope through heathery meadows set with islands of stunted subalpine fir and Engelmann spruce. From Lake Louise south, a band of subalpine larch lies just below timberline. North of Lake Louise, subalpine larch peters out; it is absent north of Dolomite Pass.

With or without larch, the subalpine zone continues downward into dark, heavy forests of tall subalpine fir and Engelmann spruce, often with a fair bit of lodgepole pine. Here one also finds whitebark pine (Peace River south), and occasional limber pines (Saskatchewan Crossing south). Crowberry, grouseberry and Labrador tea are common on the mossy forest floor.

The subalpine climate is cool and damp. This is the zone of heaviest snow accumulation—the snow forest, much the same up and down the Rockies, regardless of which side of the divide you are on.

About 300-500 m below timberline, the subalpine fir and whitebark pine are gradually replaced by lodgepole pine and aspen. White spruce mix with Engelmann spruce, shrub species change, and thus the montane forest is reached.

MONTANE FOREST

In this book the term "montane" is used to describe the typical plant community that covers the lower slopes and foothills of the Rockies. To deal with ecological variety in the montane forest (the result mostly of fire succession and a patchy climate), I think of montane forest as having several subsets. They are described below.

Eastern-slope montane forest

The eastern-slope montane forest is extensive, covering the lower mountain slopes, the valley floors and much of the foothills belt. The main tree species are lodgepole pine, white spruce and aspen, with buffaloberry, juniper, cinquefoil, wild rose and kinnikinnik the characteristic shrubbery. From Jasper south, Douglas-fir stands dot south-facing and west-facing slopes along major valleys. The foothills south of Calgary are full of Douglas-fir.

The montane woods get generally damper as you go north, most noticeably in the eastern foothills north of Calgary, where Strong and Leggat (1981) identify a portion they call the "boreal foothills." To the non-botanist, the most obvious change north of Bow River is the decrease in the number and size of clearings. The forest becomes denser and more continuous.

Special area: the southern foothills

South of Bow River the foothills are so rich in aspen, and so grassy, that they form a special part of the eastern-slope montane forest. The ecoregion system recognizes this and provides a name: "aspen parkland." On the ecoregion map of Alberta, the aspen parkland has its southern margin in this area, then sweeps northeast, out of the foothills and away from the mountains. Because the term "southern foothills" is more commonly applied to the place I am talking about, this book uses "southern foothills" instead of "aspen parkland," but the terms are equivalent. The foothills east of Glacier National Park, Montana are included in this region.

Western-slope montane forest

Generally speaking, the western-slope montane forest is simply a wetter version of what you find on the eastern slope. It is somewhat heavier and shrubbier, with the addition of a few species that seldom cross the divide: western larch, for example, and trillium. But the differences are more of degree than of kind, and it seems reasonable to continue calling this region "montane," adding "western-slope" to show that there *is* a difference.

Special areas: southern Rocky Mountain Trench and Columbian forest

Ecological differences that have little to do with elevation are best seen in the Rocky Mountain Trench, which is part dry, part wet and part in-between. This is an exceptionally varied place, botanically.

In spite of the overall wetter character of the western slope, the floor of the trench between Golden and the international boundary is the driest place in or adjacent to the Canadian Rockies (rain-haters' centre: Canal Flats). You can even find cactus growing there. Douglas-fir is common, and there are stands of sun-loving ponderosa pine from Columbia Lake south. As you approach the Montana border there is a marked increase in western larch.

Between Golden and Prince George, the floor and lower sides of the trench are heavily treed in a mixed forest of spruce, cedar, hemlock and poplar. In the dense undergrowth lurks spiny devil's-club. This is **Columbian forest** (a term used by Hosie in *Native Trees of Canada,* 1979). Columbian forest is a spillover from the wet, warm Columbia mountains to the west. Normally limited in our area to the Rocky Mountain Trench, Columbian forest appears farther east in the Rockies along storm tracks, which carry sufficient moisture for cedar groves at Mount Robson and near Fernie (the Fernie groves are mostly logged at time of writing).

Another patch of Columbian forest grows along the western boundary of Glacier National Park, Montana; it has crept eastward along the shores of Lake McDonald.

North of Prince George the Columbian forest gives way to typically montane species, although the influence of Williston Lake may change this. The lake is a huge reservoir in the northern Rocky Mountain Trench, created by damming Peace River at the mountain front in 1967. Perhaps Williston Lake will moderate the climate there and increase the humidity, encouraging the expansion of Columbian forest to the north.

FURTHER READING

See also the general botanical bibliography on page 462.

Canadian Forestry Service (1974) *Ecotour of the TransCanada Highway, Calgary-Golden* Information Canada, Ottawa. Non-technical booklet briefly describing ecological variety along the route; illustrated, 18 pages.

Hardy, W.G., ed. (1967) *Alberta: a Natural History* Hurtig, Edmonton. General naturalist's guide to the province; illustrated, 343 pages.

Krajina, V.J. (1965) "Biogeoclimatic zones and classification of British Columbia," in *Ecology of Western North America*

Rowe, J.S. (1972) *Forest Regions of Canada* Canadian Forest Service, Department of Environment, Ottawa. General ecology; illustrated, 172 pages.

Spalding, A.E., Ed. (1980) *A Nature Guide to Alberta* Hurtig, Edmonton. Mapsheet-by-mapsheet guide to the province, with good introductory material and mountain coverage; illustrated, 368 pages.

Strong, W.L., and K. Leggat (1981) *Ecoregions of Alberta* ENR Technical Report T/4, available free of charge from Alberta Energy and Natural Resources, Seventh Floor, 9915 108 Street, Edmonton T5K 2C9. Summary of a major land-classification project; illustrated with photos and maps, 64 pages.

SCIENTIFIC NAMES OF VASCULAR PLANT FAMILIES AND THEIR COMMON EQUIVALENTS

Listed in botanical order

Lycopodiaceae
Clubmoss family

Selaginellaceae
Spikemoss family

Equisetaceae
Horsetail family

Ophioglossaceae
Adder's-tongue family

Polypodiaceae
Common fern family

Taxaceae
Yew family

Cupressaceae
Cypress family

Pinaceae
Pine family

Salicaceae
Willow family

Betulaceae
Birch family

Urticaceae
Nettle family

Loranthaceae
Mistletoe family

Santalaceae
Sandalwood family

Aristolochiaceae
Birthwort family

Polygonaceae
Buckwheat family

Chenopodiaceae
Goosefoot family

Amaranthaceae
Pigweed family

Nyctaginaceae
Four-o'clock family

Portulacaceae
Purslane family

Caryophyllaceae
Pink family

Nymphaeceae
Water-lily family

Ranunculaceae
Buttercup family

Berberidaceae
Barberry family

Papaveraceae
Poppy family

Fumariaceae
Fumitory family

Cruciferae
Mustard family

Droseraceae
Sundew family

Crassulaceae
Stonecrop family

Saxifragaceae
Saxifrage family

Grossulariaceae
Currant/gooseberry family

Hydrangeaceae
Hydrangea family

Rosaceae
Rose family

Leguminosae
Pea family

Geraniaceae
Geranium family

Oxalidaceae
Oxalis/wood-sorrel family

Linaceae
Flax family

Euphorbiaceae
Spurge family

Empetraceae
Crowberry family

Anacardiaceae
Sumac family

Aceraceae
Maple family

Rhamnaceae
Buckthorn family

Malvaceae
Mallow family

Hypericaceae
St. John's-wort family

Violaceae
Violet family

Cactaceae
Cactus family

Elaeagnaceae
Oleaster family

Lythraceae
Loosestrife family

Onagraceae
Evening-primrose family

Haloragaceae
Water-milfoil family

Hippuridaceae
Mare's-tail family

Araliaceae
Ginseng family

Umbelliferae Parsley/carrot family	Labiatae Mint family	Scheuchzeriaceae Scheuchzeria family
Cornaceae Dogwood family	Solanaceae Nightshade family	Juncaginaceae Arrow-grass family
Ericaceae Heath family	Scrophulariaceae Figwort family	Potamogetonaceae Pondweed family
Primulaceae Primrose family	Orobanchaceae Broomrape family	Juncaceae Rush family
Gentianaceae Gentian family	Lentibulariaceae Bladderwort family	Cyperaceae Sedge family
Menyanthaceae Buck-bean family	Plantaginaceae Plantain family	Gramineae Grass family
Apocynaceae Dogbane family	Rubiaceae Madder family	Sparganiaceae Bur-reed family
Asclepiadaceae Milkweed family	Caprifoliaceae Honeysuckle family	Typhaceae Cat-tail family
Convolvulaceae Morning-glory family	Valerianaceae Valerian family	Araceae Arum family
Polemoniaceae Phlox family	Campanulaceae Harebell/bluebell family	Lemnaceae Duckweed family
Hydrophyllaceae Waterleaf family	Compositae Composite/aster family	Liliaceae Lily family
Boraginaceae Borage family		Iridaceae Iris family
Verbenaceae Verbena/vervain family	Alismataceae Water-plantain family	Orchidaceae Orchid family
	Hydrocharitaceae Frog's-bit family	

ECO-PICTURES SECTION

Here are 31 common plant/animal communities of the Canadian Rockies. A few species characteristic of each community are given. Some very common species are not listed because they occur in so many environments. Not all parts of the mountains have all species named. One or two auto-accessible locations are named when it seemed appropriate. The arrangement is roughly from lowest elevations to highest, with some special communities grouped at the end.

This is by no means a complete discussion of ecological communities in the region; such a list is beyond the scope of this book. The intention here is to point out some important (or interesting) and easily recognized communities. For more information, consult the reading list on page 270.

1. **Southern Rocky Mountain Trench floor** (Wilmer Wildlife Refuge). Driest part of the Canadian Rockies, with Douglas-fir, lodgepole pine, ponderosa pine, Rocky Mountain juniper, sagebrush, snowbrush, Oregon grape, cactus, white mariposa lily. Western skink, yellow pine chipmunk. Extensive wetlands; species list similar to montane wetlands (item 10) with more Columbian plants (next entry), more amphibians and the painted turtle.

2. **Columbian forest** (Lake McDonald in Glacier park, or Mt. Robson area). At low elevations on the western slope; see map on page 264 for distribution. Damp, humid summer; moderate winter temperatures and longest growing season in the region. A heavy mixed-wood forest of cedar, hemlock, black cottonwood, Douglas-fir, white spruce, lodgepole pine, white pine, black spruce and western larch (southern area). Pacific willow, green alder, thimbleberry, devil's-club, sarsaparilla, orange honeysuckle, goat's-beard, lace flower, heal-all, *Lobaria* tree lichen.

3. **Southern-foothills meadow or grassland** (along the TransCanada Highway west of Calgary; especially well-developed in the Waterton/Glacier area). Dry and windy in winter from frequent chinooks, but large snowbanks accumulate in lee spots. Silty soils. Lodgepole pine, Douglas-fir, aspen, balsam poplar, limber pine; silverberry. Many grasses: timothy, junegrass, fescue, bluegrass, brome, needle-and-thread, sweetgrass. Wildflowers as per montane meadow (item 7), with horsemint common south of Crowsnest Pass. Meadow voles, thirteen-lined ground squirrel, Richardson's ground squirrel, northern pocket gopher, coyote; red-tailed hawk, prairie falcon, meadowlark, mourning dove, nighthawk.

4. **White-spruce forest** (Bow, North Saskatchewan or Athabasca valleys at the mountain front). In the eastern front ranges and western foothills, along floors of major valleys where extreme chinook conditions and high water table prevent growth of lodgepole pine. White spruce is the only common tree; there is minor aspen. Shrubs: kinnikinnik, willows, shrubby potentilla, roses. **Cryptogamic soil:** lichens, mosses and fungi forming a crust between shrubs and tufts of grass.

5. **Aspen grove** (along highways in southern foothills, Bow Valley Parkway; Pyramid Lake Road). Mostly eastern-slope montane, on gently sloping, gravelly soil. Trembling aspen with minor spruce and white birch; water birch, Bebb's and Scouler's willows, bracted honeysuckle, buffaloberry, mertensia, wild rose, common juniper, buckbrush; wild pea, red paintbrush, Solomon's seal, twisted stalk, cow-parsnip, clematis. Thrushes, flycatchers, warblers; thirteen-lined ground squirrel (southern region), mule deer.

6. Montane forest (environs of Banff and Jasper). Most common community in the Canadian Rockies, dependent on forest fire. Mostly lodgepole pine, with white spruce, Douglas-fir, aspen and white birch. Shrubs: buffaloberry, common juniper, wild roses, low-bush cranberry; thickets in damp spots of Scouler's and Bebb's willows, alder and Rocky Mountain maple. Wildflowers: red paintbrush, arnica, calypso orchid, yarrow, goldenrod. Grasses: ryegrass, ricegrass, spike trisetum, common timothy. *Cladonia* and *Peltigera* lichens. Branch-tip spiders, carpenter ants, beetles; woodpeckers, ruffed grouse, sharp-shinned and Cooper's hawks, owls, goshawk, thrushes, chickadees, juncos, pine grosbeak, crossbills; deer mouse, red squirrel, snowshoe hare, marten, black bear, coyote, wolf, mule deer, white-tailed deer, elk, moose.

7. Montane meadow (environs of Banff and Jasper). Typical of open dry places on valley floors in the front ranges and foothills. Cold in winter, but with little snow accumulation; receives most moisture as summer rain. Shrubs: common juniper, shrubby potentilla, buffaloberry, silverberry, wild rose, saskatoon. Many wildflowers: pasque flower, pasture sage, daisy fleabane, showy androsace, aster, stonecrop, gaillardia, yarrow, wind flower, harebell, *Antennaria* species; showy locoweed, ragwort, goldenrod, three-flowered avens, silverweed. Grasses: montane timothy, trisetum, ryegrass, junegrass, brome, fescue, bluegrass, ticklegrass, foxtail barley. Wood tick, ants, butterflies; raven, sparrows, robin; Richardson's or Columbian ground squirrels, snowshoe hare, elk, coyote, wolf.

Pictures of ecological communities

8. Montane feather-moss forest (Jasper area). North-facing subset of montane forest, at low elevations from Bow River north. (At higher elevations, this is part of the lower subalpine forest). Feather mosses cover the ground under closely-spaced lodgepole pine, white spruce and black spruce. Gooseberry, wild rose, common juniper; bunchberry (but few wildflowers); *Peltigera* and *Cladonia* lichens. Ruby-crowned kinglet, winter wren; red squirrel.

9. Douglas-fir woods (Radium area, southern foothills, environs of Banff and Jasper). Subset of montane forest; see page 299 for distribution. Grassy woods (ryegrass, fescue) with moderately spaced Douglas-firs; minor white spruce and lodgepole pine, with little shrub growth (some common juniper, buffaloberry, wild rose) and few wildflowers. Red-breasted nuthatch, junco, chickadees; elk, mule deer, white-tailed deer, coyote.

Pictures of ecological communities   277

10. **Montane or subalpine wetland** (along Fenland Trail or at Vermilion Lakes near Banff; at Cottonwood Slough near Jasper). Standing water and ponds. White spruce, black spruce, alder, many willows (especially *Salix commutata, S. discolor, S. planifolia, S. rigida* and *S. candida).* Labrador tea, shrubby potentilla; bulrushes, bur-reed, cattail, water hemlock, bog orchids, little elephants, swamp laurel, cotton grass and other sedges, rushes, horsetails, peat mosses. Mosquitoes, dragonflies, water insects and larvae; long-toed salamander, chorus frog, spotted frog, western toad, garter snakes; dabbling ducks, snipe, sora, blue heron, red-winged blackbird, hummingbirds, northern waterthrush, yellow warbler, yellowthroat, sparrows; water shrew, meadow vole, water vole, beaver, muskrat, mink, moose, wolf.

11. **Lake communities** (many locations). Shoreline vegetation as per montane marsh, with horsetails and chives. Water plants: mare's-tail, bladderwort, water smartweed, pondweed, pond lily, water hemlock. Leeches, water insects and larvae in water, dragonflies near shore; snails and fingernail clams; rainbow trout, brook trout, lake trout, suckers; loon, grebes, Barrow's goldeneye and other diving ducks, osprey, bald eagle, sandpipers, yellow-rumped warbler, swallows; beaver, muskrat, moose.

Pictures of ecological communities

12. **Montane and subalpine river communities** (many locations). Banks and islands often with sandbar willows *(Salix exigua* and *S. caudata);* river alder, red-osier dogwood, shrubby potentilla, Labrador tea, blueberries, cow parsnip, false hellebore, yellow paintbrush, white camas. Rainbow trout, brook trout, brown trout, whitefish; western toad, wood frog; yellow-rumped warbler, osprey, bald eagle, kingfisher, swallows; water shrew, mink, moose, black bear. Photo courtesy Jasper National Park.

13. **Dryas flats** (along the Sunwapta River north of Athabasca Glacier). Central and northern regions, mostly eastern slope, where yellow dryas covers gravel along streams and on highway shoulders. Broad-leaved willow-herb also common.

Pictures of ecological communities   279

14. Montane or subalpine canyon (Maligne Canyon, Johnston Canyon). Damp, shady environment. Black spruce, white spruce, white birch, alders, willows, ground birch, Labrador tea, menziesia; ferns, clubmoss, feather mosses, *Hygrohypnum* and *Scouleria* mosses by the water. Least chipmunk, red squirrel, raven, black swift. Photo courtesy Jasper National Park.

15. Lower subalpine forest (Lake Louise, or Mt. Edith Cavell Road). Cool, short growing season; heavy snowfall. Subalpine fir, Engelmann spruce, lodgepole pine, whitebark pine; Barclay's and Drummond's willows, Labrador tea, menziesia, Rocky Mountain rhododendron, crowberry, mountain cranberry, bunchberry arnica, larkspur, monkshood, columbine; Clark's nutcracker, gray jay, spruce and blue grouse, three-toed woodpecker, merlin, goshawk, hawk owl, Townsend's solitaire, shrike; red-backed vole, red-tailed chipmunk, snowshoe hare, ermine, marten, fisher, porcupine, lynx, cougar, moose, grizzly bear, caribou (winter).

Pictures of ecological communities

16. **Subalpine meadow** (Bow Pass, Sunwapta Pass, Sunshine). Damp, with cool, short growing season; very cold in winter. Bluegreen willow, Barratt's willow, rock willow, dwarf birch; valerian, western lousewort, Drummond's anemone, larkspur, monkshood, saussurea. Grasses: trisetum, bluegrass, fescue, alpine foxtail, mountain timothy. Horse flies, butterflies, mosquitoes; Brewer's sparrow, Savannah sparrow, northern harrier; pygmy shrew, heather vole, northern bog lemming, Columbian ground squirrel, ermine, marmot, grizzly bear, moose, elk.

17. **Upper subalpine woods** (Bow Pass or Parker Ridge along Icefields Parkway; Sunshine area near Banff; Going-to-the-Sun Road). Cool, very short growing season; cold, snowy, windy winters. Island-like patches of subalpine fir and Engelmann spruce, spaced subalpine larch; grouseberry, crowberry, heather; beargrass in Waterton/Glacier area. Rich in tree lichens such as *Usnea, Bryoria, Hypogymnia* and *Letharia;* ground lichens also common from Banff north (*Cladonia, Peltigera, Cladina, Stereocaulon*). Golden-crowned sparrow, fox sparrow, robin, blue grouse, warblers, gray jay; grizzly bear, elk (summer), caribou.

Pictures of ecological communities   *281*

18. Larch grove (Going-to-the-Sun Road; Highwood Pass along Alberta 40). Subset of upper subalpine forest, found from Bow Pass south. Grows just below the krummholz zone. Main species: subalpine larch and white heather.

19. Alpine meadow/alpine tundra (Logan Pass, The Whistlers via Jasper Tramway). Cool, very short growing season; highly variable snow depth; very windy. Many small communities in this environment, but two main ones are meadow (fairly dry, grassy, with many wildflowers) and tundra (damper, carpets of heather, ponds). White, pink and green heather, willows (bluegreen, alpine, rock, snow), dwarf birch; forget-me-not, moss campion, white dryas, western anemone, alpine anemone, blue-bottle gentian, yellow paintbrush, arctic poppy, Lyall's saxifrage, head-shaped and alpine louseworts; alpine bluegrass, trisetum, alpine foxtail, mountain timothy; *Cladina* and *Stereocaulon* ground lichens. Gray-crowned rosy finch, ptarmigan, pipit, horned lark, northern harrier, golden eagle; brown lemming, Columbian ground squirrel, marmot, grizzly bear, wolverine, caribou, bighorn sheep (summer).

20. **Krummholz** (Logan Pass along Going-to-the-Sun Road in Glacier park). Patches of densely growing subalpine fir and Engelmann spruce at timberline. See page 328.

21. **Summit** (top of The Whistlers, short walk from Jasper Tramway). Highest community, found near tops of peaks. Very cool, extremely short growing season; very cold, extremely windy winters with patchy snow accumulation. Mosses and lichens (*Xanthoria, Rhizocarpon, Umbilicaria, Thamnolia,* encrusting types), prickly saxifrage, purple saxifrage, mountain sorrel. Snow worms, springtails and hill-topping insects; raven, golden eagle, mountain goat, wolverine, marmot.

Pictures of ecological communities   283

22. **Avalanche track** (Going-to-the-Sun Road; TransCanada Highway near Kicking Horse Pass; Icefields Parkway at Parker Ridge). Green alder, willows, krummholz at higher elevations. Grizzly bear, moose.

23. **Burn** (Vermilion Pass, along Highway 93 in Kootenay park). Young lodgepole pines, fireweed; woodpeckers, mule deer. Photo courtesy Kootenay National Park.

24. Blowdown (watch for occurrences along highways in southern Alberta). A gust of powerful wind blows down a stand of timber covering an area that can be as large as a mountainside. Like a burn or avalanche, an accident that changes an existing community. Happens mostly in montane lodgepole and aspen communities, primarily on the eastern slope and especially south of Crowsnest Pass. Provides excellent habitat for carpenter ants, woodpeckers, grouse, wrens, snowshoe hare, porcupine.

25. Rocky slope or cliff at lower elevations (Disaster Point along Highway 16 east of Jasper, Alberta 40 in Kananaskis country). Scraggly white or Engelmann spruce, Douglas-fir, limber pine, whitebark pine; creeping and common juniper, kinnikinnik, shrubby potentilla, gooseberry, wild roses; white camas, pasture sage, silver plant and other buckwheat-family members, alpine potentilla. Kestrel, mountain bluebird; wood rat, least chipmunk, golden-mantled ground squirrel, bighorn sheep, mountain goat.

Pictures of ecological communities   285

26. **Talus or rockslide** (Maligne Valley slides or Moraine Lake). Lichens on the boulders, mosses on and between them; prickly saxifrage, gooseberry, sorrel. Long-tailed vole, least chipmunk, golden-mantled ground squirrel, pika, marmot.

27. **Scree slope** (many locations). Scree (small rock fragments that have come from cliffs above) is too unstable for most plants, but in spots that have not been covered for a few years there may be raspberry, bladder locoweed, dwarf hawksbeard and bladder campion.

Pictures of ecological communities

28. Glacial melt-back area (Toe of Athabasca Glacier, or road's end at Mt. Edith Cavell). Recolonization of bare ground by young Engelmann spruce, willows, broad-leaved willow-herb, mountain sorrel, sedges, rushes. Photo by S. Lal Mattu.

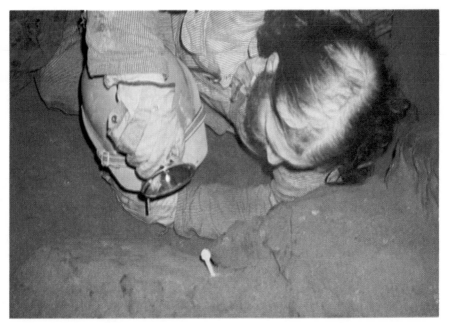

29. Cave (no easy access). Molds and sometimes mushrooms on organic matter (microscopic material such as pollen, dead animals, wood rat and bat feces, human waste and trash). Blind, eyeless water insects (crustaceans), such as *Salmacellus steganothrix* (an isopod) and *Stygobromus canadensis* (an amphipod known only from Castleguard Cave), ice insects (see page 534; wood rats (near entrance) and bats. Martens must travel far into mountain caves, perhaps in search of bats; I have found marten skeletons over a kilometre deep in Cadomin Cave.

Pictures of ecological communities 287

30. Dunes (Jasper Lake area along Highway 16 in eastern Jasper park). White spruce, silverberry, creeping juniper, kinnikinnik and other dry montane species overgrowing stable sand dunes; active dunes are covering vegetation. Photo courtesy Jasper National Park.

31. Summer snowbank (high points along mountain highways). There is an interesting ecological community here, based on red algae living in the snow. See page 532 for more information. Photo by Cia Gadd.

Pictures of ecological communities

Plants
Starting with trees and working down

Some 660 plants are pictured and described in this book—about half of all Canadian Rockies flora. The listings include all the common species, plus some uncommon ones that are bound to attract your attention if you happen to see them. The species not listed are close relatives of the ones pictured, or rare, or likely to catch the eye only of the professional botanist—who can get what he needs from the technical literature.

The common name of the family to which a particular plant belongs is given (in parentheses) on the same line as its Latin genus and species names. On page 271 there is a list of these common family names, matched with their Latin equivalents. The order of the list is the accepted botanical order. (To make look-ups easier for amateurs, the plant listings in this book don't always follow that order.)

For our purposes, a **tree** is a tall plant (normally 5 m high or taller) with a single woody stem (the trunk), although there may be more than one trunk per plant.

A **shrub** is any woody plant that is not a tree. (Isn't botany easy?) Most shrubs have multiple stems. Some are vines.

Strictly speaking, wildflowers are **forbs:** the seed-bearing non-woody plants, excluding grasses, sedges and rushes. But most wildflower books include flowering shrubs as well as forbs.

Grasses, sedges and rushes have a wonderful collective name: the **graminoids,** meaning the "grass-like" plants.

The forbs plus the grass-like group comprise the **herbs.** So an herb is something different to a botanist than it is to a cook or a naturopath.

Then there are the **ferns, clubmosses** and **spikemosses,** which are tricky to identify because they don't bloom. Not to worry; the listings are short.

Lower on the evolutionary scale are the **bryophytes** (mosses and liverworts), the **lichens** and the **fungi.** This book lists some of the more interesting lower plants, including a kind of algae that lives in snowbanks (page 532).

USING THE LISTINGS

Non-botanists, and I am one of them, can have a lot of trouble identifying plants—even the most obvious, showy-blooming ones, never mind the little plain-Jane ones. Perhaps you do your identifications like I do them: by brute force, looking at picture after picture until—aha!—there's the little beggar on page 418.

A botanist gets around this by using a **key system,** which requires knowledge of plant families and plant parts. There is nothing mysterious about keying out plants, but who has the time to learn how to do it? Especially when there are other ways.

In these pages you will find some of those "other ways," as used in non-technical botany books. They work.

The idea is to go right to the section where your plant is likely to be, thus eliminating most of the endless page-turning. To use the listings, ask yourself some questions:

1. **What sort of plant is this?** Is it obviously a **tree?** A **shrub?** A **wildflower** of some kind? Does it look to be at home in the **water?** Is it a **fern** or a **horsetail?** Does it look rather like **grass?** Or is it a **moss?** A **lichen?** Perhaps a **mushroom,** or some other kind of **fungus?**

    Each of these groups has its own section, and most readers should get to the right section without any trouble. Just in case, though, the fern look-alikes are cross-referenced ("see also") and the little low-growing shrubs that look like wildflowers are stuck in with the wildflowers.

    Once you are in the right section, it probably won't take long to find the mystery plant—unless it is a wildflower. There are a *lot* of wildflowers listed in this book.

    Suppose it is a wildflower. You can get two steps farther in the identification game before the page-turning starts. Check your surroundings and ask yourself the next question:

2. **Am I above or below timberline?**

    The section on wildflowers has been split into those below timberline and those above.

    Sometimes it may be hard to tell if you are above or below the treeline. Maybe the terrain is so rough and rocky that few trees are growing there. When in doubt, you can save time by checking the alpine flowers first, for that list is shorter. Then go to the below-treeline section.

3. **What color is the bloom?**

    The wildflower listings have been further divided by color. There is no need to be precise here, because most wildflowers fall easily into one of six color groups:

    > **White**
    > **Green or greenish**
    > **Yellow or orange**
    > **Red or pink**
    > **Purple or blue**
    > **Brown, reddish brown or otherwise drab**

    Having decided on the color, find the appropriate section and *then* start turning the pages. There won't be terribly many to turn.

    But what about the greenish-white flowers, or the purplish-pink ones? There are certainly a few in-betweens, and there also can be a lot of variation in the color of a single species. Well, if you can't find a particular flower under one color, then try another color. To help with troublesome species, all possible colors are mentioned and some cross-referencing has been done.

4. **What part of the flowering season is it?**

    The listing for each flowering plant shows the time of year during which it normally blooms.

    Willows are the earliest plants to bloom in the Canadian Rockies. The fuzzy **catkins** (pussy-willows) are the flowers, and on some species the catkins appear in late February. I have even seen them once in late *January* during a warm winter at Jasper. A few wildflowers and shrubs begin to bloom in March on the western slope, and sometimes pasque flowers appear in March in the eastern-slope foothills, but don't expect to find many flowers on either side of the divide until the latter half of May, when frosts at the lower elevations are nearly finished and the growing season is on.

    Deciduous trees leaf out in mid-May at Jasper, about a week earlier in the southern section and in the Rocky Mountain Trench; a week later north of Peace River.

    Most shrubs bloom in June, many of them with white flowers.

Mid-July to the end of the first week in August is the height of the wildflower season—spectacular at all elevations. This is the warmest time of year in the Rockies, when pollinating insects are the most active.

The show has wound down noticeably by mid-August. By the end of the month there are few flowers to be seen. The first week in September often brings a killing frost, although the odd showy aster, gentian or harebell doggedly blooms through the middle of September and sometimes you will find a flower in early October. Shrubby cinquefoil (page 318) sometimes puts out a batch of flowers *after* the leaves have turned!

If you are interested in **mushrooms,** you probably know that there are two seasons for looking: in early spring, meaning late April through mid-May in the Canadian Rockies, and again in early fall, from mid-August through September. Of the two seasons, the fall one is far richer in the number of mushrooms and in the diversity of species.

Of course, the time that a particular plant blooms depends on its elevation, the weather, and the blooming site—whether north-facing or south-facing, sheltered by rocks, open and windy, and so on. A flower that blooms early on the montane valley floor may bloom in midsummer up near timberline.

The Canadian Rockies are 835 km long, covering nearly twelve degrees of latitude, so one would expect a pronounced lag in blooming time from south to north. But the difference isn't great. Given equivalent plant communities at Banff and west of Fort Nelson, the more northerly community will be about a week behind. During late July, widely distributed species are at the same stage of development throughout the Rockies. Fall color creeps over the whole range at once, beginning in early September.

The big north-south difference is not so much a matter of time as it is a matter of elevation: Banff is at an elevation of 1387 m, but the same plant community west of Fort Nelson occurs at only 650 m above sea level. A given plant grows (and blooms) at a lower elevation as one goes north.

So check the blooming period when looking up a plant. During the first week in June you can safely ignore the entries that are supposed to bloom in August.

5. **Finally, if the illustration looks close to what you've got, read the entry, checking the ecological information first.**

You can close in on the correct identification by using the ecological data: the elevational zone or region the plant grows in (see the previous chapter for an explanation) and the sort of environment it likes (wet, dry, wooded, open, etc.). This information has been placed at the beginning of each entry so that you can skim it and decide whether it fits. Following that, the key features of the plant are described, which should clinch the identification.

These listings are *mainly* for identification. There is a lot more to learn about Rocky Mountain botany, of course. If you want more detail, be it on certain species or certain ecological relationships, then it is time to head down to the library—preferably a university library.

Another source of detailed information is the government. The libraries of the national parks contain unpublished checklists, studies, copies of journal articles and theses. The Western Regional Office of Parks Canada in Calgary also holds duplicate copies of much of this material.

Easily obtainable publications on Rocky Mountain botany at time of writing are listed on page 462.

● *SCALE BARS USED IN BOTANY SECTION:*

Thick scale bars (|) are one centimetre long.

Thin scale bars (|) are one millimetre long.

TREES

What is the tallest tree in the Canadian Rockies? There is no documented record that I could find. One would think that it would have to be a conifer of some kind, perhaps a cedar or Douglas-fir, but until the record is known, I'll put my money on one of the immense **black cottonwoods** of the western slope. *Native Trees of Canada* (Hosie, 1979), states that the black cottonwood reaches 40 m, which sounds about right. The specimens along Lake McDonald in Glacier National Park seem outstandingly huge.

The same publication lists western red cedar as the tallest of the tree species in western Canada (up to 60 m), but the cedars in the Rockies seem considerably shorter than their counterparts farther west, where the trees are generally taller. After decades of logging, there are precious few big cedars left. Yet the loggers have often ignored the cottonwoods, which are worthless to them. A strange but common sight in British Columbia is a large clear-cut area, everything reduced to rubble except a few giant cottonwoods.

The *shortest* mature trees are undoubtedly the timberline trees: subalpine firs and Engelmann spruces that in extreme cases are creeping (spreading flat to the ground).

Now: how about the *oldest* tree? Currently the champion is a whitebark pine found on the west side of the Ramparts in Mount Robson Provincial Park.* The coring tool crossed 713 rings and didn't reach the centre. That tree would have been a seedling about 750 years ago (1230 AD). An Engelmann spruce in the grove just northeast of Icefield Centre along Highway 93 had 680 rings, for an estimated age of 720 years (described in same journal article).

Potentially, the oldest trees in the Canadian Rockies are subalpine larches. J.W. Campbell, of the Research Council of Alberta, reports larches 650 years old in Kananaskis Country and perhaps 800 years old to the south. But these dates are approximate.

A Douglas-fir just east of Banff has been dated to over 674 years (Canadian Forestry Service, 1984). That is not very old in comparison with the Douglas-firs of Vancouver Island, one of which has been ring-counted to 1306 years. In the White Mountains of eastern California there are bristlecone pines 4600 years old—the world record for trees. These are timberline trees, which have grown very slowly. Timberline trees in the Canadian Rockies are mostly subalpine fir, which live only a couple of hundred years.

Limber pine is a close relative of bristlecone pine, and one would think that the gnarled limber pines of the southern Alberta foothills are old. But they date to about 200 years.

The oldest plants of any kind in the Rockies are almost certainly lichens. See page 435.

In the listings that follow, the blooming date is given at the end of the line with the scientific name and family. If no blooming date is given, then the species does not produce flowers.

Evergreen conifers

There are only 14 needled, cone-bearing trees that grow in the Rockies, so learning them all is easy. Pine, spruce, fir, hemlock, Douglas-fir and larch are all members of the pine family (Pinaceae); cedar belongs to the cypress/juniper family (Cupressaceae). Most of these species are evergreen (they do not lose their needles for part of the year), but some, such as the larch, are deciduous.

---

*Luckman, B.; L. Jozsa and P. Murphy (1984) "Living seven-hundred-year-old *Picea engelmannii* and *Pinus albicaulis* in the Canadian Rockies" *Arctic and Alpine Research* 16, 419-422.

Lodgepole pine
Pinus contorta (pine family)

A characteristic montane tree, with a very straight, gradually tapering trunk, useful for making tipi poles (hence the name). Mature height 5-20 m, with the foliage mainly in the upper third. Needles 2-5 cm long, in bunches of two (the only pine in the Canadian Rockies with needles in twos). The bark is brown and scaly.

Job Kuijt, a botanist with the University of Lethbridge, once found a three-needled lodgepole pine (since destroyed) in Jasper park. See also the entry on three-needled ponderosa pines (page 295).

Lodgepole pine is the most common tree in the montane forest, perhaps the most common tree in the Canadian Rockies. In late June and early July, lodgepole pollen drifts through the mountains in greenish-yellow clouds, accumulating as a yellow scum on any quiet water body. People sometimes ask if the scum is somehow related to acid rain. The answer is no; neither is the stuff particularly allergenic.

The cones are egg-shaped, hard, and may take many years to open for seed release and germination. More commonly, though, the cones open quite suddenly, by the thousand, during a forest fire. Solid stands of lodgepole pine mark areas that have burned; the heat-resistant seeds germinate readily in the carbon-rich soil. The trees grow quickly, forming a dense **dog-hair forest** in which all members are the same age.

Dog-hair forest gradually thins itself out. The faster-growing trees reach above the slower ones, which weaken and die because they can't tolerate shade. In winter, snow overloads the tufts of foliage atop the long, skinny trunks of the weaker trees; they bow over to the ground and die. Disease also attacks weaker trees. As the years go by a lodgepole forest becomes open and sunny.

Eventually one of two things happens: (a) another fire goes through, repeating the process, or (b) over the course of 100 years or so most of the lodgepoles become rotten inside, succumb to disease and blow over—a hazard to campers—to be replaced by shade-tolerant spruce (and Douglas-fir in some regions) that have been patiently growing under the pines. These species owe their success to the low reproductivity of lodgepole in the absence of fire.

Fire suppression through the twentieth century has blanketed the Rockies with old, unhealthy lodgepole forests. Fire is now recognized by foresters as a normal and essential part of forest ecology. It will be allowed to occur more often.

South of Crowsnest Pass Over half the lodgepoles have been killed by mountain pine beetles (page 478). Although the northward spread of the bugs has slowed, indicating that the outbreak is nearly over, they have reached Valemount on the western slope and Banff on the eastern slope. Efforts to resist them are needless; it is time to let nature take its course.

The trunks and branches of lodgepole pine are sometimes marked by swellings that collectors call **burls** and forest-disease specialists call **galls**. They are commonly caused by insect or fungal parasites, all evoking the same response from the tree: it quickly grows tissue at the infected or damaged site, walling off the intruding organisms and thus forming the gall. Perhaps the most common gall-causing organism is **western gall rust** *(Endocronartium harknessii).*

Pine dwarf mistletoe is a parasitic plant *(Arceuthobium americanum)* that grows along the branches of lodgepole pine. It does not produce galls (although the branches can become somewhat thickened) and does not infect spruce, fir or other pine species in the Canadian Rockies, although it attacks jack pine, *P. banksiana,* which grows east of the Rockies.

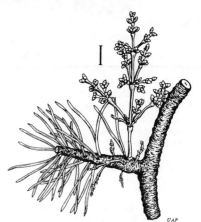

Pine dwarf mistletoe

Mistletoe has greenish-yellow or yellowish-brown stems up to 10 cm long, with no leaves. The roots reach into the host-tree's bark and sap-wood for nutrients. The bud-like blooms take two years to mature into the seeds, which are spread by exploding from their cases. The seeds can travel several metres, lodging in other parts of the tree and spreading the infestation through the forest.

Look for mistletoe in old stands of lodgepole, where it does best. You can often spot it from a distance because some branches of the infected trees grow in dense bunches that look different from the rest of the tree. These branches are called **witches' brooms.** (See also witches' brooms on spruce and fir caused by *Chrysomyxa arctostaphyli,* a fungus that is sometimes mistakenly called mistletoe, page 298).

Red-belt is another lodgepole affliction. This one is caused by the weather. Warm chinook winds in winter (page 257) cause the needles to dry, but the rest of the tree is frozen and sap movement is too slow to replace the moisture. The needles turn reddish-brown and drop off. The condition can affect whole mountainsides, producing reddish streaks of timber (thus "red-belt").

Broomed lodgepole

Red-belt may be the cause of an anomaly in the occurrence of lodgepole pine. Common at montane elevations throughout the Canadian Rockies, the species is surprisingly scarce close to the mountain front in the major cross-cutting valleys (Athabasca, Bow, etc.). These valleys experience the most sudden rises in temperature during chinooks and the greatest wind velocities. White spruce and Douglas-fir, the two common conifers in these lodgepole-free areas, are not as prone to red-belt damage, which may explain why they survive here in place of the pines.

Ponderosa pine
Pinus ponderosa (pine family)

Grows at low elevations in the southern Rocky Mountain Trench from Radium Hot Springs south. Can reach 30-40 m in height. The trunk is straight, but the crown (overall shape of the tree) is rather irregular. Easiest identifier: long needles (7-20 cm) in bunches of three. Cones hard and prickly, 7-15 cm long. Reddish bark, with large, plate-like scales. Heavily logged, the ponderosa pine is a beautiful tree that needs protection in its few remaining stands. Unfortunately much of what remains has fallen to the pine beetle (page 478).

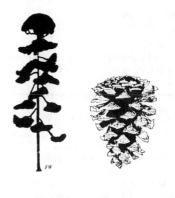

Of the three versions of this tree, the one found in the Canadian Rockies is the Pacific ponderosa (variety *P. p. ponderosa*). In southern Montana, Wyoming and northern Colorado, the **Rocky Mountain ponderosa** (var. *P. p. scopulorum*) looks like a cross between ponderosa and lodgepole. It grows mixed with lodgepole and is difficult to tell apart, for it has two or three needles in a bundle rather than always three. The needles are intermediate in length between the two species, and the bark is brown rather than reddish. For that reason, scattered Rocky Mountain ponderosa may be present in the southern part of the Canadian Rockies, where "three-needled lodgepoles" have been reported. (The other ponderosa, *P. p. arizonica* or Arizona ponderosa, is limited to southeastern Arizona.)

Western white pine
Pinus monticola (pine family)

Occasional in Columbian forest as far north as Valemount, perhaps most common along Lake McDonald in Glacier National Park. Has been reported once in Waterton park but otherwise not in Alberta. Grows 30-40 m tall, but mature individuals are uncommon and most of the trees seen are only 5-10 m in height.

Note how branches are present lower on the trunk than in lodgepole pine, and that there are five needles per bundle, rather than two or three. The bark is gray, roughening with age. Differentiate from whitebark pine and limber pine by habitat, size, and shape (the other two trees are subalpine, shorter, and squatter) and by the cones: western white pine

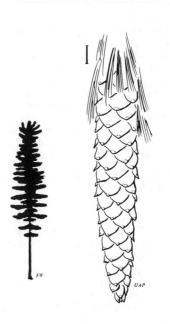

cones are long (12-20 cm), narrow, and tend to curve.

Whitebark pine
Pinus albicaulis (pine family)

Not common, but found throughout the Rockies in the subalpine zone from Peace River south. Prefers windswept, cliffy locations, but also occurs in the forest. The bark is smooth and light gray in young trees, becoming brown and scaly with age. Mature height seldom over 10 m; the trunk tapers rapidly. Needles in bunches of five.

How do you tell whitebark pine from similar-looking limber pine? Whitebark cones are squat and egg-shaped, like lodgepole cones, and 5-10 cm long; limber pine cones are much larger (15-20 cm long). The seeds of both are favorite foods of Clark's nutcracker (page 624).

Limber pine
Pinus flexilis (pine family)

Mainly western-slope montane and subalpine, between Golden and Radium. On the eastern slope, scattered individuals and small stands grow at timberline in Waterton/Glacier and at much lower elevations in the southern foothills around Crowsnest Pass. The species has been reported as far north as Saskatchewan Crossing.

Limber-pine needles grow in bunches of five. The gray, smooth branches are so flexible that they can be tied in knots (this is hard on the tree). Distinguish from similar-looking whitebark pine by the cones: limber pine to 20 cm long; whitebark never longer than 10 cm. At time of writing, many limber pines in the Rockies are diseased with white pine blister rust *(Cronartium ribicola),* which produces large orange galls.

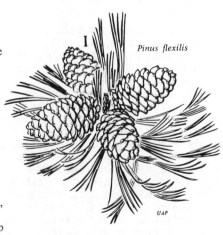

Pinus flexilis

Engelmann spruce and white spruce
Picea engelmannii, P. glauca
(pine family)

These are the more common spruce species in the Canadian Rockies, sometimes difficult to tell apart because they interbreed. Mature size 20-30 m; cone-shaped and symmetrical when young, becoming less so with age. Brown, shreddy bark. The papery cones are 5-10 cm long, carried mostly near the top of the tree—often so densely on mature

white spruce that the tops look brown
from a distance. The needles are 1-2 cm
long and prickly; they are square in
cross-section and can be rolled between
your fingers. (Fir needles are flat; will
not roll. Pine needles are longer and
form a round bundle when held
together).

If you are determined to
differentiate white spruce from
Engelmann (providing the specimen you
are looking at is not a cross), then
consider first your location. White spruce
grows throughout the Rockies, but
Engelmann peters out north of Grande
Cache. South of there, check your
elevation: except in cliffy places,
Engelmanns grow higher on the
mountain (upper montane to timberline).
White spruce is more common at lower
elevations, never found in the upper
subalpine tree islands or krummholz (for
more on krummholz, see page 328).
Engelmann needles tend to curve
upward; white spruce needles grow
straighter and more evenly around the
twig, and are somewhat less prickly. For
a positive identification of a pure-strain
tree, check the cones: the scales of
Engelmann cones are thin and flexible,
with irregular edges, while those of
white spruce are stiffer and
smooth-edged.

Picea glauca

Picea engelmannii

Black spruce
Picea mariana (pine family)

A short spruce (10-15 m), reaching 25 m
occasionally, growing in bogs and damp
places. Look for it on the eastern side of
the divide from Calgary north, and on
the western side from Valemount north.
This is the easiest spruce to identify
from a distance: the top is often a dense,
pointed tuft, while the rest of the crown
is more open. The tree is slim
throughout, with short branches. The
needles are short (1-1.5 cm) and straight,
darker than other spruce needles (hence
the name), and softer—not prickly. The
bark is shreddier than Engelmann or
white spruce bark, exposing a dark,
purplish layer underneath.

Picea mariana

Subalpine fir/alpine fir
Abies lasiocarpa (pine family)

Characteristic of the subalpine forest
throughout the Rockies, at home along
with Engelmann spruce in both the
heavy timber of the lower subalpine zone
and the tree-islands at timberline.
Subalpine fir can sneak quite far down
the hill in steep-walled east/west valleys
that are cold and dark in winter. For
example, there are can find tall
subalpine firs only a few kilometres west
of Jasper along the Miette River. The
species also does well in heavy-snowfall
areas of the Columbian forest; there is a
grove below Mt. Robson, and you will
find them at low elevations on the
western slope from Prince George north.

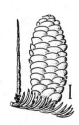

  This is the only true fir of the
Canadian Rockies (Douglas-fir is an
imposter; see page 299). Its shape is
high-spired to shed the deep subalpine
snows. Fir needles are soft and flat; they
don't roll between your fingers. Young
trees have smooth, gray bark that
becomes rougher with age. The cones are
distinctive: purple and sticky, sitting
upright on the upper branches rather
than hanging down like those of other
conifers. The cones don't fall off whole;
instead, the scales drop off one by one,
leaving little candle-like rods on the
branches.

  Subalpine forest is notably more
fragrant than that of lower elevations,
thanks to the aromatic resin of the fir.

Witch's broom

Spruce and occasionally fir suffer in
common the strange, bushy growths
among their branches that many people
take to be squirrel nests. But a witch's
broom is part of the tree: a dense mass
of needles on twisted twigs that spring
from a single point, often along the
trunk. Some trees are afflicted with
several witches' brooms, yet they don't
seem to kill the tree, nor even to damage
it much. The cause is a fungus
(*Chrysomyxa arctostaphyli*), a parasite
that causes the tree to pervert its growth.
  There is a yearly cycle: from the
mass of twigs, bare of needles and
seemingly dead (looking very much like
a nest of some sort), the short yellowish
needles come out in May and June. The
color is from masses of spores, which

Witch's broom

produce a musty smell that can be quite strong but difficult to place. I have seen people on all fours under an infected spruce or fir, hunting for what they assume to be a malodorous wildflower of some kind. The odor diminishes as summer passes. By October the needles have dried and fallen out, to regenerate next spring.

In some books, *Chrysomyxa* witches' brooms are called mistletoe, which is a mistake. Pine dwarf mistletoe is a very different plant (see page 294).

Swollen, salmon-colored branch tips, very common on white and Engelmann spruce and sometimes on Douglas-fir, are caused by the **Cooley spruce gall aphid,** *Adelges cooleyi.* The galls look a little like cones, but closer inspection shows them to be new-growth needles and twigs gone wrong. Fresh, greenish galls form in May. Breaking one off the tree and tearing it open will reveal tiny black aphids, one in each chamber of the gall, surrounded by a thin cottony layer. These are nymphs: immature insects. Later, when they mature to the adult stage, which is also very small, the aphids leave their galls and suck plant juices from needles. When the females reproduce, they lay eggs along the twigs, each brood covered under a cottony speck. Sometimes the branches are practically white with these specks. Surprisingly, Cooley spruce-gall aphids do little damage to the trees.

Typical aphid-affected branch tip (most apparent after aphids have emerged)

Douglas-fir
Pseudotsuga menziesii (pine family)

Increasingly common at montane elevations as you follow the Rocky Mountain Trench south from McLeod Lake, perhaps the predominant tree in the trench south of Golden. Douglas-fir also grows at low elevations on the eastern slope along the Athabasca, North Saskatchewan, and Bow rivers. The most northerly stand on the eastern slope is at Brule Lake, just east of Jasper National Park. South of Bow River the species forms scattered stands in the southern foothills, becoming common from Waterton south.

Smooth-barked, symmetrical and delicate-looking when young, Douglas-fir becomes gnarled and picturesque as it grows old. Mature trees have deeply furrowed bark (usually pocked with

woodpecker holes), heavy limbs, and often a gently curved trunk. This species lives a long time (some have been ring-counted to over 1300 years), mainly because it withstands forest fire. Look for blackened bark on the trunk, especially around the base.

Persons familiar with the enormous Douglas-firs of the Coast Mountains (variety *P. m. menziesii*) will hardly recognize the interior Douglas-fir of the Rockies (variety *P. m. glauca).* It is much shorter, though still a good-sized tree for the Canadian Rockies: 30-40 m tall at maturity.

Douglas-fir resembles both fir and hemlock, but is actually neither (thus the "pseudo-" part of the scientific name). It has the flat needles characteristic of both groups. The cones are unusual: pick one up and note the bracts (little spiny flaps) that stick out between the scales, like the tails and hind legs of tiny mice. There is a Stoney Indian story that ends with mice hiding in the cones to escape the wrath of Naapi, a legendary figure. (Cones of larch, page 302, also have spiny bracts.)

The Douglas-fir is picky about sunlight, temperature and soil moisture. In the southern Rockies of Colorado and New Mexico it favors north-facing slopes; farther north, in Wyoming and Montana, it does equally well on either side of the mountain, while in Canada it grows mainly on south-facing exposures.

Between Brisco and Edgewater in the southern Rocky Mountain Trench there grows the **Cauliflower Tree,** a Douglas-fir with some sort of affliction that has made the top a lumpy mess of twisted foliage. Look for it on the west side of Highway 95. A species of mistletoe has been known to parasitize Douglas-fir in Canada *(Arceuthobium douglasii),* but mistletoe is not the culprit in this case.

Western hemlock
Tsuga heterophylla (pine family)

Western slope only, at low elevations in the Columbian forest between Golden and Prince George; also around Fernie. Hemlock is often easily identified by looking at the top of a mature tree: the tip (properly called the **riser**) nods limply over to the side. The needles of the hemlock are small (1-1.5 cm long),

Oldest known living Douglas-fir in Alberta, 676 years in 1986. Photo by Les Jozsa, Forintek, Vancouver.

The Cauliflower Tree. Photo by Les Jozsa.

soft, flat and dark green, growing on short, hair-like stalks. The cones are also small (2 cm long), the scales tightly closed at first, then opening widely and showing a rectangular shape. Bark is reddish brown when young, darker and rather deeply furrowed when old; always scaly.

Hemlock becomes irregular in shape and ragged-looking as it grows older. This relaxed-looking tree isn't very strongly rooted, and it doesn't last long in windy places. Like cedar, the wood of the hemlock is valued for its resistance to rot (it contains tannin). Unlike cedar, western hemlock is also quite strong.

Western red cedar
Thuja plicata (cypress/juniper family)

Along with hemlock, cedar is a characteristic species of the Columbian forest. Cedar grows only on the western slope and mainly west of the Rockies, but crosses to the eastern side of the Rocky Mountain Trench from Golden north. It fades out north of Prince George. Farther east in the Rockies it occurs wherever storm tracks lay down enough moisture for it; there are cedar groves at Mt. Robson and near Fernie (the small stand now mostly logged); the best stands are along Lake McDonald in Glacier National Park.

Identifiers: the straight, vertically lined gray trunk and scaly needles that look rather like juniper. (Folk names often confuse juniper and cedar; they are also called "cypresses" in some regions.) Western red cedar is a tall tree, commonly reaching 40 m. It has been heavily logged for its redwood-like lumber, which resists rot. Rapidly disappearing in British Columbia, the trees are not being replanted. Loggers complain that the best are gone; the cedars they cut these days are mostly hollow, rotten on the inside. Good—maybe the cutters will give up and a few stands of cedar will remain for their grandchildren to admire. Some cedar groves fall within national and provincial parks and are thus protected, but like the California redwood groves, the western red cedars of British Columbia will soon be scarce unless the government begins to exercise tighter control.

Conifers that aren't evergreen: the larches

Larches and tamaracks are peculiar
conifers because they are not evergreen:
in October the needles fall. Through the
winter the trees appear dead and
skeletal—until the following May, when
new needles emerge. You can tell a
wintering larch from a leafless
broad-leaved tree by checking the
branches. On a larch, they are covered
with little nipple-like needle bases.

Subalpine larch/Lyall's larch
Larix lyallii (pine family)

Subalpine larch grows just below
timberline, in open stands. Mature trees
are branching and scraggly, 5-10 m tall,
thinly clad in very soft, pale-green
needles. Found mainly on the eastern
slope, the current northern limit of this
species in North America is Clearwater
Pass, in the front ranges east of Bow
Summit. A long-dead *L. lyallii* was found
recently near the toe of the Athabasca
Glacier, 95 km farther north; it lived
from about 1000-1250 A.D., when the
climate was somewhat warmer than it is
now (see page 204).
   Subalpine larch becomes less common
south of Crowsnest Pass. The trees are
most conspicuous in the fall, when the
needles turn golden and give the upper
subalpine forest some fall coloration to
match the aspen groves far below.

Western larch
Larix occidentalis (pine family)

This is the western-slope larch, common
at low elevations from Canal Flats south,
patchy as far north as Golden. In Alberta
it is found in the first few kilometres
east of Crowsnest Pass, with one report
in the Kananaskis area.
   Western larch is tall: up to 30 m in
the Canadian Rockies. This sets it apart
from the much-shorter tamarack (next
entry), which is restricted to the eastern
slope. Unlike subalpine larch (previous
entry), western larch is fairly
symmetrical, with a single, straight
trunk; it grows at much lower elevations
than subalpine larch. The leaves of all
three larches are the same: soft,
pale-green needles that turn golden in
mid-September and drop off in
mid-October. Western larch seldom grows

in pure stands; usually it mixes with pine
and spruce.

Tamarack/American larch
Larix laricina (pine family)

Eastern-slope montane, common in the
foothills north of the Red Deer River,
sharing boggy places with black spruce.
Tamarack is symmetrical and short,
5-10 m tall in the Rockies, with pale
green needles that turn golden in the fall
and drop off. For a superb display of
fall tamarack color, drive west from
Rocky Mountain House on Highway 11
in the first week of October.

See also the yew, page 318.

Leafy trees

The six species of broad-leaved trees
native to the Canadian Rockies are all
described here, plus one that isn't native
(Manitoba maple) but seems determined
to stay. If you see a tree that you can't
identify, it may be another non-native
species that has been planted by
someone, or one that has escaped into the
wilds.

Trembling aspen
Populus tremuloides (willow family)
Mid-April to early May

Most common leafy tree of the Rockies,
found everywhere at montane elevations
and characteristic of that ecosystem.
Smooth, white bark; gray and furrowed
only near the base (or not at all).

    Stark black scars mark points of past
injury to aspen bark. A common one is
from the aspen-borer beetle, which keeps
a slit open as it tunnels in the wood.
Fungal infections introduced at this
stained opening frequently cause death
of the branch or trunk higher up.

    Large animals scar the trunks of
aspen. Members of the deer family,
especially mule deer, rub small trees with
their antlers, leaving scent from glands
at the bases; they also eat the bark in
hard winters. Bears claw their way up
when danger threatens, and they also
scratch the trunks to head height,
apparently to mark territory. Small
mammals such as the snowshoe hare will
eat aspen bark from branches and twigs
bent near the ground under coatings of
ice and snow.

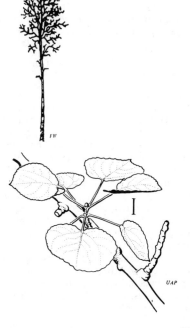

A waxy white material forms on the trunks of aspens exposed to strong sunlight; it protects the sensitive bark from ultraviolet injury and helps to limit water loss.

Frost cankers are so common on aspen in the Rockies that I see them on nearly every tree. Sections of bark up to 5 m long can be so badly frozen during cold snaps that they discolor and peel away in spring. If a canker doesn't heal, the bark sloughs off, leaving a brownish/blackish sickly-looking scar. Frost damage can continue year after year, enlarging the scar and eventually exposing the heartwood. Somehow the trees survive hideous frost cankers, in part by growing heavy, ribbed bark on the uninjured side of the tree, which strengthens it.

Aspen branches are fairly short. Foliage is sparse, concentrated near the top of the tree. The leaves are 3-5 cm across, rounded, pointed at the tip, finely toothed and waxy green; they rustle on their thin stalks in the slightest breeze (hence "trembling aspen") and in the fall turn brilliantly yellow, gold or reddish. The leaf buds and young leaves exude a nectar that attracts ants; the ants kill many of the forest tent caterpillars (page 528) that would otherwise defoliate the tree at this sensitive time. Later in the summer, look for other caterpillar species inside leaves they have rolled into tubes by sticking the sides together with silk.

In early spring the trees produce willow-like catkins. They leaf out in May. In early July the seed pods burst, ejecting downy seeds that travel by air and water.

Differentiate aspen from white birch (page 305) by the bark: peeling and often pinkish on the birch, solidly attached on the aspen. You can tell aspen from balsam poplar or black cottonwood by the leaves: smaller and rounder on the aspen. When these trees are young, i.e. less than 5 m tall, aspen, balsam poplar and black cottonwood all have bark that is smooth right to the ground. In winter, when leaves are absent, I find these three hard to differentiate.

Aspens commonly grow in groves of clones (genetically identical individuals) formed by propagation along roots, but they are also found singly. The species does very well on gravelly places such as alluvial fans. Looking across to a slope heavily timbered in conifers, you can often spot a fan by noting the triangular shape of a nearly pure stand of aspen growing on it. Most aspen groves include scattered white spruce.

Aspen is the shortest-lived of the poplars, averaging less than 80 years. Mature trees vary considerably in height, from only 5 m high in rough locations to 30-40 m in protected places. The wood is soft and brittle when dry. It easily makes a roaring fire, but gather a lot: aspen burns very quickly.

Balsam poplar
Populus balsamifera (willow family)
Early May

This is the common eastern-slope poplar, replaced by black cottonwood on the western slope. Larger, more elongated leaves than aspen, dark glossy green on the upper surface and paler underneath. The bark is gray and furrowed well up the trunk, smooth and yellowish-white only near the top or when the tree is young. Balsam poplar prefers montane and lower subalpine streamcourses, where it can grow to 30 m in height. But any gravelly spot will do; in such locations the tree is usually stunted and rather ill-formed, with a curving trunk and a few twisting branches. Unlike aspen, balsam poplar will grow in rather nasty places; I have found it within 100 m of glacial snouts. The species is

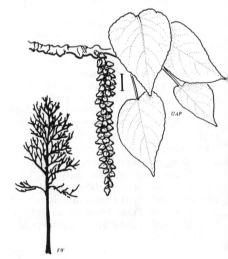

prone to the same afflictions as aspen, which see. In July, balsam poplar produces cottony seeds in two-parted pods. This is how to differentiate it from black cottonwood (next entry), which is practically identical but has three-parted pods.

Black cottonwood/plains cottonwood
Populus trichocarpa (willow family)
Late April to early May

Common on the western slope, in stands along montane and lower subalpine streamcourses, and in the dense Columbian forest of the Rocky Mountain Trench. Scarce in the eastern-slope mountains, except in the southern foothills, where it is common along streams south of Crowsnest Pass.

    This tree closely resembles balsam poplar, but black cottonwood is usually larger and heavier-looking: up to 40 m tall, with the trunk up to 2 m in diameter. The leaves are somewhat bigger and broader, but otherwise similar. The pod-like fruits are diagnostic: black cottonwood pods split open in three parts; those of balsam poplar (previous entry), in two parts. As the name implies, cottonwoods are prolific cotton-fluff producers. Groves become ankle-deep in the stuff, which can trouble people with allergies.

White birch/paper birch
Betula papyrifera (birch family)

Common at lower elevations, except in the southern Alberta foothills and in the Waterton/Glacier area, where the species is only occasional. The bark is white, sometimes discolored to gray, always reddish on the smaller branches, and usually peeling off the trunk in papery sheets—hence the traditional use in canoe-building.

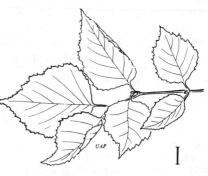

    In the Rockies, birch is not a very tall tree: 20 m or so. It looks rather like aspen, and grows in mixed groves. Tell the two apart by the peeling birchbark and the leaves: birch leaves are smaller, with coarsely toothed margins, while the teeth on aspen leaves are finely, bluntly toothed. Willow-like catkins appear in spring, before the leaves come out. Both male and female flowers bloom on the same tree; male flowers are skinnier and shorter than female ones. Seeds are not cottony.

Columbian hawthorn and black hawthorn
Crataegus columbiana, C. douglasii
(rose family) May

Contrary to what the name implies, Columbian hawthorn is not common in the Columbian forest; black hawthorn is. Columbian hawthorn is more common in the southern Rocky Mountain trench from Golden south.

These are similar small trees (5-10 m tall), with toothed, alder-like leaves and very rough, dark-gray bark. The smaller branches and twigs are covered with sharp, woody spines 1-3 cm long, which make identification easy: hawthorn is the only tree or tall shrub in the Canadian Rockies that has thorns.

Growing mainly on the western slope, both types of hawthorn have been reported as shrubs from Waterton/Glacier on the eastern slope. Where the two are found together (mostly in the Golden area), differentiate by the thorns: Columbian-hawthorn ones are longer. Clusters of rather malodorous flowers in May are followed by apple-shaped fruits in August (proper name: "haws"), purplish on black hawthorn, scarlet on Columbian. They are edible but seedy.

Crataegus douglasii

Crataegus columbiana

Manitoba maple/box elder
Acer negundo (maple family) Early May

A small tree, usually less than 10 m high and often reduced to shrub size. Eastern slope only, where it occurs west of its normal range on the prairies. Seen mainly near the towns in which it has been extensively planted, the Manitoba seems to be escaping from cultivation. Recognize it by the leaves, which are in groups of seven leaflets. The tree is squat, with spreading branches that break in heavy snowfalls. The bark is gray-brown and furrowed. Drooping clusters of small yellowish-green flowers with pink stems come out before the leaves; the seeds (a favorite food of the evening grosbeak) are in twos, with back-sloping wings. See also Douglas maple, page 314.

See also Scouler's willow, wild choke cherry, pin cherry, river alder, water birch and Rocky Mountain juniper.

SHRUBS

Shrubs are multiple-stemmed woody plants too small to be called trees. In the Rockies some species grow to tree height (5 m or taller); others are so low-growing that they form ground cover. In this book the dwarf shrubs are listed with the wildflowers, because non-botanists tend to think of them as wildflowers. The reverse applies as well: tall, shrubby-looking wildflowers such as goatsbeard are listed with the shrubs. But in each case the true nature of the plant (woody or non-woody) is noted.

Nearly all the shrubs that grow in the Rockies are included in this section. A look through the listings will show that the western slope has more species. Shrubs tend to grow taller on that side of the divide, too, which is not surprising; it is warmer and wetter there. The next time you are thrashing through some Columbian-forest green hell, be sure to have this book along for looking up the bush that just poked you in the eye.

Another reason to learn the shrubs: many of them produce edible berries.

The listings below are divided by height into a section for tall shrubs and one for short ones. This is rather arbitrary, for shrubs vary greatly in size from one location to the next. If you can't find a plant in the tall section, then check the short section. The willows, a tricky group, are listed together—and first.

Willows
Salix spp. (willow family) Late February to June

Willows produce catkins (pussy-willows) in the spring and cottony seeds later. Most species grow in dense clumps near water (or even in it) and have elongated bluegreen leaves. Beyond that, they are all different. At least 25 species grow in the Rockies, of which perhaps six are easy to identify. The rest are difficult, requiring in some cases a specialist.

So, what can the non-botanist do? Rather than merely presenting a few species, which causes identification errors because others are overlooked (a big problem in any condensed guide like this one), I have included them all, with illustrations—but not with exhaustive descriptions or complicated keys, which would take up too much space. Instead, I have worked out the summary list and quick key below. Using it carefully will get you to the correct identification in many cases—or at least to a choice of only two or three species. Where possible, the common name is given as well as the scientific one.

Bright-red galls on willow are common. They are caused by insect larvae that live within the gall. Try cutting open a gall; you will probably find a little white worm-like larva inside it.

See also silverberry, page 312.

Tall (usually 2 m or more), lower montane, in bogs or beaver ponds

Dark, hairy twigs: *S. commutata*
Purplish-brown bark: *S. maccalliana*

Tall, lower montane, near water, but not in it

Drooping branches: *S. amygdaloides,* **peach-leaf willow**
Reddish twigs, netted leaf veins, earliest catkins:
    S. discolor, **pussy willow**
Purplish twigs, leaves only 2-3 cm long: *S. planifolia*
Yellowish-brown branches, finely toothed leaves: *S. rigida*

Tall, lower montane, in thickets or open woods

Gray-brown bark, hairy leaves: *S. bebbiana,* **Bebb's willow**
Yellow twigs, bark on branches fissured: *S. lasiandra,* **Pacific willow**
Reddish-brown bark, rather broad leaves: *S. monticola*
Club-shaped leaves, early catkins: *S. scouleriana,* **Scouler's willow**

Tall, low-elevation montane on alluvium; long, narrow leaves

> Spreading, droopy branches: *S. caudata*, **whiplash willow**
> Gray-brown bark: *S. exigua*, **sandbar willow**

Tall, upper montane and subalpine, any habitat

> Reddish-brown bark: *S. barclayi*, **Barclay's willow**
> Smooth, purplish-brown bark: *S. drummondiana*, **Drummond's willow**
> Gray bark, shiny yellowish-brown twigs: *S. serissima*, **autumn willow**

Medium-sized (50-150 cm), lower montane, usually in water

> Gray bark, narrow leaves: *S. candida*, **hoary willow**
> Brown branches, green twigs, wider leaves: *S. myrtillifolia*

Medium-sized, subalpine and alpine

> Purplish-brown bark, leaves 4-7 cm: *S. barrattiana*, **Barratt's willow**
> Leaves 1-3 cm, hairy underneath: *S. brachycarpa*
> Leaves 1-2 cm, not hairy, prefers open slopes: *S. glauca*, **bluegreen willow**
> Yellowish twigs, prefers boggy places: *S. farriae*
> Leathery, heavily veined leaves: *S. vestita*, **rock willow**
> Toothed leaves: see dwarf birch, page 319.

Alpine, low-growing (under 50 cm) or creeping

> Leaves club-shaped, 2-3 cm long: *S. arctica*, **alpine willow**
> Leaves only 0.5-1 cm long, rounded: *S. nivalis*, **snow willow**

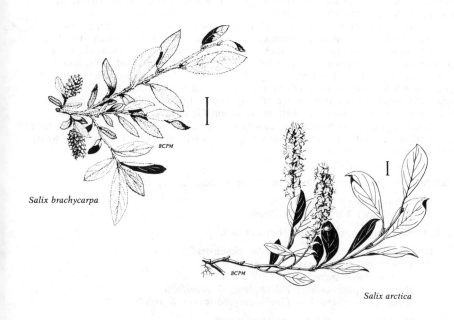

Salix brachycarpa

Salix arctica

Willows are illustrated in alphabetical order by species

Salix bebbiana

Salix candida

Salix commutata

Salix discolor

Salix drummondiana

Willows

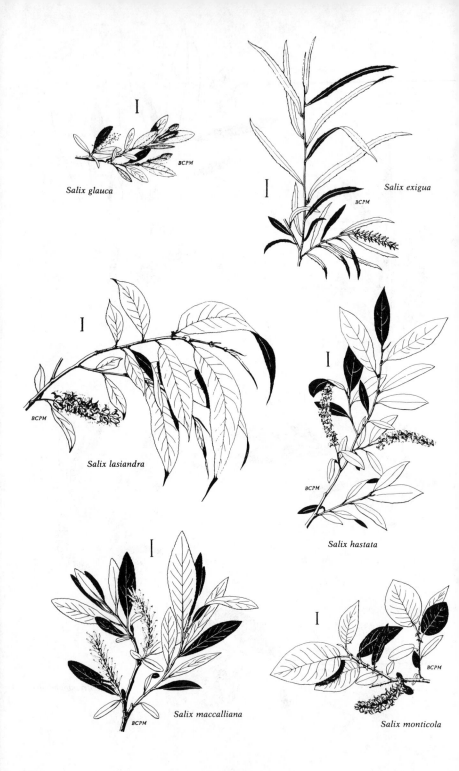

Salix glauca

Salix exigua

Salix lasiandra

Salix hastata

Salix maccalliana

Salix monticola

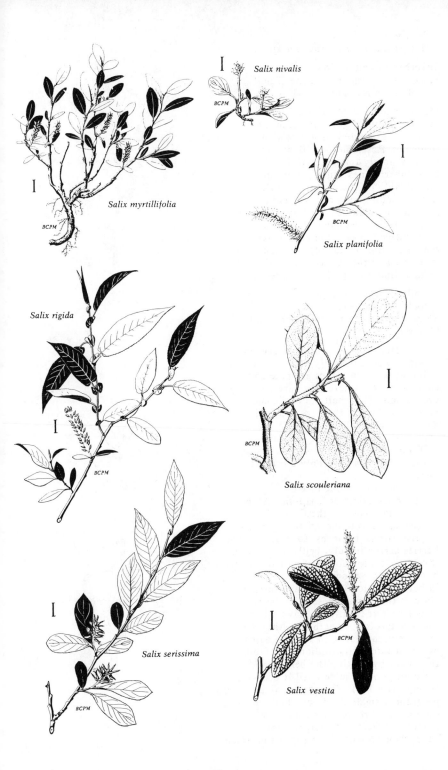

Salix nivalis

Salix myrtillifolia

Salix planifolia

Salix rigida

Salix scouleriana

Salix serissima

Salix vestita

Tall shrubs
(1.5 m or taller, sometimes tree-size)

Silverberry/wolf willow
Elaeagnus commutata (oleaster family)
Late June to mid-July

Montane, at low elevations. Silverberry
thrives in rough, gravelly places and on
disturbed ground—look for it along
roadsides. Resembles a willow, but isn't;
is more closely related to the
buffaloberry (next entry). Immediately
identifiable by the coating of pale gray,
silvery-looking material that covers all
parts of the plant: stems, leaves, even the
berries. Hence the name. The flowers,
tiny and yellow, are the most fragrant in
the mountains. Following the scent will
take you to either a silverberry thicket
or to a dimestore perfume counter.

Canadian buffaloberry/
soopolallie/soapberry
Shepherdia canadensis (oleaster family)
Mid-May

Most common shrub in the eastern-slope
montane woods. Usually about 1.5 m tall.
Shiny dark-green leaves are pale and
fuzzy beneath, where there are also tiny
brown dots. The small flowers come
before the leaves; they are inconspicuous
and pale yellow, but look closely: the
male and female flowers are quite
different. Males have several rod-like
anthers; females have only a central
pistil.
    Soopolallie (pronounced
"soap-uh-LAY-lee" or "soap-uh-LAL-ee")
is an Indian word in the Chinook
language, a creole incorporating many
English forms. It means "soap-berry." The
berries arrive in July, brilliantly red and
thus very conspicuous red on most plants
but strangely yellow on some (no
in-between colors) and always carried
close to the stems. These juicy berries
taste sweet at first, then leave a bitter,
soapy aftertaste. Nonetheless, they are
extremely popular with bears. You can
make an interesting Indian dish from
this plant by beating the berries and
whipping up the juice until it becomes
foamy. At a Parks Canada evening
program, a small child once told me that
she and her brother made up some
soopolallie foam that actually tasted
good: they drowned it in sugar and grape

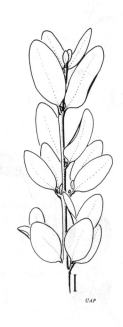

Kool-aid. Compare this species with buckbrush, page 324.

Red-osier dogwood
Cornus stolonifera (dogwood family)
Late May to mid-July

Montane, along streams and other damp places. Another willow look-alike, it also resembles white spirea (page 326), but the leaves are not toothed and spirea flowers have five petals, not four. Smooth red twigs and shiny green leaves, arranged in typical dogwood fashion. They turn dark red in fall. The flowers are small and greenish white, in little clusters at the ends of the stems. Round gray berries are not tasty.

River alder/thinleaf alder
Alnus tenuifolia (birch family) Late May

More common in western-slope montane forest than on the eastern slope; grows along stream courses in drier, more southern areas, spreading onto moist slopes farther north. Can reach 10 m in height; commonly 3-4 m. Grows densely and makes for rough going wherever you find it. Leaves are dull green above, often brown underneath. Small teeth along the margin, superimposed on larger teeth. Branches gray or light brown with small white horizontal lines, bark flaking off with age. Willow-style flowers; long seed heads hang down.

Green alder/speckled alder/ mountain alder
Alnus crispa (birch family)
Late May to early June

The avalanche-track alder, growing densely in mountain gullies. Mainly subalpine, but sometimes higher or lower. Common on the eastern slope; very common on the western slope. Similar to river alder, but with shiny green leaves rather than dull ones; bark marked in speckles rather than lines. Cone-like flowers and fruits.

Beaked hazelnut/filbert
Corylus cornuta (birch family) March

Mainly Columbian forest. Spreading, 2-3 m tall; grows in both woods and meadows. Toothy, alder-like leaves and long yellow catkins hanging down in early spring, replaced by conspicuous green husks in July, each enclosing an edible nut.

Alderleaf buckthorn
Rhamnus alnifolia (buckthorn family)
June

Lower montane, western slope south of
Golden, eastern slope south of Crowsnest
Pass, in marshy areas; sometimes in aspen
groves. Spreading, gray-brown branches,
sparsely leaved, no thorns. Alder-like
toothed leaves. Very small, greenish
flowers carried inconspicuously along the
stems; black one-seeded berries. Not
terribly common, but often in large
patches when you find it.

Snowbrush/deer brush
Ceanothus velutinus (buckthorn family)
June

Dry lower montane slopes, south of
Radium on the western slope and south
of Crowsnest Pass on the eastern slope.
Shiny evergreen leaves; rounded and
with the finest of teeth. Compare with
buffaloberry, page 312. Sticky fragrant
yellowish-green twigs. Small white
flowers in sprays, each flower on a
hair-thin stalk. Pods rather than seeds.

Water birch/ground birch
Betula occidentalis (birch family)
Late May

Scattered clumps in well-drained,
gravelly places from valley floors to
timberline (mostly montane). Shiny
reddish branches with wart-like glands;
small, dark-green toothed leaves. Can
become quite tall (up to 6 m), and may
hybridize with white birch (page 305).
See also **dwarf birch,** page 319.
Water-birch catkins are capsule-shaped
and coarse, 2-3 cm long.

Rocky Mountain maple/Douglas maple
Acer glabrum (maple family) June

Primarily a western-slope montane shrub
that occurs sporadically east of the
continental divide in the Athabasca, Bow
and Crowsnest drainages. Up to 5 m tall,
but stunted on the eastern slope. Prefers
rocky places. Reddish-brown bark,
roughened and patchy-looking with age,
typically maple-shaped leaves.
Inconspicuous flowers, but the buds and
new twigs are bright red—as are the
leaves in fall. The seeds have wings.
Compare with high-bush cranberry (next
entry). The only other maple in the

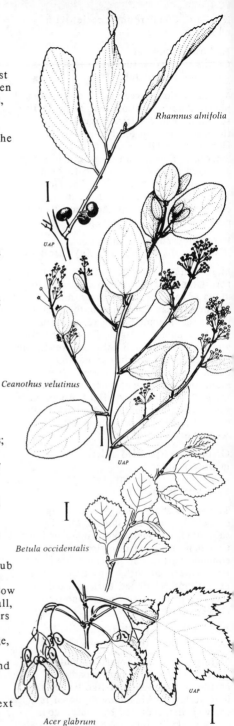

Rhamnus alnifolia

Ceanothus velutinus

Betula occidentalis

Acer glabrum

Canadian Rockies is Manitoba maple (page 306).

High-bush cranberry
Viburnum opulus (honeysuckle family)
Late May to mid-June

Occasional in moist places in western-slope montane woods; sometimes subalpine. Known from the eastern slope south of Crowsnest Pass, but rare. Low-bush cranberry, page 326, is much more common in the Rockies. High-bush cranberry reaches 4 m in height; usually 1-2 m. Not a true cranberry, like the mountain cranberry (page 369), but the red fruits are edible and used in making jam once the large flat seeds, characteristic of *Viburnum* species, are removed. Sweeter after a frost. Has maple-like three-lobed leaves, but differentiate from Rocky Mountain maple (previous entry) by high-bush cranberry's showy flat-topped clusters of white flowers at ends of stems, which are not red.

Wild choke cherry
Prunus virginiana (rose family) May

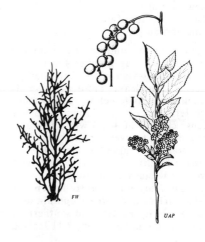

Montane, throughout the Rockies, in sunny places at low elevations, bordering woods. On the western slope, wild choke cherry is often a small tree (less than 10 m tall). On the eastern slope it is usually shrub-sized. As an ornamental it reaches tree height on both sides of the divide. Shape: squat and spreading, often with multiple trunks. The bark is dark and purplish-brown. Leaves are fairly broad and finely toothed. White flowers are carried in dense cylindrical clusters up to 10 cm long, followed in fall by small purplish-black sour cherries. Compare with pin cherry, next entry.

Pin cherry
Prunus pennsylvanica (rose family)
Early May through June

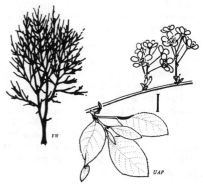

Montane, lower elevations, usually in clearings bordering woods. Extensively planted in towns. Reddish-brown bark, marked with powdery horizontal orange lines **(lenticels)** on older specimens. Shiny yellowish-green lance-shaped leaves taper to a point; they are finely round-toothed. White blooms in small clusters of 5-12 flowers; small, sour cherries on long stalks in August. Very similar to choke cherry, previous entry. Differentiate by

Tall shrubs

the blossoms (choke cherry has many more, in long cylindrical clusters), leaves (those of choke cherry are broader, sharp-toothed rather than blunt-toothed) and fruits (darker and shorter-stemmed on choke cherry).

On the western slope between Radium and Valemount you may find the occasional **bitter cherry** *(P. emarginata)*. It is very similar to pin cherry, but has grayish-brown bark and *dull* yellowish-green leaves that have fine *blunt* teeth.

Ninebark
Physocarpus malvaceus (rose family)
Mid-June to early July

Columbian forest; occasional in the Waterton/Glacier area. Spreads from a tight cluster of stems, growing 2-4 m tall. Very shreddy bark, in many layers (hence "ninebark"). Sharply lobed leaves, white flowers in clusters. No berries; reddish seed cases instead.

Mountain ash
Sorbus spp. (rose family)
June and July

Upper montane and lower subalpine, in shady places. Can grow to 4 m tall, but is usually chest-high in the Canadian Rockies. The leaves are distinctive: dark green above, pale below, in 7-13 toothy leaflets. Bark is dark brown. Blooms in dense clusters of small white flowers. The berries are very showy, bright red-orange, in large bunches. They attract flocks of waxwings. We have two species: **western mountain ash** *(S. scopulina)* with slightly larger leaves, 9-13 leaflets, and **Sitka mountain ash** *(S. sitchensis),* central and southern areas only, with smaller leaves, 7-11 leaflets.

Red elderberry
Sambucus racemosa (honeysuckle family)
Late May to early July

Common in Columbian forest clearings; occasional elsewhere. Five leaflets, dark branches, creamy white flowers carried in upright clusters. Berries small, round, and red or black. They are tart; some sources say edible, others say possibly poisonous. In the southern Rocky Mountain Trench, look for **blue-berry elder** *(S. cerulea),* distinguished by its flat-topped flowerheads and bluish berries.

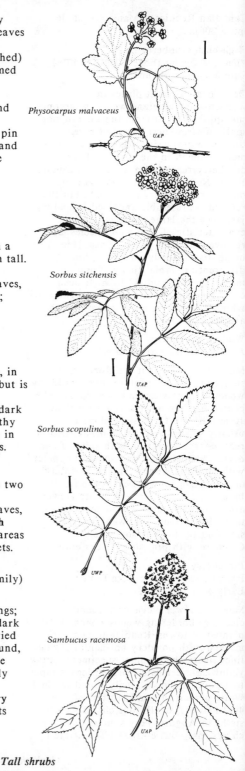

Physocarpus malvaceus

Sorbus sitchensis

Sorbus scopulina

Sambucus racemosa

Orange honeysuckle
Lonicera ciliosa (honeysuckle family)
May

Columbian forest. A high-climbing vine,
twisting around stems and branches to
heights of 10 m. Leaves have a chalky
surface that rubs off; look for tubular
orange flowers and small clusters of
orange berries in the cuplike holders of
fused leaves that are typical of
honeysuckle. See also twining
honeysuckle (page 326).

Ocean spray/mountain spray
Holodiscus discolor (rose family) June

Dry areas at low elevations in the Rocky
Mountain Trench from Golden south.
Can reach 4 m, but usually about
head-high. Small white flowers in long
drooping plume-like clusters; no berries.
Leaves both toothed and notched; green
above, pale and hairy below.

Goat's-beard
Aruncus sylvester (rose family)
Late June to mid-July

Columbian forest, in damp, shady places;
on the eastern slope noted only within a
few kilometres of Pine Pass. Up to 2 m
tall; usually less, with lance-shaped,
toothed leaflets along tough, ribbed stems
that regrow each year—not a true shrub,
but shrub-like enough to include here.
Distinctive blooms: long, pencil-shaped
pale-pink flower clusters at right angles
to the stems. Strings of brown seeds later.

Devil's-club
Oplopanax horridum (ginseng family)
June

Common in Columbian forest,
occasionally western-slope montane, not
reported on the eastern slope except in
Waterton/Glacier, in the Peace-area
foothills and east of the mountains in
the Fox Creek/Valleyview area. Stands
1-2 m tall, growing in patches in cedar
groves and other damp, shady places. The
name of this plant says it all. The stems
are covered with long poisonous spines
(contact causes inflammation). The very
large, deeply notched, pale green leaves
are spiny on the underside.
Greenish-white flowers bloom in clusters;
brilliantly red berries are carried in
upright bunches that are quite pretty.

Lonicera ciliosa

Holodiscus discolor

Aruncus sylvester

I

Rocky Mountain juniper/ scopulorum juniper
Juniperus scopulorum (cypress family)

Western-slope montane, Columbian forest, and a few locations in southern Alberta (Kananaskis area, Waterton/Glacier). Easily identified as a juniper by the needle-like scaly leaves, small bitter berries (blue when mature; otherwise green or gray) and shreddy brown bark. Compare with prickly juniper (page 328), with which it interbreeds. Rocky Mountain juniper grows taller than prickly juniper (up to 5 m), sometimes symmetrically but more often raggedly, and it is not prickly.

Western yew/Pacific yew
Taxus brevifolia (yew family) May

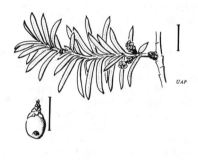

Western-slope montane from Valemount south, perhaps most common on the west side of Glacier park. Primarily a Columbian-forest species, yew grows at a few eastern-slope locations in Glacier park and along the Bertha Lake trail in Waterton park. This is a tree that stays shrub-size in the Rockies, with spreading multiple trunks. The bark is reddish and scaly. The sharp-pointed, flat needles are dull-green above and two-tone pale green below. Male flowers are very small cones (2-33 mm) among the needles. Seeds are more conspicuous: bright-red berry-like cups 4-5 mm across, each holding a brown or bluish seed. The seeds are poisonous, as are the branches and leaves of this plant.

Short shrubs

How tall is short? The shrubs in this section grow about 1-1.5 m tall.

Shrubby potentilla/shrubby cinquefoil
Potentilla fruticosa (rose family)
Late June to early September

Common montane-to-lower-subalpine shrub, growing nearly anywhere, wet or dry. Shreddy brown stems and small leaves that are deeply divided, almost needle-like. The plant looks prickly but isn't. Most easily recognizable by the many yellow blossoms, which are five-petalled, showy, and bloom all summer. I have seen this species blooming in early October, when the leaves had turned. There are many potentilla species in the Rockies, but this is the only woody one. It closely resembles garden-variety potentilla, derived from this species.

Labrador tea/trapper's tea
Ledum groenlandicum (heath family)
Late June to early July

Upper montane and subalpine forests, in wet, shady places. More common north of Bow River; absent at Waterton/Glacier (but see next paragraph). A short shrub (1 m or less), easily recognized by the leaves: 2-6 cm long, oblong (but usually strongly curled-under along the edges and thus narrow-looking) and shiny green on top; rusty brown and furry beneath. They are evergreen. The flowers are small and white, with five petals; they bloom in dense tufts at the stem ends.

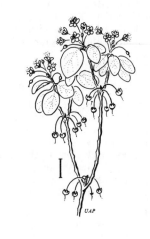

UAP

    South of Crowsnest Pass, another Labrador-tea species is prevalent: *L. glandulosum,* which is very similar but with broader leaves that are not furry underneath and less curled-under. Kuijt (1982) notes that Labrador tea to the north and west of Waterton is usually hybridized *L. glandulosum / groenlandicum*; Moss (1983) notes similar hybrids in Banff park.

    There is yet another Labrador-tea species, this one limited to the northern Rockies: *L. palustre,* whose range overlaps with *L. groenlandicum.* Differentiate by *L. palustre's* size (shorter: 10-50 cm), shorter leaves (1-4 cm) and fewer stamens *(L. palustre* 8-11; *L. groenlandicum* 5-7).

Betula glandulosa

I

UAP

Dwarf birch
Betula glandulosa (birch family)
Late May

Subalpine and alpine meadows, usually near water. Less than a metre high, with small (1-2 cm) round, toothed shiny green leaves. The bark is black and warty. Flowers are oval catkins about a centimetre long, carried upright along the stems. Dwarf birch and rock willow (page 311) often grow together.

Sagebrush
Artemisia tridentata (composite family)
Mid- to late September

Common western-slope montane shrub, occasional on the eastern slope in the Waterton/Glacier area. I have also seen it

Artemisia tridentata

UAP

on dry hillsides along the Peace River near Hudson's Hope. Grows at low elevations, in open, dry places. Can reach 2 m, but is usually waist-high or lower. Easy to recognize by the sage fragrance of the gray-green leaves, which are unusually shaped: widening toward the tip, which is toothed. Shreddy, gnarled gray-green bark. Small yellowish flowers are inconspicuous on their short spikes. No berries.

Antelope bush/greasewood
Purshia tridentata (rose family) April

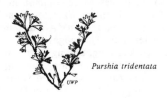

Purshia tridentata

Western-slope montane, at low elevations. A sagebrush look-alike, but not even in the same family. The leaves are similar, but greener, and they lack the sage fragrance. They grow close to the stems, which are widely spaced. Can grow to 3 m tall, but usually chest-high. Small yellow flowers in spring.

Rabbitbrush
Chrysothamnus nauseosus
(composite family)
Late August to mid-September

Chrysothamnus nauseosus

Western-slope only, in the driest parts of the Rocky Mountain Trench around Wasa and Fort Steele. Another sagebrush look-alike, but smaller (usually less than half a metre tall) and greener, with erect stems and thin, pointed leaves. Masses of tiny yellow flowers atop the stems make the plant showy in late summer and early fall. Resembles broomweed (page 357), which also has yellow flowers, but snakeweed stems are not woody and the flowers are larger, the ray-flowers larger and more petal-like.

Wild roses
Rosa spp. (rose family)
Late May to early August

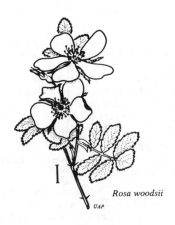

Rosa woodsii

Perhaps the most-easily recognized montane plants are the wild roses. At their best in the open, they are also very common in lodgepole and aspen forests. Small, toothed leaves grow in bunches of seven or nine, and large pink (sometimes purple or white) five-petalled flowers bloom with the typical rose fragrance.

The three eastern-slope species grow together and interbreed. One can quickly be told apart by the prickles on the stems: scattered curved thorns on the **common wild rose/thorny wild rose** *(R. woodsii)*. Stems of the other two are densely covered with straight spines, but one species *(R. arkansana,* **dwarf prairie rose)** is rare on the eastern slope, where it is found mostly in Waterton/Glacier. It is shorter (less than 40 cm tall), with stems that die back each year. The other is the **prickly wild rose/spiny wild rose** *(R. acicularis),* the provincial wildflower of Alberta. It is taller than the dwarf prairie rose (head-high sometimes) and much more common throughout the mountains. It blooms mostly in June, earlier than either of the other eastern-slope roses.

To complicate things for western-slope rose-fanciers, two additional species occur here: **Nootka wild rose** *(R. nutkana),* which is tall (up to 3 m) and thorny, and **baldhip rose** *(R. gymnocarpa),* which is shorter and has spiny stems, with no sepals adhering to the back of the fruit.

In the fall, all these species produce **rosehips:** fleshy fruits that are rich in vitamin C and make tasty jam or tea.

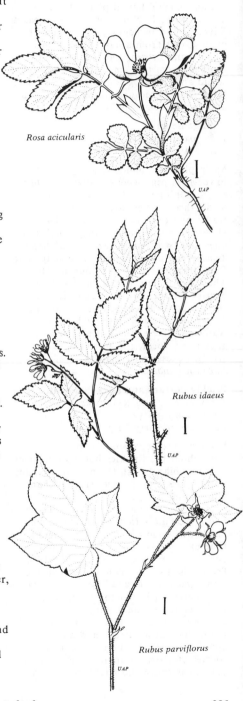

Rosa acicularis

UAP

Wild raspberry
Rubus idaeus (rose family)
Mid-June to early July

Very prickly shrub found in gravelly places and on disturbed ground (often grows along highways) in montane areas. Grows 1 m to 2 m tall, but can be quite short—less than 10 cm—in damp places. Flowers white, about 5 cm across, with five petals like other rose-family plants. Dull-green leaves in threes are reminiscent of poison ivy, but the spiny stems prove otherwise. Tasty red berries appear in mid-August. Caution: keep an eye out for bears before plunging into *their* raspberry patches.

Rubus idaeus

UAP

Thimbleberry/salmonberry
Rubus parviflorus (rose family)
Late June to mid-July

Common Columbian-forest plant, also throughout the western-slope montane woods, but occasionally eastern-slope as well (fairly common at Waterton/Glacier, Pine Pass, Peace River; occasional elsewhere, close to the continental divide). A handsome shrub, with big three-lobed leaves up to 20 cm broad and large white flowers. Stems are smooth. Fruits raspberry-like, though mealy and not as sweet or flavorful.

Rubus parviflorus

UAP

Cloudberry/baked-apple
Rubus chamaemorus (rose family)
Mid-June *See thimbleberry, previous page, for picture*

An uncommon, boreal plant of the
eastern-slope Rockies north of Athabasca
River, found in boggy places where it
often grows from a mossy bed. Stems
smooth and brown, leaves lobed and
toothed, 2 cm to 7 cm wide. Flowers are
white and showy, about 2 cm across. The
large fruit is red or yellowish; soft, juicy
and sweet—worth looking for.

Wild gooseberry
Ribes oxyacanthoides (saxifrage family)
Late May to mid-June

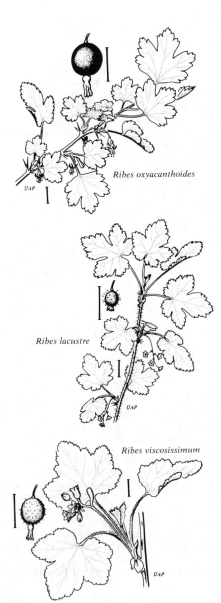

Ribes oxyacanthoides

Moist places in montane and
lower-subalpine woods, growing up to a
metre tall, open and ragged-looking.
Small three-parted coarsely toothed
leaves and densely spiny stems. The
flowers are small and white, hanging in
ones and twos from near the leaf bases.
The berries are pale green and striped at
first, turning dark red to purple later.
They are smooth, unlike the finely hairy
berries of the currant species found in
the Canadian Rockies. In the southern
Rocky Mountain Trench and at
Waterton/Glacier there is another
gooseberry species: *R. inerme*. The stems
are much less spiny than those of
R. oxyacanthoides.

Prickly currant and sticky currant
Ribes lacustre and *R. viscosissimum*
(saxifrage family)
Late May to early July

Ribes lacustre

Ribes viscosissimum

Montane and subalpine, found
throughout the Rockies but most common
in Columbian forest. Open, sparse shrubs
up to a metre tall; leaves smaller than
wild gooseberry (1-2 cm for swamp
gooseberry; 2-3 cm for wild gooseberry)
and more finely toothed; prickly stems.
Small white flowers carried 6-8 cm at a
time on a stalk. The best way to tell
currant from gooseberry is to check the
fruits: the two common currants in the
Canadian Rockies are finely hairy, while
gooseberries are smooth. At maturity,
gooseberries are dark purple while
currents are nearly black. Once you
know that it's a currant and not a
gooseberry, telling the two common
species of currants apart is easy: prickly
currant is spiny and sticky currant is

Short shrubs

not; nor is sticky currant found north of the Porcupine Hills. There are several other species around, but they are less common (and difficult to differentiate).

Blueberry/bilberry/ huckleberry/whortleberry
Vaccinium spp. (heath family)
June and July

At all elevations, but mostly upper montane and subalpine. Common on both slopes but especially plentiful on the western side. Patch-forming plants, sometimes blanketing open valley bottoms and lower slopes. All species have smooth stems and spring-green, finely toothed leaves, often with yellow spotting. Small white or pink bell-shaped flowers come in clusters. The fruits are dark blue (except for one species, next entry), with a characteristic circular rim on the bottom. Look for berries about the middle of August; they are excellent raw or baked.

Discovering that all the common names above are applied mainly to one species *(V. caespitosum)*, I thought I had broken the mystique of blueberry-group names. Then I found out that there were other species of blueberries and got mixed up all over again. Here is how to sort them out:

V. caespitosum: commonest species, 20-30 cm tall. The only one with reddish twigs. Prefers lightly wooded upper montane and subalpine slopes.

V. membranaceum: greenish twigs, leaves 2-5 cm long; tallest one (up to 1 m) and with the largest berries (8-10 mm). Upper montane and subalpine, in open woods.

V. myrtillus: dwarf subalpine and alpine species less than 30 cm tall, but producing berries 5-8 mm thick. Leaves only 1-2 cm long. Prefers open slopes.

V. occidentale: in bogs on the western slope; berries 4-5 mm across and very dark blue to black.

See also grouseberry (page 369).

Vaccinium caespitosum

Vaccinium membranaceum

Vaccinium myrtillus

Vaccinium occidentale

Saskatoon/serviceberry/Juneberry
Amelanchier alnifolia (rose family)
Late May to early June

Montane, forming patches in dry clearings. Usually less than 1 m tall on the eastern slope, but frequently 2 m on the western slope. Purplish-brown twigs and gray branches. Leaves oval, lightly toothed, strongly veined; tend to fold upward along the centre. Flowers with five well-separated white petals. Fruits appear in late July and August; they are round and purple when ripe, about 1 cm in size, with a characteristic mouth-like feature at the end. Bears stuff saskatoons into their own mouth-like features. Humans may prefer their saskatoons in pies.

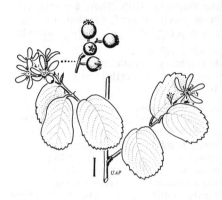

Buckbrush/wolfberry/snowberry
Symphoricarpos occidentalis
(honeysuckle family) July

A common montane shrub of dry, open areas, often bordering aspen and poplar groves. Usually knee-high, but can get taller. Leaves 3-7 cm long, oval and toothy, growing opposite one another on the grayish-brown stems. Each set of leaves (thick, rather hairy beneath) grows at 90° to the ones above and below, a common arrangement but especially visible on this plant. Small, funnel-shaped flowers are pinkish-white, blooming in clusters at points where the leaves attach to the stems. Greenish berries darken with age; not tasty. Note the other snowberry, next entry.

Snowberry
Symphoricarpos albus
(honeysuckle family)
Late June to early August

Knee-high montane shrub of dry hillsides, often growing with saskatoon, which it resembles. Most easily recognizable by the snow-white berries, which are about 5 mm thick and round, with a brown dot on the bottom. They are bitter. Leaves are oval, 2-3 cm long, pale and hairy beneath. Small, bell-shaped white flowers with a bit of pink, blooming in small clusters.

Spreading dogbane
Apocynum androsaemifolium
(dogbane family) July

Dry montane hillsides, often with
saskatoon and snowberry. Knee-high or
lower. Leaves are in pairs; dark glossy
green on top and pale below, prominently
veined, drooping down like those of
poison ivy. Clusters of pretty white
bell-shaped flowers with pink tips; long
seed pods later. Broken stems or torn
leaves exude milky sap.

Poison ivy/poison oak
Rhus radicans (sumac family)
June and July

Rare in the Rockies, but it does occur
here, at low elevations in the Rocky
Mountain Trench from Radium south.
Occasionally poison ivy is reported from
the eastern slope, in southern Glacier
National Park; there are a few records in
Waterton. Leaflets in threes, each
10-15 cm long, glossy, drooping, dark
green, heavily veined with wavy edges.
Stems are reddish at junctions. Enough
information to identify without
touching? A maddening rash follows the
slightest contact—if you are sensitive.
Clusters of small yellowish-green
flowers; photogenic white berries against
red leaves in the fall.

Bracted honeysuckle/black twinberry
Lonicera involucrata
(honeysuckle family)
Late May to early July

Montane and subalpine, usually in aspen
woods along streamcourses. Waist-high at
low elevations; shorter near timberline.
Nondescript-looking, with dull green
wavy-edged leaves, but easily
recognizable when in bloom or bearing
fruit. The small flowers are yellow, in
twos. Dark-purple, inedible berries also
form in twos, held in a pair of large red
or purplish bracts (modified leaves) that
curve back.

Red twinberry/Utah honeysuckle
Lonicera utahensis (honeysuckle family)
Late May to mid-July

Lower subalpine, from Crowsnest Pass
south. Resembles bracted honeysuckle
(previous entry), but usually shorter and
with smaller leaves that are rounder.
Similar yellow flowers; the fruit, though,

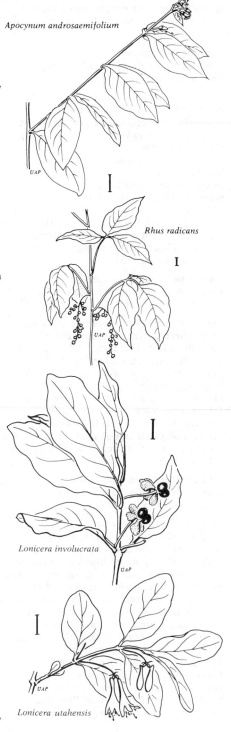

Apocynum androsaemifolium

Rhus radicans

Lonicera involucrata

Lonicera utahensis

is red rather than purple, and hangs in
twos without the bright bracts typical of
L. involucrata.

Twining honeysuckle
Lonicera dioica (honeysuckle family)
June and early July

A vine, common in Columbian forest,
occasional in the Waterton area,
strangely not reported in nearby Glacier.
Grows on most anything. Messy-looking
clusters of showy yellow or orange
trumpet-shaped flowers darken just
before they fall. Very fragrant, sweet
smell; popular with hummingbirds. As in
bracted honeysuckle, the leaves
immediately below the flowers fuse into
a cuplike shape that holds a cluster of
berries (not just a pair, as in bracted
honeysuckle). See also orange
honeysuckle (page 317).

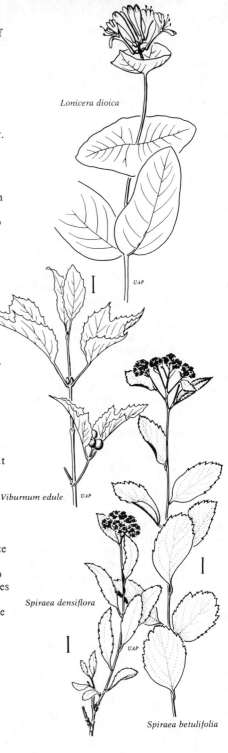

Lonicera dioica

Low-bush cranberry/squashberry
Viburnum edule (honeysuckle family)
Late May and June

Montane and lower subalpine, common
everywhere except in the southern
foothills and the Waterton/Glacier area,
where it is scarce. Prefers open spots in
damp woods. Looks very much like the
high-bush cranberry, but is shorter
(1-2 m). Large glossy-green three-lobed
leaves with toothed margins turn
brilliantly red in the fall. Blooms in
clusters of small star-shaped white
flowers. Berries are red with a large flat
seed in each.

Viburnum edule

White spirea/white meadowsweet
Spiraea betulifolia (rose family)
Late June to early August

Montane, bordering woods. Up to 1 m
tall, usually shorter. Gardeners recognize
this plant immediately by the showy
clusters of tiny white blooms, similar to
the domestic bridal-wreath spirea. Leaves
are distinctive: plain oval shape, but
growing more deeply toothed toward the
tip. Stems are smooth and reddish, with
flowerheads atop them rather like red
osier dogwood (page 313), which can be
differentiated by the smooth-edged
leaves. There is also a pink-flowering
form (**pink spirea,** *Spiraea densiflora*),
that is similar but subalpine and found
mainly south of Crowsnest Pass. Plant
produces seedpods rather than berries.

Spiraea densiflora

Spiraea betulifolia

Mock orange/syringa
Philadelphus lewisii (hydrangea family)
July

Occasional in the Rocky Mountain
Trench south of Elko and in the
Waterton/Glacier area. Up to 2 m tall,
but usually much shorter. Large,
four-petalled white flowers in small
clusters at stem-ends. Light-green leaves
2-5 cm long, each with three prominent
veins and scalloped edges. Compare with
Rocky Mountain rhododendron (next
entry).

Rocky Mountain rhododendron/
white rhododendron
Rhododendron albiflorum (heath family)
Early July to mid-August

Very common in damp Columbian-forest
clearings, where it reaches 2 m in height;
occasional (and half that height)
elsewhere, in upper montane and
subalpine areas. Broad white
five-petalled flowers are cup-shaped and
2-3 cm across, in floppy clusters of two
or three along the stem below the new
leaves, which are narrow and oblong,
rather diamond-shaped, spring-green and
glossy. Compare with menziesia (next
entry) which grows in the same places.

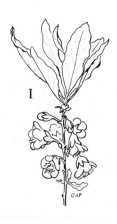

Menziesia/false azalea/false huckleberry
Menziesia ferruginea (heath family)
Late May to early July

Pronounced "men-ZEE-see-uh "or
"men-ZAY-see-uh." A common subalpine
species in moist forest, also found at
much lower elevations in Columbian
areas. Blueberry-like leaves, but slightly
hairy, with rather irregular margins and
sunken veins. The leaves form
fan-shaped clusters. The bark is brown
and shreddy. The flowers are small
peach-pink bells (no white on them) in
drooping, long-stemmed clusters; they
have a sharp, rather skunky smell,
pungent when a large patch is blooming.
No berries; seeds are enclosed in dry
capsules. When not in bloom, menziesia
strongly resembles Rocky Mountain
rhododendron (previous entry), but
menziesia leaves are not glossy and often
are stained red at the tips by disease.

Prickly juniper/common juniper and creeping juniper

Juniperus communis and *J. horizontalis* (cypress family) late June to early July

Very common, easily recognized montane and lower subalpine shrubs. **Prickly juniper** grows up to a metre tall in roughly circular knee-high patches, the branches drooping outward from the centre, while **creeping juniper** lies on the ground in irregular patches. The two species are not supposed to interbreed, but I have often seen specimens with intermediate characteristics.

Both species have needle-like leaves that are prickly in prickly juniper and scaly in creeping juniper, both with the distinctive juniper odor. Brushing against the plants in late June or early July produces yellow smoke: pollen from the inconspicuous brown flowers. The berries vary from green (new) through gray (this year's) to purple (last year's). They are very bitter—the original flavoring used in gin—but in spite of that I have seen squirrels eating them. Grouse like them as well.

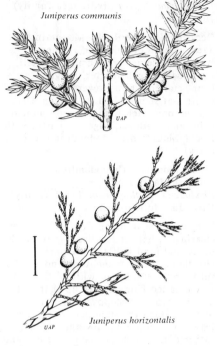

Juniperus communis

Juniperus horizontalis

Krummholz spruce and fir

Krummholz ("KRUM-holts") means "crooked wood" in German, or more idiomatically "elfin forest." The name fits perfectly the scrubby, shrub-like patches of evergreens that mark timberline (photo on page 282). Not shrubs at all, these are trees stunted in their extreme environment to knee-high size. Any part that grows tall enough to poke up above the protective winter snow is likely to die, so the foliage thickens below. Thus, patches of krummholz indicate places in which the snow tends to accumulate.

Readers familiar with the Rockies of Colorado and Wyoming may notice that in the Canadian Rockies there are few **flag trees**: tallish timberline trees with foliage on only one side. This may be the result of stronger winds in the American Rockies (to cause the flagging), and at the same time warmer winter temperatures (to allow taller growth at timberline).

The two tree species that commonly produce krummholz in the Canadian Rockies are subalpine fir *(Abies lasiocarpa),* with flat needles and smooth gray bark (page 298), and Engelmann spruce *(Picea engelmannii),* with square, prickly needles and rough brown bark (page 296).

Sometimes there will be the odd whitebark pine *(Pinus albicaulis),* with half-round needles in bunches of five and squat cones (page 296), or in southern areas limber pine *(Pinus flexilis),* similar to whitebark pine but with longer cones (page 296).

Like the alpine meadowland, krummholz has a fragile beauty that is easily destroyed. When walking at timberline, I go around the dense krummholz patches rather than thrashing through them, for a small branch might have taken fifty years to grow. Even the dead branches have a job here: to protect the living wood from the bitter alpine gales.

WILDFLOWERS BELOW TIMBERLINE

If you can't find it here, try the alpine flowers or the shrubs.

White
Or cream-colored, or champagne ivory, or bleached-poodle blonde.

Trillium/wake-robin
Trillium ovatum (lily family)
Mid-April to late May

Western-slope montane and subalpine,
from Radium south (has been reported
from Waterton/Glacier), in moist, shady
places. A large flower with three narrow
white petals, going pinkish or purplish
with age, offset against three green
sepals underneath. Three broad leaves,
10-15 cm long.

White mariposa lily/sego lily
Calochortus apiculatus (lily family)
Late June to early July

Western-slope montane south of Radium,
eastern-slope montane south of Crowsnest
Pass. Prefers dry, open slopes. Very
showy three-petalled flower; white or
yellowish, more yellow toward the centre.
The long, thin leaves grow only at the
base. Like other large-flowered lilies, it
makes a big three-sided seed capsule
after blooming. Unlike the others, the
mariposa capsule hangs down.

    There is a pale-purple mariposa lily
in the southern Rocky Mountain Trench.
See page 377.

One-flowered clintonia/
queen cup/beadlily
Clintonia uniflora (lily family)
Early June to mid-July

Western-slope montane and lower
subalpine shady forest. Most common in
Columbian forest; on the eastern slope
mainly in Waterton/Glacier. A low plant,
usually about 10 cm high, with two to
four glossy green leaves at the base. The
flower is reminiscent of Easter lily but
smaller, in six parts with long yellow
anthers. Has perhaps the most beautiful
fruit in the mountains: a single bead-like
bright-blue berry, not edible.

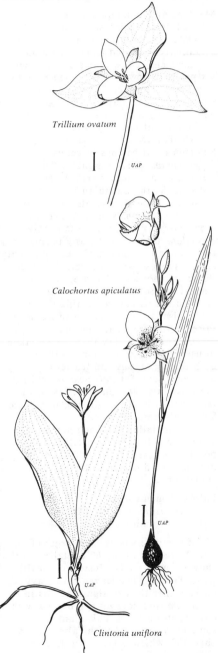

Trillium ovatum

Calochortus apiculatus

Clintonia uniflora

Star-flowered Solomon's-seal/false Solomon's-seal/"western" Solomon's-seal and three-leaved Solomon's-seal
Smilacina stellata and *S. trifolia*
(lily family) Mid-May to mid-June

Montane and subalpine, mostly on wooded north-facing slopes. *S. stellata* stands 20-40 cm tall. Seven or so smooth, spring-green pointed leaves angle upward off the stem. A few delicate snowy white six-petalled flowers are carried near the top. Fruit is an inedible striped green berry that grows darker with age. Three-leaved Solomon's-seal *(S. trifolia)* is similar, but has only three leaves.

Confusing names department: true Solomon's-seal belongs in genus *Polygonatum,* which resembles *Smilacina* but grows in eastern North America and not here. So the Canadian Rockies version is false. But we also have our own false Solomon's seal, *S. racemosa* (next entry), which is a close relative of *S. stellata,* the one that many people think to be true Solomon's seal but really isn't. I suppose we could call *S. stellata* "false Solomon's seal" and *S. racemosa* "false-false Solomon's seal, but teachers of logic tell us that something that is false-false is true. Which in this case is false, if you see what I mean.

Clear as mud. Try this. I have taken to using "western Solomon's-seal" for both the *Smilacina*s and "eastern Solomon's seal" for *Polygonatum,* calling the false-false version *(S. racemosa)* by its commonest common name, just "false Solomon's-seal."

Incidentally, Solomon's seal itself is a star symbol with six interlocking points, thought to ward off disease. It does not ward off lexicological confusion.

False Solomon's seal
Smilacina racemosa (lily family)
Late May to mid-June

Moist montane woods. The larger of the two *Smilacina*s (up to 60 cm tall) and the showier, with puffy clusters of small white flowers. The leaves have wavy edges rather than straight ones, as in *S. stellata* (previous entry). Berries with dark spots on them. This plant is sometimes confused with false hellebore, page 350, which is taller (up to 2 m),

Smilacina stellata

Smilacina racemosa

UAP

with straight-edged leaves and cascades of green flowers.

White camas and death camas
Zygadenus elegans and *Z. venenosus*
(lily family) Late May to mid-August

Common montane plants, preferring open areas or light woods. *Z. elegans* is sometimes found much higher, growing in dwarf form above timberline. Long, narrow, pale-green leaves rise gracefully from the base. The flowers are creamy or greenish, carried on a showy spike above the leaves. The two species look similar; differentiate by their ranges, blooming times and flowers: smaller and tighter on the spike in death camas, which has a very poisonous bulb *(Z. venenosus,* southern areas, late May to mid-June) and larger on white camas *(Z. elegans,* all areas, July) which is more common and less poisonous. The flower stalk is taller and less crowded on white camas.

Fairy bells
Disporum trachycarpum (lily family)
Late May to mid-June

Fairly common, growing knee-high in montane aspen woods; fading out north of Grande Cache. Drooping white flowers, sometimes tinged yellow or green, in groups of one to four at the ends of stems. The flowers are bell-shaped at first but soon split into separate petals and wilt, becoming ragged-looking. The large red-orange lumpy berries grow in twos; they are velvety looking and sweet-tasting but contain large seeds. Slightly zig-zagging stems and wavy-edged leaves resemble those of twisted-stalk, page 350.

Western clematis/traveler's joy
Clematis ligusticifolia (buttercup family)
July

Southern montane, not common, usually in thickets. A woody vine (shrub); likes to grow on other shrubs. Leaflets are lance-shaped, often notched, always toothy. Showy white flowers with four sepals and long, spread-out centre parts. See also blue clematis (page 377).

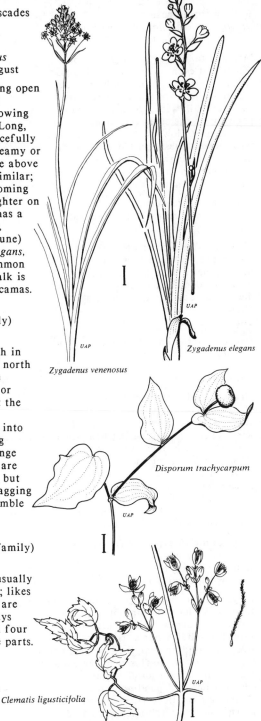

Zygadenus elegans

Zygadenus venenosus

Disporum trachycarpum

Clematis ligusticifolia

Western spring beauty
Claytonia lanceolata (purslane family)
Late April to late June

Montane to alpine, in meadows, open
woods and even scree slopes well above
timberline. Common in southern areas,
especially in Waterton/Glacier. Grows
10-20 cm tall, with two broad leaves
partway up the stem. One or more white
or pale-pink flowers about 1 cm across,
with purple lines. Can bloom very early
at low elevations. There is a strictly
alpine version (page 393). See also wild
white geranium (next entry).

Wild white geranium
Geranium richardsonii (geranium family)
Late May to early July

Montane woods, common in the southern
region but less so farther north. Grows
up to a metre high; usually about 50 cm.
Easily recognized as a geranium by the
deeply divided, lightly hairy leaves.
Showy white or pale-pink flowers with
pink to purple lines in them.

Sweet-flowered androsace/rock-jasmine
Androsace chamaejasme
(primrose family)
Mid-May to early July

Montane and higher, in open places. One
of those striking little flowers that
makes you say "awww . . ." Straight,
wirelike stems are usually (though not
always) reddish; they reach up about
5 cm from a tuft of small overlapping
leaves. A cluster of several small (1 cm
or less) white flowers atop each stem is
fragrant. Each flower has a hole in the
centre with a yellow rim. Compare with
fairy candelabra (next entry).

Fairy candelabra/pygmy flower
Androsace septentrionalis
(primrose family)
Late April to early June

Tiny, delicate montane plant that prefers
open, rocky locations and blooms early.
Rosette of narrow basal leaves. Straight
wire-thin reddish stems reach up
5-20 cm, dividing near the top; each one
carries a tiny white flower at the end.
This plant shows a lot of variation,
which seems to depend upon the
blooming time. In April the stems are
short, sometimes unbranched, and bear
very small flowers. Plants blooming later

Claytonia lanceolata

Geranium richardsonii

Androsace chamaejasme

Androsace septentrionalis

in the season, in June, have longer stems
and the flowers are somewhat larger.
Differentiate from *A. chamaejasme*
(previous entry) by the branching in
fairy candelabra and the single flower at
the end of each stem. Otherwise they are
quite similar, especially early-blooming
ones.

White draba/whitlow-grass
Draba spp. (mustard family)
May to early June

Western-slope montane and the
Waterton/Glacier area. Most of the
drabas are yellow, but a few are white.
All are difficult to identify to the
species level. General characteristics:
four-petalled flowers, each petal in two
lobes, carried in a small cluster atop a
stem 10-20 cm long. Small basal tuft of
little lance-shaped hairy leaves. Elliptical
seedpods.

Mountain sandwort
Arenaria spp. (pink family)
Mid-May through July

Mainly subalpine, but can grow higher or
lower on dry, rocky slopes or ridges.
Height 10-15 cm, with very narrow,
hair-like leaves, mostly basal; the edges
are yellow and minutely spiny. Small
star-shaped flowers have narrow petals
and 10 stamens. Several species; leave
them to the botanists to figure out.

Chickweed/starwort
Stellaria spp. and *Cerastium* spp.
(pink family) May to August

At all elevations, but when below
timberline mostly montane in exposed
places (see also the alpine species,
page 393). More common south of Peace
River, especially in the Waterton/Glacier
area. Look for the cleft petals, sometimes
so deeply indented that they look like
double petals. These are characteristic of
the two genera. The leaves are narrow
and short; compare with fringe-cup (next
entry). There are many species, all very
similar; most are *Stellaria*. See also
mountain sandwort (previous entry), and
dwarf epilobium, page 375.

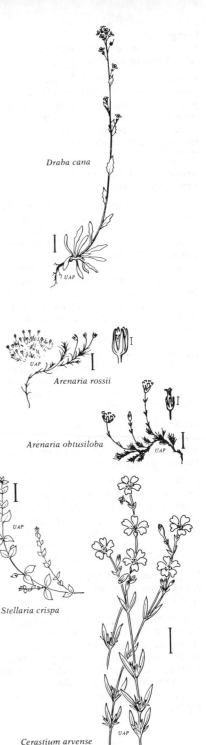

Draba cana

Arenaria rossii

Arenaria obtusiloba

Stellaria crispa

Cerastium arvense

Fringe-cup
Lithophragma parviflora (saxifrage family)
Late April to early June

Western-slope montane, in open areas.
Flowers resemble chickweed, but the
petals are notched in threes rather than
twos and the leaves are different:
spreading, five-lobed and bluntly toothed
rather than lance-shaped.

Windflower
Anemone multifida (buttercup family)
Late May to late June

Common montane plant of dry meadows
and open woods. Ankle-high, with a
fuzzy stem and a fringe of fern-like
leaves partway up the stem, which is
capped by 1-3 flowers. Flower color
quite variable; usually white, tinged with
purple on the back. Sometimes purple on
the front, too—or even red. Produces a
dense, woolly ball of downy seeds. The
seedhead opens for distribution by the
wind.
   Windflower closely resembles
Drummond's anemone *(A. drummondii),*
which lacks the fringe, produces a single
flower, and is mostly alpine/subalpine
rather than montane. See also alpine
anemone, page 392.

**Prickly saxifrage/common
saxifrage/spotted saxifrage**
Saxifraga bronchialis (saxifrage family)
July to early August

Rocky places at all elevations. Wire-thin
reddish stems growing 10-20 cm above a
cushion of prickly needle-like leaves.
The small white flowers are exquisite up
close: each petal is marked with a
pattern of tiny red and yellow dots. See
also three-point saxifrage, page 394.

Leather-leaved saxifrage
Leptarrhena pyrolifolia
(saxifrage family) July

Subalpine and alpine, along mossy stream
banks. Numerous small white flowers
clustered near the top of a hairless stem
10-20 cm tall. Shiny, broad, evergreen
toothed leaves are clustered at the base,
but there is usually one along the stem.
Compare with western saxifrage (next
entry).

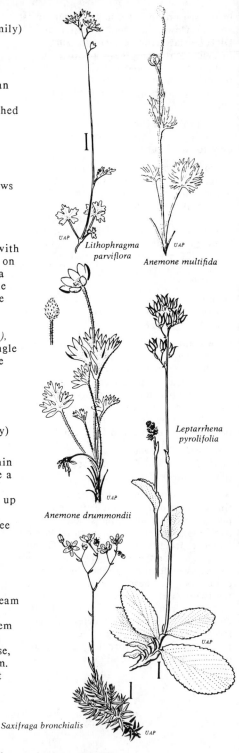

Lithophragma parviflora

Anemone multifida

Leptarrhena pyrolifolia

Anemone drummondii

Saxifraga bronchialis

Western saxifrage/ false leather-leaved saxifrage
Saxifraga occidentalis (saxifrage family)
Early May to mid-August

At all elevations, in nearly any habitat; most common saxifrage in southern sections. Closely resembles leather-leaved saxifrage (previous entry), but has no leaf on the short-haired stem and is not evergreen. Flowers very early at low elevations, much later in the alpine zone.

Alum-root
Heuchera parvifolia
(saxifrage family)
Late May to early July

Columbian forest, western-slope montane around Fernie, and in the Waterton/Glacier area. At all elevations, on rocky outcrops and cliffs. Leaves are all basal, 2-3 cm wide on long stems and deeply divided into three or five lobes. The reddish flower stalk, 30-40 cm tall, is hairy; the small flowers may be yellowish as well as white. See also *H. cylindrica,* page 362.

One-flowered wintergreen/single delight
Pyrola uniflora (heath family)
Mid-July to early August

A small plant, growing under evergreens in montane forests. One nodding flower, waxy white with a green ovary in the middle surrounded by yellowish stamens. The rounded leaves are glossy green with finely toothed edges.

Grass-of-parnassus
Parnassia spp. (saxifrage family)
July and August

Mostly subalpine, but also montane and sometimes above timberline. Grows in wet places. Looks rather like a straightened-up one-flowered wintergreen, with prominent ovary and stamens, but is not even in the same family. Glossy, round, basal leaves, plus one leaf low on the stem on *P. palustris* (lower elevations, beside streams; July to early August) and one leaf higher and smaller on *P. fimbriata* (**fringed grass-of-parnassus,** the most common species, high-subalpine and alpine, late July to mid-August). The other species in the Rockies *(P. kotzebuei,* page 392) lacks the upper leaf.

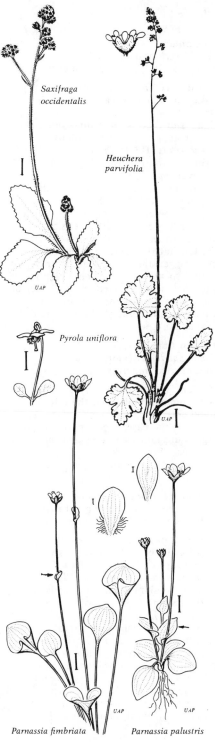

Saxifraga occidentalis

Heuchera parvifolia

Pyrola uniflora

Parnassia fimbriata *Parnassia palustris*

Moss phlox
Phlox hoodii and *P. alyssifolia*
(phlox family) Late April to early June

Southern foothills and the
Waterton/Glacier area, in dry, open
places. Looks like an alpine cushion
plant, and there is an alpine phlox of
similar appearance (**white phlox,
*P. multiflora,*** found farther south in the
Wyoming and Colorado Rockies);
however, moss phlox grows at low
elevations. A cushion of prickly green
leaves is dotted with showy white
flowers, sometimes a bit pink or purple,
with yellow centres; the petals are
squared at the ends. *P. alyssifolia* is very
similar, but the leaves and flowers are a
little bigger and often pink. It grows in
similar locations and blooms slightly
later; has been reported from Glacier but
not from Waterton (one reported a
kilometre northeast of the Waterton
boundary).

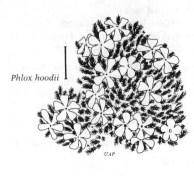

Phlox hoodii

Western Canada violet
Viola canadensis (violet family)
Late May to mid-July

Montane woods, in shady places. The
most common violet and the tallest:
10-30 cm. Large, wrinkled heart-shaped
leaves at the base, becoming more oval
higher up; indented veins and lumpy
margins. Flowers are white or pale
purple, with dark veining and yellow
centres.

Bunchberry/dwarf dogwood
Cornus canadensis (dogwood family)
Late June to mid-July

Common in montane and subalpine
evergreen woods, but rare on the eastern
slope south of Crowsnest Pass. Often
thought of as the provincial flower of
British Columbia, but the official flower
is the bloom of the dogwood *tree*
(C. nuttallii), not the wildflower.
Low-growing, usually in patches; leaves
in a bilaterally symmetrical grouping of
four or six. Distinctive bloom: four
petal-like bracts turn from green to
white, surrounding the tiny, greenish
flowers that look like the central part of
a single flower. Cluster of pretty red
berries in August; bland taste.

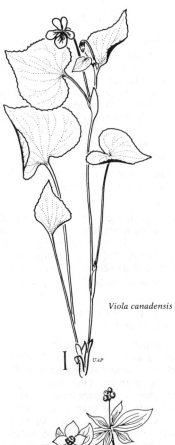

Viola canadensis

Cornus canadensis

Wild strawberry
Fragaria virginiana (rose family)
Early May to late July

Montane, usually in dry open woods.
Easily recognized by the three-parted
toothy leaflets and the red stems running
across the ground. Small but showy white
flowers, yellow-centred; berries in July
and August. All the flavor of a big
grocery-store strawberry is concentrated
in the wild version, which is about as big
as the end of your little finger. Can be
confused with trailing raspberry (next
entry). See also sibbaldia (page 400).

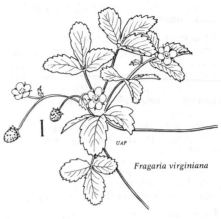

Fragaria virginiana

Trailing raspberry
Rubus pedatus (rose family)
June and July

Montane and subalpine north of Peace
River, and in Columbian-forest areas. A
trailing vine, resembling strawberry but
with leaflets in fives and thin dark
woody stems. Raspberries in September;
not very flavorful.

Rubus pedatus

Kinnikinnik/bearberry
Arctostaphylos uva-ursi (heath family)
Early May through July

Common ground-covering shrub; grows
best on dry, south-facing montane slopes.
A mat of small, thick, glossy oval leaves
on woody stems. Leaves are evergreen
but may become purplish through the
winter. Blooms in small inconspicuous
white flowers that are urn-shaped, with
out-turned pink lips. Berries are bright
red, rather mealy and bland, but edible.
Can be confused with mountain
cranberry (page 369), which has pink
flowers without lips, and twinflower
(next entry) before it blooms.
   Pronounced "KINNY-kin-ick,"
Algonquin for "smoking mixture." The
dried leaves can indeed be smoked,
resulting in a sore throat and no
intoxication. The berries were an Indian
staple, pounded up with saskatoons
(page 324) and animal fat to make
pemmican. A close relative of
California's manzanita, kinnikinnik has
two sister species in the Canadian
Rockies: **alpine bearberry** *(A. alpina),*
with netted, finely toothed leaves and
black berries; and **red bearberry**
(A. rubra), a subalpine version with
larger, thinner, bright-green leaves (also

Arctostaphylos uva-ursi

strongly netted) and larger berries. Both
these species lose their leaves in fall.

Twinflower
Linnaea borealis (honeysuckle family)
Late June to late July

Montane and subalpine. A
ground-covering shrub with small round
leaves rather like kinnikinnik (previous
entry) or mountain cranberry (page 369).
But the leaf tips of twinflower are
toothy. Common except in the
Waterton/Glacier area and easy to
identify by the two white or pale-pink
bell-shaped flowers hanging from bent
stalks. Fragrant.

Creeping wintergreen/
creeping snowberry
Gaultheria hispidula (heath family) July

Damp spots in montane evergreen woods;
absent at Waterton/Glacier. Low-growing,
with tiny oval leaves that are dark above
and hairy brown beneath. Even tinier
flowers (2 mm across) are cup-shaped,
hidden among the leaves. Produces small
white berries. *G. humifusa* has similar
flowers but grows at subalpine levels in
the Waterton/Glacier area and the
berries are red, not white.

White pussytoes/
small-flowered everlasting
Antennaria microphylla
(composite family)
June and July

Eastern-slope montane, in patches on dry
slopes. The tight flowerhead is off-white
and fizzy; looks like the underside of a
cat's paw. The leaves are also distinctive:
pale green or gray, fuzzy, and spreading
at the base. Compare with pearly
everlasting (next entry). There is also a
red- or pink-flowered *Antennaria*
(page 370).

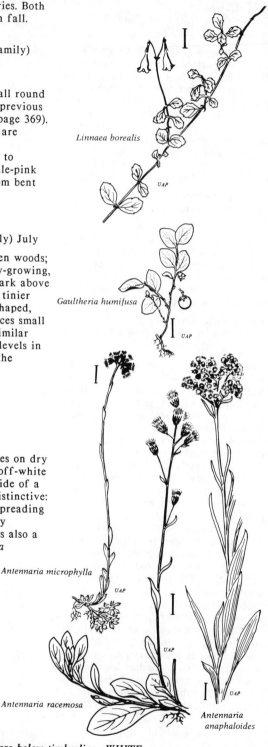

Linnaea borealis

Gaultheria humifusa

Antennaria microphylla

Antennaria racemosa

*Antennaria
anaphaloides*

Pearly everlasting
Antennaria anaphaloides
(composite family)
Early July to early August

Montane, common in dry open places.
Resembles pussytoes (previous entry), but
a much larger plant, with bigger,
more-expanded flower heads. Leaves
felty and green on top, furry underneath.
"Everlasting" refers to the longevity of
cut flowers in this genus.

Molecule plant
Antennaria racemosa
(composite family)
Late June to early July

Montane and subalpine woods; 10-30 cm
tall. Okay; I made up the common name.
But there doesn't seem to be one
otherwise, and the thing really *does* look
like a molecular model. There are up to a
dozen ball-like white flowerheads on
bare stems. You have to see it to believe
it. The leaves mostly are basal, green and
glossy on the top, gray and felty
underneath, broadly lance-shaped, not
toothed.

Coltsfoot, white lettuce and brickellia
Petasites, Prenanthes and *Brickellia*
(composite family)
Late April to early May

Damp places at low elevations—or
sometimes alpine. Coltsfoot is a
coarse-looking plant with broad, deeply
lobed or toothy, woolly leaves 5-7 cm
long and tuft-like flowers. Grows
15-20 cm high and blooms very
early—often before the leaves are out.
Along the eastern slope the species is
mostly *P. frigidus,* which has notched
leaves, or another type: **arrowleaf
coltsfoot** *(P. sagittatus),* with toothed but
not notched leaves.

In the Waterton/Glacier area there is
a look-alike plant called **white lettuce**
(Prenanthes sagittata) that has smaller
leaves (2-3 cm long). And, just to confuse
things thoroughly in that part of the
mountains, there is yet another look-alike
called *Brickellia grandiflora* that can be
distinguished by arrow-shaped leaves
that are toothy at the base, smooth
toward the tip. This species avoids the
damp sites favored by coltsfoot and
white lettuce. Strangely, *P. frigidus* also
grows in the alpine zone.

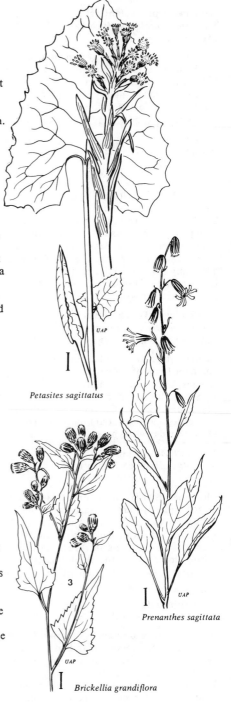

Petasites sagittatus

Prenanthes sagittata

Brickellia grandiflora

Wild sweet pea/vetchling
Lathyrus ochroleucus (pea family)
May to July

A montane vine, often found in aspen
woods or in thickets. Smooth oval leaflets
2-3 cm long; tendrils along the stems.
Cream-colored to pale-yellow flowers in
clusters of a few; edible pea-pods later.
Compare with milk-vetch, next entry.

Lathyrus ochroleucus

Milk-vetch
Astragalus spp. (pea family)
May and June

Southern montane. Showy white or
yellowish-white blooms, sometimes with a
line of pink or purple along the back.
Small leaflets are very narrow and set
along the stem like sawteeth (typical
vetch arrangement). Pea-family members,
the vetches produce small pods. There
are many species, difficult to
differentiate. Compare with wild sweet
pea, previous entry.

White clover/Dutch clover
Trifolium repens (pea family)
Late June to early August

Astragalus americanus

Montane and lower subalpine. Most
common form of clover, an introduced
species. Grows in low patches in
meadows, lawns, roadsides and grassy
places everywhere. Clover leaves (three
leaflets; sometimes four), ball-shaped
flowerheads—with bees.

White sweet clover
Melilotus alba (pea family)
Late June and July

Montane, usually on disturbed land such
as roadsides, where it has been seeded.
Can grow to 2 m high, but usually a
metre or less. Bushy plant with curving
stems; toothy leaflets in threes; small
white flowers in cylindrical clusters.
See yellow sweet clover (page 365) for picture.

Trifolium repens

Sundew
Drosera spp. (sundew family)
Mid-June to mid-July

Strange little montane/Columbian-forest
plants of wet, mossy streambanks and
bogs. Absent at Waterton but present at
Glacier. Reddish rosette of sticky, hairy
leaves attracts and holds insects; a leaf
folds in and the plant digests the bugs.
Tiny white flowers bloom at the top of a
bare 15-cm stem growing up from the

Drosera rotundifolia

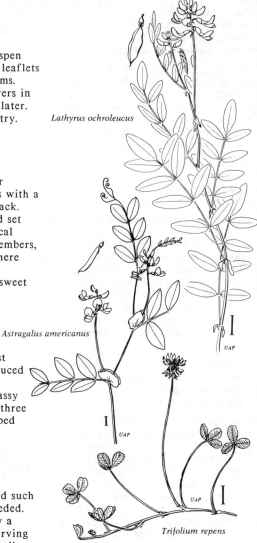

centre. **Round-leaved sundew**
(*D. rotundifolia,* round leaves) is found
on both slopes. Two long-leaved species
(*D. anglica,* leaves 1-3 cm long and
3-4 mm wide, and *D. linearis,* with
longer, even narrower leaves) are mainly
western-slope. See also butterwort,
page 385, another insectivorous plant of
the Rockies.

Indian pipe
Monotropa uniflora (heath family)
Mid-July

Shady places in moist montane woods.
Never common, absent at Waterton but
known from Glacier. Instantly
recognizable by the pipe shape, this
dead-white plant has no chlorophyll; it is
a saprophyte, rooting in decaying matter.
But it is also a proper flowering plant,
not a fungus.

Sparrow's-egg orchid/ northern lady's-slipper
Cypripedium passerinum (orchid family)
Mid-July

Western-slope montane and Columbian
forest, occasionally eastern-slope
montane north of Bow River, in shady
protected places. Grows 15-30 cm tall,
usually in small groups. Finely hairy
stem and leaves; pure-white egg-like
flower partly covered with green sepals.
Look for purple dots inside. Compare
with mountain lady's-slipper, next entry.

Mountain lady's-slipper
Cypripedium montanum (orchid family)
July

Western-slope montane, at low elevations
in damp places; on the eastern slope
known only from Waterton/Glacier. A
tall orchid (up to 50 cm); leaves broader
and fewer than sparrow's-egg. Closely
resembles the yellow lady's-slipper,
page 353, but is white rather than
yellow, although it has a yellow tongue.

Bog orchids/rein orchids
Habenaria spp. (orchid family)
Late June to mid-July

Damp places in montane meadows and
woods. Several species, all with the same
general form: a spike 20-60 cm high of
many small white or greenish flowers.
Long leaves grow up from the base;
sometimes there are a few on the stem.
Sometimes called "rein orchids" because

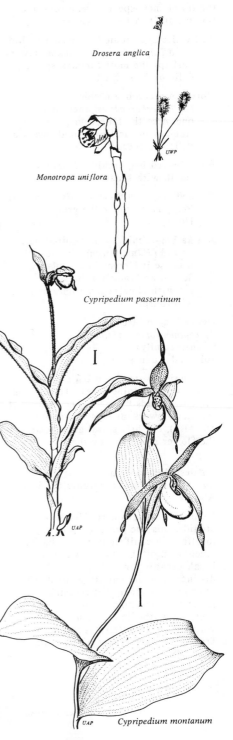

Drosera anglica

Monotropa uniflora

Cypripedium passerinum

Cypripedium montanum

the lip of most species has a rein-like feature on it. A few to know:

Tall white bog orchid/white rein orchid *(H. dilitata):* has the whitest flowers. Perhaps the most common species; deliciously scented.

Northern green bog orchid *(H. hyperborea):* another common one. Also the tallest one, with brown stamens in the flower and two small yellow anthers.

Blunt-leaved bog orchid *(H. obtusata):* small, with broad leaves.

Bracted bog orchid *(H. viridis bracteata):* long bracts under the greenish flowers.

Alaska bog-orchid/slender-spired bog orchid *(H. unalascensis):* unusual because it blooms in dry places. Scale-like bracts up the stem; greenish flowers sometimes marked with purple.

Hooded ladies' tresses
Spiranthes romanzoffiana
(orchid family)
July and August

By running water or in bogs, montane and lower subalpine forest. Tell it from the bog orchids by the larger, somewhat showier flowers (always white, not greenish), by their spiral arrangement on the flower spike and by their vanilla scent.

Rattlesnake plantain
Goodyera oblongifolia (orchid family)
August

Montane, southern area. Unlike most orchids, this one prefers fairly dry locations in coniferous woods. Easily recognized by the leaves, which are basal, broadly lance-shaped, with a distinctive white pattern against the dark-green surface that resembles rattlesnake markings. Spike of greenish-white flowers. Another white-on-green pattern is found on freshly emerged leaves of toadflax, page 348.

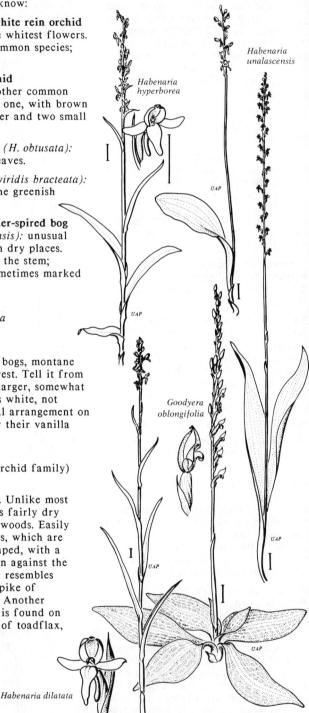

Habenaria obtusata

Habenaria unalascensis

Habenaria hyperborea

Goodyera oblongifolia

Habenaria dilatata

Round-leaved orchid/spotted orchid
Orchis rotundifolia (orchid family)
Mid-June to early July

Eastern-slope montane, usually in spruce
woods; rare in Waterton/Glacier. Not
common but worth hunting for: the small
flowers look like angels in purple-dotted
white robes, with mauve hats and
wings—really! One rounded leaf at the
base.

False asphodel
Tofieldia glutinosa (lily family) July

Northern montane, at edges of bogs and
ponds. Rare south of Bow River. Tuft of
white (sometimes greenish or yellowish)
flowers atop a green stem 10-40 cm tall.
Warty glands roughen the stem and make
it sticky. Narrow leaves reach up from
the base about half the length of the
stem.
    Dwarf false asphodel *(T. pusilla)*
grows in wet upper subalpine and alpine
areas in the northern Rockies. It is
shorter (under 25 cm tall) with shorter,
broader leaves that form a basal tuft.

Beargrass
Xerophyllum tenax (lily family)
Late May to mid-July

Waterton/Glacier only, in open woods
and meadows at subalpine and low
alpine elevations, but also found along
Lake McDonald in Glacier park. Very
long (40-50 cm) olive-colored grass-like
leaves reach up from the base; shorter
leaves clasp the stem, which can be up to
a metre tall. Large, easily recognized
bloom: a dense, club-shaped tuft of tiny
white flowers that trail down the stem.
Often the lower part of the club is in
bloom before the upper part has opened.
A large patch of beargrass looks for all
the world like a grassy meadow, but in
fact it is a field of lilies.

Antenna plant/sweet cicely
Osmorhiza depauperata (carrot family)
Late June to early July

Montane and subalpine. Fairly tall (up to
60 cm), with peculiar branching stems at
the top that *do* look rather like television
antennas, especially when the plant is in
seed. Indented, carrot-like leaflets grow
below the antenna-like part. Blooms are
inconspicuous and white. See also
western sweet cicely, page 349.

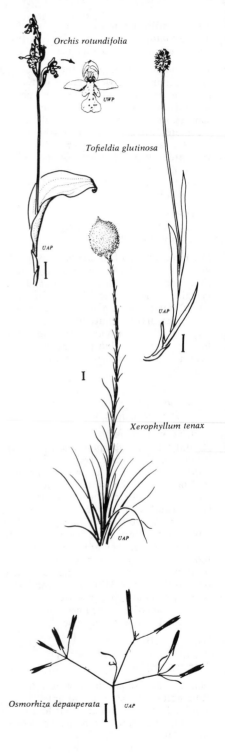

Orchis rotundifolia

Tofieldia glutinosa

Xerophyllum tenax

Osmorhiza depauperata

Yarrow/milfoil/tansy
Achillea millefolium (composite family)
Early June to early September

Very common throughout the Rockies up
to timberline, and well known in Europe,
too. One or more flat clusters of small
white flowers with pale yellow or white
centres atop a stem 20-50 cm tall.
Characteristic sage-like smell, though it
is not a sage. The frilly, fern-like
gray-green leaves are narrow and tend to
clasp the stem. They speed up
blood-clotting when crushed and placed
on a wound.

Baneberry
Actaea rubra (buttercup family)
Late May through June

Montane woods, often among aspen. Can
grow to a metre tall; leaflets droop in
threes or fives, with deeply toothed
margins. Dense, conical heads of tiny
white flowers with 4-10 petals carried
above the plant. Beautiful clusters of
large, bright red (sometimes white) shiny
berries; attractive but poisonous, so don't
keep them around the house where little
kids might eat 'em.

Cow parsnip
Heracleum lanatum (carrot family)
Mid-June through July

Tall, very common
montane/lower-subalpine plant growing
beside running water, frequently in
aspen woods. Thick, hairy stems grow up
to 2 m high on the western slope, shorter
on the other side of the divide. Heavy,
flat flowerheads atop the plant are dense
with tiny white flowers that give off a
musty smell. Very large leaves sit lower
down in threes; they are deeply lobed,
toothed, dark green and hairy
underneath. The leaves resemble those of
devil's-club (page 317), which you will
sometimes find lying in wait for you
among otherwise-innocuous cow-parsnip
patches on the western slope.

White angelica
Angelica arguta (carrot family)
July to early August

Montane and subalpine, southern area.
Resembles cow parsnip and grows in
similar locations, but it is not hairy and
the flower clusters are ball-shaped rather
than flat.

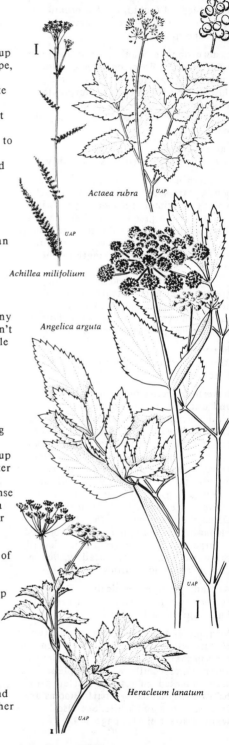

Actaea rubra   UAP

Achillea milifolium   UAP

Angelica arguta

Heracleum lanatum   UAP

UAP

Pathfinder/trail plant
Adenocaulon bicolor (composite family)
July

Western-slope montane south of Golden
and the Waterton/Glacier area. Small
tufted flowers on long stalks, reminiscent
of coltsfoot (page 339), but pathfinder
leaves are broader and coltsfoot flowers
are earlier (April to May). Compare
also with arrowleaf balsam-root,
page 356. When you walk through a
patch of pathfinder the leaves turn over,
marking your path with the
light-colored, hairy undersides. The seeds
catch on clothing.

Lace flower/foam flower/false mitrewort/Nancy-over-the-ground
Tiarella trifoliata (saxifrage family)
Late June to late July

Western-slope montane and subalpine,
very common in Columbian forest; on the
eastern slope most common in the
Waterton/Glacier area, occasional near
the continental divide at least as far
north as Jasper. Height 10-30 cm.
Maple-shaped leaves about 8 cm across;
tiny white flowers on drooping stalks in
a showy open cluster atop the plant.

Valerian
Valeriana spp. (valerian family)
May to August

Subalpine meadows to a little above
treeline. Stout square stem up to a metre
tall, with large, deeply lobed and toothed
leaves; those of *V. dioica* (late May
through June) more delicate than those
of *V. sitchensis* (late May to mid-August).
Dense tuft of small flowers at the top,
purplish at first, turning white later.
After a frost this plant spreads a strong,
rather unpleasant odor. The seed-like
fruits have feathers. This plant is
sometimes called "wild heliotrope"—a
poor name, for it is not a heliotrope
(genus *Heliotropium)* at all.

Northern bedstraw
Galium boreale (madder family)
Late June to early August

Common in open montane woods.
Calf-high plant with narrow dark-green
leaves and showy tufts of tiny white
four-parted flowers. Leaves are in fours,
too, growing symmetrically from each
node.

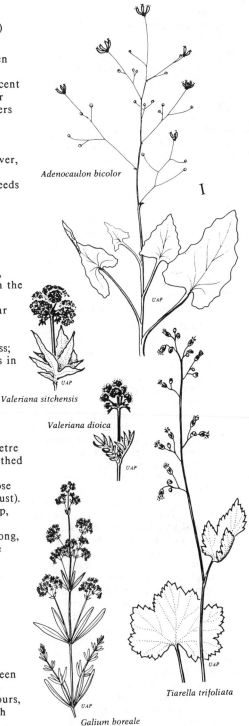

Adenocaulon bicolor

Valeriana sitchensis

Valeriana dioica

Tiarella trifoliata

Galium boreale

Fleabane
Erigeron spp. (composite family) April to
August

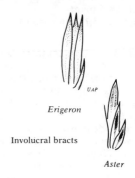

Erigeron

Involucral bracts

Aster

If it looks like a daisy, but it's growing a
long way from the roadside, then it is
probably a fleabane. That is the general
rule in the Rockies, where real daisies
(*Chrysanthemum* spp., see next entry) are
not native.

There are many fleabane species in
the Canadian Rockies, some very
difficult to identify, and to make
matters worse the asters (page 347) are
quite similar. I am content just to be able
to tell a fleabane from an aster. Try this,
ahem, simple procedure. Look at the
little green cup under the flower—the
scaly **involucral bracts**. If there is just
one row of bracts then it is a fleabane;
if there is more than one row, it is an
aster.

Having got that far, here are two
fleabanes that are fairly easy to know.
See also the alpine varieties on page 395.

Daisy fleabane *(E. compositus),*
mid-April through June: common at
all elevations throughout the
Rockies, very common on grassy
montane slopes, where it is one of
the early spring flowers. Frilly,
hairy leaves at the base are each
divided into three lobes at the end.
Stem has narrow, clasping leaves or
leaflets, 10-20 cm tall. One flower
(flowerhead, really, for in members
of the composite family the
petal-like parts are all individual
flowers, as are the little bumps that
make up the centre) per stem, 2-3 cm
across. This plant sometimes has the
petal-like white **ray-flowers**. The
early ones around Jasper don't; they
just have mustard-colored **disk
flowers** (the ones in the centre). A
week or so later, ray flowers may
appear on the same plants—or they
may not—while later-blooming ones
seem to have ray flowers from the
start. Regardless, they all produce
fuzzy round seedheads the size of
marbles in July and August.

Erigeron compositus

Common fleabane *(E. caespitosus),* June
and July: montane, often in large
patches. Ankle-high, very daisy-like
plant with narrow, undivided leaves
covered in fine hairs, as are the

Erigeron caespitosus

stems. Flowerheads are white, though sometimes pinkish or bluish and rather wide compared with other fleabanes; centres are the color of hot mustard.

Western willow aster
Aster hesperius (composite family)
July and August

Low-elevation montane, in moist grassy meadows. Often a metre tall, this aster has white or pinkish ray flowers (most asters are purple). The leaves are narrow and lack stalks, but the most distinctive thing about the plant demands that you get your eye close to the stems: they have thin white lines of hair running down them.

Ox-eye daisy
Chrysanthemum leucanthemum (composite family)
June to August

A true daisy, unlike the fleabanes and asters, and thus not native to the Rockies. Look for this species around towns, where it has spread from gardens, and along roadsides. At 40-60 cm it is taller than any white fleabane, with bigger flowers (4-6 cm across). The basal leaves are paddle-shaped and cleft, becoming narrower and more pointed up the stems.

Aster hesperius

Chrysanthemum leucanthemum

Not wishing to nag, I still feel obligated to point out that picking wildflowers is an absolute no-no. Wildflowers are protected by law throughout the Canadian Rockies, and for a very good reason: experience has shown that even light picking of some species can wipe them out. Most plants must maintain an adequate density for successful fertilization and maintenance of ongoing generations, and the rarer ones are often right at the threshold of viability. To my way of thinking, we have no right to destroy anything lovely and natural simply because we wish to possess it. When identifying wildflowers, I bring my eye to the flower, not the flower to my eye.

Wildflowers below timberline: greenish
Often with other colors, but mostly
greenish

One-sided wintergreen
Pyrola secunda (heath family)
Mid-July to early August

Montane and lower subalpine woods. A
small plant, 10-20 cm tall, with rounded
basal evergreen leaves and small
ball-shaped greenish-white flowers
hanging in a row beneath the arching
stem. The styles stick out.

Green pyrola
Pyrola chlorantha (heath family) July

Montane, usually in dry lodgepole woods.
Very similar to pink pyrola (see
page 370), but with green flowers and
stems rather than pink ones. Green
pyrola is also smaller (10-20 cm rather
than 20-30 cm for pink pyrola) and
flowers a little earlier.

Northern false toadflax/
northern bastard toadflax
Geocaulon livida (sandalwood family)
Late May to early June

Montane woods. A single stem per plant,
10-20 cm tall, with smooth lance-shaped
leaves, often stained brown. Most of the
new plants are sickly-looking, afflicted
with a common virus that patterns the
crinkly leaves yellow and green. They
become smooth and more evenly
pale-green later. But in late summer the
leaves become splotched with brown.
Look for tiny greenish flowers along the
stem, at leaf nodes. Showy red berries in
fall are inedible. Plant is partly parasitic
on tree roots, producing some of its own
food as well. True toadflax is *Linaria
vulgaris,* page 366. See also rattlesnake
plantain, page 342.

Meadow-rue
Thalictrum spp. (buttercup family)
June and July

Montane and subalpine, in damp
sheltered places. Up to a metre tall.
Leaves the shape of yellow columbine
(page 361), but smaller, bluegreen and
veined. Female flowers are greenish and
nodding; male flowers are purplish and
star-shaped, with long stamens. The two
common species are difficult to
differentiate, even for botanists. Leaves

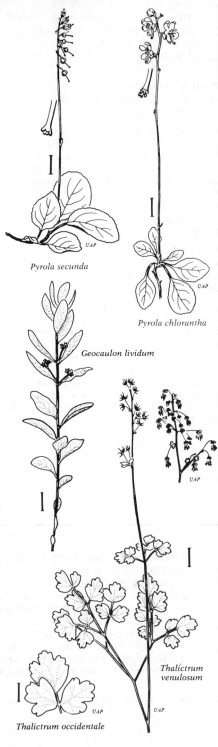

Pyrola secunda

Pyrola chlorantha

Geocaulon lividum

*Thalictrum
venulosum*

Thalictrum occidentale

of *T. venulosum* are more heavily veined than those of *T. occidentale*.

Mitrewort/bishop's-cap
Mitella spp. (saxifrage family)
Late June to mid-July

Southern montane and subalpine, in damp shady places. Small plants of the forest floor; easy to pass by. But the flowers are distinctive: yellowish-green stars, with strange frilly petals that extend well beyond the petal-like sepals. The fruit opens to show a cup with tiny black seeds in it. We have three species that are similar, of which the commonest one is the round-leaved *M. nuda*. *M. pentandra* is taller. The other *Mitella* has mauve flowers; see page 382.

Peppergrass
Lepidium densiflorum (mustard family)
Mid-June to early August

Montane forest, on disturbed ground. Spikes of tiny greenish flowers up to 50 cm tall. Narrow, toothed leaves up the stem to the point at which the flowers begin. There are usually no petals, only sepals. Showy sprays of small pods in fall.

Western sweet cicely
Osmorhiza occidentalis (carrot family)
Late May to early July

Eastern-slope montane, from Crowsnest Pass south. Tall (up to 1 m), with toothy leaflets in threes. Tiny greenish flowers in upright clusters on very thin stems, carried above the leaves. See also the antenna plant, page 343.

Wild sarsaparilla
Aralia nudicaulis (ginseng family) June

In deep montane woods. Common on the western slope; fairly common in central and northern sections of the eastern slope. Absent at Waterton and eastern-slope Glacier. Distinctive-looking: the leaves are carried flat on three stems atop the plant, like an umbrella. The leaflets resemble poison ivy, especially when they are young and in threes (they later go to fives). But leaves of wild sarsaparilla are dull, while those of poison ivy are shiny. Small, greenish-white flowers bloom in ball-like clusters, usually three to a plant. Dark purple berries, not edible.

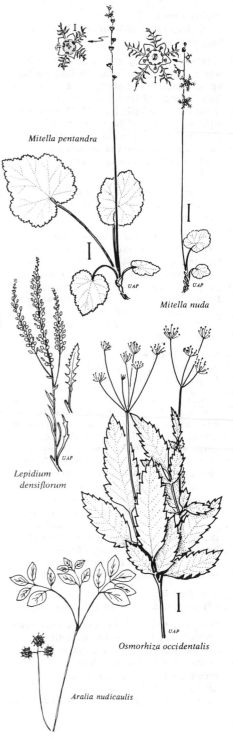

Mitella pentandra

Mitella nuda

Lepidium densiflorum

Osmorhiza occidentalis

Aralia nudicaulis

Twisted stalk
Streptopus amplexifolius (lily family)
May and June

Montane, in shady places near running
water. The tallest Canadian Rockies lily:
up to a metre. The stems zig-zag slightly.
Wavy-margined leaves are rather like
those of fairy bells (page 331), but often
with yellow spots. Small greenish-white
flowers hide underneath, hanging from
twisted stalks. The red berries are
oval-shaped, also hanging from twisted
stalks.

Bronze bells/western stenanthium
Stenanthium occidentale (lily family)
June and July

Moist montane and lower-subalpine
woods, southern and central sections.
Delicate plant 20-40 cm tall, with 6-10
small greenish (or brownish, or even
purplish) bell-shaped flowers hanging
from a thin stalk. The sides of the bells
have purplish streaks and there is a
yellow clapper. Narrow leaves grow up
from the base.

False hellebore
Veratrum viride (lily family)
July and August

Montane and subalpine woods, often near
running water. A tall plant (often
head-high) with very long parallel-veined
leaves, often called skunkcabbage
(page 412) by non-botanists, though the
two plants look quite different. Compare
also with false Solomon's seal, page 330.
Flowers of false hellebore are small and
yellowish green, but there are lots of
them in streamers atop the plant. *All
parts are quite poisonous;* they contain
the alkaloid protoveratrine, which slows
heartbeat and breathing. (True
hellebores, of the European genus
Helleborus, cause digestive upsets.)

Wild licorice
Glycyrrhiza lepidota (pea family) July

Southern montane, in dry places. Grows
up to a metre tall, with vetch-like
sawtooth leaves. Flowers are small and
greenish or yellowish-white;
inconspicuous. The seed pods are
distinctive: 1-2 cm long and covered with
prickles. Roots taste weakly of licorice.

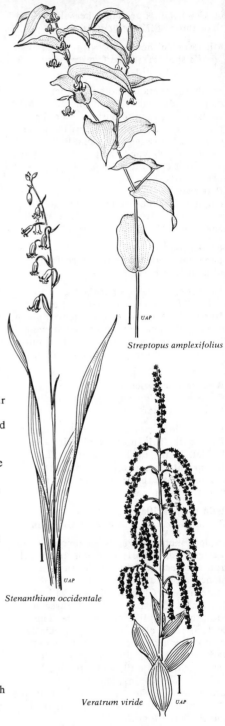

Streptopus amplexifolius

Stenanthium occidentale

Veratrum viride

Russian thistle/tumbleweed
Salsola kali (goosefoot family)
June and July

An introduced weed in disturbed places
at low elevations, common in the
southern region. Not a true thistle, but
prickly when dead and dry. The stiff,
rounded plant breaks off at the root and
goes tumbling along with the wind,
spreading its seeds. The plant is prickly
when alive, too; the leaves are narrow,
hard and pointed. Look for the tiny
greenish flowers along the stems.

Salsola kali

Stinging nettle
Urtica dioica (nettle family)
Late June and July

Montane, mainly on disturbed ground.
Usually about a metre tall, but can grow
larger. Avoid this plant: merely brushing
it lightly will cause a burning sensation
that lasts for hours. The toothy,
lance-shaped leaves have small spines
that break off in the skin and discharge
an irritant. From a (safe) distance, you
can spot stinging nettle by noting the
small green flowers in drooping strings;
otherwise it looks much like wild mint
(page 386), immediately recognizable by
the minty smell (which stinging nettle
lacks). Like other nasty plants in the
Rockies, stinging nettle is more common
on the western slope.

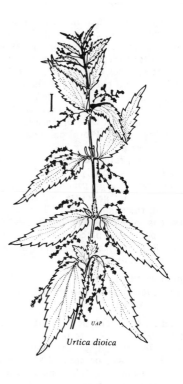

Urtica dioica

Glycyrrhiza lepidota

Wildflowers below timberline: yellow or orange

Glacier lily/snow lily/ avalanche lily/dogtooth violet
Erythronium grandiflorum (lily family)
Mid-May to mid-July

Upper montane to subalpine, common in southern areas of both slopes; scarce north of Bow Pass. Unmistakable, large brilliant-yellow flower that follows the snowline up the mountains. Usually two upstanding, in-curling leaves 10-15 cm high, with the single flower (sometimes two) nodding atop a slightly higher stem.

Western wood lily
Lilium philadelphicum (lily family)
Mid-June to mid-July

On south-facing open montane slopes and aspen woods; also common in Columbian forest. Large, very showy orange flower faces upward (flower of true tiger lily, next entry, faces downward), with black dots inside and black-ended stamens. Narrow leaves grow from the stem, not from the base like most other lilies. Height is 5-50 cm tall. Often mistakenly called "tiger lily." Floral emblem of Saskatchewan.

Despite protected status throughout Canada, the wood lily is always a picker's target. And picking kills it, for the bulb cannot generate two sets of leaves in the same summer. That explains why it is so seldom seen beside highways and in populated places—except in the national parks, where visitors generally follow the no-picking rule.

Columbia lily/tiger lily
Lilium columbianum (lily family)
June to August

Western-slope montane and subalpine, in moist places. There are only a few short, narrow leaves, but several large orange flowers nod over on stems 20-70 cm tall. The black-dotted petals bend backward, exposing long anthers. Again, this is not the true tiger lily, *Lilium tigrinum*, which is a native of Asia.

Yellow mountain violet and evergreen violet
Viola glabella and *V. orbiculata*
(violet family) Late June and early July

Both grow in damp, mossy montane and subalpine woods. Rounded, bluntly toothed leaves, notched in at the stem.

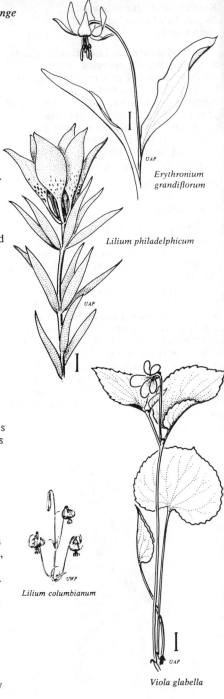

Erythronium grandiflorum

Lilium philadelphicum

Lilium columbianum

Viola glabella

Bright yellow flowers with purple veins, five-petalled and not radially symmetrical. Differentiate the two species by the short stems in the low-growing evergreen violet. Mountain violet can reach 30 cm.

Yellow prairie violet
Viola nuttallii (violet family)
Early to mid-May

Mainly western-slope southern montane, but also at Waterton/Glacier and in the southern foothills. Prefers dry, open spots at low elevations, but sometimes grows quite high, in alpine scree slopes. Note the long, scalloped, un-violet-like leaves. Flowers are yellow with purple veins and purple tinge on the back of the upper two petals. Sometimes called "Johnny jump-up," a name applied to various garden violets and pansies. Compare with yellow monkey-flower, next entry.

Yellow monkey-flower
Mimulus guttatus (figwort family)
July to September

Mainly western-slope, montane to subalpine; eastern slope south of Crowsnest only. Grows in wet, open spots. Up to 30 cm tall, with large blooms and toothed, pointed leaves. Look for dots on the calyx (cup under the flower). Monkey-flower is sometimes mistaken for yellow violet (previous entry).

Yellow lady's-slipper/moccasin flower
Cypripedium calceolus (orchid family)
Mid-June to early July

Shady moist montane woods, all areas, though scarce on the eastern slope north of Jasper and south of Crowsnest Pass. Large, very distinctive bloom: bright yellow and bag-like, with a brown sepal above and two more on the side, spiralling. Grows about 20 cm high. Several smooth, parallel-veined leaves at the base. Very similar to mountain lady's slipper except for the flower color. See page 341 for illustration.

Northern coral-root orchid/ pale coral-root orchid
Corallorhiza trifida (orchid family)
May and June

Damp places, montane woods. The most distinctive feature is the lack of leaves: the plant is a saprophyte. It roots in dead

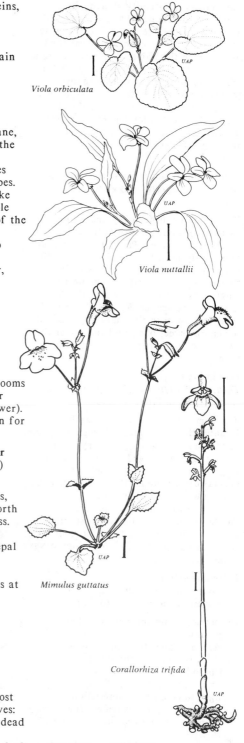

Viola orbiculata

Viola nuttallii

Mimulus guttatus

Corallorhiza trifida

material, symbiotically sharing its substrate with fungi that further break the food down, releasing nutrients. The stubby roots look rather like branched coral; hence the name. The flowers are a combination of yellow, green and white, usually looking more yellow than anything else. Other coral-roots you may see: **spotted coral-root** *(C. maculata),* which is very similar but reddish, and the **striped coral-root** *C. striata,* which has larger flowers that are marked with thin red lines.

Yellow penstemon/yellow beard-tongue
Penstemon confertus (figwort family)
Early June to August

Central and southern regions, common from Lake Louise south (very common south of Crowsnest Pass) in dry montane and subalpine meadows. The only yellow penstemon in the Canadian Rockies, and thus easily identified. Plants mostly on single stems less than 30 cm tall with lance-shaped leaves. Radial clusters of small yellow trumpet-shaped flowers, the lower lip three-lobed and the upper lip two-lobed in characteristic penstemon fashion.

Dandelion
Taraxacum officinale (composite family)
Early April to late September

The common, lawn-variety dandelion. Usually the first yellow flower of spring, found in every grassy, clovery place. Very familiar: ragged leaves, all basal; large, brilliant-yellow bloom with no central disk; round, fluffy seedhead that blows away in the wind. But don't confuse with look-alike flowers: false dandelion and goatsbeard (next entries). Or look-alike seedheads of the anemones, white dryas (page 393) and yellow dryas (page 361).

False dandelions
Agoseris spp. and *Microseris nutans* (composite family) June to August

In meadows and open woods. The **large-flowered false dandelion** *(Agoseris glauca,* montane, July and August) is a good imitation, but the petals are fewer and broader, and the leaves are narrow and not toothy. A related species, **orange-flowered false dandelion** *(A. aurantiaca,* all elevations, June and July), has a showy red-orange bloom. The

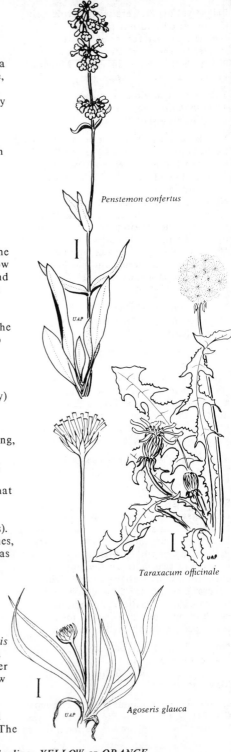

Penstemon confertus

Taraxacum officinale

Agoseris glauca

leaves have a few broad, cuspy teeth. In southern western-slope montane meadows and at Waterton/Glacier there is yet another false dandelion: *Microseris nutans.* The leaves are long and very narrow, often with backward-pointing teeth. The blooms are 1-2 cm across, yellow (often with purple lines) and nod before they bloom. See also goat's-beard (next entry).

Goat's-beard/yellow salsify/ oyster plant/giant dandelion
Tragopogon dubius (composite family)
Late June to mid-July

Low-elevation montane, usually on disturbed ground. Looks rather like a dandelion but is much larger: up to 60 cm tall. Leaves are long and grass-like, rather than broad and toothy like a dandelion. Bloom is bright yellow; the petal-like ray flowers are rather sparse and blackish toward the centre; sharp-looking green bracts extend beyond the edges. Seedhead is dandelion-like but much larger. You will see this plant in gardens, along with a purple variety *(T. pratensis).*

Hawkweed
Hieracium spp. (composite family)
July and August

Common montane and subalpine plants, growing in dry open areas and often forming patches. About a dozen species, difficult to differentiate and easily mistaken for sow thistle (next entry). All hawkweeds have bright-yellow, dandelion-like blooms (no central disk) 2-3 cm across, a few to a dozen per plant. The flowers bloom on stalks rising from the places where the leaves join the stem; look for dark hairs under the blooms, another hawkweed identifier.

Two low-elevation hawkweeds to look for are **narrow-leaved hawkweed** *(H. umbellatum),* with leaves that are shallowly toothed at the base, becoming narrower and less toothy up the stem, and **prairie hawkweed** *(H. cynoglossoides),* which has club-shaped leaves and is very hairy. At subalpine elevations look for **slender hawkweed** *(H. triste).* It can be mistaken for arnica (page 356), but in slender hawkweed the blooms are smaller (less than 3 cm across) and they lack a central disk.

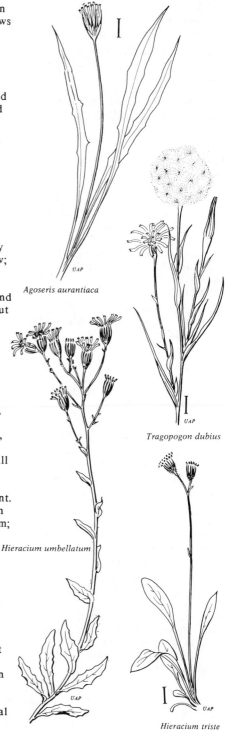

Agoseris aurantiaca

Tragopogon dubius

Hieracium umbellatum

Hieracium triste

Sow thistle
Sonchus arvensis (composite family)
Late July and early August

Montane, along roadsides and in
disturbed, dry, sunny places. Common in
most places but absent at Waterton
(present at Glacier). Resembles
hawkweed, but sow thistle is taller (up to
2 m) and with large (10-20 cm), toothy,
prickly leaves.

Arnica
Arnica spp. (composite family)
Mid-June through August

Montane and subalpine, usually in
evergreen woods. An easily identified
perennial genus, *except in alternate
years, when the plants do not bloom.*
Large, bright-yellow ray flowers curl a
bit at the edges, with small teeth at the
petal ends. Small yellow centres. Many
species, sometimes interbreeding. Some
common ones:

Heart-leaved arnica *(A. cordifolia):*
upper montane and subalpine; has
broadest leaves.

Broad-leaved arnica *(A. latifolia):*
resembles *A. cordifolia,* but the
leaves have either no petioles (stems)
or short ones. Most common
western-slope species.

Narrow-leaved arnica *(A. fulgens):*
narrowest leaves, mostly basal.

Aspen-rich woods around Jasper townsite
are full of *A. chamissonis,* a tall species
(up to 80 cm) with several blooms. The
oblong leaves have a prominent white
vein in the middle.

Arrowhead balsam root/spring sunflower
Balsamorhiza sagittata
(composite family)
Mid-May through June

Lower western-slope montane from
Golden south, and the southern foothills.
Arnica-like flower but very different
leaves: long (up to 20 cm), all at the base,
arrow-shaped and fuzzy underneath.
Grows on dry open slopes, not in the
woods, which distinguishes it from
pathfinder, page 345.

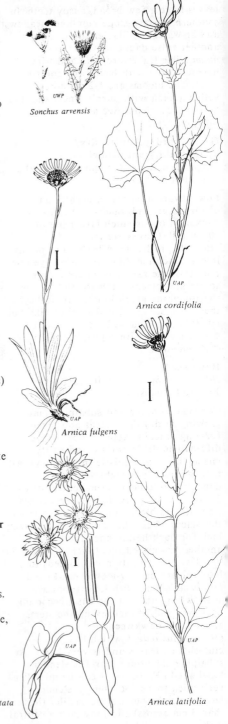

Sonchus arvensis

Arnica cordifolia

Arnica fulgens

Balsamorhiza sagittata

Arnica latifolia

Wild gaillardia/brown-eyed Susan
Gaillardia aristata (composite family)
Early July to late August

Dry, grassy montane meadows. True brown-eyed susans belong to the genus *Rudbeckia* and grow in the southern and eastern USA, but the name fits wild gaillardia so well (and is such a good identifier) that I guess we're stuck with it. Wild gaillardia is up to 50 cm tall, with scalloped leaves and hairy stems. The blooms are large, 5-10 cm across and very showy: domed brown centres with long yellow petals that often droop backward, each getting wider toward the end, which is divided into three small lobes that give the illusion of many more ray flowers (petal-like parts) than there actually are.

Golden aster
Chrysopsis villosa (composite family)
July to late August

Southern montane, in dry meadows at low elevations. Not really an aster (there are no yellow asters), but close enough. A sprawling plant with hairs on stems and leaves, and somewhat sticky. Flowers are showy; bloom at the ends of the stems.

Gumweed
Grindelia squarrosa (composite family)
August and early September

Western-slope montane from Golden south at low elevations, and in the southern foothills. Prefers dry, open places. An unkempt-looking plant, despite the pretty yellow blooms; it exudes a sticky harmless juice. Disk flowers (centres) are paler than the ray flowers.

Broomweed/snakeweed
Gutierrezia sarothrae (composite family)
Late August and early September

A southern-Alberta prairie plant that creeps into the foothills, although it hasn't made it into Waterton or eastern-slope Glacier. Look for it also around Cranbrook. A bushy rabbitbrush look-alike (page 320) with very thin, hairy leaves 1-3 cm long on slender dark-green stems 30-40 cm long. Lots of small yellow blooms cover the top in showy clusters.

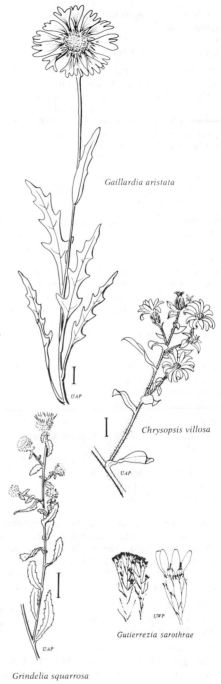

Gaillardia aristata

Chrysopsis villosa

Gutierrezia sarothrae

Grindelia squarrosa

Yellow puccoon/woolly gromwell/lemonweed
Lithospermum ruderale (borage family)
Late May to Mid-July

Mostly southern montane, in open places.
A showy, bushy plant 20-50 cm tall with
hairy dark-green leaves that turn up at
the ends. Clusters of bright-yellow
flowers have dark centres. Puccoon is a
prairie plant found in the mountains
where horses use the trails (figure that
out).

Creeping mahonia/Oregon grape
Berberis repens (barberry family)
Late May and June

Southern western-slope montane, eastern
slope only in the Waterton/Glacier area,
in open woods and rocky places.
Holly-like leaves are distinctive, as are
the sour blue berries. Blooms are small
and yellow, in tight clusters near the
centre of the low-growing plant.
B. nervosa, also called Oregon grape, has
leaves that are even more holly-like;
grows in open areas of the Columbian
forest.

Pineapple weed and scentless chamomile
Matricaria matricarioides
and *M. perforata* (composite family)
July and August

Pineapple weed is common on disturbed
ground at low elevations throughout the
Rockies. This is a small plant, 10-20 cm
tall; very lacy leaves emit the odor of
pineapple, especially when crushed. The
blooms are mustard-colored, lacking ray
flowers (petal-like parts).
Scentless chamomile *(M. perforata)* is
similar and also common, but the blooms
have white ray flowers and the plant is a
little taller. **Wild chamomile** *(Matricaria
recutita)* is also found in the Canadian
Rockies, but it is not common. All these
are introduced species.

Potentilla/cinquefoil
Potentilla spp. (rose family)
May through August

At all elevations, in various habitats.
This genus is familiar to gardeners, but
there are many wild forms as well. Good
identifiers: five-fingered leaflets and
brilliant-yellow, five-petalled flowers,
often indented at the petal-ends and
alternating with five smaller green

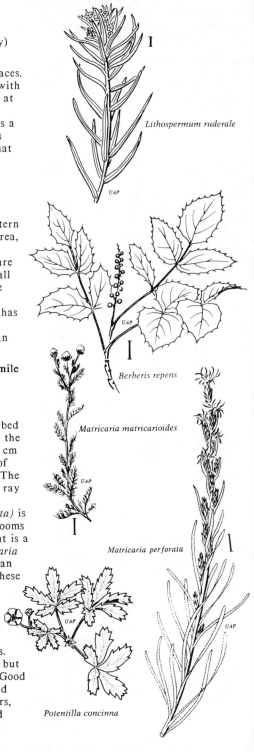

Lithospermum ruderale

Berberis repens

Matricaria matricarioides

Matricaria perforata

Potentilla concinna

sepals. Unfortunately, there are a lot of
potentilla species, some of which are
easily confused with one another and
with certain buttercups and avens. The
common potentillas are listed below,
followed by the buttercups and avens,
for comparison.

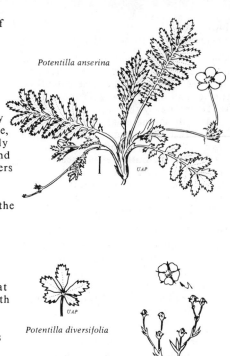

Potentilla anserina

Early potentilla *(P. concinna)* early May
through July: eastern-slope montane,
on south-facing hillsides. Very early
starter; leaves come out in April and
early May. Typical potentilla flowers
set close to a disorderly looking,
ground-hugging mat of very hairy
five-pointed leaves, pale-green on the
top and light-gray beneath.

Silverweed *(P. anserina)* late May to
early August: on dry, gravelly
montane slopes. Grows with early
potentilla, blooms early, and looks
like it—but the leaves are somewhat
different: toothed, green and smooth
above, silvery and hairy beneath.
Rather than forming an unkempt
cushion, they grow in orderly rows
on straggling, vine-like roots.

Potentilla diversifolia

Montane potentilla *(P. gracilis)* late June
to early August: most common
montane species; grows everywhere.
Spreading, geranium-like toothed
leaves are slightly hairy underneath
and 4-7 cm across at the plant's base,
becoming smaller and less numerous
up the reddish stems, which can
reach 60-70 cm in height, topped by
typical potentilla flowers with
indented petal-ends.

P. diversifolia closely resembles montane
potentilla (previous entry), but grows
at higher elevations and has smaller
leaves that are only lightly hairy.

Potentilla glandulosa

Subalpine potentilla *(P. glandulosa)*
mid-May through July: subalpine and
alpine, in open dry spots. Grows
20-30 cm tall, with rounded, toothy
leaflets and petal ends that are not
indented.

See also shrubby potentilla, page 318,
and the alpine potentillas, page 399.

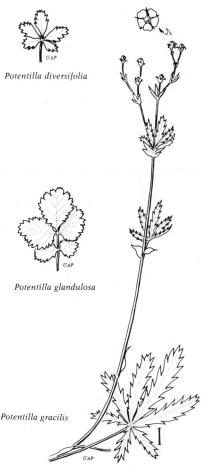

Potentilla gracilis

Buttercup
Ranunculus spp. (buttercup family)

There are many members of this species,
and they run the gamut of Rockies
habitats. They look like some potentilla
species and often grow with them.
Differentiate by the shiny,
varnished-looking petals and green
centres in buttercup flowers; potentillas
have yellow centres and less-glossy
leaves. But the buttercups closely
resemble yellow avens (page 361).
Differentiate by the small leaves that
grow just below an aven's flowers, and
their absence in buttercups.

Here are some common buttercups:

Western buttercup *(R. occidentalis)* April
   through June: most common
   western-slope buttercup, found
   everywhere at low elevations.
   Three-lobed toothed leaves, stems
   5-50 cm tall.

Hairy buttercup *(R. uncinatus)* May
   through July: in shady western-slope
   montane and Columbian forests,
   central region. Occasional on the
   eastern slope from Saskatchewan
   Crossing south. Three-lobed leaves as
   above, but narrower; hairy stems and
   smaller flowers.

Macoun's buttercup/hairy buttercup *(R.
   macounii)* June and July: montane
   meadows. The hairiest buttercup.
   Resembles (and grows with) tall
   buttercup (next entry); has larger
   leaves but smaller flowers.

Tall buttercup *(R. acris)* June to
   mid-August: damp meadows at low
   elevations. Hairy stems; similar to
   Macoun's buttercup (previous entry),
   but with smaller leaves and larger
   flowers.

As you can see, identifying buttercup
species is a job for botanists. Thankfully,
I'm a geologist. See also yellow water
crowfoot (page 414) and the alpine
buttercups (page 399).

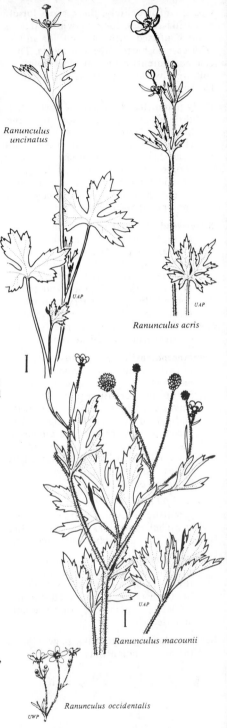

Ranunculus uncinatus

Ranunculus acris

Ranunculus macounii

Ranunculus occidentalis

Yellow avens

Geum aleppicum (rose family)
Early June to early August

Montane meadows, in wet ground.
Strikingly similar to tall buttercup
(above) and sometimes growing with it,
but note the cone-shaped green centre in
the flower and small leaves growing not
far below it (tall buttercups have long,
hairy flower-stems). **Large-leaved avens**
(G. macrophyllum) is another common
species; note the difference in leaf size.

Yellow columbine

Aquilegia flavescens (buttercup family)
June to early August

Mainly eastern-slope subalpine meadows,
occasional at lower elevations.
Uncommon on the western slope. Fairly
tall plant (up to 1 m) with large, very
showy, complicated flowers, normally
pale yellow, but often tinged with pink
or purple. There is also a blue-and-white
version (northern blue columbine,
page 385) and a red species (page 373).
Flower stems emerge from a bushy
growth of distinctive leaves: dark green,
a few centimetres across, with rounded
lobes. See also meadow-rue, page 348.

Purslane

Portulaca oleracea (purslane family) July

Montane, on disturbed ground. This is a
low-growing weed everyone has seen, but
hardly anyone knows. Easily identified
by the glossy, fleshy green leaves. Look
closely—the small white-and-yellow
flowers are lovely.

Yellow dryas/yellow mountain avens

Dryas drummondii (rose family)
Mid-June to early July

Montane version of white dryas
(page 393), very common on the eastern
slope of the central region; less so
elsewhere. This mat-forming shrub
quickly covers stony ground such as
glacial outwash flats, front-range
streambeds and roadsides. *Something* has
to, I guess. The leaves are green above,
gray or brown below, and blunt-toothed;
flowers on stalks 5-10 cm tall, nodding
over, with 8-10 short yellow petals. As
the flowers go to seed they gradually
straighten up, sending a twisted cone of
plumes out from the centre. The cone
expands into a dandelion-like seed head.

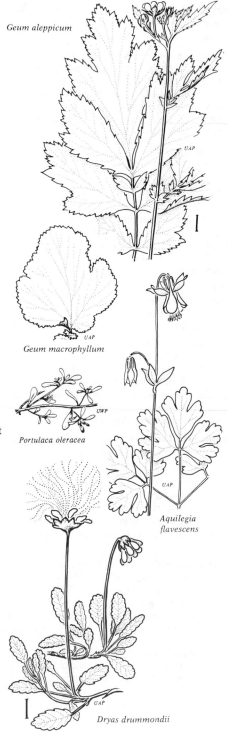

Geum aleppicum

Geum macrophyllum

Portulaca oleracea

Aquilegia flavescens

Dryas drummondii

Pasture sage/pasture wormwood
Artemisia frigida (composite family)
August

Montane, in dry places on sandy soil.
Most easily identified by the strong
fragrance of the leaves when crushed:
they smell like the desert. Tufts of finely
divided, fuzzy gray-green leaflets with
inconspicuous small flowers hidden along
the stems. Yellow centres; no petals.

Stonecrop/sedum
Sedum stenopetalum (orpine family) June

Throughout the Rockies at all elevations,
in exposed places. A **succulent** plant (in
the botanical sense; not particularly good
to eat), easily identified by the fleshy
pinkish stem (5-10 cm tall) and short, fat
leaves. Flowers are about 1 cm across,
yellow with green centres and long
stamens.

Yellow alumroot
Heuchera cylindrica
(saxifrage family)
Early July to mid-August

Montane to alpine, in dry, rocky
locations. Small yellow upright
bell-shaped flowers in a spike atop a
leafless stem. Leaves are all basal,
stick/hairy. Flowers are near the top of
the stem. Compare with *H. parvifolia,* a
whitish species (page 335).

Mustard family
(various species) May to July

Small plants, all with four-petalled small
flowers that embody the word "cute." The
seed pods are often distinctive, as shown
in the illustrations. There are many
species; differentiating them is best left
to botanists, but here are a few easy
ones.

Draba/whitlow-grass *(Draba* spp.) early
  May through July: rocky, stony
  places at all elevations. Several
  species, all low-growing and
  similar-looking, with the same small
  yellow four-petalled flowers (white
  in some species) and finely hairy,
  mostly basal gray-green leaves. Seeds
  are in small upright pods. *D. incerta*
  is probably the most common species

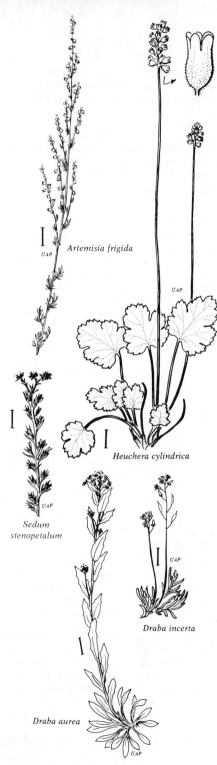

Artemisia frigida

Heuchera cylindrica

Sedum stenopetalum

Draba incerta

Draba aurea

in the Rockies; *D. aurea* is the tallest (20-30 cm), preferring dry montane locations.

Yellow rocket *(Barbarea vulgaris)* June and July: montane, often on disturbed ground. An uncommon introduced species identified by its irregularly indented small leaves. Fairly tall: 20-50 cm.

Flixweed *(Descurainia sophia)* June and July: a common montane weed. The tallest mustard (up to 1 m), with finely divided, frilly-looking leaves and slender pods.

Wallflower/small-flowered rocket *(Erysimum inconspicuum)* late May to mid-July: montane, at low elevations; common in the southern region. Loose clusters of small but showy bright-yellow flowers atop a stem 40-60 cm tall. Narrow, slightly hairy leaves. Long skinny pods in fall. There is also a purple alpine version, page 405.

In April or May you may find many mustard-family plants with tiny yellowish leaves on short stems above a basal rosette. The yellow color comes from pinpoint-sized yellow dots on the leaves, giving the plant a colorful, flower-like appearance. Such plants are infected with a fungus that is quite common on *Draba;* the infected plant sends up the stem and yellowish leaves but seldom grows taller than a few centimetres. After a week or two it withers back to the basal leaves. I have seen only one infected plant that had normal flowers as well as the yellowish leaves.

Ragwort/groundsel
Senecio spp. (composite family)
June to August

Montane and subalpine, in open places. Often growing with goldenrod (next entry) and rather similar-looking, but ragwort blooms occur in clusters of a few right at the top of the plant, while goldenrod blooms are smaller and trail partway down the stem. The ray flowers (petal-like parts) of the head sometimes come out later than the disk flowers at the centre, which vary from red to orange on the same plant. There are many ragwort species, some of which

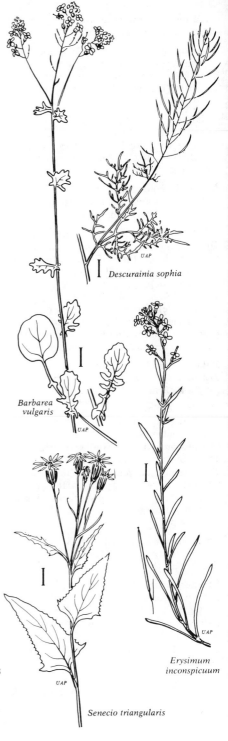

Descurainia sophia

Barbarea vulgaris

Erysimum inconspicuum

Senecio triangularis

have no ray flowers at all. Here are two easy-to-identify ragworts:

Prairie ragwort *(S. canus)* June and July: eastern-slope montane, in dry places; 10-20 cm tall, with smooth-edged basal leaves and irregularly toothed stem leaves.

Triangular-leaved ragwort *(S. triangularis)* July and August: a tall (1-1.4 m) subalpine species with large, coarsely toothed arrow-shaped leaves.

Mountain goldenrod
Solidago spathulata (composite family)
Late July to early September

Montane, in dry places, blooming late. Grows 10-30 cm high, often in small patches. Showy tufts of small all-yellow flowers in a loose spike atop erect stems with long oblong leaves. There is a tall version *(S. gigantea;* 20-50 cm, multiple open flower clusters) and one with denser flowerheads *(S. missouriensis;* plume-like branching flower clusters); both are common in southern areas.

Buffalo bean/false lupine
Thermopsis rhombifolia (pea family)
May and June

Handsome plant of eastern-slope montane meadows, Bow River south. Strangely unreported in Waterton; Glacier reports *T. montana,* which is similar. Grows 15-45 cm tall in sandy, open spots. Clusters of rich yellow pea flowers against contrasting green leaflets in threes, hairy on close inspection. Makes curved, hairy gray pods about 5 cm long holding poisonous seeds.

Early yellow locoweed
Oxytropis sericea (pea family)
Early May through June

Southern montane. Not a tall plant, but showy in bloom. Compact mat of gray-green hairy leaves, with tufts of pale yellow pea-type flowers above it on stems 15-40 cm high. Poisonous. A very similar species, *O. campestris,* blooms later in the summer.

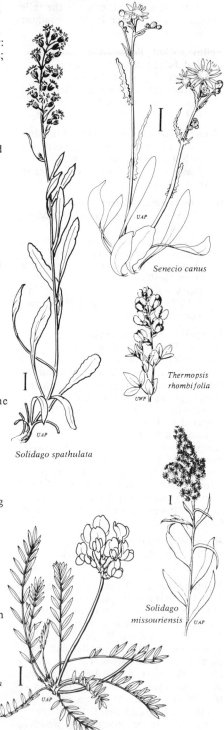

Senecio canus

Thermopsis rhombifolia

Solidago spathulata

Solidago missouriensis

Oxytropis sericea

Yellow sweet clover/yellow alfalfa
Melilotus officinalis (pea family)
Mid-July to September

Common on disturbed ground at low
elevations. A tall plant with narrow
cylindrical flower clusters like white
sweet clover (page 340), but with bright
yellow flowers. Introduced.

Golden corydalis
Corydalis aurea (fumitory family)
May to early July

Montane, on south-facing dry hillsides;
often on disturbed ground. Easily
mistaken for a sprawling pea-family
plant, the flowers are rather similar and
so are the pods produced later. But note
how the leaves are different.

Yellow paintbrush
Castilleja lutescens (figwort family)
June and July

At low elevations, in meadows and in
gravelly places along streams. Yellow
version of the familiar red paintbrush
(page 368). Color tends to be pale and
greenish. See also alpine yellow
paintbrush, page 402, and compare with
owl clover, next entry.

Owl-clover
Orthocarpus luteus (figwort family)
July to early September

Southern montane at low elevations,
occasional north to Jasper. Erect hairy
stems 10-30 cm high; short leaves. Small
yellow tubular flowers along the upper
two-thirds. The leaves continue through
the flower spike. Resembles western
lousewort (above), but the leaves are
different.

Western lousewort/
bracted lousewort/wood betony
Pedicularis bracteosa (figwort family)
July and August

Subalpine and alpine meadows. Plant
stands 20-40 cm high, with fern-like
leaves that range from green to
olive-drab. Dense spikes of small, tubular
yellow flowers (often with a pinkish or
purplish tinge) and green bracts;
distinctive in that the whole spike does
not flower at once.

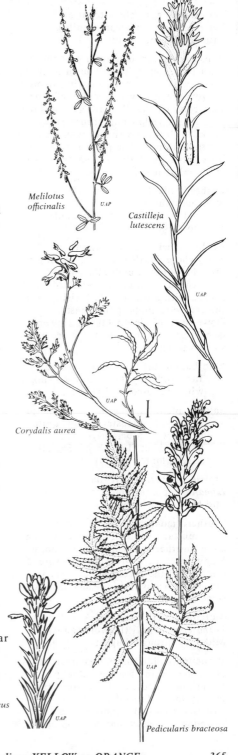

*Melilotus
officinalis*

*Castilleja
lutescens*

Corydalis aurea

Orthocarpus luteus

Pedicularis bracteosa

Butter-and-eggs/yellow toadflax
Linaria vulgaris (figwort family)
Late June through July

In patches along montane roads and on
disturbed ground. Tall plant (a metre or
more), with long gently curving stems.
Narrow green leaves drooping off the
stem contrast sharply with a long spike
of brilliant yellow-and-orange flowers.
Looks rather like a snapdragon, and is in
the same family. The plant is an
introduced weed, disliked in agricultural
circles—but it is beautiful.

Umbrella plant/sulphur plant/
wild buckwheat
Eriogonum spp. (buckwheat family)
June to August

Rocky places at all elevations
everywhere. Small plants, all having the
same half-round, umbrella-shaped
flowerhead. Oval or lance-shaped basal
leaves, with a leafless stalk rising from
the centre to support the dense
flowerhead of tiny petal-less flowers
(sepals provide the color). Two common
species to know:

Wild buckwheat *(E. umbellatum)* early
   June and July: tall (up to 40 cm),
   with cream-colored flowers.

Sulphur plant *(E. flavum),* mid-June to
   early August: eastern-slope, quite
   hairy, with a bright-yellow,
   less-compact flowerhead. See also
   silver plant, page 401.

Prairie parsley/biscuit root
Lomatium spp. (carrot family)
Mid-May to early July

Southern montane. Several clusters of
tiny, mustard-yellow flowers blooming
close together to form a loose canopy.
Many small, carrot-like leaflets spread
out around the base. Edible stems and
taproot. Various species; some larger,
some smaller, all similar.

Mullein/miner's candlestick
Verbascum thapsus (figwort family)
Mid-July through August

Pronounced "MULL-in." Common at low
elevations in the southern Rocky
Mountain Trench; on the eastern slope
mainly in the foothills south of
Crowsnest Pass. But mullein is an
introduced species that can pop up

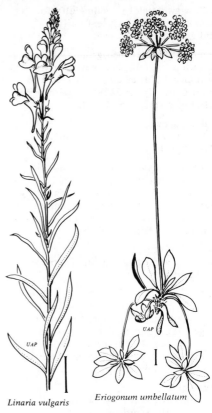

Linaria vulgaris

Eriogonum umbellatum

Lomatium dissectum

anywhere: I have seen it along the railway just west of Jasper. Prefers disturbed ground. A ramrod-straight plant often a metre or more tall; coarse and stout, with large oblong soft fuzzy olive-colored leaves that get smaller up the stem. Flowers are bright yellow, 1-2 cm across, packed in a spike atop the plant, which turns brown and stiffens in the fall.

Cholla cactus/brittle cactus
Opuntia fragilis (cactus family)
Mid-June to mid-July

Pronounced "CHOY-ah." Fairly common in sunny, dry places in the southern Rocky Mountain Trench from Radium south. Small and inconspicuous compared to the large cholla patches of the American southwest, but still easily identified as cactus: spiny greenish or salmon-colored fleshy joints each a few centimetres long, lying on the ground. Showy yellow flowers develop into reddish/purplish fruits.

Other entries to check:

Wild sweet pea and milk-vetch, page 340.
Skunkcabbage, page 412.
Yellow water crowfoot, page 414.

Opuntia fragilis

UWP

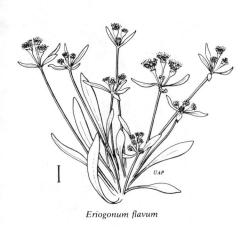

Eriogonum flavum

UAP

Verbascum thapsus

UAP

Red paintbrush
Castilleja spp. (figwort family)
June to late August

Montane and subalpine meadows,
sometimes above timberline. Perhaps the
best-known flower of the Rockies and
very easy to identify. A close look shows
that the color, which ranges from
red-orange to purple, is not carried on
the petals (they are green), but on the
bracts. Another little-known fact about
paintbrush is that the plant is a parasite,
attaching its roots to those of other
plants to gain part of its nutrients.

    There are many species and keying
them out is difficult. The most common
red species is *C. miniata;* its color varies
from red-orange to crimson. Purplish
flowers are probably *C. rhexifolia.* Along
the Alaska Highway you may see one
with purplish stems: *C. raupii.* See also
yellow paintbrush, page 365; there are
also red/yellow hybrids.

Thin-leaved owl-clover
Orthocarpus tenuifolius (figwort family)
June and July

Low elevations, western-slope montane
from Radium south; occasionally seen on
the eastern slope south of Crowsnest
Pass. Colored bracts like paintbrush, but
also tiny trumpet-shaped flowers hidden
among them. The leaves are very narrow,
hairy and divided into threes.

Pale sweetvetch/pale hedysarum
Hedysarum alpinum (pea family)
Late-June to early August

Pronounced "heddy-SAIR-um." Montane,
in clearings. Pale pink flowers on tall,
pointy spikes; rows of small paired
leaves. Compare with wild vetch
(page 378) and purple sweetvetch
(page 379). Members of this genus have
jointed pods, which distinguishes them
from the other pea-family plants.

Red clover
Trifolium pratense (pea family)
Mid-June to early August

Montane, in open grassy places and on
disturbed ground. Leaves larger than
lawn-variety clover (white clover,
page 340), smooth-edged and
lighter-veined, with round flowerheads

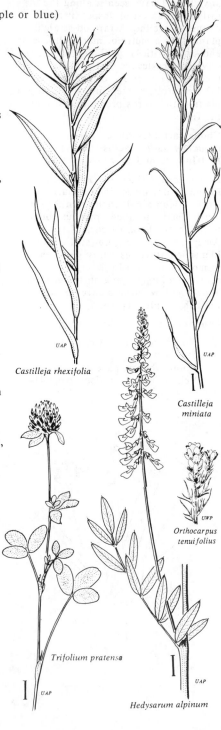

Castilleja rhexifolia

*Castilleja
miniata*

*Orthocarpus
tenuifolius*

Trifolium pratense

Hedysarum alpinum

blooming pale pink or reddish, not white.
Differentiate from similar **alsike clover**
(T. hybridum) by red clover's toothy
leaves with whitish markings, and the
small leaves under the flowerhead.

Horsemint/wild bergamot
Monarda fistulosa (mint family)
Mid-July to mid-August

Southern montane and lower subalpine,
occasional as far north as Columbia
Icefield, in meadows. Showy flowerhead
looks like the frayed end of a pink or
mauve rope; flowers are tube-like with
stamens sticking out. Stem is straight,
about 50 cm tall, with pairs of toothy
leaves. Just below the flowerhead the
leaves are smooth-edged.

Mountain cranberry/
lingonberry/cow-berry
Vaccinium vitis-idaea (heath family)
June

In subalpine and damp montane woods,
common from Bow River north, absent at
Waterton/Glacier. A ground-covering
shrub that resembles kinnikinnik
(page 337) and largely replaces it in
subalpine forest. The leaves are smaller
than kinnikinnik and have tiny black
glands underneath; the plant blooms in
small clusters of little pale-pink
bell-shaped flowers without the
out-turned lip of the kinnikinnik flower,
which is mostly white. The red
cranberries are tart, sweetening after
several frosts; they may be left on the
plant all winter, then collected in spring.

Grouseberry
Vaccinium scoparium (heath family)
June and July

Upper-subalpine shrub, common in open
woods of the central region.
Low-growing and straggly, with
pale-green stems and a thin foliage of
small, pointed pale leaves. (See
Vaccinium myrtillus, page 323, for
picture.) Flowers appear at places where
the leaves join the stem; they are small,
urn-shaped and pink. The red-to-purple
berries are BB-sized and flat-ended—like
tiny blueberries, which is what they are.
Delicious.

Monarda fistulosa

Vaccinium vitis-idaea

Pink pussytoes/rosy everlasting
Antennaria rosea or *A. microphylla*
(composite family) June to August

Meadows and open montane forest,
usually in small patches. A tight cluster
of small, rounded flowers on
short-leaved stems above larger, finely
divided felty gray-green basal leaves.
Each flower in the cluster has a white
centre with a narrow red border, making
the whole flowerhead appear pink. Some
botanists think that *A. rosea* is a variety
of white pussytoes (page 338), not a
separate species.

**Old-man's whiskers/prairie smoke/
three-flowered avens**
Geum triflorum (rose family)
Mid-May through June

South-facing open montane slopes, more
common on the eastern side of the
Rockies. Strange-looking plant: three
round red closed blooms with bright-red
hairy sepals hiding cream-colored petals
within, nodding on reddish stems over
finely divided leaves. Stands only
10-15 cm tall.

Pipsissewa/prince's pine
Chimaphila umbellata (heath family)
July

Montane forests, southern area and
mostly western slope. Small plant with
leaves near or on the ground; several
flowers on stalks radiate from a central
leafless stem 10-20 cm tall. Flowers red
and globe-shaped at first, later opening
out in pale-pink petals (note the shape)
and pink centres. Leaves are distinctive:
rather holly-like, glossy green, oblong
and toothy, in basal whorls.

Common pink wintergreen/pyrola
Pyrola asarifolia (heath family)
Early July to early August

Montane evergreen woods. Striking plant:
a greenish-pink, leafless stem, 10-20 cm
high, with about a dozen nodding pink
flowers (if they are greenish-white, see
green pyrola, page 348). The leaves are
round and glossy green, lying at the base.
    None of the wintergreens listed in
this book smells of wintergreen oil. They
are so named because their leaves stay
green through the winter. The
wintergreen for which the fragrant oil is
named is *Gaultheria procumbens*, native

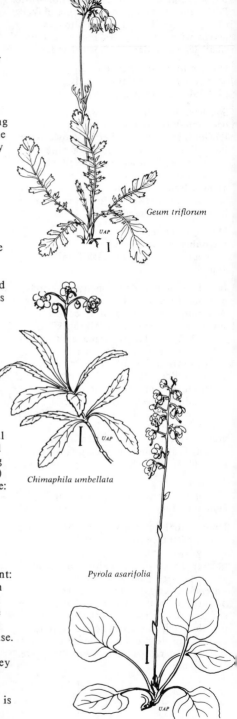

Geum triflorum

Chimaphila umbellata

Pyrola asarifolia

to southeastern Canada and northeastern USA.

Elephant-head/little elephants
Pedicularis groenlandica (figwort family)
Late June to early August

Montane and subalpine, in wet places. A spike of small pink flowers, each of which looks like the head of an elephant, complete with trunk and ears. Leaves are frilly and drab purplish-green.

Calypso orchid/fairy's-slipper/venus's-slipper
Calypso bulbosa (orchid family)
Mid-May to early July

Shady montane woods. The most beautiful of the Rocky Mountain orchids; once seen, always remembered. Upper part pink to pale-purple; below, bright-yellow stamens with black tips hang over the purple-marked white lower lip of the flower. Often in small patches, each plant has only one basal leaf, round and dark-green.

Heart-leaved twayblade
Listera cordata (orchid family)
July and August

Subalpine, in shady woods. Can range in color from green to purple, but most often red. Two round leaves, pointed at the tip and indented at the back, are paired partway up the stem. At the top of the plant, which is only 10-15 cm tall, are five to ten small flowers, each with a long split lower lip and a canopy of five petals. See also the bog-orchid listings, pages 341-342.

Red monkey-flower
Mimulus lewisii (figwort family)
Mid-July through August

Subalpine to low alpine, along streams; common in southern areas, scarce north of Crowsnest Pass. Large, showy pink or red flowers that are sometimes mistaken for violets (there are no red or pink violets known in the Canadian Rockies). Yellow centres with dark dots. Leaves grow in pairs on the stems (30-50 cm tall); they are pointed and shallowly toothed.

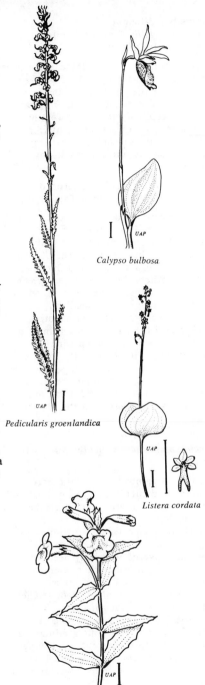

Calypso bulbosa

Pedicularis groenlandica

Listera cordata

Mimulus lewisii

Lyall's beard-tongue
Penstemon lyallii (figwort family)
June to early August

Upper montane and subalpine, sometimes
alpine, found mainly south of Crowsnest
Pass. The smallest penstemon in the
mountains. Large, showy pink-to-purple
flowers, seemingly too heavy for the
weak stems, which let the plant flop
untidily on the ground. Narrow leaves.

See also the purple penstemons,
page 380.

Shooting star/peacock/roosterhead
Dodecatheon spp. (primrose family) June

Mostly montane, but also subalpine and
low alpine, in damp meadows. Large,
very striking flower: the deep-pink or
purple petals bend straight back,
exposing yellow stamens and dark,
pointed anthers. Don't confuse with the
small bog cranberry (next entry), which
is similar though much smaller.

We have two species of shooting
stars, best differentiated when in seed.
In *D. conjugens* the pod opening has
squared edges; in *D. pulchellum* the
opening is saw-toothed. Both species are
equally common in southern areas;
D. conjugens is unreported north of
Saskatchewan Crossing on the eastern
slope.

Small bog cranberry
Vaccinium oxycoccus (heath family)
June

Swamps, streambanks and lakeshores,
montane and subalpine bogs, central and
northern areas. More common on the
eastern slope, but absent at
Waterton/Glacier. Often growing with
Labrador tea. A shrub. The low-growing
stems are covered with tiny needle-like
(but soft) green leaves that resemble
crowberry (page 408) or heather
(page 396) until the plant blooms. Then
the small flowers identify it
immediately: each has four pale-pink
petals bent backward, like a miniature
shooting-star (previous entry), leaving
the yellow anthers exposed. The berries
are tasty, true cranberries, sweeter after
a frost or two.

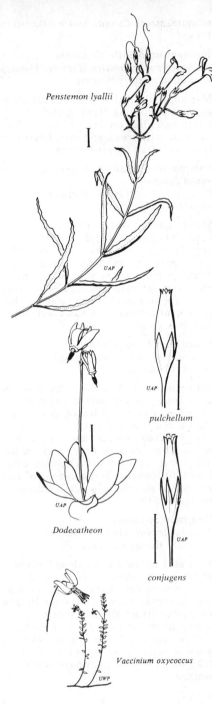

Penstemon lyallii

pulchellum

Dodecatheon

conjugens

Vaccinium oxycoccus

Swamp laurel/mountain laurel
Kalmia polifolia (heath family)
Late June and July

Subalpine, sometimes alpine, beside
streams and in bogs; rare in southern
areas. An ankle-high shrub with thick
evergreen leaves that are dark-green on
top, paler beneath and often rolled under
like those of Labrador tea (but not fuzzy
underneath as in Labrador tea). The
five-lobed pink flowers are small but
showy, with an elongated style sticking
out. See also *K. microphylla*, page 403.

Kalmia polifolia

Red columbine
Aquilegia formosa (columbine family)
Early June through July. See page 361 for illustration.

Western-slope montane to alpine;
occasional on the eastern slope in central
sections. Bushy plants up to a metre tall.
Large, very showy flowers with
characteristic nectar-laden spurs in the
back. Color ranges from crimson to
orange. Typical columbine leaves: broad
but deeply indented, with rounded edges.
Compare with leaves of meadow-rue,
page 348. This plant may hybridize with
yellow columbine (page 361), especially
through mountain passes in the central
section, where many flowers are both
pink and yellow.

Common fireweed/mountain fireweed/ and broad-leaved willow-herb/ river beauty
Epilobium angustifolium
and *E. latifolium*
(evening primrose family) mid-July to
late-August

Montane and subalpine. Showy plants
with large four-petalled pink flowers.
Fireweed is a tall plant (up to 1.5 m),
with dozens of flowers carried on a tall
spike along with many rod-like seed
pods. It grows best on disturbed
ground—roadsides, logged areas and
recent burns. Official floral emblem of
the Yukon.

    Broad-leaved willow herb has
somewhat larger flowers, but there are
fewer on the spike (perhaps half a
dozen) and the whole plant is
lower-growing than fireweed, seldom
more than 30 cm tall. Broad-leaved
willow herb likes gravelly places such as
alluvial fans—especially the outwash
flats downstream from glaciers. It is

Epilobium angustifolium

Epilobium latifolium

common from Bow River north. Both
species produce long, cottony seeds in
late summer.

Collomia
Collomia grandiflora
(phlox family) June and July

Western-slope montane, at low elevations.
Grows 15-20 cm tall, with narrow leaves
along the stem and a cluster of large,
trumpet-shaped flowers at the top.
C. linearis grows in the Waterton/Glacier
area; is similar but with smaller flowers.
Collomia is sometimes mistaken for
scarlet gilia/skyrocket *(Gilia aggregata),*
which grows south and west of the
southern and central regions of the
Canadian Rockies.

Bird's-eye primrose and mealy primrose
Primula mistassinica (primrose family)
Late May and June

Montane and subalpine, near water.
Common in northern areas and
occasional south to Bow River; absent at
Waterton/Glacier. **Bird's-eye primrose** is
a small plant (10-15 cm), often
overlooked. Small, toothy basal leaves
and a leafless erect stem bearing one or
more flowers with five distinctive
notched pale-pink or purplish petals.
There is a pit in the flower centre,
surrounded by a yellow rim.
    Mealy primrose *(P. incana)* is similar
but taller (up to 40 cm) with a larger
number of smaller flowers and
smooth-edged basal leaves. See also
dwarf raspberry (next entry) and dwarf
epilobium (page 375).

Dwarf raspberry/arctic raspberry/
dewberry/
Rubus arcticus (rose family)
Late June to mid-July

Montane and lower subalpine, in moist
meadows. Scarce in Waterton/Glacier,
becoming fairly common north of Banff.
Close relative of the raspberry
(page 321), with similar leaves, but this
plant straggles along the ground. Pink,
widely separated petals with interspersed
green bracts that quickly become ragged,
giving the flowers a wilted appearance.
Insipid raspberries in August. In
Columbian forest this species is absent;
in its place is a smaller, white-blooming
one: *R. pedatus,* trailing raspberry
(page 337).

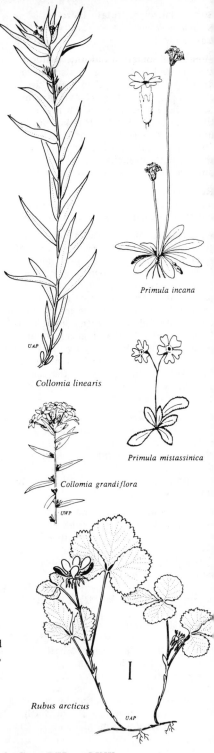

Primula incana

Collomia linearis

Primula mistassinica

Collomia grandiflora

Rubus arcticus

Dwarf epilobium/alpine willow-herb/ dwarf willow-herb
Epilobium spp. (evening primrose family)
Late June to early August

Subalpine and alpine, sometimes at low elevations but nearly always beside running water. Members of the fireweed tribe, though you would never know it. The plants are small (10-15 cm high) and so are the flowers (only a centimetre or so across). But they are eye-catching: four petals meet at right angles like an X. Each petal is deeply notched, so that it looks like a double. The color varies a lot from site to site; most plants are pink, but pure white ones have been reported from Vermilion Pass and Waterton. There are several species, difficult to differentiate; *E. anagallydifolium* is the most common in the Canadian Rockies. This species has smooth-edged leaves that tend to hug the stem.

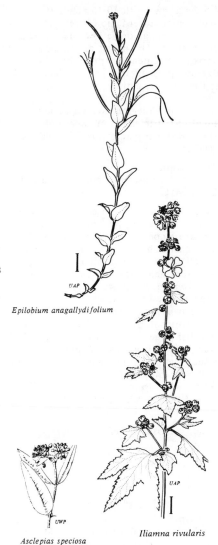

Epilobium anagallydifolium

Mountain hollyhock
Iliamna rivularis (mallow family)
June through September

At low elevations, western-slope montane and Waterton/Glacier. A tall plant (up to 2 m), bushy and showy, with large pale-pink flowers (5-10 cm broad) in spikes. The leaves are large and maple-shaped, with toothed margins.

Showy milkweed
Asclepias speciosa (milkweed family)
June and July

Found mainly in the driest part of the Rocky Mountain Trench (Wasa, Fort Steele), on sunny slopes. Reported from Glacier and the southern Alberta foothills but not from Waterton. Rounded clusters of star-shaped pink or purplish flowers atop stems with lance-shaped leaves showing distinctive white veining. Milky juice. Large pods split open, spilling cottony seeds; the stalks dry and remain upright for much of the winter.

Asclepias speciosa

Iliamna rivularis

Bitterroot/rock rose
Lewisia rediviva (purslane family)
April and May

Southern western-slope montane, in dry, rocky places; reported from the southern foothills near Pincher Creek. Low-growing but showy: pink flowers

Lewisia rediviva

4-6 cm across with 10-15 petals that are
often paler toward the flower centre,
which is orange or yellow. State flower
of Montana. The leaves are thick and
narrow, succulent in spring but then
drying up as summer goes by. The thick
taproot is distinctive, often wedged in
rock.

In the Waterton/Glacier area a
subalpine species *(L. pygmaea)* blooms in
exposed damp places; has 6-8 petals on a
smaller flower.

Lewisia pygmaea

Townsendia
Townsendia hookeri (composite family)
Early May

Southern foothills and eastern parts of
Waterton/Glacier, possibly on the
western slope south of Radium. At first
glance this showy flower looks like a
pink fleabane, but it belongs to a
different genus (all the fleabanes are
Erigeron, and most are paler; see
page 346).

Townsendia varies in color from
pure white to purplish; there is a
purplish-blue species in the Rockies from
Red Deer River south *(T. parryi).*
Usually at least one bloom on *T. hookeri*
will have pink-tipped petals. Hairy
leaves with up margins, mostly at the
base. Large flowers on short stalks, only
2-5 cm high.

Townsendia hookeri

Other pinkish flowers:

Lyall's saxifrage, page 394.
Windflower, page 334.
Showy locoweed, page 379.
Moss phlox, page 336.
Buckbrush, page 324.

Many pink flowers can also be purplish.
If you can't find what you are looking
for here, try the next section.

Townsendia parryi

Pasque flower/prairie crocus
Anemone patens (buttercup family)
Late March to mid-May

Montane, usually on south-facing slopes.
Earliest showy flower in the Rockies
(earliest flower of all is the pussy
willow, page 307). Look for pasque
flowers only a few days behind the
melting snow. Not really a crocus, but
the shape is crocus-like. Pale-blue or
pale-purple with a yellow centre, open by
day and closed by night. Grows close to
the ground on a short, very fuzzy stem;
leaves are frilly, also fuzzy, and appear
beneath the flower after it has come up.
As in all anemones, the stem grows
continuously, so the plant is taller when
in seed.

Sagebrush mariposa lily/
green-banded mariposa
Calochortus macrocarpus (lily family)
Late May to early June

Rocky Mountain Trench floor from
Radium south, on dry slopes. Easily
identified: one, sometimes more large
lavender flowers, each with three broad
petals marked by a central green band.
The stem stands 20-50 cm tall, with one
long, narrow leaf at the base.

Blue-eyed grass
Sisyrinchium montanum (iris family)
Mainly June; again in August

Montane, in open places near water.
Grass-like leaves 10-40 cm tall, with
star-shaped, yellow-centred blue flowers
individually on stems as long as the
leaves. This plant blooms early, then
repeats in August, although in lesser
numbers.

Blue clematis
Clematis columbiana (buttercup family)
Late May and June

Most any pronunciation is acceptable.
Take your pick: "KLEM-uh-tiss," or
"klem-AH-tiss," with long or short *a*. A
woody vine, clematis twines among the
shrubbery in montane woods and brushy
places, central and southern sections.
Down-turned flowers each have four
long sepals, blue to purple, that tend to
twist near the ends. They look like
petals. Leaves 3-8 cm, lance-shaped, with
indented veins.

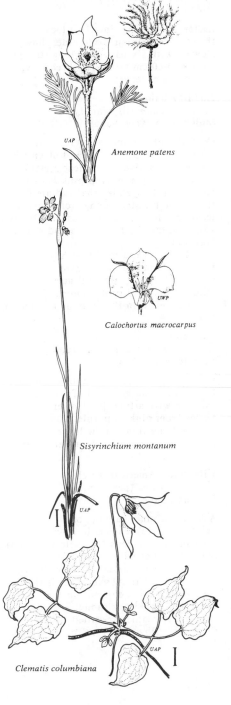

Anemone patens

Calochortus macrocarpus

Sisyrinchium montanum

Clematis columbiana

Blue camas
Camassia quamash (lily family)
Mid- to late-June

Eastern slope only, in a few locations in
the southern region. Deep blue, showy
flowers with six parts and long stamens.
Grows 30-60 cm tall, with three long,
narrow basal leaves.

Nodding onion
Allium cernuum (lily family)
Mid-July to early August

Central and southern montane and
subalpine, in open places and often near
water. Distinctive flowerheads: many
lavender, purple or even pink bell-shaped
flowers on long stalks that radiate from
the top of the stem. Long, very narrow
leaves smell of onion if crushed. Grows
15-50 cm tall; bulb is edible and strongly
flavored.

    However, you might wish to pass
such edible plants by in favor of the
grocery-store varieties. All native
wildflowers need protection—and many
of them get it, in the form of no-picking
laws.

Wild chive
Allium schoenoprasum (lily family)
Late June and July

Montane, in moist ground; often along
lakeshores. Another kind of wild onion,
this one with a tuft-like flowerhead that
varies from pink to purple, usually
mauve. Long thin hollow leaves grow
upward from the base. Seeds are in small
dark pods.

Wild vetch/American vetch
Vicia americana (pea family)
June and July

A montane vine, hanging onto its
neighbors. Oval leaflets in rows, and
tendrils at stem ends like wild sweet pea
(page 340), but with bluish-purple
flowers rather than cream or yellowish
ones. Pea-pods in August. This is the only
true vetch that is common in the
Canadian Rockies, although many other
pea-family plants are called "vetch."
Compare with sweetvetch, next entry.

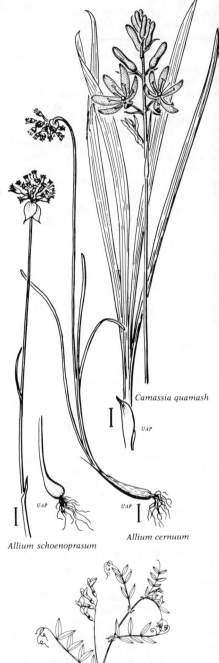

Camassia quamash

UAP

Allium schoenoprasum

UAP

Allium cernuum

UAP

Vicia americana　UAP

Sweetvetch/Mackenzie's hedysarum
Hedysarum boreale (pea family)
Late May to early July

Pronounced "heddy-SAIR-um." Common montane and lower subalpine species, in dry clearings. Very fragrant reddish-purple pea-type flowers in floppy clusters. Small dark-green leaflets in rows. Bears dig up and eat the roots of this plant in spring. See also pale sweetvetch, page 368.

Showy locoweed
Oxytropis splendens (pea family)
Late June to mid-July

Montane, in dry open places; often on disturbed ground such as highway shoulders. Common on the eastern slope; occasional on the western slope.

    This a hard one to classify by color. Both pink and purple occur on the same plant; some people think of it as pink (perhaps because the plant is so white-hairy that the purple is diluted). It looks purple to me. At any rate, it blossoms in dense spikes above fuzzy gray-green leaves. Not tall (10-20 cm), but easy to spot and identify. Unlike some other locoweeds, this one is not harmful to cattle.

Wild lupine
Lupinus spp. (pea family)
Late June to early August

Montane and subalpine, common on the western slope but on the eastern slope common only in Waterton/Glacier and north of Peace River. With its pea-like flowers, lupine would be difficult to tell from the other pea-family members were it not for the leaves, which spread out in frondy leaflets rather than looking like rows of teeth.

    There are many lupine species, varying in minute ways. Most are blue or lavender, although the flowers of **arctic lupine** *(L. arcticus)*, a common form along the Alaska Highway, are blue with white tips. From Jasper northward, and from farther south on the western slope, look for the very showy *L. nootkatensis,* which has white and yellow patches at the bases of the large blue petals. *Lupinus sericeus* is a common species in the southern region; it has the typical lupine leaf shape and flowerhead.

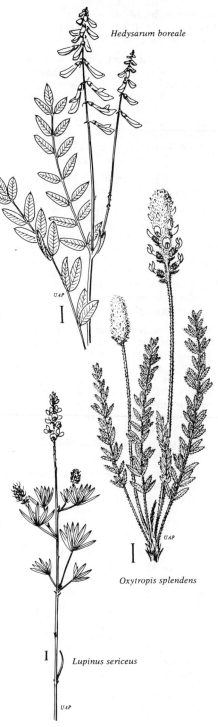

Hedysarum boreale

Oxytropis splendens

Lupinus sericeus

Penstemon/beard-tongue
Penstemon spp. (figwort family)
May to August

At all elevations, but mainly montane
and subalpine, in a variety of habitats.
Many species, difficult for the
non-botanist to differentiate. All have
spikes of tubular flowers with
asymmetric lips (two petals above, three
below). Shades of color differ inside and
outside. Hairiness within the flower
accounts for the name "beard-tongue."

Here are five common species, easier
than some others to tell apart:

Slender blue beard-tongue *(P. procerus)*
June and July: perhaps the most
common penstemon in the Rockies
north of Crowsnest Pass. Its flowers
are smaller than the others (about
1 cm long), carried in a dense spike.
The plant stands 10-20 cm tall. Look
for it in moist, open places, montane
and subalpine.

Smooth blue beard-tongue *(P. nitidus)*
May to June: limited to the southern
foothills/Waterton/Glacier area in
dry, sunny places. Easily identified
by the fleshy bluegreen foliage
(basal leaves narrow, ones on the
stem broader) and interestingly
colored trumpet-shaped flowers: blue
inside, with a long yellow stamen;
pink or pale purple outside. Tall for
a penstemon: 20-30 cm.

Lilac-flowered beard-tongue *(P. gracilis)*
June and July: a dainty-looking
species with pale-lavender or even
white flowers, 2-3 cm long. Grows
10-20 cm tall in grassy places in the
southern foothills, although it is
absent at Waterton/Glacier.

Crested beard-tongue *(P. eriantherus)*
June: husky, colorful lavender to
deep-purple blooms (pink inside) that
seem to overweigh their stem. The
throat of each flower is very hairy.

Elliptical-leaved penstemon *(P. ellipticus)*
late June to August: a low-growing
penstemon with bluntly toothed,
rather broad leaves and large
lavender flowers on short, hairy
stems. Subalpine and alpine.

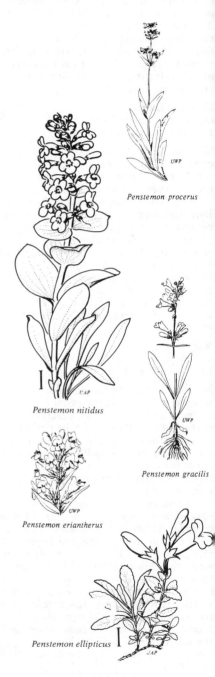

Penstemon procerus

Penstemon nitidus

Penstemon gracilis

Penstemon eriantherus

Penstemon ellipticus

One-flowered broomrape/cancer-root
Orobanche uniflora (broomrape family)
April and May

Western-slope mostly, from Prince George south; on the eastern slope from Bow River south. Normally low-elevation montane, it sometimes grows well above timberline in moist places where its host-plants (stonecrop and saxifrages) live. Like paintbrush or toadflax, broomrape is a root parasite. It has no green leaves. Small (2 cm) penstemon-like, violet-like flower varies in color from yellow to mauve; usually blue. Always yellow inside. One flower atop each hairy stem, 5-10 cm long.

Clustered broomrape *(O. fasiculata)* has three or more purple or yellowish flowers and is less common; grows at low elevations in southern areas. Scaly stems, sticky and hairy.

Sticky geranium and Bicknell's geranium/crane's-bill
Geranium viscosissimum
and *G. bicknellii*
(geranium family) late May to August

Montane meadows and open woods. Both plants have spreading, deeply divided leaves like those of cultivated geraniums, but the flowers are smaller, purple or pink-purple with reddish lines in the petals. Sticky geranium (Saskatchewan Crossing south) is tall (20-60 cm), sticky and blooms from June to mid-August. Bicknell's crane's-bill (all areas) has smaller blooms (about 1 cm across), is shorter (15-25 cm), not sticky and flowers from late May to early July. See also wild white geranium, page 332.

Rock cress
Arabis spp. (mustard family)
Late April through July

Montane to subalpine, in grassy meadows and rocky places. Many species, difficult to distinguish from one another. Each has a tuft of short, lance-shaped basal leaves; the stem (usually hairy) is 10-20 cm tall, clasped by small leaves. The four-petalled flowers are on short stalks at the top and vary from pale purple to cream. Most species bloom early, in May or June. In July and August long, pod-like seed cases typical of the mustard family are carried erect in some species, drooping in others.

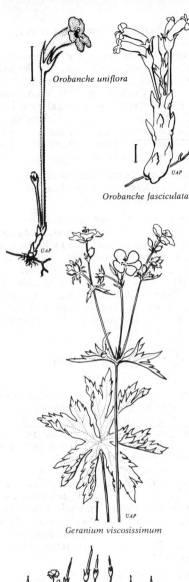

Orobanche uniflora

Orobanche fasciculata

Geranium viscosissimum

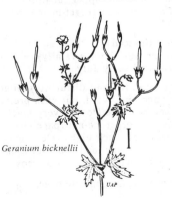

Geranium bicknellii

Individual identification is tricky; perhaps the classic species in the Canadian Rockies is *A. drummondii*—yet another Rockies plant bearing the name of Thomas Drummond (page 750).

Like *Draba* (page 362), *Arabis* can become infected by a **fungal rust**. The first tiny leaves to appear in spring are colored yellowish by the dot-like rust colonies. The diseased plants don't grow much and seldom bloom.

Mauve mitrewort/three-tooth mitrewort
Mitella trifida (saxifrage family)
Late May to early July

Western-slope upper montane and subalpine, Waterton/Glacier, in damp woods. Delicate plant up to 40 cm tall with toothy heart-shaped basal leaves on rather long stems and one or more leafless flower stalks. Near the top there is a line of 10-20 small mauve (sometimes nearly white) flowers, each with the strange trellis-like petals characteristic of mitrewort.

Speedwell/veronica
Veronica spp. (figwort family)
July to early September

Montane, in moist places. Various sizes, but usually less than 50 cm tall. The flowers bloom in sprays from leaf junctions; they are small, four-petalled and pale-blue to violet. Look closely: the petals are unequal in length.
V. americana is low-growing, with bluntly fine-toothed leaves; *V. catenata* often grows in water; *V. peregrina* has its flowers tucked up against the stem. See also alpine speedwell (page 404), a common alpine and upper-subalpine plant. Compare with forget-me-not, page 404.

Blue-bur/stickseed
Lappula echinata (borage family)
Late June and early July

Montane meadows and disturbed ground. A wiry knee-high weed, but with pretty yellow-centred blue flowers very much like those of forget-me-not (page 404), which grows at much higher elevations. In August, blue-bur loads up your socks and shoelaces with tiny barbed seeds.

(Drawing is on opposite page.)

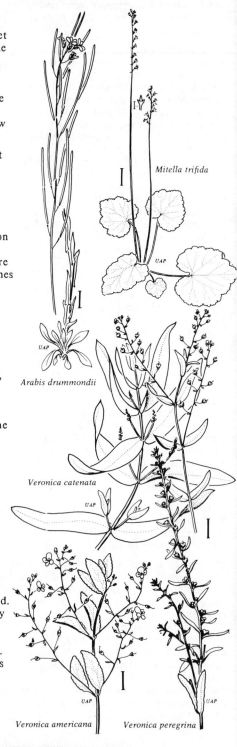

Mitella trifida

Arabis drummondii

Veronica catenata

Veronica americana *Veronica peregrina*

Jacob's ladder
Polemonium pulcherrimum
(phlox family) Late May to mid-July

Mostly montane but sometimes much
higher; common in southern areas,
occasional elsewhere. Prefers dry, open
places. Looks like a taller,
larger-flowered forget-me-not (page 404),
but the leaflets are small and fern-like,
arranged in sawtooth rows on reddish
stems 20-30 cm high. See also western
Jacob's ladder, next entry, and sky pilot,
page 406.

Western Jacob's ladder
Polemonium acutiflorum (phlox family)
June and July

Clearings in dry montane woods, common
from Peace River north. An eye-catching
plant: showy blue flaring bells ride in
clusters atop stems 20-30 cm tall with
incongruous sawtooth, pea-like leaves.
Taller than *P. pulcherrimum* (previous
entry). Harebell (next entry) has
different leaves, as does wild blue flax
(page 384).

Harebell/bluebell
Campanula rotundifolia (harebell family)
Late June to late September

Very common in dry eastern-slope
montane meadows and open woods. Less
common on the western slope. Easy to
recognize: several large sky-blue bells on
a skinny stem 10-40 cm tall. But
sometimes confused with Jacob's ladder
(previous entry), wild blue flax (next
entry) and mertensia (page 384).
    The name is puzzling. If it were
"*hair*bell," referring to the thin stems,
that would be sensible, but it is *hare*bell,
as in bunnies. The Scots seem to have
done this to us. The plant is common in
Scotland, where it is variously "bluebell"
or "harebell." (Further confusing the
issue is Robert Burns's "Bluebells of
Scotland," which are actually *Endymion
nonscriptum*, a wild hyacinth.) "Harebell"
is an old term, perhaps having something
to do with witches turning themselves
into hares, for an even older name is
"witch's thimble." On the other hand,
some sources say that harebell is just a
phonetic spelling of the way people used
to say "heather bell" in Britain long ago.
The species does indeed grow in the
heather over there.

Polemonium pulcherrimum

Polemonium acutiflorum

Campanula rotundifolia

Lappula echinata

People use "bluebell" for so many plants that I think we should stick to "harebell" for this one. There is only one species called "harebell" in the Canadian or American Rockies, although there are two versions: an alpine one, page 404, and the common one growing below timberline.

Wild blue flax
Linum lewisii (flax family)
June and July

Montane meadows and open woods. Fairly tall plant (up to 1 m) covered with individual showy blue flowers, yellow-centred, on slender stalks with small narrow leaves. The flowers are flatter than harebell (previous entry) and the leaves are not sawtoothed like those of Jacob's ladder (page 383). Each flower blooms but a day. Close relative of cultivated flax.

Mertensia/bluebells/tall lungwort
Mertensia paniculata (borage family)
Late June to mid-July

Common in montane woods, especially in aspen groves, through northern and central areas. Absent south of Crowsnest Pass. Bushy plant up to a metre high, but not a shrub. Dark-green, heavily veined leaves and clusters of small nodding bells that are pink in the bud and blue upon opening. In the Waterton/Glacier area *M. paniculata* is missing, replaced by a smaller, less-bushy version: *M. longiflora*.

Early blue violet/dog violet
Viola adunca (violet family)
Mid-May to early June

Montane meadows and open woods, often in grass. A low-growing violet, usually in patches. Typical violet flower, often more purple than blue, with a white centre marked by dark lines. You may find an albino. Many small rounded leaves (1-3 cm) with blunt teeth, indented at the stem.

This plant may bloom again in the fall. In Jasper, early blue violets flowered *after* a hard frost in September of 1984, carrying on gaily in my lawn until October 16, when several centimetres of snow finally shut them down.

Linum lewisii

UAP

Mertensia paniculata   *Mertensia longiflora*

Viola adunca

Butterwort
Pinguicula vulgaris (bladderwort family)
June and July

Montane and subalpine woods, in shady,
wet places. A small plant with pale-green
slightly in-curled glossy basal leaves
covered with the bugs that it traps and
digests; like sundew (page 340),
butterwort is insectivorous. The bloom is
pretty and blue, a violet-like flower with
a spur on the back, nodding on a stalk
10-15 cm high.

Pinguicula vulgaris

Brook lobelia
Lobelia kalmii (bluebell family)
Mid-August to early September.

Central and northern montane, in wet
places. Usually on sites with limestone
bedrock. Small but distinctive blue or
purple flowers: two narrow petals on the
upper part (with a bump between them)
and three wider petals below. White and
yellow in the centre. Plant is only
10-20 cm tall.

Lobelia kalmii

Northern blue columbine
Aquilegia brevistyla spp.
(buttercup family) June and July

Occasional in montane and subalpine
meadows or open woods from Bow River
north; absent at Waterton/Glacier, where
an alpine species *(A. jonesii* page 406)
has a similar bloom. Large, very showy
flowers like yellow columbine (page 361)
or red columbine (page 373), but blue,
mauve or purple with white trim.
Columbine is bushy, with spreading,
deeply divided round-edged leaves. The
flowers of northern blue columbine are
reminiscent of those of their
southern-Rockies kin *(A. coerulea,*
Colorado columbine, not in the Canadian
Rockies) but smaller. Hybridization of
northern blue columbine with yellow
columbine and red columbine can
produce some odd color combinations.

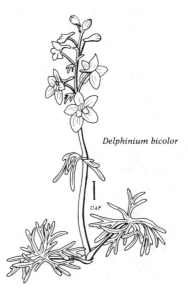

Delphinium bicolor

Tall larkspur/tall delphinium
Delphinium glaucum (buttercup family)
Mid-July to mid-August

Subalpine meadows, central and northern
areas; not found at Waterton/Glacier.
Tall, very showy spikes of deep blue or
purple flowers, each with a spur on the
back. Leaves are dark-green, spreading
and finely divided. Poisonous; animals
do not eat it. A much shorter version

(D. bicolor, mid-May to late June) grows at all elevations in the Waterton/Glacier area; the flower has white on it as well as blue. In the southern Rocky Mountain Trench look for a shaggy version, *D. menziesii.* See also monkshood, next entry.

Monkshood/aconite
Aconitum delphinifolium (buttercup family)
Late June and July

Aconitum delphinifolium

Subalpine meadows, central and northern areas. Monkshood often grows with larkspur (previous entry), which it resembles in size, color and leaf shape—but the flowers are different. Like larkspur, monkshood is poisonous.

Purple alfalfa/lucerne
Medicago sativa (pea family) July

Dry montane meadows, fields and disturbed ground. Not as tall as white sweet clover (page 340) or yellow sweet clover (page 365), but with the same pea-family leaves. The purple flowers are in small clusters rather than long cylindrical ones; the pods are coiled. This plant shows an incredible range of color: from golden yellow through green and blue to purple.

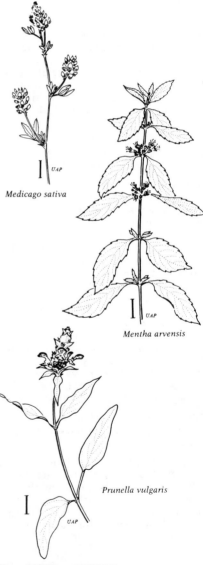

Medicago sativa

Wild mint
Mentha arvensis (mint family)
July and August

Montane, near water. Knee-high, in bushy patches. Dark-green color and coarse toothy leaves make it resemble stinging nettle (page 351), but you can tell the two apart without having to touch the plant: smell the strong fragrance given off by all parts of the mint. Further, the small mauve or purple mint flowers snuggle against the stem, while stinging-nettle flowers hang in greenish strings.

Mentha arvensis

Heal-all/self-heal
Prunella vulgaris (mint family)
July and August

Western-slope montane, in moist places; rare on the eastern slope outside Waterton/Glacier. A strange-looking plant about 20 cm tall. Small orchid-like blue or pale purple flowers protrude from a heavy, dense club at the top. The flowers don't all bloom at once; the non-blooming portions of the club are

Prunella vulgaris

green with brown-tipped sepals. The
pointed leaves are olive-colored, in pairs.
Heal-all is medicinal: an extract helps to
stop internal bleeding.

Aster
Aster (composite family)
July through September

Montane to alpine, but mostly growing at
lower elevations, in dry places. Asters
are very difficult to differentiate from
the fleabanes (page 346), but nearly all
the fleabanes are white to mauve, while
most of the asters (more than half of the
dozen or so species in the Rockies) are
blue to purple. Also, many asters bloom
later in the summer than fleabanes.

   To place a flower in the right group,
check the cup holding the bloom. Asters
have several rows of scaly bracts there,
while fleabanes have just one (see
illustration on page 346). The individual
species of either tribe are notoriously
hard to identify, but everyone should be
able to spot showy aster (next entry) and
showy fleabane (the following one).

Aster conspicuus

Showy aster/large purple aster
Aster conspicuus (composite family)
August and September

Low-elevation montane, very common in
clearings and meadows. Up to 70 cm tall,
with rather wide, coarsely toothed leaves
that are rough to the touch. The upper
stems tend to be sticky. The blooms are
purplish-blue or violet, with yellow
centres; the ray flowers (petal-like parts)
are rather thin and sparse, not toothed at
the ends like those of showy fleabane
(next entry).

Showy fleabane
Erigeron peregrinus (composite family)
July

Montane to alpine, but mostly in
subalpine meadows, often in large
patches. A tall fleabane (50 cm) with
large blooms that range from pale blue
or purple (almost white) to pastel shades.
Large yellow centre with upturned ray
flowers that look like upturned
petal-ends. One to several blooms on
stems up to 60 cm tall. Smooth-edged
leaves, toothed ray-ends, plant not
sticky—all of which serve to
differentiate from showy aster (previous
entry). But there are similar fleabanes.

Erigeron peregrinus

Gentians
Gentiana spp. (gentian family)
June to September

All elevations, but mostly subalpine.
Gentians are known for the beautiful
saturated blue color of their flowers,
which are mostly in the form of upright
bells. There are many species, including
several alpine ones (page 406). Two that
are easy to recognize and grow below
timberline are given below.

Fringed gentian *(G. detonsa)* July and
August: a montane species, at lower
elevations in moist places. A single,
large flower, deep blue, at the top of
the plant (height 15-40 cm) and well
above the very narrow leaves.

Northern gentian/felwort *(G. amarella)*
late June to mid-September: mostly
montane, in the woods, but reaching
well above timberline on occasion
and often growing out in the open.
(Don't confuse alpine specimens with
blue-bottle gentian, page 407).
Felwort is the only common gentian
with flowers that may be other than
blue; they range from pink to purple
and tend to bleach out as the flower
ages. Many straight stems up to
50 cm tall. Leaves and flowers
arranged along the stems in tiers,
each composed of two leaves with
several small flowers clustered just
above the leaves and next to the
stem.

Bull thistle/Scottish thistle and Canada thistle
Cirsium vulgare, C. arvense (composite
family), late July and early August

Montane meadows and disturbed ground,
often in patches that one learns to avoid.
Very coarse-looking plants with
extremely prickly leaves and
flowerheads. Blooms of the bull thistle
are large rose-purple tufts 5-7 cm across,
anchored in a bulbous calyx; Canada
thistle blooms are smaller (1-2 cm across)
and lighter-colored. The plant is shorter:
a metre or less. Bull thistle can reach
well over a metre.

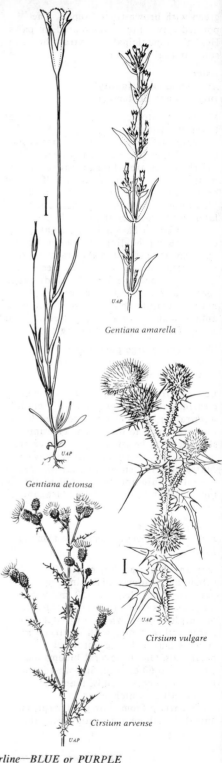

Gentiana amarella

Gentiana detonsa

Cirsium vulgare

Cirsium arvense

Spotted knapweed
Centaurea maculosa (composite family)
July and August

Western-slope montane, eastern slope south of Crowsnest Pass. Knapweed looks like a thistle, but there are no prickles. Thistle-like purple flowerheads at ends of stems branching from a central stalk up to a metre tall. Leaves are narrowly divided, and the entire plant is hairy. Feathery seeds in fall.

Other flowers that can be purplish:

Windflower, page 334.
Bronze bells, page 350.

Wildflowers below timberline: drab
Brown, reddish-brown, greenish-brown or even black.

Dock
Rumex spp. (buckwheat family) July

Eastern-slope montane, occasional western-slope; usually on disturbed ground such as highway shoulders. Typically half a metre tall, but can reach well over a metre in southern areas. Bloom is greenish-white, in long spikes of tiny flowers, but these plants are better known for their showy streamers of reddish-brown seeds. Each is carried in a round envelope that looks like a cap-gun cap. See also mountain sorrel, page 398.

Dragon sagewort/false tarragon
Artemisia dracunculus
(composite family) August

Low-elevation montane, southern Rocky Mountain Trench and Waterton/Glacier, in dry, open places. Often aromatic like sage, but not always. Narrow, dull-green leaves set rather sparsely on the stems, which are smooth, woody, and grow to a metre tall. Tiny brown or olive-drab bell-shaped flowers hang from drooping stems on the upper part of the plant.

Cudweed sagewort/prairie sagewort
Artemisia ludoviciana (composite family) August

Low-elevation montane, in southern sections. Silvery, fairly narrow leaves angle upward along the single stem, which can be a metre tall. The small blooms are upright and brown, cupped by hairy white bracts.

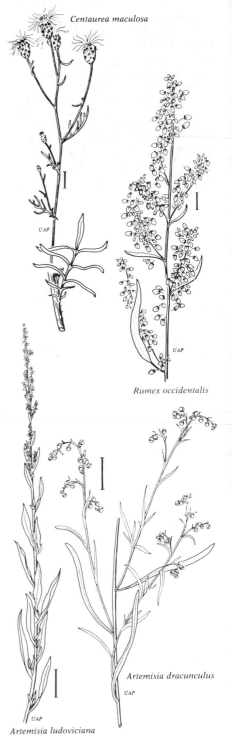

Centaurea maculosa

Rumex occidentalis

Artemisia dracunculus

Artemisia ludoviciana

Black henbane
Hyoscyamus niger (nightshade family)
July and August

Occasional in the southern Rocky
Mountain Trench and the southern
foothills, but not reported from
Waterton/Glacier. Can be tall (up to
1.5 m), but usually 20-40 cm. Hairy all
over, with ragged-edged drab-green
leaves. Large bell-shaped flowers are
carried along the stem; they are
greenish-yellow with purple veining. The
odor is unpleasant, and the plant (a
European import) is poisonous. Yecch.

ALPINE WILDFLOWERS
What's a nice plant like you doing in a place like this?

Postcard scenes to the contrary, the high country is actually a rather nasty place. Go there on a warm morning in late July; you may catch a few hours in the meadows before the rain starts and the wind comes up.

When everything is perfect, though—when the day is calm, the skies are clear, the hummingbirds are about and the fragrance of a hundred nectars drifts through the heather—when all cliches are in gear—then you know why people get silly over the alpine zone.

Strictly speaking, an alpine plant is one that grows above timberline. But some typically alpine species (white dryas, for example) may grow well below timberline on cliffs, in scree and talus, among rockslide blocks—in places that are bare, rocky, windy and alpine-*like*.

Summer comes late to the alpine zone, and it is very short: most flowers bloom between late June and the middle of August. Further, the blooming dates for a particular species can vary a great deal, depending on the date at which the snow melts. That date is just as unpredictable as the weather in the high country.

I used to wonder why so many alpine plants have large, cup-shaped flowers rather than the flower clusters or nodding blooms one sees more often at lower elevations. Recently I learned the reason: concave, up-turned flowers collect solar heat. Having attracted insects by color and fragrance, these plants offer a bit of warmth, encouraging bugs to linger awhile. They tramp about in the pollen and thus aid fertilization.

Flower-learners, here is good news: at high elevations there is little difference in the botany of the eastern-slope and western-slope Rockies. In fact, you are likely to see many of the same species anywhere above timberline in North America. So let's get going; it's all uphill to the alpine meadows.

Alpine wildflowers: white

Western anemone/chalice flower
Anemone occidentalis (buttercup family)
Late June and July

In grassy alpine and subalpine meadows. Blooms early, poking up behind the retreating snow like its close relative of lower elevations, the pasque flower (page 377). Large, creamy white cup with a yellow centre. Each flower is on a furry stem 15-40 cm tall, with a collar of frilly, fuzzy leaves partway up the stem. Basal leaves are also frilly; they grow taller after blooming. Distinctive shaggy seedheads. Compare with globeflower, next entry.

Globeflower
Trollius albiflorus (buttercup family)
June to mid-July

In damp places, often near water. Resembles western anemone (previous entry), but the stem is not furry and the flower has a cone of green pistils at the centre (surrounded by yellow stamens), while the anemone centre is all yellow. The leaves are different, too: smooth, not as finely divided as those of the anemone and growing at more than one

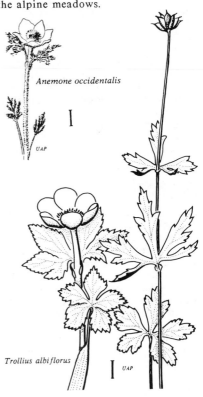

Anemone occidentalis

Trollius albiflorus

place up the stem. Blooms later than the anemones.

Alpine anemone/northern anemone
Anemone parviflora (buttercup family)
Early May to mid-August

On exposed alpine and high subalpine slopes, sometimes much lower, flowering early at low elevations and much later higher up. Smaller flower (2-3 cm) than the western anemone or globeflower (previous entry), with yellow stamens and a green pistil. Single flower has petal-like sepals, often bluish on the back; it sits upright on a slender hairless stem above glossy basal leaves, each divided into three lobes and notched as well. Similar leaves in a fringe about halfway up the stem. Round, tight seedhead is dark-colored, but with white wool. See also windflower, page 334.

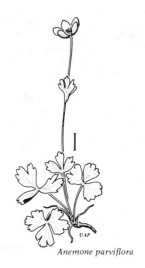

Anemone parviflora

Drummond's anemone
Anemone drummondii (buttercup family)
Early June to mid-July

Very similar to the windflower (page 334), but growing mainly above timberline and in subalpine meadows. The single flower is 2-3 cm across, creamy white, with petal-like sepals that are often blue-tinged underneath. To differentiate from windflower, which sometimes grows in subalpine meadows and even above timberline, note that there is just one flower on Drummond's anemone, not two or more as on the windflower, and that there is no fringe of leaves partway up the stem of Drummond's, as there is on windflower.

Alpine grass-of-Parnassus
Parnassia kotzebuei (saxifrage family)
July

In damp places, often near streams and in patches; fairly common in northern and central areas, scarce in the south. Glossy green, oval basal leaves with parallel veins. One small white flower per leafless stem, carried 10-15 cm high. Finger-like stamens. Strictly an alpine/high-subalpine species, but often mixed with fringed grass-of-Parnassus (page 335), which also grows at lower elevations. Differentiate by the unfringed petals on the alpine version.

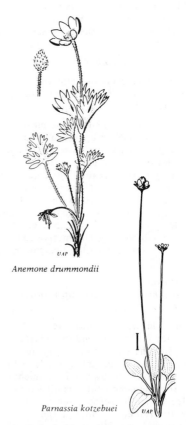

Anemone drummondii

Parnassia kotzebuei

Alpine spring beauty
Claytonia megarrhiza (purslane family)
Mid-July to early August

From Highwood Pass south, on scree slopes and rocky, exposed places. A small, fleshy plant with reddish-green leaves in a rosette. Small white flowers bloom around the edge of the plant rather than in the middle as you might expect; the petal ends are toothed. Compare with double bladderpod, page 401.

Claytonia megarrhiza

Alpine starwort/chickweed
Stellaria monantha, Cerastium spp.
(pink family) May to mid-August

On scree slopes, among rocks and along ridges. Alpine starwort has small white flowers on short (5 cm) stems and lance-shaped bluegreen leaves, very common in Waterton/Glacier, where it grows in big white patches that are very showy against the red argillite slopes. In chickweed patches the leaves are not blue-green. If the patch is small, with small, pure-white flowers having petals that are not notched or cleft, you may be looking at mountain sandwort, page 333.

Stellaria monantha

White dryas/mountain dryas/ white mountain avens
Dryas octopetala and *D. integrifolia*
(rose family) Mid-June to early August

Very common alpine ground-cover of stony, rocky places. Small, bluntly toothed leaves, dark green above and dull brown or gray below. Short-stalked showy white flowers up to 2 cm across, with 8-10 petals; they look straight up at you and beg not to be stepped on. Seedhead forms a twisted plume that later opens, looking like a dandelion. Compare with yellow dryas, page 361.

From the Columbia Icefield north you may also find *D. integrifolia:* *identical to D. octopetala,* but with smaller, narrower, glossier leaves.

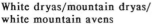

Dryas octopetala

Alpine marsh marigold
Caltha leptosepala (buttercup family)
June to August

On wet ground, often growing with globeflower and buttercups. Common elsewhere, this plant is absent in the Waterton/Glacier area. Showy white flowers with yellow centres have 6-12 petal-like sepals, resembling mountain

Caltha leptosepala

dryas (previous entry) but the oval leaves are large and glossy. Stems 5-10 cm tall, smooth and purplish.

Alpine pyrola/lesser wintergreen
Pyrola minor (heath family) July

On moist ground; more common in northerly sections. Has glossy basal leaves, a bare stalk and white or pale-pink flowers like its lowland relatives, but is a dwarf species, growing only about 10 cm tall (others are 20-30 cm).

Three-point saxifrage
Saxifraga tricuspidata (saxifrage family) Late June and July

Alpine, on rocky ground, from North Saskatchewan River north. Identical to prickly saxifrage (page 334), except that the leaves of *S. tricuspidata* end in three small points. In the Canadian Rockies the plant is nearly always alpine, while prickly saxifrage is found at all elevations.

Lyall's saxifrage
Saxifraga lyallii (saxifrage family) Early July to late August

Near running water, often in large patches that look reddish from a distance. Each plant has several small white flowers, each with a prominent reddish pistil but no dots on the petals like three-point saxifrage (previous entry) or prickly saxifrage (page 334). The stem of Lyall's, up to 30 cm tall, is also reddish, but the leaves, which are fan-shaped and toothed on the ends, are green.

Nodding saxifrage and romanzoffia
Saxifraga cernua (saxifrage family) Mid-July

In protected places. Note the leaves: pale green, with 3-5 prominent teeth. Mostly basal, they also grow on the stem. The flowers are single, on green stalks 10-15 cm tall.

A similar species is *S. hyperborea* (July to early August); differentiate by the flat or indented petal ends on *S. cernua* (those of *S. hyperborea* are round) and the presence of more than one flower on a stem in *S. hyperborea*. *S. cernua* frequently carries little bulblets (parts that drop off to form new

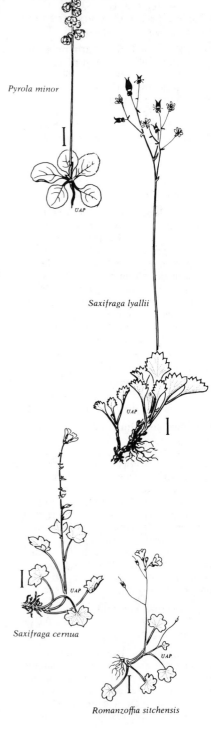

Pyrola minor

Saxifraga lyallii

Saxifraga cernua

Romanzoffia sitchensis

plants) in the spots where the leaves join the stem.

To further complicate things, *Romanzoffia sitchensis* (mid-June to mid-August) looks very much like *S. hyperborea*. They have similar habitats, too. Tell them apart by the petals: those of romanzoffia are fused, while those of *S. hyperborea* are separate from one another.

Alpine fleabane and woolly fleabane
Erigeron pallens and *E. lanatus* (composite family) July and August

There are many fleabane species, but only a few white-flowered alpine ones, all rather rare. These two are both quite woolly, with flowers that can be pinkish as well as white. Separate them by the leaves: alpine fleabane has notched leaf-ends; woolly fleabane does not. As well, the flower of woolly fleabane is larger—about 2 cm across, while alpine fleabane is rarely more than 1 cm across.

Contorted lousewort
Pedicularis contorta (figwort family) June and July

In sunny alpine and subalpine locations; fairly common between Bow River and Crowsnest Pass. A tall plant by alpine standards: 20-30 cm, with olive-drab fern-like leaves. Showy cream-colored or yellowish-white flowers in an open spike atop the stem, each flower in the shape of a down-curled tube.

Luetkea/meadow spirea/partridge-foot
Luetkea pectinata (rose family) Late July to late August

Alpine and high subalpine, fairly common north of the North Saskatchewan River. Grows in damp meadows. Rod-like clusters of small creamy-white flowers, five-petalled with lots of stamens, atop a short stem (10 cm) with small frilly leaves, each part cleft into two or three at the tip. More frilly leaves at the base, forming mats when the plant grows in patches. See also bistort (next entry) and false asphodel, page 343.

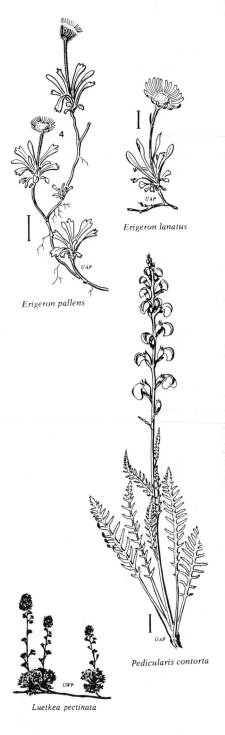

Erigeron lanatus

Erigeron pallens

Pedicularis contorta

Luetkea pectinata

Bistort
Polygonum viviparum
(buckwheat family)
Late July to early August

Polygonum vivparum

Alpine and subalpine, in meadows. A small white tuft near the ground, resembling luetkea (previous entry), but with simple rather than complex leaves, and larger overall. Also looks like false asphodel (page 343), which grows at lower elevations bordering water and has a rounder flowerhead.

In addition to the usual flowers-and-seed method of reproduction, bistort can reproduce asexually by forming little purple bulblets that drop off from the lower end of the flower cluster and take root. The bulblets sometimes sprout leaves while still on the parent plant.

Alpine everlasting
Antennaria alpina (composite family)
July

In dry meadows. Less than 10 cm tall and rather hairy, with a cluster of very short, woolly narrow leaves at the base. They continue up the stem. Dishwater-white flowers on top, not densely packed. *A. lanata* is more common in northern sections; similar to *A. alpina* but somewhat taller (10-15 cm), with larger, longer leaves, mostly up the stem, and a denser flowerhead.

Antennaria alpina   *Antennaria lanata*

Alpine coltsfoot
Petasites frigidus (composite family)
Late June and July

An alpine variety of the montane species (page 339), preferring wet, well-vegetated meadows. It is a little shorter, but otherwise the same.

White heather
Cassiope tetragona, C. mertensiana
(heath family) Late June to early August

Similar-looking alpine and high subalpine dwarf shrubs, common in central and northern areas but absent in Waterton (although reported from Glacier). Both species form large patches of upward-curving dark-green scaly stems 10-20 cm long. The scales are actually tiny leaves lying close to the stem.

White heather often grows with pink heather (page 403), green heather (next

Cassiope

entry) and crowberry (page 408), all of
which look rather alike until they bloom.
But these latter three look thicker and
fuzzier than the two white heathers,
because their leaves are a little longer
and stick out from the stem at right
angles. In bloom, the white heathers are
easy to tell from the others: they are the
only ones that have pure white flowers.
These are small but numerous and showy;
little nodding white bells on which the
petals turn outward at the lip. There are
no berries.

 C. mertensiana is nearly identical to
C. tetragona but has slightly thinner
stems and no groove on the back of the
leaf. It forms bright-green mats, while
C. tetragona grows in dark-green tufts.

Alpine wildflowers:
yellowish green, reddish green, odd colors

Green heather/yellow heather
Phyllodoce glanduliflora (heath family)
June and July

Alpine and high subalpine, common in
central and northern areas, scarce south
of Crowsnest Pass. A ground-covering
shrub that often grows with pink heather
and white heather (page 403). Stems
5-10 cm long, covered with needle-like
leaves that are not prickly. Flowers are
urnlike, with out-turned lips, in small
nodding clusters atop the stems; the color
ranges from pale yellowish green to pale
yellow. No berries are produced. See also
crowberry, page 408.

Longstem greencaps/alpine wormwood
Artemisia norvegica (composite family)
August

In alpine and subalpine meadows, central
and northern areas; absent at
Waterton/Glacier. Frilly bright-green
leaves, mostly at the base of a hairy stem
30-60 cm tall, with a dozen or so
odd-looking blooms at the top. Each is a
nodding flattened green ball about 1 cm
across with dark-green ribs on it, like
lines of longitude. The flowers look like
they are going to open further, but they
don't. See also bladder campion (next
entry).

Artemisia norvegica

Bladder campion/alpine campion/ nodding pink/chinese lantern
Lychnis apetala (pink family)
June and July

Stony, high-alpine scree slopes and moraines. Rare in southern sections, not common anywhere, but with an arresting bloom that looks like a greenish oriental lantern with purple stripes. This is actually the calyx, not the flower; to see the petals, which are purple, look inside the mouth of the calyx. The plant is only 5-10 cm tall and lightly fuzzy all over; the leaves are lance-shaped and mostly basal.

Mountain sorrel
Oxyria digyna (buckwheat family) July

In protected spots, often among boulders. Leaves round, reddish brown to olive drab and indented at the stem. Atop the stem, 20-30 cm tall, there is a spray of tiny reddish/greenish flowers, each on the thinnest of stalks. The small seeds are typical of sorrel or dock: each in a little circular envelope, carried by the hundred in reddish-brown plumes.

Alpine wild flowers: yellow or orange

Arctic poppies
Papaver kluanensis, P. pygmaeum
(poppy family) July and August

In rocky, exposed places well above timberline. Not common, but unmistakable: frilly basal leaves and a few skinny, black-haired stems 10-40 cm tall that kink below the showy poppy-like flowers, one per stem, yellow to orange. Hairy pods later on.

North of Crowsnest Pass the main species is *P. kluanensis*, 20-40 cm tall but otherwise very similar to *P. pygmaeum*, 10-20 cm tall, which is limited to Waterton/Glacier. Differentiate by the hairiness: *P. kluanensis* is densely hairy on both the tops and undersides of the leaves, while *P. pygmaeum* is fuzzy, not hairy, and mainly on the undersides of the leaves.

These plants amaze me. Often I have come upon a half-dozen fragile-looking poppies flopping about in some forlorn, wind-raked col. This is heart-rending—they are so *brave*.

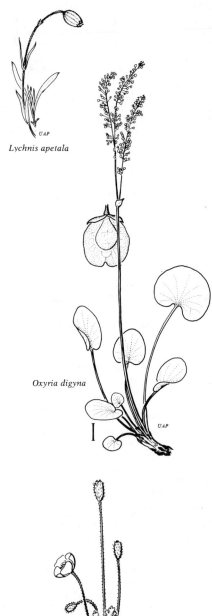

Lychnis apetala

Oxyria digyna

Papaver pygmaeum

Alpine potentilla/alpine cinquefoil
Potentilla nivea (rose family)
Early June to mid-July

A cushion plant with brilliant yellow
flowers blooming on a mat of silvery
green fuzzy leaflets (in threes, with
teeth). One of the showier alpine plants;
look for it in rocky, windy places both
above and below timberline. It is part of
the climber's rock garden. A very similar
species, *P. ledebourniana,* makes
less-compact cushions and tends to have
longer flower-stems with larger flowers.
See also the other potentillas (page 359).

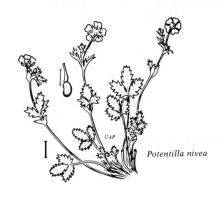

Potentilla nivea

Alpine buttercup/snow buttercup
Ranunculus eschscholtzii
(buttercup family)
Late June to early August

Ranunculus eschscholtzii

Alpine and subalpine, in sheltered damp
places. The only common buttercup that
grows at high elevations, which solves
the usual problem of differentiating
species in this complex genus
(*R. verecundus* is similar—but rare.)
Look for the shiny-yellow buttercup
flower with its green centre, and the
bright-green, deeply cleft leaves.

Alpine arnica
Arnica alpina (composite family)
July and August

Prefers dry spots that are sandy or
gravelly. This is the most common
high-country arnica, identified as such
by the showy all-yellow arnica bloom,
which has three teeth on the end of each
ray. Low-growing for an arnica species
(20-30 cm), with lance-shaped leaves and
a woolly stem.

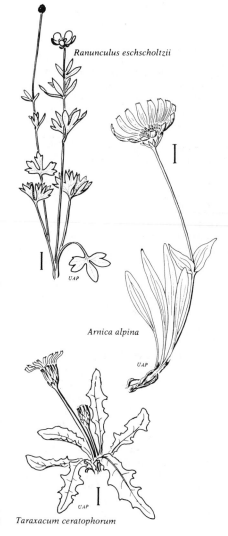

Arnica alpina

Alpine dandelion
Taraxacum spp. (composite family)
June through August

Yup, the lowly dandelion grows way up
here. In fact, there are more alpine
species (three) than low-country ones
(two), all very similar. Easily identified
as dandelion by the ragged-looking
leaves spreading from the base, the
brilliant yellow blooms made of
ray-flowers only (no disk-flowers in the
centre) and the fluffy, round seedhead.
All these parts are smaller in the
high-country versions than they are in
the lawn variety. If the flowers are right

Taraxacum ceratophorum

but not the leaves, see hawksbeard (next entry).

Alpine hawksbeard
Crepis nana (composite family)
Late July and August

In exposed places, among scree and broken rock; prefers limestone outcrops. A small rosette of smooth, spoon-shaped leaves 1-2 cm across, dark green or slightly purplish—but don't confuse with mountain sorrel, page 398. A cluster of purple tubes at the centre of the rosette opens into little dandelion-like flowers.

Crepis nana

Golden fleabane
Erigeron aureus (composite family)
July and August

The only yellow fleabane at any elevation, but can be confused with Lyall's goldenweed (next entry). Alpine fleabane grows in alpine and subalpine meadows; it is found between Brazeau River and Crowsnest Pass. The bloom is 1-2 cm across, all-yellow, with rather wide ray-flowers (petal-like parts) for a fleabane. Stem is hairy and leafless; basal leaves are also hairy.

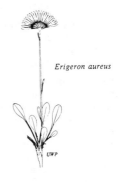

Erigeron aureus

Lyall's goldenweed/Lyall's iron-plant
Haplopappus lyallii (composite family)
July and August

Distribution and appearance similar to golden fleabane, above, but the bloom is larger (up to 3 cm across) and the stems have small leaves on them that are sticky as well as hairy. This plant and golden fleabane (above) are the only yellow daisy-like flowers you are likely to see in the high country.

Haplopappus lyallii

Sibbaldia
Sibbaldia procumbens (rose family)
Early June to early July

A mat-forming plant; grows in rocky places. The three-parted leaves are rather like those of strawberry (page 337), but smaller (1-2 cm long) and toothed only at the ends of the lobes, which tend to fold inward along the centreline. Distinctive flowers: star-like, with small yellow petals alternating with larger, pointed green sepals. Leaves turn beautifully red in fall—meaning late August in the alpine zone.

Sibbaldia procumbens

Silver plant
Eriogonum ovalifolium
(buckwheat family) June and July

Mostly south of Crowsnest Pass. Prefers
rough, rocky places at high elevations,
but can be found much lower at
alpine-like sites. Plant is a cushion of
silvery-looking felty leaves with several
hairless stalks rising about 10 cm and
each carrying a tight, rounded cluster of
tiny cup-shaped flowers that are yellow
and green with red tips.

Eriogonum ovalifolium

Head-shaped lousewort
Pedicularis capitata (figwort family)
July and August

Prefers stony places. The shortest
lousewort, often rising only a few
centimetres above the ground. A central
and northerly species, not reported from
Waterton/Glacier. Leaves small and
fern-like. Striking flowers: 3-4 cm long,
each a curved pale-yellow tube with
brown lips and a tiny tongue hanging
out. See also western lousewort, page 365.

Pedicularis capitata

Double bladder-pod
Physaria didymocarpa (mustard family)
Late May through June

From Brazeau River south, in exposed
places at any elevation, but mostly alpine
and always on limy soils. Not a large
plant, but conspicuous for its shape:
spokes of prostrate flowerheads radiating
from a central rosette of gray-green
diamond-shaped hairy leaves. Small
bright-yellow flowers have the four
petals typical of mustard-family plants.
The seed cases are interesting:
transparent round inflated pods. See also
bladder locoweed (page 406) and alpine
spring beauty (page 393).

Physaria didymocarpa

Alpine early yellow locoweed
Oxytropis sericea (pea family) July

On sparsely covered ground. This variety
of early yellow locoweed is much like its
low-elevation relative (page 364), but is
slightly smaller in every dimension, has
black hairs on the stems and lies flat on
the ground. See page 364 for picture.

Alpine yellow paintbrush
Castilleja occidentalis (figwort family)
Late June to mid-August

Alpine and subalpine meadows, usually in small patches. Pale yellow or greenish-yellow blooms on reddish or purplish stems 10-20 cm tall. Narrow leaves climb the stems, becoming denser near the top, where they merge with the flowerhead. Like the yellow paintbrush of lower elevations (page 365), the yellow alpine paintbrush carries its color on petal-like bracts that surround the spiky green flowers. The whole plant is lightly hairy.

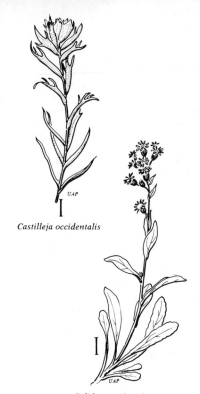

Castilleja occidentalis

Alpine goldenrod
Solidago multiradiata (composite family)
August

Mostly alpine, but also subalpine. The only common high-country goldenrod and obviously so: a cluster of about a dozen small yellow flowers atop a leafy stem 10-20 cm tall. Resembles mountain goldenrod (page 364) but is smaller.

Flowers to check in the below-timberline listings:

> Stonecrop, page 362.
> Western lousewort, page 365.

See also green heather, page 397.

Solidago multiradiata

Alpine wildflowers: red or pink

Moss campion
Silene acaulis (pink family)
Mid-June to early August

Alpine, in open rocky places. The classic cushion plant: tiny bright-green leaves packed into a domed mat that looks a lot like moss, but studded with small pink flowers (mosses don't have flowers). One of the better-known alpine plants, common throughout the Rockies. Compare with spreading phlox (next entry).

Silene acaulis

Spreading phlox/carpet pink
Phlox diffusa (pink family)
June to August

Alpine and subalpine, in open rocky places. Absent at Waterton/Glacier. A pink moss-campion look-alike (see previous entry), but rare and found mainly on peaks west of the continental

Phlox diffusa

divide—one of only a few high-country plants with a preference for one watershed or the other. Differentiate from moss campion by the less-compact character of spreading phlox, and by the leaves, which are longer.

Alpine lousewort
Pedicularis arctica (figwort family)
Early July to early August

Alpine, in rocky spots; not found in the Waterton/Glacier area. Low-growing plant with small fern-like leaves. A showy spike (5-15 cm) of purplish-pink flowers, each an upward-curved tube.

Pedicularis arctica

Rose-root
Sedum roseum (sedum family)
June and July

Normally alpine, but can be found much lower in exposed rocky places. A small plant, less common on the western slope, identifiable immediately as a sedum by the fleshy leaves. The stem is about 10 cm long, carrying a dense cluster of small red or reddish-purple flowers at the top.

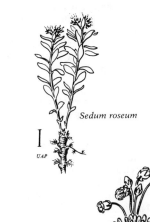

Sedum roseum

Pink heather
Phyllodoce empetriformis (heath family)
July and August

Alpine and high subalpine meadows, in ground-covering patches. A dwarf shrub. The stems are 5-10 cm long and covered with needle-like (but soft) leaves. The flowers are small pink bells in clusters atop the stems. Compare with alpine laurel (next entry). When not in bloom, this plant is difficult to tell from green heather (page 397) or crowberry (page 408). Pink heather does not produce berries.

Phyllodoce empetriformis

Alpine laurel
Kalmia microphylla (heath family)
Late July to early August

In moist tundra and high subalpine forest, central and northern areas. Resembles pink heather (previous entry), but the flowers are somewhat larger and flatter; the stems have fewer, larger leaves. Closely resembles *Kalmia polifolia,* a subalpine species sometimes growing in same area, but has smaller, rounder leaves (*K. microphylla* 1-2 cm long; *K. polifolia* 2-4 cm long). See page 373 for picture.

Other species to check:

Lyall's beardtongue, page 372.
Lyall's saxifrage, page 394.
Red monkey-flower, page 371.
Lapland rosebay, page 405.

Alpine wildflowers: blue or purple

Alpine forget-me-not
Myosotis alpestris (borage family) July

Myosotis alpestris

Alpine and subalpine, in open areas
throughout the Rockies. Small (10-20 cm),
with fuzzy lance-shaped leaves.
Well-loved for its small yellow-centred
(sometimes white-centred) sky-blue
flowers borne in small clusters atop the
plant. Prefers limy soils. Compare with
alpine speedwell and alpine rock cress
(next entries).

Veronica wormskjoldii

Alpine speedwell/alpine veronica
Veronica wormskjoldii (figwort family)
Late June to August

Subalpine and alpine, in moist meadows.
Flowers are rather like forget-me-not
(previous entry), but smaller and
four-petalled rather than five-petalled,
deeper blue (sometimes almost purple)
and without a yellow or white centre. A
single stem 10-30 cm tall, with paired
hairy oval leaves. Flowers in a cluster at
the top. Compare with moss gentian
(page 407) and see also the other
veronicas (page 382).

Arabis lyallii

Alpine rock cress
Arabis lyalli, A. lemmonii
(mustard family) June and July

Alpine and subalpine, in exposed places.
Small, deep-purple flowers with four
petals, carried in a small cluster atop the
stem, 10-20 cm tall. Leaves are small and
shaped like elongated arrowheads; plant
is hairiest at the base. *A. lemmonii* is
similar but not quite as hairy. Both
species produce long slender seed pods.

Alpine harebell
Campanula lasiocarpa (bluebell family)
July and August

Alpine. Showy, bell-shaped bloom like
that of its montane relative (page 383),
but a much shorter plant, restricted to
the high alpine zone and not nearly as
common. Absent at Waterton/Glacier. A
single flower on a short stem (2-10 cm)

Campanula lasiocarpa

Arabis lemmonii

with mostly basal leaves; look for a little furriness just behind the flower.

Purple saxifrage
Saxifraga oppositifolia
(saxifrage family) Mid-July

Common on alpine slopes, except in Waterton/Glacier where it is strangely absent. This low-growing plant looks nothing like the other members of the genus. Bright-violet bell-shaped flowers stare up from a mat of tiny scraggly leaves set close to the spreading stems. This plant blooms for only a few days after the snow goes, so see it while you can.

Alpine purple wallflower
Erysimum pallasii (mustard family) July

Alpine, in stony places, rare but seen occasionally from Bow River north. Four-petalled lavender flowers in a ring-like cluster above a rosette of narrow dark-green leaves that tend to fold inward. The flower cluster grows taller as the days go by.

Lapland rosebay
Rhododendron lapponicum
(heath family) July and August

Northern area, occasional as far south as North Saskatchewan River, in rocky places and tundra, usually on limy soil. A dwarf shrub, ground-hugging to 30 cm tall. Large, brilliantly purple or pink flowers in low clusters. The leaves are small, oval, drab and leathery-looking, with rust-colored scales underneath.

Telesonix
Telesonix heucheriformis
(saxifrage family) July

Alpine and subalpine, mostly eastern-slope, fairly common from Columbia Icefield north; absent at Waterton/Glacier. Dense colonies in crevices on limestone or dolomite outcrops, often under overhangs. Round, deep-green leathery leaves 3-5 cm across, with toothy edges. They smell like turpentine. Reddish-purple bell-shaped flowers a centimetre across, carried erect on prominent red stalks. Bristly flower bases and red sepals. Imagine: a wildflower with a name like an electronics company.

Sky pilot/skunkweed
Polemonium viscosum (phlox family)
June and July

Rocky alpine areas and scree slopes
south of Crowsnest Pass, fading out to
the north. A striking plant: large flowers
(2-4 cm across) with yellow centres. But
the leaflets, which are tiny, give off a
strong, unpleasant odor.

Polemonium viscosum

Aquilegia jonesii

Alpine columbine
Aquilegia jonesii (buttercup family) June

Waterton/Glacier, in limestone scree
slopes at high elevations. A rare plant
with rather un-columbine-like leaves that
form a small tuft. Instantly recognizable
as columbine when it blooms: a single
large, deep-blue flower with five spurs,
carried on a short stem.

Bladder locoweed
Oxytropis podocarpa (pea family) July

Rocky places, often in scree slopes.
Common in northern and central sections
but missing at Waterton/Glacier. A
low-growing plant, forming a scraggly
rosette; the only blue or purple locoweed
at high elevations, identifiable as such
by the pea-type blossoms and leaves.
After blooming, the plant produces large,
eye-catching reddish inflated seed pods
lying on the ground at the ends of long
stalks.

Oxytropis podocarpa

Alpine milk-vetch
Astragalus alpinus (pea family)
Late June and July

In meadows and on scree slopes.
Fragile-looking and fairly small
(10-20 cm), blooming in dense clusters on
straight leafless stalks that rise above the
straggly stems bearing hairy leaves.
Pea-type flowers are bright blue, with
white parts.

Astragalus alpinus

Alpine gentians
Gentiana spp. (gentian family)
July and August

Like their montane relatives, the
high-country gentians listed below have
beautiful deep-blue flowers.

Mountain gentian/explorer's gentian
    (G. calycosa) July and August: a
    subalpine and alpine species that is
    fairly common in the
    Waterton/Glacier area but not
    reported elsewhere. Grows 10-20 cm

high, with small but broad, pointed
leaves in pairs up the stem. The deep
blue flower is the largest gentian
bloom—very lovely—with dots inside
against a white background.

**Blue-bottle gentian/smooth alpine
gentian** *(G. glauca)* mid-July to
mid-August: in alpine and subalpine
meadows; absent at
Waterton/Glacier, occasional through
Banff and common from Jasper
north. Low-growing but erect, with
several waxy deep-blue flowers atop
each stem, which bears pairs of
rounded leaves. All parts of the
plant quite glossy-looking. Resembles
four-parted gentian (next entry), but
that plant has tiers of small flowers
while smooth alpine gentian bears its
flowers only at the top.

Four-parted gentian *(G. propinqua)* July
and August: in subalpine and lower
alpine meadows. Resembles
blue-bottle gentian (previous entry),
but the lavender-blue flowers occur
farther down the plant as well as on
the top.

Moss gentian *(G. prostrata)* July to early
August: a ground-hugging alpine
species with small deep-blue flowers
and small paired leaves. The flowers
close in cloudy conditions, or when
touched. Compare with alpine
speedwell, page 404.

See also northern gentian, page 388.

**Scorpionweed/silky phacelia/
purple bee-plant**
Phacelia sericea, P. lyallii
(waterleaf family)
Late May to mid-August

Sheltered alpine spots and subalpine
meadows, but sometimes growing at
much lower elevations. A striking plant,
unlikely to be confused with anything
else. Spikes 15-40 cm high crammed with
small purple flowers from which project
long stamens, hairs and whatnot. The
leaves are long and frilly; they tend to
droop.
    Look for *P. lyallii* south of
Crowsnest Pass. It has the same flowers
in clusters rather than spikes. The leaves
are not quite so finely divided.

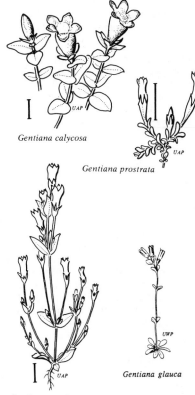

Gentiana calycosa

Gentiana prostrata

Gentiana propinqua

Gentiana glauca

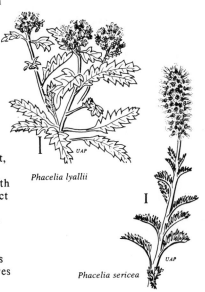

Phacelia lyallii

Phacelia sericea

Saw wort/saussurea
Saussurea nuda (composite family)
July and August

Saussurea nuda

UWP

Alpine scree slopes and subalpine
meadows from Crowsnest Pass north.
May grow fairly tall (up to 40 cm), but is
usually short (5-20 cm). Thistle-like at
first appearance, but lacking spines.
Large, heavy, hairy flowerheads above a
ground-hugging rosette of hairy leaves.

Crowberry
Empetrum nigrum (heath family) June

Another fuzzy-stemmed ground-covering
shrub of subalpine and alpine meadows,
common everywhere except in the
Waterton/Glacier area. Short needle-like
leaves, very similar to green heather
(page 397) or pink heather (page 403).
The flowers, though, are quite different:
small and purplish, carried close to the
stem. Juicy berries appear in August,
dark purple to black. They are sweet (the
flavor seems apple-like to me), but each
has a large seed in it.

Empetrum nigrum

See also:

Western lousewort, page 365.
Bladder campion, page 398.
Rose root, page 403.
Elliptical-leaved penstemon,
page 380.

WATER PLANTS

Many plant species can tolerate occasional flooding, and some prefer soil so damp that it is nearly saturated. Still, this chapter is reserved for plants that *normally grow in water,* whether it be a puddle, a pond, a marsh, lake, stream or river.

Believe it or not, there are plants from tropical-fish aquariums growing outdoors near Banff Hot Springs. Turn to page 556 to find out more.

Algae

Although there are thousands of microscopic algal plant species in the Canadian Rockies, few are very conspicuous. Here are a couple of groups to know.

Plankton

All Rockies lakes have plenty of planktonic (free-floating) algae in them. Even the clearest lake water carries plankton. Some lakes are murky with it. The normal plankton in Canadian Rockies waters are not harmful to drink, although human pollution with intestinal bacteria and the protozoan *Giardia lamblia* (page 824) has rendered all surface water in the southern and central regions suspect.

What interests me about lake plankton is the **bloom** phenomenon: a planktonic population explosion in late summer. On Maligne Lake, for example, if you are out on the water in August you may see a yellowish scum that looks a bit like the pollen scum of June or July (see page 293). But this is not pollen; it is one or more red algae species that are reaching the peak of their annual growth and reproduction cycles at that time. The individual cells are too small to see without a microscope, but if you dip out a bit on a white card (or even on your finger) you can see the yellowish clots of cells.

Attached algae

The other kind of algae that you may notice are those species that can send you headlong into the creek if you step on a boulder or a log coated with them. Beware the slippery surfaces early in the day, when water levels are low in the mountains.

How can you tell attached forms of algae from similar-looking mosses? Look closely; they really aren't similar at all. Mosses are far more complicated plants than algae. If the thing you are looking at is nothing more than green slime or filaments in water, then it is a species of algae.

There are algae that live in snow. See page 532 for these and other interesting snow-and-ice organisms in the Canadian Rockies.

Water mosses

Few mosses actually grow in standing water, but the peat mosses *Drepanocladus* and *Tomenthypnum* do. They are brown and frilly; for more information on them, and on the other water-loving moss species in the Canadian Rockies, turn to page 431.

Higher water plants

Duckweed
Lemna and *Spirodela* spp.
(duckweed family)

In bright-green floating colonies on shallow, warm ponds at low elevations, often covering a good deal of the surface. Each plant is a small leaf-like pad called a thallus, 2-8 mm across, with one or more tiny roots hanging down. Duckweed reproduces mostly by budding, but occasionally it puts forth microscopic flowers. In the fall, tiny bulblets drop off the thalli to overwinter at the bottom; in spring they rise to the surface and begin covering the pond anew.

   There are three duckweed species in the Canadian Rockies. **Common duckweed** *(Lemna minor)* is by far the most common one; the thalli are oval, 2-5 mm across and not connected. They float at the surface. In **ivy duckweed** *(L. trisulca)* the thalli are elongated and interconnected in mats that float below the surface. **Larger duckweed** *(Spirodela polyrhiza)* is not really much larger (4-8 mm across, oval), but has several tiny roots hanging off the thallus rather than just one.

Mare's-tail
Hippuris spp. (water-milfoil family)
July and August

In or beside shallow water at low elevations, rooted in the mud. A segmented plant resembling horsetail (page 426) but with flat leaves rather than round horsetail-type stems. As well, mare's-tail produces tiny green flowers along the stem where the tiers of leaves join, while horsetail does not flower.

   There are two species in the Canadian Rockies: *H. vulgaris*, with stems 5-30 cm long, and *H. montana*, with stems only 1-10 cm long. The latter prefers moving water rather than lakes and grows from Saskatchewan Crossing north.

Eurasian water-milfoil
Myriophyllum spicatum
(water-milfoil family) July and August

In quiet water up to 2 m deep at low elevations. A very frilly plant, reaching up a metre or so from roots in the bottom and floating just below the

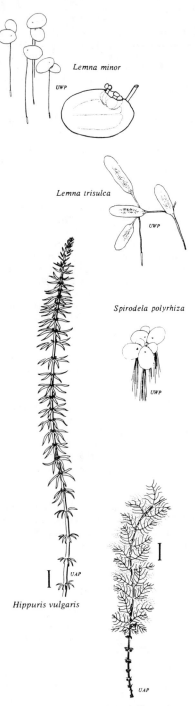

Lemna minor

UWP

Lemna trisulca

UWP

Spirodela polyrhiza

UWP

Hippuris vulgaris

UAP

Myriophyllum spicatum

UAP

surface. Usually a single stem per plant.
Tiers of little green flowers stick up a
few centimetres above the surface.
Compare with bladderwort (next entry).

Bladderwort
Utricularia spp. (bladderwort family)
Late June and July

A floating, unrooted plant, growing in
tangled masses below the surface in
shallow water at low elevations. Stems up
to a metre long with very frilly leaves
and little bladders that not only support
the plant at its proper depth but also
feed it in an interesting way. Like its
relative butterwort (page 385),
bladderwort is carnivorous. The bladders
are sensitive to the slightest touch,
opening when tiny water creatures bump
into them. The animals are swept in,
where they die; their remains are
ingested by the plant. Bladderwort has
one to several showy flowers, yellow and
snapdragon-like, carried above the water
on a stem.

Of the three species in the Canadian
Rockies, all rather similar, *U. vulgaris* is
by far the most common. See also
water-milfoil (previous entry).

Common cattail
Typha latifolia (cattail family)
Late June to early July

Montane, at low elevations; often in
roadside ditches. Common colonial marsh
plant, rooting in shallow water (less than
half a metre deep). Stands up to 2 m tall.
Very long leaves, often with dried-out
papery tips; round stems the same color.

Most people recognize the
hot-dog-shaped brown seedheads of the
cattail, but what about the flowers?
Check the plant in early summer; you
will find that the hot-dog part is made
up of umpteen thousand female flowers,
each nothing more than a hairy pistil.
There are no petals. The male flowers
occur on the same plant; they make up
the spike atop the hot-dog. When cattail
goes to seed the male flowers dry up and
the spike hardens. The female flowers
become fluffy seeds that disperse in the
wind after birds break up the heads.

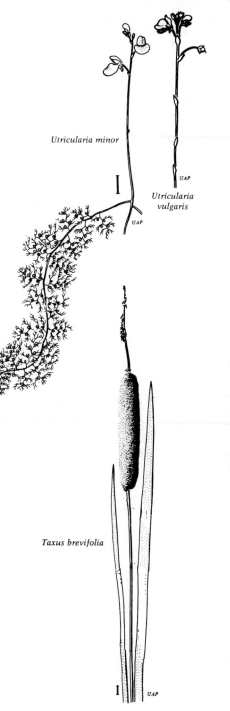

Utricularia minor

Utricularia vulgaris

UAP

UAP

Taxus brevifolia

UAP

Common great bulrush/tule
Scirpus validus (sedge family)
June to July

Montane, fringing lakes in colonies.
Stands 1-3 m tall; all parts dark green or
drab. What you notice are the stems. The
leaves grow down near the base,
underwater, and they look like loose
parts of the stem. The flowers are also
drab; they spring from a point near the
top of the stem, forming a loose cluster
on stalks.

There is also a small bulrush
(*S. caespitosus;* 10-50 cm tall) that looks
like any other sedge (page 420) except
for the very short, scaly leaves at the
base of the plant (most sedge leaves are
much longer). Common in bogs.

Giant bur-reed
Sparganium angustifolium
(bur-reed family) July and August

At low elevations in water up to half a
metre deep. True reeds *(Phragmites
communis)* do not grow in the Canadian
Rockies, so the bur-reed will have to do.
Long thin grass-like leaves clasp the
stems, often floating on the surface of
the water; leaves are flat on one side and
slightly rounded on the other. Fluffy
round flowerheads produce spiky green
ball-like fruits up to 2 cm across. There
are several other species of bur-reed,
similar-looking and sometimes
hybridizing with giant bur-reed, which is
the most common.

Yellow skunkcabbage
Lysichitum americanum (arum family)
Late April and early May

Western slope only, in Columbian forest
marshes and wet spots, often mong
cedars. Huge, broad leaves (often a metre
in length or longer) spread out from the
centre; they give off a pungent odor
when crushed.

This plant can be mistaken for false
hellebore (page 350) before the
skunkcabbage has grown very large. But
skunkcabbage leaves have stalks and
false hellebore leaves do not. Further,
false hellebore is far more widespread,
and it prefers a drier habitat. Yet many
people call false hellebore
"skunkcabbage." This can be a fatal
mistake if you eat false hellebore; it is
quite poisonous.

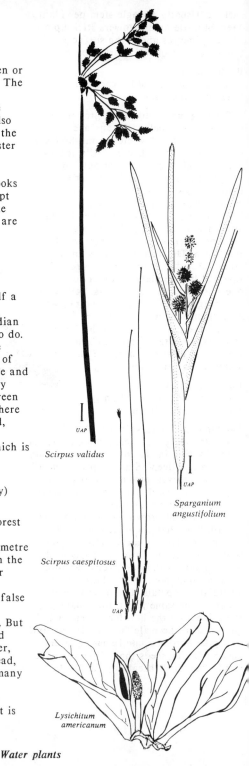

Scirpus validus

Sparganium angustifolium

Scirpus caespitosus

Lysichitum americanum

The tiny yellow flowers of skunkcabbage crowd along a club-shaped structure wrapped in a sheath. Inside the sheath the temperature is a constant 22 °C during the early-spring blooming period; this may attract pollinating insects. The leaves come later, edible after boiling to remove stinging calcium oxalate crystals. The large rootstock was an Indian staple, made into flour.

Arrow-grass
Triglochin maritima (arrow-grass family) July

Montane, fringing marshes. Grass-like, about half a metre tall, drably colored and not very noticeable until it blooms, when it makes a spike of small green flowers. These look like little bumps on the lower part of the spike, becoming a dense head farther up. See also pondweed, this page.

Water smartweed/water knotweed
Polygonum amphibium (buckwheat family)
July and August

At low elevations in very shallow water or shoreline mud, sometimes in water deep enough to float the leaves. More common on the western slope. Stands 5-10 cm tall, with glossy green leaves, prominently white-veined. One large pink-to-red bistort-like flower cluster (page 396) atop a straight stem; one or more smaller clusters underneath.

Broad-leaved water-plantain
Alisma plantago-aquatica (water plantain family) July

Western-slope and Waterton/Glacier, in marshes and along the shores of shallow lakes at low elevations. Large glossy green leaves 10-30 cm long, rather like water smartweed (previous entry), but with parallel, ladder-like veins. Has a pretty bloom: small white three-petalled flowers, each at the end of a stalk, starburst-like.

Pondweed
Potamogeton spp. (pondweed family) August

Rooted in montane ponds and slow-moving streams. Most of the plant is submerged, but sometimes the leaves are floating. The flowers always stick up out of the water; they are tiny, in greenish

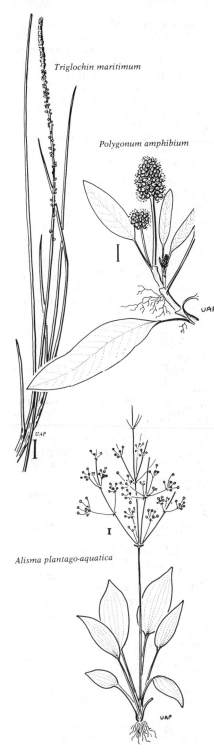

Triglochin maritimum

Polygonum amphibium

Alisma plantago-aquatica

Water plants

clusters a couple of centimetres long.
When not in bloom, pondweed can be
differentiated from water-plantain or
water smartweed (previous entries) by
the translucent sheaths along the stems at
the bases of pondweed leaves. Bloom is
rather like arrow-grass (page 413), but
the leaves are much broader on most
species of pondweed, of which there are
nine in the Rockies. Most common is
P. richardsonii, illustrated. Others are
difficult to tell apart.

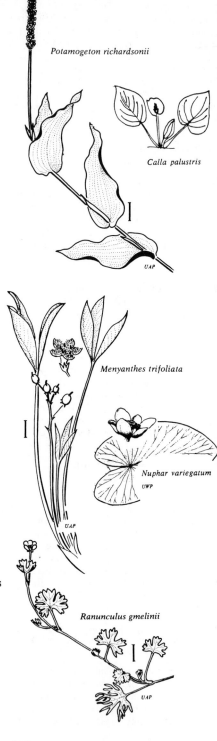

Potamogeton richardsonii

Calla palustris

Menyanthes trifoliata

Nuphar variegatum
UWP

Ranunculus gmelinii

Water arum/wild calla
Calla palustris (arum family)
June and July

Montane marshes and shallow ponds in
the northern-region foothills. Glossy
green heart-shaped leaves, each with a
prominent yellow central rib. This plant
tries hard to hold its leaves up out of the
water, and it mostly succeeds. The
flowers are interesting: the top of the
stem has a large white leaf-like bract,
partly surrounding a club of tiny
yellowish-green flowers.

Buckbean
Menyanthes trifoliata (buckbean family)
June and July

In shallow standing water at montane
elevations. Erect leaves held above the
water are each divided into three lobes.
A spike of showy white-to-purplish
fringed flowers is carried higher still;
the anthers are bright red or purple.

Yellow pond lily
Nuphar variegatum (water lily family)
June and July

Occasional on low-elevation ponds and
sometimes slow-moving streams. Easily
identified by the large heart-shaped
floating leaves. Strongly rooted in the
bottom mud, the plant produces large
yellow flowers with red-fringed centres.
The flowers are carried singly atop stems
that stick up above the surface.

Yellow water crowfoot
and white water crowfoot
Ranunculus gmelinii and *R. circinatus*
(buttercup family) July

In shallow ponds or sluggish streams.
Yellow water crowfoot is fairly common
on the western slope and at
Waterton/Glacier, occasional elsewhere.
It has weak stems, so it either floats or

lies on the shoreline mud when the water is low. Divided leaves 1-2 cm across, forming tangled mats. Typical buttercup flowers.

White water crowfoot has white flowers and is absent at Waterton. Several other buttercup species sometimes grow in water: *R. cymbalaria* (lies on the mud; tiny yellow flowers), *R. aquatilis* (very frilly leaves, sometimes floating) and *R. flammula* (small bunches of leaves along a sprawling stem that roots).

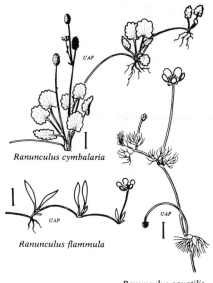

Ranunculus cymbalaria

Ranunculus flammula

Ranunculus aquatilis

Water hemlock
Cicuta maculata (carrot family)
July and August

In bogs up to timberline, often in standing water. Up to 2 m tall; usually less than a metre, with prominently veined sawtooth leaves. The flowers are tiny and white, carried in clusters above the plant like cow parsnip (page 344), which is a relative. Water hemlock is quite poisonous, especially the lower parts and the roots; cattle die after eating only a few plants. Compare with water parsnip (next entry).

Water parsnip
Sium suave (carrot family)
July and August

Western slope mainly; grows in boggy places, often with water hemlock (previous entry), which looks like it. Differentiate by the simpler arrangement of the leaves on water parsnip, compared with the doubly compound arrangement on water hemlock. Water parsnip is also reportedly poisonous, although supposedly not as dangerous as water hemlock.

Cicuta maculata

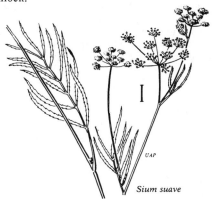

Sium suave

GRASSES AND GRASS-LIKE PLANTS

What is a "grass," anyway? It's something that looks like . . . well, *grass,* you know. Grasses, sedges and rushes all fit the non-botanist's image of grass: anything with skinny leaves. Nothing is that easy, of course; each of these three groups is in a different family.

True grasses are round-stemmed and hollow. They grow in joints rather than as single, continuous, tubular stems (bamboo is a grass). Grass leaves may be very narrow or perhaps curled inward, but essentially they are flat.

Sedges, on the other hand, have stems that are solid. Both the stems and the leaves are triangular in cross-section (although the leaves are often flattened so much that they look flat).

Rushes have round stems that are hollow, like grass. But they don't grow in joints; the stems are continuous. And the leaves, rather than being flat, are usually round.

The botany student's way of remembering all this is to say to himself, over and over before the exam:

Rushes are round, sedges have edges, and grasses have joints.

You might not know it to look at them, but all these plants produce flowers. What they lack is color in the blooms. That is why one overlooks the flowers of grasses, sedges and rushes: they are just collections of tiny brown or purplish parts. Actually, there *is* a little color in the flowers of the grasses and sedges (although not in the rushes). The tiny anthers are bright yellow.

Grasses

There are over a hundred grass species in the Canadian Rockies, of which 21 species have been selected for this book. All are in the grass family (Gramineae), so the family is not given in the listings. The blooming date is not particularly important—the same picture suffices for both bloom and seedhead in grasses—so it isn't given in the listings either.

How does one identify grasses? By getting acquainted with their morphology, especially all the little parts of the flowerheads, then sitting on the ground for hours with a magnifying glass and a botanical key. This is too much trouble for me; I am content to casually pick out the few species described below, which besides being very common can be identified mostly by shape, size and color. But for confident identification that magnifying glass will be required.

Nature-lore note: the seeds of many grass species are self-planting. Sharp-pointed on one end, with a long spine on the other, they fall to the ground and tend to land point down, sticking in like spears. Whenever the wind blows the spine vibrates, sending the seed deeper and deeper into the soil.

In the identifications that follow, note that "broad leaves" means broad *for a grass leaf* (3-5 mm); narrow is *really* narrow (1-2 mm). Few grasses grow singly (just a stem and a few leaves); most grow in tufts (many stems and leaves growing from a single point). Very large tufts become tussocks, which are especially common in high subalpine and alpine meadows. Only a few species form sod (lawn-like patches).

Timothy
Phleum spp.

Grows in sparse tufts 10-50 cm tall,
usually in moist meadows. The two
Rockies species of timothy occur at
different elevations. **Common timothy**
(P. pratense) is mostly montane, although
it may grow higher. Note the
hotdog-shaped head, which is purplish
green. **Mountain timothy**
(P. commutatum) is mostly alpine, but
also subalpine; similar head, but shorter,
as is the whole plant.

  Timothy is easily confused with
foxtail (next entry), and can be reliably
differentiated only with a magnifying
glass. Check the tiny parts (spikelets) of
the head; in timothy, each spikelet has a
fringe of coarse bristles on the sides,
while in foxtail the spikelets have
scattered hairs all over them.

Foxtail
Alopecurus spp.

Up to 80 cm tall. Oddly, the two species
we have in the Rockies closely match the
two timothy species and even grow with
them.

Water foxtail *(A. aequalis)* is lower
  montane, most common in the
  southern region, often growing
  singly; it prefers muddy places and
  can stand shallow water, while its
  look-alike, common timothy
  (previous entry), will grow in damp
  places but not in water.

Alpine foxtail *(A. alpinus)* grows in
  tufts, often with mountain timothy,
  in moist subalpine meadows. Alpine
  foxtail is usually a few centimetres
  taller than timothy, but the only way
  to differentiate for sure is with a
  magnifying glass, as described in the
  entry on timothy.

Spike trisetum
Trisetum spicatum

Grows everywhere, upper montane and
higher, in tufts with narrow leaves. The
purplish-to-silvery heads look like lumpy
timothy, with longer hairs.

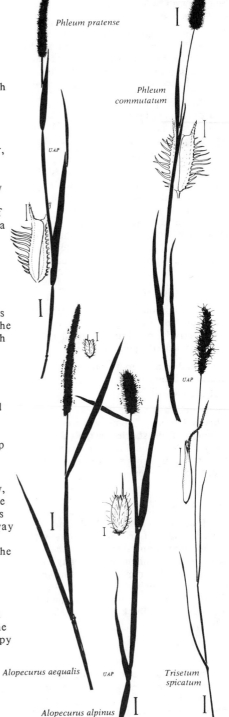

Phleum pratense

Phleum
commutatum

UAP

Alopecurus aequalis   UAP

Alopecurus alpinus

Trisetum
spicatum

Grasses and grass-like plants   417

Smooth ryegrass
Elymus glaucus

Tufts up to a metre tall in montane
woods. The leaves are broad and tend to
droop. Compare with the heads of the
foregoing grasses; rye is coarser but still
compact, and green rather than purplish.

Marsh/bluejoint reedgrass
and purple reedgrass
Calamagrostis canadensis
and *C. purpurascens*

Marsh reedgrass (120 cm) is common
along fringes of montane marshes and
lakes. Heads are large and feathery; each
grain is small (3-4 mm long), with a
spray of fine hairs at the base.
    Purple reedgrass is shorter
(30-70 cm); has similar grains but a much
tighter head. Grows in dry, often rocky
montane and lower subalpine locations.

Junegrass
Koeleria macrantha

Dry, grassy montane meadows. Grows
20-50 cm tall, in tufts; the narrow leaves
are mostly basal. Note the divided head,
which is usually purplish-green.

Awnless brome/smooth brome/
northern brome
Bromus inermis

Montane, on dry slopes, growing singly.
This is a typical brome, the most
common of six species in the Canadian
Rockies. Note the dozen-or-so parts in
the head, each about 1 cm long and
bluegreen. The leaves are broad.

Fescue
Festuca spp.

Montane and subalpine, in dry meadows.
Nine species, all growing in tufts with
narrow leaves and coarse, branched
heads. Two common species: **rough fescue**
(F. scabrella), common in the southern
region and growing 50-100 cm tall, and
sheep fescue *(F. saximontana),* common
throughout the Rockies and 10-50 cm
tall.

Bluegrass
Poa spp.

Bluegrass is native to the Rockies, where
it grows at every elevation in meadows.
There are 19 species in the Canadian
Rockies, very tricky even for botanists to

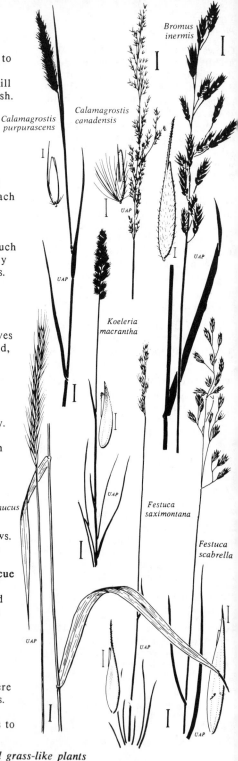

*Bromus
inermis*

*Calamagrostis
canadensis*

*Calamagrostis
purpurascens*

*Koeleria
macrantha*

Elymus glaucus

*Festuca
saximontana*

*Festuca
scabrella*

tell apart. Try going by your location.
Here are two species to know:

Kentucky bluegrass *(P. pratensis)* is all
over the Rockies at low elevations.
And in nearly any lawn you see. It
forms sod under good conditions;
otherwise it grows in tufts. The
heads are denser and heavier than
the other two common Rockies
bluegrasses. But you will have to
leave the lawn uncut to check this
out.

Alpine bluegrass *(P. alpina)* is common
above timberline, growing in tufts or
small patches 10-30 cm tall. The
heads are well-branched and mostly
green, the leaves wide.

Ticklegrass/hairgrass
Agrostis scabra

Montane meadows. Grows in dense tufts
up to 50 cm tall. Medium-wide erect
leaves and very thin stems. The heads are
ticklish, all right—small purple parts on
long, skinny stalks.

Sweetgrass
Hierochloe odorata

Most common in the southern foothills,
in dry meadows, but found at least as
far north as Jasper. Grows 30-60 cm tall,
with short leaves (2-3 cm) that are also
broad. The head is well divided on long
stalks, and the plant gives off a sweet
smell, especially when it burns. The
Blackfoot Indians hold sweetgrass
especially dear; they use it in religious
observances.

Foxtail barley
Hordeum jubatum

Montane, usually growing in tussocks and
often on disturbed ground. Foxtail has
the largest, fluffiest head of any Rockies
grass. This is a beautiful plant; the winds
of late summer and early autumn set
fields of foxtail nodding in
coppery-hued waves.

Needle-and-thread/spear grass
Stipa comata

On dry slopes at low elevations, mostly
south of Bow River but also found at
Jasper and perhaps farther north. When
you see it up close, you realize that
needle-and-thread is aptly named, for the
seed heads look like small threaded

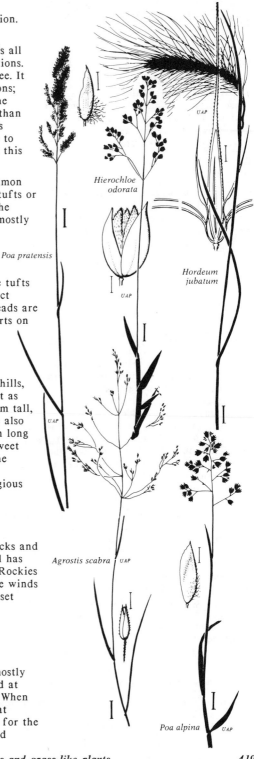

Hierochloe odorata

Poa pratensis

Hordeum jubatum

Agrostis scabra

Poa alpina

Grasses and grass-like plants

419

needles. And the needles are even sharp.
The species grows in spreading tufts.

Timber oatgrass
Danthonia californica

Dry montane meadows and gravelly
places, sometimes subalpine. Grows in
dense tufts 10-50 cm tall. The leaves are
moderately broad and often hairy, but
this grass is easy to identify by the very
large parts that make up the heads.

Ricegrass
Oryzopsis asperifolia

Open montane woods, common from
Banff south, in tufts. The leaves are
mainly basal, reaching upward along the
stems. Distinctive heads with rice-like
parts on short stalks.

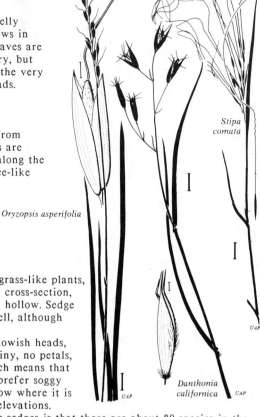

Stipa comata

Oryzopsis asperifolia

Danthonia californica

Sedges

Sedges (family Cyperaceae) are grass-like plants,
but their stems are triangular in cross-section,
not round, and solid rather than hollow. Sedge
leaves are often triangular as well, although
more flattened than the stems.

Green with brownish or yellowish heads,
sedges have grass-like flowers (tiny, no petals,
brownish or purplish parts) which means that
they are not at all showy. Most prefer soggy
places, although some species grow where it is
dry. You can find sedges at all elevations.

The horrible thing about the sedges is that there are about 80 species in the
Rockies and nearly all belong to only one genus: *Carex*. Thus they are extremely
difficult to identify because they look so much alike. Even professional botanists
agonize over them. Job Kuijt, who produced a weighty tome on the flora of
Waterton Lakes National Park, summed it up well when he introduced the
70 *Carex* species known from Waterton as "an extraordinarily large and difficult
genus," the identification of whose members requires "a special kind of courage
and devotion." (Kuijt, 1982, page 207)

That explains why, in so many botanical checklists for various places in the
Rockies, one finds the sedges under "*Carex* spp.," with nary a species name given.

What if, like me, you are not even a botanist? You give up early in the game.
For this book I have simply picked out a few common, representative sedges and
stuck them in. The idea is not to try to identify species, but just to see what
sedges look like.

Here are a couple of things to look for in sedges:

- The peculiar, beaked, flask-like **perigynium**, the seed-carrying part of the sedge,
  which is what the botanist uses to differentiate species.

- The difference between male and female flower spikes on the same plant. Male
  flowers are usually above, with lots of stamens dangling out; female flowers are
  usually below and fatter-looking.

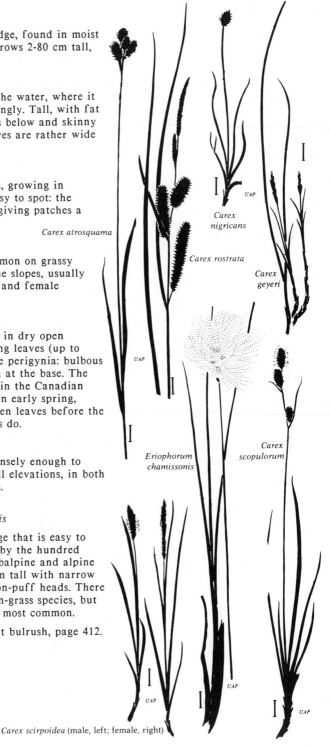

Carex atrosquama

A classic mountain sedge, found in moist subalpine meadows. Grows 2-80 cm tall, in tufts.

Carex rostrata

Montane marshes, in the water, where it grows in clusters or singly. Tall, with fat female flower-clusters below and skinny male ones above. Leaves are rather wide and flat, for a sedge.

Carex nigricans

A small alpine species, growing in patches on tundra. Easy to spot: the heads are very dark, giving patches a blackish look.

Carex atrosquama

Carex scirpoidea

This one is quite common on grassy montane and subalpine slopes, usually singly. Note the male and female flowerheads.

Carex geyeri

Southern region only, in dry open coniferous woods. Long leaves (up to 40 cm) and distinctive perigynia: bulbous at the top rather than at the base. The only evergreen sedge in the Canadian Rockies. Look for it in early spring, when it will have green leaves before the other grass-like plants do.

Carex scopulorum

This species grows densely enough to form sod. Found at all elevations, in both wet and dry locations.

Cotton grass
Eriophorum chamissonis

Finally, here is a sedge that is easy to identify. These grow by the hundred along the edges of subalpine and alpine bogs, standing 1-30 cm tall with narrow basal leaves and cotton-puff heads. There are a few other cotton-grass species, but this one is by far the most common.

See also common great bulrush, page 412.

Carex nigricans

Carex rostrata

Carex geyeri

Carex scopulorum

Eriophorum chamissonis

Carex scirpoidea (male, left; female, right)

Rushes

Rushes (family Juncaceae) are nondescript green-and-brown plants with tiny purplish flowers that have three petals and three sepals, like those of the lily family. They belong mostly to the genus *Juncus,* which (get ready) resembles the *Carex* sedges.

Fortunately it is easy to tell the sedges and rushes apart: rushes have hollow, round stems like grasses (but no joints), while sedge stems are solid and triangular in cross-section. Further, rushes have round leaves, not flat ones like grasses or flattened triangular ones like sedges. The flowering parts of rushes are usually larger, so the heads look coarser.

Juncus spp.

These are all short, easy-to-miss plants. They are mostly 10-20 cm tall (although some grow to 60 cm), usually found singly or in small groups—not densely colonial like many of the sedges. Only a few are tufted. Here are some common representatives from the 15 species in the Canadian Rockies.

Wire rush *(J. balticus)* prefers mud or shallow water at low elevations. Rigid, wire-like stems 20-60 cm tall, with a few brownish clasping leaves near the base.

Toad rush *(J. bufonius)* is a lower-montane plant, found in wet places. Tufted, but not colonial, 10-20 cm tall. The heads are at the ends of branches.

J. mertensianus grows in subalpine bogs. Note the solitary head.

Small-flowered woodrush
Luzula parviflora

Woodrushes are rushes that prefer drier places than *Juncus* rushes. So they grow in meadows and among the trees. Of the six Canadian Rockies species, this one is both the commonest and the easiest to identify. Note the many small nodding or drooping heads on branched stalks. The leaves are wider and flatter than those of other rushes.

Juncus balticus

Luzula parviflora

Juncus bufonius

Juncus mertensianus

FERNS, HORSETAILS AND CLUBMOSSES/SPIKEMOSSES

These plants do not bloom. Like the mushrooms, mosses and lichens they produce spores instead of seeds.

Lacking flowers, members of this group are perhaps harder to identify than the flowering plants—although the ferns have a lot of variety in their leaves, and that helps. Eleven common ones are included here. The horsetails are trickier to differentiate, while the clubmosses (and their close relatives, the spikemosses) are intent on remaining anonymous to anybody but a botanist. Still, there are two clubmosses that are fairly easy to pick out, and one spikemoss that is unmistakable. Three species of horsetail are quite common in the Canadian Rockies and easy to identify; they, too, are included.

Ferns

Ferns are moisture-loving plants, which means that one finds many more of them, and more species, on the western slope than on the eastern slope. The best places are in Columbian-forest areas of the Rocky Mountain Trench.

Note how some species have two distinctly different kinds of leaves: fertile ones, which carry the spore cases, and sterile ones, which do not. They look different.

A fern pokes out of the ground in a wheel-like roll called a **fiddlehead**. The fiddlehead unrolls and grows. Fiddleheads are tasty, but recently at least one species (bracken, page 424) has been shown to cause cancer in cattle.

Grape fern/moonwort
Botrychium spp. (adder's-tongue family)

Montane and lower subalpine meadows, but sometimes above timberline. Small (5-20 cm tall) but striking: the spore cases are carried above the leaves on a stalk. Several species, difficult to tell apart, except for *B. virginianum*, which is the easiest to identify because it has frillier leaves than other members of the genus. This is also the most common grape fern. Of the others, *B. lunaria* is also fairly common.

Steller's rock brake
Cryptogramma stelleri
(common fern family)

Western-slope montane, central and southern regions; occasional on the eastern slope from Banff south. Prefers mossy cliffs. Sparsely leaved and pale, it's not much to look at, but rock brake is interesting for its two kinds of leaves: narrow fertile leaflets and oval sterile ones. The fertile frond is taller, and the fertile leaflets have translucent edges that roll inward. The stems are yellowish. Compare with parsley fern (next entry).

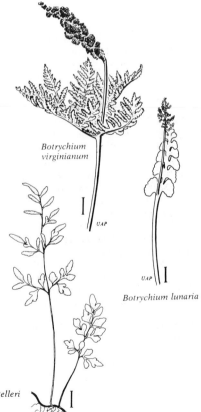

Botrychium virginianum

Botrychium lunaria

Cryptogramma stelleri

Parsley fern
Cryptogramma crispa
(common fern family)

Alpine and high subalpine, among rocks; sometimes much lower. Similar to Steller's rock-brake (previous entry), but the sterile leaflet edges are toothy and the fertile leaflets, which point upward, do not have translucent edges. Plant has more foliage and often grows taller (20-30 cm) than Steller's rock brake.

Lady fern
Athyrium filix-femina
(common fern family)

Montane and subalpine, in moist, shady protected places; common in Columbian forest. One of the larger ferns you are likely to see in the mountains: fronds up to 2 m long. Note how each frond has short leaflets at the base and the tip; there are wider ones between.

Bracken
Pteridium aquilinum
(common fern family)

Montane woods, western slope and occasional in Waterton. Another big fern, up to 2 m high. Simple shape: branches and leaflets along a stem—a single leaf, actually, growing from the rootstock. Lacy, delicate appearance.

Bladder fern and northwestern woodsia
Cystopteris fragilis, Woodsia oregana
(common fern family)

Bladder fern is the most common fern in the mountains, growing everywhere, in almost any situation. Small and delicate, with easily broken fronds 20-30 cm long. The stem is shiny and translucent.

This plant is easily confused with northwestern woodsia but is much more common. The only reliable way to distinguish the two is to look at the spore cases (the brown dots under the leaflets). On bladder fern, small veins pass under the spore cases and continue to the edge of the leaflet; on northwestern woodsia the veins end at the spore cases.

Cryptogramma crispa

Athyrium filix-femina

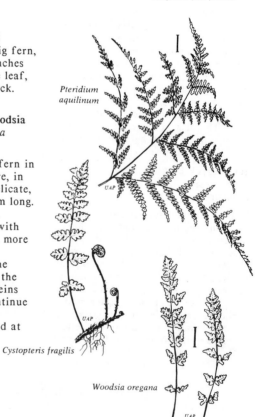

Pteridium aquilinum

Cystopteris fragilis

Woodsia oregana

Oak fern
Gymnocarpium dryopteris
(common fern family)

In deep forest, mostly lower subalpine. A
medium-sized, rather delicate-looking
fern, standing 20-40 cm tall. The stem
branches into three, each branch roughly
equal in size. Leaflets are dark green
down the centre and paler toward the
edges.

Cliff woodsia
Woodsia scopulina (common fern family)

A small fern, growing at all elevations
(but mostly subalpine and alpine) among
rocks in sunny places. More common on
the eastern slope. Prefers soil derived
from sandstones and shales rather than
from limestones or dolomites; common on
quartzites. Stems are dark-brown at the
base and yellowish near the ends. The
leaves are sparsely hairy but the stems
are smooth.

Holly fern/Christmas fern
Polystichum lonchitis
(common fern family)

A southern-region plant, rare north of
Bow River, often found among broken
rock and talus; sometimes growing in
meadows. Easy to identify: tough shiny
green prickly leaves. Several erect fronds
20-40 cm tall; stems covered with brown
scales. Leaflets are not symmetrical (see
illustration), and they stay green all
winter.

Other plants with fern-like leaves:

Lousewort, pages 365 and 403.
Yarrow, page 344.
Jacob's ladder, page 383.

Gymnocarpium dryopteris

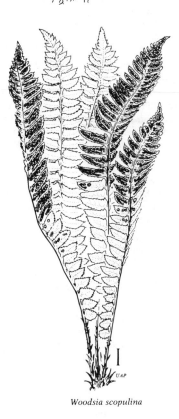

Woodsia scopulina

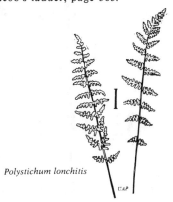

Polystichum lonchitis

More common in the Canadian Rockies than one might think, there are nine species you are likely to see here. Identification isn't easy in most of these. In addition to the short descriptions, pay close attention to the enlarged drawings of the stem joints, which are diagnostic features.

Common horsetail and other horsetails with side branches
Equisetum arvense and others
(horsetail family)

Ubiquitous along montane and lower subalpine roadsides, in meadows and woods. Can manage in ground that is rather dry; need not grow in wet places. Common horsetail normally stands 10-30 cm tall (although it can grow much taller), is medium green and has lots of side branches that give it a frilly look. After the first hard frost of fall, these plants lose their color and fall over, looking like fish skeletons before the silica in their bodies turns to dust.

Common horsetail produces two kinds of shoots: unbranched fertile ones, which come up in early spring, and branched sterile ones (thus lacking cones), which come up later.

Here are the other horsetails in the Canadian Rockies that usually have side branches.

E. pratense: in same habitat as *E. arvense* and often growing with it, but less common. Grows 20-50 cm tall. Distinguish by the slender, pointed branch ends with green margins in *E. arvense* and the triangular branch ends with white margins in *E. pratense,* which produces branched fertile shoots and a few sterile ones that are slender and pale, also branched.

E. sylvaticum: from Jasper north, usually in the woods; 30-60 cm tall. The branches usually curve down—unique in the Rockies. Like *E. pratense,* this species produces both sterile and fertile plants.

E. palustre: 20-60 cm tall; grows in marshy spots at low elevations. Uncommon.

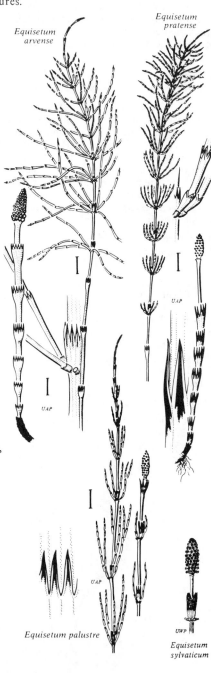

Equisetum arvense

Equisetum pratense

Equisetum palustre

Equisetum sylvaticum

Sedge-like horsetail
Equisetum scirpoides (horsetail family)

Common in damp montane and subalpine woods of the central region, usually growing in patches bordering marshes. Easily identified by its short size (5-15 cm). It is jointed and has no side branches; the stems are wavy rather than straight. From a distance, a patch of this plant looks grass-like.

Scouring-rush tribe
Equisetum spp. (horsetail family)

These species match the standard image of a horsetail: straight dark-green hollow jointed stems without side branches (although side branches are sometimes present).

E. variegatum: fairly short (10-40 cm), montane and subalpine, in moist meadows and gravelly stream flats or along lakeshores. Stems are evergreen (remain green under the snow), have 5-10 fine ridges. Most common unbranched species in the Canadian Rockies, but less so in the southern region.

E. fluviatile: central and southern montane and subalpine, usually growing in water. Up to 1 m tall, sometimes with side branches; stems delicately ribbed.

E. hyemale: central and southern montane, on streambanks and lakeshores. Up to 1 m tall, with tough gray-green evergreen stems that have 18-40 very rough ridges.

E. laevigatum: 30-80 cm tall, in open spots at low elevations from Bow River south. Can tolerate dry conditions. Stems have 14-20 ridges.

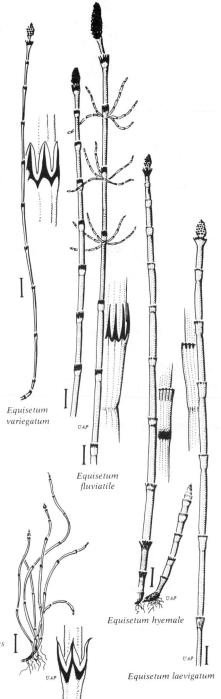

Equisetum variegatum

Equisetum fluviatile

Equisetum scirpoides

Equisetum hyemale

Equisetum laevigatum

The clubmosses and spikemosses look like heather (page 396) or crowberry (page 408): short stems covered with needle-like leaves. The way to tell them from heather or crowberry is to look for the cone-like spore cases on the clubmosses. You won't find anything resembling a cone on heather or crowberry; further, clubmosses and spikemosses are much less common than either heather or crowberry, so if you are strolling through heathery meadows there is no need to worry that you may in fact be strolling through clubmossy/spikemossy meadows. There may be patches of clubmoss/spikemoss to look at if you keep an eye open for them.

Stiff clubmoss
Lycopodium annotinum
(clubmoss family)

Montane and subalpine, in damp, shady places. Look for this one growing among feather mosses (page 429) on north-facing slopes. Erect spring-green stems 10-20 cm tall with sharp-ended leaves; yellowish cones at the stem ends. There are several other species of *Lycopodium* in the mountains, but they are much more difficult to recognize and differentiate than this one.

Ground-cedar
Lycopodium complanatum
(clubmoss family)

Mainly western-slope montane, in the woods; common in Columbian forest, occasional on the eastern slope. Looks very much like little fronds of cedar growing up out of the mossy forest floor. Scaly olive-drab stems branch repeatedly from the creeping rootstock.

Spikemoss
Selaginella densa (spikemoss family)

Mostly low-elevation montane, but occasional to timberline, in open dry places. Looks very much like some sort of coarse moss: fuzzy olive-drab stems, silvery near the tips, reaching up a couple of centimetres. But a close look will often reveal little cones at the ends of the stems, which would never be found on moss. During rainy periods this plant brightens up considerably.

Lycopodium annotinum

Lycopodium complanatum

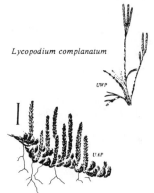

Selaginella densa

MOSSES AND LIVERWORTS

Mosses have only themselves to blame if they are largely anonymous to most of us. They are not flashy like wildflowers, poisonous like mushrooms or conspicuous like trees. Yet the mosses—especially the feather mosses—cover a lot of the forest floor in the Canadian Rockies. One might as well get to know a few species.

Mosses and liverworts (the two branches of the phylum Bryophyta) are not vascular plants: they have no roots and little means of moving water around in their bodies—no plumbing at all, really, which means that they quickly suck up any moisture that comes their way and hold onto it for as long as possible. Moss leaves are very small, while some liverworts are merely one large leaf-like body. Both groups stay green all the time, winter and summer, although they dull down a bit under the snow or during dry spells.

This dependence on incidental moisture leads mosses and liverworts to favor damp places in which to grow: along streams, at springs and seeps, or in bogs. To cut losses by evaporation, many bryophytes live in the shade. The cool, damp subalpine forest is just right, as are Columbian-forest areas of the western slope.

Still, a few species are good enough at hoarding moisture to make a go of it on the driest of bare-rock cliffs and sunbaked slopes. Cold is not a particular problem; mosses can spend a good part of the year frozen to some high-country crag, revving up the photosynthetic factory whenever there is liquid water about.

Most bryophytes are colonial, living shoulder-to-shoulder (well, gametophyte-to-gametophyte) with many others of their own kind.

This is cozy, no doubt, but possibly boring. Fortunately the monotony is relieved by interesting sex. To reproduce, the bryophytes have several choices. They can grow sexual organs, contribute sperm and egg, then send up a sporophyte and release spores. If that is too much trouble they can create little reproductive packets called "gemmae," which fall off and germinate. If all else fails, this group has the choice of going to pieces: fragmenting, each bit starting anew.

Except to the specialist, mosses and liverworts are difficult to identify. It's all done through a magnifying glass (or, worse, through a microscope). And, of course, there are many species. For the purpose of this book it seems adequate to introduce the more common groups in the Rockies, illustrating them with species likely to catch your eye. The many nondescript ones—the Little Green Mosses—can be left for the bryologists to sort out.

Mosses of the forest floor:
the feather mosses

Easily the most obvious and perhaps also the most common bryophytes of the Rockies, feather mosses cover the shady ground in montane and subalpine coniferous forests. They don't do well in deciduous woods, where the falling leaves tend to bury them. We are speaking here of very frilly mosses, the tiny leaves growing along branching stems 5-10 cm long.

Stepping off a dusty, hard-packed trail into pillowy feather moss is a treat for tired feet—although not particularly kind to the moss. The thing to do is to lie down on your tummy and get nose-to-moss, preferably with a magnifying glass. Don't worry; there are no tiny beasties in this micro-jungle to bite you, although in spring you should

Feather mosses

check yourself for ticks (page 481) when you get up.

There are four kinds of feather mosses you are likely to see in the Canadian Rockies, as described below.

Stairstep moss *(Hylocomnium splendens)* is the most common feather moss on the eastern slope. Tiers of curving branches come off the main stem, each tier representing a year's growth; these stair-like tiers give the plant its common name. The tiny leaves stay pressed tightly together. The branches have branches.

Big red-stem *(Pleurozium schreberi)* is the most ordinary-looking feather moss, but still easily differentiated by the red stem; all the others have green stems. The leaves are larger than those of most feather mosses, though smaller than those of *Rhytidiadelphus* (next entry), growing on the stem and on branches that stick out from the stem at right angles. The upper stem often nods to one side.

Goose-neck moss *(Rhytidiadelphus triquetrus)* has the largest leaves but the fewest branches. It looks very fuzzy; the leaves grow on the stem as well as on the branches, and the tips hang over, goose-necked. The color is spring green. On the western slope this is the most common feather moss.

Knight's-plume *(Ptilium crista-castrensis)* is the featheriest feather moss. The many branches are regularly arranged left and right along the stem like an ostrich feather, becoming gradually longer farther down. The tiny leaves curl downward, each like a sickle.

Dicranum spp. are also common among the feather mosses of the subalpine forest floor. They are coarse and fuzzy, standing erect with no side branches. If it is possible for a moss to look windswept, these do.

Barbilophozia lycopodioides is another plant you may find in this community. It's an olive-green single-stemmed liverwort (moss relative; see page 434) that looks a lot like a moss. The tiny

Drawings in this section labeled *WS* have been reproduced from *Bryologia Europea*, by W. Ph. Schimpher (a 1971 reprint of the classic 19th century work).

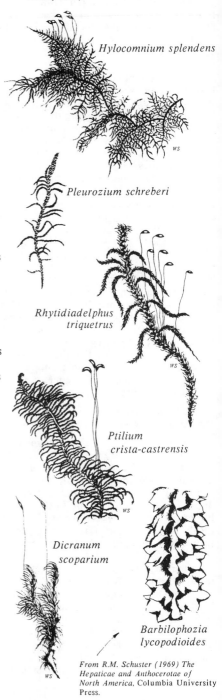

Hylocomnium splendens

WS

Pleurozium schreberi

Rhytidiadelphus triquetrus

WS

Ptilium crista-castrensis

WS

Dicranum scoparium

Barbilophozia lycopodioides

WS

From R.M. Schuster (1969) *The Hepaticae and Anthocerotae of North America*, Columbia University Press.

Mosses and liverworts

four-pointed leaves are arranged in two opposite rows along a single unbranched stem; they are translucent and a little slimy-looking.

Polytrichum commune hides among the feather mosses and humus. This is the largest moss in the mountains, easily identified by the heavy stems, which are up to 3 cm thick and 30 cm long.

Swamp mosses (peat mosses)

In the central and northern Canadian Rockies there is a special kind of swamp called **muskeg**: a heavily vegetated black-spruce bog with hummocks and hollows. Sometimes the surface will support your weight. Breaking through puts you up to your knees (or deeper) in smelly black muck.

It takes dedication to be a peat-moss bryologist.

There are two main mosses that grow in Rockies peat bogs, neither of them a species of the genus *Sphagnum,* which is the only true peat moss (in the botanical sense). *Sphagnum* is common elsewhere in the world and does grow here, but not abundantly. Instead, we have mainly *Drepanocladus* species, which prefer the soggy hollows, and *Tomenhypnum nitens,* which forms the hummocks. Both are golden-brown, long-leaved and frilly looking; tell them apart by the curving, overlapping leaves of *Drepanocladus* and the fuzzy stems of *Tomenhypnum.*

Speaking of peat: what exactly is it, and how does it form? Peat is the first stage of what eventually becomes coal. In bogs, the stagnant water carries little oxygen, so the decay process is very slow. It can take hundreds of years for the cellulose that makes up the plant fibers to break down into its main components (carbon, hydrogen and oxygen).

The oxygen is quickly used by other organisms, while the hydrogen combines with sulphur, always present in living tissues, to be released as stinky hydrogen sulphide (H_2s). Some of the carbon winds up in the other common swamp gas, methane (CH_4), but much of it simply collects as peat, becoming purer as time goes by. After several thousand years the stuff is concentrated enough to burn, once it has dried out—ask any Scot.

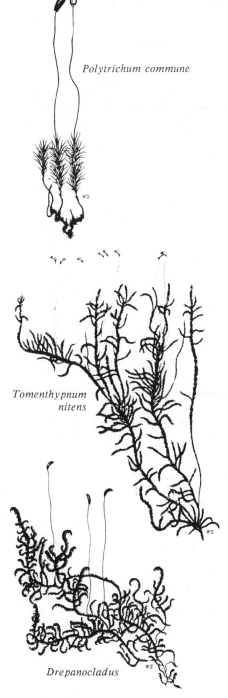

Polytrichum commune

Tomenhypnum nitens

Drepanocladus

On our side of the Atlantic we don't burn peat; we wait a hundred million years or so until it has become nearly pure carbon, i.e. coal. But we destroy our muskegs anyway, digging them up to get at the blackened bottom layers of dead moss, which go into our gardens and around our potted plants. The next time you see a bulldozed-out bog in the foothills, you will know what happened.

Beyond commerce, peat has value to science. Swamp and lake bottoms can be cored, yielding peat records of the recent geological past and telling us what the weather was like thousands of years ago.

Mosses along streams and at springs

Small perennial streams and springs with steady water levels are terrific places for bryophytes to grow, so there will be lots of anonymous Little Green Mosses there, many of them species of the genera *Bryum, Pohlia* and *Cratoneuron.*

If the water level varies a good deal, which is typical of front-range streams, you may find *Hygrohypnum luridum,* a coarse brownish-green moss that grows in the narrow zone between high and low water (the splash zone). In winter, anyone walking up the dry streambed of Maligne Canyon between Fifth Bridge and Fourth Bridge can easily locate the summer water level, which is marked along the canyon walls by *H. luridum.*

On the western slope, look for *Scouleria aquatica* on wet rocks just above the water line. This moss prefers to stay soggy all the time.

Mosses on cliffs and in other rocky places; alpine mosses

The north side of any rocky outcrop is likely to be very mossy in the Canadian Rockies, especially if the rock is limestone. Cliffs at any elevation mimic the alpine-zone environment: they are extremely variable in surface temperature, alternately wet and dry, with little or no soil. For this reason many of the moss species one sees atop The Whistlers, a mountain overlooking Jasper, also grow on Old Fort Point, a hill just across the river from the town.

The mosses that live in this difficult environment depend on rain and snowmelt for water, but as bryophytes they are good at conserving it—especially

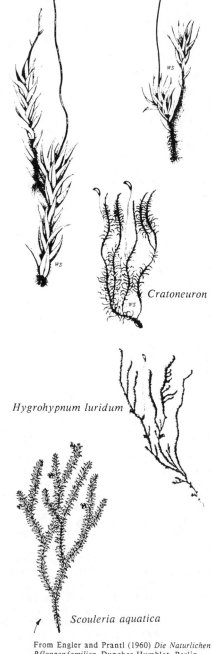

Bryum

Pohlia

Cratoneuron

Hygrohypnum luridum

Scouleria aquatica

From Engler and Prantl (1960) *Die Naturlichen Pflanzenfamilien.* Duncher Humblot, Berlin.

Mosses and liverworts

on the shady side of the rock. Vascular plants such as wildflowers, which have roots, require soil in which to grow; they fare poorly on vertical rock. But mosses don't have roots, don't need much soil (if any), and thus fit the cliffside ecological niche quite nicely. Bryophytes do well on the stony ground above timberline for the same reasons.

Grimmia species are small and tufted, often very dark green or even black. Look for tiny white hair points sticking up above the surface. This genus is the aridity champion, growing in amazingly dry spots. The drier the conditions, the blacker the moss. *Grimmia* survives on south-facing rocks in the hot summer sun, on the ground on sunny, open slopes at low elevations; it luxuriates in the relative comfort of a cool north-facing cliff.

Orthotrichum species look a lot like *Grimmia* (previous entry) and grow in similar places, but are larger and lack hair points. The surface sometimes has a whitish look. Capsules (spore cases) are often present, peeking up from the leaves.

Thuidium abietinum is frilly and branched, rather like a small feather moss. It is thready when wet and fluffy when dry.

Tortula ruralis is orangish and fuzzy-looking, with white hair points. It takes up water very quickly, swelling noticeably in only 10 or 15 seconds; the leaves clasp the stem when dry, but stand off it when wet.

Encalypta species are easily identified by the prominent dunce-cap-like structures that stick up from the surface on wire-like red stalks. Called **calyptras**, they cover the plant's spore-bearing capsules. How modest.

Ditrichum flexicaule has very fine, narrow leaves arranged spirally around the stem. It resembles *Distichum capillaceum*, which has two rows of tiny leaves on a shiny stem. Both species grow back in limestone or dolomite crevices that

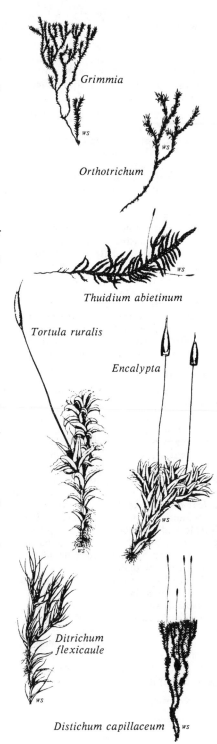

Grimmia

Orthotrichum

Thuidium abietinum

Tortula ruralis

Encalypta

Ditrichum flexicaule

Distichum capillaceum

seep slowly. Here they get a little
moisture.

Hypnum revolutum and *H. vaucheri* are
creeping and branched. All the tiny
leaves curl down the same way, and
they are tightly pressed together
along the stem.

Hypnum vaucheri

Polytrichum and *Pogonatum* are called
the **hairy-cap mosses.** Low and
round, they resemble nothing so
much as tiny pincushion
cacti—especially when wet, which
causes the radially arranged leaves
to spread out. When dry, these mosses
close up. They grow singly or in
small groups on the ground,
preferring non-calcareous soil and
usually choosing sandy places among
rocks at high subalpine and alpine
elevations. A good place to see
hairy-cap mosses is along the Path of
the Glacier Trail at Mt. Edith Cavell.
In *Polytrichum juniperinum* the
leaves are shiny with red tips; in
Polytrichum piliferum the tips are
white. *Pogonatum alpinum* is similar
but with dull leaves and green tips.

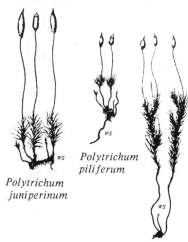

*Polytrichum
piliferum*

*Polytrichum
juniperinum*

Pogonatum alpinum

Liverworts

Liverworts resemble some lichen species. But liverworts are not algae-fungi
cooperatives, so they are not lichens.

Marchantia polymorpha is a common and interesting liverwort. It looks like
green plastic that someone poured onto the ground. The thallus (technical names
for a plant body that has no stem or leaves) is bright green, thick and leathery,
somewhat scaly and thready underneath. It gets 4-6 cm long.

Look for small colonies of
Marchantia in damp spots at any
elevation—especially in areas that burned
a year or two ago. Note the eye-catching
reproductive structures: umbrella-like
female and male organs, and cup-like
green or brown holders for gemmae that
are scattered by raindrops (the gemmae
grow into new plants).

The only plant likely to be mistaken
for *Marchantia* is the lichen *Peltigera
aphthosa* (page 438), which is white
underneath, rather than green, and lacks
umbrellas or gemmae cups.

Other liverworts are more moss-like.
Barbilophozia lycopodioides, a leafy
liverwort described on page 430, is a
good example.

*Male
stalk*

*Female
stalk*

Marchantia polymorpha

LICHENS*

Sometimes it can be hard to tell a moss from a lichen, especially in the case of the tree lichens, which many people mistakenly call "Spanish moss." This is wrong on two counts: (1) Spanish moss is not a moss, it is an epiphyte (rootless higher plant) called *Tillandsia usneoides* that hangs from trees, and (2) it grows from the southern USA to Peru, not in Spain. It doesn't grow here.

If the object in question is found any higher than about a metre up a live tree in the Canadian Rockies, it is always going to be a lichen. You might find a few mosses huddling around the base of the trunk, but they don't get more than a little way up.

What about mosses and lichens growing on rocks and on the ground? How do you tell *them* apart? Again, this is easy: mosses have leaves, no matter how tiny, while lichens do not. Lichens have crust-like lobes, worm-like tubes, or other definitely un-mossy structures. Further, mosses are nearly always green (although *Grimmia,* page 433, can be quite dark, practically black), while lichens are usually other colors: gray, yellow, red, black, white—although there are a few lichen species that are quite green.

The main difference between bryophytes and lichens, though, requires a microscope to see: lichens are strange composite plants made up of an alga and a fungus living together. The fungus provides the plant structure, cradling the algal cells safely inside. The algal cells contain chlorophyll, so they photosynthesize food. This is shared with the fungus in a classic example of **symbiosis:** a partnership that benefits both members.

Something to consider as you hop from one lichen-covered boulder to the next: these are beyond a doubt the oldest plants in the mountains. Growing outward slowly and steadily, some colonies may date back to the end of the last major glaciation 11,000 years ago.

Lichens on trees

Lichens that grow on wood are plentiful in Rockies forests, especially in heavy subalpine stands. They hang in hair-like masses, encrust the bark and tuft the gnarled, barkless trunks and branches of dead conifers. Here are the common ones.

Usnea (pronounced "UZ-knee-uh") species, which can be called **old man's beard,** are commonly misidentified as Spanish moss, which doesn't grow here. *Usnea* is pale greenish gray, hanging from twigs in coarse hair-like masses. It is never black like *Bryoria* (next page). Gently pulling a strand of *Usnea* apart reveals a central cord that is just a little stronger that the sheath. The trees along Highway 93 upstream from Radium Hot Springs are loaded with old man's beard.

Alectoria species are less common in the Canadian Rockies than *Usnea*. They are yellowish green and lack the elastic central cord.

Photos followed by "DV" are by Dale Vitt.

Usnea

Alectoria

*Proper English pronunciation is "LIKE-ens," not "LITCH-ens."

Bryoria species (until recently included in the genus *Alectoria*) are called **hair lichens.** They hang from trees rather like *Usnea* and *Alectoria,* but are much darker in color and thinner, like wisps of black horsehair hanging from dead twigs and branches. There is no central cord. The genus is especially common in subalpine forests, where the height above ground of the lowest hair lichens shows the maximum winter snow depth in an average year.

Bryoria

Hypogymnia physodes and *Parmelia sulcata* are scaly, covering the surfaces of twigs with gray-green lobes. In color and form they closely resemble each other, but pulling apart a lobe of *Hypogymnia* shows that it is hollow, while *Parmelia* is solid.

Hypogymnia

Parmeliopsis ambigua resembles *Parmelia sulcata* (previous entry), but grows mainly on the lower trunks of trees rather than on branches and twigs, never higher than the portion covered in snow.

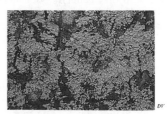

Parmeliopsis ambigua

Cetraria pinastri is another twig-encrusting lichen. The thallus is green with yellow edges.

Wolf lichen *(Letharia vulpina)* is brilliantly greenish yellow. It grows in showy tufts on dry wood that has lost its bark, most plentifully in the high-subalpine woods. Reputed to be toxic, the common name comes from its supposed use in poisoning wolves.

Cetraria pinastri

Lobaria pulmonaria is instantly recognizable: large and papery, loosely swaddling the lower limbs of trees in Columbian forest. The upper surface is pale gray-green, bright green on a rainy day (or within a minute of wetting), and coarsely veined. The back side is quilt-like, with white lumps against light-brown channels. White **soredia** (powdery clumps of algae and fungal threads) cluster along the edges. This weird plant looks vaguely evil, like something out of the science-fiction film *Aliens.*

Letharia vulpina

Lichens on the ground

The farther north you go along the Rockies chain, the more lichens you will find on the ground, especially above treeline. There is some sort of lichen divide at the latitude of the Columbia Icefield; north of there the ground-growing lichens (folk name: "reindeer lichens") are markedly more common—and it is from the Columbia Icefield north that you find caribou, which are dependent on lichens.

Lobaria pulmonaria

Cladonia species are the commonest forest-floor lichens in the Canadian Rockies. The many species are mostly greenish gray, sometimes pale tan, and always erect. Most produce **podetia**: hollow structures up to 10 cm tall. These take three forms:

1.
Worm-like rods.

2.
Irregular branching rods that end in knobs.

3.
Cupped structures that look like little gray golf tees.

Cladonia chlorophaea

If the podetia are rather irregular and tipped with bits of brilliant red color, the species is probably *C. coccifera,* a common one here. Worm-like ones are often *C. cornuta.* The very golf-tee-like ones are likely to be *C. chlorophaea, C. gracilis* or *C. pyxidata,* all going by the folk name **pixie cups.**

Thamnolia vermicularis is a tundra lichen. Like *Cladonia* (previous entry) it produces worm-like rods, but they are bone white, not gray-green, and shorter (3-6 cm) than those of *Cladonia.* Each rod is a separate plant; it is not attached to anything and simply lies on the ground, or sometimes on rock surfaces. Yellow rods 2-3 cm tall in tundra are *Dactylina arctica.*

Thamnolia vermicularis

Dactylina arctica

Cladina spp. are the reindeer lichens proper, known to model-railroad buffs as the miniature bushes they use in their layouts. The hobby-shop variety, usually *C. stellaris,* has been dyed; the natural color is a pale yellowish gray. Sponge-like and

Cladina mitis

rounded, 5-10 cm across, the species prefers alpine tundra. The other common species are more irregular. In this latter group we have gray-green ones *(C. rangiferina)* and yellow-green ones *(C. mitis).*

Stereocaulon spp. are steel-gray masses up to 8 cm tall, tightly convoluted and reminiscent of cauliflower. Below timberline the usual species is *S. tomentosum;* above it is often *S. paschale.*

Stereocaulon

Peltigera spp. are common on the forest floor, often growing with feather mosses. Two species are easily identified:

    P. canina, the **dog-ear lichen,** is flat and spreading, wrinkly at the edges, growing to 20 cm across. The color is dull olive-drab on top (from the bluegreen algal component) and white or tan underneath, with rootlike threads (**rhizines**) that anchor the plant to the soil.

Peltigera aphthosa

    P. aphthosa is similar but green—brilliantly green when wet—because the algal component is green rather than bluegreen. But there are dark, warty dots (**cephalodia**) scattered on the surface that are colonies of bluegreen algae. Underneath there are hairy veins.

Cetraria tilesii

Cetraria tilesii is the most common yellow tundra lichen. It is foliose, resembling peeling paint, and it prefers calcareous soil. There are other *Cetraria* species, identified mainly by color: *C. nivalis,* which is cream-colored, and *C. cucullata,* which is also cream-colored but has greater in-turning at the edges.

Cetraria cucullata

Solorina crocea is a small but distinctive alpine ground lichen that prefers acidic (non-limy) soil, especially along trails used by horses. It is flat, like *Peltigera,* but smaller: only 4-6 cm across. The top surface is nondescript pale greenish brown, but check the edges: they are brilliantly orange.

Icmadophila ericetorum is also easy to recognize. It looks like patches of powdered sugar with pinhead-sized, salmon-colored spots called **apothecia.**

Icmadophila ericetorum

A bryology student at the University of Alberta has given *Icmadophila* the perfect common name: **fairy upchuck**. Look for this delightful stuff on the cut banks of trails in moist forest, where it is often found overgrowing mosses.

Lichens on rocks

Many rock-encrusting lichens are of the **crustose** type, a large group whose members are notoriously hard to identify. Most are gray or black, in various shades, and they require laboratory work with microscope and chemicals to differentiate to even the genus level. Thus, we have Little Gray Lichens to go with our Little Green Mosses, Little Brown Mushrooms and Little Gray Birds.

However, some lichens that grow on rocks *can* be identified rather easily. These are mostly **foliose** lichens: attached to the rock, but not very tightly. They can be removed without scraping them to dust, as is the case with crustose lichens. Sometimes you can even peek under foliose lichens to inspect their diagnostic underparts without scraping them loose. As always, a true-blue naturalist brings his eye down to the plant rather than ripping the plant up for inspection.

Xanthoria is the easiest of the rock lichens to identify. It's orange, the only orange lichen of its size in the Canadian Rockies, reaching 5 cm across and often intergrowing to form wider colonies. We also have *Caloplaca,* another orange crustose lichen, but this species is usually pinhead-sized and thus easily differentiated from *Xanthoria.*

Xanthoria elegans

Xanthoria looks to be a crustose lichen, but close inspection shows that it is foliose: the lobes are lumpy, fairly thick and rather easily removed from the rock. There are several species in the Canadian Rockies, colonizing limestone, sandstone and shale from the lowest elevations to the highest rocky summits; the most common is *X. elegans.*

This ecological success has come in spite of a need for nitrogen, a rare commodity in forms usable by plants. *Xanthoria* gets its nitrogen by growing where small animals and birds regularly excrete. That is why one so often sees orange lichens on high points where hawks and eagles perch, on cliff walls below ledges where ravens have nested, or anywhere that wood rats or chipmunks scurry about the rock.

Rhizocarpon geographicum, the **map lichen,** is also easily identified. It is uniquely lime green with black mottling. Crustose, it grows only on non-calcareous substrates such as quartzite, which it colonizes extensively in the main ranges.

Rhizocarpon geographicum

    R. geographicum lives a very long time: up to 9600 years in the arctic. It colonizes glacial moraines soon after the ice moves back, and it grows at a known rate (in the central Rockies about 0.42 mm/yr for the first 110 years, 0.114 mm for the next 140 years and perhaps even more slowly from then on). By measuring the diameter of this lichen on moraine boulders, geologists have established the history of glacial advances and retreats over the last few hundred years in quartzite-rich parts of Jasper and Banff parks. The Path of the Glacier interpretive trail at Mt. Edith Cavell develops this topic.

Even more geographical-looking are the intergrown colonies of **crustose lichens** one commonly finds on streambank boulders (as long as they are not of limestone or dolomite). The many species—too numerous and too taxonomically difficult to be covered here—look much like varicolored maps, complete with black dividing lines between colonies. Some common ones: *Bacidia, Buellia, Lecanora* and *Lecidea*.

Crustose lichens on quartzite

Umbilicaria is a genus that should be familiar to anyone who has crossed a quartzite boulderfield in the rain. These dark-brown lichens swell when wet, becoming gelatinous and amazingly slippery underfoot. Each plant is anchored at only one point, so not only is it slippery, it breaks loose when you step on it.
    U. krascheninnikovii is a common species, the "krasch" part being most appropriate.

Umbilicaria

MUSHROOMS AND OTHER FUNGI

Mushrooms grow all over the Rockies, from the wooded valley floors to the barren heights. I have seen them popping up in patches of white dryas on the rocky summit of Yamnuska Mountain and growing on discarded food deep in Cadomin Cave. But there is a difference in occurrence on either side of the continental divide: mushrooms, puffballs, shelf fungi and the like do better on the warmer, wetter, shadier western slope than they do on the cooler, drier, sunnier eastern slope. One sees more fungi (and more fungal variety) in Columbian-forest areas (see map on page 264) than anywhere else.

We are speaking here of primitive plants that lack chlorophyll and thus do not manufacture their own food. They must get it somewhere else. Where? From dead organic matter, from soil, from feces, from living things. From rotting logs, elk droppings, dead animals, live insects—but most often, surprisingly, from the roots of living plants. The notion that mushrooms are all saprophytes is quite wrong. The vast majority are **mycorrhizal**. They surround and penetrate the roots of green plants, taking starches from them. In doing so, the fungi somehow increase the absorptive powers of the host roots, providing more moisture, more minerals, more nitrogen. In the case of lichens (page 435), specific fungi and algae combine to prosper where neither organism could manage alone, and the same is doubtless true of many mushroom/green plant associations.

While we are dealing with misconceptions, it is important to say that toadstools and mushrooms are the same thing. But just as geologists don't have any use for the word "dirt," so botanists in Canada and the United States seldom use "toadstool." They use "mushroom."

Mushroom life is fairly simple. Below ground, or usually otherwise out of sight, is the **mycelium**: a collection of thread-like **hyphae** that spread through or around the food source. If you have seen mold, you have seen a mycelium. The mycelium, which is a rather primitive thing, manages to grow a far more complex **carpophore**—the mushroom proper—which emerges into the air and sun. The carpophore is the reproductive equipment of the plant. It produces spores that grow new mycelia.

Spore dispersal is so effective that many mushroom species are distributed worldwide. The same mushroom species you see at Bow Lake might turn up in the Alps, the Andes, the Himalayas—or in your front yard, if the growing conditions are right.

Edibility

Dare you *eat* the mushroom in your front yard? Here is a wonderful ambiguity, the source of man's fascination with mushrooms. Many are tasty, but some are poisonous, even life-threatening. Others will make you crazy for awhile. If the squirrels eat a particular species, is it safe for us? If the juice discolors silver, is it poisonous? Do the poisons disappear if the mushroom is cooked or dried?

Reject these folksy notions, for they are all false. The only safe way to go about this game is to know exactly what you are doing—that is, *you've got to know exactly what you have picked.* When in doubt, don't eat.

Further, don't eat much the first time. Many people have allergies to various foods, and mushrooms are famous for going down well with one person while coming up rather nastily with another. Be cautious. Never sit down to a mushroom dinner hosted by someone who might not be reliable as a collector.

Avoid alcohol when eating mushrooms. Some species are perfectly harmless until you take a drink, then the symptoms come on. For the same reason, don't mix mushrooms at the same meal. Eat only one kind at a time or risk upsets caused by chemical clashes.

More words to the wise: always cook wild mushrooms. Don't eat them raw. Fungal tissues are for the most part indigestible by humans, but cooking helps the body to handle them. Eat mushrooms for their interesting flavor and texture, not for their nutritive value. In most species it is practically nil. At least mushrooms won't make you fat, unless you overdo the butter when frying them.

If all this puts you off eating mushrooms, please remember that anyone writing about them feels obligated to point out all the bad stuff first. And, in line with the preservationist outlook of this book, I'm not encouraging mushroom-picking. Like everything else in the Rockies, it is better to leave the fungi alone. Although less sensitive to mass picking than wildflowers, some mushroom species (particularly the boletes) disappear in heavily picked places.

Intoxicating and poisonous mushrooms known to occur in the Canadian Rockies

We have *Amanita muscaria* here, which will make you sick as well as high—although this magic mushroom is reportedly much less potent in North America than it is in Europe and Asia. I seldom see the hallucinogenic *Psilocybe* species, which are at least easy on your body if not on your mind. They prefer the wet, warm climate of the west coast, Vancouver Island and the Queen Charlottes over the relatively drier, colder climate of the Rockies.

Neither do we have many really poisonous species. The deadly *Amanita virosa* can turn up here, though. *Amanita pantherina*, which is supposedly toxic enough to kill small children, is fairly common, as is false morel, another nasty one. Fungi in the Canadian Rockies known or thought to be poisonous are noted as such in the text.

Identifying mushrooms

Making positive identifications of mushrooms is tricky. Mushrooms are fairly simple in structure; thus, there are few diagnostic features. Further, mushrooms can change considerably in appearance over a matter of a few days. The general pattern is this: the cap is rounded and brightly colored (if a colored species) when coming up, then it flattens, dries and becomes paler, finally blackening and shriveling.

A solid identification requires that you correctly determine:

- The texture, color and size of the cap surface. Shape is not as important in mos species as these other factors, for mushroom caps tend to be rounded when new flattening and turning upward at the edges later.
- The texture of the stalk, and whether rings are present.
- The gill type, arrangement and color.
- The color of the spores, as revealed in a **spore print**. To make a print, set the cap on a piece of white paper. After an hour or two, preferably overnight, lift the cap and look at the color of the spores left on the paper. In most species the color is unvarying and thus a reliable characteristic—although using a specimen that is too young or too old may give a spore print that is too light (or no spore-print at all).

Many identifications can be made without spore prints, but until you get to know a particular species you shouldn't neglect this step, particularly if eating is the goal. Making a print need not mean picking the mushroom. If you remove only part of the cap, leaving most of it and the stem intact, the mycelium will not be overly damaged and the mushroom will be back next year.

Ordinary capped mushrooms

Herewith the common, normal, mushroom-like mushrooms of the Canadian Rockies.

King boletus
Boletus edulis (August to October)
Choice edible

Very common in montane spruce/pine/aspen woods, found in soil and usually singly. A large mushroom, the cap buff to reddish-brown and often resembling a nicely browned bun. Smooth in dry weather, sticky in wet. Can be large: up to 30 cm across, usually 10-20 cm. Under the cap, but easily visible from the side, is a sponge-like mass of white to greenish-yellow pores instead of gills. The stalk is usually white, though sometimes brown, with a net-like texture. It thickens downward. King boletus goes buggy very quickly. Spore print: olive brown.

Admirable boletus
Boletus mirabilis (August to October)
Very good edible

Favors rotting hemlock, thus more common in Columbian forest than elsewhere. Smaller than king boletus (7-15 cm), but similar. The cap is rougher, the spongy pores underneath tend to be browner, the stem is pale brown rather than white, rough/pitted, taller/thinner than that of king boletus and not thickening as much toward the base. Spore print: olive brown.

Rough-stemmed boletus
Leccinum scabrum (July to August)
Edible

Look for this bolete around birch trees, sometimes near dwarf birch in high subalpine and alpine situations. It's a northern species on the western slope but fairly common all along the eastern slope. Looks like the other boletes described, but with a rougher stem marked by lines of raised black dots. The cap is large (up to 20 cm), grayish brown to yellowish brown and tends to be flatter than that of the other boletes. Spore print: brown.

Suillus
Suillus tomentosus (August to November)
Edible

In lodgepole pine forest. Boletus-like mushroom, 5-10 cm across, differentiated by its scaly, rather slimy cap (especially in wet weather) with brown flecks on yellow background, and yellow stem with brown dots and barely noticeable ring. Edible, although not particularly tasty. Spore print: dark olive drab.

Hedgehog mushroom
Dentinum repandum
(July to November; often quite late)
Edible

Tends to grow in groups or fairy rings under conifers in mixed-wood forests. Small to medium-sized mushroom, easy to recognize by looking under the cap: instead of gills or spongy pores, it has soft fragile white spines. The cap is creamy white and 5-15 cm across, usually with a depressed centre and a fold on one side. Stem always white and usually thickening upward. The hedgehog mushroom resists bugs and thus lasts a long time. New ones are good eating. Spore print: white.

Scaly tooth/shingle-top
Hydnum imbricatum (August to October)
Edible

Common in montane forests, usually in groups. A larger version of the hedgehog mushroom, up to 25 cm across the cap. Easily recognizable by the very rough cap surface, which is tiled with large brown scales. White spines underneath go gray to brown with age; the stem is pale brown and fairly smooth. Long-lasting like its relatives, the cap of scaly tooth gradually turns upward, becoming almost funnel-shaped as the days pass. Tasty when new; older ones become tough and acrid. Spore print: reddish brown.

Shaggy mane
Coprinus comatus (August to September)
Choice edible

In dense groups on disturbed ground, common in grassy places or pushing out of hard-packed earth—even paved road shoulders. Yet the plant is very delicate. Easily identified by the bullet-shaped, scaly white cap that gets speckled with black as the gills underneath deteriorate.

Eventually, only the stalk is left. Shaggy mane tastes rather like asparagus. But eat it soon; like inky cap (page 450), it soon liquifies. Unlike inky cap, shaggy mane won't make you ill if you have a drink after eating it. Spore print: black.

Shaggy parasol
Macrolepiota rhacodes
(September to October) CAUTION

On disturbed ground, compost heaps, along roads, single or in groups and fairy rings. Covered with large cinnamon-to-pink scales, the white cap shows more and more as the mushroom flattens. There is always one big scale at the centre. Stem smooth and white with a ring near the top. Gills are white at first; darken later. A choice edible mushroom and not likely to be confused with any other in the mountains, *except* a poisonous outsider named **green-spored lepiota** *(Chlorophyllum molybdites),* which looks similar (lighter-colored scales) and gives a green spore print. Spore print of shaggy parasol is white.

Russet-scaly trich
Tricholoma vaccinum (July to November)
Not palatable

Usually under pine or spruce. Scaly reddish-brown mushroom with lighter gills and a rough stem. Cap is 2-8 cm across, conical at first, flattening somewhat later; cobwebby veil bits stuck to the edge. Spore print: white.

Fly agaric
Amanita muscaria (June to August)
POISONOUS, mind-altering

Fly agaric is fairly common in montane woods, under conifers or birches—and on your lawn if you have these trees. This is a very beautiful gilled mushroom up to 30 cm across, frequently bright red but sometimes pink, orange or yellow. Bits of the white veil that covers the mushroom as it emerges adhere to the cap, although rain can wash them off. The cap is rounded at first, flattening out later as it grows larger. The stem is always white, with a skirt-like ring near the top and others at the base.

Fly agaric is famous as a dope mushroom (especially in Siberia), although the drug content is extremely variable and differs between North American and Asian specimens. The

Mushrooms

effects of our version are not pleasant: dizziness, uncoordination, muscle cramps and delusions, although without hallucinations. Intense activity, often violent, is followed by deep sleep. Three alkaloid drugs: ibotenic acid, which goes to muscimol and muscazone, all apparently used by the fungus as insecticides. Milk in which a cap is sitting will kill flies attracted to it. Spore print: white.

Panther agaric
Amanita pantherina (April to September)
POISONOUS, mind-altering

Similar in form and habitat to fly agaric (see previous entry for drawing), but pale brown or greenish rather than red or yellow. Same adhering bits of veil on the cap and rings (or more often a bulb) on the stem. Similar sort of poisoning, too, but worse. Spore print: white.

Giant clitocybe
Clitocybe gigantea (August to October)
Edible

Favors disturbed ground and open woods, singly or in groups and fairy rings. A big mushroom, 10-45 cm across, with a smooth white cap that tends to lift at the edges, exposing white gills that run a little way down the short, smooth, white, ringless stem. Edible but sometimes foul-smelling and bad tasting. Spore print: white.

Silvery-violet cort/silvery cortinarius
Cortinarius alboviolaceus
(August to October) Edible

In mixed woods, solitary or a few at a time. There are many *Cortinarius* mushrooms, most of them hard to differentiate, but this one stands out: it is shiny-gray with a violet cast. Cap is 3-6 cm wide, bell-shaped at first and flatter later, silky-textured with the edge turned under. The stem is thick and smooth or a bit gnarly, with that silvery-violet tinge. Gills are pale violet at first, becoming rusty brown later. Confirm the rusty spore-print before eating.

Tacky green russula
Russula aeriginea (July to September)
Edible if cooked

Common under aspen and lodgepole pine
in montane woods. Slightly sticky,
faintly radially lined cap 5-8.5 cm across,
greenish at least near the centre, which
becomes depressed. Gills and stalk
yellowish white. No rings on stalk. Not
recommended for eating raw. Spore print:
pale yellow.

Emetic russula
Russula emetica (August to September)
POISONOUS

Boggy places in montane and subalpine
woods, often among mosses in small
groups. Slimy, sticky, bright-red cap
2.5-7.5 cm across, flat or concave;
yellowish-white gills and stem. Stem is
dry and without rings. This one has a
bitter taste and makes you throw up.
Spore print: white.

Shellfish russula/woodland russula
Russula xerampelina
(August to September) Not tasty

Fairly common in Columbian forest, but
found everywhere under spruce,
Douglas-fir and hemlock. Cap
purplish-red to brown, 2.5-15 cm across,
smooth in dry weather, slimy in wet;
radial lines along the edge. Stem white to
pink and unringed, gills pale yellow.
Mushroom smells (and tastes)
unpleasantly fishy. Spore print: pale
yellow.

Meadow mushroom
Agaricus campestris
(August to September) Choice edible

In grassy meadows, where it can be quite
abundant. Medium-sized mushroom
3-10 cm across, convex cap white to
gray-brown, dry; fat stalk same color;
one ring at the top. Gills pink at first,
then darkening to brown. A close relative
of the common commercial mushroom,
but with more flavor.

    Be careful, though, that you are not
gathering a deadly *Amanita virosa* by
mistake. The poisonous amanitas have a
skirt-like ring on the stem and a cup or
bulb at the base; *Agaricus* species have
the ring but lack the cup or bulb. Spore
print is dark brown. See also poison pie
(page 448).

Bleeding agaricus
Agaricus haemorrhoidarius
(July to October) CAUTION

In moist mixed-wood forest, single or a
few at a time. Cap is 5-15 cm across,
brown-flecked and scaly; white or
pinkish stem has one ring on the upper
part. Gills are white at first, becoming
pinkish and then purplish-brown. Main
feature: flesh instantly turns bright red
when injured. Edible for most people;
upsetting for some. Spore print: dark
brown.

The prince
Agaricus augustus (July to September)
Choice edible

Prefers to grow singly in disturbed
ground; often found along montane roads
and paths. A big mushroom: cap up to
35 cm across, unfolding flat, with
down-curved edges, yellowish with
circular rows of brown scales. Flesh
bruises yellow. Whitish gills turn pink,
then brown. Stem is thick and short,
scaly and white, with a ring at the top.
This mushroom gives off an odor of
anise and almond; it is renowned for
taste and meatiness. Spore print: dark
brown.

Poison pie
Hebeloma crustuliniforme
(September to November) **POISONOUS**

In mixed-wood forests, often in fairy
rings on disturbed ground. Fairly small
cap (3-9 cm), buff at centre and paler at
edges, usually convex, but sometimes flat
or with uplifted edges. Stem white, flaky
near the top, no ring. Odor of radishes.
Most common of the *Hebeloma* species in
the Canadian Rockies; there are others,
but difficult to differentiate. All have
that sharp, radishy odor. Spore print:
brown to rust.

Anise-scented clitocybe
Clitocybe odora (July to September)
Edible

Montane and subalpine woods, more
common on the eastern slope.
Medium-sized (2-10 cm) rough gray-green
cap, aging paler with a dark bump in the
centre. Gills white to greenish, no ring
on the stalk. Strong odor of anise
(licorice). Spore print: pale pink to white.

Blewit
Clitocybe nuda (August to November)
CAUTION

In deep woods, common in Columbian
forest, found everywhere and usually in
small groups or alone. Also called *Lepista
nuda*. Cap convex to flat, with in-rolled
or at least down-turned margins,
10-15 cm across, uniformly gray-brown
with a purplish cast and dry, silky feel.
Rough white stem, often thick, no ring.
Gills notched where they meet the stem.
Tasty but not recommended by
mycologists because some *Clitocybe*
species are poisonous. Spore print: peach.

Honey mushroom
Armillariella mellea
(August to November) CAUTION

In clusters on living or dead trees; often
very common. Tends to kill its host.
Quite variable in appearance because of
variable stalk thickness. Cap usually
light brown, convex with in-rolled white
edge, 2-10 cm across and sticky with
erect dark hairs at the centre, becoming
scaly toward the edge. Gills white, stem
same color as cap toward base but white
and often thickening abruptly at the top,
where there is a ring.

 The honey mushroom produces black
rhizomorphs (runners) from its base;
these may be up to 100 m long.

 Oily odor and taste, but still relished
by some eaters, who must boil the thing
first or risk upset. Further, there are
some nasty look-alikes around, so be sure
of identification. Spore print of
A. mellea is white.

Fawn mushroom
Pluteus cervinus (May to October) Edible

Common on and over rotting wood, in
mixed-wood forest, present all summer
and well into fall, especially after rain.
Cap is 3-12 cm across, smooth or a bit
rough and brown to light gray. Stem
smooth and white. Gills creamy, pale
yellow or pink. Tasty only when freshly
emerged. Spore print: salmon-pink.

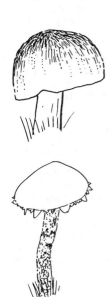

Questionable stropharia
Stropharia ambigua
(September to October) CAUTION

Occasional in Columbian forest, standing
singly. Easily identified by the cap:
5-15 cm across and slimy, the color of

brown mustard, with bits of white veil adhering to the edge. Stem is long and thin, quite rough, white, with a ring near the top. Gills are off-white to purplish-gray. Not tasty, and one of its relatives (*S. coronilla,* not known from the Canadian Rockies), is poisonous. Spore print of questionable stropharia: dark purplish-brown.

Slimy-sheathed waxy cap
Hygrophorus oliveaceoalbus
(September to October) CAUTION

Near Engelmann spruce, subalpine zone. An unappealing mushroom: slimy gray cap 3-12 cm across, white gills underneath, and a slimy white stalk with scabs of dark gray ick on it. Yet people eat it. The books recommend caution but don't say why. Spore print: white.

Inky cap/alcohol inky
Coprinus atramentarius
(May to September) CAUTION

In clusters near buried wood. A common and easily recognized mushroom: droopy, vertically lined gray cap 5-6 cm wide; slender pure-white stem with one ring at the base. Nipple-like touch of brown atop the cap; often pale brown or darker gray at the pleated cap margin. The gills of inky caps self-destruct in a few days by turning into a black liquid.

   If you want to eat this mushroom, do so before it starts to liquify and don't drink alcohol the day before or after. Inky caps take away the body's ability to break down any alcohol in the bloodstream; if you mix booze and inky caps you will probably have flushing of the face and neck, tingling in the extremities and an instant hangover. Symptoms last a few hours. Spore print: black.

Fuzzy foot
Xeromphalina campanella
(May to November) Not tasty

In clusters on well-decayed wood, most common on hemlock in Columbian-forest areas but found everywhere. Small orange mushroom only one or two centimetres across but easily identified by the hairy tuft at the base. Cap has radiating lines, is smooth and usually moist; stem yellowish at the top and unringed; gills cross-veined. Spore print: pale buff.

Buttery collybia
Collybia butyracea (July to September)
Not tasty

Under conifers. The cap feels greasy and looks buttery; this is one of the few mushrooms that is lighter in the centre and darker toward the edges. Looks as if a lump of butter were melting over the top of it, and even smells rancid. Cap 1-5 cm across; stem is gray to yellowish, narrowing upward, ringless. Spore print: white.

Dung-loving psilocybe
Psilocybe coprophila (June to October)
Hallucinogenic

On dung, especially that of domestic cattle. Sticky brown cap 1-3 cm across, with a yellowish stalk; very umbrella-like mushroom. A widespread psilocybe and not strongly psychoactive, but in quantity it will turn your mind into something like its substrate. Spore print: brownish purple.

Fairy-ring mushroom
Marasmius oreades (May to September)
CAUTION

In lawns or other grassy places, many at a time in the shape of a ring. This is an anonymous-looking small mushroom, cap 1-4 cm across and cream to pale brown with most color near the centre, where there is usually a knob. Long, thin, rubbery stems; creamy gills.

    Like other fairy-ring species, this one sends up mushrooms from the edge of a mycelium that grows steadily outward from the original growing site. Fairy rings can be quite old: up to 500 years. They are also attractive to young children playing on lawns. Eating the mushrooms from this kind of fairy ring won't do them any harm, but there are several poisonous ones (notably *M. cystidosius, Clitocybe dealbata,* and *Inocybe umbratica)* that can do a nasty number. So if you have little kids, keep their play spots clear of fairy rings. Spore print of *M. oreades*: white or buff.

Little brown mushrooms (LBMs)

Speaking of fairy rings: anyone interested in them will have to learn a great many species of small mushrooms before he knows what he is doing. Every biological branch has its little-brown-something-or-others; these are the mushroom versions. Some of them, such as the common lawn-growing *Galerina* species, are deadly, and there are other poisonous ones. Unless you are a real or aspiring mycologist, you may, like me, be happy to label the whole crowd LBMs and let them go at that. And not eat them.

Chanterelles and chanterelle look-alikes

If the cap is irregular and strongly turned up at the edges, so that the gills are easily visible, check this group.

Chanterelle
Cantharellus cibarius
(September to October) Choice edible

Montane, fairly common in Douglas-fir woods and brushy areas, in soil. Egg-yolk yellow to pale orange, medium-sized mushroom (10-15 cm across); vase-shaped, with a crinkly-edged cap and prominent coarse gill-like folds that are cross-veined between the ribs. Often smells like apricot. The flesh is white and solid.

This is a spicy, peppery mushroom; very popular in Europe (in Germany they call it the "Pfefferling": pepper mushroom). There are other edible chanterelles you may find: most commonly a white one *(C. subalbidus,* western-slope montane, white spore print) and a scaly one *(C. floccosus,* up to 20 cm across, reddish woolly scales). Be careful not to confuse these with the possibly-poisonous *Clitocybe aurantiaca* (next entry), which is smaller, doesn't have cross-veined gills and gives a white spore print. The spore print of the colored chanterelles is pale yellow or buff.

Orange clitocybe/false chanterelle
Clitocybe aurantiaca (August to October)
CAUTION

Montane forest, often in groups on soil or decaying wood. Resembles chanterelle (above), but is usually smaller (5-10 cm across), paler in color, with finer gills that lack the ladder-like cross veins of chanterelle. Rumored to be poisonous. Spore print: white.

Orange-latex milky/delicious lactarius
Lactarius deliciosus
(October to November) CAUTION

Singly in pine and Douglas-fir forests,
where it may be abundant. Another
chanterelle-like mushroom, this one with
smooth margins and zones of
lighter/darker orange color around the
cap. As it gets older, it becomes
green-stained. The *Lactarius* group ooze
a milky fluid when cut; in this species it
is orange. Eat with caution, for some of
the group are poisonous. Spore print:
cream.

Apricot jelly
Phlogiotis hellevoides
(May to July, August to October) Edible

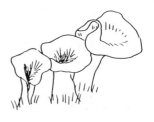

Under conifers, sometimes on rotting
trees. Translucent funnels 1-7 cm across
and up to 10 cm tall; reddish-orange to
pink. Resembles a chantarelle, but there
are no gills. Edible, but with rubbery
texture and little taste. Spores are white.

True and false morels

In these species the spores are carried on
top of the cap rather than underneath,
an arrangement that produces
weird-looking and thus readily
identifiable mushrooms. An easily
recognized group and common on the
western slope, the morels are tricky to
identify to the species level. But all are
edible and some are choice. Just be
careful that you haven't got a false
morel (page 454), for they can be quite
poisonous.

Yellow morel/sponge mushroom
Morchella esculenta (April to June)
Choice edible

The yellow morel is perhaps the most
common morel, coming up a few days
behind the last spring snows in
aspen/birch woods and bushy places.
Note the strange cap: deeply pitted, with
raised ridges between the pits. Cap is
pale yellow to medium brown, 4-5 cm
across. The white stem attaches at the
base of the cap, and the whole thing is
hollow—which means you have to slice it
open and check well for bugs before
cooking. Very tasty; dries well. Spores
are white.

Black morel/narrow-capped morel
Morchella angusticeps/elata
(April to May) CAUTION

This species prefers mixed woods and
can be plentiful in areas that have
recently burned. Similar to yellow morel
above, but more pointed and with a
darker cap. The stem is often deeply
grooved or even divided. This is perhaps
the tastiest of the morels, but may be
upsetting if eaten with alcoholic
beverages. Spores are white.

Conifer false morel
Gyromitra esculenta (April to June)
POISONOUS

Here is a potentially lethal mushroom
that looks rather like the prized morels:
lumpy brown cap with a white stem.
Further, this species of false morel
appears at the same time of year as the
true morels, although it prefers to grow
under conifers rather than broadleaf
trees. Differentiate by the cap: wrinkly
in false morel (3-10 cm across) rather
than pitted as in true morel.

False morel poisonings are caused by
monomethylhydrazine (MMH); symptoms
are severe gastrointestinal upset followed
by muscle cramps and uncoordination. In
the worst cases there is fainting,
convulsions, coma and death. Spores are
white. See also saddle-shaped false morel
(next entry).

Saddle-shaped false morel/
hooded gyromitra
Gyromitra infula (August to October)
CAUTION

Singly or a few at a time on disturbed
ground. This false morel has a
distorted-looking pale-brown cap
10-15 cm across. The stem is pale and
often inward-folded. Some people eat the
saddle-shaped false morel with no ill
effects; others experience upsets. The
problem is in differentiating from the
poisonous conifer false morel (previous
entry). Spores of *G. infula* are pale
yellow.

Fluted white helvella
Helvella crispa (September to October)
Edible

Montane woods. Rather similar to
saddle-shaped false morel (previous
entry), but white, with a ribbed, holey

stem. Cap 1.5-6 cm across. Not poisonous and fairly tasty. Spores of *H. crispa* are white.

Club-like fungi

These look like mushrooms that have lost their caps. That is not the case; in the club fungi there is no cap. The spores are on the exterior surface, although usually colorless and thus not very obvious.

Flat-topped coral
Clavariadelphus truncatus
(August to October) Edible

Common eastern-slope mushroom of montane woods. Pale orange, ochre or yellowish, 2-8 cm tall, with a flattened or depressed top and wrinkled sides. Sweet-tasting, although there are other species that are bitter. Spores are ochre.

Pestle-shaped coral
Clavariadelphus pistillaris
(July to October) Unpalatable

In lodgepole woods, in groups. Yellow to salmon-pink rods, rarely branching, 5-20 cm tall with swollen ends. Pale and hairy near the base of the stalk. Bitter taste. Spores white.

Cudonia
Cudonia circinans (July to September)
Unpalatable

In coniferous woods. Like the above, but browner and smaller, with more expansion at the top; looks at bit like it's wearing a shower cap. Spores white.

Dead-man's fingers
Xylaria polymorpha (June to October)
Edibility unknown

On rotting wood. Dark-gray fingery clubs 2-8 cm long, whiter in early stages. Spores are very dark.

Coral fungi

Usually on the ground but sometimes on wood, there are many coral fungi species, mostly of the genus *Ramaria* or *Clavaria*, which all look rather alike. Colors range from yellow-tipped orange to bright red and runs evenly along the branches.

The coral-like lichens *Cladonia*, *Thamnolia*, and *Dactylina* (page 437) resemble the coral fungi. But the fungi are hollow while the lichens are solid. The fungi last a few weeks and

Ramaria

disappear, while the lichens remain all the time.

The **cauliflower fungus** *(Sparassis radicata)* looks leafier. It is huge (up to 75 cm across) and bright yellow, going brown as it ages. Look for it in Columbian-forest areas in September and October.

Clavaria

Shelf fungi

When one thinks of a mushroom one thinks of a round-capped thing with a central stem. But if the stem is stuck on asymmetrically, off to one side of the cap, then you have the basic structure of many shelf fungi. Eliminate the stem entirely and you have the rest. Most shelf fungi (also called **bracket fungi**) are members of the polypore family; they have pores on their under surfaces rather than gills. Shelf fungi are hardier than most other fungi, maintaining their carpophores longer than the mushrooms do, even through the winter in some cases.

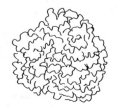

Cauliflower fungus

A shelf fungus requires something to make a shelf on. This is usually rotting wood (often a stump), but can also be live wood. Polypores tend to spread through a stump or a log in ever-expanding tiers; the mycelium within can cause a lot of damage in live trees—though, like insect infestations, shelf fungi are natural eliminators of old, weak trees.

Although some shelf fungi are edible, and even choice, most of them are woody-textured and unpalatable. But they are lovely to look at. I leave them where they be; many take a long time to grow and their mycelia are badly harmed when the carpophores are ripped off their moorings.

Included with this bunch is the smoky polypore (page 458), a lichen-like encrusting fungus.

Oyster mushroom
Pleurotus sapidus
(April to May; again in September)
Edible

Damp places, on decaying broadleaf trees. Colonies of very pale, wavy-edged delicate mushrooms 5-20 cm wide with short off-centre stems—or none at all. Is it a mushroom or is it a shelf fungus? Only its mycologist knows for sure. Spore print: white to violet-gray.

The oyster mushroom has a taste for the nematodes (microscopic worms) that live in dead wood. A toxin released by the mushroom paralyzes any nematode venturing into the mycelium. Hyphae then grow down the worm's throat and digest it from inside out—while it is still alive.

Angel wings
Pleurocybella porrigens
(September to October) Edible

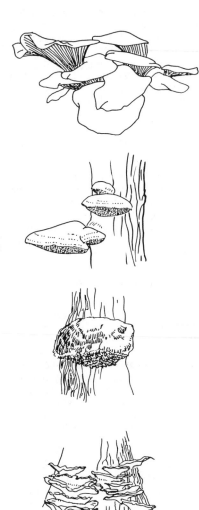

In colonies on rotting conifers. Common in Columbian forest, on hemlock and cedar. Angel wings look rather like the oyster mushroom (previous entry), but thinner and whiter. Spores are white.

Birch bracket-fungus/birch polypore
Piptoporus betulinus (year-round)
Unpalatable

On live or dead birch trees, in the Canadian Rockies on white birch. A fleshy, tough semicircular growth with concentric rings in varying shades of tan and brown, pale underneath, where there are pores instead of gills. Spores are white.

White spongy polypore
Spongiporus leucospongia
(August to November) Unpalatable

On stumps of subalpine-zone conifers. Rough brown top 3-10 cm across and rather irregular, with distinctive cottony underside. Spores are colorless.

Chicken mushroom/sulfur shelf
Laetiporus sulphureus
(May to November) CAUTION

In closely spaced tiers on stumps and logs; sometimes on living trees. Smooth-surfaced wavy-edged red-orange tops 5-30 cm across, often turned up at the edge and displaying brilliant yellow tubes underneath. Tastes like chicken, but eat it when it is young or risk swollen lips (allergic reaction). Spore print: white.

Jelly crep
Crepidotus mollis (June to October)
Unpalatable

In tiers on rotting deciduous trees. Brown to reddish brown hairy/scaly shelves 1-8 cm across with lighter margins; brown gills underneath (a stalkless mushroom, really). Spore print yellowish brown.

Violet toothed polypore
Trichapum biformis (May to November)
Unpalatable

Common in damp forests, sometimes by the hundred in open tiers on dead deciduous material. Tough, semicircular, mostly detached shelves 1-7 cm wide, concentrically zoned in grays and browns, becoming more violet toward the edge. Creamy violet pores underneath that get tooth-like with age. Spores are white.

Turkey tail
Trametes versicolor (May to December)
Unpalatable

On dead wood or at injured spots on live trees. A very beautiful, fan-like fungus of closely spaced tiers 3-10 cm across, each member with concentric zones of warm browns and tans; contrasting white margin. White to yellow pores underneath. Spores are white.

Smoky polypore
Bjerkandera adusta (July to November)
Unpalatable

Usually parasitic on living trees, often in drier locations. This species is inclined to kill the host, so you may also find it on dead wood. A smoke-colored lichen-like encrustation, sometimes shelf-like, paler gray around the edges. Actually it is a colony; on most specimens you can see concentric zones that show where the plants, individually 1-7 cm across, have grown together. Spores are white.

Cup fungi

Cup shaped, with the spores carried on the top of the plant rather than underneath. They scatter in wind and rain.

Yellow rabbit ears
Otidea leporina (August to September)
Edibility unknown

Single or in small groups on soil in coniferous woods. Each cup is elongated and tilted upward, so that it resembles a rabbit's ear. Smooth, 1-3 cm across, varying in color from deep yellow to pale orange. Spores are larger than those of most fungi; each contains two tiny droplets of oil.

Eyelash cup
Scutellinia scutellata (June to November)
Edibility unknown

In dense colonies on and around rotting
wood. Easily recognized: small red or
orange cups 1-2 cm across with dark
hairs around the edges that look just like
eyelashes. Underneath, the cups are
short-hairy. The spores are oily.

Bird's-nest fungi
Nidula, Cyathus, and *Crucibulum* spp.
(September to November)
Edibility unknown

On plant debris and on the ground, often
in the dung of browsing (twig-eating)
animals. Small cups a centimetre wide or
less, with egg-like spore packets inside,
waiting in gel to be tossed out when hit
by a raindrop. The airborne packet trails
an adhesive thread that catches in
nearby vegetation, often wrapping onto a
twig like a bolo. When an animal eats the
vegetation the spores pass through,
starting a new bird's-nest fungus in the
droppings.

    There are many species of bird's-nest
fungi in the mountains. They are allied
more closely with the puffballs
(page 460) than with the cup fungi, but
placed here because they look rather like
cup fungi.

Nidula candida

Jelly fungi

Here we have a weird group of plants
that most people will react to by saying
"yecch." Yet they are interesting, very
simple fungi without gills or stems. Some
folks actually *eat* them.

Witch's butter
Tremella mesenterica (year-round) Edible

Montane and lower subalpine, on alder
branches (page 313). Bright yellow or
orange lumpy blobs, soft and jelly-like in
damp weather, tougher when dry. A
similar plant, *Dacrymyces palmatus,* is
orangish and grows from a single point.

Tree-ear
Auricularia auricula
(May to June, again
September to November) Edible

In coniferous forest, a few at a time to
many in colonies. Fairly large (3-15 cm
across) and, as the name says, ear-like,

translucent brown and rubbery with
wart-like bumps. Spores are white.

Puffballs and earthstars

This chapter ends with the only group of
fungi that is any fun to play with: the
puffballs. Once a puffball has dried out
inside, and a small hole has opened in
the top, it begs to be squeezed, which
will eject the spores in little puffs of
dark-colored dust. This is most amusing
for kids, although inhaling the spores is
rumored to be unhealthy.

Puffballs are renowned for flavorful
eating. But before digging into one, be
sure that it isn't a poisonous amanita
mushroom (pages 445 and 446) still in
the bud stage. If there is any internal
structure—the developing cap, gills, veil
and so on—then leave it alone. Further,
don't eat a puffball that is anything but
white inside. Other colors indicate that it
is either past the palatable stage or
unsafe.

Gem-studded puffball
Lycoperdon perlatum (July to October)
Edible

On the ground at practically any
elevation. A little egg-shaped ball 2-6 cm
across; white with soft, short spines that
tend to disappear as the puffball ripens.
The white spore masses inside become
olive-drab about the same time the
covering becomes papery and the hole
opens. Tasty in the early stages. If it is
purple inside (or any color other than
white), don't eat it; it may be a
poisonous puffball-like fungus called
Scleroderma citrinum that has a tan
pigskin-like cover and splits open rather
than puffing.

Western giant puffball
Calvatia booniana (July to August)
Choice edible

In meadows; uncommon but seen more on
the western slope. A great big puffball
20-60 cm across, with buff warts. White
inside at first; later it goes olive brown
as the spores mature. Rather than exiting
through a hole as in most other
puffballs, the spores expand until the
ball cracks open. Don't eat if there is
any internal structure (the proto-cap and
gills of a potentially poisonous
mushroom), or if not white inside.

Buried-stalk puffball
Tulostoma simulans (April to December)
Edibility unknown

In sandy soil, sometimes growing up
through feather mosses. Usually as a
cluster of small puffballs only 1-1.5 cm
across on long stalks. The hole in each
protrudes a bit. Spores are pinkish
yellow, leaving a brown stain around the
hole.

Barometer earthstar
Astraeus hygrometrus
(September to November)
Edibility unknown

What's this? A little puffball with *petals?*
Looks like it, but the rays are the outer
skin of the puffball that has curled back
and cracked in a star-shaped pattern
2-4 cm across, revealing an inner sac of
spores that puffs through a central hole.
The rays lie out on wet days and curl
inward when it is dry—thus the common
name: barometer. A charming, terribly
intelligent fungus and my favorite. Look
for earthstars in sandy places, in groups,
talking about the weather.

FURTHER READING ON CANADIAN ROCKIES BOTANY

Alberta Energy and Natural Resources (1977) *Trees of Alberta* Free
  poster/pamphlet available from Alberta Recreation, Parks and Wildlife,
  10405 Jasper Avenue, Edmonton T5J 3N4.

Alberta Forestry Association (1984) *Alberta Trees of Renown: an Honour Roll of
  Alberta Trees* Alberta Forestry Association, #311, 10526 Jasper Avenue,
  Edmonton T5J 1Z5. Catalogue of notable trees in the province:
  record-holders, unusual, historical. Illustrated, 32 pages.

Alberta Recreation and Parks (undated) *Tracking the Trees and Shrubs of
  Kananaskis Country* Free illustrated, keyed booklet; 32 pages. Order from
  Kananaskis Country, #412, 1011 Glenmore Trail SW, Calgary T2V 4R6.

Bandoni, R.J, and A. Szczawinski (1964) *Guide to Common Mushrooms of British
  Columbia* British Columbia Provincial Museum Handbook No. 24.
  Photographs, non-technical; 179 pages. Order from the Provincial Museum,
  Victoria.

Clark, L. (1974) *Wild Flowers of Forest & Woodland in the Pacific Northwest*
  Douglas & McIntyre, Vancouver. Handy guide to the western-slope forbs
  and shrubs. Photo illustrations; 80 pages.

——, completed by J. Trelawney (1974) *Lewis Clark's Field Guide to Wild Flowers
  of Marsh and Waterway* Gray's, Sidney, BC. Good treatment of wetland
  forbs and shrubs; photographs, 64 pages.

Conard, H.S., and P. Redfearn, Jr. (1979) *How to Know the Mosses and Liverworts*
  Wm. C. Brown, Dubuque, Iowa. Good introduction to North American
  mosses. Keyed, illustrated; 302 pages.

Cormack, R.G. (1977) *Wild Flowers of Alberta* Hurtig, Edmonton. Good
  descriptions of many eastern-slope wildflowers, with so-so photo
  illustrations; 415 pages.

Goward, T. (1974) *20 Plants of Interior Parks* Free illustrated booklet available
  from British Columbia Parks and Outdoor Recreation, #308, 1011 Fourth
  Avenue, Prince George, BC V2L 3H9.

Hale, M.E. (1979) *How to Know the Lichens* Wm. C. Brown, Dubuque, Iowa. The
  best book for amateurs on North American lichens; textbook material at the
  front. Keyed, illustrated; 246 pages.

Hitchcock, C.L.; Cronquist, A. and J. Janish (1973) *Flora of the Pacific Northwest*
  University of Washington Press, Seattle. The botanist's companion for our
  region; comprehensive, though some species are not illustrated and the text
  is both technical and condensed in cryptic abbreviations; 730 pages.

Hosie, R.C. (1979) *Native Trees of Canada,* Fitzhenry and Whiteside, Toronto. The
  authoritative source. Easy to understand; 380 pages.

Kessell, S.R. et al. (1979) *Checklist of Vascular Plants of Glacier National Park,
  Montana* Comprehensive list, but no descriptions or illustrations. Available
  from Glacier National Park, West Glacier, Montana 59936.

Kuijt, J. (1982) *A Flora of Waterton Lakes National Park* University of Alberta
  Press, Edmonton. The best all-round guide on Canadian Rockies botany
  (Waterton has most of the species found in the region), written for both the
  amateur and the professional. Illustrated; 684 pages.

Lincoff, G. and C. Nehring (1981) *The Audubon Society Field Guide to North
  American Mushrooms* Alfred Knopf, New York. Comprehensive,
  photographs; 928 pages but still pocket-sized.

Little, E.L. (1980) *The Audubon Field Guide to North American Trees, Western
  Region* Alfred A. Knopf, New York. Comprehensive and pocketable.
  Photographic illustrations, range maps; 640 pages.

Lyons, C.P. (1965) *Trees, Shrubs and Flowers to Know in British Columbia* J.M.
  Dent & Sons, Toronto. The best thing available for the amateur on
  western-slope flora. Illustrated, range maps; 194 pages.

Moss, E.H., and J.G. Packer (1983) *The Flora of Alberta* University of Toronto Press, Toronto. The standard guide for Alberta, newly revised. Very technical, no illustrations, but with range maps for most species; 687 pages.

Nelson, D. and S. (1978) *Easy Field Guide to Trees of Glacier National Park* Tecolote Press, Box 217, Glenwood, New Mexico 88039. Illustrated with black-and-white drawings of cones and leaves; 32 pages.

Parks Canada (1982) *Wild Flowers of Waterton Lakes National Park* Illustrated 32-page booklet with brief descriptions of 104 species, available from Waterton Lakes National Park, Waterton Park, AB T0K 2M0.

Pohl, R.W. (1954) *How to know the grasses* Wm. C. Brown, Dubuque, Iowa. Keyed, illustrated guide to 293 North American species, written for the amateur; 192 pages.

Porsild, A.E. and D. Lid (1974) *Rocky Mountain Wildflowers* National Museum/Parks Canada. Excellent illustrations of 325 eastern-slope plants, but basis for inclusion seems arbitrary and the text is skimpy; 454 pages.

Scotter, G.W. and H. Flygare (1986) *Wildflowers of the Canadian Rockies* Hurtig, Edmonton. A new guide covering 228 species on both eastern and western slopes. Index, glossary, color-photo illustrations; 170 pages and expensive for that length.

Shaw, R.J. and D. On (1979) *Plants of Waterton-Glacier National Parks and the Canadian Rockies* Mountain Press Publishing Company, Missoula, Montana, and Summerthought, Banff. Very good photos of 220 species, including both flowers and fruits of species that make berries. Non-technical text; 160 pages.

Stanton, C. and N. Lopoukine (undated) *The Trees and Forests of Waterton Lakes National Park* Free poster/brochure by the Forestry Service, Environment Canada, available from Waterton Lakes National Park, Waterton Park, AB T0K 2M0

Stevenson, R. et al. (1976) *Trees and Forests of Jasper National Park* Illustrated booklet by the Forestry Service, Environment Canada, available for .75 from Jasper National Park, Box 10, Jasper T0E 1E0.

Trelawney, J.G. (1983) *Wildflowers of the Yukon* Gray's; Sidney, B.C. Excellent guide to common northern species; covers 332 forbs and shrubs. Good text and unusually good photo illustrations; 214 pages.

Underhill, J. (1979) *Guide to Western Mushrooms* Hancock House, Surrey, BC and Blaine, WA. Handy booklet on 45 common western-slope fungi. Photo illustrations; 32 pages.

—— (1980) *Northwestern Wild Berries* Hancock House, Surrey, BC and Blaine, WA. Excellent treatment of western-slope shrubs, with information on edibility and suggested preparation. Photos; 96 pages.

Rocky Mountain wood tick. Photo courtesy Jasper National Park.

Insects and spiders

Insects and spiders
Phylum Arthropoda, classes Insecta and Arachnida

How are the bugs in the Canadian Rockies? Doing just fine, thank you. We have lots: mosquitos, flies and ticks to bite you, bees and wasps to sting you, giant ants that plod over your bare feet. What we don't have are the really nasty ones: no black widows, no scorpions, no fire ants. Nor are we likely to acquire any in our cold northern climate.

Insect awards presentation: the mosquito wins, hands down, in the Most Annoying category. Bald-faced hornet gets Most Painful, although the horse fly walks off with Most Vicious. Award for Most Maddening Itch goes to the black fly, which shares honors with the Rocky Mountain wood tick for Sneakiest Mode of Attack. Most Frightful-Looking goes to the huge, wasp-like Horntail, which is harmless.

Of course, insects are beautiful in their own way. Their strange, alien lives are quite interesting. And remember this, while you are slapping and swearing: if it were not for the bugs the wildflowers wouldn't get pollinated and we mountain-dwellers would be up to our navels in unprocessed elk poop.

Of the 100,000 or so species of arthropods in North America, there are perhaps 20,000 species found in the Canadian Rockies—far too many to present in any sort of detail. Rather, I have singled out a few individuals and groups that are bound to attract your attention (in one way or another). To help in looking up the myriad species that are not covered here, the scientific family name is given with each entry rather than just the common family name.

Getting your hands on insect specimens is surprisingly easy (and I'm not talking about swatting mosquitoes). Just walk or bicycle along any highway shoulder. So many bugs are killed by auto traffic that a goodly number are always lying beside the driving lanes, many in un-crunched condition.

Another place to look for insects is at the top of a hill. It need not be high; any fairly prominent point will do. Plan to arrive at about 10 a.m. on a June morning, when you will probably find plenty of varied buzzers, flutterers and droners **"hill-topping"**: the entomologist's term for hill-top mating. Hill-topping is especially common among the fly clan. Only on hill tops are you likely to see the males of many fly species.

But be prepared for a little interest from the bugs, particularly if it's a rocky prominence and *you* are the highest point. A sting or bite isn't likely; just a mass landing. While sitting on the tip of a rock spire in Colorado, my climbing partner and I were "hill-topped" by literally thousands of winged beasties, all vying for the choicest places on which to alight (on eyelids, inside ears, etc.). The situation was so outrageously funny that we could not get the ropes set up for the descent, and we might have rolled off the rock in hysterics if we hadn't been tied in.

The listings begin with bugs that normally live on land or fly over it. There are separate sections on bugs in, on or over water (page 486), butterflies (page 494), moths (page 525) and caterpillars (page 528). For the ice insects, snow cranefly and other cold-adapted arthropods, see page 532.

BUGS ON LAND AND IN THE AIR

Might as well start off with the *flies* (order Diptera).

Mosquitoes
(family Culicidae)

There are some 28 species of mosquitoes in the Canadian Rockies, of which four common ones are described here. They are all flies (order Diptera). The eggs hatch in spring and the larvae are all water-dependent, staying just under the surface and feeding mostly on algae, floating pollen and decaying plant matter. The pupal phase is interesting: while the pupae of most insects are motionless, well-hidden in their capsules as they change to adults, mosquito pupae float openly at the water's surface and can swim away to the bottom when threatened.

Mosquito larvae and pupae are a common food of other pond dwellers, who are faced with such a sudden glut that they cannot eat them all in the small time (a week or two) that it takes for the larvae to metamorphose to adults. This is the mosquito's survival strategy.

The adults use their slender, piercing probosci to feed on plant juices. Male mosquitoes have very feathery antennae; females have skinny ones.

After mating, the male dies. The fertilized female in some species overwinters by hibernation; in most species she lays eggs in the summer or fall and then dies. In either case she must have a blood meal to obtain proteins necessary for successful egg production. She homes in on the carbon dioxide in your breath, not your body warmth or clothing color, although clothing color is important during final approach. Repellents work by jamming the females' CO_2 detectors with the wrong molecule, in most cases N, N-diethyl-metatoluamide (commonly abbreviated DEET). Formulations that are 75 percent or more DEET work for several hours and are effective against black flies and other biting flies as well as mosquitoes.

But DEET is a smelly solvent that attacks most kinds of plastic. Whenever I use it to go birdwatching in buggy places, my binoculars get tacky to the touch. This leads me to wonder what the stuff is doing to my body. Like any other chemical, we should use bug repellents cautiously, only when (buzz, whine, ouch!) one must either smear up or go indoors. Two layers of upper-body clothing and long pants will keep the vulnerable areas small. Try a turtleneck shirt under a tightly-woven outer layer. If you can't wear repellent, or don't want to, just slip on some light gardener's gloves and a head net (available at many outdoor equipment stores). Some shops sell anti-bug anoraks made of netting; these are great for hot days, because they can be worn with no shirt. You keep the anorak in a bag impregnated with repellent.

Mosquito season in the southern and central Canadian Rockies is mercifully short. Except in prime breeding sites (marshes, shallow ponds, sluggish streams), which are buggy all summer, the worst time for mosquitoes comes in late June or early July and lasts only a couple of weeks in the valleys, where most dwellings area. Higher up, though, in the subalpine forest and above timberline, mosquitoes are a bother throughout July and well into August. The wetter, warmer western slope is worse than the cooler, drier eastern slope. The northern region is the worst of all.

To get instant relief from a swelling, itching mosquito bite, try indenting the skin over the bite with your fingernail. Use lots of pressure, making two marks that cross each other. The annoyance will subside for a while. For sensitive individuals (the kind who get big lumps from mosquito bites), an antihistamine insect-bite ointment provides relief through the I-can't-stand-it stage.

House mosquitoes
Culex spp. (family Culicidae)
April to September

Southern and central regions mainly.
Uncommon only at very high elevations, where
the temperature dips below freezing nearly
every night. In hordes near shallow ponds and
marshes, where they breed. Length 4-5 mm.
Worst time is mid-June through mid-July. The
most common mosquito genus in the mountains;
members are light brown all over with faintly
banded abdomens. Not very hairy. They keep all
legs down when inserting the proboscis.
C. tarsalis is perhaps the most common species;
she overwinters in talus slopes, caves and rodent
burrows, emerging in May to bite and lay eggs.
Most active at night. Transmits the virus of
western equine encephalitis, mainly a disease of
birds but also a killer of horses. Humans get it
occasionally.

Malaria mosquito
Anopheles earlei (family Culicidae)
May to August

Montane and subalpine, in woods and near
towns; more common on the western slope.
Length 4 mm. Same size and similar to house
mosquito (above), but the abdomen is not
banded. Easiest way to identify one of these is
to let it light on you; the malaria mosquito
raises its tail nearly straight up, hind legs in
the air, as it inserts the proboscis. As the name
says, these mosquitos may carry malaria (and
other diseases). Although malaria is supposedly
not present in Canada, it is wise *not* to let these
ladies under your skin. They overwinter by
hibernating in animal burrows, beaver lodges
and such, emerging in May.

Snow mosquito
Aedes communis (family Culicidae)
July and August

At all elevations, near small pools of water.
This is a little yellowish mosquito that reaches
its greatest numbers in midsummer. Eggs are
laid the previous summer under leaves or among
needle duff in low places that hold water for
a while in spring, frequently beside a melting
snowbank. Neither sex survives the winter. The
young may hatch under the snow, but develop
very slowly until early spring brings the
meltwater they need.
   Aedes vexans is a similar species, although
reddish brown rather than yellow. It is known
for persistence in attacking and for population
explosions, both of which are reflected in the
species name.

Other kinds of flies
Order Diptera

Crane fly
Tipula spp. (family Tipulidae) June to August

Montane and subalpine, often near water. Looks
like a great big mosquito, with dangling legs up
to 50 mm long, but it is not. Brown body with
clear wings. Poor flyer; bumbles through the air.
Often winds up indoors for some reason.
Despite its size and appearance, the crane fly is
harmless—it doesn't even eat, existing only to
mate and die. Males are smaller than females
and have skinny abdomens with a ball on the
end; females have cigar-shaped abdomens.

Midges
(Chaoboridea and Chironomidae families)
July and August

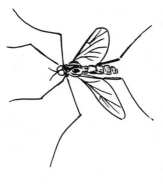

Montane and subalpine, along lakeshores and in
the woods, hovering in compact swarms that are
often just at head-level (cough, choke). To most
people, they are "gnats," although true gnats are
rare around here while midges are plentiful.
Midges are very mosquito-like in appearance,
but they either have short probosci or none at
all. The ones we have don't bite—which is a
good way of telling a cloud of midges from a
cloud of mosquitoes. Midges sit with their wings
held out to the side rather than parallel like
mosquitoes do. There are lots of species, some
very specialized. One type lives in limestone
cave openings. Some species have red larvae
that wiggle about in the water (see bloodworms,
page 486). What fishermen call "black gnats" are
actually midges.

House fly
Musca domestica (family Muscidae)
June to October

In any habitat and at any elevation, although
especially common around garbage, human food
and mammal feces. Scarce above timberline.
This is the common fly that walks around on
the rim of your teacup with its dirty feet.
Length about 7 mm, body gray with four black
stripes on the **thorax** (part with wings; behind
that is the **abdomen,** the typical layout of any
insect) and reddish eyes. Clear wings that fold
parallel to the body.
      House flies do not bite; they vacuum up
liquids that are sweet or decaying. While
vacuuming you, a house fly may be transferring
such things as typhoid, cholera, dysentery and
various parasitic worms. So brush a fly off;
don't squash it on your skin.

Intensely reproductive, house flies produce 5-6 broods a year of 75-120 eggs that hatch within 12 hours. The larvae (maggots) live in poop, dead stuff and garbage. They reach adulthood in only 12 days, living for 15-26 days and making more flies as fast as possible. Support your local birds.

Blue bottle flies
Calliphora vomitoria, C. cadaverina
(family Calliphoridae) June to September

Montane, around dead animals, meat and garbage. The possessors of these charming species names are large flies (about 13 mm long), with dark-gray bodies, red eyes and metallic blue abdomens. Rather bristly all over. They buzz loudly around the house.

The life style of the blue bottle fly is wonderfully attractive: eggs laid on decaying flesh hatch almost immediately; the maggots suck decay juices, crawl off to pupate in a drier place, then emerge after 2-3 weeks in adult form to feed on carrion and in the wounds of live animals (females only; the males mate and die).

Oddly enough, blue bottle flies are not known as disease transmitters. In fact, a festering wound attacked by these flies will become sterile, although it takes longer to heal.

Green bottle fly
Lucilia illustris (family Calliphoridae)
June to September

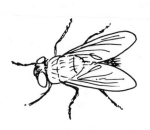

Montane, around dead fish, carrion and garbage. Large (10-14 mm long), with brilliantly metallic green thorax and abdomen, black head with red eyes; clear wings.

Green bottle flies eat dead stuff, hanging around garbage cans and carrion. One of their favorite things is rotting trout guts left out for them by thoughtful fishermen.

Dung fly
Scathophaga stercoraria
(family Scathophagidae) June to August

Montane, common around stables and domestic animals. Easily recognized by the color: coppery or yellowish, especially on the abdomen. Bristly all over, with red eyes and clear wings that are yellowish near the front. A bit larger than the house fly (10 mm), which is the prey of the adult dung fly. Thus, dung flies are friends, not foes. The larvae are the dung-eaters, tunneling in (oh boy, oh boy!) from eggs deposited there.

Deer flies
Chrysops spp. (family Tabanidae)
June to August

Montane and subalpine, usually in the woods.
More common on the western slope. Looks
rather like a house fly, but the difference is
obvious when it lands: it bites.

Ten millimetres long, the typical deer fly
is a little larger than a house fly and sits with
its wings held out a little to the side, while the
house fly folds its wings pretty well straight
back. As well, deer fly wings are darkly
banded. There is a bit of yellow on the thorax
and head, and the eyes are patterned greenish
or gold.

The larvae live in water, preying on small
insects (which they kill by injecting venom);
they pupate in mud along the shore. Like the
mosquito, only the female adult deer fly bites,
sometimes transmitting tularemia to snowshoe
hares, which can then infect us if we eat them.
DEET repellents work on deer flies, which is
good, because they are too quick to swat.

Horse flies
Hybomitra spp. (family Tabanidae)
June to August

At all elevations, but particularly common in
subalpine meadows. The largest fly in the
Rockies, up to 20 mm long. Gray head with
enormous iridescent striped green eyes; rest of
body gray (sometimes gray and orange); wings
clear.

The horse-fly larva lives in water, eating
other insects for up to three summers and
overwintering in bottom mud. One spring it
pupates, emerging a few weeks later as either a
pollen/nectar-eating adult male, which mates
and dies, or a female, which lives until fall,
taking blood from large mammals and laying
eggs in plants that hang over water, into which
the larvae drop.

A horse fly will follow a backpacker for
hours, occasionally landing to attempt a bite.
The mandibles work like a pair of scissors,
opening a wound that bleeds freely because the
fly's saliva contains an anti-clotting agent.
Repellent works, but horse flies are also a little
slow on takeoff and thus vulnerable to swatting.
They have been known to carry disease, but not
ones transferable to humans, so swat away—and
swat hard: horse flies can survive knocks that
would do in most other kinds of insects.

Black flies
Simulium spp. (family Simuliidae)
July and August

Montane and subalpine, along streams. Black
flies are uncommon south of Lake Louise,
gradually increasing in numbers as you go
north. These are small flies, only 2-4 mm long.
There are many species in the Canadian
Rockies; most are gray, some with yellow
banded legs and abdomens. There is an
interesting life cycle: eggs laid next to running
water (often in a spring) hatch in October; the
small black larvae wiggle into the water and
can sometimes be seen clinging by the hundred
to stones under the surface. They overwinter
there, pupating in silk cocoons, then pop out in
midsummer as adults, riding bubbles of
self-produced gas to the surface and flying
away. The males eat only nectar, but the
females of most species also require blood from
birds or mammals to reproduce.

That's bad news for us humans. Black flies are voracious, and sneaky: you
don't notice them biting. They usually go for the back of the neck, just under the
hairline from ear to ear, or around the eyes. You feel an itch there, bringing away
a spot of blood on your finger that signifies you are too late: the fly has struck
and gone. The wound swells to a lump about a centimetre across, with a red dot in
the middle; it itches for several days, making crusts, and takes a week or more to
go away. Treatment: don't scratch; that only makes it worse. Insect-bite ointments
help. In sensitive people, especially if bitten around the eye, the spot may swell
hugely, becoming an eye-closing purple egg that infects. Go to the doctor.

Fortunately, black flies do not bite at night (they are busiest around sunset).
During the day, a little insect repellent applied around the hairline will keep them
away. Use a brand that is at least 75 percent DEET. Wearing light-colored clothing
helps, for they prefer to light on dark colors.

In late summer black flies like to come indoors, where they seldom bite
(thankfully) and can be observed up close as they scramble around the window
panes. Before having your revenge, keep in mind that most species bite birds, not
humans.

Although black flies transmit blindness-causing parasites in the tropics, they
are not vectors for human disease in the Rockies. Birds suffer from black flies the
most: ducks, geese and swans contract waterfowl malaria from black fly bites, and
it is often fatal.

Bees, wasps, hornets and their mimics
Order Hymenoptera

Honey bee
Apis mellifera (family Apidae) June to August

Montane, in open areas with wildflowers or cultivated legumes such as alfalfa.
The honey bee is the most common bee in the world, but it is rivalled here in
numbers by the northern golden bumblebee (next entry).

The honey bee is 11-15 mm long, with furry yellowish-brown head and thorax,
black eyes, banded ochre-and-black abdomen, black legs; lower parts often covered
with pollen. Honey bees live in very large colonies (60,000-80,000 members) that
build hives of wax in tree holes, attics, woodpiles and other dry, woody places.

Of all the bees and wasps, the honey bee exhibits the most complex social behavior and has perhaps the most interesting life cycle. Eggs in waxy cells hatch to larvae that remain there, pupating into various physical forms: queens (reproductive females), drones (reproductive males) and workers (non-reproductive females). Control of types is through feeding of larvae; amount of bee-bread (pollen/honey mixture) consumed and intake of special foods such as royal jelly control who grows up into what. Adults eat nectar and honey, live a year or less—except for the queen, who lives 3-5 years, overwintering within the hive while layers of workers surround her, the outer workers perishing in the cold at this latitude. The queen leaves in early spring, taking with her a swarm of remaining workers to start a new colony. New queens emerge in the old hive, killing one another until only one remains. She then flies about, mates and produces replacement eggs for the swarm that left. The honey bee has a barbed stinger that lodges in human flesh, thus killing the bee when it stings.

Golden northern bumble bee
Bombus fervidus (family Apidae)
June to September

Montane and subalpine, in flowery meadows. A large bee (20-30 mm long), easily differentiated from other Rockies bees by its size and by its very furry, broad bands of yellow and black. Legs are black with orange pollen pouches; wings are small and smoky-looking.

Bumble bees fly sluggishly from flower to flower, eating nectar and gathering pollen to take home to the nest, which is in the ground or in the wall of a building. Like yellow-jackets and hornets (next entry), only the mated females survive the winter, starting a new nest and feeding honey to the first brood of larvae, which become under-sized workers not much bigger than honey bees. In July and August, subsequent broods of full-size adults enlarge the nest until cold weather kills all but the young, newly mated queens, who overwinter to start new colonies.

See also the thetis clearwing moth, page 526.

Western yellow-jacket
Vespula spp. (family Vespidae)
June to September

Montane, common in dry open woods. Often in campgrounds. Gaudy yellow-and-black banded body 10-15 mm long; yellow legs, clear wings. Hairy face; compare with bald-faced hornet (next entry).

Most yellow-jackets in the Canadian Rockies nest in the ground, often under prickly juniper (page 328), but there is at least one species here that builds papery, wasp-like nests under building overhangs. Hornets are renowned for attacks if the nest is disturbed. However, I have stumbled on many nests over the years without getting stung, so maybe they are less easily aroused in the Rockies than elsewhere. One hot afternoon I guzzled most a can of juice left all morning on a campground picnic table, then put the can down when I noticed a buzzing feeling on my lips—at which point several yellow-jackets zipped out. None stung me.

Life cycle: emerging from forest litter and soil in spring, a young mated female digs a shallow nest and produces eggs, feeding pre-chewed insects (or a variety of other foods, including stuff scavenged from picnics) to the larvae. They become female workers, who forage to support subsequent broods. Adults eat only nectar. At summer's end, males develop from infertile eggs laid by workers. The males mate with new queens, who are the only ones to survive the winter.

Bald-faced hornet
Vespula maculata (family Vespidae)
June to August

Montane, in meadows; fairly common in towns, around flower gardens, where they sting with very little provocation. The bald-faced hornet looks a lot like a yellow-jacket (previous entry), but it is bigger (15-20 mm long), and patterned differently: black and white rather than black and yellow, the face white and bald rather than hairy like a yellow-jacket, the abdomen unstriped.

Hornets make papery gray nests of chewed wood pulp that hang under tree branches or other woody supports; larvae in cells inside are fed insect pulp by adults. The life cycle is like that of the yellow-jacket.

Hover flies
(family Syrphidae) July and August

Montane and subalpine, near shrubbery where the larvae can eat aphids and other small insects. Hoverflies are non-bees in disguise. They mimic yellow-jackets and hornets, but cannot sting. They are also smaller (about 10 mm), with brown eyes rather than black.

Hover flies hover, all right, hanging around people in a rather too-interested way. Yet they are not after blood; the adult drinks nectar.

Black-and-yellow mud dauber
Sceliphron caementarium (family Sphecidae)
June to September

Occasional at low elevations, Banff south.
Easily recognized as a wasp by the long
thread-like waist. Body length 25-30 mm; wings
not as long as body, folded straight back.
Mostly black, with yellow legs, yellow patches
on head and thorax, yellow waist and yellow
spot on abdomen at connection.

    The female builds a nest of mud under any
overhang (rocks, eaves); places a stung spider
(alive, but immobile) in each cell and lays an
egg on it. Larvae eat the spiders, remaining in
the cells through pupation to adult stage, when
they emerge to drink nectar and mate. This
wasp packs a wallop; beware.

Western giant ichneumon
Megarhyssa nortoni (family Ichneumonidae)
June to August

Montane, often in deciduous woods. Females
very large (35-75 mm long; males 25-40 mm. A
very elegant wasp, with an extra-long waist,
long yellow antennae, long yellow legs, and in
females a very long, two-part black ovipositor
(egg-laying tube) hanging from the abdomen.
Head is yellow around black eyes; there are also
yellow and/or red markings on the body.

    Ichneumons are parasitic wasps. The
egg-laden female listens with her antennae for
horntail larvae (next entry) boring in dead
wood. Then she works her long, sharp-ended
ovipositor into the wood at several sites, laying
her eggs in the tunnels. The eggs hatch and the
ichneumon larvae enter the horntail larvae,
feeding on them until the ichneumon larvae are
grown, at which point the hosts die. The
western giant ichneumon is active by day, feeds
on nectar and cannot sting. But there are
short-tailed nocturnal species (family
Ophionidae) that *do* sting.

Smoky horntail
Urocerus spp. (family Siricidae)
July and August

Montane, around dead wood in forests; often
seen around lumber piles in towns. Big,
scary-looking wasp-like insect up to 40 mm
long. Dark-brown body with yellow or ochre
head, black eyes and yellow/ochre bands on the
thorax and abdomen. No thread-like waist,
though. Female has a prominent ovipositor
sticking out the back; she uses it to lay eggs
under the surface of dead wood.

The larvae bore galleries, sometimes becoming victims of ichneumon wasps (previous entry), which parasitize them. Despite the nightmare-bug appearance, horntails are harmless. The adults live on nectar, and they are attracted to campfires.

Sand wasp/digger wasp
Ammophila or *Podalonia* spp.
(family Sphecidae) May to August

Montane meadows, on bare earth; often seen digging in dusty trails. Body 15-20 mm long and all black, with clear wings; short thread-like waist identifies it as a wasp.

Interesting to watch; you can get quite close without disturbing it. The female digs quickly into bare soil, disappearing for a moment in the vertical burrow and then emerging. Usually she flies to another site and repeats the process. What she is doing is looking for the perfect spot for a nest: a deeper burrow with a cell at the end. She drags an immobilized insect (usually a caterpillar) to the end of the cell and lays an egg on it, then departs, sealing the entrance and leaving the prey to provide food for the larva.

Stings of bees, wasps and hornets

To avoid getting stung, stay away from hives and nests, and don't run around barefoot in flowery meadows. A sting of this group is mildly venomous and thus feels fiery, although the pain subsides quickly, especially if the site is numbed with ice. Insect-bite ointment can reduce any follow-up itching. The wound will be tender for a day or two, and it may swell. If a honeybee stinger comes off in the skin, it should be removed, for it may still contain the venom gland.

You may be allergic to the venom and not know it until you are stung. The symptoms are rapid swelling at the site, general feeling of weakness and discomfort, and in severe cases an asthma-like restriction of the bronchial tubes that makes it hard to breathe. For some people, this airway blockage can be fatal if untreated. A simple allergy test by a doctor can determine whether you are allergic and to what degree. Very sensitive people carry medication (a combination of epinephrine and an antihistamine) to take after a sting; in the past this had to be injected but now it is available in inhalers.

Ants
Order Hymenoptera (family Formicidae)

Like wasps, ants have a slender waist (a **pedicel**) between the thorax and abdomen. They also have a bend in their antennae.

Red ants
Formica spp. (family Formicidae) May to September

Montane and subalpine, southern and central sections, very common in dry lodgepole woods from Banff/Golden south, less so as one goes north. Several species, all similar: body length 5-10 mm, orangey-red head and thorax, black abdomen.

The most common ants in the Canadian Rockies, red ants nest underground, building up extensive heaps of soil particles around the entrances. Red ants are aphid farmers (aphids are discussed on page 476), finding aphids and stroking them to receive "honeydew" (sweet stuff secreted from the anus) that is a favorite food. Sometimes they carry aphids to more convenient locations, but they don't take them underground. Red ants also eat enough other things—flower nectar, small insects, human food and garbage—to make a go of it nearly anywhere, which accounts for their success.

The life cycle is typical of ants. Each colony, which can number many thousands, has one queen. She stays underground, producing eggs. The larvae remain underground until they pupate and mature in one of two castes: workers, which are wingless sterile females, and winged reproductive females and males, which number only a few in each nest. The young reproductive females and males go on mating flights, then the males die. Each mated female flies to a suitable site for a new nest, tears her own wings off and starts digging. She produces the first brood of larvae, feeding them herself until they pupate; they emerge as workers who will serve her for the rest of their lives. Red ants can bite; they also spray formic acid in the wound, which causes a stinging sensation.

Giant carpenter ant
Camponotus herculeanus (family Formicidae)
May to October

Red ant

Montane and subalpine woods, on the ground or on dead wood. Very large ant, up to 20 mm long. Body looks black at first glance, but may actually be dark reddish brown. Antennae have elbows (like all ants).

Carpenter ants make their nests in dead trees, both fallen or standing, chewing out long galleries. They don't eat the wood; they merely carry the sawdust outside and dump it. They eat insects and anything sweet, which will draw them to your picnic. Despite their size, carpenter ants are non-threatening (none has ever bitten me, even when I'm on the ground in places where they are plodding about). Life cycle is similar to that of red ants (previous entry).

Giant carpenter ant

Aphids
Order Homoptera (family Aphididae)

Montane, very common on the willows, roses, pea-family plants, aspen, poplar—you name it; it seems to have an aphid that eats it. There are thousands of species, all designed to do the same thing: suck the juice from the plant. Aphids are mostly quite small (2-3 mm long) and wingless, although at one point in their complicated life-cycle winged females appear. Only the eggs overwinter, but each summer there are many generations, producing zillions of tasty, defenseless aphids that become staple foods of other insects and birds. Some aphid species coexist symbiotically with many species of ants, which practice agriculture on them. See the entry on red ants.

There are thousands of species of beetles in the Canadian Rockies (30,000 species in North America, 300,000 in the world)—far too many to detail here. So I have written up just a few, very common ones, plus a couple that are extra-interesting for some reason. If you want to know more about Rockies beetles, get one of the reference books listed at the end.

A beetle on the ground looks wingless, but it does have wings: two sets, in fact, like a butterfly. The forewings are called **elytra** (singular: elytron). These are hard, running down the beetle's back and serving as covers for the hindwings underneath, which are clear and do the work of flying. What looks like a beetle's abdomen from above is actually the two elytra, closed and fitting together down the midline with the precision of Italian sports-car bodywork. When a beetle flies, the elytra open and swing away to the side, staying still while the hindwings buzz frantically. Catch a ladybird beetle and watch the process; it is machine-like: beetle hesitates, elytra flip up, wings buzz, off it goes. When a beetle lands, the elytra often snap down before the wings are fully retracted, leaving the tips sticking out for a moment like untucked shirt-tails.

Black ground beetles
(family Carabidae) July to September

Montane and subalpine, often in moist woods under rocks or logs lying on the ground. The most common beetles in the mountains, probably because they are the most common beetles in North America (more than 3000 species, according to the Audubon guide), black ground beetles are indeed black, and shiny. They are about 15 mm long, with many parallel grooves down the back (i.e., on the wing covers). Mostly active at night, they sometimes venture out during the day, hunting busily for caterpillars; they like their food *soft*. Eggs laid in late summer soon hatch to larvae that overwinter in the ground, growing, pupating, and reaching the adult stage in midsummer.

Ladybird/ladybug
(family Coccinellidae) May to September

Montane, in woods and brushy places. There are many genera and species of these beetles in the Canadian Rockies, all pretty similar: small (about 5 mm long), with a black-and-white front end, rounded orange back with black spots, and black legs. Differences among species are reflected in the number of spots, which vary from 13 to none (all orange or all black) and in the pattern on the thorax.

The **nine-spotted ladybird** *(Coccinella novemnotata)* is perhaps the most common one in the mountains; we also have the **three-banded ladybird** *(C. trifasciata;* three black bands across the back) and two two-spotted versions: *(Adalia bipunctata;* one spot on each side, and *A. frigida,* with two faint spots and a bar near the back). The **convergent ladybird** *(Hippodamia convergens)* is the 13-spotted one;

it also has converging white stripes on the pronotum (the head-end).

Ladybirds eat mainly aphids, which are always in plentiful supply. These beetles are also prolific, producing several generations in the short Canadian Rockies summer. Adults do the overwintering, snug below the snow under bark and leaves. The word "ladybird" comes from "Our Lady," an old European name for the beetles that honors their ability to keep the aphids under control in vineyards. Here in somewhat-colonial Canada, entomologists prefer the British "ladybird" to the American "ladybug."

Black pine sawyer beetle
Monochamus oregonensis (family Cerambycidae)
July and August

Montane, in lodgepole pine woods. A large black beetle up to 30 mm long, instantly recognizable by the extremely long antennae (males only; in females the antennae are only about half as long, and furry). These are gnawing insects. The female chews a hole into the bark of a lodgepole pine and deposits eggs there; the larvae eat inward, almost to the heartwood, then start back out, reaching the bark layer again a couple of years after starting, just as they are about to pupate. The emerging adults eat their way out through the bark, continuing to feed on bark as they seek mates.

Pine and spruce engraver beetles, and the mountain pine beetle
Ips, Dendroctonus and other genera
(family Scolytidae) July and August

Montane and subalpine forests. These beetles eat trees. Small (5-10 mm long) and black or brown, you may never see them, but they are very common, perhaps the leading killers of conifers. In midsummer the female tunnels under the bark of a pine or spruce, laying eggs. The larvae hatch in about two weeks; They excavate galleries (tunnels) just under the bark, in the nutrient-rich cambium layer. Trees that have died from heavy infestations soon lose their bark, exposing the crisscrossing galleries engraved on the wood. After overwintering under the bark, the larvae continue eating until June of the following year, when they pupate and emerge over the next two months as adults that have chewed their way through the bark and out. Flying about the woods for a couple of weeks, they mate, reproduce and die.

The mountain pine beetle *(Dendroctonus ponderosae)* is in the news these days because it is a particularly destructive member of this family. At time of writing it's having a population explosion in montane lodgepole forests south of Banff on the eastern slope and south of Valemount on the western slope. These are probably the limits of the current outbreak, during which about half the lodgepole pines (and a good bit of ponderosa and western white pine) have been killed south of Crowsnest Pass on the eastern slope and south of Golden on the western slope.

Why is this bug such a potent tree-killer?

The galleries of most engraver beetles tend to run up and down the trunk, the way the resin runs, so the resin flow is diminished somewhat but not cut off. Thus, it takes a great number of larvae to kill a large tree—although small trees succumb rather easily, as do old trees that cannot drown the invaders in sap. The mountain pine beetle, on the other hand, chews out galleries that go *around* the trunk, across the flow of resin, blocking the flow and thus starving the tree.

We humans must blame ourselves for the current pine-beetle population boom. The bug does best in stands of old, mature timber, of which there are many in the Rockies, the result of 50 years of fighting forest fires.

But trying to stop the beetle is probably doomed to failure, rather like the ill-conceived spruce-budworm poisoning campaigns in New Brunswick. Years of costly aerial spraying there, harmful to anyone and anything living nearby, have served only to keep the budworm population from reaching its limit and crashing naturally back to pre-explosion levels. That crash would take a good bit of timber with it, which the forest industry of New Brunswick is unwilling to surrender to the bugs. Chemical-spray manufacturers are enthusiastic allies in this battle.

Something is going to destroy the unnaturally old forests of the Rockies, be it fire or disease. Rather than compound the harm by trying to intervene, we might as well let this insect attack run its boom-and-bust course. It would seem that the mountain pine beetle cannot advance much farther north, for genetic weakness due to excessive inbreeding should by now be taking its toll. Further, temperatures of -35 °C to -40 °C do in the overwintering larvae, and such temperatures are reached nearly every winter in central and northern regions.

With the beetle attack has come something that the forest industry calls "salvage logging." Beetle-killed timber can still be turned into lumber and paper, so loggers go into affected areas and clear-cut tracts of forest that would otherwise recover from the infestation naturally, by ecological succession of spruce and Douglas-fir. Often permits are given for "salvage logging" in environmentally sensitive places that would otherwise be off-limits to loggers. How strange: a little bug that selectively and neatly kills only the pines, opening up the woods naturally, without removing the nutrients or damaging the soil, is used as an excuse by humans to wreck an entire ecosystem.

Grasshoppers and crickets
Order Orthoptera

Pallid-winged grasshopper
Trimerotropis pallidipennis (family Acrididae)
June to October

Montane, in dry, grassy places. Length 30-40 mm. A well-camouflaged beast, the pallid-winged grasshopper seems to disappear against the yellowy-brown foliage of late summer, the season when adults of this species are most common. Identify them by the two black bars across the white-to-yellow wings. They feed on wildflowers and grasses, mating in late fall and dying around Halloween in the first cold weather. Eggs laid in the soil overwinter, hatching in early June. The nymphs are small versions of the adults, but lack wings.

Alpine grasshopper
Malenoplus alpinus (family Acrididae)
June to October

Montane (despite its name), in dry, grassy
places. Length 20-25 mm. Gray to
yellowish-brown and shiny, as if the parts were
made of plastic. There is black trim on the back
legs (V-shaped markings), the lower parts of
which are blue with black spines. It eats grass
and has a life cycle like that of the
pallid-winged grasshopper (previous entry).

Field cricket
Gryllus pennsylvanicus (family Gryllidae)
June to October

Montane, in woods or moist stony places, seen
mainly at night. Length 15-25 mm, black.
Grasshopper-like, but more compact and with
long antennae. Two spine-like egg-laying tubes
stick out the back of females. Hiding by day in
thick foliage and under rocks, crickets emerge
at dusk to feed on seeds, plant fruits, young
growing plants or dead insects.

This species sings by **stridulating:** rubbing
the rows of raised veins at the root of one wing
against a similar organ on the other wing. The
sound is amazingly loud for a creature so small.

Eggs laid in soil overwinter (the adults die
at first heavy frost); the nymphs (like tiny
adults) emerge in early June and grow steadily
through the summer to maturity in August. You
may find adults and immatures in your
basement when September rolls around, for
crickets do not like cold weather.

Cicadas
Order Homoptera

Okanagana and *Platypedia* spp.
(family Cicadidae) July

In montane woods, clinging to trees (sometimes to shrubs or wildflowers).
Pronounced either "sick-AY-duh" (long *a*), "sick-AH-duh," or with the accent on the
first syllable. You will hear these insects before you see them; they make a loud,
continuous buzzing that is unmistakable. Finding the cicadas themselves, which
are large (20-30 mm long), is surprisingly difficult: they hold very still, and they
are often the color of the bark they sit on.

Our species are difficult to tell apart, but all are greenish or brownish and
quite fat, with large eyes and large clear wings. Often, what one finds is the
empty shell of the nymph stage, which looks a lot like the adult but lacks the
wings.

The life cycle is interesting. Eggs are forced into tree bark in late summer by
the female's strong ovipositer. They soon hatch, the nymphs dropping to the
ground right away to burrow down among the tree roots, which they eat for one
to three years before emerging in midsummer to shed their exoskeletons and fly
about on new wings. Finding trees of the right species, they sing loudly, attracting
mates. Most species don't eat anything in the adult stage; rather, they are eaten
themselves by birds and small mammals, for whom the annual cicada banquet
must be a highlight of summer.

Ticks
Class Arachnida, order Acarina

Rocky Mountain wood tick
Dermacentor andersoni (family Ixodidae)
April to June

Montane, as far north as Grande Cache on the eastern slope and perhaps farther on the western slope, common in grassy places frequented by small mammals (ground squirrels and the like). A tick looks like a little flat spider: triangular body about 5 mm long, with eight legs. It is in the same class as spiders (Arachnida), but in a different order (Acarina, which also includes the mites). Female is reddish brown with a white patch behind the head; male is reddish brown with gray mottling. Ticks move slowly, one leg at a time. They are easy to grab and cannot bite or sting. You may have occasion to do a bit of grabbing.

See also the photo on page 464.

Adult ticks (and near-adults) climb up grasses and other low-growing plants, hanging on with two legs while leaving the other six extended. Hooks on the ends catch in the hair of any passing animal—or on the pantlegs of certain kinds of passing animals. Note that ticks do not drop out of trees; they climb only a few centimetres. They also crawl toward their would-be hosts, attracted by exhaled carbon dioxide.

Once on the host, the tick then climbs higher, seeking tender skin that can be penetrated easily by its mouthparts. These are inserted very gradually, so the host doesn't notice. To make the attachment secure, the tick literally glues itself on with a secreted cement.

Note that only the mouthparts go into the skin. The rest of the tick, including the tiny head, stays outside. The notion of ticks burrowing under the skin is false.

The tick begins to feed, taking in blood under capillary pressure and injecting an anti-clotting agent to keep the blood flowing. As it fills, the tick's body swells. Mated females bloat to many times their un-fed size, looking like large gray kernels of corn when full; males take much less blood and swell only a little.

If immature, the tick then drops off, grows a bit, molts (splits out of its exoskeleton, which has become too small), and in so doing reaches maturity. It then finds another host on which to take one more meal and look for a mate.

After mating, the male dies. Mated females drop off and lay masses of 5000-10,000 eggs under rocks, leaves or logs. The eggs overwinter, hatching in June and July. The tiny larvae are also parasites; they feed on blood from small rodents. Then they metamorphose to nymphs (the immature stage mentioned in the previous paragraph), which can become adults that same summer if more blood is obtained; if not, the nymphs overwinter under the snow and emerge in early spring as adults, ready to renew the cycle.

Amazingly, an adult tick can remain unfed for up to three years before it finally gives up and expires.

Ticks are seen often in the Canadian Rockies from late April to early June, when the elk are crawling with them and hikers resting in spring-green meadows are picking them up without knowing it. Not to worry (yet); ticks don't attach right away. Like the camper seeking the best site in the campground, a tick walks slowly over a human host for several hours—at least three hours, sometimes 24—before settling down to feed.

Elk, moose and other large mammals may carry thousands of ticks. This is possible because large mammals frequent the same places year after year, lying about in swarms of well-fed parasites. Humans sometimes sit or lie in these same places; grassy clearings in the woods are particularly inviting spots for lunch and a snooze or a bit of lovemaking. It happens often: the amorous couple, oblivious to the hordes closing in, jump up in panic when they see several ticks crawling on them.

A tick remains on its host for at least a couple of days and sometimes a week or more. *The good news:* the wound left by a tick after it drops off is small and soon heals. *The bad news:* ticks can do you harm in other ways.

For example, compounds in the anti-clotting fluid injected to keep the blood flowing are toxic to the human nervous system, and a tick left on the back of the neck for several days sometimes causes bizarre symptoms as the toxin affects the upper spinal cord and brain: numbness in arms and legs, loss of coordination, drowsiness and personality changes. Yikes! All this from a bug smaller than the tip of your little finger.

That is not all. The symptoms above clear up within a few hours after the tick is removed, but ticks on the eastern slope of the Rockies can also carry a nasty disease that, if you get it, will wreck your summer at the very least and may possibly kill you. This is **Rocky Mountain spotted fever,** also called **tick fever** (there is only one type of tick fever you can get in North America, and this is it). The cause is *Rickettsia rickettsii,* a tiny organism that falls phylogenetically between the viruses and the bacteria. A small percentage of the ticks in the mountains carry these rickettsiae in their bodies, transferring them to humans through the mouthparts. Other mammals seem unaffected.

Infection begins a few hours after feeding starts. Three to 12 days later the symptoms come on suddenly: severe headache, chills and muscular pain. You definitely know that you are sick. Fever begins, reaching 39.5-40 °C by the second day and remaining high for as long as two weeks. A cough develops, followed on the fourth day of fever by a rash that appears on wrists, ankles, palms, soles of feet and forearms, spreading to neck and face, rear end and trunk. The rash gets nasty, becoming infected-looking. If untreated, the disease goes on to delirium, coma, brain and heart damage, and death in about 25 percent of cases.

Treatment is by the antibiotics tetracycline or chloramphenicol; the idea is to get to the doctor fast if you find a well-attached tick on your body and start showing the symptoms above. Even when treated early, tick fever hangs on for a long time, leaving you debilitated for weeks. Children living in Rocky Mountain communities are most commonly struck; they are outdoors a lot in spring, often on the ground, and they don't notice the beasties. Their parents had better.

That is the whole idea, here: do not let any ticks attach. Each day you are out in the mountains during tick season, strip down before supper and check yourself over well, especially in your hair (and in other hairy places). Ticks often go for the nape of the neck or behind the ears, where there is plenty of hair and the skin is thin. They also attach on the back, or beneath a belt or brassiere strap, or under the elastic band in your underwear—anywhere that clothes fit tightly, which may help a tick to dig in on our sparsely haired bodies. Get somebody to look at your back.

In the later afternoon, any ticks you picked up during the day will probably still be crawling around. Grab them and either flush them down the toilet or burn them up. They are difficult to squash (hard and flat), and people have picked up tick fever by handling crushed ticks. If you are camping, you must kill every one you find; any let go alive around a campsite will make their way back to you.

Check your pets, too. On dogs, ticks usually wind up behind the ears and under the collar. Cats don't seem to get them.

Insect repellents that contain a high concentration of DEET (check the label) will keep ticks away. If you know you are going to be passing through tick-infested places, a bit of repellent applied around the ankles and lower pantlegs will discourage hangers-on. However, you would have to bathe in the stuff to really ensure protection, so inspection for ticks each evening is still required. I don't bother with repellents, except when the mosquitoes are utterly maddening. Once-a-day tick-picking is quick and easy, avoids the use of chemicals (with their attendant odor and plastic-eating properties), and thus is almost certainly healthier as well as more convenient.

If the tick has attached, remove it by pulling *gently and steadily.* Unless the tick is well-glued-on, mouthparts firmly imbedded, it will come off intact. Folk remedies such as burning the tick's rear with a match or lighted cigarette, or pouring gasoline or whiskey on it, serve only to kill the tick while it is still hooked in. But applying a little DEET repellent is supposed to encourage the tick to let go.

If the mouthparts stay in the wound, they should be removed. Tease them out with a flamed needle or knifeblade. Then wash the wound well with soap and sterilize it with antiseptic if you have any. A bit of that whiskey will do.

Spiders and harvestmen
Class Arachnida, orders Araneae (spiders)
and Opiliones (harvestmen)

You may be pleased to know that large, hairy spiders such as the tarantula do not live in the Canadian Rockies. Neither do any dangerously poisonous ones, such as the black widow or the brown recluse—although you never know what will turn up in your basement or heated garage. Eggs imported from south of the border can hatch anywhere warm enough.

Branch-tip spiders
Dictyna spp. (family Dictynidae)
April to October

Montane woods. If you have ever walked along a mountain trail in the morning, then I'll bet you've brushed through dozens of straggly, nearly invisible webs produced by this very common, harmless little spider. By afternoon most of the webs have been ripped down by passing animals and birds; they will be rebuilt that evening.

The branch-tip spider's body is only a few millimetres long, buffy brown all over with a tiny cephalothorax (head end), longish legs and round abdomen marked on top by a series of nested brown W's. The female hangs her white egg-case in the web, which is why you may find odd little white balls on your pants and shirt after a day in the woods. The spiderlings mature by fall and overwinter under the snow.

American house spider
Achaearanea tepidariorum (family Theridiidae)
All year (indoors)

In houses, barns, garages—any sheltered places, for these spiders do not like the outdoors. Small and harmless (body only 5 mm long), they are yellowish brown, the round abdomen much bigger than the head and decorated with brown, black and white squiggles. They are very tolerant of humans, stringing their webs up in the corners of windows and ceilings. If you are tolerant of them as well, you will find them interesting to watch—as my whole family did one winter.

In classic spider fashion, it would run over to a struggling fly stuck in the web (or placed there by my sadistic children), sting the fly a couple of times to paralyze it, then wrap it up in a bit of silk. Retiring to a corner of the web, the spider would wait a few minutes for the fly to liquify inside (another nice property of spider venom). Then it would tenderly hold the fly, piercing it with its mouthparts at various points to suck up what my wife referred to as a "fly shake."

We thought it impolite of our spider to merely toss the empties onto the window-ledge when it was finished with them, although leaving the fly-shells in the web was kind of ugly, too, so occasionally we would clean up the mess.

Tetragnatha

Long-jawed orb weaver
Tetragnatha spp. (family Tetragnathidae)
June to September

In tall grass and shrubs along streams or other water bodies. Easily identified by the skinny abdomen, up to 10 mm long and pale yellowish green or silvery with a few black dots. This spider keeps its long, nearly transparent legs bundled together ahead of it and behind it, as if it were living in a straw. It builds a web for catching small insects; when disturbed, it drops out and runs away.

Misumena

Goldenrod spider
Misumena vatia (family Thomisidae)
May to September

Found hiding in yellow or white flowers, or among green leaves. I have noticed it only at montane elevations. Fairly small (body up to 10 mm long), this member of the crab-spider family matches its color to that of its shelter, so it varies from pale white or greenish to bright yellow. Always, though, there will be a red stripe on each side of the abdomen. The spider waits, legs folded, until a small insect visits the flower or plant in which it hides.

Then, zap! It grabs, bites and eats.

Pardosa

Wolf spider
Pardosa spp. (family Lycosidae)
May to September

Common in montane woods, where it pokes about on the forest floor or beside streams; also common among talus and scree at any elevation. Body 10-15 mm long, grayish brown with a ragged gray stripe along the front part and moderately long brown legs. Females bigger than males.

Phidippus

Often seen in the daytime, wolf spiders are active mostly at night. They have good eyesight (for a spider: a few inches). They move quickly and pounce on insect prey rather than spinning a web, although they use a lifeline of silk to catch themselves when they fall. There is no nest. Females carry around a white egg-case attached to the abdomen; when the spiderlings hatch they ride on mum's back, eating nothing (subsisting on their yolk-sacs) until they drop off a few weeks later to go their own ways. Wolf spiders overwinter under the snow, in pine needles and other litter.

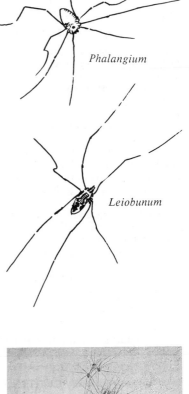

Phalangium

Leiobunum

Jumping spiders
Phidippus spp. (family Salticidae) June and July

Fairly common in dry montane places, often seen along dusty trails. Not large (5-10 mm long). The immatures are easily spotted by their quick movements and bright red or red-orange coloration with lovely iridescent green mouthparts. The legs are short and black. The adults are drably black and gray, much more difficult to see.

Jumping spiders do just that when hunting (or being hunted); they have the best vision of any spider, which you can test by bringing a finger toward one and finding the distance at which it takes notice. *Phidippus* lives in a little silken nest under a stone, fallen branch or leaf. It may move in with you; is harmless.

Harvestmen/daddy-long-legs
Phalangium and *Leiobunum* spp.
(order Opiliones, family Phalangiidae)
June to October

Montane, common on trees or on the ground, often sunning themselves low down on south-facing building sides. Small, round brown bodies (4-8 mm) and very long, extremely skinny brown legs.

Harvestmen look like spiders but are not (they are in a separate order). They have only two eyes, rather than the eight (more or less) of true spiders; the eyes of *Phalangium* are stuck on a tiny black bump on the spider's head, while on *Leiobunum* they are mounted low and in front. This latter is a little larger than the former, and a little lighter in color.

Cluster of hibernating harvestmen in a cave near Jasper.

Harvestmen eat small bugs, decaying stuff and plant juices. They don't produce silk. After mating in late summer, the female lays eggs in the soil; they overwinter and the young emerge next spring, very tiny at first, becoming large enough to notice in June (for *Phalangium;* the young of *Leiobunum* show up about a month later). Most adults cannot survive the Canadian Rockies winter, but they try to hibernate en masse. I know of one overwintering spot: a small chamber at the back of a short limestone cave along the Maligne River. The entrance is small; when I first crawled in and stood up I was nose-to-spider with patches of clustered harvestmen on the walls.

BUGS IN, ON OR OVER WATER

> *So, naturalists observe, a flea*
> *Hath smaller fleas that on him prey;*
> *And these have smaller fleas to bite 'em,*
> *And so proceed ad infinitum.*

> - Jonathan Swift

Never truer than in your average mountain pond. There are thousands of wee beasties in the lakes and streams of the Canadian Rockies, most so small you need a microscope to see them: **hydrozoans, rotifers, tardigrades, roundworms, flatworms, gastrotrichs, rhizopods, suctorians** . . . and everything is eating everything else. A few of the tiny eaters and eatees are illustrated on the next page.

Next up the ladder we have the **crustaceans** (class Crustacea), known popularly as "freshwater shrimp." You can leave your microscope at home for these, but bring a finely woven dip net and a magnifying glass if you want to catch some for a look-see. They are water arthropods, freshwater versions of their much-larger marine relatives the lobsters and shrimp. Crustaceans are year-round water dwellers, going about their lives under a metre of ice in winter. The ones illustrated are all common around here, especially in warm, low-elevation lakes in spring. Scooping up a handful of bottom mud will usually get you a few **amphipods** (scuds, sideswimmers) and **ostracods.** Sweeping a net through the water just off the bottom will often bag **fairy shrimp** (anostracads), **water fleas** (cladocerans) and **copepods.** Surface water gives up **plankton** (diatoms, algae and algae-eating copepods, water fleas and fairy shrimp).

There may be other things in your net, of course. Consider the possibilities on the next few pages.

Aquatic insect larvae

Many airborne insects begin life under water. Here are a few common insect larvae found in mountain water bodies. Note that larvae of stoneflies, mayflies, damselflies and dragonflies are called "naiads," but they are larvae all the same.

Mosquito larvae
Order Diptera, family Culicidae,
April to August

Montane to alpine, in still water. Very common in shallow lakes and temporary water bodies during June, but also found in *any* spot of water as long as its surface is not oily: in buckets, tin cans, tree holes, pitted stumps—you name it. Mosquito larvae are up to 15 mm long; they hang from the water surface upside down, each breathing (well, *respiring;* insects don't breathe) through a tube that breaks the surface. Oil kills a mosquito larva because it keeps the tube from reaching air. The larvae constantly curl and uncurl; they are known to fishermen as "wrigglers." Adult form: page 466.

Midge larvae (bloodworms and phantom midges)
Order Diptera,
families Chironomidae and Chaoboridae,
year-round

Montane to alpine, in lakes and sluggish streams. Hemoglobin in the otherwise-transparent larval bodies of midge

Microscopic

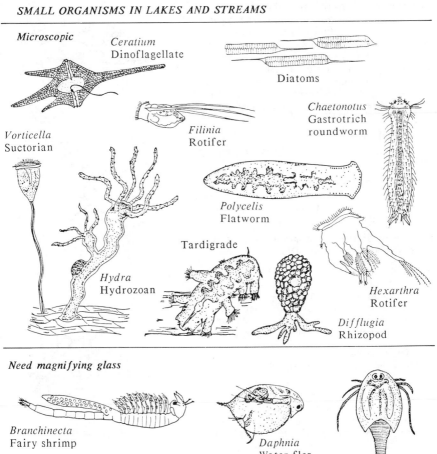

Ceratium
Dinoflagellate

Diatoms

Vorticella
Suctorian

Filinia
Rotifer

Chaetonotus
Gastrotrich
roundworm

Polycelis
Flatworm

Tardigrade

Hydra
Hydrozoan

Hexarthra
Rotifer

Difflugia
Rhizopod

Need magnifying glass

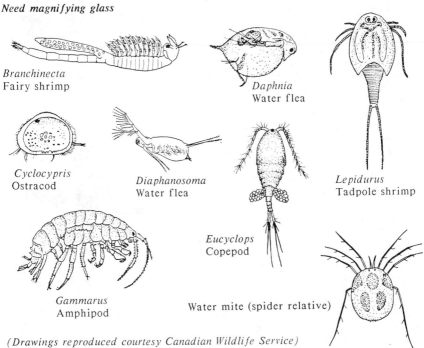

Branchinecta
Fairy shrimp

Daphnia
Water flea

Cyclocypris
Ostracod

Diaphanosoma
Water flea

Lepidurus
Tadpole shrimp

Eucyclops
Copepod

Gammarus
Amphipod

Water mite (spider relative)

(Drawings reproduced courtesy Canadian Wildlife Service)

Water insects

species colors them red; thus the name
bloodworms (although they aren't really worms).
The larvae of **phantom midges** such as
Chaoborus lack hemoglobin and are practically
invisible underwater; other midge larvae are
dark-colored. They are all 10-20 mm long and
very active, bringing their front and back ends
together and then snapping them apart. They
eat small organisms and decaying matter. See
page 468 for the adult form.

Black fly larva

Black fly larvae
Simulium spp. (Diptera, family Simuliidae)
May to September

In vigorous montane and subalpine streams.
Small (2-5 mm long), living on and under rocks,
attached by a rear-end sucker disk and eating
microorganisms. Adult form: page 471.

Water tiger

Predaceous diving beetle larvae (water tigers)
Order Coleoptera, family Dytiscidae, year-round

In montane and subalpine water bodies of any
kind. Small (5 mm long) to very large (65 mm
long), slim and agile, patrolling up and down in
the bottom waters in search of other insect
larvae. These things can catch tadpoles or even
small fish with their hefty front-end pinchers.

Dragonfly naiads
Order Odonata, suborder Anisoptera, year-round

In montane lakes and streams, on the bottom or
clinging to water plants. The largest larva to be
found in mountain water, up to 50 mm long.
Distinguished from the other naiads (following
entries) by the absence of a tail; the abdomen is
fat and the eyes are large. Like the diving
beetle larvae (previous entry), dragonfly larvae
are voracious predators, attacking nearly
anything. Mosquito larvae are staple foods.
    These naiads have an interesting modus
operandi: the lower lip (if insects can be
thought of as having lower lips) suddenly flicks
out, snaring the prey and dragging it back.
Then the lip retracts under the head.

Dragonfly naiad

Stonefly naiad
Order Plecoptera, year-round

In streams and well-oxygenated montane and
subalpine lakes, on the bottom. Length up to
40 mm, the body yellowish or brown, with
strong-looking legs, large eyes and two harmless
spine-like sensory organs sticking out the back.
The head and next three segments are
handsomely patterned in contrasting tones.
    Most stonefly naiads putter about the
bottom, shredding detritus; some are predators,
gobbling up other bottom-dwellers. They live up
to three years before changing to adults.

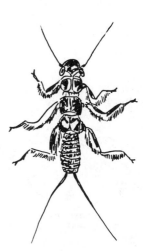

Stonefly naiad

Damselfly naiad

Order Odonata, families Coenagrionidae and
Lestidae, year-round

Montane to alpine, on bottoms of shallow ponds.
Length to 30 mm. Brown body resembling
stonefly naiad (previous entry), but slimmer,
with three large leaf-like gills at the tail.
Predatory.

Damselfly naiad

Mayfly naiad

Order Ephemeroptera, May to August

Montane and subalpine, in fast-flowing, rocky
streams. Length to 15 mm, smaller than similar
stonefly and damselfly larvae. Green, brown or
transparent body has slim legs and three
filaments on the end (two are sensors called
cerci). Feeds on plant material and tiny animals.
Can live up to four years before
metamorphosing to adult.

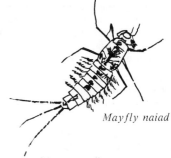

Mayfly naiad

Caddisfly larvae

Order Trichoptera, year-round

Montane and subalpine, in lakes and streams.
Caterpillar-like larvae live in cylindrical cases
up to 50 mm long made of sand, twigs or leaves
held together with silky glue secreted from
salivary glands. Caddisfly larvae extend their
heads and front legs to crawl about the bottom,
dragging the cases with them. It takes a year
for them to reach the adult stage; they pupate
in the cases.

Caddisly larva

Water bugs, water beetles

Backswimmer

Order Hemiptera (true bugs),
family Notonectidae, July to October

In montane and subalpine ponds and streams,
often at the surface in shallow quiet water.
Length 10-15 mm. Backswimmers live belly-side
up (black); the other side is white to green,
often with prominent red patches. Covered
wings are used only in spring, to fly from one
pond to another. One pair of legs is long,
sticking straight out to the side and propelling
this bug (a true bug, in the scientific sense) like
oars. The front legs, also fairly long, are used to
grab prey: small insects, mostly, held in the
tension of the surface water. Although small,
this bug can bite you. Compare with water
boatmen (next entry).

Leaf tube   *Sand tubes*

Adult caddisfly

Backswimmer

Water boatmen
Order Hemiptera, family Corixidae,
June to September

Montane and subalpine ponds, puddles and
other small or very small water bodies—even
discarded cans that hold water. And open septic
tanks. Length 5-15 mm. Resembles the
backswimmer (previous entry), but lives right
side up. Body is brown with fine white or gray
parallel wiggly lines; the hind pair of legs are
long and do the rowing; the shorter ones help.
Most water boatmen eat algae, but some are
predaceous. None bites. Often living in minute
water bodies that are inclined to dry up, they
fly from one stagnant pool to the next.

Giant water bug
Lethocerus americanus
(Hemiptera, family Belostomidae)
June to September

Shallow, montane ponds and sloughs, often just
under the surface among underwater vegetation.
Largest water insect in the mountains
(45-60 mm long), brown and flat, with thick
front legs to seize prey up to the size of a small
salamander. It grabs and stabs, thrusting a sharp
beak into the victim and injecting it with
anaesthetic saliva. It can do the same to your
foot if you step on it while wading, the reason
for its folk name: "toe-biter." The nymphs tend
to eat each other, thus keeping the number of
giant water bugs in any one pond fairly small.
Good.

Whirlygig beetles
Gyrinus spp. (Coleoptera, family Gyrinidae)
May to September

Montane and subalpine, at the surface in quiet
water. Whirlygig beetles in the Canadian
Rockies are 3-7 mm long, oval and black, often
shiny, with lines of dots and orangey legs. The
name comes from peculiar group behavior. Lots
of whirlygig beetles will congregate, each one
whirling round and round, bumping into the
others, acting nuts. No one knows why, although
it likely has to do with that great
craziness-inducer, sex. Larvae eat small
organisms, crawl out of the water to pupate and
return in the adult, whirlygig form. See also the
diving beetles (next entry).

Diving beetles
Order Coleoptera, family Dytiscidae,
May to September

Montane ponds and slow streams, in weedy
shallow water. Many species; small ones are
often 10-15 mm long, brown body with
yellowish markings and yellow, bristly back
legs. Larger species (up to 40 mm) are often of
the genus *Dytiscus;* oval body is shiny black
with a yellow rim.

    Your typical diving beetle grabs a bubble
of air on its butt and dives to the bottom,
grubbing about there among the insect larvae
and whatnot until the bubble is gone, at which
point it returns to the surface for another one.
The bubble actually extends up under the
beetle's elytra (wing coverings), so there is more
air there than it would seem. The beetles fly
from pond to pond at night, feeding mostly on
mosquito larvae; the large ones also kill
tadpoles and small fish.

    Like the whirlygig beetles (previous entry),
diving beetles pupate in damp soil and return to
the water as adults, able to fly but seldom
doing so. Adults overwinter and live three years
or more.

Giant water scavenger beetle
Hydrophilus triangularis
Order Coleoptera, family Hydrophilidae
August and September

Montane and subalpine ponds and sluggish
streams. Length 25-40 mm. Resembles a large
diving beetle (previous entry), but lacks the
yellow rim around the body and has a pair of
long palps (mouthparts) sticking out the front.
It is not predatory, preferring to scavenge along
the bottom for dead stuff. At night these beetles
fly around; you can attract them to lights. You
can also sometimes find their egg cases floating
around: silky cocoons 20-25 mm across, each
with one projecting point. Larvae live
underwater, pupate in damp dirt along the
shore and re-enter the water in late summer,
often active under ice all winter.

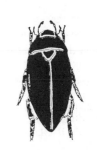

Water striders
Order Hemiptera, family Gerridae,
June to September

Montane to alpine, on still water surfaces. Body
10-15 mm long, dark brown. Long, skinny
middle and hind legs snap forward and back,
propelling these bugs (true bugs) across the
water very quickly—just try catching one! They
eat mostly insects stuck in the surface film, and
they talk to one another by making ripples.
Really! Adults overwinter on the shore, under

leaves buried beneath the snow. Texans, creators
of wonderful folkisms, call them "Jesus bugs"
because they walk on water. In Canada, true to
northern form, we often call them
"pond-skaters."

Mayflies
Order Ephemeroptera, May to August

In hovering swarms above lakes and
fast-flowing montane and subalpine streams.
Hundreds of species, differing mainly in size
(5-15 mm long) and color (white, yellow, brown,
greenish). Body layout is similar throughout:
slender, with gently up-curved abdomen, clear
or smoky wings held together vertically above
the body, and two or three long filaments
extending from the tail.

This is an ancient animal, little changed in
350 million years. The males swarm, attracting
females into the throng; a male seizes each and
they mate on the wing. Within an hour the
females drop eggs into the water. These lodge
under stones. The naiads cling to rocks, eating
small organisms and/or algae; they emerge from
the water and molt to dark-colored nearly
mature adults called subimagos (or "duns").
Subimagos molt again a few hours later to join
the dancing adults, living only a day or two and
not eating at all.

Mayflies represent all that is giddy about
the short northern summer.

Dragonflies and damselflies
Order Odonata

Dragonflies and damselflies are readily identified by the long, slender abdomen
and four equal-sized wings. These are Devonian insects; they have done well on
this planet for 350 million years. The secret of their success: possibly their
helicopter-like flying ability. Up, down, forward, back, sideways, hovering—these
flyers can do it all, making them extremely agile hunters. They catch prey with
their feet.

The difference between the dragonflies and damselflies is mainly in the eyes
(larger on dragonflies, covering most of the head) and in the wings (usually, but
not always, folded back when at rest in damselflies, held out horizontally in
dragonflies).

Dragonfly/damselfly sex is interesting. The male produces a little bag of
sperm from the tip of his abdomen, then curls the abdomen under to place the
packet in a special chamber under the second segment back from the thorax. When
a female comes along, the male grabs her around the neck with special claspers; if
agreeable, she bends the tip of her abdomen up to take the sperm bag from its
compartment, later depositing the fertilized eggs in the water or on plants nearby.

The naiads (larvae) spend one or more years eating mainly mosquito larvae
before crawling out of the water and changing over a few days into adults, which
live along the shores of lakes, ponds and streams at all but the highest elevations.
They may be seen throughout the summer, patrolling a little way out from shore.
Some species prefer to do their hunting in the woods.

Representative dragonflies and damselflies of the Canadian Rockies are
described on the next page.

Darners (family Aeschnidae): over montane ponds and lazy streams. Large (bodies 60-80 mm long; wingspans to 100 mm), brilliantly blue, green and/or brown with clear wings.

Darner

Emeralds (family Corduliidae): over cold montane and subalpine marshes, bogs or slow-moving streams. Medium-sized (40-60 mm), with iridescent green eyes, metallic green or greenish-bronze thorax and dark abdomen (sometimes with white rings). Common ones are *Somatochlora* spp. and *Cordulia shurtleffi.*

Whitefaces *(Leucorrhinia* spp., family Libellulidae): over montane and subalpine marches and bogs. Small (25-40 mm), black with red or yellow markings and white faces.

Meadowhawks *(Sympetrum* spp., family Libellulidae): over montane and subalpine marshes. Usually red or golden all over. One common species *(S. danae)* is black like *Leucorrhinia* (previous entry), but has a dark face. Meadowhawks like to land on white-colored things: rocks, bleached logs, tan pantlegs.

Skimmer

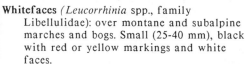

Four-spot skimmer *(Libellula quadrimaculata)* family Libellulidae): montane to subalpine, over lakes and slow-moving rivers. Length 70-80 mm; olive-brown with yellow stripes along the sides and yellow face. Each wing has two smoky spots along the leading edge.

Clubtails (family Gomphidae): montane, over small, fast-flowing streams. In the Rockies we have mainly the pale snaketail *(Ophiogomphus severis):* 45-52 mm long, thorax pale greenish-yellow with dark markings; abdomen black with yellow spots.

Clubtail

Bluets (damselflies; family Coenagrionidae), June to September: montane to alpine, common over ponds and lakes. Length 30-40 mm. Sky-blue with black markings and clear wings.

Spreadwings (damselflies; family Lestidae), June to August: montane and subalpine, near small ponds. Length 35-40 mm, the thorax bright metallic green or bronze, abdomen darker and vaguely banded, wings clear and held out from the body at rest, like those of a damselfly.

Damselfly

BUTTERFLIES

Somehow, butterflies are *not* bugs. We say "Oh, look, John—there's a blue butterfly sitting on your shoulder!" Not "John, look out—there's some kind of icky *bug* on your shoulder!"

Butterflies are not icky; to human eyes they are the most beautiful of the insects. Better yet, they are harmless. Thus we refrain from harming *them*—except when they are in the larval stage, as caterpillars. These we squash and poison just as fiercely as we do anything else that strikes us as ugly or alien.

Moths are, well, not as attractive as butterflies. Mostly drab-looking night-flyers, they are inclined as larvae to eat up the crops and make holes in our clothes. They are *almost* bugs.

Between the moths and the butterflies there are the skippers, looking rather like each group. See page 520.

The life cycle of all these creatures is in four stages: egg, caterpillar, chrysalis (pupa: the insect motionless inside a case, undergoing metamorphosis), and adult butterfly, skipper or moth. In most species the cycle lasts one year. The caterpillar feeds mostly on leaves, while the adults either feed on flower nectar or don't eat at all. Except for a few species that overwinter as adults, they fly about for a couple of weeks, mate, produce eggs and die.

Highly specialized creatures of delicate ecology, most caterpillars depend on only one or two species of plants for food—what entomologists call the **host plants**. The adult is a little less picky, sipping nectar wherever it can find it (if it is a species that eats in the adult stage), but butterflies tend to prefer the same environment they did in the caterpillar stage. So one looks for a particular butterfly in the plant community that supports it.

In the Rockies we have lots of butterflies, especially in the drier parts of the region: southern foothills, front ranges south of Bow River and the southern Rocky Mountain Trench. We have representatives of every major North American group except the metalmarks. But I don't think we have as many amateur butterfly *collectors* (per capita) as there used to be a few generations ago, when butterfly-collecting was a fad. Perhaps more of us now realize that we need not kill or possess a wild thing to enjoy it.

Nondestructive butterfly-watching is like birdwatching: you do it with binoculars. Most butterflies will let you approach within a few metres, but that isn't quite close enough for naked-eye identification. However, if you screw down your binoculars to their closest focus, you can see all the detail in those lovely wings. Choose a warm, windless afternoon and go to a meadow, alpine or otherwise, or a good-sized clearing in the woods. Settle down near a tiny spot of water, for butterflies often light around puddles to drink. Wearing bright colors will attract the Schmetterlings to you (and hummingbirds, too). It's hard work, lying about in fields of wildflowers for hours, but somebody has to do it.

Butterflies are surprisingly easy to identify. It is done by looking at the highly diagnostic colors and patterns in the wings. Note how butterflies really have two sets of wings, not just one. The **forewings** and **hindwings** overlap, giving the impression that there is only one wing on each side. But there are two. Usually the top and bottom sides of the wings are different—and frequently it is the bottom side that helps in making the identification. Body colors are sometimes useful, but less important.

There are 90-odd species of butterflies that you are likely to see in the Canadian Rockies, and 12 species of skippers. The uncommon ones have not been individually described, but there is a list at the end of the section, on page 524.

The listings below are organized in much the same way as the Audubon guide (see further reading, page 531). The month(s) given with each listing indicate the flight period. This can vary considerably, so don't put a lot of stock in it. Further, insect populations fluctuate markedly from year to year and from place to place; a butterfly listed as common around Jasper in 1985 may be rare there a couple of years later. Its range might change as well. Sizes given are wingtip-to-wingtip; if a particular specimen is at the large end of the range for that species, it is probably a female.

Butterfly experts are trying to standardize common names (as ornithologists have done), but at time of writing they are still quibbling. I have listed just the name given in the Audubon guide.

Boldly patterned butterflies
Brush-foot family (Nymphalidae)

These are the butterflies that are easiest to identify. They are all members of the brush-foot family: butterflies with small, vestigial front legs.

Mourning cloak
Nymphalis antiopa (brush-foot family)
April to October

Common in montane aspen/poplar woods and adjoining meadows. Host plants: willows, aspen, balsam poplar. A large butterfly (75-85 mm), easily recognized by the gold or cream margin on the dark-brown, velvety wings. Note also the line of deep blue or purple dots, the rough wing edges and the stubby tail on the hindwing. Underneath, the wings are woody-looking with a whitish border. Listen to this butterfly as it leaves its perch; you may hear it make a clicking sound.

Mourning cloaks overwinter as adults, which explains why they are the first butterflies you see in spring and the last in fall. They are uncommon in midsummer.

Milbert's tortoiseshell
Aglais milberti (brush-foot family)
April to October

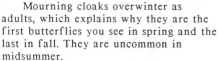

At all elevations, in any habitat. Host plants: nettles. Wingspan 45-50 mm. Milbert's tortoiseshell has an unmistakable yellow-and-orange band along the rear part of the wing. The rest is dark brown, except for red-orange bars along the leading edge, a small white crescent near the wingtip and white flecks along the irregular trailing edge. Underneath, the wings are drab brown with a lighter zone under the bright topside band.

White admiral
Limenitis arthemis (brush-foot family),
June to September

Common in and bordering aspen and poplar groves. Host plants: birch, willow, poplar and aspen. Large (75-80 mm), black except for a broad white band across the wings, both above and below. Note also the red spots behind the band,

and the blue crescents along the trailing edge.

Lorquin's admiral
Limenitis lorquini (brush-foot family)
June to September

Southern region on the eastern slope, but north to Golden on the western slope, in montane forests and meadows near host-plant willows, aspen, balsam poplar and choke cherry. Wingspan 55-70 mm. Lorquin's admiral has a broad band of white bars against a black background, with red-orange wingtips. It is colorful underneath: the white band exists there, too, against an orange background with black crescents and black veins.

 If any butterfly can be thought of as "aggressive," this one can. It will come over to check you out, and it even chases birds!

Red admiral
Vanessa atalanta (brush-foot family)
May to October

Occasional in montane and subalpine forest and moist meadows as far north as Pink Mountain. Caterpillar eats nettles. Medium-sized (wingspan 45-60 mm) and very boldly patterned: black wings with red-orange bars that form a semicircle; white markings near the forewing tips and a thin border of white scallops. Underneath, the wings are drab with a slash of orange and some white spots.

Painted lady
Vanessa cardui (brush-foot family)
June to September

Common in some years but otherwise rare, in meadows at all elevations. Host plants: thistles. A fairly large butterfly (50-60 mm), the painted lady resembles the fritillaries (page 511) or the checkerspots (page 510), with their complex orange/black/white patterns. But the painted lady is patterned more simply on top: brown body and inner wing area, orange/yellowish0 central area with black patches (and dots on the hindwing), black wingtips with white bars and spots. Underneath, the wings are complexly patterned in brown and white; look for the eyespots on the lower hindwing.

 Occurring worldwide, the painted lady can overwinter only in warm areas such as the American southwest. The new adults emerge in late winter and move north, sometimes flying all the way to the arctic. They reproduce and try to return, but it is unlikely that those reaching the Canadian Rockies can make it home before cold temperatures catch them. And the offspring cannot take the winters here. Thus, whenever there is a population explosion to the south we see many painted ladies; in lean years, very few.

White butterflies
Whites (family Pieridae)
and a parnassian (family Papilionidae)

"White" means *mostly* white. There are other colors as well as patterns in the wings of these butterflies, but most of the wing surface is white, creamy, or very pale yellow.

Veined white
Artogeia napi (whites/sulphurs family)
April to August

Montane and subalpine, in shady, damp places. Seeks mustard-family wildflowers (rock-cress and others). Small (30-40 mm). Black body, white wings with a bit of black along edges. Males often have one black spot on each forewing; females, two. Wings white underneath, hindwing with brown or greenish veins that are heavy in northern populations and often unnoticeable in southern ones. Similar cabbage white (next entry) has yellow patches beneath hindwing and no veining.

Cabbage white
Artogeia rapae (whites/sulphurs family)
May to September

Found as far north as Willmore park, around dwellings at montane elevations where the caterpillars can eat garden vegetables. Common in towns, but will also eat wild mustard-family plants such as rock cress. Introduced from Europe, this butterfly is small to medium-sized (30-50 mm), white above with pale black wingtips and usually one black spot (male) or two (female) on each forewing. Hindwing is yellowish underneath (sometimes quite bright when freshly emerged), flecked with gray. Compare with veined white, previous entry.

Northern marblewing
Euchloe creusa (whites/sulphurs)
May to July

Subalpine and alpine meadows, central
and northern regions. Host plants: *Draba*
species. Size: 30-35 mm. White wings with
charcoal pattern at tips; prominent bar
along front edge. Underside heavily
marbled in yellowish-green. Found
mainly in spring, but also later in the
summer.

Creamy marblewing
Euchloe ausonides
(whites/sulphurs family) April to August

Montane woods, in moist places. A
northern-marblewing look-alike, but
sparser marbling below, with green and
yellow along veins. At 35-45 mm across,
it is also a bit larger. Despite its long
season, we see it mainly in the spring.

Western white
Pontia occidentalis
(whites/sulphurs family)
April to September

Montane to alpine, but mostly upper
subalpine and higher, among
mustard-family plants, especially rock
cress. Often seen at hilltops. Wingspan
30-45 mm, larger than spring white (next
entry), but with similar ashy pattern on
top. Go by the underwing color: greenish
in western white. Two broods a year:
spring and late summer.

Spring white
Pontia sisymbrii (whites/sulphurs family)
May to July

Mostly montane, in dry places from
North Saskatchewan River south, around
mustard-family plants. Ashy black
pattern on upper wings like western
white (previous entry), but smaller
(30-35 mm); also, the pattern underneath
the wings is black, not greenish.

Phoebus parnassian
Parnassius phoebus (swallowtail family)
June to September

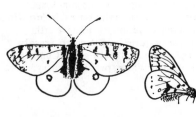

Eastern-slope, found only where
stonecrop *(Sedum* spp.) grows, in open,
meadowy places at all elevations. A large
(55-75 mm) white, dusky or
transparent-looking butterfly. Note black
markings at the wingtips and red
markings in a bar along the leading edge.

Red also in a black-edged circle on the hindwing and in three spots underneath. Males are less transparent-looking than females. Species is smaller and darker at higher elevations.

Sara orangetip
Anthocharis sara
(whites/sulphurs family) April to July

Southern Rocky Mountain Trench, and north on the eastern slope to Bow River, in montane and subalpine meadows. Like most of the whites, this one's caterpillar eats mustard-family plants. Butterfly is small (30-40 mm), with the usual charcoal-on-white markings (females may be yellow). Good identifier: the red-orange wingtips. Mottled green underneath.

Plain yellow butterflies
Sulphurs (family Pieridae) and a parnassian

Sulphurs are rather plain butterflies. Most have black-bordered wings with pink fringes along the edges and a yellow or orange spot on top of the hindwing. On females the black border is faint.

Sulphurs often sit with their wings folded, so the underside of the wing is used for identification. Key features: spots and a small smear of color on the hindwing near the back leg.

Eversmann's parnassian
Parnassius eversmanni
(parnassian family) June and July

Northern region, in alpine and subalpine meadows. Wingspan 50-55 mm; larger than the sulphurs, with dark pattern and red spots on hindwing. Males yellow, but females paler or white, with a white waxy bulb (the **sphragis**; prevents re-mating after fertilization) at end of abdomen. Host plant is golden corydalis.

Blueberry sulphur
Colias pelidne (whites/sulphurs family)
July and August

From Plateau Mountain (southwest of Calgary) north; also found in Glacier park (although not reported from Waterton). Subalpine meadows and woods, around blueberry plants. A typical sulphur: small (30-35 mm) rounded wings are pale yellow or cream, with black margin and pink edges. Two white wing spots below: black-edged on forewing, pink-edged on hindwing. Compare with Greenland sulphur (next entry).

Greenland sulphur
Colias hecla (whites/sulphurs family)
June to August

Mainly northern alpine and subalpine, but reported as far south as Nordegg. Wingspan 35-50 mm. Resembles the blueberry sulphur (previous entry), but is often larger and oranger; has smaller, fainter spots underneath the wing and is sooty-looking toward the body on the top side.

Palaeno sulphur
Colias palaeno (whites/sulphurs family)
June and July

Northern region, in boggy subalpine meadows. Wingspan 35-45 mm. Males yellow above, with small plain white spot (no rim) on forewing above/below and hindwing below. Black wing margin. Females similar but paler, with spotted wing margins topside. Both sexes olive below, sometimes quite dark. Caterpillar feeds on small bog cranberry.

Pink-edged sulphur
Colias interior (whites/sulphurs family)
June to September

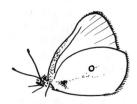

Eastern slope, in montane and subalpine meadows, often found on asters (although the host plants are blueberries). Very similar to the blueberry sulphur (page 499), but with only one spot under the wing and lighter coloring.

Labrador sulphur
Colias nastes (whites/sulphurs family)
July and August

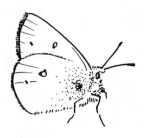

Alpine, found along ridges, over scree and in other rocky places. Yet another little butterfly with pink wing margins, fast-flying and difficult to approach, but this one has four spots under each wing (two prominent ones and two fainter ones) and is decidedly greener than the others. Blends in with the mosses and lichens it lights on. Alpine milk-vetch is the caterpillar's only food.

Mead's sulphur
Colias meadii (whites/sulphurs family)
July and August

Alpine and subalpine, from Pink Mountain south. Host plant: clover. Larger than most other sulphurs (35-50 mm) and brighter orange on top (with purplish sheen), greener below.

Sooty cast to both wings. Two white
spots below, one black-edged and one
white-edged.

Great northern sulphur
Colias gigantea (whites/sulphurs family)
June to August

Spottily distributed throughout the
Canadian Rockies, seen usually in
willowy montane and subalpine bogs.
Small to medium-sized butterfly
(35-45 mm in the mountains), usually
bright yellow, with thin black wing
borders (male only) and wide pink
fringes. Yellow spot on the hind wing.
Spot is silver below, and the hindwing is
greenish.

Common sulphur
Colias philodice (whites/sulphurs family)
March to November

In clovery montane and subalpine
meadows; common in planted or weedy
clover patches, such as you find along
highways. Large (35-60 mm); alights
spreadwinged. Pale gold or yellow with
black border and black spot on forewing.
Female has yellow spots along border.
Underneath there is a double spot on the
hindwing and single, smaller spot on the
forewing, plus ten or so faint brown
spots closer to the wing margin. See also
Queen Alexandra's sulphur (next entry).

Queen Alexandra's sulphur
Colias alexandra
(whites/sulphurs family)
May to September

Montane, in pine woods and meadows.
Found near its host plants: vetches,
locoweeds and lupines. Spreadwinged on
landing like the common sulphur
(previous entry), and resembling it, but
smaller and oranger, with reduced black
border and faint spots on upper wing
surfaces. Greenish underneath, with one
small silver spot.

Butterflies with large tails on their wings
Swallowtails (family Papilionidae)

Butterflies in this group are the Rockies' largest and perhaps most beautiful. They are also rather difficult to tell apart. The underneath wing surfaces are important identifying features.

Eastern tiger swallowtail
Pterourus glaucus (swallowtail family)
May to October

Moist montane woods and meadows; host plants are willows, aspen, balsam poplar and birches. Can be quite large (up to 140 mm), but in the Canadian Rockies usually 80-90 mm. Lots of yellow showing, with black trailing edge and black stripes, two of which intersect at the back to form a vee. Bit of red at the back. Underneath, the hindwing has red and blue spots along the trailing edge, which differentiates the tiger from the western tiger (next entry), which has red only below the tails.

Western tiger swallowtail
Pterourus rutulus (swallowtail family)
June and July

Occasional in Glacier park, in moist montane woods and meadows. Host plants: willows, aspen, balsam poplar, birches and alders. Very similar to the eastern tiger swallowtail (previous entry), but with a couple of distinct differences: it is usually smaller (70-90 mm) and has underside red spots below the tail only.

Two-tailed tiger swallowtail
Pterourus multicaudatus
(swallowtail family) June to September

Mainly in the southern Rocky Mountain Trench, in areas dry enough to support sagebrush; occasional eastern-slope montane. Host plants are choke cherries and pin cherries. Similar to the western tiger swallowtail (previous entry), but somewhat larger (90-110 mm) and with two tails—one long, one shorter—on each hindwing rather than just one.

Anise swallowtail
Papilio zelicaon (swallowtail family)
June to August

Eastern slope as far north as Kakwa area; mostly alpine but also at lower elevations. Often congregates above hilltops. Host plants are cow parsnip, angelica and other carrot-family members; named for its taste for commercial anise. A smallish swallowtail (65-75 mm); the black yoke across the leading edge is broken by yellow spots; underneath, the wings are much paler than those of black swallowtails in the region.

Old-world swallowtail
Papilio machaon (swallowtail family)
June and July

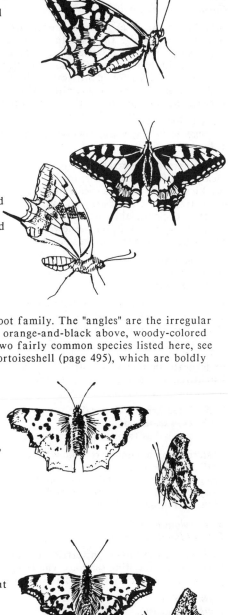

Northern region, subalpine and alpine, bordering woods and near water. Host plants probably *Artemesia* spp. Resembles anise swallowtail (previous entry), but often a little smaller (65-70 mm), with no black dot in the red patch on the hindwing, and much yellower underneath, with less black and blue.

See also Eversmann's parnassian, page 499.

Butterflies with irregular wing edges
Anglewings (family Nymphalidae)

Anglewings are members of the brush-foot family. The "angles" are the irregular wing edges. These butterflies tend to be orange-and-black above, woody-colored and moth-like underneath. Besides the two fairly common species listed here, see also the mourning cloak and Milbert's tortoiseshell (page 495), which are boldly patterned anglewings.

Satyr anglewing
Polygonia satyrus (brush-foot family)
April to October

In subalpine woods and meadows. Caterpillars eat stinging nettle—go to it, kids! Wingspan 45-50 mm. Brightly colored: orange with black spots; brown and woody-looking underneath.

Faunus anglewing
Polygonia faunus (brush-foot family)
April to September

Common in montane woods. Caterpillar feeds on willows, birch, alder and currant. Wingspan 45-55 mm. Resembles the satyr anglewing (previous entry), but the trailing edges of the wings have a black border all the way around.

Hairstreaks
Gossamer-wings family (Lycaenidae)

Most hairstreak species have strange, thready tails, usually black with white tips. But of the species in the Canadian Rockies, only the gray hairstreak has tails. (However, see also the western tailed blue, page 506.)

   Small butterflies, hairstreaks sit with their wings closed, so underside markings are used for identification. They are mostly drab on top, anyway. Males and females are pretty much alike. Although members of the gossamer-wings family, their wings are anything but gossamer.

Gray hairstreak
Strymon melinus (gossamer-wings family)
July

In southern and central montane clearings. Many host plants; in the Rockies mostly legumes (pea family) and wild strawberry. Dark gray on top, with an orange spot on the hindwing; lighter gray below, with tails on the lower hindwing and orange patches nearby.

Coral hairstreak
Harkenclenus titus
(gossamer-wings family) July

Eastern-slope montane from Bow River south, in meadows and along streams. The caterpillar eats saskatoon berries and choke cherries. Brown topside (25-30 mm), it is a little fancier underneath than most hairstreaks, with bright red dots along the edge of the hindwing. But there is no tail.

White-lined green hairstreak
Callophrys sheridanii
(gossamer-wings family) May and June

Eastern-slope montane from Bow River south, in dry places. Host plants: *Eriogonum* species. Small (20-30 mm). Gray above, iridescent bluegreen below, with white line. No tails.

Small, plain brown butterflies
Elfins (family Lycaenidae)

Elfins are little brown butterflies, the LGBs of lepidoptery. They resemble the hairstreaks (preceding section). The females tend to be lighter-colored than the males. There are only four species you are likely to see in the Rockies.

Brown elfin
Incisalia augustius
(gossamer-wings family) April to June

In montane and lower subalpine woods, often feeding on kinnikinnik nectar. Caterpillar eats flowers and budding leaves of blueberries and Rocky Mountain rhododendron. Small (20-25 mm), light brown or gray above, sometimes orangey. Rust-to-brown below, with a wavy line across both wings and rows of faint dots.

Hoary elfin
Incisalia polios (gossamer-wings family)
April to June

In montane and lower subalpine pine forests, near host-plant kinnikinnik. Small like the other elfins (20-25 mm), and resembling the brown elfin (previous entry), but grayer on top, with a silvery zone along the wing margins.

Western pine elfin
Incisalia eryphon
(gossamer-wings family) April to July

Montane and lower subalpine, in pine forests and bogs from Yellowhead Pass south. Caterpillar eats emerging needles of lodgepole pine and ponderosa pine; adults drink many nectars, including those of pussy willow, wild rose and lupine. Dark brown above, the females a bit lighter like other elfin females; quite decorative below, for an elfin: jagged bands of brown and black, with a white line midway down the wings and a narrow checkered black-and-white wing margin.

Blue butterflies
Blues (family Lycaenidae)

For once the lepidopterist's sometimes-obscure vocabulary is right on: "blues" are, in fact, small blue butterflies. Except that the females are usually brown (oh, well), with any blue found only near the body. Both sexes have a fringe of silvery hairs along the wing margins and are similar underneath.

Greenish blue
Plebejus saepiolus
(gossamer-wings family) May to August

Montane and subalpine, in open places with host-plant clover; a common roadside butterfly. Wingspan 20-30 mm. Male is gray-blue, often greenish-tinged, with dark wing border and central dark spot on forewing and hindwing. Females similar, but brown replaces blue, with orange zone near hindwing edge. Males silvery underneath; females browner. Both sexes have black dots and a faint dark line along the underside wing edges.

Blue copper
Chalceria heteronea
(gossamer-wings family) July and August

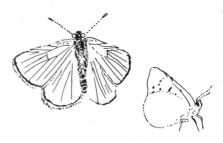

In eastern-slope montane meadows, southern region. Strongly dependent on buckwheat (*Eriogonum* species); caterpillar eats the plant and the adult sips the nectar, as well as that of other flowers. Wingspan 25-35 mm. Very blue butterfly with black border and gray wing fringe; female not as brightly colored. Differentiate from other blues by the prominent dark veining in the wings (this butterfly is really a copper, not a blue). Underneath, the wings are creamy white, spotted rather like the greenish blue (previous entry).

Common blue
Icaricia icarioides
(gossamer-wings family) May to August

In open montane and subalpine woods as far north as Lake Louise, near host-plant lupines. Wingspan 25-35 mm. Male pale blue to nearly purple, with gray fringe and black margin on forewing; dark line on hindwing with faint marginal spots but no central spot. Female brown, often with some blue near the body. Sooty gray underneath; pale-rimmed ink-drop dots on the forewing, larger than those on the hindwing.

Arrowhead blue
Glaucopsyche piasus
(gossamer-wings family) June

Southern foothills, from Bow River south, in meadows. Host plants: lupines. Wingspan 25-30 mm. Blue above (females dark-bordered), gray or brownish below, with prominent white-bordered black ink drops. Hindwing has diagnostic arrowhead-shaped markings toward the margin, sometimes with a bit of orange in the lower ones, and the fringes are checked.

Western tailed blue
Everes amyntula (gossamer-wings family)
May to August

Southern and central montane; host plants locoweeds, wild pea and vetches. Wingspan 20-30 mm. Nondescript blue above with dark margin and white fringe; female brown, but easily identified because she has a little hairstreak-like tail (however, don't

confuse with gray hairstreak, page 504).
Gray underneath, with pale blue fringe
and scattered black spots; bit of orange
by the tail. Watch these when they are
drinking at puddles and damp spots; they
wiggle their hind legs.

Northern blue
Lycaeides argyrognomon
(gossamer-wings family) June to August

Subalpine and alpine, often around
subalpine bogs with host plants laurel,
labrador tea and crowberry. Span
20-30 mm. Males blue with black margin,
plus a row of vague black dots on the
hindwing, and silvery fringe; females
brown with orange dots next to the
fringe. Below, both sexes are buffy gray
with numerous white-rimmed spots and a
line of interesting black-orange-black
bars along the wing edge. Very similar to
the orange-bordered blue (next entry) but
wider-ranging and more common. Three
subspecies, one each for southern, central
and northern regions.

Orange-bordered blue
Lycaeides melissa (gossamer-wings family)
May to August

Eastern-slope montane and subalpine as
far north as Ram River, in meadows and
dry places. Caterpillar eats lupine, wild
licorice, locoweed and alfalfa. Standard
blue above, 20-30 mm across, with black
margin and white fringe; females brown
or grayish brown with orange border.
Very difficult to differentiate from
similar northern blue (previous entry) in
other parts of North America, but in the
Canadian Rockies not so hard:
orange-bordered male has continuous
wide band of orange below rather than
discrete crescents, while the female has a
band of orange on each upper wing
surface rather than orange crescents.

Spring azure
Celastrina ladon (gossamer-wings family)
April and June

In montane and subalpine woods; host
plants dogwood, *Viburnum* and
blueberry. Wingspan 20-30 mm. A rather
distinctive blue: dark margin continues
sooty well into the wing, and the
edge-fringe is pale blue, not white.
Underneath, the color is sooty brown or
drab white, with a bordering row of

squared, dab-like sooty spots. Large spots farther in often overlap on the hindwing.

Acmon blue
Icaricia acmon (gossamer-wings family)
June to August

Eastern-slope montane, north to Ram River. Like most blues, host plants are buckwheat-family genera and legumes such as locoweed. This one also eats knotweed. Males are easily differentiated from other blues by the band of orange at the back, with black spots, a thin white line, then a dark line and silvery fringe at the edge. Female is drab brown, but the orange band is even brighter. Underneath, both sexes have white-rimmed black spots on a sooty white background.

High-mountain blue
Agriades franklinii
(gossamer-wings family) July and August

Alpine and subalpine; host plants rock jasmine and perhaps shooting star. Wingspan 20-25 mm. Males blue with black border and white fringe; row of spots next to the border on the hindwing and—important—a black bar on the forewing. Females are brown and lack the hindwing dots but have the forewing bar. Also distinctive underneath: white near the wing edge, with a thin black line and some spotting; sooty brown farther in, with black dots rimmed widely by white.

Copper-colored butterflies
Coppers (family Lycaenidae)

Coppers are usually copper-colored, all right, but often with a strange purplish sheen when viewed at an angle. Like the blues, the male and female coppers are different on upper wing surfaces (females darker, drabber) but similar underneath. The group is small in North America, and there are only four species one is likely to see in the Rockies. All are members of the gossamer-wings family.

Lustrous copper
Chalceria cupreus
(gossamer-wings family) July and August

In alpine and high subalpine meadows and talus slopes. Host plant: mountain sorrel. Wingspan 25-30 mm. The copperiest of Rockies coppers, the males are quite bright above, with black-and-white wing margins and black spotting. Females darker. Below, the wings are black-margined, with orange or pink on the forewing and a red line on the hindwing.

American copper
Lycaena phlaeas (gossamer-wings family) July and August

Eastern-slope alpine, from Kakwa River south. Host plant is mountain sorrel. Smallest copper in the mountains (wingspan 22-28 mm), but brightly patterned on top, orange against gray. Can be much darker, though, like other alpine species. Underside is rather like that of lustrous copper (previous entry), but lacks the black wing margin.

Mariposa copper
Epidemia mariposa
(gossamer-wings family)
June to September

Southern and central montane and subalpine, near bogs, ponds and in other damp places. Caterpillar may feed on knotweed. Wingspan 25-30 mm. Male orange with brown wing margins and black spots on forewing; hindwing sooty orange with row of black crescents at the rear and white fringe. Female very dark, with bright orange spots. Underneath, forewing of both sexes is similar to upper surface (orange and black), but hindwing is sooty/silvery.

Dorcas copper
Epidemia dorcas (gossamer-wings family)
July and August

In montane and subalpine wetlands and meadows; host plant probably shrubby potentilla. Wingspan 25-30 mm. Males coppery brown with notable purple sheen, dark-brown or black margins and spots. Orange half-moons are present along rear hindwing edge in about half the individuals. Females mahogany with concentric lines of black smudges and light-brown wing edges. Underwings of

both sexes tawny, with black dots in
rough concentric rings. Note pale orange
band at rear of hindwing.

Checkered butterflies
Checkerspots (family Nymphalidae)

Checkerspots are three-colored butterflies with complicated patterns. Like a birder
trying to identify flycatchers, you have to know just what to look for as a
checkerspot comes by. They are all medium-sized butterflies (40-50 mm across the
outspread wings), the males and females sometimes alike and sometimes different.

Northern checkerspot
Charidryas palla (brush-foot family)
June to August

From Bow River south, in aspen-rich
montane woods and subalpine meadows.
Lots of host plants: paintbrush,
fleabanes, asters and goldenrod. Look for
this species also around rabbitbrush in
the dry southern Rocky Mountain
Trench. Small for a checkerspot
(30-40 mm). Male upper wings orange
and black, with the white limited to rear
wing margin; females are much darker,
yet with more white. Sexes similar
underneath: hindwing has yellowish
bands with yellow crescent-shaped
markings inside a red border.

Rockslide checkerspot
Charidryas damoetas (brush-foot family)
July and August

From Athabasca River south, on alpine
scree slopes and in other bouldery places.
Host plant: goldenrod. This is another
smallish checkerspot, 30-40 mm across
and resembling the northern checkerspot
(previous entry), but buff-and-black
rather than orange-and-black, and
limited to the high country. Orange and
sooty-white below, with black netting.
Kind of greasy-looking. Sexes similar.

Anicia checkerspot
Occidryas anicia (brush-foot family)
May to September

At all elevations, but most common in
dry montane meadows and woods. Host
plants are mainly paintbrush and
penstemons. Wingspan 30-50 mm.
Confusingly variable topside, but they
are more uniform below: three bands of
white on the orange hindwing, with
black netting and an orange margin.

Edith's checkerspot
Occidryas editha (brush-foot family)
July and August

Eastern-slope, southern and central regions, at all elevations in open woods and meadows. Caterpillar eats paintbrush, owl clover, lousewort and other figwort-family plants. Wingspan 30-50 mm. Quite checkery; look for a bold white bar on the forewing that stands out from the rest of the pattern. Also checkered below.

Gillette's checkerspot
Hypodryas gillettii (brush-foot family)
June and July

Southern eastern-slope montane, in lodgepole woods and meadows. Host plants include bracted honeysuckle and snowberry. Wingspan 35-45 mm. Same pattern above and below: wide band of orange toward the rear, large orange spots among brown/white pattern forward. Sexes similar.

Orange-and-black butterflies
Fritillaries and crescentspots (family Nymphalidae)

There are *lots* of orange-and-black butterflies in the Canadian Rockies, most of them fritillaries or crescentspots (branches of the brush-foot family). Be prepared to put in some time if you want to learn the various species.

If you would rather not, though, it is easy to tell a fritillary from a member of any other group: most fritillaries are labeled with the letters "OSB" along the leading edge of the forewing. Really! Possible meanings: garbled version of "SOB," or maybe the anti-predator message "Oogy! Stinky! Barfy!" Crescentspots lack the calligraphics.

Despite their numbers, most fritillaries are dependent on only one group of host plants: the violets, of which only three species are common in the mountains (early blue violet, western Canada violet and evergreen violet). This high degree of specialization is risky, for failure of the food source (always possible in a dry year) can wipe out such a dependent species over a wide area.

Pearly crescentspot
Phyciodes selenis (brush-foot family)
June to August

In grassy or moist open places at all elevations. Host plants: asters. Wingspan 25-40 mm; small for this group. Crescentspots are like fritillaries but have more black in the wing, especially along the margin, and one or more white crescent-shaped spots under the hindwing. The pearly crescentspot is typical: blotchy orange and black on top with (females darker than males), yellowish underneath with orange netting and a line of small black dots—plus a single silver crescent

between the line of dots and the wing
edge. Compare with field crescentspot
(next entry).

Field crescentspot
Phyciodes campestris (brush-foot family)
June to August

In subalpine and alpine meadows;
caterpillar eats asters. Wingspan only
30-35 mm, smaller than the checkerspots.
Identify by the dotted row of orange
spots on the upper hindwing. Otherwise
checkered pale-yellow and dark brown
(often black in the Canadian Rockies.)
Underneath, the wings are patterned in
varying shades of burnt orange.

Zerene and aphrodite fritillaries
Speyeria zerene and *S. aphrodite*
(brush-foot family) June to September

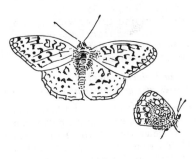

Zerene found in montane meadows
throughout the region; aphrodite very
common in southern Rocky Mountain
Trench, present on eastern slope south of
Bow River. Host plants are violets.
Wingspan 50-70 mm. Typical fritillaries
above (orange, with squiggly black
markings), but differentiated from others
by underwing pattern: brown with large
black-rimmed silvery spots. Telling the
two apart isn't easy; in the Rockies the
aphrodite fritillary has a red band
underneath while the equivalent area on
zerene is tan.

Callippe fritillary
Speyeria callippe (brush-foot family)
June to August

In the dry Rocky Mountain Trench from
Canal Flats south, and in the eastern
foothills as far north as Nordegg. Host
plants: violets. Wingspan 50-60 mm.
Another look-alike fritillary, this one
quite similar to the aphrodite and zerene
fritillaries except that the silver
underwing spots along the wing margin
are in the shape of triangles.

Edwards' fritillary
Speyeria edwardsii (brush-foot family)
July

Southern foothills, in meadows and
clearings in pine forests. Host: yellow
prairie violet. A large fritillary
(wingspan 50-70 mm), often with more
yellow topside than others. Large silvery
spots below resemble those of callippe,
aphrodite and zerene fritillaries

(previous entries); differentiate by the greenish color between the spots, the orange veining and the pinkish/orangish body.

Mormon fritillary
Speyeria mormonia (brush-foot family)
July to September

From Kakwa River south, in moist montane meadows with asters (although the host plants are violets). Smaller than the previous two fritillaries described (wingspan 40-50 mm). Similar pattern on wing surfaces, but underneath the wings are olive-hued rather than brown, there is no red/tan band, and the spots are drab rather than silver.

Hydaspe fritillary
Speyeria hydaspe (brush-foot family)
July and August

From Athabasca River south, in montane meadows and aspen groves. Host plants: violets. Wingspan 45-60 mm. Topside pattern the usual fritillary black-on-orange, but underneath there are diagnostic markings: yellow spots, black at one end, on a reddish brown or maroon background.

Atlantis fritillary
Speyeria atlantis (brush-foot family)
July and August

Mostly subalpine, in clearings and along streams. Host plants: violets. Wingspan 45-65 mm. Here is one fritillary you can identify from the upper side: there is a black border on the wings. Below, the wing border is chocolate brown or reddish against paler wing surfaces with silvery spots.

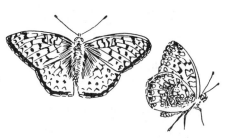

Great spangled fritillary
Speyeria cybele (brush-foot family)
July to September

Extreme southern Rocky Mountain Trench; north as far as Banff on eastern slope, in montane clearings. Host plants: violets. This is the largest fritillary in the Canadian Rockies, wingspan 55-75 mm. Often yellowish, and with a prominent dark yoke. Check the underwings for a diagnostic yellow band between the orangey margin and the brownish inner part. Males are orange on top; females, cream.

Bog fritillary
Proclossiana eunomia (brush-foot family)
June to August

In subalpine and montane black-spruce bogs; sometimes alpine. Small (30-40 mm) and darkly marked with smudgy black on orange, rather like a crescentspot, but bright underneath: pale yellow with rough orange bands, black veining and small circles.

Titania's fritillary
Clossiana titania (brush-foot family)
June to September

Common butterfly, found nearly anywhere at montane and subalpine elevations. Host plants are willows and bistort. A boldly marked fritillary, but small (30-45 mm) despite its name. On the underside, the hindwing is diagnostic: purplish or reddish and densely patterned, with several pairs of pale yellow opposed black chevrons bordered in yellow or white, making interesting, X-like figures.

Freya's fritillary
Clossiana freija (brush-foot family)
May to July

In willowy places at any elevation. Caterpillar eats blueberry plants, kinnikinnik and crowberry. Wingspan 30-40 mm. Yellowish orange on top, with usual fritillary black markings; hindwing underneath has marginal white triangles and a jagged red-and-white band farther in.

Frigga fritillary
Clossiana frigga (brush-foot family)
June and July

In subalpine bogs, especially those with willows. Caterpillar feeds on the northern species of white dryas (*Dryas integrifolia*), willows and maybe raspberry plants. A small fritillary (30-40 mm), the frigga is typical topside but has a pale purplish band underneath with smoky markings on it and a wonderful common name.

Silver-bordered fritillary
Clossiana selene (brush-foot family)
June to August

In montane wetlands from Jasper south.
Host plants: violets. Wingspan 35-50 mm.
Note the yellow-blotched, silvery
underwings, with their regular row of
black dots and the large, angular white
patches near the body.

Astarte fritillary
Clossiana astarte (brush-foot family)
June to August

Along alpine ridges and scree slopes
from Pink Mountain south. Brighter
orange topside than other fritillaries, and
fairly large (35-50 mm), with rather
fuzzy markings. Banded underneath,
with black and white dots in rows, red
near the centre.

Picture not available

Dingy arctic fritillary
Clossiana improba (brush-foot family)
July and August

In soggy alpine meadows from McLeod
River north. Host plant: high-country
willow species. Wingspan 30-35 mm.
Dusky, vaguely patterned upper surfaces;
quite brown toward the body. Oranger
underneath, with light outer band on
hindwing and rust-colored inner area.

Alberta fritillary
Clossiana alberta (brush-foot family)
July and August

On dry, rocky alpine slopes, southern
area. Host plant: white dryas. Resembles
dingy arctic fritillary (previous entry),
but on the lower surface of the hindwing
there is a pale band; at the margin there
are dots and faint crescents.

Napaea fritillary
Boloria napaea (brush-foot family)
July and August

Over alpine tundra and high-subalpine
meadows, northern region. Host plant:
alpine bistort. Yet another
arctic-fritillary look-alike on the upper
surface, but this one is quite different
below: blotchy, with yellow or cream
crescents against black or brown near the
body, and one crescent that is just the
reverse (dark against a light blob)
farther out in the lower hindwing.

Butterflies with eyespots on their wings
Satyrs (family Satyridae)

Not all the butterflies listed below actually have eyespots. But most of them do, and those that don't are close relatives of those that do, so they are included here. All are **satyrs**: medium-sized brownish butterflies with small forelegs (like the brush-foot family). Host plants for the caterpillars are various grasses and sedges; the adults tend to stay in the larval habitat.

Ochre ringlet/prairie ringlet/ northwest ringlet
Coenonympha tullia (satyr family)
May to July

Montane to alpine, southern area, in dry, grassy places. Host plant unknown, but likely to be grasses. Wingspan 25-50 mm. Ochre/orangey above, sometimes with an eyespot at the wingtip. Browner underneath, with variable underwing pattern; the illustration is fairly typical.

Large wood-nymph
Cercyonis pegala (satyr family)
June to August

Mostly south of Bow River, in eastern-slope montane woods, meadows and wetlands; also found in extreme southern Rocky Mountain Trench. Host plants: grasses. Wingspan 50-75 mm. Light brown to dark brown on top, with one or two eyespots; lighter below, with large eyespots on the forewing and small eyespots on the hindwing, all yellow-rimmed. An irregular dark line divides inner wing pattern from outer. Compare with dark wood nymph (next entry).

Dark wood-nymph
Cercyonis oetus (satyr family)
July and August

In dry, grassy places, southern Rocky Mountain Trench and eastern slope from North Saskatchewan River south. Host plants: grasses. Wingspan 35-45 mm. Dark brown above and below, with one or two prominent eyespots underneath on the forewing and a couple of small spots on the hindwing. Much like the large wood nymph (previous entry), but markedly smaller and darker, with fewer spots and no inner-wing/outer-wing pattern division underneath. Note range difference.

Uhler's arctic
Oeneis uhleri (satyr family) May to July

Eastern slope, in dry grassy spots at all
elevations from North Saskatchewan
River south. Caterpillar feeds on grasses.
Color varies from light brown to
greenish ochre; two eyespots on the
forewing and a circle of two to five on
the hindwing. Underneath, there is an
eyespot or two on the frosty, orangey
forewing, but not on the hindwing,
which is marbled brown and white.

Jutta arctic
Oenis jutta (satyr family) June and July

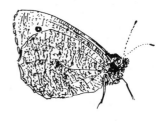

Central and northern regions, near
subalpine bogs and other wet places. Host
plant is cotton grass. Wingspan 50-55 mm.
Drab above, yellowish near the wing
edge with obvious black eyespots in the
yellow. Densely marbled black and white
underneath, with a white-dotted black
eyespot set in yellow on the forewing.
But this species can vary considerably.

White-veined arctic
Oeneis taygete (satyr family)
June to August

Alpine, often in rough, rocky places
from North Saskatchewan River north.
Hosts may be grasses and/or sedges.
Wingspan 45-50 mm. Another
orange-to-brown plain butterfly above,
sometimes with eyespots. Below, the
hindwing is diagnostic: a broad band
zigzags through, dark at the edges and
paler at the centre. Outside the crisp
edges of the band, the wing is frosty,
grading browner toward the margin and
the body. Veins are silvery-scaly.

Chryxus arctic
Oeneis chryxus (satyr family)
May to August

In pine forest and small clearings, mostly
northern but found throughout the
mountains. Host plants: grasses. Wingspan
45-50 mm. Here is an arctic with a
recognizable upper pattern: brown yoke
with pale orange zone near trailing edges
marked by black dots; dark wing
margins. Underneath there is a jagged
band crossing the hindwing, much like
that of the white-veined arctic (previous
entry), plus an eyespot.

Melissa arctic
Oeneis melissa (satyr family)
July and August

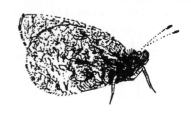

In alpine meadows and over scree slopes.
Host plants: grasses and sedges. Wingspan
40-50 mm. A well-camouflaged butterfly,
gray to brown above and dark/light
mottled below, mainly on the hindwing.
Usually no eyespots.

Polixenes arctic
Oeneis polixenes (satyr family)
June and July

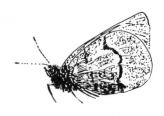

Northern and central alpine areas, on
tundra and stony ground. Host: alpine
bluegrass. Wingspan 40-45 mm.
Brownish/grayish above and below, often
with tiny white dots toward the wing
margins. Translucent-looking, sometimes
resembling smoky mica. Hindwing has a
ragged dark line underneath. This species
grows slowly; must often overwinter
twice before maturity.

Alberta arctic
Oeneis alberta (satyr family)
May and June

Occasional in the southern foothills, in
dry meadows. Host plants: grasses. A
small satyr (35-45 mm), dull ochre above,
with what lepidopterists call a **bird-beak**
pattern (eye, plus beak-like shape) along
the leading edge; more obvious
underneath. The rest of the underside is
wood-grain mottled.

Canada arctic
Oeneis macounii (satyr family)
June and July

Eastern-slope montane lodgepole forests
and clearings, from Pink Mountain south
to Kananaskis Country. Most common in
odd-numbered years. Host plants: grasses.
Wingspan 50-60 mm. Black-and-orange
pattern resembles the well-known
monarch butterfly (not found in the
Canadian Rockies) but the Canada arctic
is much smaller and has eyespots.
Underneath, the topside pattern carries
through the forewing, but the hindwing
is woody, with a smoky margin.

Arctic alpine
Erebia rossii (satyr family)
June and July)

Northern alpine and upper subalpine
meadows. Life cycle unstudied. Wingspan
35-50 mm. Dark brown above, with two
eyespots on the topside forewing circled
in orange; hindwing is banded
grayish/brownish below and lacks
eyespots or other markings.

Red-disked alpine
Erebia discoidalis (satyr family)
May and June

Eastern slope, in grassy places, montane
and subalpine meadows and wetlands.
Host plants: possibly grasses and sedges.
Wingspan 45-50 mm. Very dark butterfly,
with broad bars of dim red against
black. Similar underneath the forewing;
hindwing drab and mottled.

Spruce-bog alpine
Erebia disa (satyr family) June and July

In subalpine forests and bogs from
Canmore north. Host plants unknown;
possibly sedges. Wingspan 45-50 mm.
Drab above, although central portions of
the wings are pale orange, often with
four eyespots on the forewing.
Underneath, the forewing eyespots are
more noticeable, while the hindwing is
uniformly drab.

Common alpine
Erebia epipsodea (satyr family)
June to August

At all elevations, in damp meadows or
boggy places. Host plants: grasses.
Wingspan 45-55 mm. A distinctive
butterfly, mostly drab brown, but with
orange patches near the wing margins
and white-dotted black eyespots in the
orange. Lower wing surfaces are likewise
drab, although the forewing is orangey,
with repeated eyespots.

Erebia rossii

Erebia discoidalis

SKIPPERS
Skippers (family Hesperiidae)

What was that? Looked like a moth, sort of. More like a butterfly, but the wings seemed too small for the body. Aha—it was a skipper.

Skippers are furry-looking and drably colored, like moths. Yet, unlike most moths they are active in the daytime, and their bodies are much more butterfly-like than moth-like. A reliable way to differentiate between moths and skippers is to check the antennae: thickened and hooked at the end in skippers, whip-like or furry in moths.

The name "skipper" comes from the way these things fly: quickly, darting up and down.

There are two groups of skippers: **folded-wing** skippers and **spread-wing** skippers. The folded-wing group sits with the forewings and hindwings held at different angles; the effect is rather like that of the folding in the wings of a paper airplane. Only skippers do this, so here is a way of telling these skippers from moths or true butterflies. Spread-wing skippers sit with wings spread flat, like butterflies. But a skipper's wings are much smaller relative to its body size than those of a butterfly. And the ends of a skipper's antennae are hooked, while those of butterflies are straight.

There are only 17 species of skippers that you are likely to see in the Canadian Rockies, and they are fairly easy to tell apart, so I have listed them all.

Folded-wing skippers
Subfamily Hesperiinae

Draco skipper
Polites draco (folded-wings family)
June to August

Eastern slope from McLeod River south, at any elevation. Host plants unknown. Wingspan 20-25 mm. Streaky dull-orange and black above, greenish below with orangey, yellow-spotted forewing and diagnostic hindwing: there is a vee-shaped zone of connected yellow or cream spots.

Common banded skipper
Hesperia comma (folded-wings family)
June to August

Alpine and subalpine meadows. Host plants: grasses. Wingspan 20-25 mm. Streaky orange and black on top, like draco skipper (previous entry). Underneath, the wings are burnt-orange to brown with unconnected angular white spots that are well defined.

Long dash
Polites mystic (folded-wings family)
May to September

Eastern slope from Bow River south, in marshes, streams and wet places at low elevations. Host plants: grasses. Wingspan 25-30 mm. Upper wing surfaces are orange, with a black trailing edge and black smear just back of the centre. Underneath, the wings are brownish; the

hindwing has a curved yellow band
across it, broken with brown veining.
There is a yellow spot ahead of the band.

Woodland skipper
Ochlodes sylvanoides
(folded-wings family) July to August

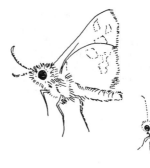

Southern montane woods, often in brushy
places. Host plants: grasses. Wingspan
20-30 mm. Orange with black trailing
edges and a black smear in the wing
centre, rather like the long dash
(previous entry). Differentiate by the
character of the trailing edge pattern
(ragged on woodland skipper, more even
on long dash), and black smear (narrower
on woodland skipper). The pattern under
the wing is also similar, but the light
band is broken on the woodland skipper,
the colors less defined, and there is no
yellow spot ahead of the band.

Nevada skipper
Hesperia nevada (folded-wings family)
May to July

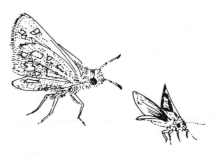

Eastern-slope montane, from Porcupine
Hills south. Host plants: needle grasses
(*Stipa* species). Wingspan 25-35 mm.
Lighter-colored than most skippers,
orange and brown above with a black
wing mark; below, the hindwing is gray,
sometimes greenish, with jagged silvery
spots.

Spread-winged skippers
Subfamily Perginae

This group of skippers sits with the wings open, like many butterfly species.
Spread-winged skippers are also a little more decorative than folded-wing
skippers, although neither group can hold a candle to the butterflies.

Alpine checkered skipper
Pyrgus centaureae (spread-wings family)
June and July

In alpine meadows, but sometimes at
lower elevations. Host plant not known
in North America, but the caterpillar
eats blackberries in Europe, and we have
several *Rubus* species here: wild
raspberry, dewberry, thimbleberry and
others. Wingspan 20-30 mm. Brown with
white checks; so similar to the
two-banded checkered skipper (next
entry) that you might as well go by
location: alpine checkered usually above
timberline, two-banded far below. When
in doubt, have a look under the wing.
Both species are complexly (and
variably) patterned in brown and white,

but the two-banded usually has some reddish color while the alpine does not.

Two-banded checkered skipper
Pyrgus ruralis (spread-wings family)
April to August

Eastern-slope montane, from North Saskatchewan River south, in lodgepole or ponderosa forest clearings. Host plants: potentillas. Wingspan 20-30. Black-and-white on top; complicated pattern in brown, white and rust on lower wing surfaces. Very similar to alpine checkered skipper (see previous entry for differences).

Common checkered skipper
Pyrgus communis (spread-wings family)
July

Eastern slope from Bow River south, at low elevations in large, grassy meadows. Host plants: mallow family. Wingspan 20-30 mm, but usually smaller than the two similar skippers listed previously. Highly variable topside (practically black to pale and quite checkery), with hairy-looking bluish scales. Below, hindwing is pale or yellowish with rows or bands of olive or tan spots with dark outlines.

Persius duskywing
Erynnis persius (spread-wings family)
June and July

Montane, in brushy areas and aspen groves. Host plants: lupines, possibly willows and balsam poplar. Wingspan 25-35 mm. Another brown-and-white checked skipper, this one with very hairy forewings and rather plain brown hindwings marked by rows of small black and pale spots. Similar underneath.

Dreamy duskywing
Erynnis icelus (spread-wings family)
May and June

Southern region, in montane meadows and deciduous groves. Host plants aspen, birch, balsam poplar. Wingspan 25-35 mm. Woody-looking topside, with zones of brown. Vague row of white dots across the hindwing and narrow black border on both wings. No white streaks.

Northern cloudywing
Thorybes pylades (spread-wings family)
May to July

Southern region, at all elevations in open areas. Host plants: legumes. Plain brown, but easily identified by the narrow white streaks along the leading edge of the wing, as if the thing had flown through a drop of ice cream. It is also brown underneath, gray near the edges.

Arctic skipper
Carterocephalus palaemon
(spread-wings family) June and July

Central and southern subalpine streams, bogs, meadows and forests. Not usually alpine, despite the name. Host plant: reedgrass. Wingspan 20-30 mm. Orange and black, rather like a fritillary (see page 511), but with smaller wings relative to body size. The only orange-patterned spread-wing skipper in the region and thus easily identified: orange and yellow underneath, with a purplish hue.

BUTTERFLIES AND SKIPPERS RARE LIST

These species are either uncommon in the Canadian Rockies (reported only a few times each summer) or rare (only a few records). When possible, I have indicated where they have been seen.

Amblyscirtes vialis (Crowsnest south)
Boloria bellona (Bow River south)
Boloria polaris (Pink Mountain north)
Callophrys siva (Invermere, Canal Flats)
Colias eurytheme (Jasper south)
Epargyreus clarus (extreme southern Rocky Mountain Trench)
Erebia magdalena (McBride, Mt. Hamel, Adams Creek Lookout)
Erebia theano (Stone Mountain park)
Erynnis pacuvius (southern Rocky Mountain Trench)
Euchloe hyantis (southern Rocky Mountain Trench)
Euptoieta claudia (Athabasca River south)
Incisalia mossii (eastern slope, southern region)
Limenitis archippus (Bow River south)
Lycaena hyllus (foothills)
Lycaena xanthoides (southern foothills)
Mitoura spinetorum (Yoho park south)
Neominois ridingsii (Plateau Mountain)
Neophasia menapia (Alberta)
Nymphalis californica (eastern slope, central and southern regions)
Nymphalis vau-album (eastern slope, central and southern regions)
Oarisma garita (Lake Louise south)
Plebejus optilete (Stone Mountain park)
Plebejus shasta (Lake Louise south)
Polites coras (Banff south)
Polites themistocles (Bow River south)
Polygonia gracilis (eastern slope, between Athabasca and Bow)
Polygonia progne (scattered)
Polygonia zephyrus (eastern slope, between Athabasca and Bow)
Pterourus eurymedon (southern foothills)
Satyrium acadica (extreme southern foothills)
Satyrium fulginosum (Waterton)
Vanessa anabella (eastern slope, north to Bow River)

MOTHS

There are far more moth species in the Rockies than butterfly species, but moths are generally small and drab, fly mainly at night and thus are not noticed as much by humans, who are mostly daytime seekers of the bright and beautiful. Still, moths have a soft beauty all their own. I have included a few common and curiosity-arousing ones.

Given a rather drab butterfly, a skipper and a moth, pick out the moth by the way it holds its wings when not flying: usually folded down over its back, tent-like, rather than folded upward or spread out. Note also the antennae: commonly whip-like or very furry, not thickened at the ends like those of skippers or true butterflies.

Acraea moth
Estigmene acraea
(tiger-moth family, Arctiidae)
June and July

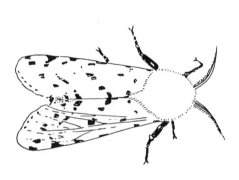

In open areas at low elevations. Host plants: poplar, choke cherry, alder, wildflowers. Wingspan 45-50 mm. Forewing mostly white, spotted with contrasting black markings; hindwing yellow in male and white in female. Black legs; black antennae that are comb-like under a magnifying glass.

Meal moth
Pyralis farinalis
(pyralid family, Pyralidae)
anytime indoors; summer outdoors

At low elevations, around dwellings, but also in the wild. Caterpillar eats mostly grain, especially the processed grains humans eat. Very small (wingspan 15-25 mm), but fairly easy to identify: V-shaped at rest, rusty brown with creamy shoulders.

Forest tent caterpillar moth
Malacosoma spp.
(tent-caterpillar family, Lasiocampidae)
June and July

Montane, in aspen or balsam poplar groves. The caterpillars are voracious eaters of aspen and poplar leaves (see page 528), but the moth does not eat anything. It is 30-40 mm across and pale brown, lightly furry all over, with darker oblique bands near the middle of the forewing. The wings are held loosely spread, although drooping in typical moth fashion.

White-marked tussock moth
Orgyia leucostigmata
(tussock-moth family, Lymantriidae)
May to September

Eastern slope, in aspen or mixed woods. Common small moth (30-35 mm), woody looking, with zones of brown across the wings. The male has big, feathery antennae; the wingless female is smaller, with whip-like ones.

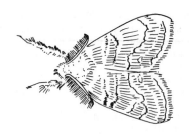

Big poplar sphinx
Pachysphinx modesta
(sphinx-moth family, Sphingidae)
May to August

Active at night in montane aspen groves and mixed aspen/pine woods. An enormous moth (wingspan 90-140 mm), readily identifiable by its size and simple color pattern: light brown across the head and forward part of the wings, chocolate brown in a band farther back, and mottled brown toward the trailing edges. In the middle band there is a small white crescent on the forewing.

Cerisy's sphinx/eyed hawk-moth
Smerinthus cerisyi
(sphinx-moth family, Sphingidae)
May and June

Montane and subalpine, near water and often in willow thickets. Host plants: willows and poplars. A large moth (wingspan 60-85 mm) with very distinctive eyespot on the hindwing. The forewing pattern varies.

Snowberry clearwing/
thetis clearwing/bee hawk-moth
Hemaris diffinis
(sphinx-moth family, Sphingidae)
July and August

In montane forest clearings, southern and central regions, flying by day. Wingspan 30-35 mm. Mimics a bumblebee: yellow and black, complete with transparent sections in the wings. But note the rusty color near the wing-roots, the tiny head and elbow-less antennae; these show that it isn't a bee at all. Harmless. The caterpillar eats several montane plant species: snowberry, honeysuckle, low-bush cranberry and hawthorne.

Hummingbird moth
Hemaris thysbe
(sphinx-moth family, Sphingidae)
May to September

In flowery montane meadows and along streambanks. Host plants: honeysuckles. Much smaller than a hummingbird (wingspan 40-50 mm), this moth is nonetheless a good imitator: colorful, with green head, reddish abdomen and reddish wings that have clear patches. It buzzes by day from flower to flower, hovering in hummingbird fashion.

Alfalfa looper
Autographa californica
(noctuid family, Noctuidae) July

Western slope montane, at low elevations around alfalfa fields and other open areas with legumes. Caterpillar eats a lot more than just alfalfa, consuming the leaves of a variety of herbaceous plants. Wingspan 30-40 mm. Woody looking, most easily identified by the difference between the forewing, which is complexly patterned in subtle shades of gray and brown, and the hindwing, which is zoned simply: light gray forward and darker gray aft.

Banded woollybear
Isia isabella
(tiger-moth family, Arctiidae)
May to August

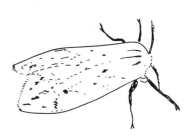

Montane. Very familiar as a caterpillar, but not so as a moth. Feeds on wildflowers. Wingspan 20-30 mm. Pale yellow with brown splotches, mostly near the wing margins. The body is more diagnostic: reddish head, yellowish abdomen with lines of black dots on the top and sides, dark legs.

Common sheep moth
Hemileuca eglanterina
(giant-silkworm family, Saturniidae)
June to August

Montane meadows, southern area. Host plants: wild roses, choke cherry, birch and aspen. A large moth (60-70 mm) and a colorful one, easily mistaken for a butterfly. Forewing pale yellowish pink, with prominent black bands and a central eye-like spot. Hindwing bright yellow with similar banding. The body is yellow and black.

CATERPILLARS

A caterpillar is not a worm; it is the larval stage of a butterfly or moth (worms are all grown up just the way they are). Unlike their attractive adult forms, caterpillars evoke in humans such responses as "yuck," or "don't touch it!" This is partly sensible; there are many poisonous caterpillars in the world, and lots of prickly ones.

To tell a caterpillar from any other insect larva, check the legs. With few exceptions, there will be three pairs of real legs on the front end and up to five pairs of knob-like **prolegs** farther back.

A caterpillar is all business. Typically hatching from eggs that have overwintered, the emergent larva must eat its way through many times its body weight in very specific plants before it is time to spin a shell around itself—the chrysalis, or pupa—and emerge in the adult, flying, butterfly form, whose job it is to find a mate, lay eggs and die (although a few species overwinter).

Here are some common, easily identified Canadian Rockies caterpillars. The sizes given are maximums, for caterpillars grow steadily larger until they pupate.

Woolly bear caterpillar
Isia isabella
(tiger-moth family, Arctiidae)
August and September

Montane, often around dwellings. Maximum length 50 mm. This must be the best-known caterpillar in North America; it occurs everywhere at summer's end. Black, with a reddish band in the middle, and very furry. Like some other brightly marked caterpillars, this one is toxic to birds.

But does a small red band mean a hard winter and a large red band a mild one, as folklore has it? According to the Audubon guide, a small reddish band means that the caterpillar is not mature yet. And does a large crop of woolly bears tally with a rough winter ahead? Probably not, although it does mean that the little darlings had a good summer.

Acraea moth caterpillar
Estigmene acraea
(tiger-moth family, Arctiidae)
May and June

Montane and subalpine, feeding on many kinds of wildflowers. A big caterpillar (maximum length 65 mm), very like the woolly bear (previous entry) but all reddish brown, without the black bars. Under the long hair it is black.

Forest tent caterpillar
Malacosoma spp.
(tent-caterpillar family, Lasiocampidae)
May to July

Montane, in groves of aspen, balsam poplar and white birch. Maximum length 50 mm. Body dark brown with blue sides

and white or yellowish spots along the
top; long white hairs sprout from the
sides. Appearing in early spring, these
caterpillars don't build nests; their "tents"
are silky mats used for moving about.
Foresters don't like tent caterpillars; they
can denude entire trees. However, this
seldom kills a tree outright, for it
usually regrows its leaves 2-3 weeks
later.

Birch leaf miner
Lyonetia saliciella
(family Lyonetiidae) July

Mainly western slope, in Columbian
forest, but possible in any stand of white
birch. Evident by hundreds of silken
strands hanging from the trees, each
strand having either a caterpillar on the
end or crawling up a strand affixed to
the ground.

White-marked tussock-moth caterpillar
Orgyia leucostigmata
(tussock-moth family, Lymantriidae)
June and July)

Eastern slope montane. Maximum length
35 mm. Another long-hair caterpillar,
this one with some black hairs and some
white hairs—the executive look. The
body is yellow, with a black top line set
with red dots; the head is brilliantly red.
It eats the leaves of deciduous trees and
shrubs.

Mourning cloak caterpillar
Nymphalis antiopa
(brush-foot family, Nymphalidae) August

Montane, on willows or balsam poplar, in
groups. Length 50 mm. White-haired,
white-speckled black body with black
spines emerging from red spots. Legs are
also reddish.

Phoebus parnassian caterpillar
Parnassius phoebus
(parnassian family, Papilionidae)
June to August

At any elevation in open places where
stonecrop grows. Length 25 mm. Simple
color scheme: black with lines of yellow
dots running down the back and sides.

Anise swallowtail caterpillar
Papilio zelicaon
(swallowtail family, Papilionidae)
June and July

Subalpine and montane, feeding mostly
on cow parsnip. Length 50 mm. Smooth
and green, with fancy yellow-dotted
black stripes.

Creamy marblewing caterpillar
Euchloe ausonides
(whites family, Pieridae) May and June

Montane and subalpine, on
mustard-family plants such as rock cress.
Length 20 mm. Skinny, the bluegreen
body striped white and gold with lots of
little black knobs.

Common blue caterpillar
Icaricia icarioides
(gossamer-wings family, Lycaenidae)
June and July

Subalpine, on lupines. Tiny, stubby
caterpillars only 10 mm long, green with
many short hairs and diagonal markings.
Well-disguised; see if you can find one.

Cabbage white caterpillar
Artogeia rapae
(whites family, Pieridae) May to August

Montane and subalpine, on
mustard-family plants. Length 20 mm.
Skinny, finely haired and spring green.
Look for the thin yellow stripes along
the back and sides.

Eastern tiger swallowtail caterpillar
Pterourus glaucus
(swallowtail family, Papilionidae)
May to September

Montane, on willows, balsam poplars and
birches. Length 50 mm. Medium brown to
green, faintly mottled in darker brown
and thus plain-looking were it not for a
bright yellow collar and scary-looking
yellow-rimmed black eyespots on the
head. There are blue dots just ahead of
the collar.

FURTHER READING ABOUT INSECTS AND SPIDERS

There is little literature for the lay public specifically about the arthropods of the Rockies, and the technical literature is enormous and difficult. So I refer to the items listed below, which tell me what family (sometimes genus, rarely species) that a particular bug belongs to. When I need detailed information, I call up experts in government and academia. Included in the list below are some free government items.

Alberta Fish and Wildlife (undated) *Common Invertebrates of Alberta* Free poster of a few selected groups, suitable for use in schools.

Arnett, R.H., Jr. (1980) *How to Know the Beetles* Wm. C. Brown, Dubuque, Iowa. 1500 species, 900 illustrated with line drawings. Introduction, key, index, glossary; 416 pages. Also in this series, but not listed here: books on mites and ticks, aquatic insects and immature insects.

Bland, R.G. (1978) *How to Know the Insects* Wm. C. Brown, Dubuque, Iowa. Keyed tour of all families, with line drawings. Introduction, key, index, glossary; 409 pages.

Borror, D.J. and R.E. White (1970) *A Field Guide to the Insects of America North of Mexico* Peterson series, Houghton Mifflin, Boston. Text is minimal but drawings are very good, including color section. Index; 404 pages.

Kaston, B.J. (1978) *How to Know the Spiders* Wm. C. Brown, Dubuque, Iowa. All known North American spiders (519 species) except Micryphantidae (difficult family comprising 20 percent of N.A. species). Line drawings, introduction, key, index, glossary; 272 pages.

Milne, L. and M. (1980) *The Audubon Society Field Guide to North American Insects and Spiders* Knopf, New York. Information-packed; the best all-round layman's publication on arthropods. Covers 550 common species, illustrated with very good color photos. Index, 989 pages.

"Pest Leaflet" series put out by Environment Canada, Ottawa. Various authors, titles, dates. Free brochures on insects that conflict with human activities. Brief and informative, although anti-bug.

Pyle, R.M. (1981) *The Audubon Society Field Guide to North American Butterflies* Knopf, New York. Comprehensive treatment of butterflies and skippers, with information on caterpillars and eggs. Color photo illustrations; special index of host plants; 914 pages.

Underhill, J.E. (1980) *Butterflies of Provincial Parks* British Columbia Ministry of Lands, Parks and Housing. Free four-page brochure on common BC butterflies, most found in the Rockies.

—— and A. Harcombe (1962) *Some Insects of Provincial Parks* British Columbia Ministry of Lands, Parks and Housing. Free four-page brochure on the commonest of BC bug groups, all of which are found in the Rockies.

Life in the snow
And other Rocky Mountain miscellany, such as molluscs

Yes, Virginia; there *are* ice worms. They live in the summer snow patches of the Rockies.

Consider the Columbia Icefield, a singularly snowy place. Cold and lifeless? Cold, yes; lifeless, no. On a sunny day in July, every square metre holds a display of insects.

Flies, beetles, butterflies and moths arrive on updrafts and storm winds, buzzing or fluttering across the rolling whiteness. Blanketing the surface there is a metre of chilled air that is deadly to warm-weather bugs.

A moth comes too close to the surface. The wingbeat slows, and it drops onto the snow.

A pair of ravens cruise by. They descend for lunch. Their big black feet step among the numb and dying insects; the birds can pick at their leisure.

Watermelon snow
Chlamydomonas nivalis (red algae), June to September

Everyone likes to play on a roadside snowbank in the middle of summer, an activity not possible in, say, Ontario but quite normal at high points along the Icefields Parkway. A word of caution, though: sliding on a steep snow patch can easily put you in hospital, for it is easy to get out of control and crash into rocks at the bottom.

But what's this? *Pink* snow? Yes, indeed. The red color in the snow is caused by millions of one-celled plants: an alga called *Chlamydomonas,* each with a red eye-spot. Sometimes the algae are so abundant in a snowfield that the snow acquires a pinkish hue. It's **watermelon snow.**

Most often you don't notice the color until the algae are artificially concentrated, which happens when you slide down a slope or walk across it. Your rump-track or boot-tracks stand out, watermelon-pink.

How does anything live in the snow? The cell content of *Chlamydomonas,* which like all protoplasm is mostly water, resists freezing through a little elementary chemistry: minerals and other substances dissolved in water depress the freezing point a few degrees. Photosynthesizing among the snowbanks, the algae get their mineral supply from dust in the snow.

In turn, watermelon-snow algae support populations of other creatures: ice worms (next entry), little bugs that eat the ice worms, birds that eat the bugs, etc., etc. All it takes is some food-producing plant at its base, and the ecological pyramid grows—in the *weirdest* places.

For some reason, watermelon snow is seldom seen in the Waterton/Glacier region. Elsewhere, look for it in the alpine zone from early June through early August. And watch out on those sloping snowpatches.

Snow worms/ice worms
Mesenchytraeus spp. (class Oligochaeta) May to August

Alpine, wriggling on top of melting snowbanks that have a high concentration of watermelon-snow algae (previous entry), which seems to be the primary food of the worm.

There are perhaps a dozen snow-worm species in the Canadian Rockies, most of them on the western slope. They are up to 2 cm long and yellowish-brown to dark reddish-brown, often curled up in little dark balls. Not much is known about them, but they seem to live only on snowbanks that melt entirely each summer, and only on snowbanks lying over soil (not on snow lying over glacial ice or rock).

Eggs laid in soil hatch in early spring. The worms work their way up through the snow to the surface and stay there until melt returns them to earth in late summer for production of next year's crop; adults may overwinter under the snow.

Springtails (snow fleas)
Order Collembola
Early winter and spring

There is a "Mount Collembola" in the Kananaskis area near Ribbon Creek. I had always wondered what the name meant, then learned one day that collembolans are tiny wingless primitive insects—springtails. Mount Collembola is well named, for the normal habitat of many springtail species is well above treeline, under rocks and among the shallow litter of tundra plants, where they eat pollen, molds and decaying vegetation. Denizens of incredibly hostile places, they even live in Antarctica.

Springtails are only 2-6 mm long, with a water-sucking tube sticking out of the abdomen. The **furcula**, an abdominal plate, cocks forward, held by a tiny catch. When a springtail decides to leap, the catch lets go and the furcula snaps back, flipping the little chap 10-15 cm into the air. Listen closely to an airborne collembolan; you may hear it saying "Wheeeeee!"

Hatching from eggs laid in soil, the tiny nymphs mature so late in the year that they reach the adult stage in early winter. Adults climb up vegetation and rocks to reach the snow surface, where they mate in a swarm, a sort of arthropod orgy. Thousands of them gather on the thin, early-winter snow of November and December (you may also see them in early spring). Because they can be quite colorful, swarming springtails produce patches up to a half-metre across that are brilliant yellow, red, orange, purple or blue. These patches look a little like lichens—until you notice that they are moving.

Small winter stoneflies
Order Plecoptera (family Capniidae)
March and April

Swarming over the snow near streams. These stoneflies are 5-10 mm long, larger than springtails (previous entry). One of my sources says the larvae feed on plants and the adults on bluegreen algae; another says the adults eat lichens.

Snow cranefly
Chionea spp.
Order Diptera (family Tipulidae)
October to April

Mostly subalpine, but sometimes at lower
elevations, picking its way slowly across
the surface of the snow. A dark-colored
wingless bug 5-12 mm long that looks at
first like a spider, but on closer
inspection turns out to be an insect: it
has six (rather than eight) long, skinny
legs. (I have seen live spiders on the
snow, too.)

Snow craneflies start to appear with the first snows of fall. In the central
Rockies one sees them all winter, sometimes at outrageously low
temperatures—down to about at -20 °C—although they are most active at
temperatures between -5 °C and +3 °C.

For most of their lives, snow craneflies live in the burrows of ground
squirrels and other small rodents, eating the tiny organisms (fleas and such) that
infest these animals. The larvae metamorphose to adults in early autumn and
disperse, looking for mates. They reach the surface by climbing up the trunks of
trees and branches of shrubs. After a few weeks of mating, the males die and the
females go back under the snow to lay eggs in the soil.

Obviously these bugs function on some kind of natural antifreeze, but at
temperatures well below freezing it is thought that their body fluids are
supercooled, which means subject to instant and complete freeze-up if the insect is
jolted—which may explain why it walks so carefully!

Compare with the snow scorpionfly, next entry.

Snow scorpionfly
Boreus spp. (Mecoptera, family Boreidae)
February and April

In mossy montane and subalpine forests,
seen on the snow surface in late winter
and early spring. Snow scorpionflies and
snow craneflies (previous entry) look

Snow scorpionfly

rather alike, but the snow scorpionfly
(3 mm long) is much smaller than the
snow cranefly (5-12 mm), so small that
you may not notice the scorpionflies,
even though they can be quite numerous
on a warmish day in April. They mate in
the snow, after which the male dies and
the female lays eggs at the base of the
snowpack, in feather mosses (page 429).
Both the caterpillar-like larvae and the
flightless adults are scavengers,
burrowing among the deep beds of moss
in search of dead insects. They may also
eat the moss itself.

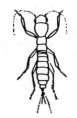

Ice insect

Ice insects
Grylloblatta campodeiformis (Order Grylloblattodea) June to September

Found under stones, wood fragments and other debris in cold, north-facing
locations at all elevations, on glacial ice near its margins, and in ice caves (rock
caves that contain ice). Length 15-30 mm, light brown, with long antennae on the
front and cerci (more sensors) on the back.

These creatures actually live in contact with ice as well as snow, although the eggs must be laid in soil. A primitive and thus probably ancient order related to the earwigs, the ice insects (only ten species worldwide, six in North America) were discovered in Banff National Park in 1914. Little is known of their lives, except that the adults feed on bugs trapped on the cold snow surface. They are nocturnal and cold-seeking, unable to tolerate temperatures greater than 8°C. Placed in a warm hand, they die.

SNAILS, CLAMS AND LEECHES

There are very few species of molluscs in the mountains, which is not surprising when you consider that most molluscs are sea creatures. Nonetheless, the floors of shallow montane lakes and ponds are sometimes covered with **snails** (order Gastropoda) of the genus *Lymnaea*. You can also find **fingernail clams** (order Pelecypoda, genus *Psidium*) in the same habitat, although they are not as plentiful.

You can thank the snails for **swimmer's itch:** attacks by microscopic parasites of the genus *Schistosoma*. At one stage in the life cycle, *Schistosoma* **cercariae** (resembling tiny tadpoles) swim out of the snail in great numbers, looking for waterfowl, their next host. But they sometimes hit swimming humans instead. Using their forked tails, they quickly penetrate the skin, only to find that they have invaded the wrong organism (man rather than duck). They soon die—but can be very annoying both before and after.

Swimmer's itch begins soon after you get out of the water. You feel an itching sensation all over (or just on the legs if you only went wading), often followed a few days later by a rash as the parasites die and fester out. The rash soon clears up and that is the end of it in our part of the world. But elsewhere, in the tropics, there are human-specific forms that can kill.

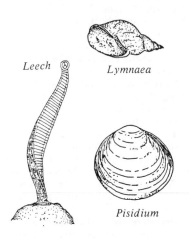

Leech   Lymnaea

Pisidium

Drawings reproduced courtesy Canadian Wildlife Service

See also *Giardia lamblia,* page 824, a waterborne parasite that does occur in the Canadian Rockies.

Finally, among the miscellaneous water dwellers of the mountains we must not forget the **leeches** (phylum Annelida, class Hirudina). These live in shallow montane ponds and sluggish streams. Leeches are black worms, half-round in cross-section and up to 10 cm long.

There is a sucker at each end. Of the many species of leeches in the Rockies, none are likely to do the thing that leeches are famous for: attaching to your body and sucking blood. Instead, they will be doing that to other creatures, usually fish. Leeches spend most of their time stuck onto rocks or submerged pieces of wood near the bottom, their bodies held upward vertically. Occasionally you may see one swimming through the water. It does so like a snake, undulating along most gracefully. Like many other worms, leeches are hermaphroditic: male and female at the same time. Think of the advantages.

Fishes
Phylum Chordata, subphylum Invertebrata, superclass Pisces

There are only some 40 species of fish you are likely to find in and about the Canadian Rockies, plus a few hybrids, so they are all included here. That is not to say that you won't come across other species, because governments and individuals are forever trying to transplant fish from one waterhole to another.

This practice is on the wane: it upsets watershed ecology, often eliminating native species. As well, the number of lakes and streams without fish—interesting to study and essential for survival of organisms that cannot coexist with fish—has shrunk considerably since stocking began in the region at the turn of the century. The entire Maligne River basin in Jasper park, for example, was originally fish-free (probably because of a high waterfall near the mouth of the river). Brook trout were introduced into Maligne Lake by the government in 1928, and rainbow trout were introduced without authorization in the 1960s. To a fisherman, a lake without fish is a lake that needs stocking. To a naturalist, anything wild is best left alone.

This book is mainly for naturalists, so this chapter is mainly about fish, not fishing. There is plenty of literature available on how and where to catch this and that; the idea here is to present the kind of information that is seldom found in fishing guides.

For example: what became of the fish in the Canadian Rockies during the Pleistocene glacial advances? Practically the entire region has been under ice at one time or another in the last two million years, which means that the fish must have been forced out. Obviously, they have come back—but from where?

At the end of the Late Wisconsinan glaciation some 11,000 years ago, it seems likely that our native species spread up the Missouri-Mississippi system on the eastern slope to the Waterton/Glacier area, and up the Columbia system on the western slope. Both these great drainage basins were unglaciated in their southern portions, providing **refugia** (literally, safe places) for fish during the ice ages. There may also have a refugium to the *north,* strangely enough, for large parts of the Yukon were never glaciated, and at least one of those regions connects with the Rockies via Liard River.

So far so good, but how did fish return to the Fraser, Bow, North Saskatchewan and Athabasca systems? These rivers drain much of the Rockies, and they all lie well within the area that was covered by ice.

As it turns out, the same ice that sent the fish packing earlier probably helped them to return later. Glaciers in the mountains melted back more quickly than the huge icecap on the prairies, and meltwater streams running out of the mountains collected in large, deep lakes dammed up against the easterly glacial mass. This chain of temporary lakes stretched all along the mountain front, at various times connecting one watershed to the next. Thus, it was possible for fish to move across the low divides of the foothills and prairies, advancing north.

At the same time, on the other side of the Rockies, a chain of glacially dammed lakes in the Rocky Mountain Trench undoubtedly provided connections between the Columbia and Fraser drainages over the low divide in the trench floor between Golden and Valemount. To the north, the Fraser and Peace systems were probably joined for a time around McLeod Lake. This would have provided an Arctic-Pacific link, for the Peace cuts right across the Rockies and drains into the Athabasca-Mackenzie system to the Arctic Ocean. There were other north-south links farther west, in the Okanagan-Shuswap area.

One must keep in mind that these connections need not have been open for very long (theoretically, a single season would have been enough), nor all at the same time. Fish could have moved across one temporary drainage link after another, their bridges burning behind them, so to speak.

On to the main purpose of this chapter: to acquaint readers with the modern representatives of those pioneers.

In describing foods eaten by fish, the word "invertebrates" is used in a special sense to include all the insect larvae, crustaceans and non-flying adult arthropods that live in the water or on its surface. Other invertebrates are mentioned separately. They include flying insects, molluscs (snails and freshwater clams), worms such as leeches, and plankton: the tiny animals and plants that live suspended in the water or floating on the surface. For our purposes, microorganisms can be considered plankton as well. (For more on plankton, see page 487.)

Fish sizes vary a lot, mainly because fish continue to grow throughout their lives. The figures given here are for average-size adults in the Canadian Rockies; you may see individuals that are much larger. Records are noted when I have been able to find them.

A note on reproduction in fish. All the species described in this chapter lay eggs, except for two live-bearing species: the mosquitofish and the sailfin molly, both present only at Banff Hot springs (see page 556).

Egg-style reproduction in fish is called **spawning.** The female produces gelatinous eggs, either simply broadcasting them over the bottom or laying them in a shallow nest scooped out of the bottom. The male emits sperm (termed "milt") that fertilizes them. Often the pair lie side-by-side as this occurs; they quiver, mouths gaping open—fish sex must be exciting. Spawning is so similar in most species that I have not described it repetitively in the individual entries. Some species, though, have different and interesting ways of spawning, and these are described in a little detail.

Fishing regulations vary considerably from place to place in the Rockies. Before throwing in your line (and maybe getting nicked for it) be sure to obtain the latest rules of the game, available at fish and wildlife offices and sporting goods shops in Alberta, British Columbia and Montana. Regulations in the national parks may differ from provincial or state regulations.

On to the listings.

SALMON, TROUT, GRAYLING AND WHITEFISH
Family Salmonidae

Trout and salmon are both members of the salmon family, as are whitefish and grayling. The word "salmon" is applied to those fish in the family that normally hatch in freshwater and then head downstream to spend most of their lives in the sea, returning inland at the end to spawn. This life cycle is termed "anadromous."

Trout, on the other hand, stay in freshwater all the time. They do not make the journey down-river as fry, and they may spawn many times before dying. This makes evolutionary sense: why go through the trauma of switching from freshwater to saltwater and back again if you can manage just fine in one medium or the other? And why expend all your reproductive capacity in one shot? The probable answer: food is available in the ocean in far greater quantities than it is in fresh water.

Some species within the salmon family can occur in either a freshwater (trout-type) form or an anadromous (salmon-type) form. Rainbow trout and steelhead, for example, are the same species, yet steelhead are anadromous, while rainbows are not.

The anadromous form usually grows much larger than the equivalent freshwater form. The freshwater kokanee, for example, averages about 22 cm long in Lake McDonald (Glacier park) but the anadromous sockeye attains 80 cm out in the Pacific. Both are *Oncorhynchus nerka.*

EXTERNAL FISH ANATOMY

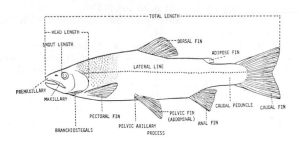

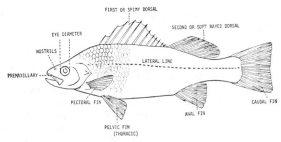

FRY (YOUNG) OF COMMON TROUT AND SALMON SPECIES

Chinook salmon

Kokanee

Cutthroat trout

Rainbow trout

Bull trout

Brown trout

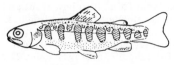

Brook trout

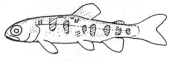

Lake trout

Fishes

The only ocean-going salmon species that spawns regularly in the Canadian Rockies is the chinook, which migrates up the Fraser as far as Mount Robson. There used to be a tremendous salmon run up the Columbia/Kootenay system, but this ended in 1939 when the Grand Coulee Dam was built on the lower Columbia in Washington state. A fish ladder (a series of artificial steps in the river to bypass the dam) failed to work. Salmon experimentally netted and trucked around the dam continued to their spawning grounds, but the young were killed in the turbines on their way downstream to the sea. This error has never been corrected, many more dams have been built on the Columbia, and it now seems that we humans have destroyed one of the world's great salmon runs. Fortunately, the Fraser remains un-dammed.

Chinook salmon/spring salmon
Oncorhynchus tshawytscha (salmon family)

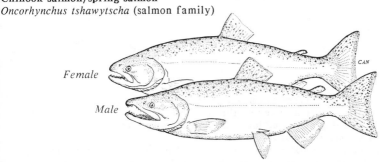

Female

Male

Seen in the Rockies only along the Fraser River and its tributaries between late August and mid-September during the spawning run. Most adults are 83-92 cm long and weigh 8-10 kg; maximum 160 cm and 57 kg. Identification: during spawning the fish are dark red, almost black in some individuals, with greenish heads and patches of white fungus on places where they have been injured while struggling up rapids and waterfalls. Males have distinctive hooked jaws and slightly humped backs.

Chinooks head for the sea after about a year, remaining there for up to five years (two or three years on the average). They normally return inland to spawn when four or five years old.

No one can fail to be impressed by the sight of enormous red chinook salmon writhing in water that barely covers their bodies as they spawn in small streams feeding the Fraser. They have come over 1000 km upstream in pursuit of the thready chemical flavor of the water in which they first swam. They haven't eaten a thing in weeks.

Each female produces a shallow depression in the gravel (called a **redd**) by fanning her tail. A male takes one or more females as mates, defending her redd from other males. Or a female may choose a particular male. The female lies on her side and quivers, releasing eggs; the male releases milt at the same time, the act repeated until 500-700 eggs are laid. The female covers the fertilized eggs with gravel, then moves on to make another redd until several thousand eggs are laid. When the females are finished, so are the males: all adults die a day or two after. Birds and bears clean up the remains.

So strong, so elemental, so sad, the salmon run is a great event to witness. You can see the spawning chinooks up close on the northern outskirts of Valemount, where Highway 5 crosses Swift Creek. There is a special government-installed viewing area there.

Another spot is at Rearguard Falls, near Mt. Robson, where the fish attempt to pass the falls—a tremendous rapid, really—by jumping from step to step. It had been thought that Rearguard Falls was the upper limit of the salmon run on the Fraser, but several hundred chinooks have been seen in the past several years spawning above Rearguard falls at Swiftcurrent Creek. Ten-metre Overlander

Falls, a few kilometres farther upstream, is impassable to the fish and thus the end of the line.

Pacific salmon species are declining in numbers, the blame placed largely on commercial fishing. Spawning salmon are protected by law upstream from Prince George, and they are not particularly good eating, anyway, this far from the sea.

Kokanee
Oncorhynchus nerka (salmon family)

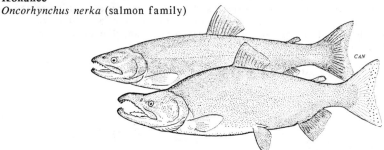

Native in western-slope lakes, but now absent through most of the Columbia system. Present in Williston Lake and thus possibly on the eastern slope, but an attempted eastern-slope introduction some years ago was unsuccessful. Adults 20-23 cm, 0.3 kg; maximum about 70 cm and 4 kg.

Kokanee look much like rainbow trout (next entry), with the pink line along the side, but kokanee are bluish rather than greenish along the back and lack spots. Spawning adults are redder all over, with greenish heads; the males develop the strange-looking enlarged, curved jaws and hump typical of salmon. Both sexes carry patches of white fungus when spawning.

The kokanee is simply a landlocked sockeye salmon, similar in all ways except smaller. The species eats mainly plankton, reaching maturity in three years. Introduced extensively as an easily caught and tasty game fish, kokanee reproduce throughout the Fraser drainage but not in the Columbia/Kootenay system—except at one well-known locality: McDonald Lake, near West Glacier, Montana. Kokanee living in McDonald Lake go through an annual spawning run upstream, just as if the lake were their ocean home. They lay eggs in upper McDonald Creek, where the gravelly bed is sufficiently aerated and at the right temperature for successful reproduction. Park staff report runs of 100,000 fish in mid-September. All adults die shortly after spawning, providing a sudden protein glut that attracts up to 600 bald eagles. Gulls, ravens, magpies, bears and even deer come to eat the dead and dying fish.

Rainbow trout/steelhead
Salmo gairdneri (salmon family)

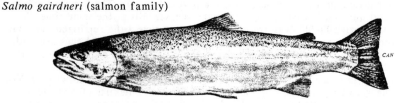

Native on the western slope (and possibly in the Peace and Athabasca drainages), introduced on the eastern side of the Rockies, now common at all elevations in streams and lakes. Average size 20 cm and 1 kg; Alberta record 9.3 kg (Maligne Lake, 1980). Identification: pale bluish or greenish back, the color often extending down the sides, which become silvery or yellowish lower down. Fish is black-spotted all over except on the belly. Pink or reddish band on the sides, starting at the gills, is prominent on spawning males.

This fish has two forms: freshwater/saltwater migrant, or freshwater only. There are no major physical differences. The ocean-going form, called **steelhead,** is native to BC and the Pacific states. It hatches mainly in coastal streams and moves to sea after 2-4 years, then returns inland about three years later to spawn, thereafter migrating annually between stream and sea and living 6-8 years. There may be steelhead in the Fraser portion of the Rocky Mountain Trench, but probably not many. The freshwater form, called **rainbow trout,** has been stocked throughout the Rockies; it is by far the more common form in the mountains.

Rainbow trout spawn in spring (early summer at high elevations); they reach sexual maturity at 3-5 years; although few live beyond their first spawning, it is not uncommon to find 12-year-old individuals. Primary foods are flying insects, leeches, snails, invertebrates and small fish. The most popular game fish, rainbow trout are easily raised in hatcheries and tolerate warm water, although they do better in cold water. Rainbows often hybridize with cutthroat trout (next entry).

Cutthroat trout
Salmo clarki (salmon family)

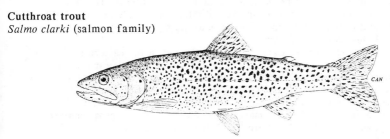

Native to headwaters lakes and streams from Athabasca River south on the eastern slope and throughout the western slope. Average size 25 cm, 0.2 kg; Alberta record weight 4 kg (Lower Kananaskis Lake, 1950). Identification: yellowish-green to beige on the back, sides paler; black spotting along the back also covers the sides rearward along the body; tail fin spotted, too. All cutthroat show a red line in a crease along the lower jaw; it fades when the fish dies.

Cutthroat trout readily hybridize with introduced rainbows, and as a result pure cutthroat are becoming rare in the Canadian Rockies. In an attempt to preserve the inland form (there is also a sea-run cutthroat that spawns in coastal BC streams), the Alberta government has introduced cutthroat, and only cutthroat, in the Ram River above David Thompson Canyon, which has waterfalls that have kept the watershed upstream previously free of fish.

Cutthroat prefer high, cold mountain lakes and streams, eating flying insects, invertebrates and small fish. Mature in two to four years, they spawn in spring and early summer and live about 4-7 years.

Brown trout
Salmo trutta (salmon family)

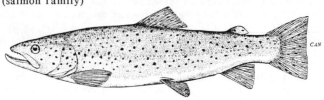

An introduced species, now fairly common on the eastern slope in the North Saskatchewan, Red Deer and Bow drainages (also in the upper Athabasca River), mainly in cool but gentle foothills streams with well-vegetated banks. Rarer, but present on the western slope in the Kootenay River. Average size 20 cm, 1 kg; Alberta record weight 7 kg (Swan Lake, 1983), length 70 cm (North Raven Creek). A 5.5-kg specimen has come from Lake Edith at Jasper. Identification: golden-brown to olive-drab along the back, lighter colored along the sides with black spots and orange-to-red spots on the body (less prominent on the fins). Spots have white halos. Tail is unforked.

Brown trout are European and Asian, introduced in the eastern-slope national parks in 1924-1925 and in coastal BC rivers in the 1930s. Active mainly at night, they eat mostly flying insects and invertebrates, although large adults take other fish, amphibians and even mice. During the day, brown trout hide under rocks and in vegetation; they are difficult to catch and not as tasty as the other trout. Spawning time is late fall; age at maturity is 4-5 years and lifespan may reach 13 years. Brown trout hybridize with brook trout (page 543).

Golden trout
Salmo aguabonita (salmon family)

Eastern slope only, stocked in scattered high-elevation lakes from the North Saskatchewan River south. Average size about 20 cm, 0.5 kg; Alberta record 2 kg (Barnaby Ridge, 1965). Identification: very similar to rainbow trout (page 540), but even more colorful: yellowish body, larger spotting and orange fin tips.

Golden trout are native to the Kern River in the Sierra Nevada mountains of California. Starting in 1959, the Alberta government has introduced them into subalpine lakes, hoping they will reproduce; they do. The fish do well at high elevations, living on flying insects and invertebrates; they spawn in midsummer.

Brook trout/speckled char
Salvelinus fontinalis (salmon family)

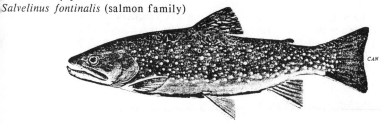

Introduced, now common in rushing eastern-slope streams and lakes between Athabasca and Bow rivers, on the western slope from Valemount south. Average size 25-30 cm, 0.5 kg; Alberta record 5.9 kg (Wood Buffalo National Park, 1967). Identification: olive-green back with yellow worm-like markings, paler green on sides, with yellow spots, plus red spots that have blue halos. Lower fins are pink to red, with white front edge and black stripe just behind.

   Brook trout are native to eastern Canada, where coastal dwellers migrate between inland and marine waters. Prized game fish, they have been stocked throughout the continent, with most success in mountain regions. They eat mostly caddisfly larvae, midges, mayflies and invertebrates, living about five years and spawning every fall when two to four years old. Brook trout sometimes hybridize with brown trout (page 542) to produce tiger trout (next entry); they also hybridize with bull trout (page 544) and lake trout (see splake, next page).

Tiger trout

Tiger trout are brown-trout/brook-trout hybrids. They are rare but reported occasionally in southern Alberta.

Lake trout
Salvelinus namaycush (salmon family)

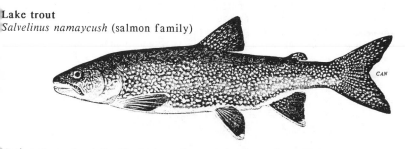

Native throughout the Rockies on the eastern slope, from Valemount north on the western slope, in deep, cold lakes. Average size 30 cm, 1.5 kg; Alberta record weight 23.8 kg (Cold Lake), length 91 cm (Pyramid Lake, Jasper). A monster 1.3 m long and weighing 46.3 kg was caught in Lake Athabasca (northwest Saskatchewan) in 1961. Identification: lighter-colored than other trout, olive to gray-green or brownish above and lighter on the sides, speckled or mottled with white. Deeply forked tail.

   Lake trout seek water that is at 10°C or colder, staying deep in the summer and feeding on small organisms; in winter they move up closer to the surface and eat mainly other fish. Juveniles feed on invertebrates. Spawning begins at age 5-10; lifespan has not been established, but if the spawning age is any indication it may be the longest of any trout. Spawning time is fall. Lake trout have been artificially crossed with brook trout (see splake, next entry).

Splake

Splake are fertile hybrid trout produced at the Banff hatchery in 1946 by artificially crossing male brook trout and female lake trout. Natural hybridization of these two is not known. Splake were introduced in many lakes in Banff and Jasper parks, but only Lake Agnes, a small tarn above Lake Louise, is known to have an established splake population.

Bull trout
Salvelinus confluentus (salmon family)

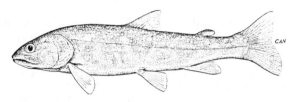

Native and common in western-slope streams and lakes, especially in the Kootenay watershed; less common in eastern-slope waters but widespread. Average size 25 cm, 1 kg; Alberta record weight 11.7 kg (Muskeg River, 1947) and length 86 cm (Clearwater River). Identification: often rather dark-colored, pale-olive to gray-green, with pale pink to orange spots that lack halos. The dorsal (top) fin is more pointed than that of other trout, the tail fin is not forked, and the lower fins are white on the front edge like those of brook trout.

Bull trout have also been called "Dolly Varden," the name of a character in the Dickens novel *Barnaby Rudge,* who dressed in pink-spotted calico that looked rather like the coloration of this fish. But the name should be dropped: recently it has been shown that the bull trout is not the same species as the Dolly Varden *(S. malma)*, which occurs mainly along the west coast.

Bottom feeders (they eat mainly invertebrates), bull trout spawn in the fifth year, in fall. They can live up to 20 years, 10-12 years on the average.

Arctic grayling
Thymallus arcticus (salmon family)

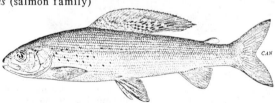

Native in cold lakes and streams in northern areas, common from the Athabasca River north on the eastern slope and in Peace River drainage. Occasional much farther south: grayling have been successfully introduced in Glacier park, from whence they have spread up the Flathead River on the western slope. Grayling also now occur in Waterton park, in the Belly River. Average size in the Canadian Rockies 20-30 cm, 0.2-0.8 kg; Alberta record 1.3 kg (Embarras River, northeastern Alberta) and 36 cm (Marten Creek). Identification is easy: look for the very large, white-spotted dark dorsal (top) fin. In spawning males, the fin becomes quite reddish. Back is iridescent green or bluish gray, lighter on the sides, with a few dark spots on the front half.

Arctic grayling need cold water and are very sensitive to pollution (especially stirred-up silt). They eat mainly flying insects and near-surface invertebrates, sometimes feeding on bottom-dwellers and occasionally on the fry of other fish.

Grayling reach maturity in 4-6 years and spawn during ice breakup (mid-April to early June in the Rockies). The fish live as long as 12 years.

Mountain whitefish
Prosopium williamsoni (salmon family)

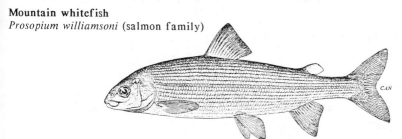

Native in larger rivers and lakes at montane and lower subalpine elevations; more common on the eastern slope. Average size 20-30 cm, 0.2-0.8 kg; Alberta record 2.4 kg, 53 cm (Athabasca River, 1976). Identification: trout-like in shape and features, but essentially uncolored (greenish or brownish along the back), with no spots and a small mouth.

Whitefish are bottom feeders, eating mostly invertebrates (especially insect larvae), snails and small fish; they prefer the main watercourses and the lakes that lie along them. Sometimes called "grayling" in southern areas, they look rather similar to immature arctic grayling (previous entry); differentiate by the large dorsal fin on the grayling. Age at maturity 3-4 years; maximum lifespan 18 years (recorded in Bow Lake); spawning is in the fall. Game fish.

Pygmy whitefish
Prosopium coulteri (salmon family)

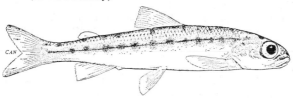

Occasional along the western slope, on the eastern slope in Peace River and Waterton Lakes; recently reported in the Athabasca near Jasper. Typically 10 cm long. Similar to mountain whitefish (previous entry), but smaller and slimmer. Habits and life history also similar.

Lake whitefish
Coregonus clupeaformis (salmon family)

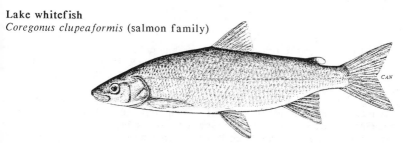

Supposedly native in larger, deeper lakes and rivers, but reported only from Upper Waterton Lake. Average size 45 cm, 1 kg. Resembles mountain whitefish (page 545), but larger, darker and more heavily built. Small mouth and dark fins.

Lake whitefish feed near the bottom, sometimes higher, eating mainly invertebrates, snails and plankton. They mature in 4-6 years, spawn in the fall and live about 10 years (maximum 28 years). They are popular among anglers and commercially important in eastern North America.

BIG FISH: PIKE AND STURGEON

Northern pike/jackfish
Esox lucius (pike family, Esocidae)

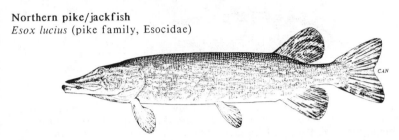

Eastern slope mainly, but also in Peace and Liard drainages, occasional in low-elevation lakes along the larger rivers. Average size 40 cm, 3 kg; Alberta record 115 cm, 17 kg (Keho Lake, 1983). Identification: large size, dorsal fin far back on the body and long snout with a big mouth full of nasty-looking teeth (fisherfolk beware: it bites!). Color pattern varies considerably, from rather plain bluish to spotted and striped, with red fins.

Except for sturgeon (next entry) and spawning chinook salmon, northern pike are the biggest fish in the Canadian Rockies (rivalled sometimes by lake trout). Yet they live in shallow lake water, hunting the weedy fringes for fish (90 percent of the diet), frogs, mice, young muskrats and ducklings. Juveniles eat mainly invertebrates and small fish. Maturity comes at 2-3 years for males, 3-4 years for females; lifespan about 10-12 years, maximum 26 years. Pike spawn in late spring. There is no nest; a pair swims about together, releasing eggs and milt at intervals. Pike are caught for sport, but be sure to cook them well, for they often carry tapeworms that can be passed to man.

White sturgeon
Acipenser transmontanus (sturgeon family, Acipenseridae)

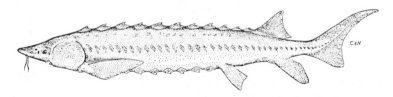

Uncommon but present in the Fraser as far upstream as Longworth (east of Prince George), possibly as far as McBride, and in the Kootenay River to at least Lake Koocanusa in the southern Rocky Mountain Trench; possibly in the upper Columbia as well.

This is by far the largest fish species found in the Rockies—the largest in North America, in fact. Individuals reaching 270 cm and 150 kg have been caught near Prince George. (Record weight in the lower Fraser is 548 kg). But white sturgeon are seldom seen upstream from Prince George, and they are usually comparatively small (about 120 cm long on the average). Regardless of size, sturgeon are readily identifiable by their shape and especially by the rows of pointed bony plates along the back and belly.

Despite their intimidating appearance, sturgeon are toothless bottom feeders. They use their sucker-like mouths to pick up anything edible there. Not only are sturgeon our biggest species, they are also the oldest: the females spawn first at 26-34 years and the males at 11-22 years. Large ones are 60-70 years old. They don't die after spawning, and may reach the age of 100!

Sturgeon can be anadromous (saltwater/freshwater), moving up the Fraser from the Pacific in early spring to spawn and returning to the sea in late summer, but individuals above Prince George seem to be strictly freshwater-dwellers.

CODFISH AND LAMPREYS IN THE ROCKIES?
Yes, me b'y.

Burbot/ling
Lota lota (codfish family, Gadidae)

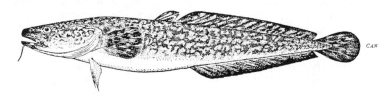

Native in large lakes and occasionally in the deeper rivers. Average size 30-40 cm; a 75-cm specimen was taken in Lesser Slave Lake, Alberta. Burbot look eel-like, long and round, with continuous fins on the back and belly; compare with Pacific lamprey (next entry). Like other codfishes (burbot is the only true freshwater cod), there are two short barbels on the nose and a long, wispy one under the chin. Coloration: dark brown with yellowish mottling.

Bottom feeders, burbot eat invertebrates when young and mostly other fish when older. Spawning is unusual: under ice in winter, at night. Ten or twelve fish spawn together, writhing, in a ball-shaped clump that moves along the bottom spewing eggs. Burbot are tasty if skinned, but often rejected by fishermen who don't know them and mistake them for catfish. However, there are no catfish in the Canadian Rockies—although the 15-cm **stonecat**, *Noturus flavus,* could show up in the southern foothills, in Milk River drainage). Burbot reach maturity at 3-4 years and may live to 10-15 years.

Pacific lamprey
Entosphenus tridentatus (lamprey family, Petromyzontidae)

Present in the upper Columbia system of the Rocky Mountain Trench, but not common; present in the Fraser below Prince George, but not reported above. Eel-like, with a prominent round disk-like mouth, no lower fin and no fin behind the gills. Average adult length 20 cm.

Lamprey are dark-colored, (brown to blue-black) and unpatterned; they are parasites, attaching to other fishes by means of a sucking mouth. Small teeth rasp off scales and skin to reach the tissues beneath, from which the lamprey withdraws blood. About a third of the host fish die.

Lamprey young spend 5-6 years buried in river-bottom mud, eating mostly microorganisms. When they grow up they move downstream to the sea, or, in the case of the Columbia-system lampreys, which are landlocked by dams, to one of the large lakes or reservoirs. There they feed parasitically for several more years, eventually heading back upstream in late summer to lie under stones along the bottom until the following year, when they spawn (April to July) and die within two weeks. Apparently they eat nothing during the entire 9-10 month spawning period.

SUCKERS
Family Catostomidae

Not loved by fishermen but interesting in their own right, suckers are the most widespread and perhaps the most numerous fish in the Canadian Rockies. We have four species. Mostly bottom feeders in lakes, they eat algae, invertebrates and snails; spawning is often at the water's edge, where you can watch the fish doing their thing in spring. Juveniles patrol the shoreline in large schools, going round and round the lake. They don't reach maturity until age five, and can easily live ten years. Suckers are frequently taken by fisherman but seldom eaten; although palatable, the fish are often parasitized by large tapeworms—as are many other fish species in the mountains.

Longnose sucker
Catostomus catostomus (sucker family)

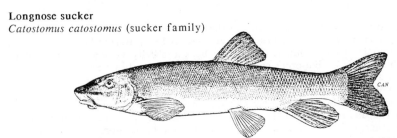

Common throughout the Rockies at all elevations, mostly in the deeper lakes. Average size elsewhere 20-35 cm, but somewhat smaller in the mountains (maximum around Jasper townsite 31 cm in Pyramid Lake; larger ones reported from Lower Kananaskis Reservoir). Readily identified as a sucker by the round, sucking mouth; differentiate from other suckers in the Rockies by the longer snout of the longnose. Body is round, dark olive to brown on the back, lighter down the sides, with dark top and tail fins, pinkish lower fins. Hybridizes with the largescale sucker (next page).

White sucker
Catostomus commersoni (sucker family)

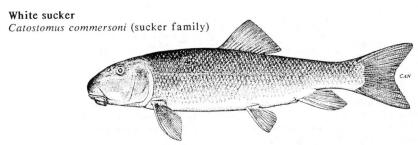

Another common sucker, tolerant of environmental variation and thus widely distributed. Average size 40 cm elsewhere but only 20-30 cm in the Canadian Rockies. Often found with long-nosed sucker (previous entry); differentiate by the paler color of the white sucker and especially by the blunter head. White suckers feed on the bottom, eating invertebrates and algae. Highly adaptable, these fish spread farther than any other species during deglaciation of the Rockies (for more on that interesting story, see page 536).

Largescale sucker
Catostomus macrocheilus (sucker family)

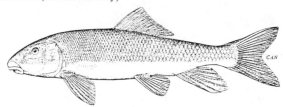

Fairly common in the upper Columbia, Fraser and Peace drainages, at montane elevations. Our largest sucker, typically 30-45 cm long and reaching 60 cm in the larger rivers. Seldom found in lakes. Dark above, pale below; during spawning, adults acquire a golden look on the back and sides, and often sport a greenish side band. Good identifier: ahead of the top fin, there is a low ridge along the back that is not present in our other suckers. Foods: snails, invertebrates and algae, all taken from the bottom. This species hybridizes with white suckers in BC, and may do the same here and there in Alberta.

Mountain sucker
Catostomus platyrhynchus (sucker family)

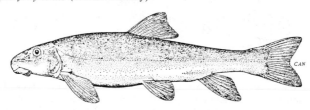

In swift eastern-slope streams from the upper North Saskatchewan south, often at high elevations. Smaller than the other suckers in the Rockies, averaging only 10-15 cm long. Body olive drab or brown, lighter down the sides, often with a brown band and black speckles. Mountain suckers eat algae; they mature in about two years and spawn in early summer. Longevity unknown, but probably less than that of other suckers.

LITTLE SILVERY FISH: THE MINNOWS
Family Cyprinidae

We are speaking here of a taxonomic group of fishes, not just any little fish (juvenile fish are properly called **fry**). True, most of the minnows are small—the little silvery fish of the mountains—but some grow nearly as large as the average trout. None has teeth, but many minnows have barbels: little projections of flesh near the corners of the mouth. Barbels are sensory organs, sensitive to smell and touch.

Northern squawfish
Ptychocheilus oregonensis (minnow family)

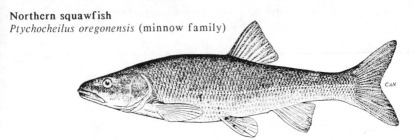

Mainly western-slope, in lakes of the Columbia and Fraser systems, but also occasional on the eastern slope in the upper Peace system. Average size 25 cm, large for a minnow; a 44-cm specimen has been reported from Peace River, Alberta. Round body like most minnows, dark gray to brown along the back and silvery down the sides. There is a prominent black spot at the base of the tail. Juveniles eat plankton and invertebrates; adults eat small fish. Squawfish spawn at six years (May to July) and may live to be 20—the most geriatric of the minnows in this region. Edible.

Peamouth chub
Mylocheilus caurinus (minnow family)

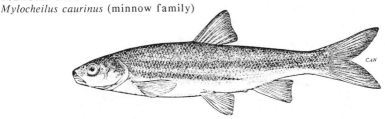

In the weedy shallows of western-slope lakes and slow-moving rivers from the Peace River south (eastern-slope only in the Peace) at low elevations. Average size 10-25 cm; reported to 36 cm. Small fish, pointed at the front with a small mouth; olive-brown along the back and often partway down the side, where there is a prominent dark stripe from front to base of tailfin. Sometimes there is another stripe below the first one, reaching from the gills about halfway to the tail. Peamouth chub are often seen in schools, feeding on invertebrates; they also spawn en masse, right at the water's edge, in May and June. Lifespan up to 13 years.

Flathead chub
Hybopsis gracilis (minnow family)

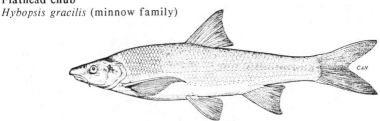

Eastern slope only, in larger rivers but seldom in lakes; most common in the Peace system. Prefers muddy water with a gravelly bottom. A large minnow (average size 15-20 cm, maximum 32 cm), faintly brownish above and white below, silvery sided with no other markings. Good identifiers: barbels at the corners of the mouth; small eyes. Foods: mainly surface fare such as water striders, beetles and flies; adults also take small fishes and have been known to eat the young of aquatic rodents. Spawning is probably in summer; lifespan unknown but may be many years.

Lake chub
Couesius plumbeus (minnow family)

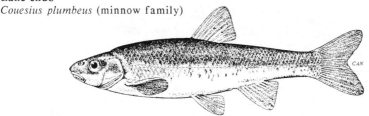

Throughout the Rockies over gravelly bottoms, common at low elevations but sometimes found in timberline lakes and streams. Average size 5-10 cm. Small greenish-silver fish, nearly round in cross-section, with a prominent dark line along the side from nose to base of tail. Lake chub eat invertebrates, plankton and algae; they spawn at 3-4 years and live about five. In early spring this species begins to move upstream, spawning near headwaters in late June and July. It is probable that most die after this run. Hybrids with longnose dace (page 552) occur in Upper and Lower Kananaskis reservoirs.

Lake chub can survive higher water temperatures than any other fish in the Rockies except the tropical species at Banff Hot Springs (see page 556); lake chub are the only fish living in the warm-water marshes below Liard Hot springs.

Pearl dace
Semotilus margarita (minnow family)

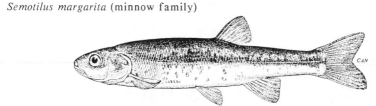

Eastern slope only, in foothills lakes and sluggish streams from Peace River south. Average size 6-11 cm. Very similar to the lake chub (previous entry): olive along the back, with a dark stripe along the side. In adults the stripe fades toward the front, which is a way of telling this fish from other single-striped minnows, whose stripe is either solid all along the body or tends to fade at the back rather than the front. Male pearl dace have a bright red stripe below the dark one from November to July; spawning is in spring. Lifespan is short, probably just a couple of years maximum. Foods for this species include algae and invertebrates.

Longnose dace
Rhinichthys cataractae (minnow family)

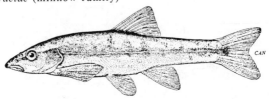

Bottom-dwellers in lakes and rivers, often in small, fast-flowing streams, where they manage to stay on the bottom by deflating their air-bladders. Average size 5-10 cm; reported to 18 cm. Easily recognized by the long, nose-like upper lip and dark, dirty-looking mottling on the back and sides. Fins are white; body is rounded. There are barbels just ahead of the eyes. Longnose dace feed on invertebrates (especially aquatic insect larvae) and live about five years. They spawn in June and July and are known to hybridize with lake chub (page 551).

Leopard dace
Rhinichthys falcatus (minnow family)

Occasional on the western slope around Prince George, in small, sluggish streams. Average length 5-10 cm. Identified by the large dark spots on the cream-colored sides. Head is rather dark, with barbels on the nose; fins are yellowish. Breeding males have orange lips. Food is mainly fly larvae and other invertebrates when very young; mainly flying insects later. Spawning is thought to occur in July; lifespan perhaps four years.

Redside shiner
Richardsonius balteatus (minnow family)

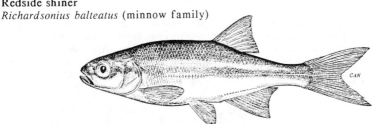

Throughout the western slope; on the eastern slope only in the Peace system. Mainly in rivers but occasionally in lakes, usually in large schools in shallow water. Small, thick-bodied silvery fish (average size 4-10 cm), dark olive along the back with a dark side stripe beginning at the front and fading out toward the rear. There are often scattered black spots along the stripe. Breeding males are colorful: the stripe is bright yellow, there is a crimson patch behind the gills, and the belly is pink. Redside shiners feed mainly on plankton and algae, the larger ones also taking insects at the surface, fish eggs and small fish. Spawning is in midsummer and lifespan about three years.

Spottail shiner
Notropis hudsonius (minnow family)

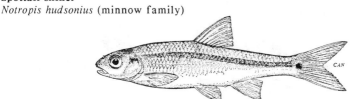

Eastern-slope only, in the foothills between the North Saskatchewan River and Waterton Lakes, usually in lakes and sluggish streams. Average size 4-6 cm. Nearly the ultimate little silvery fish, with no obvious body markings **except** a small dark spot at the base of the tail—most of the time. Some specimens lack even this identifier; another trait is that the eyes are rather large for a minnow. Spottail shiners often school in shallow lake bottoms; they eat plankton, algae and invertebrates, spawn in summer and live about four years.

Northern redbelly dace
Phoxinus eos (minnow family)

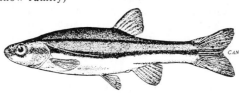

Eastern slope only, in the Peace and Athabasca rivers; not common. Preferred habitat: quiet, shallow ponds with brown-colored muddy bottoms and dark-stained water, such as one finds in beaver ponds. Average size under 5 cm. Resembles other minnows; differentiate by the two dark bands along the side with yellowish color between them. Breeding males are reddish. These are algae and plankton eaters; they spawn in summer, laying eggs in algal masses. Adults live up to six years.

Finescale dace
Phoxinus neogaeus (minnow family)

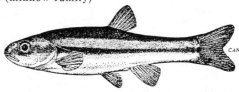

Eastern-slope only, from Peace River south, in shallow quiet water like that favored by northern redbelly dace (previous entry), with which it shares habitat. Physically similar, too; differentiate by the larger mouth of the finescale dace and single dark stripe rather than double one. Finescale dace eat surface insects, plankton and invertebrates, but there is little life-cycle information available on this species. It seems to spawn in June.

Fathead minnow
Pimephales promelas (minnow family)

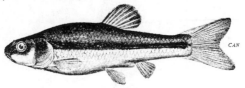

Eastern-slope only, from Athabasca River south, in warm, shallow streams and lakes; common in the Waterton/Glacier area. Small (average size 5-7 cm), thick and yellowish. Spawning males are easily identified by the large, blackish head with prominent tubercles (horny bumps) on the face and chin. Fathead minnows feed mainly on algae; they are resistant to extremes in pH and salinity, and tolerant of low oxygen levels.

Spawning in this species is well-studied and interesting. In spring the male herds a female to a log, branch or stone; he nudges her up sideways against the undersurface of the object, and she sticks eggs to it with a special ovipositor. He squirts milt over the eggs, chases that female away and attracts another for the same performance. Between cruises he defends the nest. The fry mature in only a few months, but life is short for this species: a couple of years.

SCULPINS
Family Cottidae

Small but interesting-looking, sculpins are known more as marine fish than freshwater species. Yet there are sculpins in and about the Canadian Rockies. Our two species are similarly built: very small, but with disproportionately large, broad heads, very fat lips and bulbous eyes. The fins are large and feathery. Adults tend to stay on the bottom, hiding under rocks.

Slimy sculpin
Cottus cognatus (sculpin family)

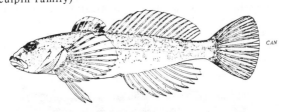

Western slope from Glacier park to Jasper, present on both slopes farther north, in lakes and cool streams with rocky bottoms. Average length about 4-6 cm. Body mottled dark brown to yellowish, slimy or smooth to the touch. Food includes mainly bottom-dwelling invertebrates such as insect larvae; the species also eats aquatic plants. Spawning is in spring, the spawning behavior somewhat like that of fathead minnow (previous entry). Other details of life cycle unreported.

Spoonhead sculpin
Cottus ricei (sculpin family)

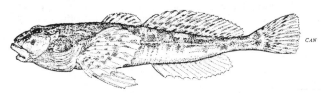

Common in muddy eastern-slope streams from Peace River south, but not reported from the upper Bow. Average length 5-6 cm. Differentiated from other sculpins by the very large, flat head; the body is round and light brown or greenish, with splotchy brown markings. Little studied.

THE REST OF THE KETTLE: GOLDEYE, STICKLEBACKS AND TROUT-PERCH

Goldeye
Hiodon alosoides (mooneye family, Hiodontidae)

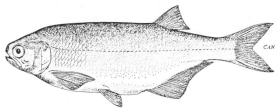

Native to the eastern slope, found mainly in the Peace drainage, in warm lakes and slow-moving muddy rivers. Have been caught in the Athabasca between Hinton and Jasper. Average size 20-30 cm. Identification: oval, silvery fish without spots or much color (a little darker on the back), very blunt head and a large yellow eye.

Goldeye are active mainly at night, eating surface bugs, invertebrates, snails and small fish. They need fairly warm water for spawning (10-13°C) and may be unable to spawn in the Rockies area, possibly arriving when 3-4 years old from eastern Alberta and the Northwest Territories. Lifespan up to 12 years. Fishermen catch goldeye for sport on light tackle; they are good eating, too, although small.

Brook stickleback
Culaea inconstans (stickleback family, Gasterosteidae)

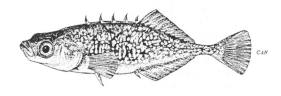

Eastern-slope only, from Peace River south, in the well-vegetated shallows of streams and lakes; often in beaver ponds. Average length about 3-6 cm; 9 cm maximum. Usually dark olive with creamy mottling; sometimes just the reverse. Good identifier: spines along the back (usually 4-6). More tolerant of high-pH, high-salt and low-oxygen conditions than other species, brook sticklebacks and fathead minnows (page 554) make a go of it where other species fail.

Sticklebacks eat mainly invertebrates, fish eggs and worms, hunting for them among aquatic vegetation. When spawning, the male builds a round nest about 2 cm across; it's made of plants and algae held together by a special glue he secretes from his kidneys. The male herds a female into the nest by nipping and nudging, then butts her under the tail until she lays the eggs. Afterward he chases her away and looks after the egg-guarding and fry-rearing himself. The young mature in about a year; lifespan is unknown but probably short.

Trout-perch
Percopsis omiscomaycus (trout-perch family, Percopsidae)

Eastern-slope only, at low elevations in deeper lakes and gentle sections of large rivers. Average size 7-10 cm. A large-headed yellowish-silver fish, with dark splotches on the upper sides, big eyes and a drooping lower lip. The body is so thin you can see the insides. Trout-perch eat insect larvae, surface bugs and invertebrates, feeding close to shore at night and retiring to deep water during the day. Spawning is in May and June, involving a run up shallow streams. Average longevity is a year or two; maximum is three years for males and four years for females.

TROPICAL FISH IN THE HOT SPRINGS AT BANFF?

No, not in with the bathers, but yes, close by in the abnormally warm marshes between the Cave and Basin Centennial Centre and Bow River. The sulphurous hot springs, flowing at about 28-33 °C throughout the year, empty into the marsh and mix with normal water. Apparently the chemistry becomes livable before the heat is gone, because a walk out onto the Parks Canada boardwalk here will reveal hundreds of little fish dependent on the warm water for survival in this climate.

Interpretive signs explain that local tropical-fish fanciers have put many exotic species into the marshes to see which, if any, would survive. The government has also experimented. In 1924 the parks branch introduced larvae-eating **mosquitofish** *(Gambusia affinis),* a native of the southeastern USA, in an attempt to cut down on the bugs around Banff. There have been only two native fish species recorded in the warm-water marshes: longnose dace (page 552) and brook stickleback (page 555).

J.S. Nelson, a fish specialist at the University of Alberta, has done the most recent study of the current hot-springs fauna (Nelson, 1983). He collected all the species now living there, and found that the mosquitofish are doing just fine. (So are the mosquitoes.) The dace and sticklebacks are still around, too. But the guppies *(Poecilia reticulata)* noted in earlier reports are now gone, as are the green swordtails *(Xiphophorus helleri)* and convict cichlids *(Cichlasoma nigrofasciatum).*

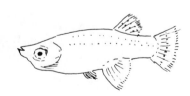

Gambusia affinis

However, the **sailfin molly** *(Poecilia latipinna)* is abundant, and **jewelfish** *(Hemichromis bimaculatus)* are present—although few jewelfish survive each winter and the species could disappear at any time. Mosquitofish have the best tolerance for hot water: they can take it as warm as 30°C, which means you can see them swimming right in the hot-springs runoff.

Poecilia latipinna

Mosquitofish and sailfin mollies, by the way, are the only live-bearing fish to be found in the Canadian Rockies. They don't lay eggs; rather, the tiny young pop out ready to swim away. Also of interest in the marsh: growths of two common aquarium plants, no doubt introduced along with the tropical fish. These include **tape grass** *(Vallisneria spirilis)* and **bushy pondweed** *(Najas microdon)*.

Hemichromis bimaculatus

So the rumors are true. Banff does indeed have everything.

What about the other hot springs in the Rockies? Do they have tropical fish? Apparently not. The only other springs with extensive warm marshes downstream are at Liard River, BC; the waters there are full of lake chub (page 551), which can tolerate temperatures of 15-20°C, but thus far no tropical fish have turned up. That is just as well; putting strange species into the Liard marshes would probably alter the unique ecology there.

Vallisneria spirilis

Najas microdon

FURTHER READING

Alberta Fish and Wildlife (1977) *Fish of Alberta* Alberta Fish and Wildlife, Edmonton. Free poster-pamphlet for fishermen with colored illustrations and short write-ups on 14 fish common in the mountains, with range maps.

Boschung, Jr., H.T. et al. (1983) *The Audubon Society Field Guide to North American Fishes, Whales and Dolphins* Knopf, New York. Comprehensive, with good photographic illustrations, short entries, no range maps; 848 pages.

Carl, G.C. et al. (1967) *The Freshwater Fishes of British Columbia* BC Provincial Museum, Victoria.

Delong, K.T. (undated) *Eagles and Salmon* Glacier Natural History Association/Glacier National Park, West Glacier, Montana. Free pamphlet describing the kokanee run in McDonald Creek.

Lee, D.S. et al. (1980) *Atlas of North American Freshwater Fishes* North Carolina Biological Survey.

Nelson, J. (1983) "The tropical fish fauna in Cave and Basin hot springs drainage, Banff National Park, Alberta," *The Canadian Field Naturalist,*" vol. 97, no. 3, pp. 255-261. Not as readily available as other sources listed here, but interesting reading.

Paetz, M. and J. Nelson (1970) *The Fishes of Alberta* Queen's Printer, Edmonton. Lots of detail, with photo illustrations and ranges maps; 282 pages.

Amphibians and reptiles
Frogs on the tundra, snakes under the snow

As you can see from the small size of this section, there are not many amphibians and reptiles in the Canadian Rockies—only 16 species. No reptiles live north of Peace River, and our only lizard and turtle species range no farther north than Crowsnest Pass. But a couple of frogs do just fine all the way to Liard River and beyond. Some species live at high elevations in the mountains; it always amazes me to find frogs in a tundra pond, where the climate allows them only four months of the year in which to grow and reproduce. Then they have to survive through the other eight months of hibernation.

There is a lot of variation within species of reptiles and amphibians, and herpetologists depend on subspecies names. So I have included them here. Subspecies identifications are difficult in places where subspecies overlap, but this is not the case in the Canadian Rockies: most species are near the northern limits of their ranges here, and thus only one, cold-adapted subspecies is present.

AMPHIBIANS (salamanders, toads, frogs)
Class Amphibia

Deemed the more primitive of the two groups and thus discussed first.

Tiger salamander
Ambystoma tigrinum
(mole-salamander family, Amphiumidae)
April to September

Present in the eastern-slope foothills from Bow River south, but you are unlikely to see it except in the morning after a rainy night. Adult length 15-40 cm. The stout shape, glossy, wet-looking skin and blotchy bright yellow-on-black pattern are easy identifiers of our subspecies, *A. t. melanostictum,* the **blotched tiger salamander.** The only other salamander in the mountains (long-toed salamander, next entry), is smaller and skinnier, with a yellow or greenish stripe down the back rather than blotches.

Salamanders live near water but spend a surprising amount of time out of it, hunting in the woods at night for earthworms, insects and one another (they are cannibalistic). They breed in water during the first heavy rains of spring, sometimes even before the ice is off the ponds, laying eggs attached to vegetation in temporary pools. Each egg is fertilized as it moves down the cloaca, for the female has picked up with her **vent** (proper name for the single egg-and-waste exit chute in amphibians, reptiles and birds) a gelatinous mass of sperm left for her by a male. The small tadpole-like larvae transform to adults either in late summer or the following spring. The young overwinter by burrowing into the mud; some of the adults do, too, but life is short for amphibians, and they rarely survive even a year.

Long-toed salamander
Ambystoma macrodactylum (mole-salamander family, Amphiumidae)
April to September

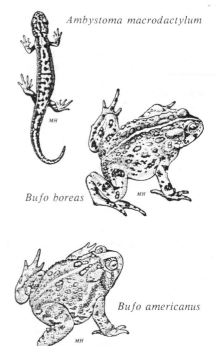

Ambystoma macrodactylum

Scattered, but locally common near montane ponds or small marshes from Peace River south. Normally active only at night and thus seldom seen. Adult length 10-17 cm. Our subspecies is *A. m. columbianum,* the **eastern long-toed salamander.** It is slender, with brown or dark-greenish glossy skin, a yellow-to-green stripe down the back and scattered white flecks on the sides. Differentiate from the tiger salamander (previous entry) by the long-toed's smaller size and different coloration. Habits and life cycle are similar.

Bufo boreas

Western toad
Bufo boreas (toad family, Bufonidae)
May to September

In moist montane and subalpine woods and meadows, usually near water, from Peace River south. Adult length 7-13 cm. A very toad-like toad, mottled olive and warty, with yellow eyes and a creamy throat. There is a creamy stripe down the back, often prominent and used to differentiate this toad from the American toad (next entry), our only other toad. In the western toad the stripe runs right up onto the head; in the American toad it doesn't. Instead, there are ridges on the head, between the eyes.

Bufo americanus

Our subspecies is *B. b. boreas,* the **boreal toad.** It is active in the early evening in hot, clear weather and all day in cool, showery weather, eating insects. This critter is easily caught and observed, but don't try to keep it; it dies. It sings rather weakly, with a sound like peeping chicks.

Like other toads and frogs in the Canadian Rockies, mating is done in the water. The male climbs onto the female's back and the water carries the sperm to the eggs as they are laid. The eggs wind up scattered in strings on aquatic vegetation; the tadpoles transform to adults in late summer and overwinter in burrows, either of their own digging or borrowed from rodents. The toads also move into vacant beaver lodges.

Handling toads is not recommended. The large glands on the head produce a toxin that is intended to burn the mouth of a predator but can also affect the central nervous system, causing salivation and slurred speech—even seizures.

American toad
Bufo americanus (toad family, Bufonidae) May to September

Eastern slope only, at low elevations near water in the southern foothills. Adult length 5-8 cm. Very similar to the western toad (previous entry), but the stripe along the back does not reach the head, which has distinctive parallel ridges on it between the eyes. And the throat is darker. Our subspecies is *B. a. hemiophrys,* the **Canadian toad.** (What's this? The Canadian toad as a subspecies of the American toad? Harumph.)

This toad is a good burrower, with two spur-like tubercles on each hind foot to use in digging. Quicker than the western toad, it plops into water when threatened. Song is a trill, low-pitched and not very loud. Life cycle and habits like those of western toad.

Wood frog
Rana sylvatica (true-frog family, Ranidae) May to September

Fairly common at low elevations in moist woods near water; occasionally subalpine or even alpine. Scarce at the southern end of its range in Glacier National Park. Small: adult length only 4-8 cm. Unlike most other frogs in the Rockies, the wood frog is unspotted, identified by the dark mask-like shading behind the eyes. Compare with the Pacific treefrog, page 562. The color varies from dark brown through pale brown and gray to pale green; there is sometimes a creamy stripe down the back. No subspecies to consider. The song is a repetitive quack.

This is the most northerly frog on the continent, ranging beyond the arctic circle. It lives in damp places with good vegetation cover, entering water to breed. Adults overwinter out of water, under logs and in leaf mats below insulating snow cover, where the temperature stays just a few degrees below freezing all winter. In the fall, the frog pulls its back legs up under it, puts its front legs over its head, and dozes off.

Then it freezes solid. Yes, *solid;* it goes clunk if you tap it. There is no heartbeat, no respiration, no detectable brain activity.

How does it survive? No one is sure, but recent work at Carleton University has shown that when the temperature reaches -2 °C, and the frog starts to freeze, the liver pumps out glucose (a sugar) in amounts that would kill other living things. The glucose floods into the cells, where it sucks up moisture. This keeps the cells from losing too much water during freezing. Freezing cells ordinarily dump their water into the bloodstream, dehydrating themselves and thus killing the organism.

Despite this water-fixing mechanism, 50 percent of the body fluid in a hibernating wood frog is ice. If you remove the frog from the cold and set it in a warm place, it soon thaws and hops away.

Northern leopard frog
Rana pipiens (true-frog family, Ranidae) March to October

Occasional as far north as the Columbia Icefield (but scarce and getting more so as the years go by) in cold montane and subalpine streams and ponds with thick vegetation. Adult length 5-13 cm. This is the froggiest-looking frog in the mountains, smooth and green to yellowish or brownish with sharply defined black spots all over and pale ridges running from the eyes back to the tail. Compared with the other western frogs, this one unmistakable. The song is varied and interesting, like a snore or a motor, mixed with clucks and grunts; Peterson's guide describes it as sounding like a balloon being rubbed.

Mainly nocturnal, the northern leopard frog stays in water by day but may go on land at night to hunt for insects. It leaps and dodges quickly into the drink if threatened; breeds in the spring or early summer.

Spotted frog
Rana pretiosa
(true-frog family, Ranidae)
April to October

Common, found throughout the region in montane and subalpine streams or ponds without much emergent vegetation. Adult length 5-10 cm. Same shape as the preceding *Rana* species, but different coloration: brown, with scattered blurry light-centred dark spots and a rusty nose. If this frog sings, it does so very infrequently; its voice is not described in the literature. The male is smaller than the female and has extra-large thumbs (frog machismo).

Spotted frogs are active in the day, mainly staying in the water. They often move upland in spring to higher ponds; in the fall they return to lower elevations to overwinter in the mud.

Tailed frog
Ascaphus truei
(tailed-frog family, Ascaphidae)
April to September

Occasional in cold, swift montane streams south of Crowsnest Pass. Adult length 2.5-5 cm. Rough-skinned, the color varying from olive to gray, usually with dark spots and mottling; there is a triangular yellow spot on the snout. Rather similar in color and pattern to the spotted frog (previous entry), the tailed frog is usually more mottled, and the male has a tail-like organ (used in copulating) while the spotted frog does not. There is no voice.

Chorus frog
Pseudacris triseriata
(treefrog family, Hylidae)
April to September

Common in shallow marsh ponds at low elevations on the eastern slope at least as far north as Peace River. The most abundant amphibian in the Canadian Rockies. This is a small frog (adult length 2-4 cm) but a very noisy one, especially during the early-spring mating time. You can hear them as soon as the ponds are free of ice. The song is a loud trill, like the sound of a fingernail run along the teeth of a comb. The animal is olive-green to brown, with bumpy skin (but not warty like a toad). Three khaki stripes or rows of spots run down the back; the upper lip is white.

These frogs are mostly nocturnal, but I often hear them in the daytime, too, sometimes just one or two frogs at a time (although the whole pond will get going if one waits quietly for a bit). The first time I bothered to investigate the sound, before I knew what made it, it seemed so loud that it had to be coming from some sort of swamp bird hidden in the bulrushes. Yet I could never find the bird. The little frog was practically under my feet, of course.

Pacific treefrog
Hyla regilla (treefrog family, Hylidae) April to September

Occasional at low elevations on the western slope of Glacier National Park and possibly around Fernie. Small; adult length 2-5 cm. Plain green, brown or yellowish—and capable of changing its color in a matter of a few minutes. It always has a broad dark stripe through the eye, rather like the mask of the wood frog (page 560). But the Pacific tree frog has knobs at the ends of its fingers and toes, the skin is rough, and it never ventures to higher elevations. Preferred habitat: up in shrubs and small trees beside water. The song is a loud, two-part rasp, the second note higher than the first, familiar to nearly anyone: it is the sound of night you hear in films and on television.

REPTILES (snakes, lizards and turtles)
Class Reptilia

Ophidiophobes: relax. Snakes are scarce this far north, and we haven't any poisonous ones. They are so small they can hardly bite you. Except for one, possibly. Read on.

Western terrestrial garter snake
Thamnophis elegans (colubrid family, Colubridae) April to October

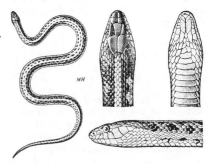

Occasional in montane wetlands and woods as far north as Grande Cache, usually in or near water. A small snake: adult length 50-85 cm. The prominent narrow pale stripe down the back and the yellow stripe along each side identify it as one of our two species of garter snakes. The upper sides are dull olive or gray, often with black spots; the lower sides and belly are lighter, with a bluish tinge. This describes *T. e. vagrans,* the **wandering garter snake** subspecies of the western terrestrial. Differentiate from the red-sided subspecies of the common garter snake (next entry), the only other garter in the Canadian Rockies, by the red-sided's black, red-spotted sides.

"Terrestrial" is a misnomer when applied to this animal; it is highly aquatic. It hunts in the water, catching tadpoles and small frogs, rodents and baby birds, fish, slugs and worms. Like other garters, it swallows its prey whole.

Garter snakes are solitary most of the time, but gang up for certain things. Sex, for example. During the spring mating, 5-10 males wrap themselves around a female, all of them trying to get close enough to impregnate her.

Okay, how do they do it? A male coils about the female and inserts a **hemi-penis** (he has a pair of these) into her vent (snake version of the cloaca). The hemi-penis has barbs on it to prevent withdrawal until the job is done.

Garter snakes are viviparous: they bear their babies without shells. The snakelets are 10-15 cm long at birth; they soon crawl away on their own.

In September or October, garter snakes seek communal hibernating quarters in abandoned rodent burrows, among boulders or deep in bedrock cracks. There they snooze the winter away by the dozen. Emerging in April, they are sluggish in the cool spring weather. The few I see around Jasper are often lying right in the middle of a trail, soaking up the sun; I have had to step over to keep from squashing them. One specimen allowed my wife to stroke it down the sides. But when I touched it the snake took offense and slithered away, lying still again in the grass all of a metre away.

Common garter snake
Thamnophis sirtalis (colubrid family, Colubridae) April to October

Occasional in or near montane streams and marshes. Most northerly reptile in North America, found to Ft. Smith in the Northwest Territories; from Peace River south in the Rockies. Adult length 50-130 cm. Prominent narrow cream stripe along the back, and a yellow stripe along each side. The subspecies here is the **red-sided garter snake** (*T. s. parietalis*). It typically has black upper sides, often with red spots; the lower sides are dark. There can be a lot of color variation in individuals, some of which may be markedly duller and thus very similar to the wandering garter snake (previous entry); note differences in the wandering garter's belly color and somewhat smaller eyes.

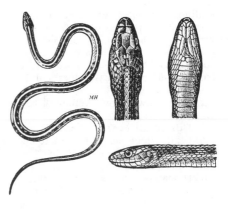

The red-sided garter snake hunts mainly in the water, taking tadpoles, frogs, salamanders, small fish and leeches, but it also pokes about on land for small rodents, slugs and insects. The habits and life cycle of this snake are essentially the same as that of the wandering garter. The young are born in late summer or early fall (depending on the temperature), take two or more years to mature and may live up to ten years.

Bullsnake/gopher snake
Pituophis melanoleucus (colubrid family, Colubridae) April to October

Rumored to be in the extreme southern end of the Canadian Rockies, in dryer eastern and southern parts of the Waterton/Glacier area and possibly on the Rocky Mountain Trench floor from Golden south. But not reported in the literature. Be the first to find one—and don't forget to tell a herpetologist.

Bullsnakes prefer grassy, sandy or rocky open woods. This is a long snake, thick and heavy-looking with a small head; adult length 120-250 cm. The subspecies, if it exists here, would be *P. m. sayi,* the **bullsnake.** It is sandy colored with contrasting earth-brown regular patches along the back, becoming smaller toward the tail. The sides are mottled in the same amazingly protective color scheme, the head sandy and unpatterned.

This snake hunts by day, eating mostly rodents, which it kills by constriction. At night it hides in rodent burrows or among rocks. It fights back if threatened, hissing and shaking its tail in imitation of a rattlesnake. Sometimes it even feigns a rattler-like strike! But there is no rattle and no poison.

Bullsnakes mate in spring, laying eggs in sandy burrows or under rocks and logs; the eggs hatch 2-3 months later, in late summer.

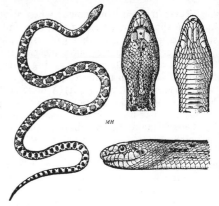

Rubber boa
Charina bottae
(boa/python family, Boidae)
May to September

Nocturnal, rare and thus seldom seen, but present in damp montane forests and meadows of the western slope from Radium south. The rubber boa ranges farther north in the Columbia Mountains just west of the Rockies, so it may be present in the Columbian forest area north of Golden. But unreported. Adult length 35-85 cm. It really does look like it's made of rubber: glossy olive to chocolate brown above, yellowish below and unpatterned.

This primitive snake has a very blunt tail, which makes it hard to decide at a distance which end is which. On adult males, two spurs (vestigial hind limbs) near the anus are prominent; females have them but they do not protrude as much.

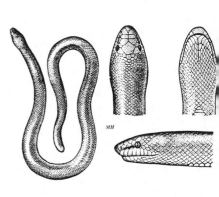

The rubber boa burrows under rocks, logs and forest litter; at night it emerges to hunt small mammals, birds and lizards, often by swimming in shallow water or climbing into shrubs or partway up trees. It kills by wrapping around the prey and squeezing it, allowing exhalation but not inhalation (a form of strangulation). So there are boa constrictors in the Canadian Rockies! However, the rubber boa is unlikely to throw a scare into anyone. This snake is a wimp, curling into a ball in your hand if you catch it. Little is reported on its breeding habits or life cycle; the young are born live (i.e., without eggs) in early fall.

Painted turtle
Chrysemys picta
(pond, marsh and box-turtle family, Emydidae)
April to October

Occasional in shallow, gentle streams and lakes at low elevations on both slopes of Glacier National Park; north in the Rocky Mountain Trench to Golden. Adult shell 10-25 cm long. Subspecies is the **western painted turtle**, *C. p. belli*. The shell is olive-brown on top, often with red or orange at the plate junctions; underneath it is brilliant red to yellow, with a dark pattern down the centre. The head, legs and tail have yellow stripes against a dark-olive background.

The only turtle in the Canadian Rockies, and barely within the mountains at that, the western painted turtle basks on mud, logs or rocks in shallow, weedy water with a muddy bottom. It eats aquatic insects, small fish, tadpoles and amphibians, becoming more vegetarian and scavenging as it grows older. It mates in spring, producing eggs in a bottle-shaped nest in the mud; the young take a long time to grow up (males 2-5 years, females 4-8 years) and may live for several years more.

Capturing and keeping painted turtles is usually unsuccessful. They need lots of clean water and the right natural foods; otherwise they die of various diseases. We have so few turtles in the mountains that they deserve every chance they can get. So please leave 'em be. The same can be said of our other reptiles and amphibians.

Western skink

Eumeces skiltonianus
(skink family, Scincidae)
April to October

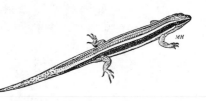

Occasional in the Rocky Mountain Trench from Cranbrook south. Adult length 17-24 cm. Juveniles are easily identified by the bright blue tail; later, it is gray. Our subspecies is *E. s. skiltonianus*, a sleek, glossy lizard with creamy stripes, brown back, black sides and creamy belly. It hunts by day among the rocks in open woods, eating insects, spiders and worms. After mating in spring, the female tends the small clutch of eggs until they hatch in late summer.

FURTHER READING

Behler, J. and F. King (1979) *The Audubon Field Guide to North American Reptiles and Amphibians* Knopf, New York. Comprehensive and portable, with photographic illustrations and range maps; 719 pages.

Carl, G. (1960) *The Reptiles of British Columbia* BC Provincial Museum Handbook No. 3, Victoria. Slim and inexpensive, with good illustrations; 65 pages.

Stebbins, R. (1954) *Amphibians and Reptiles of Western North America* McGraw-Hill, New York. Intended as a standard field reference, but a bit bulky for that. Detailed, with excellent illustrations by the author (source of the pictures in this chapter) and range maps; 528 pages.

—— (1966) *A Field Guide to Western Reptiles and Amphibians* Houghton Mifflin, Boston. In the Peterson field guide series, and up to snuff. More of Stebbins' wonderful illustrations, many of them in color; 279 pages.

Gray jay. Photo courtesy Jasper National Park.

Birds

All birds belong to the class Aves. There are 28 orders in the world (21 in North America) and 170 families, of which the 65 on our continent include some 650 species. We have only 277 species reported from the Canadian Rockies, of which 188 are seen frequently enough to be detailed in this book.

Recommended field bird guide, if you want the colored illustrations you can't get in this book: *Birds of North America,* by Robbins, Bruun and Zim. This is the renowned Golden guide, revised 1983, with excellent pictures, good range maps and a binding that can survive rainy days without falling apart. For other good bird books, check the list on page 665.

Once you are able to identify birds by sight, the next step is to learn them by sound. The best way is to get the Cornell birdsong tapes (see Kellogg on page 665), three 60-minute cassettes in a sturdy book-like folder that you can even take outdoors with you if you have a small cassette player. Jog along with the juncos. Play owl calls at night and get responses.

Some birders try to attract their prey by saying "psh-psh-psh" and making little squeaky noises by sucking on the backs of their hands. You can even buy a gadget that squeaks *for* you, so there must be something to this. But I have yet to see it work in a convincing way, and it can be annoying to go around with somebody who says "psh-psh" every few minutes and keeps kissing himself. It is not for nothing that birdwatchers are thought to be silly, you know. If you just stop in spots that seem birdy and then wait quietly for a few minutes, the birds will soon forget that you are there and go back to whatever they were doing when you arrived.

By the way, this technique—sitting very, very still until you become part of the woods—works for observing all sorts of animals. Called **Seton watching**, after the Canadian naturalist Ernest Thompson Seton, who did it a lot, the method produces astounding results. Birds will land on your head; mice will walk over your shoes. I have heard of one case in the Rockies in which a beaver climbed out of a pond and curled up in a woman's lap while she was Seton watching.

Water birds are the easiest to identify. They are boldly patterned and usually stay in male/female pairs. There is little or no vegetation to block the view, and the birds sometimes paddle close by if you are quiet. So beginners often learn the ducks, geese and other waterfowl first. You may also see the osprey and the bald eagle, fish-eaters both, around lakes and rivers. Valley-bottom lakes or ponds are the most productive; subalpine and alpine water bodies are less frequented. Getting there early (at dawn is best) will reward with the most bird business: flopping about in the water, diving and **dabbling** (tilting end-up to feed on the bottom in the shallows), singing, flying about, doing mating displays, fighting and whatnot. But any time of day is okay. Best time of year: spring, from first open water (late April, early May) until most of the breeding is over (mid-June). Except for the Waterton/Glacier area, the Rockies do not lie along a major flyway, so we don't get the enormous lakefuls of birds found farther east. However, the variety here is pretty good.

Forest birds are more difficult to find and watch as they flutter among the trees or scrabble in the undergrowth. Except for the grouse family they are mostly smaller than waterfowl and often rather drab. Beginners usually learn the common, clearly marked ones first (black-capped chickadee, raven, magpie, gray jay, Clark's nutcracker . . .) and get to the sparrows, warblers and flycatchers later. Best forest locations are around the edges of marshes, where there is the most activity and variety. Dry, grassy clearings are good, too. Again, morning is the best time and spring the best season. After mid-July the courtship displays and singing are over; to quote one Jasper birder, "Everybody just shuts up."

Open slopes at montane elevations are home to most mountain hawks (and falcons, which aren't really hawks, properly speaking); alpine areas are preferred by some. Be prepared for frustration in identifying hawks; they are notoriously variable in color pattern. Ours are inclined to be dark.

Owls are woodland birds, active mainly at dawn and dusk. A knowledgeable owler goes mainly by the calls, which are distinctive and easy to learn. Listen in April and May.

The Rockies are famous for alpine-zone birds: ptarmigan, pipits, horned larks and gray-crowned rosy finches. The ptarmigan is especially interesting: a curiously fearless and thus readily approachable high-country chicken. Northern harriers may pass close by as they fly low to the ground looking for ground squirrels, which are plentiful in the high country, especially in August and early September. Golden eagles sometimes do the same.

GOOD BIRDING LOCALITIES IN THE CANADIAN ROCKIES

People used to the tremendous numbers of birds seen in more temperate regions (the eastern United States, for example, or along major flyways) may be disappointed when they come to the Canadian Rockies, for they are far fewer birds here. This is a difficult environment for birds. Perhaps the greatest problem for them is the mountain weather, which varies so much from year to year during early summer. This is the sensitive breeding season; a week of cold rain in late June can kill many a nestling, and the rest of the summer is too short for most species to manage a second brood. So it is not surprising that fewer birds live here.

To see those that do, try some of the places listed below.

1. **The Waterton/Glacier area** is on the Trans-mountain and Central migration routes, so look for a good variety of ducks, other water birds and shorebirds in spring and fall. **Maskinonge Lake** and the adjoining marshes in Waterton are perhaps the best locations. The woods around **Lake McDonald** in western Glacier have species that prefer the deep Columbian forest found there. The foothills east of the parks feature grassland species not found farther north.

2. **Wilmer Wildlife Refuge,** just north of Wilmer in the southern Rocky Mountain Trench, offers perhaps the best assortment of wetland and lake species in the Canadian Rockies, with many tundra swans in spring. For more on this interesting place, see page 767.

3. **Kananaskis Country:** front-range species such as the mountain bluebird are regularly seen from Alberta 40. Off the main highway in Kananaskis Lakes Provincial Park, the scrubby meadows along **Pocaterra Creek** are particularly recommended. The lakes themselves are notable for shorebirds, and black swifts are seen here.

4. **The foothills west of Calgary** are known for red-tailed hawks, kestrels and other falcons. Check the hogback ridges west of **Jumping Pound Creek** along the TransCanada Highway.

5. **Lac des Arcs,** along the TransCanada Highway just west of the mountain front, has concentrations of ducks and Canada geese in spring and fall.

6. **In Banff National Park,** Banff townsite offers perhaps the best variety of woodland birds in the park. Nearby, **Fenland Trail** leads through warbler-rich wetlands with shallow ponds well known for dabbling ducks. **Vermilion Lakes Drive** gives clear views over larger (but still shallow) lakes in the same area. These are often good for grebes.

The **Bow Valley Parkway** in Banff park (Highway 1A) passes through prime mixed-wood habitat (chickadees, juncos, flycatchers, kinglets, thrushes,

RECOMMENDED BIRDING LOCALITIES IN THE CANADIAN ROCKIES

Keyed to numbered items on facing page

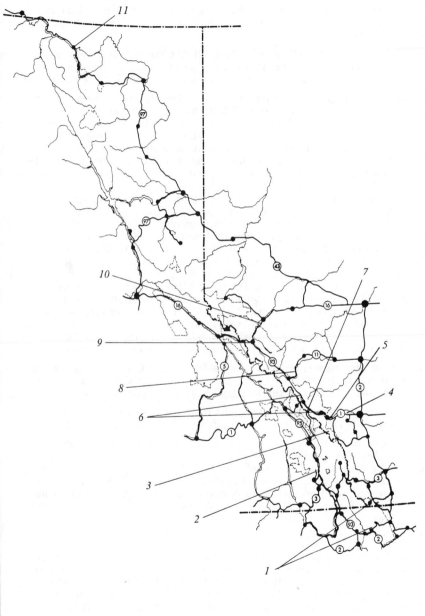

(For names of map features see base map opposite page 1)

woodpeckers) between Banff and Lake Louise. Black swifts nest at **Johnston Canyon,** which is along this route.

Bow Summit, north of Lake Louise along the Icefields Parkway, is a high subalpine area with easy walking access to alpine-zone birds. The trail up **Parker Ridge,** in the northern tip of the park, passes through similar habitat.

7. **The Vermilion Pass burn** along Highway 93 in Kootenay park is an area of ecological succession well known for hawk owl, Townsend's solitaire and woodpeckers.

8. **The Kootenay Plains** lie along Alberta 11 (the David Thompson Highway) east of Saskatchewan Crossing. This is a dry, grassy, aspen-rich region that attracts prairie species. Take a stroll in and around **Two O'clock Creek Campground.**

9. **Jasper National Park** has large wetlands at low elevations along Highway 16 (the marshes at **Pocahontas** and **Talbot Lake** are good spots).

Jasper townsite offers a good variety of montane forest birds, with many ravens, white-crowned sparrows and swallows. The trails around **Cottonwood Slough** (on the road to Pyramid Lake) are outstanding (barred and horned owl; ruffed and spruce grouse; Swainson's, varied and hermit thrushes; kinglets, red-breasted nuthatch, warblers, snipe, sora, hummingbirds). Ospreys nest just east of town along the Athabasca River.

Birders should make a point of hitting **Mildred Lake,** along the road to Jasper Park Lodge. This little lake supports a good population of water birds, supposedly because it is nutrient-rich from phosphates used in the hotel laundry. It's a sure-thing location for Barrow's goldeneye. For common loon, grebes and mergansers, try nearby lakes **Annette and Edith.**

Maligne River between Fifth Bridge and the Athabasca may be the best place in the Rockies to see dippers, especially in the cold months (the river is groundwater-fed; stays open). The upper Maligne is good for harlequin ducks and bald eagles, especially around the outlet from **Maligne Lake;** nearby, the gray jay is common at the chalet. Clark's nutcrackers are very common at the end of the road to **Mt. Edith Cavell.** It takes birders only seven minutes to reach the alpine zone on **The Whistlers** via Jasper Tramway; walking down the trail to the mountain's base allows easy birding in every life zone.

10. **East of Jasper park,** the road between Hinton and Cadomin is renowned for great gray owls and other boreal species, as is Alberta 40 north to Grande Cache, which passes by the woodland ponds of **Switzer Provincial Park.**

11. **The Liard Hot Springs marshes** along the Alaska Highway at the north end of the Rockies are bird-rich (and famous for mew gulls that buzz people).

Hunters: be careful what you shoot. Nearly all birds in the Canadian Rockies are protected. The game laws keep changing, so I can't list them here; you should contact the Alberta, British Columbia and/or Montana fish and game departments before killing anything. Likewise, it is illegal to live-trap many species or to possess them if you find them dead. You can't just pick up a road-killed hawk or keep an eagle feather found on the trail, for example. Again, check with local authorities.

USING THE LISTINGS

Order of listing: the order is essentially that of the Golden guide or Peterson's, but sometimes I have changed it so that look-alike birds can be more easily compared.

Bird names: In addition to Latin names, ornithologists have been able to agree on standard common names. So those names are used in this book. It is also common practice among birders to capitalize the names, but this is not considered to be good editorial practice in biology writing (Council of Biology Editors' *CBE Style Manual,* 1972) and they are not capitalized here. (Or in *The Audubon Society Encyclopedia of North American Birds,* a standard reference.) For French-speaking readers, the common French names are given in parentheses.

Time of occurrence: seasonal bird arrival and departure dates given here are those noted in the national parks, where the best records are kept. Same for the abundance data. Because there are no national parks in the Rockies north of Jasper, the entire northern section lacks this degree of documentation and birders there will no doubt find errors in my abundance figures and dates for arrival/departure and nesting. Please let me know, so that corrections can be made in the next edition. My address is at the front of the book.

Habitat descriptions: are based on field observations. The habitat preferred in the Canadian Rockies in summer is often different from that preferred in wintering areas far away. The ecological terms used ("montane," "subalpine," "Columbian forest" and so on) are explained in the chapter on ecology. See page 269.

Flocking: most birds migrate in flocks, even such loners as hawks and eagles, so one sees many species in flocks when they arrive in spring and depart in fall. Once the birds are established and nesting, the flocks usually break up. When a species *stays* in flocks, this is mentioned.

Relative abundance of species: in this book, *very common* means that a good birder will usually see or hear more than 25 of that species on a given day-long trip to the right habitat in the right season. *Common* means that he/she will probably find between 6 and 25, *fairly common* means 1 to 5, and *occasional* means perhaps one or two of that species over the course of the season. *Rare* means that the species has been reported in the national parks fewer than five times over the years. Rare birds aren't written up individually here, but on page 663 there is a list of rare and accidental (well out of range) species.

Voice: when it is reasonable to do so, I have tried to describe in words what a particular bird sound sounds like. This is always risky; birds don't speak English. A duck's call might sound something like "ka-peet," "ka-peet" to us, but of course it's actually saying "Helluva big fish off your port bow, Roy."

My wife is convinced that all those chickadees and other cute little forest birds are trading warnings and insults back and forth; stuff like "My terr-i-tor-EEE!" and "Get out! Get out, nest fouler!"

Most woodpeckers **drum**: they bang their bills on resonant wood. This has nothing to do with drilling for bugs; it is a way of proclaiming territory and of announcing themselves to rivals and potential mates.

A note on **foods**: in the listings, the word **invertebrates** is used as it is in the section on fishes. It refers mainly to water-dwelling insect larvae and crustaceans. Worms, snails, clams and flying insects are mentioned separately.

The **breeding dates** given here are intentionally vague; experience has shown that in the mountains a particular species can nest over a rather long period, depending mostly on elevation. The snow melts up to a month earlier in the valleys than it does at timberline, and nesting frequently begins soon after the snow leaves. Birds in the south end of the range generally nest about a week earlier than birds in the north end. Further, a species that nests in mid-May in a normal spring might nest three weeks later if the winter has been snowy and the spring late. With a complicated formula like that, it is amazing that the birds know when to do their thing at all.

Speaking of which, you may be wanting to know how they actually do it. Answer: birds are one-holers. Everything—urine, feces, eggs—comes out the **cloaca.** Birds mate by briefly touching cloacas. The male passes sticky semen to the female, and the sperm move up her cloaca.

Nesting records: seeing a bird on its nest is not an everyday occurrence; even finding a nest is rare. And identifying a species by looking at the nest is more difficult yet. Still, birders always want to know whether a given species nests in a given region. For nesting records in the Canadian Rockies I have had to rely on those kept by the national parks. If you see "No nesting record here" in the text, it means that there is no nesting record in the park checklists. The species may nest elsewhere—just outside the park boundary, for example. Please let me know if you find one of these "no-nesting-record" birds nesting in the Rockies.

Nest construction: cup-like unless otherwise indicated. Common nesting materials are twigs, shredded bark, moss, rootlets, grass and leaves; linings are usually feathers, hair and/or moss. When unusual materials are used they are mentioned.

Eggs and nestlings: the number of eggs given is the usual number; there can be more or fewer. Except as noted, all birds in the listings lay just one clutch of eggs each year. Egg colors don't seem to vary much in a particular species, but egg markings—speckles, blotches, scrawls or whatever—can vary a lot, so much so that providing detail on markings would take up too much space in a guide like this. The **incubation period** is the number of days between laying and hatching. To **fledge** is to fly, and usually is the time when a young bird leaves the nest—but not always. Ducks, grouse and sandpipers stay just a short time in the nest, often leaving as soon as they dry after hatching. These birds are **precocial,** meaning that they are ready to go right out of the egg: feathered, able to see and to feed themselves immediately. Fledging dates a week or more past hatching mean that the bird is **altricial:** coming into the world practically or completely naked, blind and helpless, requiring feeding and parental warmth for some time. Our birds are mostly altricial.

Lifespan: where possible the lifespan of each species is given, but be warned that the age information quoted here is not reliable. In ornithology, lifespan information is usually quite sketchy. Often it is based on only a few records for the species. The figures given here are maximum ones; most birds die in their first few months. But checking the listings will show that they live a surprisingly long time if they can just grow up.

Flight speed: many species have been timed in flight over known distances, but the results vary considerably. When quoted here, the flight speed is the maximum recorded.

Range: the complete summer range of a species seen here is not given for lack of space, but a brief note on the winter range is included because people want to know where the birds go. Likewise, the summer range is given for those birds that winter here.

DUCKS AND DUCK-LIKE WATER BIRDS
See also the phalaropes, page 594

Common loon (huart à collier)
Gavia immer (loon family)
Early April to early November

Common on montane and lower subalpine lakes, in ones and twos; doesn't like sharing territory. Length 60 cm, wingspan 150 cm. Dark-colored, with prominent white front; white pattern on back and two white necklaces. Red eye.

Loons carry their long bills tilted upward while swimming; they fly with the head and neck low. Song is instantly recognizable: one or more loud "whoo-EEE-ooo"s followed by an insane-asylum laugh (thus "crazy as a loon"). The birds sing in flight, occasionally at rest. They dive frequently and swim 50-100 m underwater before surfacing. Diet: mostly small fish, plus aquatic insects, snails and leeches.

Breeding is in mid-spring. The nest, a raised heap of vegetation in light cover at the waterline on an island or close to shore, is used year after year by the same pair. Two brown-spotted olive eggs hatch in about 29 days. The young ride on their parents' backs for a couple of weeks, not flying until 70-77 days after hatching. When an adult pair is approached, one bird often comes toward you, singing; you are supposed to be distracted while the other bird swims off with the children. Maximum recorded age seven years. Airspeed clocked at 85 km/h. Loons winter along the west, east and Gulf coasts, and on the Great Lakes.

These birds cannot take off from land, but must start from water. If you find a loon or a grebe (next entry) flopping about on a highway that it has mistaken for a river, just take it to the nearest body of water over 100 m long so that it can get airborne again.

Red-necked grebe (grèbe jougris)
Podiceps grisegana (grebe family)
Early April to early November

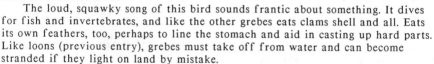

On lakes with shoreline vegetation, in ones and twos or small flocks. Common in central area, fairly common in the north, uncommon at Waterton/Glacier. Most often seen in May and June. Length 30 cm; wingspan 80 cm.

Fairly long neck, rusty red, with prominent gray throat and lower head, black toupee. Sharp yellow bill, red eye. Back is mottled brown.

The loud, squawky song of this bird sounds frantic about something. It dives for fish and invertebrates, and like the other grebes eats clams shell and all. Eats its own feathers, too, perhaps to line the stomach and aid in casting up hard parts. Like loons (previous entry), grebes must take off from water and can become stranded if they light on land by mistake.

Both species, especially grebes, hang around until cold weather hits and are thus inclined to freeze into lakes in the fall. The ice builds up around the shore, creeping out toward the centre until one day there is not enough open water for takeoff. Trapped, the bird is frozen in. Red-necked grebes nest in May/June, the nest a floating heap of rotting plants anchored in shallow water among vegetation; 4-5 white eggs hatch in 22-25 days. The young birds ride piggy-back and get fed invertebrates (plus adult feathers); don't fly until at least 10 weeks old. Wintering grounds: west and east coasts.

Western grebe (grèbe de l'Ouest)
Aechmophorus occidentalis
(grebe family)
Early April to early June,
again in September and October

On lakes; fairly common in flocks at a few locations; occasional elsewhere. The largest grebe: length 46 cm, wingspan 100 cm.

Very long white neck (black on the back) and white cheeks, with long yellowish beak and red eye; dark mottled back. Rides low in the water. Song is surprisingly high and screechy, like fingernails on a blackboard.

The western grebe runs on the water when taking off, and has a wonderful courtship display: both sexes run along the surface together, necks arched, bills tilted up and wings held out. Diet: mostly fish, invertebrates and its own feathers. No nesting records. Winters along the west coast from Alaska to Baja California.

Horned grebe (grèbe cornu)
Podiceps auritus (grebe family)
Early April to early November

Occasional on lakes and marsh ponds, usually in small flocks; most often seen in September. Length 25 cm, wingspan 60 cm.

Short neck for a grebe, rusty-red, with front and underparts also rusty, black head and back. Prominent orange tufts run from eye (red) to upper back of head; differentiate from similar eared grebe (next entry) by the neck (all black on eared) and orange tufts lower on head of eared.

Song resembles that of red-necked grebe (previous entry), although a little squeakier. Dives for small fish and bottom-dwelling invertebrates. No nesting records. Winters on the west coast.

Eared grebe (grèbe à cou noir)
Podiceps nigricolli (grebe family)
Late April to mid-May

Occasional; look for it on lakes and marsh ponds, in small flocks or among horned grebes. Length 23 cm, wingspan 58 cm.

Resembles horned grebe (above, but the neck is a little longer and black rather than red. Front is also black. The "ears" are tufts of orange feathers that sweep back from the red eye; feathers on the head form a dark topknot (on horned grebe, the orange feathers ride higher, obscuring the top of the head). Song is a series of quick reedy whistles, each one low-high.

Unlike the other grebes, this one feeds mostly at and just below the surface, eating few fish but lots of water invertebrates, water boatmen and dragonflies. No nesting records. Winters on lakes from Colorado south.

Pied-billed grebe (grèbe à bec bigarré)
Podilymbus podiceps (grebe family)
Late April and May, again in September

Occasional on lakes and wetland ponds at low elevations, usually alone. Rare in northern region.

An odd-looking grebe; small (length 23 cm), with a disproportionately large head, large brown eye, and heavy bill with a dark line across it. Dark throat and white rump; the rest is plain brown (a little mottling down the sides).

This grebe makes the sort of sounds one imagines coming from a flying saucer: rhythmic "wah-wah-wah" for a bit, then "ee-oo, ee-oo, ee-oo" for a bit. Dives for water invertebrates and small fish. Builds a small nest in late spring, the nest floating in tall vegetation near the shore of a lake or pond. Four to seven white eggs hatch in 23 days; the young are precocial, ride on parents' backs. Flying age unknown. Winter range: west coast from Vancouver Island south, through the southwest to the Gulf coast, up the east coast to New York.

Mallard (canard malard)
Anas platyrynchos (waterfowl family)
Year-round; common April through November

The most common duck in the mountains, found in flocks on lakes, marsh ponds and slow-moving streams.

Readily identified by the large size (length 40 cm, wingspan 90 cm) and male coloration: green head with yellow bill, white stripe at base of neck, rusty front, white sides with blue patch on each side near the rear, dark back with a couple of cute curls on the rump. Compare with northern shoveler (next entry), which is smaller, with white front and rusty sides (just the reverse of the mallard) and long black bill.

The female mallard is mottled brown with orange bill and the same blue patch on the side near the back. There is a band of green along the trailing edge of each wing. This is the **speculum**; it is useful in identifying the otherwise-drab females of many duck species as they fly.

Male mallards are mostly silent, sometimes rattling a little; the female song simply "quack-quack-quack," very familiar. Mallards seldom dive under water; they tip up and down in the shallows, snapping up seeds (mostly of bulrush), snails and invertebrates from the bottom, grabbing the odd tadpole and sometimes scavenging dead fish.

Nesting is in early- to mid-spring, the nest a plant-lined mud hollow at the water's edge (although up to a half-kilometre inland on occasion); 8-10 pale-green/bluegreen/white eggs are hidden under down. They hatch in 26-29 days, the young heading for the water with mum as soon as they are dry. First flight is at 7-8 weeks. Mallards can live a long time; the record is 29 years. Clocked at 95 km/h. Some of our mallards overwinter in the southern Rocky Mountain Trench; most fly southwest to lakes in Washington and Oregon. However, the species will overwinter anywhere that has shallow open water (such as at a spring-fed pond) with a good food supply.

Northern shoveler (canard souchet)
Anas clypeata (waterfowl family
Late April to beginning of June, again late August to late September

Fairly common on lakes and ponds, often with wigeons (next entry). Length 35 cm, wingspan 80 cm.

Very mallard-like duck, with green head and lots of white, but smaller, with a long black bill rather than a shorter yellow one and a white front rather than a rusty one. Sides are brown or rusty. Females are also mallard-like: mottled

Ducks and duck-like birds

brown, but again the long black bill differentiates. Voice: "cluck-luck, cluck-luck," like the tick of a large clock.

Shovelers skim the surface with their big bills, scooping up floating bugs, water boatmen and floating seeds; they also tip up and down in shallow water, getting seeds and invertebrates off the bottom. No nesting records here. Age record 16 years. Maximum flight speed 85 km/h. Wintering is from BC coast to Baja California, across American southwest, Gulf states and Caribbean.

American wigeon
(canard siffleur d'Amérique)
Anas americana (waterfowl family)
Early April and May, again
August through October

Fairly common on lakes, sloughs and gentle streams, in flocks. Length 35 cm, wingspan 85 cm.

Male easily identified by the green band from eye to nape of neck; the rest of the head is brown-speckled white, top whiter than the rest. Green-winged teal (next entry) also has a green band, but the rest of the head is rusty red, not white. Female wigeons are mottled brown; check for black on the end of the gray bill to differentiate from similar teal species and gadwall (page 578).

Ring-necked females (page 580) have a similar bill, but they are bigger, with a white eye-ring and stripe; some other female ducks are even more similar, but their heads are never mottled with white like the wigeon. Scaup females (page 580) have white around the bill base. Female ducks are tricky to identify! Fortunately they stick with the males.

The male wigeon has an endearing voice, like the squeak of a bath-toy rubber duck. Females produce a guttural quack. Pairs and groups dabble in the shallows, calling frequently and sometimes walking along the shore. They eat mostly pondweed and grasses/sedges. Breeding is in late spring, in a poorly concealed mound of vegetation lined with down, well out of the water. Eggs 9-11, white/buff, hatching in 25-26 days. Young leave nest same day, fly at 6-8 weeks. Lifespan 9 years. Slow flyer for a duck: 35 km/h. Wintering grounds are along the west coast from Vancouver Island south.

Green-winged teal (sarcelle à ailes vertes)
Anas crecca (waterfowl family)
Late March to late October

Fairly common in marshes, on lakes and rivers, in small dabbling groups. Length 27 cm, wingspan 60 cm.

Like the male wigeon, male green-winged teal is easily identified by the shiny green band from eye to nape of neck. But the head is rusty red, not mottled white like wigeon. Female is mottled brown, nondescript except for the iridescent green band near the back. Wigeon female has this too, but it is quite small and the head is whiter.

Song is a very high "ka-peet, ka-peet, ka-peet." Breeding is in late spring, the nest well concealed at the water's edge (or farther ashore) and lined with down. Eggs 10-12, elliptical and matte white; they hatch in 23-24 days. Birds leave the nest a few hours later and fly at 44 days. They winter in western and southern USA.

Cinnamon teal (sarcelle cannelle)
Anas cyanoptera (waterfowl family)
Late April to late July

Occasional on small lakes and in marshes, southern and central regions, singly or in pairs. Length 28 cm, wingspan 64 cm.

Male is the only all-over reddish duck in the Canadian Rockies (back is red-mottled black). Note green patch along the side near the rear.

Female teals of all three species are difficult to tell apart: cinnamon has a broad white line on the side, ahead of the green patch; female blue-winged has a pale blue to gray stripe in the same location, while green-winged has a brownish stripe. All have a green patch just behind the stripe.

Male cinnamons rattle when they sing. Species dabbles in the shallows, eating mainly seeds of aquatic vegetation; also snails and invertebrates. No nesting records. Flies up to 95 km/h; winters in California, Nevada, Mexico and South America.

Blue-winged teal
(sarcelle à ailes bleues)
Anas discors (waterfowl family)
Late April to early October

Common on lakes and rivers in small flocks, always at the end opposite your viewing point. A small, shy duck that flies away at the slightest alarm. Length 28 cm, wingspan 60 cm.

Male has beautiful head coloring: white crescent moon between bill and eye, rest of head pale blue with black top. Body mottled brown with blue stripe along upper side and white patch low at the back. Female is mottled brown, with pale blue stripe along the side and prominent brown eye-line. Both sexes show lovely blue wing color in flight. Squeaky-toy song, with high-pitched quacking.

This duck dabbles in the shallows, sometimes tipping to reach the bottom for snails and invertebrates but mostly skimming with its bill at and just under the surface for seeds. Nests in mid-spring, usually by a small marsh pond, the down-lined, basket-like nest well hidden on the ground. Eggs 9-11, cream to pale olive, hatching at 23-24 days; like other teal species, the young hit the water a few hours after. Age record 11 years. Speed record 45 km/h. Wintering: far to the south, in Mexico or the Gulf states, some along the coast of southern California.

Ducks and duck-like birds

Gadwall (canard chipeau)
Anas strepera (waterfowl family)
Late April to mid-June, again August
and September

Occasional; look for gadwalls in pairs,
often with wigeons (page 576) or pintails
(next entry) on lakes and marsh ponds.
Length 37 cm, wingspan 80 cm.

A drab duck; even the male has no
bright coloration. This can be an easy
identifier: any pair of ducks in which
both partners are drab is probably a pair
of gadwalls. Male has a thin white
curved line on the side, near the front;
there is a small white patch farther back,
and a bit of red between. The rump is
dark under gray back feathers. Female is
similar, lacking the curved white stripe,
with a lighter bill and brown eye-line.
Song is simple and quacky.

This dabbling duck eats mainly
stems, leaves and roots of aquatic
vegetation, but also ventures into deeper
water to dive for small fish and leeches,
going to the bottom for invertebrates and
worms. No nesting records here; winters
in the southern and southwestern states
and in Mexico.

Northern pintail (canard pilet)
Anas acuta (waterfowl family) early
April through June, again August
through October

Occasional to fairly common on lakes
and marsh ponds, a few pairs at a time,
usually dabbling among wigeons. Length
47 cm, wingspan 90 cm.

Easily identified by the long,
sharp-looking tailfeathers of the male;
compare with oldsquaw (next entry).
Pintail also sports a white front and
neck, the white continuing up onto the
brown head in a finger-like stripe. There
is a white patch low on the side, near the
rear. Female is mottled brown, plain-Jane
until she flies, when the speculum (stripe
of colored feathers along trailing edge of
wing) shows rainbowy orange, green and
white. Male song is a small "NIN-yee,
NIN-yee"; the female quacks.

Pintails tip up and down in the shallows for seeds along the bottom, also
getting snails, invertebrates, leeches and the odd minnow. Nesting is in mid-spring,
along the shores of lakes or marsh ponds in thick vegetation. Eggs 7-9, in various
pale colors in a down-lined mound. Hatching is at 25-26 days, leaving nest right
away; the young fly at 7 weeks. Age record 26 years. Maximum recorded flight
speed 105 km/h. Birds winter on the west coast.

Oldsquaw (canard kakawi)
Clangula hyemalis (waterfowl family)
Mid-April to mid-May

Fairly common in lakes, passing through.
Length 38 cm, wingspan 75 cm.
   Long, sharp tail like the pintail
(previous entry), but smaller body with
different markings: black head and neck
with large white patch on face; white
sides and dark back. Female lacks the
long tail, has white face with dark spot
below and behind the eye. Male says "ah,
ah-oo-ah"; female quacks.
   Feeding is mainly by diving,
sometimes as deep as 60 m, for
bottom-dwelling invertebrates and
freshwater clams; also eats aquatic
vegetation. No nesting records. Clocked
at 120 km/h. Oldsquaws winter along the
coasts, often well out to sea.

Canvasback (morillon à dos blanc)
Aythya valisineria (waterfowl family)
Mid-April to late May, again mid-August
to late September

Fairly common on lakes and ponds.
Rather large duck: length 38 cm,
wingspan 86 cm.
   Easily picked out among other birds by the dark-red head and neck, black
front and gray body with black tail. But closely resembles the redhead (next
entry). Differentiate by the canvasback's longer, flatter, blacker bill that curves
smoothly up into the forehead; redhead's bill is gray with black tip and stubbier.
Female canvasback is gray with light-brown front and head. Male canvasback song
is a turkey-like gobble; female quacks.
   Species dives for bottom-growing aquatic vegetation; also eats seeds,
invertebrates, snails and small fish. No nesting reports in the national parks. Age
record: 19 years. Flight record: 115 km/h. Flocks migrate in V-shaped pattern
to/from the west coast, Vancouver south.

Redhead (morillon à tête rouge)
Aythya americana (waterfowl family)
Mid-April to mid-June

Occasional on lakes in spring, passing
through. Sighted a few times in the fall.
Length 37 cm, wingspan 85 cm.
   Male closely resembles canvasback
(previous entry), and species often swims
with canvasbacks, but the redhead bill is
stubbier and gray, with a black tip. Head
is rounder. Female is plain brown with
light cheeks and underparts. Male call is
a short siren-like sound, repeated over
and over; female quacks.
   Feeding is by diving for stems and leaves of water plants, skimming duckweed
and snatching bugs. Age record 12 years; flight speed 110 km/h. No nesting record.
Wintering is along the west coast from Vancouver south.

Ring-necked duck (morillon a collier)
Aythya collaris (waterfowl family)
Early April to mid-October

Common in pairs and small flocks on southern and central lakes and marsh ponds, less common in the northern area. Length 30 cm, wingspan 72 cm.

Males resemble the redhead (previous entry) in shape and size, with similar pattern but dark purple or black on the head and neck rather than red. Male eye is yellow; female brown. A low tuft of feathers on the head makes a rounded point; black-tipped gray bill is similar to redhead. White line behind the black tip is more prominent, and there is a narrow fringe of white at the bill base.

Differentiate from scaup (next entry) by the white bill markings on the male ring-necked, and the prominent white bill base on the female scaup. Female ring-neck is brown with pale cheeks and black, white-tipped bill like that of male; she also sports a white eye-ring and line leading back, like a pair of spectacles without the nose-bridge. Male song is seldom heard; he whispers sweet nothings. Female's voice is low and quacky.

This is a shallow-diving species, picking up seeds, invertebrates, worms and snails from the bottom. Breeding is usually in small marsh ponds in mid-spring, the nest a down-lined hollow by the water with 6-12 greenish eggs that hatch in 26 days. Birds are precocial. First flight at 49-56 days. Lifespan 10 years. Wintering is along the American west coast and through the south to Mexico.

Lesser scaup (petit morillon)
Aythya affinis (waterfowl family)
Late March through October

Fairly common on lakes and marsh ponds, in flocks. Length 30 cm, wingspan 75 cm.

Male very similar to ring-necked (previous entry), but the head lacks the ring-necked's pointy bump and the bill lacks the white ring-necked's markings. Scaup head is greenish, although it often looks black from a distance. Female is brown, rather dark on the head, with a prominent white ring around the base of the bill. Both sexes have yellow eyes.

Males coo softly; females say "scaup, scaup, scaup." They feed by diving for small fish, tadpoles, snails and aquatic insects; they eat seeds and aquatic plant parts as well. Breeding time is late spring; 8-12 dark-olive eggs in a down-lined hollow near the water hatch in 26-27 days; young leave nest right away, fly at 49 days. Lifespan about 10 years. Winter range: west coast, Mexico and the Gulf states.

Barrow's goldeneye (garrot de Barrow)
Bucephala islandica (waterfowl family)
Beginning of March to mid-November

On lakes and rivers, in pairs. Very
common from Banff north, less common
to the south. Length 33 cm, wingspan
80 cm.

Male is strikingly black and white,
with a prominent white crescent on the
cheek. Female is mottled gray,
brown-headed (sometimes rusty), with a
white ring on the neck and white spot on
the front. Eyes of both sexes are bright
yellow. Compare with very similar
common goldeneye (next entry); note
smaller facial spot on the common, larger
white spots on the back, and more white
on the female common. Male Barrow's
hasn't much of a voice (grunts and
whistles softly during courting), but
makes a characteristic "woo woo woo"
sound with wings when flying.

When approached, goldeneyes are inclined not to fly. They usually just paddle
away a short distance. These ducks dive for dragonfly and damselfly larvae; they
eat a lot of pondweed and get the odd small fish. Nesting is in mid-spring, in
hollow stumps and woodpecker holes in the woods; 8-14 greenish or bluegreen eggs
hatch in 30 days. The young jump out of the nest soon after and follow mum to
water; they stay with her for a month or two before they can fly. Wintering is on
the west coast; this species may be found year-round in central BC and south
along the American Rockies.

Common goldeneye (garrot commun)
Bucephala clangula (waterfowl family)
See below for seasons

On lakes and rivers; common in
wintering areas (November to March) on
open water in southern Banff park and
south; only occasional in central areas,
where they are seen in April and May
headed north. Look for them through the
summer north of Peace River. Length
33 cm, wingspan 80 cm.

Very similar to Barrow's goldeneye
(previous entry), but the facial spot is
smaller and the head greenish and
shaped a little differently; the body is
whiter, without the plunging black mark
on the shoulder. Females have white
splotches on the back (Barrow's females
do not) but lack the white frontal spot.
Males emit a loud "jeep, jeep" and go
"woo woo woo" with their wings when
flying; females quack. Feeding and diet
like that of Barrow's.

Common goldeneyes breed in the late spring, nesting in tree cavities in the
woods near water; 6-11 greenish eggs hatch in 30 days. Young birds jump from the
nest, follow the female to water and swim with her until they fly at about

60 days. Age record: 17 years. Timed at 80 km/h. Also winter on the west coast, through southern BC and most of the USA.

White-winged scoter
(macreuse à ailes blanches)
Melanitta fusca (waterfowl family)
Early May to mid-June,
again mid-August to late October

Fairly common on large lakes, sometimes in flocks. Length 40 cm, wingspan 97 cm.

Large, very dark duck, with an apostrophe-like white eye patch on the male and another white patch on the upper side near the rear. Bill is diagnostic: small and bright orange, with a prominent black bump at the base. Female's bill is black and lacks the bump; she has two white facial patches and a white patch near the rear; looks much like female surf scoter (next entry), which lacks the white rear patch. Male white-winged is more easily told from male surf scoter by head pattern and bill shape. The male croaks but is seldom heard.

These are diving birds. They subsist mainly on invertebrates and small fish, but also eat freshwater clams (shell and all). No nesting records here. They work their way into northwestern Canada from winter homes along the west coast (Alaska to Baja California), in the Great Lakes and along the Gulf/east coast (Alabama to Newfoundland).

Surf scoter (macreuse à front blanc)
Melanitta perspicillata (waterfowl family)
Early May to mid-June,
again late September to early November

Occasional on lakes from Banff north, in ones and twos. Length 35 cm, wingspan 83 cm.

Very dark, like the white-winged scoter (previous entry). Male identified by the interesting pattern of white and black spots on the head (somewhat variable and often difficult to make out in poor light) and the heavy orange bill. No prominent bump at the bill base, as in male white-winged scoter. Female surf scoter is very similar to female white-winged, but lacks the white patch on the upper side, near the back.

Habits and range similar to white-winged; no nest records here.

Bufflehead (petit Garrot)
Bucephala albeola (waterfowl family)
Early April to mid-November

Fairly common on lakes, marsh ponds
and rivers. A small duck: length 25 cm,
wingspan 60 cm.

Both male and female are easily
identified by white head patches: male
has a large, broad one and female a
smaller, oval one. Lots of white on the
male; female is grayer. Male whistles
softly; female quacks harshly.

Species dives for insect larvae and
bottom invertebrates, snails, small fish
and seeds. Interesting courtship display:
male swims toward female, moving his
head forward and then *way* back. Breeds
on the western slope in late spring; nests
in flicker holes near water. Eight to
twelve cream/buff or pale-olive eggs in
the unlined cavity, hatching in 29 days;
the young jump to the ground soon after,
following mother to water. First flight at
50-55 days. Lifespan 11-13 years. Flight
speed 75 km/h. Species winters along the
west, east and Gulf coasts and through
the western USA.

Ruddy duck (canard roux)
Oxyura jamaicensis (waterfowl family)
Early April to mid-June,
again early August to late October

Occasional on lakes and marsh ponds. Length 28 cm, wingspan 58 cm.

Courting male has a good identifier: fan-shaped tail held stiffly upward,
black with white centre. Body is red, with prominent white patch on lower face
and black upper head with low crests over the eyes. Bill is blue. Female fairly
similar, but drab rather than red, with dark line through the white facial patch.
She carries her tail down. Male song: several quick chips, followed by "braaak."

Feeding: ruddies dive for seeds and bottom-dwelling vegetation; go especially
for midge larvae. No nesting records here. Winter range: west coast from
Vancouver Island south, across Mexico and along the Gulf and east coasts.

Harlequin duck (canard arlequin)
Histrionicus histrionicus
(waterfowl family)
Beginning of May to mid-August

Occasional on swift rivers and around
lake outlets/inlets, usually in pairs or a
few at a time. Male often leaves the
Rockies in June, leaving female to raise
the young.

Small (length 30 cm, wingspan
66 cm), but gaudy. Male is bluish-black,
with white stripes outlined in black and
red patches. Compare with wood duck
(next entry). Female is drabber, browner,

with white facial patches. Voice seldom heard; male squeals, female croaks. This species likes the torrents; it dives in the rapids and walks along the bottom, turning over stones to get larvae of mayflies, stoneflies, caddisflies. Females nest in early summer, on river islands or along the banks; male heads for the coast after breeding. Six to eight creamy eggs in a downy hollow in the ground, hatching in 27-33 days. Young fly at 40 days. Wintering is in heavy surf along the west coast, although some stay on open water in the Rockies. I have seen them all winter at the outlet of Maligne Lake.

Wood duck (canard huppé)
Aix sponsa (waterfowl family)
Early April to end of the month, sometimes to mid-June

Occasional from Waterton/Glacier to Jasper. Length 34 cm, wingspan 71 cm.

To many the most beautiful duck in north America: male is multi-colored red, brown, white, blue, green—even fancier than the harlequin (previous entry)—with a prominent drooping crest at the rear of the head. Red eyes. Female is much less colorful, although she, too, is elegant: crest, spectacles (eyes are black), lacy pattern on neck, front and lower sides, and blue patch running onto the tail. Males whistle; females say "wok."

Wood ducks spend more time on land than other species in the mountains, running about the shore for plant fruits and seeds besides their staple, duckweed. Sometimes the birds perch in trees. The few wood ducks that visit the Canadian Rockies also breed here, in mid-spring, nesting in tree holes. Eggs 8-10, cream-colored, hatching in 29-32 days. The young jump out of the nest, sometimes from 10-20 m up (!), then follow their mother to water. Fly 63 days later. Flight speed to 90 km/h. Wintering grounds: not far away in western Washington and along the coast, where wood ducks live year-round.

Common merganser (bec-sie commun)
Mergus merganser (waterfowl family)
Late March to late October

Properly pronounced "MER-gan-zer," although many people say "mer-GAN-zer." Fairly common in pairs and small flocks on lakes and slow rivers; very common in the south end of the Canadian Rockies. Large: length 45 cm, wingspan 95 cm.

Male is green-headed, with long orange bill that is hooked on the end; female is rusty-orange on the head with a crest down the back of the neck and similar bill. To differentiate from male red-breasted merganser (next entry), note crest and spotted brown front on the red-breasted; common lacks the crest and is white-fronted. Females of the two species are trickier to tell apart: common's head coloration ends abruptly on the neck; red-breasted's color changes more gradually downward. Voices: male sounds like a plucked musical string; female says "ruff, ruff, ruff."

Mergansers swim along with their heads down in the water looking for small fish to dive after; they also eat frogs, salamanders, snails, leeches, worms—nearly any water animals they can get. Breeding is in mid-spring; 7-14 cream or yellowish eggs in a down-lined tree-hole or plant-lined hollow among shoreline rocks. Hatching is in 28-32 days; nest is left a day or two later. The ducklings paddle around with momma for about five weeks before they can fly. Wintering is on inland lakes throughout much of the USA; some overwinter on open water in southern BC.

Red-breasted merganser
(bec-scie à poitrine rousse)
Mergus serrator (waterfowl family)
Late April to early June, except summer resident in north end of the Rockies

Occasional on northern lakes and rivers, rare from Jasper south. Length 40 cm, wingspan 85 cm.

Very similar to common merganser (previous entry); differentiate males by crest and spotted brown vest on the red-breasted (common lacks these) and fuzzy color edge on female red-breasted's neck. Males go "yeow, yeow," females quack.

Habits like common merganser, but red-breasted apparently doesn't nest here, although possibly at far northern end of the Rockies. Holds the speed record for our ducks: 160 km/h. Wintering is along the west and east coasts.

Hooded merganser (bec-scie couronné)
Lophodytes cucullatus (waterfowl family)
Early April to end of May, again from late July to early November

Occasional migrant, most common in the spring, seen on lakes, gentle rivers and marsh ponds. Smaller than the other mergansers (length 33 cm, wingspan 66 cm).

Males have a distinctive crest. Raised, it produces a large white patch on the head; lowered, it can still be seen as a narrow white triangle or broad white line. Compare with bufflehead (page 583). Females look very much like the other merganser ladies, but the bill is shorter and yellow rather than orange. Males make a noise like a ship creaking; females are silent.

This species dives for invertebrates, insect larvae and small fish; no nesting records here. Winters in southwestern BC and in fresh water along the west, Gulf and east coasts.

American coot (foulque d'Amérique)
Fulica americana (rail family)
Beginning of April to early November

Very common in flocks on southern-area
lakes and marsh ponds, especially in
spring and fall, becoming less common as
you go north. Length 30 cm, wingspan
65 cm.

A drab bird, except for its large
bone-white bill and red eyes. Easily
recognized by the way it paddles: the
head moves back and forth, pigeon-like.
Males and females alike.

Voice is cackly and chicken-like, as is the bird, for coots are not really ducks
(even though they act like ducks and have lobed toes). They feed both on the
shore and in the water, energetically leaping up when they dive, mainly for
aquatic vegetation but also for seeds, small minnows, tadpoles, snails, worms and
invertebrates. No nesting records here. Lifespan to 11 years. Winter range: along
west, east and Gulf coasts, often well inland.

GEESE AND SWANS

Canada goose (bernache Canadienne)
Branta canadensis (waterfowl family)
Beginning of April to end of October

Locally very common to uncommon, on
lakes, gentle rivers and marsh ponds. Big,
but quite variable in size: length
40-65 cm, wingspan 125-170 cm. Our
birds tend to be large.

Easily identified by the long black
neck with the white patch at the top. The
body is brown, lighter on the front, with
black tailfeathers and white underparts.
Males and females alike. The voice is
instantly recognizable: "a-honk, a-honk,
a-honk," an aural image of the north.

Canada geese sometimes dabble in shallow water for roots, leaves and seeds of
aquatic vegetation, but mainly they graze on land. They especially like the tender
grass of golf greens, and the Jasper Park Lodge golf course has a resident
population of geese that coexist somewhat uneasily with the golfers. (Stories of
geese stealing balls and chasing players could not be confirmed.)

Canada geese nest in mid-spring, usually on a small island or overgrown
beaver lodge; there are 5-6 large white eggs that hatch in 25-30 days. They leave
the nest the same day, swimming after the parents until able to fly at about nine
weeks; family stays together for a full year. Long-lived bird: documented record
33 years, unverified to 80 years. Mating is often for life. Speed record 90 km/h.
Wintering is along the west coast and inland through the American south and
southwest; during migration the birds fly in a V-shaped pattern that has been
shown to reduce the effort for all birds except the leader, which is usually a
female. In any particular gaggle, though, the gander of the pair with the most
goslings is the dominant bird.

Snow goose (oie blanche)
Chen caerulescens (waterfowl family)
Late April to early May, again in
September

Uncommon, resting on lakes with Canada
geese during spring and fall migrations.
Length 48 cm, wingspan 150 cm.
    The snow goose is mostly white and
thus easily mistaken for the all-white
domestic goose. But check the
tailfeathers: if they are black, it is a
snow goose. Males and females look alike.
Call is similar to Canada goose (above),
but a little higher-pitched.
    Like the Canada goose, the snow goose is a grazer: it eats the tender young
shoots of grasses and marsh vegetation. Also digs out shoreline tubers and sprouts
with its bill. Breeds in the arctic, not here. Age record: 17 years. Flight speed over
80 km/h. Winters along the west coast, from Washington to Mexico.

Tundra swan (cygne siffleur)
Cygnus columbianus (waterfowl family)
Late March to late May,
again early October to mid-November

Formerly called "whistling swan," *Olor
columbianus*. Occasional flocks rest on
lakes during spring and fall migrations;
perhaps most common on lakes in the
southern Rocky Mountain Trench.
Largest bird in the Canadian Rockies:
length 90 cm, wingspan 200 cm. The only
swan you are likely to see here.
    Identification: all white, with a very long neck and a big black bill. Males and
females look alike. Voice is an oboe-like honking, rather like Canada goose or
snow goose (above), but more musical and higher-pitched.
    Swans eat mostly water plants, using their long necks to reach the bottom in
shallow water. They also come up on land to graze as geese do. Breeding is in the
arctic. Age record 19 years; speed record 90 km/h. The birds winter in huge flocks
at scattered places in the USA. Site nearest us is in western Washington.

WEIRD BIRDS THAT LIVE IN THE SWAMP
See also the blackbirds, pages 645 and 664.

Great blue heron

Great blue heron (grand Héron)
Ardea herodias (heron family)
Beginning of August to end of September

Fairly common in southern area,
occasional in central section, rare in the
north end. Look for this bird in marshes,
along lakeshores and slow-moving rivers.
It is very large: length 97 cm, wingspan
175 cm.
    Easily recognized by the bluish
color, long S-shaped neck and big orange
bill. Head is white with a black line
extending off the back in a long crest.
Flies with neck folded back, extending it

Sandhill crane

only when landing or taking off. This habit can be used to differentiate from **sandhill crane** *(Grus canadensis,* a prairie species that is sometimes seen in the mountains), which flies with neck extended. Sandhill is also darker, has red crown, white cheeks and no crest.

Herons stand in the water on their long legs, stabbing for fish with their sharp bills. They also eat frogs, salamanders, small water mammals and aquatic insects. Breed east and west of the Rockies, but supposedly not here. Age record 21 years. Flight-speed record 55 km/h. Herons in the Canadian Rockies area fly *north* to winter along the BC and Alaska coast (there are other wintering grounds to the south).

American bittern (butor Américain)
Botaurus lentiginosus (heron family)
Early May to late June

Occasional in marshes, and quite large (length 58 cm, wingspan 114 cm), but rarely seen because it hides so cleverly among the tall vegetation.

The camouflage coloration is terrific: stripy/mottled brown and white. The bird holds its head vertically and freezes in that position when you approach; you can walk right by and never notice it—unless you pick out the red eyes. Or catch its strange song, usually uttered at dawn and dusk: "gunk-swish, gunk-swish," the sound of a pebble dropped in a bucket of water, followed by a sound like something passing by one's head at high speed. Bizarre and unmistakable.

Bitterns tramp slowly about the swamp on their long green legs, snapping up little water creatures. They breed in spring, the well-hidden nest a large stack of plants on the ground or raised above the water, with 2-5 large buff-to-olive eggs that hatch in 24-29 days. The young leave the nest at about two weeks. Bitterns winter in fresh water along the west coast, through the American southwest and south into Central America.

Sora (râle de Caroline)
Porzana carolina (rail family)
Early May to early September

A fairly common but shy marsh bird that you rarely see; listen for it at dusk and dawn. Length 17 cm, wingspan 32 cm.

Body mostly gray, with brown atop the head and down the back; the black face and throat patch are good identifiers, as are the yellow bill and the long greenish or yellowish legs. Voice is loud and distinctive: "ah-WIP," "ah-WIP," "ah-WIP," followed by a high-pitched laugh that trails off at the end.

Soras act like shorebirds, picking food from the mud; diet mostly seeds, plus snails and aquatic insects. They've been known to walk under water. Breeding is in mid-spring, the coarse nest just above the water, well-hidden among the bulrush stems that support it. Lots of eggs (8-12), buffy or olive and spotted with red or purple; they hatch in 16-20 days and the young leave the nest after only a day or two, returning at night. They can fly at 36 days. Soras winter in salt marshes along the coasts, from southern California and Virginia south through Central America and the Caribbean to Peru.

Common snipe (courlis à long bec)
Gallinago gallinago (sandpiper family)
Early April to mid-October; sometimes
year-round in the southern Rocky
Mountain Trench

Common in central and northern
marshes; less so in the southern area.
Length 23 cm.
    A sandpiper-like bird that prefers
the dense growth of marshes to the open
shoreline. Feeds by sticking its bill into
the mud for worms and insect larvae.
    Snipes perform a wonderful spring mating display known as **winnowing**. The male suddenly flies up out of the swamp to about 100 m, then plunges down at speeds up to 160 km/h, spreading his tail feathers, which show orange and vibrate in the wind to produce a strange "woo-woo-woo" sound. The female loves this, sometimes doing it herself, and lays 3-4 brown-blotched greenish eggs in a mud nest that hatch after 18-20 days. The snipelets leave the nest as soon as their down is dry; they are fed for 19-20 days, then fly away. Wintering grounds: southwestern BC and most of the USA.

SANDPIPERS AND OTHER SHOREBIRDS

Killdeer (pluvier kildir)
Charadrius vociferous (plover family)
Early March through September;
sometimes year-round

In almost any open habitat below
timberline, but in our area usually not
far from water. Length 20 cm.
    A type of plover; distinguish from
semipalmated plover (next entry) by size
(killdeer is larger) and black neck rings
(killdeer has two, semipalmated has one).
Rusty rump patch, red eye-ring. Flashy
white stripe along the rear of the wing.
    Killdeer make a variety of high-pitched calls, some of which sound rather like "kill-dee-deer," "kill-dee-deer." I don't know what they have against deer. You may sometimes hear this call at night.
    Food: beetles, grasshoppers, caterpillars, other insects. This bird is famous for faking a broken wing to lead you (or whatever else it figures to be a predator) away from the nest. Breeds in the open, the nest a simple scrape lined with whatever is handy (grass, bits of wood, or nothing at all) holding four brown-marked buff eggs. The young hatch at 24 days and immediately head for water, flying at 40 days. Lifespan 6 years. Maximum speed 90 km/h. Our birds winter from Vancouver south along the coast, across the southwest and through the American Rockies from Yellowstone south.

Semipalmated plover (pluvier à collier)
Charadrius semipalmatus (plover family)
Mid-August

Occasional flocks on shorelines around
Jasper and north, passing through to
arctic summering grounds.
　　Like the killdeer (previous entry)
but smaller (length 13 cm), with one
broad neck ring instead of two; rump is
plain brown rather than rusty. The bill is
orange with a black tip. Says "pee-wit"
and twittery things; runs quickly about
on the mud, stabbing for invertebrates
and grabbing grasshoppers. No nesting
records here. Flight speed 55 km/h.
Winters in coastal marshes from northern
California south, along the Gulf of
Mexico and up the east coast to
Maryland.

American avocet (avocet Américaine)
Recurvirostra americana (avocet family)
Mid-April and mid-August

Occasional along open shorelines, central and southern areas. Length 38 cm.
　　Easily identified by the long, upturned bill, rusty head and neck, white body
with broad black wing markings. Call: "wee-wee-wee-wee."
　　An avocet runs along in very shallow water, sweeping its bill back and forth
near the bottom to stir up aquatic insects and larvae. Skims surface for floating
bugs. Also tips in deeper water, and sometimes dives. No nesting records here. Age
record 9 years. Winters along the west coast from California south to Guatemala,
and along the Gulf of Mexico.

Spotted sandpiper
(maubèche branle-queue)
Actitis macularia (sandpiper family)
Beginning of June to mid-October

Most common sandpiper in our area, seen
along shorelines of lakes and rivers at all
elevations. Length 16 cm.
　　Several identifiers: coarsely spotted
throat (not in fall), front and underparts;
orange-and-black bill, and (especially) its
habit of bobbing its tail up and down.
Compare with solitary sandpiper (next
entry). Calls "burbledy-WEET"
repetitively as it flies; flutters with
wings down-curved.
　　Spotted sandpipers catch insects on the wing or on the ground rather than
probing for them in the mud; especially likes grasshoppers. Sometimes they dive
under water from the air to escape attack.
　　This species breeds in late spring, the nest on the ground (but seldom in the
open). Four creamy, brown-spotted eggs in an unlined nest hollow on the ground;
the female often produces more than one clutch, her assorted male mates looking
after the extra nests. Hatching is in 20-24 days, the young up and running about
immediately. Age record 8 years; flight speed 50 km/h. Winters along the west
coast from Washington south into Mexico.

Solitary sandpiper (chevalier solitaire)
Tringa solitaria (sandpiper family)
Early June to mid-October

Fairly common beside stagnant pools,
along streams and lakeshores in central
and northern areas, less common farther
south.

Seldom seen with others of its own
kind but shares habitat with spotted
sandpiper (previous entry), which it
rather resembles. Similar size (length
18 cm), but not coarsely spotted; bobs
tail, but more slowly than spotted
sandpiper. Lack of white eye-line
differentiates from other sandpipers;
note also the gray legs. Gives typical
sandpiper "pee-weet" as it flies.

Snatches flying and crawling bugs;
probes in the mud, stirring up shallow
water with forward foot. Breeds in late
spring, the female finding a tree nest
abandoned by another species, usually in
mossy woods near water. Four
brown-splotched pale-green eggs; little
known about incubation and fledging,
but the species is precocial and the
young probably jump out of the nest into
the moss below. Wintering grounds: west
and east coasts of Mexico.

Least sandpiper (bécasseau miniscule)
Calidris minutilla (sandpiper family)
Beginning of August to early September

Common along marsh ponds and
lakeshores, northern and central areas,
eastern slope; uncommon west and south.

The smallest ("least" in the biologist's
quaint usage) sandpiper, a tiny, unwary,
endearing bird only 12 cm long and
nearly invisible, even within a metre or
two, as it picks among the multi-colored
pebbles of a typical Rockies shoreline,
chasing silverfish and probing for things
in the sand. Mottled brown back and
breast with white underside. Dark bill,
quite skinny; white curved eye-line and
yellowish/greenish legs. Compare with
very similar semipalmated sandpiper and
Baird's sandpiper. Call: very cute,
high-pitched rising "peeep." Breeds in the
arctic.

One age record: 7 years. Flies
90 km/h; winters down the west coast of
the USA and along the Gulf of Mexico.

Semipalmated sandpiper
(bécasseau semi-palmé)
Calidris pusilla (sandpiper family)
Late June to late September

Fairly common shorebird in eastern-slope central and northern areas; rare elsewhere.

    Closely resembles least sandpiper (previous entry), but slightly larger (length 13 cm), with black legs rather than yellowish/greenish and white front rather than brown. Short neck, curving eye stripe. Cry is cheepy-peepy. Runs about snapping up invertebrates, probing occasionally. No nesting records here; summers in the arctic. Winters along the Gulf of Mexico and Florida's east coast.

Baird's sandpiper (bécasseau de Baird)
Calidris bairdii (sandpiper family)
Mid-August to mid-September

Occasional, mostly along eastern-slope alpine lakes and ponds, a high-arctic migrant stopping in on its annual fall journey to Chile. What a trip for such a small bird! Still, at 15 cm long, Baird's is noticeably bigger than the semipalmated or least sandpiper; otherwise it is very similar.

    Good field marks: dark legs (like the semipalmated) and brown breast (like the least), which combination effectively differentiates it. Says "kreep"; snatches insects on the ground rather than probing in the mud for them. No nesting record here.

Pectoral sandpiper
(bécasseau à poitrine cendrée)
Calidris melanotos (sandpiper family)
Late July to late September

Fairly common in eastern-slope alpine marshes and grassy meadows, rare elsewhere. Length 20 cm but can be quite a bit smaller.

    Like the least sandpiper, the pectoral has yellowish/greenish legs and a brown breast, but it is nearly twice as large (least is only 12 cm long), and the breast pattern is herringbone rather than dark-spotted chestnut. The "peep" is quite raspy. Feeds in grassy places, eating mostly flies, beetles, grass seeds. No nesting record; breeds in the arctic. Flies to Mexico and Central America for the winter.

Stilt sandpiper (bécasseau à échasses)
Calidris himantopus (sandpiper family)
Mid- to late August

Common in flocks from Jasper park
north during the fall migration; rare or
unreported elsewhere in our area. Look
for it along marsh shorelines.
    Length 20 cm, about the same size as
the pectoral sandpiper (previous entry),
which it resembles, but the neck, bill and
especially the legs of the stilt sandpiper
are longer. Very similar to lesser
yellowlegs (next entry), but a little
smaller; the stilt has ruddy streaks or
patches on the head, which the lesser
(and greater) yellowlegs lack. Voice is
surprisingly frog-like; maybe there is
some survival value in that.
    The stilt feeds in tight groups standing in water; the heads dip under as the
birds probe the bottom mud for worms, insect larvae, seeds and roots. Summers
along the arctic coast, winters from Central America to Chile.

Lesser yellowlegs
(petit chevalier à pattes jaunes)
Tringa flavipes (sandpiper family)
Mid-August to late September

Fairly common in northern area,
occasional farther south, along
shorelines, passing through.
    Yellowlegs are large
sandpipers, and the two species (lesser
and greater) are the only ones with
yellow legs. Lesser (length 22 cm) has a
shorter bill and whiter face than the
greater (next entry) and is smaller. Says
"pew" or "pew-pew," rather quickly;
probes for bugs in the mud. Doesn't
breed in the mountains; winters along
the Mexican coasts.
    I have seen this bird standing at the top of a spruce tree (the last place you
would expect to see a sandpiper), calling and calling. A short distance away,
another yellowlegs was doing the same thing.

Greater yellowlegs
(grand chevalier à pattes jauns)
Tringa melanoleuca (sandpiper family)
Beginning of May to mid-October

Common shorebird in central and
northern area; uncommon farther south
and on the western slope. The largest
sandpiper in our area (length 28 cm),
with, yes, yellow legs.
    Looks very much like the lesser
yellowlegs (previous entry), but larger,
with longer bill and darker face.
Compare also with stilt sandpiper. Calls
"cheep-cheep-cheep" in flight.

Wades, picking up floating bugs and tiny fish near the water surface; doesn't probe. Breeds near water at high subalpine and alpine elevations; four blotchy buff eggs in a hollow on the ground, sparsely lined with grass or dead leaves. Incubation: 23 days; precocial young fly 18-20 days later. Flight speed: 70 km/h. Winter range: coastal USA from California south, Texas, Mexico, Gulf coast, east coast up to New England.

Long-billed dowitcher
(bécasseau à long bec)
Limnodromus scolopaceus (sandpiper family)
Mid-July to mid-October

Fairly common in flocks on mudflats in northern and central areas, scarce in the south. Length 25 cm; quite large for a sandpiper.
　　The only large one with a short neck; incongruously long, heavy bill. Greenish-yellow legs, rather long. Unlike other sandpipers, is ruddy underneath. Call: "keek," either singly or in frantic repetition. Picks insects and seeds out of the mud, often sticking its head into pools to probe the bottom. Breeds on the northwest coast of Alaska. Flies at 70 km/h; winters along the east and west coasts south of Oregon and Virginia.

Wilson's phalarope (phalarope de Wilson)
Phalaropus tricolor (sandpiper family)
Beginning of May to mid-June

Occasional on marsh ponds and lakes, swimming. This sandpiper acts like a duck and has lobed toes like a coot (page 586). Length 20 cm.
　　Distinctive markings: black eye-line gets thicker toward the back of the head, then turns down the side of the neck, becoming a red stripe over the back. Another red back stripe parallels the first one. Gray atop the head, white front and underparts, very sharp, long bill (compare with red-necked phalarope, below). Says "rope," "rope," and makes buzzing noises. Feeds mostly along muddy shorelines, poking its head into pools for mosquito larvae. Also spins round and round in the water, stirring up larvae and nabbing them. Follows dabbling ducks, getting larvae the ducks stir up. Breeds in marsh ponds but nests not reported here; winters along the Mexican Gulf coast.

Red-necked phalarope
(phalarope hyperboré)
Phalaropus lobatus (sandpiper family)
Mid- to late May, again from beginning of August to mid-September

Occasional on montane and subalpine lakes, ponds and rivers; sometimes seen near timberline. Rare in the south. Length 15 cm, noticeably smaller than Wilson's phalarope (previous entry), the only other bird with which it is likely to be confused. Both species are sandpipers that swim about like ducks rather than sticking to the shore.

Generally darker than Wilson's, the red-necked has a dark-gray head with no white above the eye and a shorter neck. The red neck stripe becomes a colorful bib lower down, instead of running onto the back as per Wilson's. In late summer we see it in its fall plumage. Voice: quick "wip-wip-wip." Both phalaropes in our area stir up the bottom mud with their long legs, spinning around and around in the water and snapping up the insect larvae they have disturbed. Unlike Wilson's, the red-necked phalarope seldom comes to shore. Breeds in the arctic; winters on the ocean off southern California and south of the equator.

Water pipit (pipit commun)
Anthus spinoletta (pipit family)
Mid-May to mid-November,
less common after September

Very common above treeline, usually around ponds or hopping about on summer snow patches, in small flocks. Length 14 cm.

A drab little bird, the water pipit looks sparrow-like, flashes junco-like white tailfeathers when it flies and bobs like a dipper or a spotted sandpiper. But there is one sure way to know that it's a pipit: it tells you so, saying "pip-it." Also makes other calls in the same squeaky tone.

Pipits are bug-eaters, getting them at the water's edge or refrigerated in snowbanks. They also eat seeds, both on the ground and in seedheads. In fall pipits come down to lower elevations, walking along the mudflats exposed by autumn's low water levels. They breed in early summer, nesting among talus boulders or back in the natural earth cavities that form along tundra streams. Four to six heavily brown-blotched white or gray eggs are laid in a cup sheltered under a bank or grass tussock; they hatch in about two weeks, the young leaving the nest 14-16 days later.

Winter range: west coast from Washington south, through the southern USA and northern Mexico, up the east coast.

SEAGULLS IN THE ROCKIES?

Sure. Gulls live everywhere. Although they normally winter along the seashore, many species nest inland. Only the mew gull nests in the Rockies; the others we see breed north or east of the mountains.

Gulls can eat practically anything: live fish or dead, carrion of all kinds, the eggs of other species, seeds and grain—you name it. This group is smart, too: gulls open clams by dropping them on rocks from the air. (A golf course in Ontario had to be closed when the gulls kept stealing the balls and dropping them on the highway next door, resulting in broken windshields.)

Ring-billed gull (goéland à bec cerclé)
Larus delawarensis (gull family)
Late April to mid-November

Common around low-elevation lakes, rivers and (especially) garbage dumps; very common in August and September. Length 40 cm, wingspan 125 cm.

Typical gull coloration: white head and tail, gray body and wings, black wingtips, yellow legs. Identify by the black ring around the tip of the bill. California gull (below) has a red and a black spot on the tip; mew gull (also below) has no spot or ring on the bill; herring gull has pink legs. Ring-billed says "yeah, yeah," and makes a rather plaintive, sheep-like "baa."

Omnivorous like other gulls, this species has a taste for dead ground squirrels and sometimes chokes to death trying to swallow them whole. No nesting records here; prefers northern lakes. Average age 3-5 years; record 21 years. Flies up to 70 km/h. Winters all along the North American coasts from Vancouver and New York south.

California gull (goéland de Californie)
Larus californicus (gull family)
Late April to end of October

Common around low-elevation lakes, rivers and garbage dumps, especially in August and September. Similar to ring-billed gull (previous entry), but a little bigger (length 43 cm, wingspan 132 cm), with a small red spot next to a small black spot on the bill. Call includes various screechy, gull-like tones, including one like the wheezy beginning of a donkey's bray.

Habits similar to the ring-billed, although the California gull prefers prairie marshes for nesting rather than northern lakes. Eats a lot of grasshoppers and other agricultural pests; farmers like it. The Mormons built a statue in Salt Lake City to honor this bird.

The California is very dark when immature, with a black bill-tip. It doesn't get adult coloring until its third summer. Average lifespan 6-7 years, some to 12 years or more. The other gulls in our area are lighter than the California when immature, and they tend to be spotted. Wintering: west coast from Vancouver south.

Herring gull (goéland argenté)
Larus argentatus (gull family)
Mid-April to mid-March,
again late July to early October

Fairly common in central and northern sections as they cross the mountains between their west-coast wintering grounds and their boreal/prairie summer range east and north of us. Our biggest gull: length 50 cm, wingspan 140 cm.

Very similar to California gull (previous entry), but nonetheless easily differentiated by the legs: they are pink, not yellow. Voice: "karrr," with assorted squeaks and whistles; the sound of the sea, right at your local dump.

Mew gull (goéland cendré)
Larus canus (gull family)
Mid-May to mid-September

Common in the north end, occasional at Jasper, rare at the south end. Smallest of the gray-and-white gulls in our area (length 35 cm, wingspan 107 cm), but otherwise similar except for two things: there is no mark on the bill, and the mew gull has the most awful voice in birdland. "Mew" is simply too mild; this thing cries like a Siamese cat. And it does it non-stop. Diet: heavy on bugs and worms. Breeds in late spring, nesting in spruces sticking up out of swamps. The parents are very protective; people strolling along the boardwalk leading to Liard Hot Springs are routinely dived at by shrieking mew gulls nesting nearby.

Three brown-marked pale-green eggs hatch in 22-27 days; the young leave the nest in only a day or two, sticking nearby until flying time at 4-5 weeks. Age record 24 years. Wintering: Gulf of Alaska and down the west coast to the Mexican border.

Bonaparte's gull (mouette de Bonaparte)
Larus philadelphia (gull family)
Month of May, again (rarely) from
mid-August to mid-September

Named for a French biologist, not Napoleon. Fairly common in spring, northern and central areas; rare in the south.

A small gull (length 28 cm, wingspan 80 cm), easily identified by the black head and bill, but can be confused with **Franklin's gull** *(Larus pipixcan),* which is seen occasionally in the southern foothills. Check the wings: in Bonaparte's the tips are white with black trim; in Franklin's the tips are black with white trim. Both birds have bright-orange legs.

Bonaparte's gull quacks softly, like a duck; eats a lot of insects. It breeds in northwestern Canada but apparently not in the Rockies; winters along both west and east coasts of the USA.

BIRDS THAT DIVE INTO WATER FROM THE AIR, AND THE DIPPER

Common tern (sterne commun)
Sterna hirundo (gull family)
Mid-May to late June, month of
September

Occasional over lakes, diving from the sky for fish. Length 35 cm, wingspan 80 cm.

Black cap and split tail are immediate identifiers; note also orange bill, usually with black tip, and orange legs. Says "BEE-yert," with lots of buzz. Nests east of us on the big prairie lakes. Age record 25 years; flight speed 65 km/h. Wintering: along Baja California and the southeastern/Florida/Gulf coasts of the USA.

Black tern (sterne noire)
Chlidonias niger (gull family)
Mid-May to mid-June

Occasional over lakes and marsh ponds,
mostly scooping up airborne bugs rather
than diving for fish. Length 23 cm,
wingspan 90 cm. The angled wings and
split tail show that it is a tern. Very
dark all over, except under the tail,
which is white. Black head, bill and
front are distinctive. Says "ee-ah,"
sometimes just "ee" or just "ah." Breeds
east and west of the mountains; age
record 17 years. Flight speed
50 km/h—not very fast, but this bird
travels a long way each year: winters
from Panama to Chile.

Belted kingfisher
(martin-pêcheur d'Amérique)
Ceryle alcyon (kingfisher family)
Year-round; seen most often late April to
mid-September

Fairly common at low elevations around rivers, lakes and ponds. Length 30 cm.

 With its disproportionately large head, big bill and crest, the kingfisher is
likely to be mistaken only for Steller's jay or the blue jay (page 625). But the
kingfisher has a broad white neckband, which Steller's lacks; the blue jay has a
white throat and face, but the coloration does not go all the way around the neck.
Kingfisher females have a rusty band across their middles that the males lack.
Song: bursts of tuneless rattling, like the sound of a scratch-gourd in a Latin band,
given in flight.

 Kingfishers perch in trees along the water, suddenly diving in headlong after
fish. They also catch tadpoles, frogs, toads, mice and insects. Breeding is in early
spring. The birds tunnel 1-2 m (sometimes 4-5 m) into a soft bank by digging with
the bill and kicking the dirt out. Six to eight white eggs in a clutch, hatching at
23-24 days; the young fledge at 30-35 days. Flight speed 60 km/h.

 Most kingfishers in the Rockies probably winter not far to the west, in the
Columbia Mountains of BC and along the coast, where there is open water all
winter. Some remain at open spots on mountain rivers and at spring-fed lakes in
the Rockies, but these seldom survive until spring.

American dipper (cincle d'Amérique)
Cinclus mexicanus (dipper family)
Year-round

Common along fast-flowing streams.
Length 14 cm.

 A round, gray bird with a very short
tail, white eye-ring and rather large
yellow legs. In Europe there is a similar
bird called the "water ouzel." Voice:
dippers trill in flight and sing
beautifully at rest, cheeping, buzzing,
whistling, warbling and calling "zeet."

 It is amazing to hear this summery sort of birdsong on a deathly cold day in
January. But many's the time I have been skiing up a snowy, frozen stream when
the song erupts. There, at a small patch of open water, is a dipper. It plops in,
stays under a moment hunting the aquatic larvae, snails and tiny fish it eats, then

jumps back up on a rock, bobbing up and down like a kid needing the bathroom. It sees me and flies, squirting a line of blackish poop in the snow on takeoff, and lights at the next open spot. I have never seen dipper tracks in the snow.

These birds have interesting adaptations for living year-round in the torrents: enormous oil glands to waterproof their feathers; little flaps to seal their nostrils; heavy nictitating membranes (transparent extra eyelids) to cover their eyes. The species, related to the robins and wrens, breeds in early spring, building a wren-like domed nest of feather mosses in a rock crevice in a streamside cliff, usually under an overhang and often under a waterfall. There are 4-5 eggs; they hatch in 16 days. The young start hitting the water at 18-25 days, before they can fly. Lifespan 2-8 years. Non-migratory in the Canadian Rockies area.

HAWKS, FALCONS AND A PERCHING BIRD THAT ACTS LIKE A HAWK

American kestrel (crécelle Américaine)
Falco sparverius (falcon family)
Early April to mid-October

Used to be called "sparrow hawk." Common in open places, especially along dry sloping meadows at low elevations. Hangs around marshes, too. Smallest hawk-like bird in the mountains: length 22 cm, wingspan 53 cm.

A falcon; has pointy wings and a long, narrow tail. Identify by the size and coloration: red tail with black terminal band and bars (but much smaller than red-tailed hawk, page 602). Red back, red crown, black line leading down from base of beak. Voice is high and squeaky; says "killy-killy-killy."

Eats mostly insects, knocking off mice, bats, frogs and small birds when it can. Slope-soars at tree-top height; often circles and hovers before dropping on prey. Not terribly shy; one often sees kestrels on phone lines and fences along the highway. They even frequent towns—unusual for a raptorial bird. Nests in mid-spring, using an abandoned tree-hole.

Four or five brown-blotched white/pinkish eggs hatch at 29-30 days; young birds fledge at 30 days. Lifespan 4-6 years; in captivity up to 17 years. Flight speed 60 km/h. Wintering is along the west coast from Prince Rupert south, and through much of the USA and Mexico.

Merlin (faucon émerillon)
Falco columbarius (falcon family)
Early April to early September

Formerly called "pigeon hawk." Occasional in forest clearings and along lakeshores; likes the subalpine zone. A small falcon (length 30 cm, wingspan 58 cm), dark on the back like the rare **peregrine falcon** *(Falco peregrinus)* but smaller, lighter-colored on the head, without the clearly defined black cowl of the peregrine. Has several black bands on the tail, which the peregrine doesn't. Call is rather like that of the kestrel, high and squealing, but the bird is seldom vocal. Not shy; can be closely approached. Merlins hunt at tree-top level, snatching small birds out of the air; they do not stoop or soar. Also take shorebirds, squirrels, mice, bats, insects. No nesting record here; the species prefers to breed in boreal woods. Flies at 75 km/h. Winters on the west and east coasts, through the southwest states and Mexico, along the Gulf of Mexico and through the Caribbean islands to South America.

Prairie falcon (faucon des prairies)
Falco mexicanus (falcon family)
Late June to late September

Normally a prairie bird, but also seen occasionally in the foothills and above timberline in the mountains from Jasper south. Length 40 cm, wingspan 102 cm—significantly larger than the merlin (previous entry), which it resembles.

Best identifier: a dark zone under the wing, right at the root, giving the bird a sweaty-armpit look (sweaty wingpit look?). Also check the tail: underneath, there is one obvious black band. The merlin has several bands, while the rare peregrine, another large falcon, has none. The prairie falcon says "hee-hee-hee," rather like an osprey on the nest. Food is mainly small birds and ground squirrels. It soars, spots its prey and stoops (dives at it), reaching speeds of 300 km/h—wow!—as it knocks a bird from the air with its clenched feet. Then it catches the victim in its talons as it falls.

Also chases and snatches birds, drops to the ground for grasshoppers. Nests on cliffs, but apparently does not nest in the Canadian Rockies. Has lived to 10 years in captivity. Winters in the western USA and down into Mexico.

Sharp-shinned hawk (épervier brun)
Accipiter striatus (hawk family)
For season see below

Occasional at the forest fringes or in the woods. Seen most frequently from mid-August to the end of September, but has been reported year-round. Length 27 cm, wingspan 53 cm.

Resembles the merlin or American kestrel, especially in the narrow, banded tail, but note how much broader and more rounded the wings are. Differentiate from similar Cooper's hawk (next entry) by the size (Cooper's is much larger) and straight tail end (Cooper's is rounded). Voice: high-pitched, rapid "pew-pew-pew."

A sharp-shinned hunts swiftly through the woods, picking off small forest birds from their perches, sometimes grabbing a bird in mid-air or coming in low to get one on the ground. Kills by working its talons in and out. Breeds in early spring. Large nest of twigs in the woods holds 4-5 brown-blotched white eggs; hatching is at 34-35 days, fledging at 23 days. Has lived to 12 years in the wild. Wintering: along the BC coast and through much of the USA. Sometimes overwinters in central and southern Canadian Rockies.

Cooper's hawk (épervier de Cooper)
Accipiter cooperii (hawk family)
Early May to early October

Occasional in or over the woods, catching small birds and snatching rodents. Length 40 cm, wingspan 70 cm. Very much like the sharp-shinned hawk (previous entry), with dark back, mottled underside and banded tail, but much bigger. The tail is rounded at the end, not squared off. Head looks larger and heavier; black cap more prominent. To differentiate from merlin or peregrine falcon (page 599), note broad, rounded wings; falcons have sharply pointed, angular wings.

Cooper's hawk says "awk-awk-awk," quite rapidly. Like the sharp-shinned, it hunts at low levels in the woods, catching mostly squirrels, chipmunks and robin-size birds. Has a taste for domestic chickens. Sometimes dunks prey in water to drown it. Cooper's breeds in mid-spring, nesting 10-20 m up in a conifer. The male builds a platform of twigs, covering it with bark flakes. Four eggs normally, whitish/bluish, hatching in 36 days. Fledging is 30-34 days later; the young independent at eight weeks. Flight speed 82 km/h. Wintering is on the west coast and through the USA.

Northern goshawk (autour)
Accipiter gentilis (hawk family)
Year-round central, summer in the north, winter in the south

Occasional in the forest, or soaring along sparsely timbered slopes. Length 48 cm, wingspan 107 cm, the largest of the accipiters and very impressive.

Distinctively dark-colored; more uniformly colored than our other hawks and falcons. At close range, check the white eye stripe. Voice is rather like Cooper's: repetitive "eck-eck-eck-eck," but a good bit higher.

Voracious hunters, goshawks blast through the woods at high speed, taking mostly grouse; also snowshoe hares, squirrels, chipmunks, ducks, other hawks and owls—most anything that moves, it seems. Killing is by hitting with the talons open, driving them in, then quickly clenching.

Breeding is in mid-spring. The male builds the nest and supplies the food; the female broods and changes the nest lining (conifer needles and leaves). She is very protective; will attack people near the nest—and sometimes sends them to hospital for stitches in the scalp. Here is one good reason to wear a hat in the woods.

Two or three bluish-white eggs hatch in 36-41 days. The young fledge at 40 days and are particularly bloodthirsty, often killing each other and even attacking their parents, who wisely abandon them early. Lifespan in captivity 19 years; migrates at 60 km/h.

The northern goshawk, although reclusive and rarely seen, is still widespread through the Canadian taiga (far northern forest, equivalent to subalpine forest in the mountains), but its winter range in the western USA is quickly disappearing. The Coast Mountains of BC, once a vast winter refuge for this bird, are currently being savaged by clear-cut logging.

Northern harrier (busard des marais)
Circus cyaneus (hawk family)
Late April to late May,
again early July to late September

Formerly called "marsh hawk." Fairly common at any elevation, often over wetlands, subalpine meadows and tundra, flying low in search of ground squirrels and other rodents, small birds. Length 42 cm, wingspan 107 cm.

Fairly large hawk, easily identified from above (which you often are, because the bird flies so low) by the white patch on the butt. Otherwise brown on top and pale beneath, with banded tail and black wingtips. Holds wings in an upward vee while gliding, slides side to side. Makes a sound you can imitate by loudly kissing the back of your hand, quickly and repeatedly. Practice in private.

Probably nests here, but no records in the parks. Several killed in the wild at 10-16 years. Migration speed 60 km/h. Winter range: southeastern BC and most of the USA, possibly the southern Rocky Mountain Trench.

Red-tailed hawk (buse à queue rousse)
Buteo jamaicensis (hawk family)
Early April to mid-September

Fairly common in open country, especially in the eastern-slope foothills. Large: length 46 cm, wingspan 122 cm.

Body color and pattern can vary considerably, from very light to very dark, but the tail is always a good identifier: red above, pink below, spread wide in flight. Dark-phase individuals have a yoke of brown under the wing, with white on the rear surfaces and black-tipped feathers right at the wingtips. Compare with Swainson's (much less common), below.

The red-tailed's call is distinctive: a long, whistling scream ("SHEEEE-ahhhh"), repeated frequently, with a little space between blasts. A startling and spooky sound.

This hawk slope-soars low along meadowy ridges or sits on a tree, post or pole; glides cooly down to surprise ground squirrels, mice and other rodents. Occasionally takes other birds in the air by stooping; drops on frogs, salamanders, even fish. Will eat worms.

Mates for life; breeds very early in spring, the nest a mass of twigs on a ledge or in a tall tree. One to three brown-blotched off-white eggs hatch in 28-32 days; the young fly at 6-7 weeks. Long-lived: 14-16 years in the wild, up to 29 years in captivity. Flies at 35-65 km/h, but can dive at over 160 km/h. Winter range: most of the USA, Mexico, south to Nicaragua.

Swainson's hawk (buse de Swainson)
Buteo swainsoni (hawk family)
Early April to mid-September

Occasional in the foothills and on the western slope; rare elsewhere. Prefers large open areas, although seldom found above timberline. Length 45 cm, wingspan 125 cm.

Shape and size much like red-tailed (previous entry), but Swainson's is darker, with a broad, banded tail. There is usually a distinctive dark area on the trailing half of the underwing—just the reverse of the red-tailed's dark leading-edge yoke—and a brown or reddish bib, white throat and dark head. Call is much like that of red-tailed, but screamier and less whistling: "eee-aaa," the sound you are supposed to make when falling over a precipice.

One would imagine this impressive hawk diving on bunnies. Instead, it hops along the ground, eating mostly insects and mice; waits at entrances to ground-squirrel burrows to grab them in talons; catches bats. Seldom takes other birds; sits on fencelines and other low perches rather than soaring.

Swainson's breeds in early spring, preferring the intermountain valleys and the prairies, but reported to nest in the southern foothills and even in Waterton park. Bulky nest, often easily seen in a lone tree; two lightly brown-marked white eggs hatch in 28 days. Young fly 4-5 weeks later. Age data: 6-9 years.

Wintering grounds are in southern South America, requiring a very long migration in which the birds soar up several thousand metres and then glide long distances.

Rough-legged hawk (buse pattue)
Buteo lagopus (hawk family)
Mid-November and December

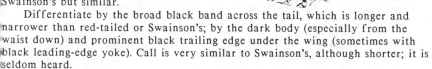

Occasional, during migration south; the only hawk you are likely to see in the snowy months, for some individuals spend the winter in the far southern foothills. Length 48 cm, wingspan 132 cm; a little larger than red-tailed or Swainson's but similar.

Differentiate by the broad black band across the tail, which is longer and narrower than red-tailed or Swainson's; by the dark body (especially from the waist down) and prominent black trailing edge under the wing (sometimes with black leading-edge yoke). Call is very similar to Swainson's, although shorter; it is seldom heard.

In its arctic breeding grounds, the rough-legged hawk eats lemmings and ptarmigan. In the Rockies it picks off mice and grouse, plus the odd ptarmigan while passing over alpine areas. Winters through much of the USA.

Osprey (aigle pêcheur)
Pandion haliaetus (hawk family)
Early March to late September

Fairly common along lakeshores and
rivers, flying to and from a massive nest
atop a tree. Large: length 57 cm,
wingspan 137 cm.

Easily identified at short range by
the white head with black eye-stripe and
black bill. Brown back and upper wings,
black-and-white underside with
prominent black patches at the wing
joints. Flies with drooped wingtips. Calls:
plain whistles, and a worried
"yee-yee-yee" if you get near the nest.

This is the fish-hawk, gliding over water and swooping down to grab anything
finny with its talons. Occasionally takes rodents, frogs, sandpipers, ducks.

The mated pair returns year after year to the same huge nest, built of sticks
atop a tree at the water's edge. Breeding is in mid-spring; three cream/yellowish,
brown-blotched eggs hatch in 32-33 days. The young birds and female are fed by
the male until fledging occurs at 7-8 weeks. Wintering: along the west coast from
California south, east coast from Florida south, and well into South America.

Northern shrike (pie-grièche boréale)
Lanius excubitor (shrike family)
Beginning of March to late May, again in
July, again beginning of October through
November

Occasional in subalpine forest, atop a
conifer. Length 20 cm.

This bird summers and winters in
different parts of the Canadian Rockies
area, as follows: winters from about Lake
Louise south, migrates between there and
the latitude of Fort Nelson; summers in
the far north end of the Rockies, and up to the Arctic Ocean. In the far south
end, western slope, you may see it all year; in central regions you see it during
spring migration from March to late May, and in the fall migration from the
beginning of October through November. In the north end you see it from April
through September. That is, if you see it at all: this bird is not common anywhere.

Identifiers: large, curved bill, black tail, black wings and black bandit's mask
against gray head. Compare with gray jay and Clark's nutcracker, page 624.
Waterton/Glacier region is also summer home of the **loggerhead shrike**
(L. ludovicianus), which is quite similar but has a shorter bill and broader
eye-mask. Loggerhead goes "tir-bzzt," "tir-bzzt" (and "bzzt-tir," "bzzt-tir"); northern
shrike says very little.

This is the hawk-pretender mentioned in the section head, a songbird
(passiforme) gone bloodthirsty, with a hawk-like tearing bill but little passiforme
feet. Shrikes catch small birds, rodents and insects, killing by biting the neck
through. They carry the prey in the bill (the legs are too weak), often sticking it
on a thorn or barbed wire fence, or hanging it in a forked branch to eat it.

Shrikes are very territorial, chasing others of their kind away. They nest in a
conifer in mid-spring, building a large cup of twigs and moss, lined with feathers,
roots and hair. Eggs 5-7, greenish-white with brown speckles, hatching at only
15 days and fledging 19-20 days later.

EAGLES

Bald eagle (aigle à tête blanche)
Haliaeetus leucocephalus (hawk family)
Mid-May to mid-September, sometimes
year-round

Fairly common along rivers and lakes,
sitting atop a tree or soaring. The
second-largest bird in the Rockies (length
82 cm, wingspan 203 cm; largest is
tundra swan, page 587) and very
impressive in its unmistakable brown
and white plumage. Doesn't say much,
though. The voice is wheezy and
high-pitched, rather like that of the little
kestrel (page 599).

    The bald eagle feeds primarily by fishing, like the osprey, but also eats
carrion and takes the odd muskrat or injured duck. Breeds in mid-spring. During
the mating display a pair sometimes lock feet in flight and tumble earthward,
releasing at the last moment. Two white eggs are laid in a nest like the osprey's: a
great big clump of sticks well up in a conifer (but seldom at the top, as per
osprey), used year after year.

    The first nestling to hatch (35-36 days) usually kills the other or starves it by
taking all the food. It fledges comparatively late: 10-11 weeks.

    Longest-lived bird in the region: up to 48 years in captivity. Migrates at
60-70 km/h. If open water is available, this species will sometimes spend the whole
winter in the mountains; usually it flies to the west coast (Alaskan panhandle
south) or to various locations inland throughout the USA. Avoids Washington, DC.

Golden eagle (aigle doré)
Aquila chrysaetos (hawk family)
Late May to early October

Occasional at high elevations and over
the tundra, a soaring alpine bird that
always impresses: nearly as big as the
bald eagle, the golden is 81 cm long with
a wingspan of 198 cm.

    Dark brown all over, often with
light patch under the tail; "golden" refers
to the neck, which looks golden only up
close. Voice is small and twittery; quite
incongruous.

    A golden eagle soars for hours, seldom flapping. When the ground squirrels
forget that it's up there and venture out of their burrows, the eagle dives to pick
one off. Also goes for snowshoe hares and marmots. Sometimes seen eating dead
sheep or goats, but stories of golden eagles snatching lambs and young mountain
goats are probably untrue.

    Nests in mid-spring, sometimes every other year. The life-mated pair build an
enormous perennial nest of sticks (up to 3 m across and a metre thick), usually on
an alpine cliff-ledge; sometimes they use very little nesting material. There are
two white eggs, blotched/streaked with reddish-brown and gray, hatching at
43-45 days but a couple of days apart. The older one usually kills the younger one.
Age record: 46 years in captivity. Flies leisurely (50 km/h) but can do nearly
200 km/h if chased; stoops at tremendous speeds: up to 320 km/h. Wintering
grounds: west coast from Alaska panhandle south and through much of the USA.

OWLS

Great horned owl (grand Duc)
Bubo virginianus (typical-owl family)
Year-round

Fairly common in the woods, but seldom
active during the day and thus
infrequently seen. Very large owl: length
50 cm, wingspan 140 cm.

    This is the only owl you are likely to
see in the Canadian Rockies area with
"horns" (feathers, really). Horned owls
hoot loudly, saying "hoo, hoo-oo-oo, hoo,
hoo," one of the more familiar night
sounds throughout North America. They
hunt mostly at night, although sometimes
during the day, gliding silently down on
prey located mainly through sound. They
catch and kill with their talons, bring
the meat home to eat it. Diet: mainly
snowshoe hares and skunks when
available, but also mice, tree squirrels,
ground squirrels, chipmunks, bats, frogs,
insects, waterfowl, perching birds,
hawks, other owls—and furry caps worn
in the woods at dusk.

    Nests early in spring, usually in a borrowed hawk-nest, sometimes in a rock
cleft or tree cavity. Very protective; don't come close. Two or three white eggs
hatch in 30-35 days. The amazingly ugly owlets flop out of the nest in 4-5 weeks;
they are fed on the ground for awhile and fly poorly until 9-10 weeks. They
follow mum and dad around for months afterward, begging food. Don't breed
until two years old; lifespan in captivity 29 years. Flight speed 65 km/h.
Non-migratory.

Great gray owl (chouette cendrée)
Strix nebulosa (typical-owl family)
Year-round

Occasional in northern area, scarce
farther south. Our largest owl: length
55 cm, wingspan 152 cm.

    More brown than gray in the
mountains, but the facial disk is quite
gray, large and concentrically ringed
around the eyes, which are yellow. No
horns. Differentiate from rather similar
barred owl (next entry) by the size
(barred owl smaller) and the eyes
(barred's eyes are black). Note vertically
streaked bib on great gray rather than
horizontally barred one.

    The great gray speaks in very low hoots; the furry creatures listen. So does the
owl; it can hear the mice under the snow. The big bird dives softly, the feathers
making no noise; it punches through the crust with its long legs to reach the little
snowy tunnel. Also hit: hares, tree squirrels and sometimes small birds.

    Often active during the day and strangely unwary, this bird will let you
approach rather closely. Breeds in early spring, taking over a crow's nest or hawk's
nest in a large conifer; sometimes nests in a snapped-off hollow tree trunk. Eggs

3-5, white. Incubation time varies from egg to egg; all birds leave the nest at 3-5 weeks but fly weakly and require parental attention for months. Non-migratory.

Barred owl (chouette rayée)
Strix varia (typical-owl family)
Year-round

Occasional in the woods; more commonly heard than seen. Large: length 43 cm, wingspan 112 cm.

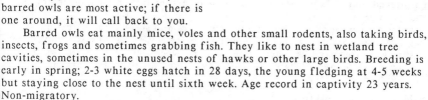

Hornless; the eyes are black, not yellow, and there is a large barred ruff below the bill and down the breast. Brown streaked buffy front.

The call is an easy one to know: a low-toned "hoo-hoo-hoo-HOO-aww," unlike any other. Listen at dusk, when barred owls are most active; if there is one around, it will call back to you.

Barred owls eat mainly mice, voles and other small rodents, also taking birds, insects, frogs and sometimes grabbing fish. They like to nest in wetland tree cavities, sometimes in the unused nests of hawks or other large birds. Breeding is early in spring; 2-3 white eggs hatch in 28 days, the young fledging at 4-5 weeks but staying close to the nest until sixth week. Age record in captivity 23 years. Non-migratory.

Northern hawk-owl (chouette épervière)
Surnia ulula (typical-owl family)
Year-round

Fairly common in northern foothills swamps; occasional in subalpine forest farther south; rare south of Banff. Length 35 cm, wingspan 85 cm.

This owl is active in the daytime. It is most easily identified by the long, hawk-like tail (which it raises and lowers when perching). Unwary; can be closely approached. Saw-whet owl (page 608) is also long-tailed and more active during the day than most other owls, but much smaller.

The hawk-owl's face is reminiscent of the great horned owl (page 606), but earless; the top of the head is speckled white on brown and the bill is yellow. Finely barred all the way down the front, which serves to differentiate from boreal and northern saw-whet owls. Voice is squeaky; sounds like glass being cleaned.

Hawk owls watch for mice and other small rodents from a tall vantage point, dropping on them. Breeding is in mid-spring, the nest usually in a natural tree cavity or in a large woodpecker hole. Sometimes manages two broods in a year. Eggs 3-10, white, hatching in 25-30 days; the young fledge at 23-27 days.

Boreal owl (nyctale boréale)
Aegolius funereus (typical-owl family)
Year-round

Occasional through most of the year, in
the woods. Rather common from
mid-April to mid-May in central and
northern sections. Smallish: length 25 cm,
wingspan 60 cm.

    Resembles hawk owl (previous
entry), but the tail is shorter and the
facial disk squared off, with a short
brown line leading up from the eye to
the top of the face. Front is mottled
rather than barred. Compare also with
saw-whet owl, below.

    Call is distinctive, associated with the northern woods at night: rather
high-pitched, quick, "hoo-hoo-hoo-hoo-hoo-hoo," rather like the winnowing of the
snipe (page 586).

    After a hard night of gobbling up mice, voles and shrews, the boreal owl
dozes away the day on a branch. You can get quite close when it's asleep. Nesting:
mid-spring, in tree cavities, often those made by woodpeckers. Eggs 3-6, white,
hatching in 26-36 days. Fledging is 30-36 days later. Has lived 15 years in
captivity. Non-migratory.

Northern saw-whet owl (petite Nyctale)
Aegolius acadicus (typical-owl family)
Year-round

Occasional year-round, more common
from mid-April to mid-May, in the
woods. Scarce in the north end of the
range. Small owl: length 18 cm, wingspan
43 cm.

    Resembles boreal owl (previous
entry), but is smaller, with a streaky
head rather than a spotted one, no
eye-line, and streaky front rather than
mottling or barring. Hoots and whistles,
the song supposedly sounding like a saw
being sharpened (thus "saw-whet").

    Hunts at night, mostly for insects, sometimes for little rodents and small birds.
By day this species is fast asleep and easily approached at its low roost. Nests in
early spring, often using a flicker hole. There are 5-6 white eggs (a lot for an
owl), hatching at 26-28 days; leave the nest 27-34 days later. The young look very
different from the adults: white eyebrow-like vee over eyes, rest of head
uniformly brown. Age in captivity: 17 years. Most saw-whets in the Canadian
Rockies go somewhere else for the winter.

Northern pygmy owl (chouette naine)
Glaucidium gnoma (typical-owl family) Year-round

Occasional year-round, common early April to late May, in the woods. Often hangs
around towns in winter, knocking off house sparrows. Our smallest owl: length
15 cm, wingspan 38 cm.

    Another long-tailed owl, but so much smaller than the hawk-owl (page 607)
that confusion is unlikely. Resembles saw-whet owl (previous entry), but is a little
smaller, with longer tail, darker face (rather fierce-looking) and diagnostic dark
markings on the back of the neck, outlined in white.

Gives forth cute little hoots, but over and over, monotonously; calls in the daytime and under moonlight. Active at dawn and dusk, more diurnal than most other owls; it perches above a clearing and swoops down on mice and insects, hitting also ground squirrels and small birds. Breeds in mid-spring, usually taking a woodpecker hole. Three to four white eggs hatch in 28 days; the young owls fledge at 29-32 days. Non-migratory.

CHICKENS:
GROUSE AND PTARMIGAN

Ruffed grouse (gellinotte huppée)
Bonasa umbellus (grouse family)
Year-round, seen most often beginning of March to end of October

Common in montane woods, often in aspen groves and near the edges of small clearings. Length 35 cm.

Of the three grouse you are likely to see in the Canadian Rockies, this is the only one with a crest (both sexes) and thus the easiest to identify. Note also the black-banded tail, reddish in males, grayer in females. Males also have a red spot above the eye. The rest of the plumage is classic camouflage, nicely matching the mottled forest floor.

Grouse don't say much (they make little soft sounds to their children and sometimes squawk when frightened), but the male ruffed grouse **drums**: standing on a log, he beats his wings up and down to produce a very low thumping sound that is repeated for eight to ten seconds, slowly at first, then faster near the end. It sounds much like a big diesel engine starting up somewhere in the woods, then stopping.

Slow-motion photography has shown that the noise is not made by thumping the body, whacking the wings together or hitting the log. It is simply made in the air. This is a mating call; despite its low frequency (40 Hz), which makes it hard for humans to pinpoint, the female finds her lover. He puts on a wonderful display: fluffs out the dark feathers on his neck (the ruff), and fans out his reddish tail.

Ruffed grouse eat insects and a great variety of plants (and plant parts) during the warm months; in winter they subsist on seeds and twig-ends, until February, when many shrubs and trees are producing nutritious buds.

Although grouse are folk-named "fool-hens" because they can often be approached so closely, the ruffed grouse is nonetheless the most skittish of the family and will suddenly fly up under your feet with a loud, startling blast of wings. Surprise! How's your heart?

Ruffed grouse breed in early spring, drumming about among the last snowbanks in the woods. The nest is a small scrape on the ground, lined with whatever is nearby. The eggs (9-12, white or buff, sometimes brown-speckled) take 23-24 days to hatch—a long time, considering the dangerous nesting site—but like all grouse and ptarmigan the young are precocious and leave the nest a just a few hours out of the shell. Almost immediately they are pecking for seeds and bugs. They are able to fly up to a little security in small trees at only 10-12 days.

Still, baby grouse is a favorite food of many predators, which explains why so many eggs are laid. If one clutch gets snapped up, the pair usually produce another. Lifespan in the wild can be 10 years. Fastest speed 65 km/h. The birds don't migrate.

Blue grouse (tétras sombre)
Dendragapus obscurus (grouse family)
Year-round

Fairly common in subalpine-fir forest, close to timberline; often on brushy avalanche slopes and burns in the front ranges. Length 43 cm; our largest grouse.

This grouse has no crest. Males have dark breasts rather than brown/white mottled ones like the other grouse species; the throat is mottled, though. There is a yellow spot above the eye (other grouse and ptarmigan males have a red spot). Both sexes have a black tail with a gray band at the end. This alone is enough to identify; tails of the others are different.

The male hoots softly during courting, five or six hoots per call. The sound is made by inflating and deflating a pouch along either side of his neck. This pouch is often bright red-orange, sometimes yellow or purplish, the color of the skin where the neck feathers have been drawn back.

Like other grouse, the blue grows little horny **pectinations** (short spines) on its toes in fall, which help it move in the snow. Blue grouse live on fruits, berries and bugs when they can get them; mostly on pine needles during the winter.

Breeding time: mid-spring. Seven to ten brown-speckled pink/buffy eggs are laid in a concealed plant-lined hollow on the ground. Hatching at 26 days, the young quickly start feeding themselves, following momma as she picks and pecks about—the pattern for all our grouse. Fly weakly in 7 days. By late summer the kids have grown up and split. No migration.

Spruce grouse (tétras de savanes)
Dendragapus canadensis (grouse family)
Year-round

Common in spruce forest; often in subalpine woods. Unwary; you can walk up within a few metres of this bird, at which point it might flop up into a tree (if it isn't there already; spruce grouse are more arboreal than their relatives). It sits there at eye-level, an easy target for hunters and thus on the decline. Length 33 cm.

No crest. The male is easily identified by his black breast patch and black throat bordered by a white line; there is a spot of bare red skin above the eye. Both sexes have a rusty brown terminal band on the white-spotted tail, which is another good identifier (and the only easy way to tell female blue grouse from female spruce grouse).

The spruce grouse doesn't have a fancy expanding neck patch like the blue grouse, but it hoots in much the same manner, only at an even lower pitch. I wondered why this spot on my bird-call tape was blank, then played it on a good machine and heard the sound for the first time. It may be the lowest-frequency bird call that the human ear can detect.

Spruce grouse also display while hooting, fanning their tails and clapping their wings together loudly. They take a little jump at the same time.

Diet: mostly spruce needles, one of the few animals to eat conifer needles. Also berries, seeds and other plant parts, mushrooms, ferns, insects. Nesting is in mid-spring, the nest on the ground but well-hidden. Seven or eight buffy or pale pink speckled eggs hatch in 24 days, the downy chicks leaving the nest right away to feed themselves. They can fly after only a week. Non-migratory.

White-tailed ptarmigan
(lagopède à queue blanche)
Lagopus leucurus (grouse family)
Year-round

Pronounced "TAR-mi-gun." Common on alpine tundra, but so well-camouflaged that you practically have to step on a ptarmigan to see it—which the bird may almost let you do, it is so unwary. Length 25 cm.

Ptarmigan plumage changes with the seasons; they are mottled brown-and-white in the summer, turning all white in the winter except for the small black bill and eye. Male ptarmigan have a red spot above the eye during breeding season. A good way to tell a summer-plumage ptarmigan from a grouse is to check the tail: it is neat and narrow on a ptarmigan, wider on a grouse. Further; ptarmigan have feathers on their feet (white ones), while grouse do not.

Of our two ptarmigan species, the white-tailed is the one with no black at all in the tail, winter or summer; the other one (willow ptarmigan, next entry), has a black-edged tail.

Ptarmigan don't say much, mostly clucking and making other soft sounds. But sometimes you may hear white-taileds scolding, shouting "boo-OW-oo" at one another.

During the summer, ptarmigan move about in family groups (normally four to eight birds), nibbling shoots, buds, flowers, fruits and seeds, and catching bugs. In the winter they flock more numerously—a dozen or two together—and subsist on seeds, twig-ends and early buds. They make well-formed, un-bird-like droppings (see page 674 for picture).

White-taileds breed in early summer, nesting on the ground in the open. There are usually 3-9 brown-speckled/spotted pinkish or buffy eggs; they hatch in 22-23 days and the young leave the nest right away, wonderfully camouflaged as they follow mom about the tundra, peeping. You can follow her, too; she doesn't get very upset. Once, when I was resting on a high-country trail near Jasper, a family of ptarmigan passed right by me, stepping over my feet and even walking under my bent-up legs. Endearingly dumb, these birds.

In winter storms, ptarmigan dig themselves into the snow; on one occasion I unknowingly skiied through a flock that all popped up at once to look at me.

If not picked off by hawks or other chicken-loving predators, ptarmigan can live up to 15 years. The white-tailed is non-migratory except in very lean winters, when it moves down to the intermountain valleys in BC and out onto the prairies looking for food.

Willow ptarmigan (lagopède des saules)
Lagopus lagopus (grouse family)
Year-round

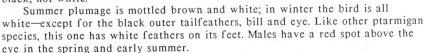

Fairly common above timberline from
Jasper north, usually near willow mats.

    Length 33 cm, noticeably larger than
white-tailed ptarmigan (previous entry),
and easily differentiated if you get a
look at the tail: the outside feathers are
black, not white.

    Summer plumage is mottled brown and white; in winter the bird is all
white—except for the black outer tailfeathers, bill and eye. Like other ptarmigan
species, this one has white feathers on its feet. Males have a red spot above the
eye in the spring and early summer.

    Willow ptarmigan are not very vocal, normally clucking and cooing quietly,
but sometimes they come out with long, loud conversations, making a variety of
quacky sounds. They walk about in small family groups, eating mostly willow
leaves. In winter you may see their tracks (as well as those of white-tailed
ptarmigan) going from bush to bush; at this time of year they eat mainly the buds,
which willows are kind enough to bring forth in early February. These buds are
amazingly rich in proteins and sugars, just the thing to get a bird through the
horrible alpine winter. During storms the birds burrow into the snow.

    This species nests in early summer among its beloved willows, laying 6-11
yellowish or reddish, heavily marked eggs in a cup on the ground. Hatching is at
20-26 days, the chicks leaving the nest right away and following the parents to the
willows, which they are dependent on for the rest of their lives. Like white-tailed
ptarmigan, willow ptarmigan prefer not to migrate, but they move to lower
elevations when the alpine food supply runs low.

A LARK IN THE HIGH COUNTRY

Horned lark (alouette cornue)
Eremophila alpestris (lark family)
Mid-April to mid-October

Common from Banff north, but only in
the alpine zone. Length 17 cm.

    Plain brown body with a black
breast-band. Very distinctive head: black
line just above the bill that crosses the
forehead and hooks downward,
broadening at the eye. There are two
little black feather-tufts on the
crown—the horns, often inconspicuous on
our birds. The face is mostly yellow,
sometimes quite pale or white. Voice is
cheepy, with bubbly/gurgly sounds. In
flight the bird folds in its wings after
each flap.

    Horned larks flit about the tundra eating bugs (mostly flies and mosquitoes)
and seeds/fruits. During late-spring courtship the male flies up 200-300 m, sings
lustily while circling, then dives earthward, pulling out at the last moment. The
female is impressed and builds a nest on the ground, protected in a hollow behind
a rock or shrub. Often there are goat/sheep poops or pebbles spotted around it.
Four brown-speckled greenish/grayish eggs hatch in 10-14 days; the young leave
the nest 9-12 days later but don't fly for another 3-5 days. Winter range: USA and
Mexico.

SWALLOWS, SWIFTS AND NIGHTHAWKS

Barn swallow (hirondelle des granges)
Hirundo rustica (swallow family)
Mid-May to late August

Very common, although subject to large
fluctuations in numbers from year to
year. Often common in towns. Length
15 cm.

Swallows put on a constant summer
airshow for people in mountain
communities, swooping about at
street-level for bugs (they feed on the
wing) and perching by the dozen along
wires. The barn swallow is easy to
recognize: bluish-black with a brown
front, it is the only swallow with a
deeply split tail.

The barn swallow is endearing in many ways, but its voice sounds like
someone loudly rubbing squeaky glass and then giving the Bronx cheer. The birds
call constantly, starting at first light (meaning five in the morning in midsummer).
Diet: strictly insects. They drink by skimming water in flight.

Barn swallows nest in mid-spring, building mud cups under any sort of
overhang—often inside buildings. If you build a little platform under an eave by a
window, a pair may move in and keep you entertained for months.

The feather-lined nest holds 4-5 small red-speckled white eggs; they hatch in
14-16 days (brooding by female only, although the male stays nearby to guard the
nest). The young fledge 17-24 days later. This short reproductive cycle allows two
broods a year in the southern section, one or two centrally and north.

The altricial nestlings lie out of sight, below the rim of the nest, until one of
the parents arrives with a throat full of masticated insects. Then all the heads pop
up at once. One or two birds get fed; the others have to wait a couple of minutes
until next time. Then they all sink back slowly, as if deflating.

Newly fledged birds are particularly fun to watch. They teeter on wires and
fences, fluttering their wings and calling plaintively whenever an adult cruises by.
The nestlings keep together for a few weeks, crowding back into the nest at night
and on rainy days. Maximum age is eight years; flight speed up to 55 km/h.

Swallows are famous for geographically precise and punctual migrations,
arriving and departing in the same week year after year. Yet they travel farther
than any other land bird, some of them round-tripping annually between Alaska
and Argentina (some sea birds travel farther).

Cliff swallow (hirondelle à front blanc)
Hirundo pyrrhonota (swallow family)
Mid-May to late August

Common, especially around towns and
under bridges, and nearly as tolerant of
humans as the barn swallow. Length
13 cm.

Resembles the barn swallow but
lacks the forked tail. There is a
prominent white patch on the forehead.
Back is lighter, with a brown patch on
the rump. They live in colonies, flying
out over water for mosquitos and such.
The calls are like those of barn swallows,
but higher-pitched and less strident.

Swallows and swifts

Cliff swallows in the Canadian Rockies seldom perch on wires, preferring instead to sit on the edges of their nests, which are little bottles made of mud stuck onto sheltered vertical or overhanging surfaces. You may see the nests on buildings, under bridges and culverts, on cliffs and under thick treelimbs. These summer condos are reused year after year if left intact.

Breeding is in mid-spring, again in midsummer in the southern section where there are often two broods each year. There are 4-5 small pinkish eggs, reddish/brownish-speckled, incubated 16 days by the female only. The young birds are fed by both parents, fledging at 23 days. Flight speed 45 km/h. Returns regularly from wintering in South America.

Violet-green swallow
(hirondelle à face blanche)
Tachycineta thalassina (swallow family)
Late April to late August

Common in the mountains proper, especially around towns; less common through the foothills. Length 12 cm.

This swallow and the tree swallow (next entry) both have white breasts and greenish backs; on the violet-green swallow the white region extends up onto the back and above the eye, while on the tree swallow it is less extensive. The tree swallow is also much less common in the Rockies.

Violet-greens behave much like barn swallows, perching in rows along wires and aerobatically chasing bugs. Their call is twittery rather than raucous, and they nest more secretively, in crevices, tree holes and nest boxes, or even in unused cliff-swallow nests.

Breeding time: mid-spring. Mud is not used in the nest. Four or five small white eggs hatch in 13-15 days; fledging is at 23-25 days. Flight speed measured at 47 km/h. Wintering is in Central America.

Tree swallow (hirondelle bicolore)
Tachycineta bicolor (swallow family)
Late April to mid-September;
less common after July

Common, but stays mainly in the woods and is thus not as obvious as the swallows listed above. Length 13 cm.

Very similar to violet-green swallow (above), with a white tummy and green back, but the white does not extend up onto the back, nor does it curl behind the eye. Voice is twittery/cheepy.

Differs in some ways from our other swallows: not colonial; will sometimes feed on the ground, taking seeds and berries as well as insects. Nests in mid-spring, usually expropriating a woodpecker hole near water, with 4-6 small white eggs that hatch in 13-16 days. The young fledge 13-24 days later. Where possible, lines its nest with white chicken feathers!

Flies at 45 km/h. Winters along the coasts from California/Virginia south, often in huge flocks.

Bank swallow (hirondelle des sables)
Riparia riparia (swallow family)
Mid-May to mid-August

Fairly common, in colonies along vertical
silty/sandy river banks. Length 12 cm.

Brown on top and white below, most
easily identified by a brown bar across
the breast. Voice is quite nasal and
buzzy. Diet: flying insects taken in the
air.

This bird, the northern rough-winged swallow (next entry) and the kingfisher
are the only birds in the Canadian Rockies area that burrow. The large river
valleys of the Canadian Rockies are generally floored in glacial silt and loess
(very fine wind-blown sand; see page 236); river-cut banks or road-cuts in these
materials, complete with an overhanging root mat at the top, make fine sites for
bank-swallow colonies.

The holes are reoccupied year after year in late spring, usually with lots of
territorial squabbling upon arrival ("Number 32? Look; we don't *want* Number 32.
We *always* take Number 33!"). New burrows are dug by hacking with the bill and
kicking soil out with the feet. The burrows are 2-5 cm in diameter, widening
somewhat inside for the nest-mat (plant parts, wool and feathers), which may be
over a metre back. Rodent burrows that open when banks collapse are used as
well.

Breeding is in May; 4-5 small white eggs hatch in 12-16 days. As in other
swallow species, only the female sits on the eggs, but both parents feed the young.
Like other swallows, they don't live very long; no records over 8 years; 4 years on
average. Bank swallows fly to South America for the winter.

Northern rough-winged swallow
(hirondelle à ailes hérissées)
Stelgidopteryx serripennis
(swallow family) Mid-May to mid-August

Fairly common in southern and central
regions, swooping above lakes and
streams. Length 12 cm.

Rather similar to the bank swallow,
the other member of this genus.
Differentiate by the lack of a brown
breast-bar on the rough-winged. Named
for tiny hooks along the primary wing
feathers, which give the wing a rough
feel.

These birds sound rather like nighthawks (page 617), the call note a buzzy
"preet." Diet is like that of other swallows: insects scooped up by the wide mouth
while in flight.

Unlike bank swallows, rough-wings are seldom colonial. They nest mostly by
burrowing, like the bank swallow, but they also move into rock crevices,
drill-holes in dynamited road-cuts or the little pipes that drain bridges. Breeding
time: mid-spring. A pair produces 6-7 small white eggs (a lot for a swallow) that
hatch in 15-16 days. Young leave the nest 15-16 days later. Wintering is in Central
America and South America.

Black swift (martinet noir d'Amérique)
Cypseloides niger (swift family)
Early June to mid-October

Fairly common but rather reclusive and high-flying for such a small bird. Mostly eastern-slope; uncommon on the western slope. Length 18 cm, larger than any of our swallows. But otherwise rather swallow-like in design.

The body of a swift is short in comparison to the wingspan, and black, with a small bit of white on the face that doesn't show except at close range. Compare with Vaux's swift (next entry), which is common only in the far south end.

Swifts fly constantly all day. They take a few quick, fluttery wingbeats (once thought to be alternate, but since shown to be together), then glide. I often see them around dusk, cruising home in formation several hundred metres above the ground. Usually traveling in small flocks, they cover hundreds of kilometres daily, seeking the most delectable insect swarms.

Not deigning to perch in the usual way, swifts hang from some sort of edge—usually the edge of the nest, which is hidden away in a cool, drippy gorge, often near a waterfall. There is but one egg in a mossy cup; it is white and rather elongated. Black swifts are so secretive that little is known of their lives, but Geoff Holroyd, an Alberta ornithologist, has discovered that in the Canadian Rockies the birds breed in midsummer. The egg hatches in late July, and the young bird grows slowly (probably because it is fed only once or twice a day). It fledges 45 days later, meaning in early September—long after other birds have fledged.

Baby swifts can survive several days unattended by going into torpor. This can happen often, for swifts hate bad weather and the adults will fly long distances to reach sunny skies (and the ant caravans they relish), before returning to feed the children.

Like the swallows, black swifts head for Central America and South America in the fall. Flight speed is unknown, but these birds seem to fly more slowly than their speedster relatives.

Vaux's swift (martinet de l'Ouest)
Chaetura vauxi (swift family) August

Common in the western-slope portion of Glacier National Park, nesting in stands of cedar, but unreported in Waterton (which is not surprising, for Waterton is strictly eastern-slope). Occasionally seen elsewhere in the Canadian Rockies, in Columbian-forest areas.

Vaux's swift (pronounced "vox," not "voe") is small (length 11 cm), more easily confused with the swallows than with the black swift. It is dark, with a white throat and breast. The call is a squeaky "chip-chip."

In mid-spring a pair of Vaux's chooses a hollow tree or some other deep shaft-like structure—sometimes a chimney—and sticks a cup of twigs onto the inside with salivary glue as the chimney swifts do. In Asia this glue is boiled from swifts' nests, forming a protein-rich broth: the famous bird's-nest soup.

The eggs (4-7) take 18-20 days to hatch; the nestlings leave the nest at 20-21 days and cling to the wall beside it for a few days more before flying. Vaux's swift winters from Mexico to Panama.

Common nighthawk
(engoulevent commun)
Chordeiles minor (nightjar family)
Beginning of June to early October

Occasional in dry, partly forested places below treeline. Length 23 cm, wingspan 58 cm.

Usually active at dusk, cruising in pairs for bugs, these dark-colored birds are not easy to see. They look somewhat like large swallows or swifts: narrow-winged, with a diagnostic white bar across each wing about two-thirds of the way to the end. Males have a white tail band; females don't. Note also the pale throat and the enormous flat head.

An easy identification is by sound: nighthawks say "beer!" in a buzzy way.

Nighthawks are not hawks; the owls do any night-hawking that comes along. Nighthawks are members of the nightjar family, a group of nocturnal or twilight birds that includes nighthawks, whip-poor-wills and nightjars proper. These birds sit longwise on their perches instead of crosswise.

Nighthawks nest in late spring, laying the eggs right on the ground, sometimes on a gravelly roof. There are two eggs, whitish/greenish and heavily marked; they hatch in about 19 days and the young fly at 23 days. Wintering is in southern Mexico and South America.

WOODPECKERS

Common flicker (pic doré)
Colaptes auratus (woodpecker family)
Late March to mid-October

Common in the woods. Length 27 cm.

Our most common woodpecker, best identified on the wing by the barred brown back and white rump patch. Perches by clinging to a tree trunk. Note the spotted breast with black throat bar and black tail feathers. Beyond that, there are three different races, of which we have two: red-shafted and yellow-shafted. (The other race, limited to the southwestern USA and Baja California/northwestern Mexico, is called "gilded," with yellow-shafted-type underwings and red-shafted-type face).

Flicker races can often be differentiated in flight, for the red-shafted flicker (more common on the western slope) has pink underwings and the yellow-shafted flicker (more common on the eastern slope) has yellow underwings. The heads are also different: red-shafted has gray crown with red band across the nape and brown cheeks; yellow-shafted has a *brown* crown with no nape patch and *gray* cheeks, plus a red blob at the corner of the bill.

Now the kicker: the races interbreed, producing all sorts of odd combinations, which why birders now call them races instead of separate species. All races have one thing in common: they say "wick-wick-wick," and "kee-arr," the flicker calls, loud and ubiquitous in the forest.

Flickers may be woodpeckers, but they don't drum on trees (a way of calling) and they don't drill for bugs. They eat mainly ants, using their long, sticky tongues to reach into anthills and carpenter-ant galleries. Other foods: other insects.

Flickers nest in large cavities they hack out of either live or dead trees, the oval entrance about 7-10 cm across. Begun in mid-spring, this is a three-week effort, but, as is true for other woodpeckers, it is repeated every year—and often in the same tree. The resulting surplus of nesting holes provides chickadees and other small cavity-nesters with lodgings far larger and more solid than they could hope to produce themselves.

Flickers lay 6-8 white eggs on a nest-mat of wood chips; they hatch in 11-12 days. The young are fed regurgitated insects and fly away 22-26 days later. Lifespan to 12 years. Flight speed 40 km/h. The yellow-shafted race winters in the eastern USA; the red-shafteds like it west of the Mississippi; some overwinter in southern BC.

Pileated woodpecker (grand Pic)
Dryocopus pileatus (woodpecker family)
Year-round

Occasional in montane woods. Although many birders say "PILL-e-a-ted," the correct pronunciation is "PILE-e-a-ted."

This is a great big woodpecker (length 38 cm, the largest in the Canadian Rockies) but so shy that you rarely see it. Aside from the size, it is easily identified by the large crest, red on males and black on females. No other woodpecker is crested. Its voice is like that of the flicker, (page 617): "wick-wick-wick." The species also drums 3-5 seconds at a time.

Pileated woodpeckers eat carpenter ants (page 476), the big black ants that live in dead or dying trees, fallen logs and stumps. The bird drills deeply into the ant galleries and drags the bugs out with its long sticky tongue. It also chops out several large cavities that are used strictly for roosting. For this it prefers dead wood in big poplars and cottonwoods, 10-20 m up. A square or rectangular entrance 8-12 cm across (diagnostic for this species) leads into a cavity up to 60 cm deep and 20 cm wide.

Nesting is in a similar cavity in mid-spring. Three to five white eggs hatch in about 18 days; the young fledge 22-26 days later. Age record is 13 years. Non-migratory.

Hairy woodpecker (pic chevelu)
Picoides villosus (woodpecker family)
Year-round

Occasional in the woods, often in damp places. Length 20 cm.

A black-and-white woodpecker with a white back; male has a red spot on the back of the head. Very similar to the downy woodpecker (next entry). Differentiate by size: the downy is noticeably smaller, with a disproportionately smaller bill. Differentiate female hairy or downy from three-toed woodpeckers (this page) and female black-backeds (page 620) by the white backs of the hairy and downy. Voice: "pweet," "pweet." Drums in short bursts. Hairy woodpeckers eat mainly wood-boring beetle larvae, cutting into their galleries under the bark. Also takes ants, other insects on the ground, berries and sap at sapsucker wells (page 6203.

Breeds in early spring, whacking out a cavity in a dead trunk or limb on a live tree; rectangular entrance is about 4 cm across and 5 cm tall. Four eggs on a chip mat hatch in 11-12 days; the young can climb to the entrance for feeding after 17 more days (most woodpecker nestlings are fed at the entrance, all the little heads sticking out at once) and fly at 28-30 days. Maximum age 14 years. Flies 30 km/h; does not migrate.

Downy woodpecker (pic mineur)
Picoides pubescens (woodpecker family)
Year-round, but seen mainly from early
May to end of September

Occasional in willow thickets, aspen woods or on poplars. The smallest woodpecker: length only 15 cm.

Black and white; male has red nape. Nearly identical to hairy woodpecker (previous entry), but markedly smaller, especially the bill, and less wary. Female told from other black-and-white woodpeckers by the white back (others are black except for downy, which is smaller than female hairy). Voice: quick "weet"s, trailing off at the end. Drums in short bursts.

Diet is like that of hairy woodpecker. Picks out winter roosting cavity as well as nesting hole. Breeds in early-spring, drilling a cavity in dead wood; entrance hole is round, about 3 cm in diameter. Four or five small white eggs hatch in 12 days; the young leave the nest 20-22 days later but are fed by adults for another 2-3 weeks. Non-migratory, but seldom seen in the winter.

Three-toed woodpecker (pic à dos rayé)
Picoides tridactylus (woodpecker family)
Year-round

Fairly common in subalpine forest on the western slope and on the eastern slope from Jasper north; scarce on the eastern slope farther south. Seen most often in April and May. Length 20 cm.

Yet another black-and-white woodpecker, but the males are easily identified by the yellow crown—that is, if you haven't got a black-backed woodpecker (next entry), which also has a yellow crown. Females lack the yellow. In these cases, check the back. If it is barred black and white, then it's a three-toed woodpecker. ("Three-toed" because, sure enough, it has three toes. Other woodpeckers have four toes.)

Voice: a very short "pert." The three-toed also drums, the hits getting quicker as they trail off.

Unwary and easily watched, this bird eats mainly wood-boring beetle larvae and other under-bark bugs, sometimes sampling the cambium layer itself. Nests in mid-spring, excavating a cavity in a dead conifer. Four or five white eggs hatch in about two weeks; fledging date unknown.

Most woodpecker children will make sounds if you tap the tree holding the nest. In this species, they set up quite a row. Non-migratory.

Black-backed woodpecker (pic à dos noir)
Picoides arcticus (woodpecker family)
Year-round

Occasional on conifers. Uncommon on the eastern slope south of Jasper. Length 21 cm, a little bigger than the three-toed woodpecker (previous entry), which it closely resembles. Check the back: the black-backed is all black, while the three-toed is barred (birders say "laddered") black and white. Males are yellow crowned; females not. Voice: very short "pert," "pert," like that of the three-toed.

Most woodpeckers drill for their food, but the black-backed *peels the bark* instead, a subtle behavioral difference that gives the black-backed its own ecological niche.

Nesting (not reported from Banff or Jasper parks, but must occur in the region) is in mid-spring, the cavity in dead wood with an oval entrance 4 cm by 5 cm. Four white eggs hatch in about two weeks; fledging date unknown. Non-migratory.

Yellow-bellied sapsucker (pic maculé)
Sphyrapicus varius (woodpecker family)
Late April to late August

Common in aspen and poplar groves, but shy. Length 20 cm.

Yet another black-and-white woodpecker (male; females are brownish), but rather easily distinguished if you can see its tummy, which is buffy or yellowish rather than the usual white. There is a large white patch on the top surface of each wing, near the body, and a white patch on the rump.

The male has two red patches, one on the forehead and one on the throat. It says "keer," every now and again; doesn't have a drawn-out call like most other woodpeckers.

This bird drills in very short bursts, sometimes just a couple of taps at a time. It drums a lot, a few taps at first, then a roll, then a few disconnected ones at the end.

True to its name, the sapsucker does drink sap. It has a special brush on the end of its tongue for licking up the stuff. Also eats bugs that are attracted to the feeding holes, called "wells." Wells are easily recognized: small holes in rows across the trunk, usually in birches, aspens or poplars but also in conifers. Eastern foresters don't like the bird much; they say that it damages hardwoods. But in the west we don't have much commercial hardwood, so it's okay to like the sapsucker. With a name like this it needs friends!

Sapsuckers nest in mid-spring, drilling out a dead section in a live aspen or poplar; entrance hole round, 3-4 cm across. Five or six white eggs hatch in 12-13 days. The young leave 25-29 days later. Age record only six years. Unlike most woodpeckers, sapsuckers migrate, wintering from western Oregon south into Texas and Mexico, up into the midwest and the eastern USA.

Williamson's sapsucker
(pic de Williamson)
Sphyrapicus thyroideus
(woodpecker family)
Mid-May to late August

In montane pine forest, occasional in the southern Rocky Mountain Trench, reported from the eastern slope at Waterton and Glacier. Length 21 cm.

This bird is a little larger than the closely related yellow-bellied sapsucker. In fact, Williamson's is even brighter-yellow on the belly; this, and the lack of the red forehead mark on the Williamson's male, distinguish it from the yellow-bellied. The female is quite unlike the male: she has a brown head, black spot on the breast, but again a bright-yellow belly.

This species is normally silent but sometimes lets go with a scream like that of the red-tailed hawk (page 602), which must shake up the neighbors. It drums in very short bursts like the yellow-bellied sapsucker (above). Breeding is in late spring. The nest is in a dead conifer trunk; like the flicker, this species seeks the same tree each year but produces a new hole each time. Five or six white eggs are laid in late May; the incubation time is not known. The bird winters from Nevada and Arizona into Baja California and northern Mexico.

Lewis's woodpecker (pic de Lewis)
Melanerpes lewis (woodpecker family)
Mid-March to mid-June

Occasional in open or brushy areas of the foothills and southern Rocky Mountain Trench; sometimes seen in Banff National Park.

A large woodpecker (length 23 cm) that doesn't act like its relatives: it perches in trees rather than clinging to the bark. It also sits on fenceposts and catches flying bugs.

Readily identifiable by the red face and pink belly; the back is greenish black. Sexes are alike.

This bird makes little kissing noises rather than the usual flicker-like woodpecker cries, but it nests like a woodpecker: 6-7 eggs in late spring, in a cavity carved in dead wood. Incubation is 12-13 days; the young fledge at about 21 days.

RAVENS, CROWS AND OTHER MEMBERS OF THE CORVID FAMILY

Common raven (grand Corbeau)
Corvus corax (corvid family) Year-round

One of the more common birds in the
Canadian Rockies, found in nearly any
habitat but most often in montane
lodgepole-pine woods, in towns and at
very high elevations. Unwary and
approachable.

Large (length 53 cm; the largest
songbird) and completely black—likely to
be confused only with the American
crow (next entry). Differentiate by size
(ravens are usually larger), by the bill
(heavier in ravens), the tail (raven tail is
wedge-shaped across the back, or at least
quite rounded; crow tail is flat or
slightly rounded), the plumage (shaggier
on raven, especially on the neck), the
flight (crows flap steadily; ravens often
coast and soar) and lastly the time of
year (crows leave the mountains in
winter; ravens stay).

I have noticed something else that seems diagnostic: watch the bird walk. If it
moves its head briskly back and forth like a pigeon, then it is a crow; if it moves
its head only slightly back and forth (often from side to side), then it's a raven.

Skulking about, big and dark, ravens are the image of malevolence in
literature. They are not cute; not well liked. But I think they are the most
interesting birds in the mountains.

Ravens live everywhere and eat anything. Preferring to scavenge, they cluster
by the hundred at dumps and are quick to converge on a wolf kill.

Slow-moving but surprisingly agile, a raven will suddenly fold its wings and
make a twisting somersault in the air, dropping several metres before pulling out
of the stunt with a self-satisfied (?) "rawk." The bird uses the same maneuver as
defense against harrassing kestrels.

The ravens of Jasper townsite, which seem typical, spend most of the day in
ones or twos. They perch atop the street lights, keeping an eye out for anything
edible we humans may drop. The birds talk to one another from their posts, saying
"croak," "tock" and many other things. Sometimes one will bark like a dog, or make
little mewing sounds like a kitten. In the late afternoon they gather and flap off
together to one roost or another. ("Where'll we stay tonight? Out by Maligne
Canyon again?") They are terribly smart, as birds go, with a complex social
structure that somebody should spend 20 years studying.

Ravens mate for life. They breed in late winter, preferring a cliffside niche
when they can get one, otherwise nesting in a tree. Both sexes work on the nest,
carrying up substantial sticks and twigs to the site. Not just any stick or twig will
do: it must be old and bare of bark. A fair bit of the building material gets
chucked overboard. It doesn't seem to be clumsiness—it's pickiness.

The nest is lined with moss, grass and leaves, then with an inner layer of hair
(often bighorn wool). The eggs (4-6) are large, variously greenish or bluish and
often heavily scrawled with other pigments. For some unknown reason there is
frequently one egg in the nest that is plain blue. The nestlings hatch in 20-21 days,
are brownish/purplish/blackish and incredibly ugly. Fed regurgitated or piecemeal
foods, they leave the nest five or six weeks later, following the parents about and
begging piteously, even when grown nearly to full size. Age record: 24 years.
Flight speed: 65 km/h. Non-migratory.

American crow (corneille d'Amérique)
Corvus brachyrynchos (corvid family)
Mid-March to early November.

Very common birds at lower elevations,
in open areas and in the woods, usually
in small flocks. Length 43 cm.

Very similar to the common raven;
see previous entry for ways to
differentiate.

Not as talkative as ravens, crows caw
rather than croak; they eat most
anything, including the unattended eggs
and newly hatched young of other
species (as do most corvid-family birds).

Nesting is in early spring, the nest usually in a dead tree, although sometimes
on a utility pole and often near other crows' nests. A large cup of sticks is lined
with mud, grass, leaves and hair; 4-5 greenish/bluish, variably marked eggs hatch
in 18 days. The young leave the nest 35 days later. Age in captivity more than
20 years. Flight speed 50 km/h.

Crows are most common from early spring to late September; after that they
slip away south and west for the winter, some of them going no farther than the
Rocky Mountain Trench south of Golden.

Black-billed magpie (pie bavarde)
Pica pica (corvid family) Year-round

Locally common to occasional in small
family flocks in and around towns at
lower elevations; irregularly distributed
(some places have many; others have
none) and quite variable in population
from year to year. Length 45 cm.

For its size, the magpie has the
longest tail of any in the region (but see
also mourning dove, page 632). That, and
the bold black-and-white wing pattern,
make it easily identifiable.

Magpies say "hack-hack," and make soft mewing sounds; they fly very low,
often just above the ground, alternately flapping and gliding.

An Old World import that got out of hand, these birds are decorative but not
particularly welcome in North America; like other jays, they have a taste for
garbage, carrion, eggs and baby birds. They are noisy, too. Early in the morning,
on Sundays.

Magpies are highly social, living in small, carefully ordered flocks. They
breed in mid-spring, nesting in brushy places near water, often several life-mated
pairs in the same spot. The nest is a bulky igloo of sticks with one or two
entrances; a mud-lined cup within holds lots of eggs (usually 5-9, maximum of 12),
hatching in 17-18 days. The young leave the nest 22-28 days later. Age record
14 years. Flight speed 35 km/h. Non-migratory.

Clark's nutcracker
(casse-noix d'Amérique)
Nucifraga columbiana (corvid family)
Year-round, but mainly April to
November

Common in subalpine woods in southern
and central sections, less so farther
north. Especially common in upper
subalpine campgrounds and picnic sites.
Length 28 cm.

Clark's nutcracker has a gray body
with flashy black-and-white wings. The
beak is long and black, an easy way to
tell it from the gray jay (next entry), a
similar bird that lives in the same
habitat.

A folk name for Clark's nutcracker is "camp robber," which aptly describes its
behavior around people. Calling all day long in harsh, loud voices ("KRAW!"
"KRAW!") the birds fly from tree to tree, folding their wings between flaps. They
frequently drop to the ground or onto picnic tables looking for seeds, bugs, crumbs
or other goodies. They will also drop unexpectedly onto whatever is dangling at
the end of your fork.

Clark's favorite natural food in the Canadian Rockies area is the nut of the
whitebark pine. The long, strong bill is just the tool for ripping into cones and
extracting the seeds. It also uses the bill like a woodpecker does, getting into
rotten wood for beetle larvae and ants.

Like the gray jay, Clark's nutcracker hides its food, tucking it behind flakes
of bark, poking it among conifer fronds and sticking it into the ground. Recent
studies of this behavior have shown that the bird actually *remembers* where each
item is—and there can be thousands of items.

Nesting is often in April, when the subalpine forest is still deep in snow; the
mated-for-life pair builds a typical bulky jay-style nest of sticks on a stout
conifer branch. Two or three brown-speckled greenish eggs hatch in 16-18 days;
the young leave the nest 22 days later and follow the parents about, hounding
them mercilessly for food. This noisy begging is what accounts for the
dawn-to-dusk din in high-country campgrounds.

Supposedly non-migratory, the birds largely desert the main ranges in late
fall, moving to good pine-nut supplies in the southern foothills and southern
Rocky Mountain Trench. You seldom see them at Jasper or Banff between early
November and late April.

Gray jay (geai gris)
Perisoreus canadensis (corvid family)
Year-round

Common in the upper montane and
subalpine forest, gliding from tree to
tree. It shares that environment with its
look-alike, Clark's nutcracker. Both birds
go by the folk names "camp robber" and
"whiskey-jack." The latter is from the
Cree, "wiskatjon," anglicized to "whiskey
John" and thence to "jack." An older
birder's name for the gray jay was
"Canada jay."

Differentiate by the plumage (gray jay is smoky-colored, with lighter head and dark nape; Clark's is uniformly gray on the body, with black-and-white wings) and by the bill: fairly short on gray jay and quite long on Clark's nutcracker. Gray jay is slightly smaller (length 25 cm), stays in the mountains all winter, and is much more endearing. It arrives just as you are getting out the sandwiches, sitting atop your ski pole and waiting quietly to be offered some lunch. The patience lasts a couple of minutes, then it simply jumps on the sandwich and takes what it wants.

All fluffed up on a cold day, gray jays evince softness. They usually speak softly, too, saying "whee-ooo" from time to time. But underneath that gentle exterior lurks the rowdy soul of the jay tribe. It bursts out from time to time, when the birds squabble loudly, steal eggs, that sort of thing.

Perhaps you will be lucky enough to hear a gray jay sing. It sits atop a conifer and whistles, warbles, cheeps—an amazing production.

Gray jays eat most anything: seeds, bugs, carrion, unattended nestlings; they have been known to do in the odd mouse when it is in distress. They hoard food for the winter, coating it with sticky saliva and pasting it to conifer branches, making large stores in unused woodpecker nesting cavities and remembering where everything is stashed.

Breeding is in late winter. The life-mated pair builds a warmly lined cup nest in a conifer, producing 3-4 brown-spotted greenish/grayish eggs that hatch in about 15 days. The young leave the nest a couple of weeks later, begging from the parents for two or three weeks more.

When you see one gray jay you will usually see three, which would appear to be either the young birds staying together until they mate or perhaps the parents and one offspring. Maximum recorded age 10 years. Non-migratory, although bad winters will send gray jays to better foraging grounds at lower elevations.

Steller's jay (geai de Steller)
Cyanocitta stelleri (corvid family)
Year-round, but mostly from beginning
of October to end of April

Fairly common in coniferous woods on the western slope and south of Crowsnest Pass on the eastern slope, occasional elsewhere. Length 28 cm.

The only crested jay you are likely to see in the Rockies. **Blue jay** (geai bleu; *Cyanocitta cristata*) is rare. Steller's is mostly dark, shiny blue, with a smoky black crest, head and upper back; it has frosty-looking eyebrows and other small white markings on the forehead and throat. Blue jay is much lighter, with white breast and face, blue crest and white wing bars.

The call of Steller's jay is easy to recognize: a loud "shack," "shack," "shack," rather like that of the magpie (page 623).

Habits and life history of Steller's jay are much like those of other jays, but it has a specialty: imitating the calls of red-tailed hawks and thus scaring other birds. There must be a reason for this; perhaps it causes other birds to drop their food and fly to safety—whereupon the jay makes off with the loot.

Diet: mostly pine seeds, fruits and bugs. Rather shy, for a jay; not a camp-robber. Nesting is in early spring, the mud-lined cup of sticks holding four bluish/greenish eggs that hatch in about 16 days. Fledging date not known, but the young follow their parents around for several weeks after. Maximum recorded age seven years. Non-migratory, but seen more in the winter months, when it comes down from the high country and into towns.

Corvid (crow and jay) family   625

HUMMINGBIRDS

Rufous hummingbird (colibri roux)
Selasphorus rufus (hummingbird family)
Mid-May to end of August

Common in nearly any habitat with
wildflowers, above or below treeline;
often seen flying from a dead snag in or
beside a pond. Length 9 cm.

The problem in identifying
hummingbirds is that they don't sit still
for very long. However, there are only
two species in the Canadian Rockies. The
rufous male is easy to identify: he is the
reddish one. This is the most northerly
hummingbird species on the continent; it
reaches the southern Yukon.

Much of the body is red, especially the brilliant **gorget** (pronounced
"GOR-jet"): a scarf-like patch of shiny feathers around the neck of many
hummingbird species, sometimes covering the head as well. Female rufous is green
on the back and mostly white underneath, much like the calliope hummingbird
(next entry). Differentiate by size (rufous is much larger, if anything this small
can be called large) and by the red tint on the tail and abdomen of the rufous.

Rufous males make short buzzing sounds, with voice as well as with wings.
They put on a wonderful courtship display: vertical loops in the air, sometimes
over and over, each loop 5-10 m in diameter.

Hummingbirds have the fastest metabolisms in the bird world; they need a lot
of sugar, which they get from flower nectar, the bulk of their diet. They feed by
sticking their long, brush-tipped tongues out the ends of their needle-like bills and
lapping away. Protein comes from tiny bugs picked off the flowers. The birds eat
constantly, carrying extra food in their crops to live through the night; if they run
out of gas, which happens during bad weather, hummingbirds become dormant for
a day or two and thus survive. Rolling their shoulder joints back and forth
enables them to hover; even to fly backward. No other group of birds does this.

Rufous hummers are strongly attracted to red flowers—paintbrush,
penstemons, columbine—or anything else that is red. A friend who was trying out
a new red sleeping bag in a flowery alpine meadow was beset by hummingbirds
trying to get in with him. ("Wow! If this thing is fulla juice, my summer's made!")

The rufous breeds in late spring, the tiny nest low down in a conifer or shrub,
made of plant down wrapped up in spiderwebs and camouflaged with lichens.
There are two itsy-bitsy white eggs, incubation period unknown; the young birds
fledge about 20 days after hatching. Flight speed of hummingbirds can reach
80 km/h. The rufous winters in Mexico.

Calliope hummingbird
(colibri de Calliope)
Stellula calliope (hummingbird family)
Late May to end of August

Fairly common in any flowery habitat.
Length only 7 cm, the smallest bird in
North America (the bee hummingbird of
Cuba is about 20 percent smaller, the
smallest bird in the world).

Emerald green on top and white
below, the male calliope has a streaky
reddish-purple gorget (see previous
entry).

Females are similar but lack the gorget. They have green-freckled throats. Voice: a loud, long "see-ree" when doing the display flight, which is a series of climbs and dives. One hears this often in the mountains, sometimes without seeing the tiny bird that makes it. It zooms from flower to flower, drinking nectar and nabbing small bugs in the blooms.

This hummingbird, like its relatives, is outrageously aggressive for its size, chasing much larger birds away from its nesting site or food.

Feeding and breeding habits are like that of the rufous hummingbird. Incubation time is 15 days, fledging date 21-23 days after hatching. Wintering: Mexico.

ROBINS AND THEIR RELATIVES

American robin (merle d'Amérique)
Turdus migratorius
(thrush/kinglet family)
End of March to end of October
(but see below)

Common in any wooded habitat. Length 22 cm.

The best-known bird in North America lives here, out on the lawn, but also way up at timberline, nesting in the krummholz (dense stands of dwarf fir and spruce). Easily identified by the gray back and wings against the orangey breast. Females are a little paler on the head but otherwise similar.

Robins make a familiar burbly cheeping that is not easily imitated; it goes something like "cheer-ee-er-i-lee." They also utter a sharp alarm call and make other sounds that don't seem robin-like at all. Robins spend a lot of time on the ground, intent on worms, grubs and bugs.

Does the red, red robin go bob-bob-bobbing along, as in the popular song? No; the bird runs a few steps, then stops suddenly and holds stock-still for a moment, head turned to the side. Studies show that it is not really listening, as commonly supposed; it's looking down at the ground for food. Because their eyes are on the sides of their heads, robins must turn their heads sideways to do this.

Nesting is in early spring, usually in a conifer; four light-blue eggs in a cup made of mud and grass hatch in 11-14 days; the young fledge about two weeks later. Age record 17 years. Flight speed 60 km/h. Robins winter not far south of the Canadian Rockies, through much of the USA. South of Crowsnest Pass they arrive a month earlier and leave up to two months later than they do farther north. Sometimes they stay all winter in the southern Rocky Mountain Trench.

Varied thrush (merle à collier)
Ixoreus naevius (thrush/kinglet family)
Mid-March to mid-November

Common in spruce forests (very common in the Columbian forest of the western slope), but secretive. Seen most often from early April through August. Length 20 cm.

Robin-like in size and shape, the varied thrush is decked out for Halloween: black and orange. The orange eye-stripe and black bar across the breast are good field marks.

But one seldom sees the bird. Rather, one hears it. The song is weird: a long note, followed a moment later by another, a little higher pitched, then a third, again higher pitched. The notes are buzzy. This unique song readily identifies the bird. People who can whistle while humming can imitate it.

Like its relatives, the varied thrush scuttles about the forest floor eating insects and worms. It breeds in early spring, nesting low in a conifer, and is extremely secretive at this time; there are three light-blue eggs, but the hatching and fledging times are not known. Winter range: west coast from Prince Rupert south to the Mexican border.

Swainson's thrush (grive à dos olive)
Catharus ustulatus
(thrush/kinglet family)
Beginning of May to mid-September

Very common in coniferous woods, heard for about a half-hour at dawn and dusk. Length 16 cm.

Secretive and thus infrequently seen, Swainson's is built like a robin (a little smaller), with a dark olive-brown back. But the front is buffy and spotted/streaked with black—very much like the hermit thrush (next entry). Differentiate by the reddish-brown tail and rump of the hermit thrush. See also northern waterthrush, page 642.

Swainson's has a beautiful, flute-like song, clear and liquid, rising up the scale in a series of warbling jumps. Once heard, easily recalled. The birds also say "whit."

Swainson's feeds in the trees rather than on the ground, eating beetles, ants, caterpillars and flies; it also likes berries. The species breeds in mid-spring, laying 3-4 brown-speckled light-blue eggs in a cup-like nest made of plant matter and mud. The nest is low but well hidden 1-2 m up in a conifer. Hatching is at 10-13 days; fledging 10-12 days later. Winter range is from southern Mexico to Argentina.

Hermit thrush (grive solitaire)
Catharus guttatus (thrush/kinglet family)
Early May to end of September

Common in coniferous forest, but secretive. Length 15 cm.

Looks very much like Swainson's thrush (previous entry) but the tail and rump are rusty or cinnamon-brown rather than dark olive. The bird raises its tail often, something the other thrushes don't do. The song is robin-like, preceded by a single note.

Hermit thrushes pick for bugs, worms, fruits and berries on the ground, and usually under concealing shrubbery. But they often fly up into the lower branches of aspens to sing.

Nesting is in mid-spring, in a well-hidden cup on the ground; 3-4 light blue eggs hatch in 12-13 days. The young leave the nest 10 days later. Lifespan at least 7 years. Wintering is along the west coast from Vancouver south to Guatemala, across the Gulf states and up the east coast to Boston.

Veery (grive fauve)
Catharus fuscescens
(thrush/kinglet family)
Mid-May to early-September

Occasional in deciduous groves, southern area; rare farther north. Length 15 cm.

The veery closely resembles the hermit thrush (previous entry), but is brown or rusty all over rather than just on the rump and tail. And the veery is uncommon in the mountains. It says "veet—veer, veer, veer" and spends most of its time on the ground in pursuit of creepy-crawly food.

The species nests on the ground too, mostly farther east of us, but occasionally in the mountains. Goes to Central America and Brazil for the winter.

Townsend's solitaire
(solitaire de Townsend)
Myadestes townsendi
(thrush/kinglet family)
Mid-April to end of September

Common in open subalpine forest, usually sitting atop a conifer; seen at much lower elevations in spring. Length 17 cm.

Drab-colored, but still rather easily identified by the long tail outlined on each side by a white feather. There is also a white eye-ring and some thin white barring on the wings, which have a bit of burnt-orange in them. Song is loud, beautiful, burbly and robin-like, but much longer, a little higher-pitched and crisper. Also makes a soft "peet."

Townsend's acts like a flycatcher (page 634), leaping nimbly off its tree-top perch to grab buzzing things out of the air. Also eats insects in trees and descends for fruits, berries and worms. But it nests like a thrush, on the ground, often among rocks or at the base of a big spruce or subalpine fir, where there are often natural cavities in the soil around the roots. You may find them nesting in road cuts, too.

Breeding time: late spring. There are four white/pinkish/bluish eggs, heavily marked in darker colors. The incubation time is not known; neither is there any information about the nestlings or fledging date. Slow flyer: 30 km/h.

Townsend's solitaire winters just south and west of us, in the western mountains of the USA and in the southwestern corner of BC. The bird is occasionally seen as late as Christmas in southern Alberta, and sometimes year-round in the southern Rocky Mountain Trench.

A BLUEBIRD, WAS IT?

Mountain bluebird
(merle bleu des montagnes)
Sialia currucoides
(thrush/kinglet family)
Mid-March to mid-October

Fairly common in the eastern front
ranges, in dry, open montane areas;
occasional farther west and at higher
elevations. Length 15 cm.

This is the bluest bird found in the
Canadian Rockies. Of the other two
birds that are blue, Steller's jay
(page 625) is readily distinguished by its
black, conspicuously crested head; the
lazuli bunting (next entry) is smaller and
has an orangey breast.

The mountain bluebird is robin-like in shape, part of the same family. The
male is quite blue on top, grayish beneath with a white belly. Females are mostly
gray-brown, with blue in the wings and tail, and on the rump. Song is varied, with
soft cheeps and trills.

Mountain bluebirds are bug eaters, zooming from a low perch, gobbling, then
flying back. Sometimes they hover. The birds nest in old woodpecker holes and
other tree cavities, sometimes in borrowed bank-swallow lodgings, rodent burrows
or rock crevices. They will move into bird boxes placed in open places for them.
Breeding is in mid-spring, 5-6 pale blue eggs hatching in 13-14 days, but the
fledging date is unknown. Flies at only 30 km/h. Winter range: Vancouver area,
down the coast to California, then a broad area encompassing most of western
USA and northern Mexico.

Lazuli bunting (bruant azuré)
Passerina amoena (finch family)
June to August

Fairly common in the foothills from Bow
River south (occasional north to Jasper)
and in the southern Rocky Mountain
Trench, in aspen groves and deciduous
shrubbery; occasional in Kootenay
National Park. Length 11 cm.

Likely to be confused only with the
mountain bluebird (previous entry), the
lazuli bunting is smaller, has an
orange-and-white breast, white wing bars
and a heavier beak.

It eats mainly insects and seeds, the
male flying up into aspens to sing his
varied cheepy song. Breeding is in June;
the nest is in low shrubbery, with three
pale blue or greenish eggs that hatch in
12 days. The young birds fledge at
10-15 days and are attended for a few
days longer by the male. Winter range:
American southwest and Mexico.

See also the kingfisher, page 598.

FAMILIAR FEATHERED FRIENDS (SOMETIMES ENEMIES)

See also the house sparrow, page 654

European starling (étourneau sansonnet)
Sturnus vulgaris (starling family)
Present year-round from Jasper south; a
summer resident farther north

Common around towns, in flocks. Length
15 cm. Starling plumage changes with the
season. The birds are dark brown all
summer (in good light one can see
purplish/greenish iridescence on head
and breast), identifiable by the rather
long yellow beak, short tail and constant
squeaky chatter. In winter they become
spotted, especially on the breast and
head; the beak becomes black. And the
young birds, newly fledged, look
different again: brown above, gray
below, with black bills.

   Starlings have done all too well in North America since 100 of them were
released in New York City in 1890; they have pushed native species out of their
habitats. In the Canadian Rockies the flocks are currently small (usually a few
dozen birds) and the species is not a problem, but elsewhere they eat up crops and
spread disease around their communal roosts.

   Starlings are sociable and thus quite interesting to watch. Their tinkly,
whistling calls are varied; they imitate other bird calls, too. When alarmed they
say "veer!"

   Diet: insects, fruits and seeds, taken mostly on the ground. Starlings nest in all
kinds of cavities (woodpecker holes, hollow trees, rock crevices, attics, birdhouses),
beginning in early spring. Five to seven white, light-blue or greenish eggs hatch in
12-15 days; the young fledge 20-22 days later and beg food from the parents for
several weeks more. Long-lived for a songbird: 20 years. Speedy, too: 90 km/h
reported. Northern Rockies birds may move into central and southern areas for
the winter.

Rock dove (pigeon biset)
Columba livia (dove family) Year-round

Fairly common in small flocks around
towns, farms and ranches, although
scarce in the south end of the Canadian
Rockies. Length 28 cm. This is an
introduced species, formerly called
"domestic pigeon."

   Most rock doves in the Canadian
Rockies are the wild form: mostly gray
with black banding, a white rump patch
and purplish/greenish iridescent feathers
on the throat. However, mating with
domesticated showy breeds produces
birds with wildly varying plumage: white
to brown, red or black, variously mottled
and streaked.

   Rock doves coo, usually in a series that starts low, gets higher, and ends low.
At the same time they often turn round and round. When a rock dove takes off, its
wingtips hit noisily together and whistle; when the bird glides, the wings are held
in a vee.

Doves and pigeons pick about on the ground for seeds and fruits; as they walk, their heads snap back and forth. The eyes of birds that do this cannot fix an image while the head moves; the odd head motion allows these species to walk and see at the same time.

This species nests in groups, preferring holes in buildings to natural sites in cliff crevices. They can breed almost any time from early spring to the end of summer, sometimes producing two broods in a summer if they start the first one early enough. Two white eggs are laid in a minimal nest of twigs or roots (or, in towns, sometimes bits of wire); they hatch in 17-19 days and fledge 30-35 days later—rather late in comparison to other songbirds.

The young are fed in their first few days on **pigeon milk**: thick mucus secreted in the adult's crop. Rock doves are long-lived: 16 years for sure, possibly as long as 32 years. They are quite fast on the wing: up to 150 km/h. Non-migratory.

Mourning dove (tourterelle triste)
Zenaida macroura (dove family)
Mid-April to end of August

In open areas at low elevations, fairly common in Glacier, scarce farther north (seen a few times each summer in Jasper park); often in pairs. Length 27 cm, about half of which is tail—like the magpie (page 623).

Mourning doves are rather plain birds, light brown above, paler below, with sooty gray wings that are spotted in black. A close look reveals pink iridescence behind the neck, a black patch low on the head, and blue rings around the eyes.

The song of the mourning dove is a very soft and, yes, rather mournful "coo, coo, coo-WOO-oo." The birds are hunted in the USA, but protected in Alberta and British Columbia.

Mourning doves live almost entirely on seeds, feasting in foothills grain fields. They breed in early spring, sometimes raising two broods a year. Nest is a rough platform in a tree or tall shrub; it is built by the female from twigs supplied by the male. There are only two eggs, which are white; they hatch in 14-15 days and the young fledge 13-15 days later. Age record 17 years; speed record 90 km/h.

The species is non-migratory throughout much of the USA, but our birds move south onto the central great plains or west to the Pacific states for the winter.

Familiar perching birds

WAXWINGS

Bohemian waxwing (jaseur de Bohême)
Bombycilla garrulus (waxwing family)
Year-round, most common late August
through April

Common in fall, in flocks (sometimes
quite large flocks) at low elevations,
especially around towns. Length 16 cm.

Sleek-looking crested birds, mostly
buffy gray, with a distinctive yellow
terminal band on the tail, black mask
and a small but brilliant red spot on
each wing. The spot looks and feels like
wax; no one knows what it's for.

Differentiate from similar cedar waxwing (next entry) by the Bohemian's
larger size, white markings on the wings, lack of yellow on the breast and rusty
coloring under the tail. Both species talk constantly; Bohemians say "zirrr,"
high-pitched and twittery.

Waxwings are insect-eaters and berry-gobblers, with a particular craving for
the fruit of the mountain ash (page 316). After a summer of secretive nesting in
the forest, when you rarely see them, the birds congregate by the hundreds in late
September, when the red mountain-ash berries are ripe. This tree is frequently
planted in yards, so the flocks hit the towns.

Some 2000 (yes, two thousand) waxwings settled on my neighbor's rowan tree
in 1982, stripping all the berries in a couple of hours. The birds would wolf down
six or seven berries, then fly off and circle back for another round, pooping red
rowan bits all over the place and sometimes flying into my windows. When no
berries were left on the tree, the birds swarmed over the ground, picking up
dropped ones. My twelve-year-old boy walked out among them; they scuttled over
his shoes and perched on his head and shoulders, calling constantly in their
whispery voices.

But the annual pig-out soon ends for these birds. As winter drags on, the
berries get scarce and the flocks of waxwings shrink and shrink. Many birds head
east onto the prairies, where big flocks arrive in Edmonton in January. By spring
their numbers around Jasper are perhaps only a quarter of what they were in the
fall.

Waxwings breed in late spring, laying five sparsely spotted bluish eggs in a
cup-shaped nest in a conifer or birch. Very fond of string and hair for nest-lining,
waxwings will pick at clothes hanging out to dry and steal strings from a mop left
outside. Hatching is at 13-14 days, fledging 15-17 days later. Their winter flights
to better sources of berries are not true migrations.

Cedar waxwing (jaseur de cèdres)
Bombycilla cedrorum (waxwing family)
Beginning of June to end of September

Fairly common in the southern section;
less so farther north. Length 15 cm, a
little smaller but otherwise very similar
to the Bohemian waxwing (previous
entry).

To differentiate, note how little
white there is in the cedar's wings. But
under the tail it is white, not rusty
brown like the Bohemian, and the lower
breast of the cedar waxwing is yellowish.
Voices are similar: high, thin whistles,

trills and soft notes. "Waxwing" refers to the small spot of red on the wing, like a bit of sealing wax.

Cedar waxwings have much the same life cycle as Bohemians, but we see them only in the summer rather than year-round and never in great numbers. They winter not far south of the Canadian Rockies, through most of the USA and into Mexico.

LITTLE GRAY BIRDS (LGBs): THE FLYCATCHERS AND VIREOS

These are tough to identify. Bring your best binoculars and somebody who knows what he is doing.

Eastern kingbird (tyran tritri)
Tyrannus tyrannus (flycatcher family)
Early May to late September

Common in open places, often at ponds, perched on a snag. Length 17 cm.

Here is one of the few flycatchers that is easy to identify: black-and-white, with a white band at the end of the tail (no other perching bird has this). The Latin name says it all: *T. tyrannus* is *fierce*. A pair of kingbirds will chase much larger birds away from their territory.

Kingbirds sit on a tree top or snag with a good view, flying off after bugs and intruders. At dawn the species gives a raspy call frequently and loudly; the song proper is chittery and more subdued. Breeding is in late spring, the nest often out on a rather low branch over water. Three or four scrawled-up white or pinkish eggs hatch in 12-13 days; the nestlings fledge a couple of weeks later, but they beg food from the parents for another month. Flight speed 35 km/h. Wintering: South America.

Least flycatcher (moucherolle tchébec)
Empidonax minimus (flycatcher family)
Mid-May to mid-September

Usually in aspen groves. Common on the eastern slope from Banff north; uncommon on the western slope, rare at Waterton/Glacier.

A small flycatcher (length 11 cm), but typical: mostly olive-gray, with darker wings that have two white wingbars. Belly is lighter. Head large and slightly crested; there is a light eye-ring.

As with other flycatchers, the best identifier is the song: a quick, rather high-pitched "che-BECK," just like the French common name, repeated often and accompanied by a sneeze-like twitch.

Least flycatchers actively flit among deciduous trees, eating flying insects and caterpillars. They are quite aggressive, chasing other small birds away. Breeding is in late spring. The nest is typical for this genus: compact and deep, made of shredded bark and other fibrous plant matter, lined with grass, hair, and feathers. Spider webs and cocoons add strength. Four creamy eggs hatch in 14-16 days; the young leave two weeks later. Lifespan 5 years. Winter range: Mexico, Central America.

Hammond's flycatcher and dusky flycatcher

(moucherolle de Hammond;
moucherolle sombre)
Empidonax hammondii
and *E. oberholseri*
(flycatcher family)
Mid-May to mid-August.

See least flycatcher (previous page) for picture

Hammond's in mature coniferous forest; dusky in dry open woods or shrubbery at lower elevations. Length 11-12 cm. Both species small, very much like least flycatcher (previous entry), but with yellow-tinged bellies.

Hammond's and the dusky flycatcher are nearly identical, but Hammond's is the only flycatcher found at subalpine elevations. It is fairly common; says "pee-WIT, cha-lirp." Dusky flycatcher stays at lower elevations, where it's occasional in the montane woods; says the same thing but the second part is higher-pitched.

Both species perch on the upper branches of a conifer and fly out after bugs. They also chase other small birds away. Breeding: dusky in late spring, Hammond's in early summer. Three or four creamy eggs are laid in a nest like least flycatcher's, usually in a conifer (well up for Hammond's; 2-3 m up for dusky). Hatching is at 12-15 days; fledging is 17-18 days later. Young birds are fed by the parents for another 20 days. Winter range: Mexico, Central America.

Willow flycatcher and alder flycatcher

(moucherolle des saules,
moucherolle des aulnes)
Empidonax trailli and *E. alnorum*
(flycatcher family)
Mid-May to mid-August

Common in brushy places and willow marshes. Alder flycatcher is more common from Jasper north; willow is more common from Banff south, always at montane elevations. Length of both 12 cm.

Another case of nearly identical flycatchers. The two species were formerly one, known as "Traill's flycatcher," but they are now separated because the songs and breeding habits are different.

Identification: small birds with large pointed heads, mostly olive-gray but greenish/yellowish on the breast with darker wings and yellowish wingbars. This combination, plus a white throat, helps to differentiate from other flycatchers. Mainly, though, go by the voices: willow flycatcher says "fitz-bew"; alder flycatcher says "fee-BEE-o." If the bird isn't singing, it is proper to call it Traill's.

These birds stay in the shrubbery, hopping about and grabbing bugs. They nest in late spring, 3-4 white eggs (tiny brown speckles on one end) in a neat nest among dense foliage. Hatching is at 13-15 days, fledging 12-15 days later. Lifespan of alder flycatcher is at least 7 years. Wintering is from Mexico south to Argentina.

Western flycatcher
(moucherolle du Pacifique)
Empidonax difficilis (flycatcher family)
Beginning of June to end of July

Occasional in mixed-wood stands and along rivers; habituates canyons. Length 13 cm.

Typical flycatcher layout: large, pointy head; olive-gray body with black wings and white wingbars, distinguished from the rest by the yellow throat. Lower half of bill is also quite yellow, and the yellowish belly, which it has in common with several other species in the Canadian Rockies, is bright. Voice is squeaky, higher-pitched than other flycatchers; the bird says "pretty-pretty-pretty."

The western flycatcher flits about, bug-hunting in the shade of large trees. Probably breeds on the western slope, in mid-spring, the nest in a tree-hole or rock crevice; four brown-marked creamy eggs hatch in 14-15 days. Fledging is at 14-18 days. The birds winter from Baja California to Honduras.

Western wood-peewee (pioui de l'Ouest)
Contopus sordidulus (flycatcher family)
Mid-May to mid-August

Fairly common in damp montane woods and wetlands. Length 13 cm.

Yet another nondescript flycatcher, although not of the genus *Empidonax*. The difference is very small, but it is one you can often see clearly: there is no eye-ring. Song is whistling and nasal, with a loud "cheee" call on the end.

The bird often perches at the edge of a clearing, flying out after bugs and returning to a different branch. Nesting is in late spring, the nest of plant matter placed midway up a conifer and wrapped with spider webs. Three cream or pale-yellow brown-spotted eggs hatch in 12-13 days. Young birds fledge 15-18 days later. Lifespan 6-7 years. Winter range: Panama to Bolivia.

Olive-sided flycatcher
(moucherolle à côtés olive)
Contopus borealis (flycatcher family)
Late May to mid-August

Common in open coniferous woods, near water. Often seen at timberline and in burned places. Length 16 cm, large for a flycatcher.

Typical flycatcher shape and olive-gray plumage, but with two good identifiers: dark, vest-like coloring alongside the lighter breast and small white tufts on the back, visible in flight and tending to overlap the wings at rest. The song is distinctive, too: olive-sided flycatchers say "quick, THREE beer!" (beers in the USA, of course) and "pip-pip-pip." They sit high up in a conifer, darting after flying insects and returning.

Nesting is in late spring, three creamy or pinkish, brown-spotted eggs in a nest made mostly of greenish *Usnea* tree lichens (page 435). Incubation: 16-17 days; fledging: 15-19 days. Wintering: South America.

Warbling vireo (viréo mélodieux)
Vireo gilvus (vireo family)
Beginning of April to end of August

Very common in aspen and poplar groves, in wetlands, sometimes among pines and Douglas-firs. Length 12 cm.

    An LGB with a vague white eye-stripe and a slightly hooked bill, no wingbars. Go by the song, heard in the same spot for a long time: "bring it here, bring it here, bring it." Calls "kwee," rising and harsh. Stays high in the trees, eating caterpillars, insect eggs and bugs that live on branches and leaves. Breeds in mid-spring, the deep nest slung in the fork of a branch high up. Four sparsely speckled white eggs hatch in 12 days; the young fledge about 12-14 days later. Lifespan 10 years. Winter range: central Mexico and Central America.

Red-eyed vireo (viréo aux yeux rouges)
Vireo olivaceous (vireo family)
Mid-May to end of August

Fairly common in deciduous groves. Length 13 cm.

    Brown on top with a gray crown, white underneath; best field marks are the red eye (the only obviously red-eyed perching bird in the Canadian Rockies) and the white eye-stripe bordered by thin black lines.

    This bird sings a great deal, the song warbling and robin-like at times. It carries on all day, all summer, continuing after the nesting season is over; it even sings at night. Eats mostly caterpillars and sleeping moths on tree branches and leaves; will occasionally take flying insects, including bees and wasps. Also likes berries. Breeds in late spring; four finely speckled white eggs in a deep cup hanging in a fork 2-3 m up a deciduous tree. Incubation: 11-14 days; fledging: 12 days. Lifespan 12 years. Winters in the Amazon basin of South America.

Solitary vireo (viréo à tête bleue)
Vireo solitarius (vireo family)
Early May to mid-September

Common in deciduous stands and in pine/Douglas-fir woods. Length 12 cm.

    An LGB that closely resembles the warbling vireo (top of page) but with white wingbars and a white line running from bill to front of eye. This is the Rocky Mountain version; farther east the same species has a yellow vest and olive back. You may see in-betweens along the foothills.

    Like the other vireos, this one sings beautifully, usually in two-note or three-note phrases that rise and fall. It patrols the treetops for caterpillars, moths and walking/crawling insects, also eating some flying types.

Breeds in mid-spring, a typical vireo hanging cup built low in a deciduous or coniferous tree. Very reclusive, this bird stays on the nest when approached. One can usually come right up to it, even touch it, pick it up and peek at the eggs. (But disturbing any nesting bird to this extent seems unfair.) Four speckled white eggs hatch in about 11-12 days; fledging date unknown. Winters from Arizona through the American south and Mexico, to Nicaragua and Cuba.

LITTLE YELLOW BIRDS: THE WARBLERS

Yellow warbler (fauvette jaune)
Dendroica petechia
(American wood-warbler family)
Late August to late September

Common in mixed woods and marshes, in the shrubbery. Length 10 cm.

This is the only North American bird that is essentially yellow all over. It's a bit greenish on top, and the breast of the male is streaked with cinnamon. Female is paler yellow on the breast and a little grayer all over. Voice is rather high-pitched, the song a series of regular cheeps at the start and quick warbled ones later.

Yellow warblers go mainly for caterpillars and other insect larvae that live on shrubs and trees. The birds are not very shy and tend to stay in one place for a minute or two, which makes them fairly easy to see.

Breeding is in mid-spring, the urn-like nest usually low in a shrub fork. Four or five white/greenish/bluish eggs, brown/olive-speckled on one end, hatch in 11 days. Fledging is only 9-12 days later (warblers are altricial, but grow quickly) and the birds live 5-7 years. Winter range: Mexico, Central America, Peru and Brazil.

Wilson's warbler
(fauvette à calotte noire)
Wilsonia pusilla (wood-warbler family)
Early May to late September

Common on avalanche slopes, in willow marshes and scrubby coniferous growth. Length 11 cm.

Nearly all-yellow, but with a black cap. Breast is pure yellow; compare with yellow warbler (previous entry). Olive on the back; wings are dark and without wingbars. Song: a short series of quick cheeps, rather like a chipping sparrow (page 656), but cheepier and rising/falling in pitch.

Wilson's warbler feeds low in the shrubbery, catching both flying and walking/crawling insects. Twitches its tail as it hunts. Breeds in mid-spring, nesting on the ground, usually in dense shrubbery or hidden in a tall grass tussock. Five white, finely brown-speckled eggs hatch in 11-13 days; fledging is 10-11 days later. Winter range: Mexico, western Gulf coast south to Panama.

Common yellowthroat (fauvette masquée)
Geothlypis trichas (wood-warbler family)
Late April to end of September

Very common in wetlands, in the bushes;
the only warbler known to frequent
cattails. Length 11 cm.

Easily identified: a little yellow bird
with a raccoon-like black mask. Back,
wings, tail and top of head are olive.
Song is also easy to recognize: loud
"witchity, witchity, witchity"; also calls
"chat," "chat."

Yellowthroats flit and hop through shrubbery, usually near the ground. They
catch mostly flying insects (small dragonflies and grasshoppers are favorites) as
well as insects and larvae on leaves.

Breeding is in mid-spring. The cup nest, low in a dense shrub, is sometimes
built up along one side of the rim, hood-like. Four brown-speckled white eggs
hatch in 12 days; fledging is 9-10 days later. Lifespan: 7 years. Wintering: west,
east and Gulf coasts from California/New York south through Mexico to Panama
and the West Indies.

MacGillivray's warbler
(fauvette des buissons)
Oporornis tolmiei (wood-warbler family)
Mid-May to late September

Common in dense brushy places, often in
wetlands and along streams; also in aspen
groves, avalanche slopes and logged
places. Length 12 cm.

An odd-looking warbler: yellow body
(olive on the back) with a gray head.
Note also the white eye-ring broken by
black eye-line. Says "ta-weet, ta-weet,
ta-weet" and then "peachy peachy
peachy," or some other trill. Stalks
elusively about in the shrubbery, getting
beetles and caterpillars. Nests in
mid-spring, low in a thicket; four
brown-marked white eggs hatch in
11 days. The young fledge 8-9 days later.
Winters from central Mexico to Panama.

Townsend's warbler
(fauvette de Townsend)
Dendroica townsendi
(wood-warbler family)
Early May to end of August

Very common in tall coniferous forest, but usually up high and thus difficult to
see. Length 11 cm.

Yellow and black on the head, back and breast; black wings with white wing
patches, white belly. Voice: high and wheezy, in a variety of cheeps and trills.

Townsend's warbler sticks to the woods, picking bugs off spruce and subalpine
firs. It breeds in late spring, nesting high in a conifer (but sometimes only 2-3 m
up); lines the nest with moss spore-cases and hair. Three to five brown-speckled
white eggs; hatching and fledging times not known. Winter range: west coast from
Vancouver south, spreading east into Mexico and south as far as Nicaragua.

Orange-crowned warbler
(fauvette verdâtre)
Vermivora celata (American
wood-warbler family)
Beginning of April to end of September

Very common in brushy woods and
wetlands up to treeline, but hides in the
bushes. Length 11 cm.
    Greenish-yellow bird, sometimes on
the gray side, with a yellow-and-black
eye-line. The orange spot atop the head is
usually covered. Sings in trills with
cheeps at the end.
    Orange-crowns flit through the bushes eating caterpillars, other larvae and
insects. They nest in late May, when they can find dry spots on the ground among
shrubs (sometimes the nest is a half-metre up). There are five red/brown-spotted
white eggs in a rather large cup for a bird this size. Incubation time and fledging
date unknown. Lifespan 6 years. Winters across the American southwest and south,
through Mexico to Guatemala.

WARBLERS THAT ARE NOT MAINLY YELLOW

Yellow-rumped warbler
(fauvette à croupion jaune)
Dendroica coronata
(wood-warbler family)
Mid-April to mid-September

Very common in the woods, along
shorelines and in wooded marshes.
Length 12 cm.
    Our most common warbler, mainly
bluish-black and white but readily
identified by yellow patches in at least
three places: top of the head, bend in the
wing and on the rump. Compare with
magnolia warbler (next entry).
    If the bird has a yellow throat, then it is a member of **Audubon's race,** which
used to be called "Audubon's warbler." If the throat is white, then it's one of the
myrtle race, which used to be called "Myrtle warbler" and was once thought to be
a separate species. You may see in-betweens, one of the reasons for combining the
two species into one. The song is high, with regular cheeps; begins with several
"tsip"s.
    Yellow-rumps eat mainly flying insects, but also creepy-crawlies and ants; the
birds often perch on a snag hanging over a river or lake and dart out over the
water for flies, returning to the same perches between runs.
    Breeding time is variable; mostly in mid-spring here. Four brown-marked eggs
1-15 m up in any sort of tree hatch in 12-13 days, the young fledging 12-14 days
later. In August the upper subalpine forest is full of immatures, grayish and not
easily identifiable were it not for the bright-yellow rump patch that already
shows. Winter range: the midwest, southeastern USA, Mexico and the west coast
from Oregon south.

Magnolia warbler
(fauvette à tête cendrée)
Dendroica magnolia
(wood-warbler family)
Mid-April to end of June

Occasional in coniferous stands and black-spruce bogs. Length 11 cm.

Resembles the yellow-rumped warbler (previous entry) but has a black-streaked yellow breast, yellow throat and white eye-line. There is no yellow crown spot, but the rump is yellow. Note also the white tailband and broad white wingbar. Voice: like that of yellow warbler (page 638), but softer and less complicated. Magnolia warblers eat bugs that live on or just under the bark of conifers (beetles, larvae, aphids, spiders). Probably doesn't breed in the Canadian Rockies. Lifespan: 6-7 years. Wintering: Mexico and Central America.

Tennessee warbler (fauvette obscure)
Vermivora peregrina
(wood-warbler family)
Mid-May to mid-September

Fairly common in montane woods, especially in aspen groves and clumps of spruce in marshes. Length 11 cm.

Greenish-yellow on the back, but otherwise not yellow. Gray crown, white breast with a big gray bowtie, black-and-white eye-stripes; compare with the vireos, page 637. Song is long but rather easily recognized: high-pitched "witchy-witchy-witchy-witchy-witchy, cheep cheep cheep cheep cheep," finishing with a trill.

Tennessee warblers search the branch-ends of trees and tall shrubs for bugs, dropping to the ground occasionally for seeds, berries and fruits. Breeding is in late spring, the nest is on the ground. Four to six brown-speckled white eggs in the cup; no information on incubation or fledging. Lifespan 5 years. Winters from southern Mexico to northern South America.

Blackpoll warbler (fauvette rayée)
Dendroica striata (wood-warbler family)
Beginning of May to end of August

Common in montane and subalpine spruce forest, especially bordering wetlands. Length 12 cm.

A black and white warbler, the best male field marks being the black cap, white cheeks, black moustache and streaked vest. Females are greener and lack the white cheeks. Both sexes have white patches under the tail feathers. Song is very high and thin, a monotone of quick "tsit"s, becoming louder, then softer.

Blackpolls stay fairly low in conifers, eating a lot of aphids and other tree-crawlers as well as flying insects. They breed in the dwarf forest at timberline, sometimes above treeline in willow mats, in early summer. Four or five

brown/purple-speckled white or greenish eggs in a low cup hatch in 11 days.
Fledging is 10-12 days later. Species winters in South America.

Northern waterthrush
(fauvette des ruisseaux)
Seiurus novaboracensis
(wood-warbler family)
Mid-May to mid-August

Fairly common in marshes and along the
shores of woodland ponds. Length 13 cm.
    Identifiers: olive-brown back,
heavily streaked buffy or yellowish
breast and light-brown eye-line. Song is a
loud "sweet sweet sweet sweet" and then
some warbles.
    This bird walks on the muddy
ground and out on floating logs, bobbing
along like a spotted sandpiper. It eats
water insects and flying bugs, turns over
leaves to find slugs and crawly bugs, and
even grabs the odd tiny fish.
    It breeds in early summer, nesting among the roots of a fallen tree, in a
streambank hollow or in a cavity in rotten wood. There are four or five
brown-marked white/buff eggs; incubation time and fledging time unknown.
Lifespan 7 years. Winter range: western Gulf coast, southern Florida, Mexico,
central America and northern south America.

American redstart (fauvette flamboyante)
Setophaga ruticilla
(wood-warbler family)
Early May to mid-September

Locally common in alder and willow
thickets, wetlands and bushy places.
Length 11 cm.
    Males are black with flashy orange
trim on the wings and tail; compare with
varied thrush (page 627), the only other
bird in the mountains that is orange and
black. Females are quite different:
gray-headed (white eye-ring),
olive-brown back, dark wings and tail
with yellow patches, white breast. Song:
"wee wee wee wee," a little warbling and
strongest at the middle.
    Redstarts perch in the woods, waiting for flying insects. They usually let their
wings droop and fan their tails before leaping into the air after a bug. Breeding is
in early summer, the nest 2-4 m up in a vertical Y of a small deciduous tree or
shrub. Four brown-speckled cream/greenish eggs lie in a tidy cup lashed with
spiderwebs and often ornamented with *Usnea* tree lichens. Hatching: 12 days;
fledging: 9 days later. Lifespan: 5 years. Winter range: central Mexico and southern
Baja California through the West Indies to northern South America.

YELLOW BIRDS THAT ARE NOT WARBLERS

Western tanager (tangara à tête rouge)
Piranga ludoviciana (wood-warbler
family)
Early May to end of August

Fairly common in montane forests, often
among aspens or Douglas-firs. Length
16 cm, larger than the warblers.
    The western tanager is not a
warbler, but it looks like one: female all
yellow (greenish on the back), with black
wings and white wingbars. Males have
red heads. A good identifier for both
sexes is the bill, heavier and paler than
any warbler's. Song is three quick rising
rasps traded off with two rasps and a
chirp.
    Mainly bug eaters, tanagers relish wasps and ants, working both the treetops
and the ground. They also eat berries. Western tanager breeds in late spring,
nesting in conifers. There are 3-5 brown-marked light-blue eggs; they hatch in
13 days, but the fledging date is not known. Lifespan: has lived to 15 years in
captivity. Winter range: Mexico to Costa Rica.

Evening grosbeak (gros-bec errant)
Coccothraustes vespertinus (finch family)
Year-round

Fairly common on the eastern slope, less
so on the western side, in subalpine
forest. Flocks often spend the winter in
town. Length 18 cm.
    A chunky yellow-and-black perching
bird with a very heavy, stubby pale bill.
Males have a big yellow eyebrow and are
more brightly colored than females; both
sexes have white wing patches, but the
male and female patterns are different.
Song is twittery/whistling, sung often in
the flock.
    Evening grosbeaks eat mostly conifer seeds, also grabbing any bugs that
happen to be sitting nearby. In winter they head for lower elevations and easier
pickings: fruits, berries and especially the winged seeds and buds of the Manitoba
maple, an ornamental tree that attracts these birds into yards. Evening grosbeaks
are also fond of the sand and salt spread along highways, where they get run over.
    The birds breed in early summer, nesting in either conifers or deciduous trees.
A large, rather untidy-looking nest is made of sticks, with lichens woven in. Three
or four light-blue or greenish eggs hatch in 12-14 days; the young fledge about
two weeks later. Lifespan: 4-9 years in the wild, up to 17 years in captivity.
Evening grosbeaks winter throughout the Canadian Rockies, but they will leave
when food is scarce here, moving down into the central and southern USA.

Yellow-headed blackbird
(carouge à tête jaune)
Xanthocephalus xanthocephalus
(wood-warbler family)
Mid-April to mid-May

Occasional in eastern-slope wetlands,
rare on the western slope. Sometimes seen
in towns. Length 22 cm.

The male of this species is the only
North American bird that is half yellow
and half black. Note the white in the
wing. Females are quite different:
orange/ochre-colored breast with unique
white lace along the bottom, ochre
cheeks, white throat, brown back and
crown. Song: a variety of chirps, buzzes,
and whistles, fascinating to listen to.

Yellow-headed blackbirds are seen
here during the spring northward
migration, picking up worms and bugs
along the edges of marsh ponds and
lakes. No nesting records here. Lifespan
in the wild perhaps 8-9 years, in
captivity up to 18. Flight speed 55 km/h.
Winter range: California coast from San
Francisco south through Mexico.

Western meadowlark
(sturnelle de l'Ouest)
Sturnella neglecta (wood-warbler family)
Mid-April to end of May

Occasional in the eastern foothills, front
ranges and Rocky Mountain Trench, in
large grassy meadows. Length 22 cm.

A yellow-breasted bird with
brown-and-black mottled back, easily
identified by the broad black necklace
on the breast. Long bill, yellow and
white eye-line, white outer tailfeathers.
Song is well-known, although difficult to
describe; an up-and-down trill/warble
that some people can imitate by
whistling.

Meadowlarks feed on the ground,
picking up such insects as beetles,
grasshoppers, weevils and sow bugs; they
also eat worms, snails, grain and carrion.
No nesting records here. Flight speed
65 km/h. We see them during the spring
migration north and east; they winter
from Vancouver south, throughout the
desert states, plains states and Mexico.

BLACKBIRDS, COWBIRDS
See also yellow-headed blackbird, page 644

Red-winged blackbird
(carouge à épaulettes)
Agelaius phoeniceus
(wood-warbler family)
Mid-March to mid-August

Very common in marshes, especially those with cattails (page 411). Length 18 cm.

Males are glossy black with a brilliant red shoulder patch bordered in gold; females are streaky brown and sparrow-like, the streaking extending all over the breast and abdomen, unlike any of our sparrows. Male red-wingeds have a wonderful song, loosely translated as "konk-la-REEE."

The birds nest communally, yet the males are very territorial and aggressive, constantly bickering with others in the flock, chasing other birds away and making aerial dives at anything else venturing near the nest—birdwatchers, for example.

Blackbirds feed together in flocks, eating mainly seeds, also bugs, berries and other fruits. Breeds in mid-spring, the nest a deep, bag-like cup woven between cattail stems or willows growing in water. Four pale-blue eggs, often scrawled with black/purple, hatch in 10-12 days; the young are out of the nest 10-11 days later, but hang around another 10 days for feeding. Lifespan 8-14 years in the wild. Flying speed 45 km/h.

Winter range: most of the USA and Mexico. Red-winged blackbirds have been reported in Banff park through December, so a few may overwinter in the marshes of the southern Rocky Mountain Trench.

Brewer's blackbird
(mainate à tête pourprée)
Euphagus cyanocephalus
(wood-warbler family)
Beginning of April to mid-October

Fairly common in the foothills, often in shrubby meadows and along roads, in small flocks. Length 20 cm.

Appearing all black, the male Brewer's is actually slightly greenish and has a purplish, iridescent head. The yellow eye is sufficient to differentiate from male cowbird (next entry). Females are plain brown, nearly identical to the female cowbird. Differentiate by the bill: longer and thinner on the blackbird, shorter and thicker on the cowbird.

The rusty blackbird (mainate rouilleux; *E. carolinus*) migrates through the Canadian Rockies in spring to nesting areas north of the Rockies and is seen occasionally. It has been known to nest in Jasper park. It looks just like Brewer's, but lacks the purplish/greenish iridescence. Female is the only blackbird in the mountains that has yellow eyes; she is mottled on the head and breast.

Brewer's blackbird makes a sound like a rusty gate-hinge, also calling "chack." It walks about picking up bugs and leaping at flies, snapping its head forward as it moves; also eats grain and weed seeds.

Breeds in early spring, the nest often near water but otherwise quite varied in location: high up in trees, low in shrubs, in tree cavities, or under grass tussocks and overhanging banks. Nest includes conifer needles and mud with the usual plant matter. Five or six gray/brown-marked pale-blue or greenish eggs hatch in 12-13 days; the young fledge 13 days later but continue to be fed for another 12-13 days. Lifespan 5 years. Flight speed 60 km/h. Wintering: from southeastern BC through much of the western and southern USA, Mexico.

Brown-headed cowbird
(vacher à tête brune)
Molothrus ater (wood-warbler family)
Mid-April to mid-September

Common around ranches, following cattle. In the wilds it follows herds of elk and sheep. Also follows hiking and horseback-riding humans; frequently seen in campgrounds and towns. Length 13 cm.

Males are greenish-black like Brewer's blackbird, but the brown head is plainly visible in good light; further, the eye of the cowbird is brown, not yellow like that of Brewer's, and the cowbird is much more common. Females are more difficult to tell from Brewer's; note the stubbier, heavier cowbird bill. In his courtship display the male hunches up and spreads his tail, meanwhile uttering a rising squeak. The birds also gurgle and say "chuck" to one another.

Female cowbirds are bizarrely unwary of humans, walking among groups of hikers having lunch, hopping over their feet and flying up to catch bugs. If there are a lot of mosquitoes buzzing around you, and you are not moving about, a cowbird may light on your head or shoulder to get closer to the swarm. Still, this bird eats more seeds than anything else.

Their nomadic lifestyle prevents cowbirds from building a nest and raising their young in the normal avian way. Instead, the species is parasitic, leaving its eggs in the nests of other birds to be raised unknowingly by foster parents. It breeds from late April through much of the summer. The female deposits 10-12 brown-speckled white or greenish/bluish eggs in the egg-laden nests of other species, one egg per nest, usually throwing one of the host's clutch overboard (or eating it) to keep the number the same.

Many species are parasitized in this way, and about half of them accept the cowbird egg. Robins are among the species that reject it; some birds get rid of a cowbird egg by removing it, while others build a new nest over the whole brood and lay another clutch.

Hatching in 11-12 days, the young cowbird is often larger than the host's offspring and manages to get the most food, sometimes starving the other nestlings or throwing them out of the nest. It fledges after about 11 days, staying near the nest to beg food from the hosts for another two weeks. Lifespan is 7-13 years in the wild. Flight speed: 45 km/h. In the fall the young cowbirds find their own kind and flock south into the USA and Mexico.

Pine grosbeak (gros-bec des pins)
Pinicola enucleator (finch family)
Year-round

Fairly common in coniferous woods at
subalpine elevations, occasional at lower
elevations. Found in small flocks. Length
20 cm.

Chunky bird with a heavy black bill,
the males quite red on head, back and
breast, with patches of gray; the females
gray with brown crowns and rumps. Both
sexes have black wings with white
wingbars. Males look a good deal like
male crossbills (next entry) but are
noticeably larger. Crossbills have wider
white wingbars and (a sure identifier)
the prominently crossed bill. To
differentiate pine grosbeak from purple
finch (page 648), go by size (purple finch
is much smaller), by lack of white
wingbars on the finch and by the bill
(black on the grosbeak, buffy on the
finch).

Pine grosbeaks sing in a burbly, robin-like way. They live mostly on seeds of
deciduous trees and shrubs (birch, alder, Manitoba maple), spruce cones, shrub
fruits (rose hips, mountain ash, snowberries), spring buds and insects. The birds
are on the ground a lot, yet not very shy. Breeding is in mid-spring; four
black/purplish-marked light-blue/greenish eggs in a bulky nest of sticks hatch in
13-14 days. The nestlings fledge 20 days later. Lifespan 6-9 years. Pine grosbeaks
are non-migratory, but they often move to lower elevations and into towns for the
winter.

White-winged crossbill
(bec-croisé à ailes blanches)
Loxia leucoptera (finch family)
Year-round

Common in coniferous woods, usually a
few birds together. Length 15 cm.

Noticeably smaller than the
look-alike male pine grosbeak (previous
entry), another red bird with white
wingbars. But crossbill wingbars are
wider, and the bill is conspicuously
crossed: the upper mandible overlaps the
lower, curving off to one side. This odd,
asymmetrical arrangement helps in
opening spruce cones to extract seeds, an
important food of this bird (although it
also eats many insects).

The white-winged crossbill sings in rapid cheeps, like a chipping sparrow
(page 656), and says "dee-dee-dee" in the chickadee manner. Breeding habits are
like those of red crossbill (next entry). Non-migratory.

Red crossbill (bec-croisé rouge)
Loxia curvirostra (finch family)
Year-round

Common in lodgepole forest. Length
14 cm.

Resembles the white-winged crossbill
(previous entry), but lacks the white
wing bars and is thus easily
differentiated from male pine grosbeak
as well. To tell a male red crossbill from
a purple finch, note the buffy bill on the
finch and the black, crossed bill of the
crossbill. Females are mottled
reddish/brownish.

This species sings in short, high-pitched cheeps, slower than the white-winged.
The red crossbill is a seed-eater, but goes mainly for pine cones rather than the
spruce cones and insects eaten by the white-winged.

Crossbills breed in late winter; they nest in conifers, building a platform of
twigs supporting a cup made of grass, leaves, moss and lichens lined with hair and
feathers. Three or four brown-spotted pale-blue eggs hatch in 13-16 days; the
young fledge 17-22 days later and beg food from the adults for a month longer.
The birds don't migrate.

Purple finch (roselin pourpré)
Carpodacus pupureus (finch family)
Early March to late August

Occasional in open montane woods and
around towns, where they come to
feeders. Length 14 cm.

The reddish males resemble the red
crossbill (previous entry), but the bill is
not crossed and the head is slightly
crested. There are no white wingbars like
those of the similar pine grosbeak, which
is also red. Female purple finch is
brownish and sparrow-like.

Purple finches are talkative birds, with whistling, warbling voices. They eat
small seeds (mostly of grasses), fruits, berries and buds. Breeding in mid-spring,
they lay four or five black/brown-spotted light-blue eggs in a cup of twigs, grasses
and tiny roots lined with moss and hair. Hatching is at 13 days, fledging at about
two weeks. Lifespan 7-12 years. Wintering: through most of the USA, excluding the
Rockies.

Rosy finch (roselin brun)
Leucosticte arctoa (finch family)
Mid-February to early November

A common alpine bird, flying low over
the tundra in flocks. Length 15 cm.

Our rosy finches are of the
gray-crowned race, diagnostically gray
atop the head and with a black forehead
patch. (Other races have a larger or
smaller gray zone on the head; they live
south of the Canadian Rockies). The rest
of the bird is reddish brown, with pink
belly and wings; the bill is pale. Voice:
simple repetitive cheeps, quicker when
alarmed.

Rosy finches eat the seeds of tundra plants, often flocking on snowbanks and searching cliff bases where such food accumulates and is easy to see. The birds grab the odd insect and have a taste for snow worms (page 533), which is another reason they congregate on snow patches.

Breeding is in early summer, 4-5 pear-shaped white eggs laid in a soft cup of grass or moss hidden back in a rock crevice or built on a ledge. Incubation period is 12-14 days; fledging is 18-20 days later. The young birds are fed by the adults for another two weeks.

Rosy finches form flocks of up to 500 in the fall, moving down to lower elevations as the snow arrives; with the onset of cold weather, eastern-slope birds cross the mountains to winter from the Rocky Mountain Trench west.

Common redpoll (sizerin à tête rouge)
Carduelis flammea (finch family)
Beginning of November to end of April

Common winter resident in birch groves, alder thickets and weedy lots, usually in small flocks but sometimes numbering in the hundreds. Length 13 cm.

A little round bird with a brilliant red patch on the forehead and a black chin. Most males are also red on the breast; females are not. Both sexes have pink rumps, something to remember because sometimes you may see a few **hoary redpolls** *(C. hornemanni,* sizerin blanchâtre) in with a flock of common redpolls. The hoarys look just the same, but are white on the rump instead of pink.

Both species make a variety of sounds, calling "bzeee" (up at the end, rather like the siskin's call), cheeping and warbling, especially when in flocks. They are seed-eaters, preferring birch and alder cones but with a taste for the weed seeds they find on disturbed ground (in settled places and along highways). Redpolls aren't shy; you can get quite close.

They nest in the near-arctic **taiga:** the land just south of the northern treeline, equivalent to our high subalpine zone (but the birds very rarely nest here).

Redpolls can survive colder weather than any other songbird; the Canadian Rockies in winter are a southern holiday spot for them. They leave in April, when the daytime temperatures go above freezing—insufferably hot weather for these chaps. Lifespan is about seven years.

LITTLE FOREST BIRDS:
CHICKADEES, KINGLETS, NUTHATCHES, WRENS AND CREEPERS

Black-capped chickadee
(mésange a tête noire)
Parus atricapillus (chickadee family)
Year-round

Very common in conifers or mixed woods, in small flocks; may be our most numerous species. Length 11 cm.

Chickadees are little round birds with inordinately large heads and tiny bills. The bodies are gray/brown and drab; identify the three species in the mountains mainly by looking at the head and listening to the song. Black-capped is the most common chickadee. Has a black cap, all right, with white cheek patches and a black throat. Breast is gray/buffy, not white. Similar boreal chickadee (next entry) has a dark-brown cap (not easy to discern; looks black), with diagnostic white breast and cinnamon-colored vest. Mountain chickadee (this page) has a white eye-line.

Call of all three species is "chick-uh-dee-dee-dee," but the sound is subtly different for each species. The black-capped's "chicka" is very squeaky. The number of "dee"s varies, and sometimes the "chicka" is missing. In spring one hears the plaintive song: three clear notes, the first higher and longer than the other two. Chickadees move energetically through the woods in groups, calling frequently.

Woodsy lore: every flock has its own special *way* of saying "chickadee," which enables two different flocks crossing paths to keep themselves sorted out.

The birds search the branches for small bugs, insect eggs, larvae and seeds, often hanging upside down as they poke about with their little bills. Breeding is in early spring, the pair excavating a small cavity in a rotten tree low to the ground (often in a stump) or moving into an unused woodpecker nesting hole. They line the space with moss, plant down, feathers, spider cocoons—anything soft. Six to eight brown-speckled white eggs hatch in 12-14 days; the young fledge 16 days later. Lifespan 6-12 years.

Chickadees are non-migratory, staying at low elevations in winter and sometimes moving into towns.

Boreal chickadee (mésange a tête brune)
Parus hudsonicus (chickadee family)
Year-round

Common in coniferous woods. Length 11 cm.

Resembles black-capped chickadee (previous entry), but the cap is dark brown and the breast is white with cinnamon-colored sides rather than plain gray. The call is similar to that of other chickadees but is a little lower-pitched and more guttural; it sounds wheezy. Song is sometimes heard in spring; it is shorter and a little more warbling than that of the others.

Habits are like those of black-capped, but the boreal breeds somewhat later than the black-capped, in mid-spring; 4-9 brown-speckled white eggs lie in a rotten-wood or woodpecker cavity low in a tree or in a stump. Incubation time 15 days; fledging is 18 days later. Lifespan at least seven years. Non-migratory.

Mountain chickadee
(mésange de Gambel)
Parus gambeli (chickadee family)
Year-round

Common in montane conifers. Length 11 cm.

Resembles the other chickadees in the Canadian Rockies, but with a white eye-line in the black cap. Breast is white with gray sides. Call is a little raspier than the other chickadee calls, not wheezy like boreal's or clear like black-capped's; says "uh-dee-uh-dee-uh-dee" rather than

Little forest birds (chickadees etc.)

"dee-dee-dee." The spring song is similar to black-capped's, clear and musical. Habits and breeding like that of other chickadees; 5-7 white brown-spotted or unspotted eggs, hatching dates and fledging dates unknown. Lifespan at least seven years. Non-migratory.

Ruby-crowned kinglet
(roitelet à couronne rubis)
Regulus calendula
(old-world warbler family)
Early April to mid-October

Very common in fairly open spruce stands to timberline, usually near water. Length 10 cm.

A little gray bird, undistinguished and rather flycatcher-like except for two things: a bright red patch on top of the male's head (patch not always exposed) and the song, which is readily identified once it is heard.

In the Rockies the bird goes "tsip-tsip-tsip" a bit, then "chow-chow-chow," then the main event: "CHEEP, cheepa-cheepa CHEEP, cheepa-cheepa CHEEP," usually trailing off in more "tsip"s. This song is *loud;* a great performance for such a small creature.

Kinglets move through the lower branches of conifers in singles and pairs, looking for insects. According to a recent radio item the average Christmas-tree-sized spruce has about 60,000 mites, spiders, aphids and such on it, so there would seem to be plenty to pick at. The birds also take the odd belt of sap. Kinglets are unwary; you can get quite close.

Breeding in late spring, a pair builds a small, very cozy deep-dish nest made of plant fibers, *Usnea* tree lichens and grass. Lined with feathers, it hangs between twigs and is tied on with spider webs and hair. Seven or eight brown-speckled teeny white eggs hatch in about two weeks; the fledging date is not known.

Winter range: southwestern BC, south and east through the American southwest, Mexico, through the southern states and up the Atlantic seaboard to New England.

Golden-crowned kinglet
(roitelet à couronne dorée)
Regulus satrapa
(old-world warbler family)
Mid-March to end of December, most common from beginning of May to end of September

Common in conifers. Length 9 cm.

A very small bird, mostly greenish-gray. The male has a brilliant yellow crown with a red stripe down the middle; the female's crown is yellow only. Both sexes have a long white stripe just above the eye, which differentiates from the golden-crowned sparrow (no stripe; see page 657).

Bug-eaters like the ruby-crowned kinglet, pairs and small flocks of golden-crowned kinglets prowl the upper foliage of spruce and Douglas-firs (sometimes pines), calling "tsip" constantly. The full song is fairly complicated but seldom heard. Instead, you find yourself surrounded by twittering golden-crowns that are maddeningly difficult to locate. One would think there were far fewer of these little birds than there really are.

Nesting habits are like those of the ruby-crowned, but there are usually 8-9 eggs instead of 7-8. The bird's winter range extends farther north than the ruby-crowned's; a fair number of golden-crowns hang around Jasper until New Year's, even later in the south end of the area and on the western slope.

Red-breasted nuthatch
(sittelle à poitrine rousse)
Sitta canadensis (nuthatch family)
Year-round

Common in coniferous woods, especially on Douglas-firs. Length 10 cm.

A little gray-backed bird with a rusty breast; black cap like a chickadee but no black bib on the throat. Long, wide white eye-line runs from bill to nape of neck. White patch on the tailfeathers.

Nuthatches say "ank" often as they scuttle about on the trunks and branches of conifers, especially old lodgepole pines and Douglas-firs. These trees are loaded with the beetles and other bark-dwelling bugs that this bird uses to supplement its staple diet of conifer seeds. It hacks open the cones with its light-looking but powerful bill; hence the name "nuthatch," meaning "nut-hacker."

This is the only bird you are likely to see that walks headfirst *down* the trunk; in this way it spots tidbits that the woodpeckers and other normal, head-up trunk-walkers miss. Red-breasted nuthatches breed in mid-spring, nesting in a cavity the pair have pecked out of rotten wood (sometimes with help from unmated birds, who may also help rear the young) or in a natural wood shelter, unused woodpecker nesting hole or birdbox. The birds wipe conifer resin around the entrance. No one knows why.

Five or six brown-speckled white or pinkish eggs hatch in 12 days; the young leave the nest 18-21 days later. Lifespan seven years. Non-migratory, but seldom seen in winter; may move well south into the USA in some years.

Winter wren (troglodyte des forêts)
Troglodytes troglodytes (wren family)
Mid-April to mid-August

Common but inconspicuous, in heavy, mossy-floored montane and subalpine forest, densely overgrown swamps—any place that is so thickly vegetated it's dark.

Very small bird (length 8 cm) with a short, sharply upturned tail that flicks up and down. Dark reddish brown, with vague black barring on top; lighter below. The barring is quite visible on the lower abdomen, which is a good way to differentiate from the very similar house wren (next entry), which is barred even farther back, under the tail. Throat of the winter wren is pale and there is a faint eye stripe. Song: long and high, composed of thin insect-like trills, interspersed with whistles; scolds "tick-tick."

The winter wren is hard to pinpoint by sound. Don't look up into the trees; the bird will be on the ground, poking about among the deadfall, mosses and shrubbery for bugs.

It breeds in early spring, the male building one or more large, rough, domed nests hidden among tree roots and tangles on the forest floor. He is often polygamous, attracting several females to the various nests, which his mates line with feathers. There are 5-8 white eggs (sometimes minutely brown-spotted) in each nest; they hatch in 14-17 days. Males help with the feeding, which keeps them quite busy as first one clutch then another hatches. Fledging is at 15-20 days. Lifespan 5 years.

"Winter wren" is a misleading name in the Canadian Rockies; the birds winter on the west coast and in the American east—although some stay here as long as January (and then probably die).

House wren (troglodyte familier)
Troglodytes aedon (wren family)
Mid-May to end of September

Occasional in the bushes at low elevations. Length 11 cm.

Very similar to winter wren (previous entry), but larger, with a longer tail and black barring on the rump rather than on the belly. Up-cocked tail flicks down. Sings in trills and whistles, often at length; scolds "chak-chak-chak." Flits secretively among the shrubbery grabbing bugs, but sings so much and so often that it makes its presence known.

Breeding habits are like those of the winter wren, but the house wren also nests in tree holes and birdhouses. Age record 7 years. Winters on the west coast from California south, through the Gulf states and up the east coast.

Rock wren (troglodyte des rochers)
Salpinctes obsoletus (wren family)
Early May to end of August

Occasional on eroded till banks, dry cliffs and other sparsely vegetated places at low elevations. Length 12 cm.

Uplifted tail and curved bill identify this bird as a wren; to differentiate from the other two wrens in the Canadian Rockies, note the buff terminal band on the tail, the very light belly and the finely streaked breast. Rock wrens say "chew-EEE," "ee-or," and many other things; the voice has a buzzy quality. The bird busies itself on dry slopes, chasing insects and spiders. No nesting records here. Winters in the American southwest.

Brown creeper (grimpereau brun)
Certhia americana (creeper family)
Year-round

Fairly common in mature coniferous
woods, southern and central sections;
usually among recently fallen timber and
walking up the trunks of live trees.
Length 11 cm.

The creeper is a reclusive little
camouflaged bird that is more common
than one might think. Brown with white
streaking on top, white below, with
longish down-curved bill and very short
legs. The thin five-note song is seldom
heard and hard to imitate, but it is
distinctive and unvarying.

Starting at the bottom of a tree, a creeper climbs up in a spiral, looking for
bugs on the bark and under loose flakes. It also clings to the underside of limbs
and fallen trees. Eats seeds, too. Breeds in late spring, building a horn-shaped nest
that nearly fills a vertical crevice in live or dead wood. Six brown-dotted white
eggs are laid in a cup at the top of the horn; they hatch in 14-15 days. The young
climb out of the nest 14-16 days later. Lifespan six years.

My information sources disagree on migration; brown creepers may move over
to the warmer western slope and Columbia Mountains in winter, or may remain in
the Rockies.

SPARROWS AND SPARROW-LIKE BIRDS WITH UNSTREAKED BREASTS

House sparrow (moineau domestique)
Passer domesticus
(old-world sparrow family) Year-round

Very common in towns and other
habitations at low elevations, the females
in small flocks. Length 13 cm.

Male easily identified: brown back
and wings, gray head and breast with
large black bib, black bill. Females look
quite different, and the fact that they
flock separately from the males leads to
the illusion that they are a separate
species. Females are all brown with a
pale bill, lighter on the breast and often
streaky gray on the abdomen, with a
diagnostic dark-brown facial line that
hooks down behind the eye (no other
bird with an unstreaked breast has this).

House sparrows, formerly called "English sparrows," are European, introduced
in Brooklyn in 1851. By 1900 the birds had colonized all of North America except
the arctic. One sees and hears them in any Rockies town, loudly calling "cheep,"
"cheep" all day long. They eat mainly beetles, grasshoppers and other
crawling/jumping bugs in the summer, switching to seeds and plant fruits in the
winter.

When automotive transport took over from horses in North America, the
number of house sparrows declined, for the birds had been getting many of their
seeds from horse droppings. Nowadays one sees house sparrows picking bugs out of
the radiators of parked cars and eating scraps in the parking lots of fast-food
restaurants, so they seem to be adapting to the situation.

Breeding begins variably in the spring, usually in May but sometimes much earlier, during warm periods in March or April. Several males gather about a female, usually on the ground, then fight for her, rolling about in the dust and mud in Hollywood-cowboy fashion. The winner then mates up to 14 times with his lady, who flutters her wings and says (no kidding) "tee hee."

The male builds most of the nest, a dome of twigs (sometimes a simple cup) under an eave, back in a crevice or in a birdhouse. House sparrows love to nest behind ivy. Sometimes two broods are raised in a summer. Three to five gray/brown-dotted white/greenish/bluish eggs hatch in 11-14 days; the young fledge 15 days later. The life span is very long for such a small bird: up to 23 years in captivity. Non-migratory. The birds fly rather weakly, but can reach 60 km/h.

Dark-eyed junco (junco ardoisé)
Junco hyemalis (wood-warbler family)
Mid-March to end of December, most
common from beginning of April to end
of August

Formerly called "slate-colored junco."
Very common in the woods, from low
elevations to treeline. Length 13 cm.

Slate-colored race

On the eastern slope, juncos are
mostly of the **slate-colored race,** the
grayest of little gray birds, marked only
with a white belly, and—the main
identifier—white outside tail feathers
that are obvious only when the bird
flies. Some other sparrows in the
Canadian Rockies also flash white
tailfeathers, but none is otherwise gray.
Throughout the area (and particularly in
the spring) you may also see juncos
belonging to the **Oregon race,** which has
a gray cowl, sometimes very dark,
contrasting with brown back and vest,
white breast and belly, plus the same
diagnostic white tailfeathers.

Oregon race

Regardless of race, the junco song is a long trill, very much like that of the chipping sparrow (next entry), but a little slower and less buzzy; not heard as frequently as the chipping-sparrow's song.

Juncos flit among the lower branches of conifers, saying "tick" to one another. The white tailfeathers flare out as a bird darts into a spruce and disappears. The species is secretive sometimes and approachable at others; it seldom sings from an exposed perch like a chipping sparrow does. Feeds on the ground, hopping after beetles and other bugs; also takes seeds and is easily attracted to feeders.

Breeding begins in early spring; the species often rears two broods a year. The nest is usually on the ground in a natural cavity of some kind (among roots, under deadfall, under an overhanging bank or in a grass tussock) and the cup is always well hidden. Three to five sparsely brown/gray-marked white or greenish/grayish eggs hatch in 11-12 days; the young fledge 10-13 days later. Lifespan 3.5-6.5 years, one record of ten years. Slow flyer: 30 km/h.

Winter range for juncos is not far from us, the birds moving west to the Columbia Mountains and Coast Mountains of BC and south through nearly all the USA; some of our juncos overwinter at Waterton/Glacier and in the southern Rocky Mountain Trench.

Chipping sparrow (pinson familier)
Spizella passerina (wood-warbler family)
Beginning of May to mid-September

Very common in conifers. Length 12 cm.

Brown on back and wings with white wingbars, unstreaked white or cream breast and face, reddish cap on the head—the only sparrow likely to be seen in the Canadian Rockies with a rusty crown. Black-and-white eye-line.

An easy sparrow to identify by sight, the chipping sparrow is even easier to recognize by sound: a sustained one-note buzzy trill, usually sung from a conspicuous perch in a conifer or on a fencepost, often only head-high.

Despite its preference for the woods, this bird eats mainly grass seeds, supplemented with bugs. It breeds in mid-spring; four pale-blue, lightly brown/blue/black-marked eggs lie in a cup 1-6 m up in a conifer. Hatching is at 11-14 days; the birds leave the nest at 9-12 days, a few days before they are able to fly. Lifespan is rather short: 2.5-7 years. Winter range: coast-to-coast in the southern quarter of the USA, south to Nicaragua.

White-crowned sparrow
(pinson à couronne blanche)
Zonotrichia leucophrys
(wood-warbler family)
Mid-May to mid-October

Very common in small flocks in nearly any habitat (most often in open, shrubby places), including alpine meadows and towns. Length 15 cm.

The white-crowned is one of two sparrows with three prominent white stripes through a black cap on the head. The other is the white-throated sparrow (next entry), which has a dab of yellow ahead of the eye and is much less common.

The white-crowned has no yellow anywhere on the head, which differentiates it from the golden-crowned sparrow. Song of the white-crowned is easily recognized and heard often: a musical two-note beginning followed by buzzy "chee-zee-zee" and often a trill.

White-crowneds feed on the ground, scratching for seeds and bugs; they also eat moss capsules and willow catkins. But they fly up to sing, often from the top of an aspen or poplar. The birds are not shy; you can get within a couple of metres.

Breeding is in mid-spring at low elevations, in June at timberline. The birds nest in mossy or bushy places on the ground, sometimes low in a dense shrub or up in a tree, the nest concealed in moss or undergrowth. Two to five reddish-speckled bluish/greenish eggs hatch in 9-15 days; fledging is 9-11 days later but the feeding tapers off over another 25-30 days. If one clutch is lost, the pair produce another. When a predator comes near the nest, the parents fly up nearby, calling "pwit" very sharply. Under this stimulus the babies make no sound or movement.

Average age of 198 banded birds recovered 1920-1963 was only 1.2 years; maximum lifespan about 13 years in the wild. Flight speed: 30 km/h. Winter range:

southeastern BC, American northwest and Rockies from Wyoming south through most of USA and Mexico to Cuba.

White-throated sparrow
(pinson à gorge blanche)
Zonotrichia albicollis
(wood-warbler family)
Early May to late August

Occasional from Banff north in montane forest and bogs, in the bushes, sometimes in small flocks. Length 15 cm.

Very similar to white-crowned sparrow (previous entry), with similar stripy head, but has a small patch of yellow just ahead of the eye and a prominent white patch on the throat, bordered with a black line on each side. Unstreaked gray breast, pale bill. Song is clear and slow, like someone absent-mindedly whistling 5-6 notes, last few a little warbling. Call: "pick."

Like the white-crowned sparrow, this bird scuttles about the ground scratching for weed seeds and bugs. It breeds in mid-spring, nesting on the ground in dense shrubbery at the edge of a clearing; 4-6 reddish-spotted pale-blue/greenish eggs hatch in 11-14 days, the young leaving the nest 8-9 days later but not flying for 2-3 more. Lifespan 8-9 years. Winter range: American west coast, southern states, midwest, New England.

Golden-crowned sparrow
(pinson à couronne dorée)
Zonotrichia atricapilla
(wood-warbler family)
Mid-May to early October

Common in upper montane and subalpine forest from Banff north, often at timberline or above. Length 17 cm.

Yet another little brown bird with a gray breast, but this one has a small black cap with a bright-yellow centre. Compare with golden-crowned kinglet, page 651. Immatures look somewhat like female house sparrows (page 654). Song is three slow and wistful notes: "O-ver there," like the first phrase of the First World War marching song, followed by a short trill.

Like the other *Zonotrichia* species, the golden-crowned spends most of its time on the ground picking for seeds and bugs. The birds breed in early summer; they build their nests (often incorporating ferns and moosehair) on the ground among timberline willows or under a grassy overhang. There are three to five eggs like those of the white-throated sparrow; incubation and fledging times not known. Lifespan 8-10 years. Flight speed 35 km/h. Wintering: west coast from Vancouver to Baja California, inland through Cascades and Sierras.

Clay-colored sparrow and Brewer's sparrow
(pinson des plaines)
Spizella pallida and *S. breweri*
(wood-warbler family) Mid-May to
mid-September

Common in open places, clay-colored
seen most often in wetlands at lower
elevations, Brewer's frequenting
subalpine meadows. Length 11 cm.

The two species are nearly
identical—brown back and wings, white
wing bars, creamy unstreaked breast,
same facial pattern—except for one
thing: the clay-colored has a white line
down the top of the head and Brewer's
does not. The song of the clay-colored is
simple and buzzy, but Brewer's can bring
forth an amazingly eloquent song, with
cheeps and whistles added to the
insect-like noises. Note also the
difference in habitat.

Both birds feed on the ground, picking up seeds and bugs. Birds seen early
and late in the Canadian Rockies are mainly clay-coloreds; Brewer's arrives about
two weeks later and departs about three weeks earlier.

Breeding is in mid-spring, both species nesting low in the shrubbery but
Brewer's preferring high-subalpine locations, often in krummholz conifers
(page 328). Three or four eggs are brown-blotched light-blue. Clay-colored's eggs
hatch at 10-11 days and the young fledge only 7-9 days later. No information on
Brewer's incubation and fledging. Clay-colored lifespan is about five years. Winter
range: Brewer's from southern California across to western Texas and down into
Mexico, clay-colored mainly in Mexico.

Snow bunting (plectrophane de neiges)
Plectrophenax nivalis
(wood-warbler family)
Beginning of November to early April

Very common in the central front ranges
and foothills, after October, in flocks
along highway shoulders and other
weedy places, sometimes in towns. Less
common in the north end of the
Canadian Rockies, which they pass
through, and in the southern section,
which they avoid. Length 15 cm.

The whitest small bird in the mountains, round and big-headed with a small
bill, like a parakeet. Males are mostly white, with black tail and black patches on
wings, cinnamon back and crown, cheeks and collar. Females are generally
browner, with rusty vests, but still look quite pale compared to other birds.

Song: whistles and trills, sung frequently as the birds move through a field or
along a highway shoulder picking up seeds and the last of a summer's bug
population. They feast on grain spilled along the railway. Look for the odd
lapland longspur (page 662) or horned lark (page 612) in the flock.

Snow buntings spend a lot of time along highways but they pay little attention
to the traffic, with predictable results.

Lifespan eight years; flight speed 40 km/h. Snow buntings spend their summers in the high arctic, wintering on the west coast down to Vancouver and east across southern Canada and the northern USA.

SPARROWS WITH STREAKY BREASTS, LONGSPURS AND SISKINS

Savannah sparrow (pinson des prés)
Passerculus sandwichensis
(wood-warbler family)
Late April to early October

Very common in open, grassy places and wetlands up to timberline. Length 12 cm.
   A little brown bird with no central spot on the streaked breast. Main identifiers: a touch of yellow in the light eye-line, pink legs and notched tail. Song: a few "tip"s, then a buzzy, insect-like section, with a couple of cheeps at the end.
   The savannah sparrow hops secretively through the grasses looking for seeds and bugs; in wetlands also eats snails. Stays put until one is almost on top of it, then darts out of the grass and nips back in a few metres away.
   Breeding: in early spring, the nest in a hollow scratched out of the ground and lined with grasses/sedges, rootlets, hair (never with feathers). Four or five faintly greenish or bluish brown-spotted eggs hatch in 12 days; fledging date unknown. Lifespan seven years. Flies fast for a sparrow: 70 km/h. Winters along both coasts from US border south, through the southwest, Gulf states, lower Mississippi valley, Mexico to El Salvador.

Vesper sparrow (pinson vespéral)
Pooecetes gramineus
(wood-warbler family)
Mid-April to early September

Fairly common in dry, grassy places at low elevations. Length 14 cm.
   This bird is a little larger than the savannah sparrow (previous entry), which lives in same habitat and is generally similar except for the tail: vesper sparrow has junco-like white outer feathers that show in flight, the only brown sparrow with this feature. No yellow in eye-line like that of savannah, and there is a patch of reddish-brown at the vesper's shoulder.
   Vesper sparrows forage on the ground for bugs and seeds. They like to take dust baths. Not secretive, the birds can be closely approached. The species sings from the highest perch it can find; song is cheepy and easily recognized: two low notes, two high ones, then a couple of trills. Often heard just after rain.
   Breeding is in mid-spring. The bird digs a small hollow in the ground, usually sparsely concealed but sometimes in the open, and then builds a cup in it. Three to five speckled white eggs hatch in 11-13 days; the young leave the nest 9-13 days later but cannot fly for a few days more. They get fed for another 20-22 days. Lifespan more than six years. Flight speed only 30 km/h. Wintering is through the American southwest and southern states, up the Atlantic seaboard to New England, south through Mexico.

Lincoln's sparrow (pinson de Lincoln)
Melospiza lincolnii
(wood-warbler family)
Early May to mid-September

Very common in shrubby wetlands and
along grassy streams. Length 12 cm.

Quite similar to the vesper or
savannah sparrows, but check the tail:
there are no white tailfeathers like the
vesper sparrow's, and the end is round,
not notched like the savannah's tail; nor
is there the savannah's yellowish
eye-line. Song is long and interesting;
cheepy, buzzy, with trills. Named for
Thomas Lincoln, an associate of John
James Audubon.

A shy bird, Lincoln's sparrow prowls the undergrowth along the shoreline and
sings from cover. It scratches with both feet together (picture that) to get bugs and
seeds. Breeds in mid-spring, the cup on the ground and well hidden. Four or five
pale-green brown-speckled eggs hatch in 13-14 days; fledging is 10-12 days later.
Winters from coastal California south through the American southwest, northeast
as far as Missouri, through Mexico into central America.

LeConte's sparrow (pinson de LeConte)
Ammodramus leconteii
(wood-warbler family) June

Occasional in eastern-slope marshes, rare
south of Jasper. Length 11 cm.

Still another little brown sparrow,
this one differentiated by the white
stripe down the top of the head, ochre or
orange eye-line and buffy streaked
breast. End of tail looks ragged and
sharp. Voice is also a good identifier:
high insect-like buzz, with no birdy
cheeps at all (the only one like it in the
Rockies).

LeConte's pokes furtively among dense shrubbery and grasses for bugs and
seeds, prefers to hide or run along the ground rather than fly. When flushed, it
flies a short distance and drops back into cover like the savannah sparrow.

There are no nesting records for this species in the national parks, but it may
breed in the foothills in late spring. The nest is on the ground or raised a few
centimetres in a dry spot in a marsh, well concealed in dense cover and made of
woven grasses. Four white, heavily brown-marked eggs hatch in 11-13 days;
fledging date unknown. Winter range: the Gulf states and up the east coast to
Georgia.

Song sparrow (pinson chanteur)
Melospiza melodia (wood-warbler family)
Late March to early October, seen less often after July

Common in shrubby montane meadows, wetlands, deciduous groves and towns.
Length 14 cm.

Yet another little brown sparrow, this one is well known all over North
America. It is told from its kin by the following combination: spot in the centre of
the streaky breast, gray-on-brown face and round-ended tail. When it flies, the tail
pumps up and down. The only other sparrow in the Canadian Rockies with a

breast spot is the fox sparrow (next entry), which is noticeably larger and more evenly brown, especially on the face.

Appropriately named, the song sparrow sings beautifully and at length, whistling, cheeping, buzzing and trilling. The first part of the song seems to follow the famous first four notes of Beethoven's Fifth Symphony, although it is "tweet-tweet-tweet-BUZZ" instead of "dum-dum-dum-DOM."

The bird picks and scratches on the ground for awhile, then flits up into the shrubbery or even into the treetops; it eats bugs, seeds, fruits and berries. Not shy. Breeds in early spring, nesting on the ground under a grass tussock or sometimes low in a tree. Will nest twice if the first brood doesn't make it. Occasionally produces two healthy baby-bird batches in a summer.

There are 3-5 reddish/brownish-marked pale bluish/greenish eggs; incubation time is 12-14 days; the young leave the nest 10 days later but don't fly well for another week. Average lifespan about 2.5 years, maximum ten years. Flight speed 50 km/h. Winter range: west coast from Aleutian Islands all the way to Baja California, inland across the southwestern and southern USA, through much of the east up to the St. Lawrence River.

Fox sparrow (pinson fauve)
Passarella iliaca (wood-warbler family)
Mid-April to late September

Common at timberline during the breeding season; at other times occasional on brushy avalanche slopes and in dense subalpine alder and willow thickets. Length 16 cm, our largest sparrow.

Fox sparrows are quite brown on the back, wings and head. The breast is heavily streaked and there is a central spot. Compare with song sparrow (previous entry). The eastern version of this bird is rather reddish (thus the "fox" name), but the western type is so large and so brown that it is sometimes mistaken for a hermit thrush (page 628), which has a spotted breast, not a streaked one. Sings very beautifully from a concealed perch, chirping, whistling and trilling as well as the song sparrow but seldom buzzing.

Breeding is in late spring, often in the krummholz, nesting on the ground in dense cover or low in a shrub or tree. Three to five heavily brown-marked bluish/greenish eggs hatch in about 12-14 days; fledging date unknown. Lifespan 6-9 years. Wintering is along the west coast from Vancouver Island south to Baja California, inland through the southwest and southern USA, up the east coast to New England.

Lapland longspur (bruant lapon)
Calcarius pictus (wood-warbler family)
Early September to early October

Occasional in winter, in grassy places at
any elevation, sometimes among a flock
of snow buntings. Length 15 cm.

Male looks like a cross between a
sparrow and a horned lark (page 612),
with the black breast-band of the lark
and the face of a sparrow—the only
sparrow in the region with such a breast
marking (but compare with house
sparrow, page 654). Note also the streaky
vest and cinnamon patches on back of
neck and wing.

This bird changes plumage with the seasons, and you may see it in summer
dress, with its aviator's hat and orange breast. Females are plain streaky brown.
The song is squeaky/buzzy, reminiscent of red-winged blackbird (page 645) or
western meadowlark (page 644). Longspurs passing through the mountains are
heading south from the arctic to winter in the American northwest and through
the plains states. They fuel up on weed seeds and late-season insects.

Pine siskin (chardonneret des pins)
Carduelis pinus (finch family)
Beginning of April to mid-December

Very common in small flocks at low
elevations in the woods and in town.
Length 11 cm.

Pine siskins were once called
"linnets," for which Linnet Lake in
Waterton was named. They are streaky
brown birds that look like some kind of
sparrow—until you notice the yellow
patches in the wings, which are quite
flashy in flight. There is also yellow on
the rump and under the tail. Siskins say
"zeeeee," the voice rising in pitch as if
asking a question. They also jabber a lot
in fussy-sounding squeaks.

Although they are "pine" siskins, I see this species more often in birches and
alders, picking apart the catkins in summer and the cones in fall. They eat many
different foods: insects, seeds of all kinds (they relish dandelion heads in summer),
buds, nectar, even oozing sap. Towns offer a smorgasbord for these unwary little
birds, but they are stupid about windows and frequently break their necks flying
into them.

Breeding is in early spring; 3-5 bluish/greenish purplish-speckled eggs lie in a
nest halfway up a conifer. Hatching is at 13 days, fledging at 14-15 days. Most
songbird parents remove droppings from the nest in the form of tidy capsules that
are easily carried away, but siskins let the nest go foul after nine days. Lifespan
3-7 years, to 11 years in captivity. Winter range: west coast and most of the USA.

RARE LIST

These are birds that have been recorded in the national parks only one to five times. They are unlikely to be seen, but you never know. This list is in the sequence adopted by the American Ornithologists' Union for their North American checklist.

Arctic loon (huart arctique) *Gavia arctica*
Red-throated loon (huart à gorge rousse) *Gavia stellata*
American white pelican (péelican blanc d'Amerique) *Pelecanus erythrorynchos*
Double-crested cormorant (cormoran à aigrettes) *Phalacrocorax penicillatus*
Green heron (héron vert) *Butorides striatus*
Great egret (butor Americain) *Casmerodius albus*
Brant (bernache cravant) *Branta canadensis*
European wigeon (canard siffleur d'Europe) *Anas penelope*
Turkey vulture (vautour à tête rouge) *Cathartes aura*
Broad-winged hawk (petite buse) *Buteo platypterus*
Ferruginous hawk (buse rouilleuse) *Buteo regalis*
Gyrfalcon (gerfaut) *Falco rusticolus*
Sharp-tailed grouse (gélinotte à queue fine) *Tympanuchus phasianellus*
Ring-necked pheasant (faisan à collier) *Phasianus colchicus*
Gray partridge (perdrix grise) *Perdix perdix*
Sandhill crane (grue Canadienne) *Grus canadensis*
Virginia rail (râle de Virginie) *Ralus limicola*
Yellow rail (râle jaune) *Coturnicops novabonracensis*
Lesser golden-plover (pluvier doré d'Amerique) *Pluvialis dominica*
Black-bellied plover (pluvier à ventre noir) *Pluvialis squatarola*
Long-billed curlew (courlis à long bec) *Numenius americanus*
Eskimo curlew (courlis esquimau) *Numenius borealis*
Upland sandpiper (maubèche des champs) *Bartramia longicauda*
Wandering tattler (chevalier errant) *Heteroscelus incanus*
Ruddy turnstone (tourne-pierre roux) *Arenaria interpres*
Sanderling (sanderling) *Calidris alba*
Western sandpiper (bécasseau du Nord-Ouest) *Calidris mauri*
Dunlin (bécasseau à dos roux) *Calidris alpina*
Short-billed dowitcher (bécasseau roux) *Limnodromus griseus*
Buff-breasted sandpiper (bécasseau roussâtre) *Tryngites subruficollis*
Marbled godwit (barge marbrée) *Limosa fedoa*
Red phalarope (phalarope roux) *Phalaropus fulicarius*
Parasitic jaeger (labbe parasite) *Stercorarius parasiticus*
Long-tailed jaeger (labbe à longue queue) *Stercorarius longicaudus*
Thayer's gull (goéland de Thayer) *Larus thayeri*
Franklin's gull (mouette de Franklin) *Larus pipixcan*
Sabine's gull (mouette de Sabine) *Xema sabini*
Forster's tern (sterne de Forster) *Sterna forsteri*
Band-tailed pigeon (pigeon du Pacifique) *Columba fasciata*
Western screech owl (petit Duc) *Otus kennicottii*
Snowy owl (harfang des neiges) *Nyctea scandiaca*
Burrowing owl (chouette de terrier) *Athene cunicularia*
Long-eared owl (hibou à aigrettes longues) *Asio otus*
Short-eared owl (hibou des marais) *Asio flammeus*
Ruby-throated hummingbird (colibri à gorge rubis) *Archilochus colubris*
Western kingbird (tyran de l'Ouest) *Tyrannus verticalis*
Eastern phoebe (moucherolle phébi) *Sayornis phoebe*
Say's phoebe (moucherolle à ventre roux) *Sayornis saya*
Yellow-bellied flycatcher (moucherolle à ventre jaune) *Empidonax flaviventris*
White-breasted nuthatch (sittelle a poitrine blanche) *Sitta carolinensis*
Pygmy nuthatch (petit Sittelle) *Sitta pygmaea*
Marsh wren (troglodyte des marais) *Cistothorus palustris*
Northern mockingbird (moquer polyglotte) *Mimus polyglottos*
Gray catbird (moquer-chat) *Dumetella carolinensis*
Gray-cheeked thrush (grive à joues grises) *Catharus minimus*
Eastern bluebird (merle bleu à poitrine rouge) *Sialia sialis*
Western bluebird (merle bleu à dos marron) *Sialia mexicana*
Sprague's pipit (pipit des Prairies) *Anthus spragueii*
Philadelphia vireo (viréo de Philadelphie) *Vireo philadelphicus*
Black-and-white warbler (fauvette noire et blanche) *Mniotilta varia*
Nashville warbler (fauvette à joues grises) *Vermivora ruficapilla*
Cape May warbler (fauvette tigrée) *Dendroica tigrina*
Black-throated gray warbler (fauvette grise à gorge noire) *Dendroica nigrescens*
Black-throated green warbler (fauvette verte à gorge noire) *Dendroica virens*
Bay-breasted warbler (fauvette à poitrine baie) *Dendroica castanea*
Palm warbler (fauvette à couronne rousse) *Dendroica palmarum*
Ovenbird (fauvette couronnée) *Seiurus aurocapillus*
Canada warbler (fauvette de Canada) *Wilsonia canadensis*
Bobolink (goglu) *Dolichonyx oryzivorus*
Northern oriole (oriole du Nord) *Icterus galbula*
Common grackle (mainate bronzé) *Quiscalus quiscula*

Rose-breasted grosbeak (gros-bec à poitrine rose) *Pheucticus ludovicianus*
Black-headed grosbeak (gros-bec à tête noire) *Pheucticus melanocephalus*
Dickcissel (dickcissel) *Spiza americana*
Cassin's finch (roselin de Cassin) *Carpodacus cassinii*
House finch (roselin familier) *Carpodacus mexicanus*
American goldfinch (chardonneret jaune) *Carduelis tristis*
Rufous-sided towhee (tohi commun) *Pipilo erythrophthalmus*
Lark bunting (pinson noir et blanc) *Calamospiza melanocorys*
Grasshopper sparrow (pinson des prés) *Passerculus sandwichensis*
Baird's sparrow (pinson de Baird) *Ammodramus bairdii*
Sharp-tailed sparrow (pinson à queue aiguë) *Ammodramus caudacutus*
American tree sparrow (pinson hudsonien) *Spizella arborea*
Harris' sparrow (pinson à face noire) *Zonotrichia querula*
Swamp sparrow (pinson des marais) *Melospiza georgiana*
Chestnut-collared longspur (bruant à ventre noir) *Calcarius ornatus*

SCIENTIFIC NAMES OF BIRD FAMILIES (Rockies-area species)

Loons: order Gaviformes, family Gaviidae
Grebes: order Podicipediformes, family Podicipedidae
Herons and bitterns: order Ciconiiformes, family Ardeidae
Waterfowl (ducks and geese): order Anseriformes, family Anatidae
    Ducks: subfamily Anatinae
        Surface-feeding (dabbling) ducks: tribes Cairinini (wood duck) and Anatini (all others)
        Bay ducks: tribe Aythyini (scaup, ring-necked, redhead, canvasback)
        Sea ducks and mergansers: tribe Mergini (goldeneye, harlequin, bufflehead, oldsquaw, scoters, mergansers)
        Stiff-tailed ducks (ruddy duck): tribe Oxyurini
    Swans and geese: subfamily Anserinae
        Swans: tribe Cygnini
        Geese: tribe Anserini
Hawks and falcons: order Falconiformes
    Hawks, osprey, eagles: family Accipitridae
    Falcons: family Falconidae
Grouse and ptarmigan: order Galliformes, family Phasianidae, subfamily Tetraoninae
Cranes and allies: order Gruiformes
    Rails and coots: family Rallidae
    Cranes: family Gruidae
Shorebirds and gulls: order Charadriiformes
    Plovers (including kildeer): family Charadriidae
    Avocets: family Recurvirostridae
    Sandpipers and phalaropes: Scolopacidae
Gulls and allies: family Laridae
    Gulls: subfamily Larinae
    Terns: subfamily Sterninae
Doves: order Columbiformes, family Columbidae
Owls: order Strigiformes, family Strigidae
Nightjars (nighthawk): order Caprimulgiformes, family Caprimulgidae
Swifts and hummingbirds: order Apodiformes
    Swifts: family Apodidae
    Hummingbirds: family Trochilidae
Kingfishers: order Coraciiformes, family Alcedinidae
Woodpeckers: order Piciformes, family Picidae
Perching birds (many groups): order Passeriformes
    Flycatchers: family Tyrannidae
    Horned lark: family Alaudidae
    Swallows: family Hirundinidae
    Crows, jays, magpies: family Corvidae
    Chickadees: family Paridae
    Nuthatches: family Sittidae
    Creepers: family Certhiidae
    Wrens: family Troglodytidae
    Dippers: family Cinclidae
    Kinglets, thrushes and bluebirds: family Muscicapidae
        Kinglets: subfamily Sylviinae
        Thrushes and bluebirds: subfamily Turdinae
    Pipits: family Motacillidae
    Waxwings: family Bombycillidae
    Shrikes: family Laniidae
    Starlings: family Sturnidae
    Vireos: family Vireonidae
    Wood warblers (many groups): family Emberizidae
        Wood warblers: subfamily Parulinae
        Tanagers: subfamily Thraupinae
        Sparrows: subfamily Emberizinae
        Blackbirds, cowbirds: subfamily Icterinae
    Finches: family Fringillidae, subfamily Carduelina
    Old world sparrows (house sparrow): family Passeridae

GOOD REFERENCE BOOKS ON BIRDS

Harrison, C. (1984) *A Field Guide to Nests, Eggs and Nestlings of North American Birds* Collins; Toronto. Species-by-species info on all aspects of breeding except courting behavior. Bird-egg photos, 416 pages.

Godfrey, W. (1966) *The Birds of Canada* Queen's Printer, Ottawa. The authoritative source for this country, but getting out of date; 428 pages. French edition available.

Kellogg, P. (1975) *A Field Guide to Western Bird Songs* Houghton Mifflin, Boston. Three 60-minute cassette tapes in a plastic folder, with index. Excellent recordings of some 500 species, announced by Roger Tory Peterson.

Peterson, R. (1980) *A Field Guide to Western Birds* Houghton Mifflin, Boston. A standard work.

Robbins, C.; B. Bruun and H. Zim (1983) *Birds of North America* Golden Press, New York. The best field identification guide available, recently updated, with excellent colored illustrations and up-to-date range maps; 360 pages.

Salt, W. and J. Salt (1976) *The Birds of Alberta* Hurtig, Edmonton, Alberta. Readable text, with interesting information on each species in the province. Hardbound, but small enough to be carried along. Mixed photos and painted illustrations; information and range maps sometimes don't agree with other sources; 498 pages.

Savage, Candace (1985) *The Wonder of Canadian Birds* Western Producer Prairie Books, Saskatoon, SK. Up-to-date, interestingly written items on 55 species, including many in our area; emphasis on behavior. Excellent photo illustrations; index, species bibliographies; 209 pages.

Terres, J. (1980) *The Audubon Society Encyclopedia of North American Birds* Knopf, New York. A magnificent book, comprehensive and well-illustrated; expensive and worth it. Includes hard-to-get data on breeding, diet, weight and lifespan, with a big bibliography; 1109 pages.

Udvardy, M. (1977) *The Audubon Society Field Guide to North American Birds, Western Region* Knopf, New York; Random House, Toronto. More information on each species than in most field guides, but the text is organized by habitat, a system I find difficult to use. Barred owl has been left out. Illustrations are photos, organized by appearance; 854 pages.

CHECKLISTS are available for Banff, Jasper, Kootenay, Yoho, Waterton Lakes and Glacier national parks, and for Kananaskis Provincial Park, Alberta. Pick them up at information centres in the individual parks, or order from the addresses given below. At time of writing there was no charge for checklists.

Parks Canada, Western Regional Office
Box 2989, Station M, Calgary, Alberta T2P 3H8
Street address: 220 Fourth Avenue SE, Calgary

Glacier National Park
West Glacier, Montana 59936

Kananaskis Provincial Park
General Delivery, Seebe, Alberta T0L 1X0

Bighorn ram. Photo courtesy Jasper National Park.

Mammals
Furry animals of the Canadian Rockies

Members of the class Mammalia have hair and teats. With few exceptions, young mammals are born without that cozy halfway-house, the egg. These things are sufficient to differentiate the mammals from other animal groups.

In the Canadian Rockies we have 69 naturally occurring species of mammals. This includes the wood bison, which now lives almost exclusively in paddocks (there is at least one wild one in the region, possibly two) and *Homo sapiens.*

Because they are mostly ground-dwellers and larger than many other creatures, mammals leave **sign:** tracks, trails, droppings, the discarded remains of meals, the burrows and dens, the squirrel middens and pika haystacks. This messiness is handy for mammal-watchers, because many of their subjects are shy creatures of the night. In daylight one can tell who has been around the evening before if he knows what to look for, especially in winter, when tracks abound. Check the tracks-and-scats pictures on the pages 673 and 674.

Anyone exploring the montane woods is bound to run across mammalian bones and antlers occasionally. See pages 668 through 672 for pictures of the skulls of most mammal species in the Canadian Rockies; antlers are illustrated in the drawings of deer-family members (pages 730-736).

Here is how the species listings work. In each listing the English common name is followed by the French common name. The **dates** given bracket the time of year in which a species or its sign is seen. Some of our mammals hibernate, while others stay under the snow in winter and are not seen, even though they are active.

The **body measurements and weights** given are averages for adults *in the Canadian Rockies.* To save space the range of size and weight for each species is not given, although it can be considerable. The overall length includes the tail, the length of which is given separately. The average height of the larger animals is measured at the shoulder. Among the larger mammals, males are usually 10-30 percent bigger than females and a good deal heavier.

Each year, most mammals go through two or more **moults:** loss of one coat of hair and its replacement by another, often of a slightly different color. Where the difference is eye-catching, it is indicated.

The most interesting thing to many people about mammals is their **behavior,** so much of each entry is devoted to that. Details of reproduction are important to biologists; they include mating behavior, breeding season, the length of gestation (time in the womb), what time of year the young are born, how many are in a litter and how they grow up. This is a lot to put in a field guide, so it has been kept brief. **Longevity** data are provided where possible, but as in the case of birds, information on lifespan is usually based on few records and should not be relied upon.

Hunters: many species of mammals are protected in Alberta, British Columbia and Montana. Be sure you know the game laws before you shoot.

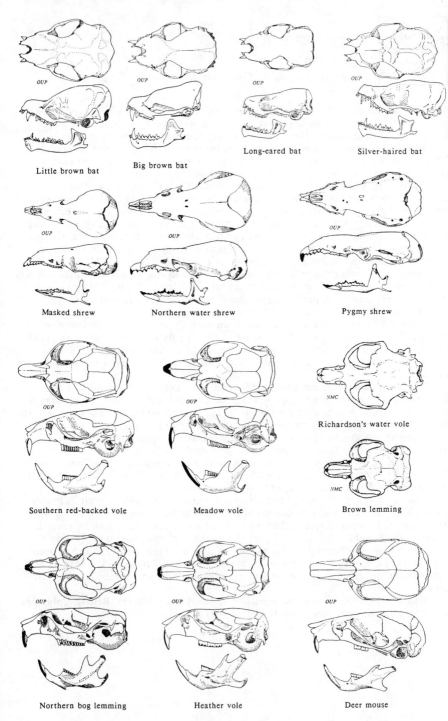

Little brown bat

Big brown bat

Long-eared bat

Silver-haired bat

Masked shrew

Northern water shrew

Pygmy shrew

Southern red-backed vole

Meadow vole

Richardson's water vole

Brown lemming

Northern bog lemming

Heather vole

Deer mouse

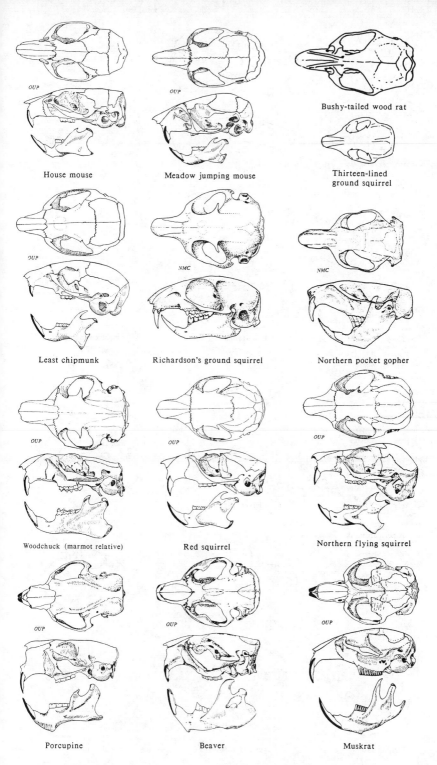

Bushy-tailed wood rat

House mouse

Meadow jumping mouse

Thirteen-lined
ground squirrel

Least chipmunk

Richardson's ground squirrel

Northern pocket gopher

Woodchuck (marmot relative)

Red squirrel

Northern flying squirrel

Porcupine

Beaver

Muskrat

MAMMAL SKULLS   669

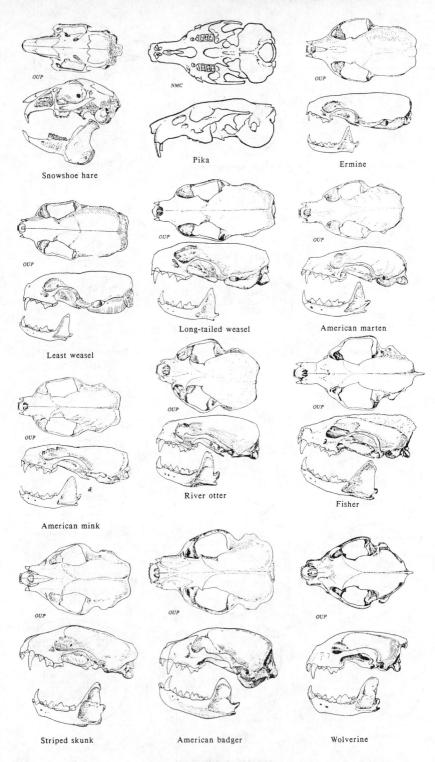

Snowshoe hare

Pika

Ermine

Least weasel

Long-tailed weasel

American marten

American mink

River otter

Fisher

Striped skunk

American badger

Wolverine

MAMMAL SKULLS

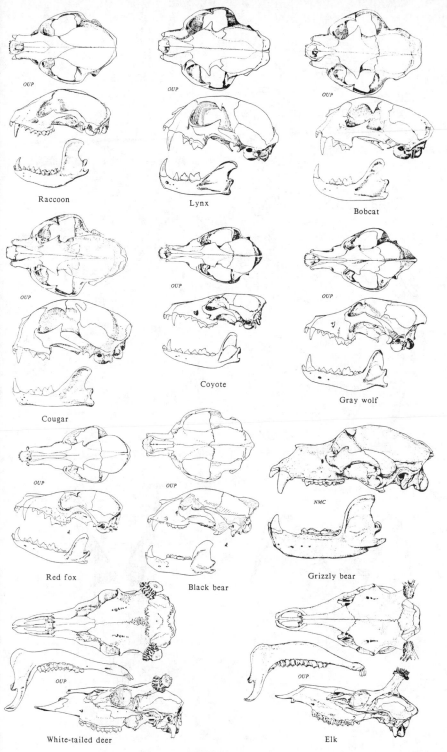

Raccoon

Lynx

Bobcat

Cougar

Coyote

Gray wolf

Red fox

Black bear

Grizzly bear

White-tailed deer

Elk

MAMMAL SKULLS

671

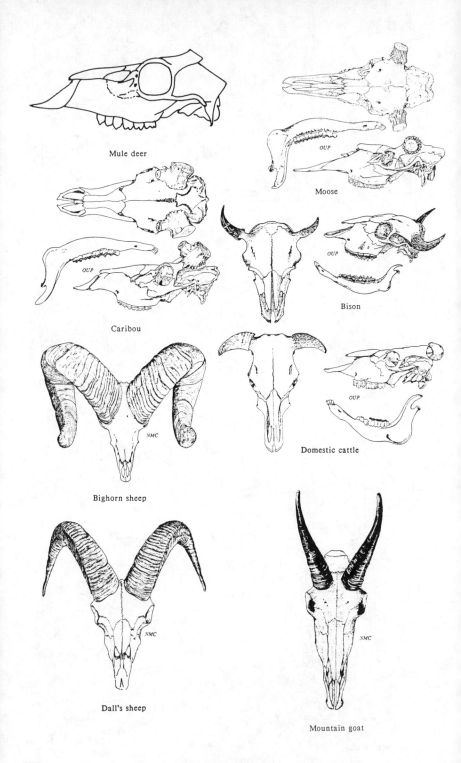

Mule deer

Moose

Caribou

Bison

Bighorn sheep

Domestic cattle

Dall's sheep

Mountain goat

MAMMAL SKULLS

TRACKS AND SCATS IN THE CANADIAN ROCKIES
Top of each track is forward direction
Distance between tracks is for walking gait unless otherwise noted

(*Redrawn from various sources*)

Red-backed vole
Running; 5 cm between sets

Meadow vole
Track 1 cm across,
running sets 5.7 cm apart

Deer mouse
Track 0.6 cm across,
sets 3 cm apart

Wood rat
Track 1.5 cm across,
running sets 19--20 cm apart

Beaver
Track 13--14 cm across

Muskrat
Hind foot 5.5--6 cm,
sets 7.5 cm apart

Red squirrel
Track 2--2.5 cm long,
leaping sets 50--70 cm apart

Chipmunk
Track 1 cm wide,
running sets 15 cm apart

Ground squirrels
Track 2.5--3 cm wide,
running sets 25--40 cm apart

Marmot
Track 4.5 cm long,
running sets 35 cm apart

Weasels
Track 2--3 cm long

Mink
Track 3.5 cm wide

Snowshoe hare
Track set 25 cm long,
hops same length

Hind

Front

Hind

Pika
Track 2--2.5 cm,
scats 0.5 cm pellets

Front

Hind   *Front*

Porcupine
Front 6.5 cm long,
hind 8 cm,
linked scats
(links 2.5 cm each)

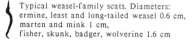

Typical weasel-family scats. Diameters:
ermine, least and long-tailed weasel 0.6 cm,
marten and mink 1 cm,
fisher, skunk, badger, wolverine 1.6 cm

Fisher
Track 5.5--6 cm long

Front   *Hind*

Wolverine
Track 11--20 cm long

Marten
Track 4--5 cm long

Typical weasel-family
loping pattern

Badger
Track 5 cm long

Hind

Front

Skunk
Track 3.5 cm long

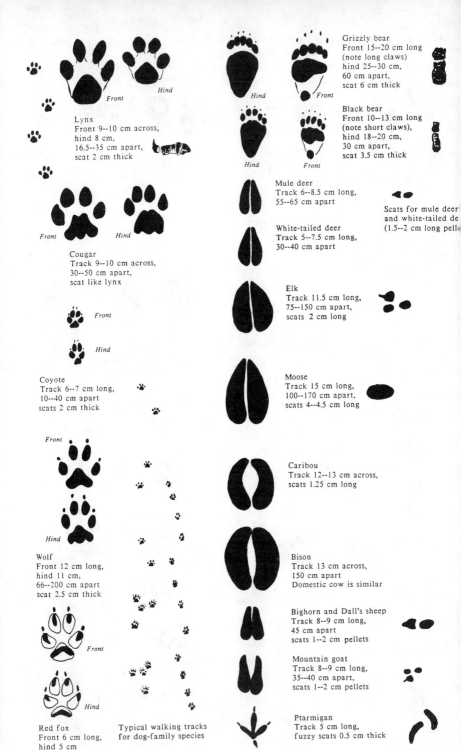

Lynx
Front 9--10 cm across,
hind 8 cm,
16.5--35 cm apart,
scat 2 cm thick

Front   *Hind*

Cougar
Track 9--10 cm across,
30--50 cm apart,
scat like lynx

Front   *Hind*

Front
Hind

Coyote
Track 6--7 cm long,
10--40 cm apart
scats 2 cm thick

Front

Hind

Wolf
Front 12 cm long,
hind 11 cm,
66--200 cm apart
scat 2.5 cm thick

Front

Hind

Red fox
Front 6 cm long,
hind 5 cm

**Typical walking tracks
for dog-family species**

Hind   *Front*

Grizzly bear
Front 15--20 cm long
(note long claws)
hind 25--30 cm,
60 cm apart,
scat 6 cm thick

Hind   *Front*

Black bear
Front 10--13 cm long
(note short claws),
hind 18--20 cm,
30 cm apart,
scat 3.5 cm thick

Mule deer
Track 6--8.5 cm long,
55--65 cm apart

Scats for mule deer
and white-tailed de
(1.5--2 cm long pell

White-tailed deer
Track 5--7.5 cm long,
30--40 cm apart

Elk
Track 11.5 cm long,
75--150 cm apart,
scats 2 cm long

Moose
Track 15 cm long,
100--170 cm apart,
scats 4--4.5 cm long

Caribou
Track 12--13 cm across,
scats 1.25 cm long

Bison
Track 13 cm across,
150 cm apart
Domestic cow is similar

Bighorn and Dall's sheep
Track 8--9 cm long,
45 cm apart
scats 1--2 cm pellets

Mountain goat
Track 8--9 cm long,
35--40 cm apart,
scats 1--2 cm pellets

Ptarmigan
Track 5 cm long,
fuzzy scats 0.5 cm thick

BATS: HUNG UP ABOUT CAVES
Order Chiroptera, family Vespertilionidae (evening-bats)

The only truly airborne mammals, bats fly with membranes of naked skin that stretch between their elongated finger-bones. The membrane also fringes the sides of the body, incorporating the weak back legs and extending along the tail. The wings are uniformly thin, not thickened in the centre to provide the sort of airfoil that gives lift to the wings of birds, but curvature in the bat's membrane creates an airfoil anyway, and thus bats fly essentially as birds do.

Bats have also evolved sonar for navigating and locating prey in the dark. A bat squeaks at frequencies of 30,000-100,000 hz, too high for humans to hear (although bats make audible noises as well). As each pulse leaves the bat's nose and mouth, the ears seal off the sound so that the animal hears only the returning echo. The brain interprets the timing of the echos to give distance and direction to whatever bounced the sound back. A bat seems to form a sonar image of its surroundings; it catches flying insects with ease, differentiating them from complex forest backgrounds.

Bugs are usually caught on a wingtip, then passed down to a pocket formed by curling the interfemoral membrane (the skin between legs and tail) inward, like the pocket of a baseball mitt. After the fly is fielded, so to speak, it is eaten immediately if small (the bat ducks its head down) or taken to a perch for eating if large. A bat typically catches one bug every seven seconds, dispatching a gram of arthropods an hour all night long.

Coupled with these skills is a prodigious memory for terrain and cave passages. Most bats overwintering in the Canadian Rockies travel deep into caverns for hibernation, flying through complex passages. They find their way home to the same cave each winter, although it may be hundreds of kilometres from where they spent the summer and the cave entrance may be tiny.

Bat coordination is terrific: bats have been known to escape from a locked laboratory room by flying unscathed through a turning ventilator fan.

In this climate, bats can carry on their nightly foraging flights only from about mid-April to mid-October, when the evening temperature is above freezing and insects are plentiful. During the other six months of the year the non-migratory species must survive without eating. Having put on a surprising amount of fat for an airborne animal (about one-third of body weight), they become dormant, hanging head-downward in tightly packed underground colonies. Their body temperature drops to that of the air temperature, which in Canadian Rockies caves is just a few degrees above freezing year-round.

The little brown bat, which is the most common species in the mountains, often mates in late August or early September, but the female keeps the male sperm alive in her uterus until the following spring—a period of about eight months. She ovulates at the end of dormancy, when she begins to eat again and is thus able to grow the embryo. Whether this is true of other species is unknown.

Females of most species bear only one baby each year, sometime between mid-June and mid-July. Each mother bat carries her baby with her when it is very young; it clings crosswise to her furry chest (she has two tiny nipples located like human ones). The young can fly on their own only three weeks after birth.

Finally, the lifespan of bats is amazingly long for such small mammals: up to 30 years, which explains why they survive with such a low rate of reproduction.

Bats can carry rabies, so it is unwise to touch them. But we need not fear them. Just the opposite; as ravenous bug-eaters and biological marvels bats deserve our respect and protection. When entering caves in winter, people should be careful not to disturb dormant bats, causing them to fly around and use up precious fat reserves needlessly. This can kill them. You can shine a light on a bat without awakening it, but only for a few seconds.

Little brown bat
(petite chauve-souris brune)
Myotis lucifugus (evening-bat family)
April to October

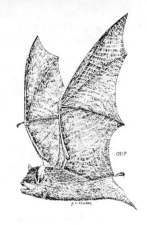

Very common from valley floors to timberline, seen from dusk to dawn flitting silently about the sky nabbing insects. In daytime, found roosting in colonies in tree hollows, rock crevices, caves and unused parts of buildings. Overwinters in the region, mainly in caves. Length 8 cm (tail 3.5 cm); weight 7.5 g. Dark-brown back, lighter underside, dark face, ears, wings, legs and tail. Compare with similar big brown bat (next entry).

Little brown bats emerge from hibernation in early spring, when small flying insects (especially mosquitoes) become active. Mating occurs in fall (in the Rockies; often in spring farther south) with delayed fertilization until after hibernation; gestation takes 50-60 days and delivery of the single young occurs from mid-May to July. Carried about in its first few weeks, the young bat soon flies; it matures during the first annual hibernation, which begins with the disappearance of flying insects in fall, often in early October in the Canadian Rockies. The longevity of this species (to 30 years) explains why I keep seeing bats banded in the 1970s hibernating year after year in Cadomin Cave.

Big brown bat
(grande chauve-souris brune)
Eptesicus fuscus
(evening-bat family)
April to October

Fairly common from Jasper south, seen chasing airborne bugs in forests and meadows from dusk to dawn. Often seen in towns. Length 11 cm (tail 4.5 cm); weight 15 g. Very similar to the little brown bat (previous entry), but noticeably larger and often rustier in color, the coat glossier and the face lighter brown. Positive identifier: no extra-small tooth behind the canine.

Habits and life cycle are like the little brown bat, but the big brown bat is bolder and more urban, hanging around dwellings and often choosing attics for winter roosts rather than caves. Big brown bats sometimes come inside houses through open doors, then refuse to leave. Quite hardy, these bats become dormant later in the fall and emerge earlier in spring than other bats in the area.

Long-legged bat
(chauve-souris à longues pattes)
Myotis volans (evening-bat family)
April to October

Occasional in woods and meadows from
Grande Cache south, seen mostly at dawn
and dusk. Length 9.5 cm (tail 4.5 cm);
weight 7 g. Dark brown like the bats
described previously, but can often be
differentiated by looking closely at the
wings: the underside of the wing
membrane is lightly furry between the
elbow and the knee.

Not much is known about the long-legged bat, but it probably spends its time
much as the little brown bat does. One difference: it is likely that this bat
migrates south for the winter, out of the Canadian Rockies, rather than
overwintering in caves—although there is one record for Cadomin.

Long-eared bat
(chauve-souris à longues oreilles)
Myotis evotis (evening-bat family)
April to October

Occasional from Prince George south,
emerging later in the evening than other
bats. Length 9.8 cm (tail 4.4 cm); weight
10 g. Yet another brown bat with black
wings, this one differentiated from the
rest by the ears: they are noticeably
longer (2-2.5 cm).

Not studied much; probably behaves
like the other *Myotis* species. Probably
migrates south rather than overwintering
here.

Silver-haired bat (chauve-souris argentée)
Lasionycteris noctivagans
(evening-bat family)
Late May and late August

Occasional from Prince George south,
usually seen in spring and late summer
when bats are migrating to and from
their winter ranges in the USA. Length
10.3 cm (tail 4.2 cm); weight 8 g. Easily
identified by color: dark brown to black
all over, with silver-tipped fur. Compare
with hoary bat (next entry).

Silver-haired bats appear earlier in the evening than other bats, sometimes in
afternoon daylight. They often fly over water, catching mayflies and other insects
that hover above the surface. Slower on the wing than other bats, and somewhat
clumsy-looking, they have been known to crash into the drink and then swim out
of it. Daytime roosts are solitary, in tree hollows, sometimes in large abandoned
bird nests. The silver-haireds migrate rather than going into dormancy.
Reproduction and life cycle are typical of bats, although two young are born
annually instead of one.

Hoary bat (chauve-souris cendrée)
Lasiurus cinereus (evening-bat family)
Late May and late August

Occasional to rare from Jasper south, flying well after dark in heavily wooded areas. Our largest bat: length 13.5 cm (tail 6 cm); weight 26 g. Silvery like the silver-haired bat (previous entry), but the underlying fur of the hoary bat is much lighter, and the hoary is quite a bit larger and stouter. There is often a yellowish collar, with tawny patches on the arms; the rear parts of the wing membranes are lightly hairy. Note the round ears.

Hoary bats are solitary, even during migration (when we see them), which takes them to the southern USA and Mexico. They usually feed over water, picking off the larger night-flying insects (mostly moths) and perhaps killing other bats. The species mates in August and gives birth to twins in June, but little else is known of its life cycle.

SHREWS
Order Insectivora, family Soricidae

If it looks like a mouse with a long, pointy nose and a wire-thin tail, then maybe it's a shrew. But shrews are not rodents; they are insectivores, a primitive order of mammals.

Shrews are active year-round, in winter staying under the snow. Busiest just before dawn and just after dusk, shrews have incredibly fast metabolisms (heart rate up to 1200 beats per minute) and must eat at least their weight in food each day to stay alive. Menu: insects (mostly moth and beetle larvae), slugs and snails, fungi and seeds. Shrews hunt mainly by rooting among ground litter. They are hunted by many small predators (especially weasels and owls), and have been known to eat one another. But they are fierce for their size, taking over the burrows of larger creatures (they don't seem to dig their own) and defending solitary territories.

Unlike most other small rodents, shrews are quite vocal, twittering away as they make their rounds. Why? Shrews have been shown to use echo-location, although not as well as bats do.

Mating is usually in the spring (sometimes in the fall). The nest is built of grass under a log or rock, usually with two entrances. Gestation time: about 18 days. There are one or two litters of 2-10 (average 4-5) young each year, the offspring reaching maturity in about four months and living at the most only two summers and the intervening winter. When threatened, a family of young shrews quickly take each other's tails in their mouths, one of them clamping onto mommy's tail and all running off in a line.

Masked shrew (musaraigne cendrée)
Sorex cinereus (shrew family)
Spring to fall

In damp meadows and forests, sometimes
above timberline, usually near water.
Probably our most common shrew, but
secretive, normally foraging under leaf
litter, concealing itself there and thus
seldom seen. Length 10 cm (tail 4 cm);
weight 4.1 g.

Recognized as a shrew by the long, whiskery nose. Fur color: grayish-brown or
sepia-colored, grayer below. Coat is much heavier in winter than in summer, and
usually darker. Very small eyes, flattened ears almost hidden in fur. Long
unfurred tail, pinkish feet with five toes on each foot (mice, sometimes confused
with shrews, have four toes on their front feet, five on the back). A little smaller
than the very similar dusky/vagrant shrews (next entry), but to differentiate
confidently you have to check the teeth. In masked shrew the front teeth along the
upper jaw grow smaller gradually toward the molars; in the dusky/vagrant species
the last tooth ahead of the molars is quite a bit smaller than the rest.

See the previous page for habits.

Dusky shrew and vagrant shrew
(musaraigne sombre, musaraigne errante)
Sorex monticolus and *S. vagrans*
(shrew family) Spring to fall

Grassy/willowy shores of bogs and streams, montane to alpine. Dusky shrew fairly
common from Crowsnest Pass north; vagrant shrew in Waterton/Glacier. Length
11 cm (tail 5 cm), weight 5 g.

Both species closely resemble the masked shrew (see previous entry for
picture), but they are a little longer and heavier, with redder fur. The upper jaw
includes one tooth (the one just ahead of the molars) that is noticeably smaller
than any of the others. Differentiate the two species by geographic range. Habits
and life history are like those given in the introduction.

Pygmy shrew (musaraigne pygmée)
Microsorex hoyi (shrew family)
Spring to fall

Fairly common in grassy subalpine
meadows; prefers drier habitat than
other shrews. The smallest mammal in
the New World: length only 8 cm, of
which 2.5 cm is tail. Weight about 3 g.

Typical shrew features: pointy whiskered nose, skinny scantily furred tail,
pink feet. Coat sepia above, smoky below. Differentiated from other shrews in the
Canadian Rockies by size (noticeably smaller), by the tail (proportionately shorter)
and dentition: in the upper jaw, two of the teeth behind the incisors are so small
that you need a magnifying glass to see them. Thus, at first glance, pygmy shrews
appear to have only three teeth between the incisors and the molars, whereas the
others clearly have five.

Life cycle of the pygmy shrew is probably like that of other shrews, but the
species needs more study. It seems even more frantically hungry than its relatives,
eating about three times its weight each day in insects and carrion.

Northern water shrew (musaraigne palustre)
Sorex palustris (shrew family) Summer and fall

In or at the edge of small mountain streams, often in heavy subalpine forest. Our largest shrew: length 15 cm (tail 7 cm), weight 13 g.

Typical shrew-like pointy face with long whiskers. Coat is dark gray, but appears quite silvery in the water from bubbles adhering to the thick fur. The hind feet are unique among our shrews: bristly along the toes and partly webbed to help in paddling.

Water shrews swim well, and watching one is fascinating. It appears to run across the water's surface when swimming quickly. Paddling furiously to overcome its bubbly buoyancy, it dives to the bottom in shallow water to grab insect larvae (caddisflies, mayflies, stoneflies), other invertebrates and fish eggs, sometimes taking small fish—and sometimes making a meal for a large trout. Emerging from a stream, a water shrew shakes the water off and quickly combs itself dry with its bristly hind feet. The species also hunts on land, searching the shoreline rocks for insects.

Mating begins in late winter. Two or three litters of about six young are raised before summer's end; gestation period unknown. Like other shrews, this one mates again shortly after giving birth. The nest is at the water's edge, often hidden among the sticks of a beaver dam or lodge. The animal is short-lived, going about its frantic little life for only two summers. What does it do during the winter, when everything is frozen up? I could find nothing on this, but shrews don't hibernate. Perhaps, like the beaver, the water shrew has a connection from its nest to water, keeping it open through constant use under the insulating snow blanket. Or it may abandon the water in winter, living as other shrews do in rodent runs under the snow.

MICE—AND A RAT
New-World mice and rats (order Rodentia, family Cricetidae), Old-World mice and rats (family Muridae) and jumping mice (family Dipodidae)

Deer mouse (souris sylvestre)
Peromyscus maniculatus
(New-World mice/rats family)
Year-round

Very common in any dry habitat; found from valley floors to timberline and sometimes higher. Nocturnal. Size quite variable; in the mountains often large: length about 20 cm (tail about 10 cm), weight about 35 g.

The deer mouse is reddish/grayish-brown above, with white tummy, chin, legs and feet. The eyes and ears are larger than those of the voles—the deer mouse was the model for Walt Disney's Mickey Mouse—and the long, lightly fuzzy tail is dark on top and white underneath.

Deer mice are nocturnal, thus seen less often than their numbers warrant. Quick and agile, using their long tails for balance, the animals travel widely on the ground, running about in overlapping one-hectare territories and crossing highways (this is the mouse that you see in your headlights). They climb trees to the top for buds and fruits. Other foods: mostly seeds (especially those of conifers), but also berries, insects (mostly larvae) and an underground fungus called *Endogone* that is popular with most mice.

Deer mice are active year-round, leaving lots of tracks on the winter snow. If you follow the tracks, easily identified by the tail print, you may come to a little snow tunnel going down toward the nest, which is a ball of grass or feather moss about 10 cm across, hidden in a grass tussock or low tree cavity, in a hollow among roots, an abandoned burrow or (a favorite) an empty container. The mice store several litres of seeds nearby for winter use.

Given a low entrance hole, deer mice will move indoors with you, not so much to eat your food (which they *will* do) as to share accommodations—including your mattress stuffing. They are fond of nesting in cupboards and drawers; in 1980, users of the Hilda Creek Hostel (along the Icefields Parkway near Columbia Icefield) opened and shut a silverware drawer many times, never pulling it out far enough to see the deer-mouse nest at the back.

If you sleep outdoors, a deer mouse may come up to your head, often walking on your sleeping bag or even on your face, to gently nibble loose a few strands of hair for nesting material. I have always found this amusing, but one time it gave the horrors to a British climber bivouacked with me under a boulder. "Bloody 'ell!!" he cried at 2 a.m. "There's a *raht* in me 'air!" And he started flailing with a piton hammer, somehow missing me as well as the raht. A couple of fig bars flung into a corner of our kip distracted the beast, which was the size of a cat according to the hammer-wielder, and we went back to sleep listening to it going "tsit-tsit-tsit" as it ate. At dawn I awoke with crumbs rolling into my eyes. It was a deer mouse, perched on my forehead as it finished the last fig bar.

Seldom vocal, deer mice drum with their front feet when alarmed. They are prey for night-hunters such as weasels and owls, sustaining their numbers through prolific reproduction. The breeding period is March to October; there are normally four litters a year averaging four babies per litter. Gestation is 22-35 days, the nursing period the same length. Papa leaves when the young are born, then returns to help out with the washing and nest-tidying when they are a few days old. Mom weans the young'uns at 22-35 days, then chucks them out; they often move in with dad, who meanwhile is seeing mom again.

Females mature at 32-35 days; males at 40-45 days. Lifespan in the wild is normally less than a year, although deer mice have lived for eight years in captivity.

House mouse
(souris commune)
Mus musculus
(Old-World mice/rats family, Muridae)
Indoors year-round

Common in townsites, in dwellings with accessible food. Nocturnal. Length 17 cm (tail 8.5 cm); weight 20 g.

Brown above, dark-gray below, with large dark ears, pink nose and feet, pale tail. Looks like the deer mouse (previous entry), but smaller and not white underneath. The white mice used in laboratories and kept as pets are albino house mice.

House mice are colonial; they evolved on the east-European steppes (grasslands, like those of the Canadian prairie provinces), then moved indoors for an easy life with the Russians of Turkestan. Like the Norway rat (not reported in the Canadian Rockies), house mice have spread throughout the world as stowaways.

They nest in walls, behind cupboards, under the floor—anywhere out of sight and safe from the cat. There are sometimes communities in grain and hay fields, for seeds are their natural foods; as human commensals they prefer cereals, flour and sugar, fruit, vegetables and whatever appeals in the garbage.

House mice come out at night, gnawing noisily into bags and boxes, leaving little rod-like droppings on the counters and carting off mattress stuffing, newspaper and hair for nesting material. One or two in a cabin can be tolerated, for they don't carry disease as some rats do, but given their reproductive rate (a litter of four to eight every couple of months, year-round) it usually becomes necessary to crack down with traps or feline help. Gestation is 21 days, maturity 35 days after birth.

Bushy-tailed wood rat/pack rat
(rat à queue touffue)
Neotoma cinerea
(New-World mice/rats family)
Year-round

GNHA

Common in coniferous woods, living in rock crevices, under boulders, in caves and under or in buildings. Nocturnal, most active just after dusk and before dawn. This is our largest mouse-like land rodent (length 42 cm, half of which is tail; weight 400 g) and is thus easily identified.

The tail is so bushy that some people mistake the wood rat for a squirrel, but none of our squirrels has the large ears and beady, protruding eyes of the wood rat. The soft coat is brownish gray, with black-tipped hairs; sometimes it is quite pale. Feet are white.

One seldom sees a wood rat, for they are usually active after dark. Instead, one sees (and smells) their dwellings. Nearly any deep crevice in a rocky outcrop below timberline could be home to a solitary wood rat, the entrance piled high with old conifer needles and twigs. There are sludgy deposits of black feces nearby, and the rocks surrounding the nest are stained yellowish from urine.

But don't get the wrong idea. These animals are actually very clean and tidy. Behind the midden and shielded by it is the nest, made like a bird's nest of soft mosses and hair. Curled up by day in the nest is the rat, often surrounded by a collection of shiny man-made objects: bits of glass, coins, cutlery, bottle caps and (currently in fashion) pop-tops from aluminum cans. Wood rats living far from human activity collect colored rocks, crystals and feathers. Thus the folk-name "pack rat" for these creatures. Another folk name, "trade rat," comes from the animal's supposed practice of leaving one object in place of another. What actually happens is that the rat drops what it is carrying in favor of a more attractive item.

Wood rats are excellent climbers. I have passed by their nests 50 m up on difficult rockclimbing routes.

Main wood-rat food: foliage, mostly of deciduous shrubs and trees, but also of conifers. The rat often drags a leafy or needle-covered branch back to the nest, where it is dried for awhile before being eaten. Fruits and seeds are also on the menu. In fall, wood rats stockpile cuttings in and near their dens; they are active all winter, mainly under the snow, but you sometimes see their tracks on the surface. They look like those of the deer mouse (page 680) but are larger.

Breeding begins in February, the males marking territory with their anal musk glands and fighting viciously among themselves as they search for females. But they are gentle with the ladies, nuzzling them and purring before mating. Gestation is 27-32 days; normally there are two litters of 3-4 (range 1-6) young each year, weaned at 26-30 days. Maturity, though, takes a long time by rodent standards: nearly a year. Maximum longevity in the wild is about four years.

Longevity in someone's cabin is often considerably shorter. Wood rats make a stinky mess of borrowed lodgings, building large middens on the beds and in the stove and cupboards. All collectibles are dragged thereto. They eviscerate mattresses, shred up blankets and clothing, poop everywhere and piss on the walls—real party types, and quite noisy at night as they waddle clumsily about and send things crashing. Not nice to have indoors. But interesting!

Western jumping mouse and meadow jumping mouse
(souris sauteuse de l'Ouest,
souris sauteuse des champs)
Zapus princeps and *Z. hudsonius*
(jumping-mouse family, Dipodidae)
Spring to fall

Fairly common in moist meadows and grasslands at all elevations, usually near water. Mostly nocturnal. Length 25 cm (tail 15 cm); weight 18 g.

The **western jumping mouse** has a brown back and tawny sides in the southern part of the Canadian Rockies; is overall gray in the north. Both races are cream-colored underneath, with a long skinny tail that is dark on top and light below. Big back legs, large ears.

From Valemount north on the western slope and Pine Pass north on the eastern slope, one also finds the **meadow jumping mouse,** quite similar but a little smaller (length 21 cm, tail 13 cm, weight 15 g), brown and tawny like the southern race of the western jumping mouse, but with a broad olive-brown band down the centre underneath. Neither species is very vocal, but adults sometimes rasp, chatter their teeth and drum with their tails. The babies squeak.

Both the western and meadow jumping mice jump, all right: 1-2 m at a time, holding very still for a moment after landing. To predators, this combination makes the mouse seem to disappear. Then it goes quietly about its business in short hops, eating grass seeds, berries and other plant fruits, sometimes climbing grass stems. It is also a good swimmer, diving over a metre deep on occasion.

Territories are about 100 m across, although a jumping mouse moves around more than other small-rodent species and may finish life a kilometre away from where it began.

A true hibernator, the species practically doubles its weight in fall, curling up tightly in a grass ball at the end of its burrow (either dug or borrowed) in September and not stirring until May. Then it mates, producing just one litter of 5 (range 2-7) young in June. Gestation is probably 18 days. The tiny babies are born pink and hairless, blind and deaf, like those of most rodents. But they are on their own a month later and mature at two months. Few live more than a year.

VOLES AND LEMMINGS
New-World mice and rats family (Cricetidae)

Voles and lemmings are mouse-like, but they have much shorter ears, smaller eyes, blunter heads and shorter, furrier tails.

Southern red-backed vole/
Gapper's red-backed vole
and northern red-backed vole
(campagnol à dos roux de Gapper,
campagnol à dos roux boréal)
Clethrionomys gapperi and *C. rutilus*
(New-World mice/rats family)
Summer and fall

Common (although populations fluctuate markedly) in subalpine forest, usually near water. Length 14 cm (tail 4 cm); weight 24 g.

The red-backed voles are easily identified by the broad stripe of reddish-brown to bright red fur running from head to tail-base. The two species are very similar, but their ranges divide at Peace River with little overlap. The southern red-backed vole (south of Peace River) has a browner stripe than the northern red-backed vole (north of Peace River), on which the stripe is quite red.

Mainly nocturnal, red-backed voles sometimes come out during the day. The northern species eats all parts of many kinds of shrubs and wildflowers. The southern species is pickier; it prefers the petioles (stalks) of leaves, supplemented with berries when it can get them and buds, twigs, seeds and even bark when leaves are scarce. Doesn't cache food. Both species will eat carrion, including their own kind.

Neither species swims much, but they both climb up into shrubs and trees. Each vole ranges through 1-2 ha, tunneling in the feather mosses of the subalpine forest floor. There is a ball-shaped nest of grass, leaves and moss hidden under deadfall or in the natural hollows that one always seems to find among the roots of large trees in boggy subalpine forest.

Active all winter, voles (red-backed and others) build an extra nest right on the ground, under the snow, joined to the extensive tunnel network that rodents maintain in the sugary-textured depth-hoar at the base of the snowpack. Occasionally they come out on the surface, leaving tiny tracks (page 673).

Everything seems to eat voles, so they reproduce prolifically. Two to four litters of 4-7 young are born from May to October each year. Gestation period 17-19 days; 18-21 days later the young are weaned and chased out of the nest to make way for the next batch. Maturity comes at four months, although most females wait until the following spring to mate. Lifespan is unknown, but certainly not very long in the wild.

Vole populations vary enormously from year to year, a boom-and-bust cycle made worse by man's killing of weasels, wolves, coyotes and predatory birds. In years of overpopulation, cabin-dwellers (especially north of Peace River) find themselves beset with waves of hungry voles; in other years they see very few.

Meadow vole (campagnol des champs)
Microtus pennsylvanicus
(New-World mice/rats family)
Spring to fall

Very common in damp montane meadows, grassy marshes, hay or grain fields and untended yards. Length 16 cm (tail 4.5 cm), weight 35 g.

Its gray coat (brown-tipped in summer), gray feet and lightly hairy tail cause many people to mistake this animal for a mouse (its folk name is "field mouse"). But the small ears and eyes show that it is a vole, not a mouse.

This is the most common rodent of open areas at low elevations; it is active in the morning and late afternoon in habitat that humans use, so we see it frequently. Meadow voles live in runways among grasses and sedges, their usual foods. They are active year-round, but they seldom venture above the snow, preferring to stockpile in fall rather than forage in winter. They also swim well, diving in marshes to escape predators (but sometimes getting eaten by trout in so doing).

Like most small mammals, the meadow vole has a home territory when the population is low (5-50 per hectare; 15-150 per acre). But the population density often increases dramatically (up to 150 voles per hectare, or 400 per acre), and when this happens the species becomes communal, sharing runways, toilet places and food caches. Despite this degree of social organization, the animals spend a lot of time fighting, and they maintain tiny inviolate territories around their individual nests. It's life in the city.

The nest is a ball of grass about 15 cm across, placed under a rock or down an unused ground-squirrel burrow when possible, in a grass tussock when not. The species is very clean; soiled bedding is discarded, and in winter new nests are built everywhere under the snow. When it melts, you can see the little abandoned nests and runs.

Female meadow voles pop out babies at such a rate that a single breeding pair would chain-produce a million descendants in a year if it were not for very heavy predation—and cannibalism: unattended children are often eaten by the neighbors.

Breeding starts in April and runs through October. The promiscuous females call squeakily to the males, who run about obliging one and all. There are three or four litters of about six each; gestation time is 20-21 days, weaning 12 days later and maturity at only 25 days. That quick growing up is essential to meadow-vole survival: the average lifespan is only two months for the spring batch, with 90 percent mortality in the first month. Meadow voles born in fall are more likely to last the winter, when their predators find them harder to get, and thus the species survives until the following spring.

Heather vole (phenacomys)
Phenacomys intermedius
(New-World mice/rats family) Spring to fall

Fairly common in shrubby montane and subalpine forest, and in shrubby alpine meadows from Pine Pass south; occasional north of Peace River. Length 14 cm (tail 3.5 cm), weight 30 g.

Resembles the meadow vole (see previous entry for picture) but is paler and occurs in the same habitat as the red-backed voles (page 684). A little grayish-brown beast with a silvery tummy, small ears and eyes and a short wire-like tail. Has white feet like a deer mouse (feet of the meadow and long-tailed voles are dirty gray, not white).

More common than once thought, heather voles scuttle unnoticed through forest-floor debris, brush and shrub patches. They are active mainly at twilight, munching the leaves of many subalpine shrubs, chewing up wildflowers and eating berries. In winter they eat the buds and bark of willows, dwarf birch, blueberries and kinnikinnik, caching twigs under the snow for lean weeks. These caches can reach a couple of litres in volume. Life-cycle: breeding from May through August, averaging five to the litter; gestation period is 19-24 days, weaning is 17 days later and sexual maturity is reached at only six weeks. Lifespan probably less than a year in the wild.

Long-tailed vole (campagnol longicaude)
Microtus longicaudus (New-World mice-rats family) Spring to fall

Fairly common in several kinds of habitat: in grassy forest glades, along stream banks and in bouldery places such as talus slopes.

A large vole: length 18 cm (tail 7 cm), weight 45 g. Closely resembles the meadow vole (see page 685), but besides the larger size a good identifier is the long tail. The fur is brown on top, going gray down the sides; belly and feet are gray. Habits not well known, but probably similar to those of meadow vole: grass/sedge eater, diurnal, active under the snow, communal runways in grass or among rocks. Reproduction is unstudied, although this species is not as prolific as the meadow vole.

Richardson's water vole
(campagnol de Richardson)
Arvicola richardsoni
(New-World mice/rats family)
Summer and fall

Fairly common from Grande Cache south, in subalpine and alpine marshes, along stream banks and in wet meadows. Length 25 cm (tail 83 cm), weight 85 g; our largest vole, almost twice the size of the meadow vole.

Easily identified by size when seen out of water. In water it looks like a miniature muskrat (page 700). Reddish-brown back, gray belly and feet; furry tail, dark-brown above and light gray below. Very blunt head and small eyes for its size; long claws.

Water voles do spend a lot of time in the water, although they don't seem to feed there; they eat mainly subalpine and alpine wildflowers (especially valerian, lousewort, arnica and lupine). In winter they subsist on willow buds and twigs.

So what are they doing in the water? I have no information on this, except that it seems a good place to avoid enemies (they are too large to be eaten by most fish). They are also burrowers, digging networks of shallow tunnels 5-10 cm in diameter in streambanks and along shorelines. The water vole creates a ridge of soil over the tunnel like a mole, the only animal in the Canadian Rockies to do so. (We have no moles. In the far south end, the northern pocket-gopher, page 694, also pushes up soil from underground, but in piles, not in ridges.)

Water voles construct runs at the base of the snowpack, building winter nests in them that are larger than those of other voles and caching vegetation; the nests litter the ground in spring.

Not much is known of the water vole's life cycle, but it breeds from mid-June to early September, producing at least two litters of five each year. Like the other voles, this species is prone to population explosions.

Brown lemming (lemming brun)
Lemmus sibiricus (New-World mice/rats
family) Summer

On alpine tundra and talus, and in
subalpine bogs, from Peace River north.
Length 15 cm (tail only 2 cm), weight
70 g.

A vole-like creature rather easily
identified by the coloration (gray head
with yellowish cheeks, gray shoulders,
brown back with yellowish sides, buffy
gray tummy) and the very short tail.
Pikas (page 703) live in much the same
habitat; differentiate by size (pika is
larger), color (pika is gray), ears (much
larger on the pika) and voice (pikas say
"eek"; lemmings say very little).

This is the famous lemming that lives in the north and flings itself into the
sea. We have it!

Lemmings are colonial burrowers, active day and night (although less so on
bright days). They dig shallow burrows down to the permafrost, one burrow per
family, with a nesting room, an indoor toilet and a couple of bare chambers
(function unknown). Lemmings eat grasses and sedges mostly, one another
occasionally. They are not true hibernators, but neither do they cache food for the
winter; they nibble away at grasses, sedges and willows under the snow, producing
snow-runs and grass-ball nests that are exposed when the snow melts.

Now the interesting part. This creature produces one to three litters of seven
(4-9) each year, breeding from June through August and sometimes all winter.
Despite the best intentions of numerous lemming-devourers (hawks, eagles, weasels,
marten, foxes, wolverines, wolves, bears; you name it, it eats lemmings), the
population builds and builds—as becomes evident in May or June, when lemming
business shuts down so that everybody can leave home and move to higher ground
during the spring melt.

This is to avoid drowning in a flooded burrow, but it has the effect of
reapportioning territory. When one of these emigrations occurs at the peak of the
population cycle (once every 2-5 years), the whole arctic suddenly becomes
ankle-deep in lemmings. The creatures swim quite well, so they plop into the
ocean, probably figuring to be across the pond shortly. In the mountains, where
populations are never as dense, the craziness is much less noticeable.

Gestation: 23 days; lifespan: less than a year for nearly all; up to 14 months
for a few.

Northern bog lemming (campagnol-lemming boréal)
Synaptomys borealis (New-World mice/rats family) Summer and fall

Occasional in black-spruce bogs, grassy marshes and damp shrubby meadows at all
elevations, but mostly subalpine. Scarce south of Crowsnest Pass. Length 13 cm
(tail 2.5 cm), weight 33 g.

Smaller than the brown lemming but similar (see previous entry for picture),
this species is differentiated by features of the skull—which is hard on the
subject. A peek in the mouth will tell the tale sometimes: if the incisors appear
quite broad and have conspicuous lengthwise grooves, it's a bog lemming.

Bog-lemming foods include grasses and sedges, winter and summer. The
animals are burrowers in summer and snow-tunnel dwellers in winter; they store
food in runways and build winter nests of grass, like the voles do. Reproduction
habits are little known; breeding is May to August, four to the litter (2-8). This
species does not have mass emigrations and doesn't seem to suffer the
boom-and-bust cycle of its relatives.

Voles and lemmings

CHIPMUNKS AND STRIPED GROUND SQUIRRELS
Squirrel family (Sciuridae)

Chipmunks are solitary, active only in daylight and not very shy; they run about nervously with their tails held upright, while ground squirrels let their tails droop. Chipmunks have stripes on their heads as well as on their backs (striped ground squirrels do not have stripes on their heads), and pouches inside their cheeks, which they stuff with food to be eaten later or carried home.

During summer, most chipmunks like to spend their evenings in woody places: abandoned woodpecker tree-holes (they are good climbers) hollow logs and stumps. But in late summer each digs a winter burrow about 2 m long, with two entrances leading to a roomy nesting and storage chamber about a metre underground. One entrance is used to eject the soil; when the nesting chamber is finished, this hole is plugged well and the other one, which has no dirt around it, is used for going in and out. This is a clever bit of work, but it also leaves the animal no emergency exit in case a snake or weasel comes slithering down.

Least chipmunk (tamia mineur)
Eutamias minimus (squirrel family)
Spring to fall

Common along forest edges and in rocky places at any elevation, except between Golden and Peace River on the western slope (the Columbian forest area); common again to the north. Length 22 cm (tail 10 cm), weight 43 g.

Of our three chipmunks, this is nominally the smallest (the range of sizes overlaps). The least chipmunk is striped like the others, with two white lines on the face (one from nose to ear above the eye, the other from lower eye to ear) and four gray ones along the back, bordered in black. There are burnt-orange patches on the shoulders and flanks; the belly is white. The tail is fluffy, dark-brown above and yellowish below. To differentiate positively from the very similar yellow pine chipmunk (next entry) is difficult, requiring dissection, but note that the least chipmunk is grayish while the yellow pine chipmunk is, in fact, yellowish, and that the habitats are somewhat different.

The least chipmunk eats strictly seeds, especially those found in succulent fruits and berries—but it eats *only* the seeds, carefully removing them from the sweet pulp that other animals crave. If you see a pile of discarded raspberry pulp, you know who has been there. Its fruit-eating neighbors must love this critter.

A grassy nest is built in the burrow, right on top of a couple of litres of stored seeds. These it needs for the winter; the least chipmunk hibernates fitfully, awakening every now and again and heading to the kitchen for a bite to eat. Torpor begins in mid-October and ends in mid-April, which is breeding time. Gestation of 28-30 days produces 4-7 young once a summer (in the Rockies); they hang around with mum for two months before leaving home. She sometimes carries them around by the loose skin on their tummies or necks.

Yellow pine chipmunk (tamia amène)
Eutamias amoenus (squirrel family) Spring to fall

Common in dry montane forests, especially so in the Douglas-fir woods of the southern Rocky Mountain Trench. Length 22 cm (tail 10 cm), weight 50 g.

Very similar to the least chipmunk (see previous entry for picture), with same marking pattern, but brighter and with more yellow. Differentiate also by habitat: yellow pine chipmunk tends to stay in dry areas at low elevations, while the least prefers moist forest openings and fringes at higher elevations. Otherwise the habits and life cycle are quite similar.

One difference: yellow pine chipmunk eats more than just seeds, taking flowers, fruits and roots as well.

Red-tailed chipmunk
(tamia à queue rousse)
Eutamias ruficaudus (squirrel family)
Spring to fall

Fairly common in the Waterton/Glacier area, usually in subalpine forest but also at lower elevations. Length 23 cm (tail 10 cm), weight 60 g.

A little larger and stockier than the yellow pine chipmunk, and rather easily differentiated in the small part of the Canadian Rockies in which the ranges overlap: red-tailed does indeed have a reddish tail, both top and bottom (tails of yellow pine and least chipmunks are brown above and tawny or ochre-colored below). The red is especially noticeable underneath.

There is little information available on the red-tailed chipmunk. It is diurnal like other chipmunks, known to spend much of its time scampering through the lower branches of Engelmann spruce and subalpine firs. It's inclined to be noisy, the chatter reminiscent of the red squirrel's scolding (page 695). Eating habits and life cycle unknown.

Golden-mantled ground squirrel
(spermophile à mante dorée)
Spermophilus lateralis
(squirrel family)
Spring to fall

Common from Grande Cache south, in dry, rocky places at subalpine and alpine elevations. Length 30 cm (tail 10 cm), weight 230 g.

Much bigger than any chipmunk, this ground squirrel nonetheless looks and acts rather like one. It has two white stripes running from neck to hips, bordered by black; the rest of the back is salt-and-pepper gray. The lower sides and tummy are buffy, while the head and shoulders (the "mantle") are yellow-ochre, brown or reddish.

This species is gregarious, living in small groups and often in the company of chipmunks, hoary marmots (page 693) or pikas (page 703). It is livelier than other ground squirrels, running quickly about by day to eat and gather the seeds, leaves, flowers and fruits of a wide variety of subalpine shrubs and wildflowers. Like the voles, it also eats underground fungi and grabs what insects it can.

What the golden-mantled ground squirrel likes best is anything coming from human hands. These are the junk-food junkies of the rodent world. At the roadside viewpoints that frequently fall within their rugged habitat they are out in force on any sunny summer day, boldly coming up to be fed, climbing onto the shoes of delighted humans and even climbing up their legs.

This is cute, but it is not particularly healthy behavior; most of the food the squirrels receive is either very sweet or very salty, and it's loaded with chemical preservatives. Late in the season this overindulgence may alter their body chemistry, such that they may die in hibernation from accumulated Cheezie toxins and Ding-Dong byproducts unknown to nature.

This is the prevailing wisdom passed on by many a park naturalist (including me) during his or her obligatory don't-feed-the-animals remarks at the evening campfire program. But a study of the effect of human foods on mice and voles (S. Gilbert and C. Krebs, 1981, *Oecologia* 51) suggests that these animals do better with junk food than without it! Whether the same can be applied to ground squirrels and chipmunks is unknown.

This still leaves one very good reason for discouraging people from attracting ground squirrels to their hands and allowing them to scamper on their clothing: the animals often have fleas, and the fleas have been known to carry bubonic plague in the Rockies.*

Unlike the burrows of other ground squirrels, there is no mound of dirt to mark the entrance to a golden-mantled's rather simple workings. These are usually 1-2 m in length and only half a metre deep, with a single chamber at the back holding a bed of shredded vegetation and a litre or two of seeds. A couple of side passages serve for pissoir and additional storage.

Hibernation is deep but not continuous for chipmunks in the Canadian Rockies. Nodding off in September, the squirrels rouse themselves every few days to eat and urinate. They don't seem to drink anything all winter. The males emerge first, in mid-April. When the females come out a couple of weeks later the breeding season is on and one litter of 4-6 young is produced in early summer. Gestation time is probably similar to that of other ground squirrels (about 28 days). The kids leave home in mid-summer; they are ready to mate by the following spring. In captivity these animals have lived for 11 years, a very long time for a small rodent species.

Thirteen-lined ground squirrel
(spermophile rayé)
Spermophilus tridecemlineatus
(squirrel family)
Spring to fall

Occasional in the southern foothills from Calgary south, in shrubby areas and aspen stands not far from water. Length 27 cm (tail 10 cm), weight 150 g.

Much bigger than a chipmunk, but stripy and thus often mistaken for one. However, there are no lines on the cheeks of the squirrel, the ears are small and the tail is not as bushy. The 13 lines include seven wide brown stripes with pale dashes in them; there are six pale stripes separating the brown ones.

Like the golden-mantled ground squirrel (previous entry), this one is likewise diurnal, but eats far more insects (mostly grasshoppers, crickets and caterpillars) than greenery. Insects are salty, which explains why this species needs to drink

---

*Although plague is not associated with the golden-mantled, it is with Richardson's (page 691) and the Columbian ground squirrel (page 692). Plague is easily cured nowadays, but there have been *deaths* from it in the Rockies because doctors have failed to recognize the flu-like symptoms in time.

water (the other ground squirrels do not). Further, it is the only one that would rather live in the shade than out in the open.

The thirteen-lined is fairly vocal, uttering shrill cries that are difficult to pinpoint among the shrubbery. It is solitary, digging a long, deep burrow (up to 5 m long and 2 m deep). There is a large chamber at the end, with a ball-nest of grasses among hoarded seeds. A second entrance is dug from the inside under a grass tussock. The tailings are used to plug the first entrance and thus to provide a hidden entry point with no telltale dirt. There is a 90° bend a little way along to discourage excavation by badgers.

Hibernation begins usually in late September. Lab study shows that the body temperature drops from the normal 36-38°C to just above freezing; the pulse drops from 100-200 per minute to 1-15, which is typical for species of ground squirrels in the Canadian Rockies. The animal cannot be aroused by prodding, but wakes up voluntarily every week or two for a nibble and a pee.

In early April it is time to head outside for breeding. Because this species is solitary, the males must search widely for females. Males fight each other when they meet. The litters are large (average of eight) but there is just one each year. Gestation period is 27-28 days. The young venture above ground in early July, leaving about ten days later to dig their own burrows. They are sexually mature by the following spring.

UNSTRIPED GROUND SQUIRRELS, THE MARMOT AND OUR ONLY TRUE GOPHER

Richardson's ground squirrel
(spermophile de Richardson)
Spermophilus richardsonii
(squirrel family, Sciuridae) Spring to fall

Very common in the foothills from Bow River south, in grassland, dry open places such as pastures and along roadsides. Length 28 cm (tail 7.5 cm), weight 300-600 g.

Identifiers: buff belly and flanks, black-tipped hairs peppering the head and back, and black streaks in the tail, which is furry but not lush. Large almond-shaped black eyes set high on the head, small ears, black whiskers.

There are various folk names for this beast. "Gopher" and "prairie dog" are commonly used, but both are erroneous, for we have no prairie dogs and only one species of gopher (see page 694). Another name, "picket pin," is more on the mark. It refers to the animal's habit of sitting up so straight that it looks from a distance like a wooden stake of the kind used to tie a horse out in pasture.

Handling ground squirrels is not recommended; they often have fleas, and the fleas can carry bubonic plague.

Richardson's ground squirrel is a creature of the open prairie, living at the northwestern limit of its range in the Canadian Rockies. It is active in the daytime, spends a lot of time above ground and is thus easy to watch. When not out foraging on the ground for grasses and wildflowers (it eats all parts, including roots and seeds), the animal sits motionless on its heels atop the dirt pile at the main burrow entrance. This gives it a good view and makes it hard to see from above. When something threatens—a hawk, a coyote, a person—it cries "tweep!", twitches its tail once and pops underground. Because the squirrels are loosely colonial (they live near one another but don't share burrows or food stores), there is usually at least one squirrel on guard while the others are concentrating on in food-gathering; thus warned, all rush below ground, squealing.

The burrows are 7-8 cm in diameter, 4-15 m long and 1-2 m deep; they are maze-like, with interconnecting passages and several rooms. The main entrance is obvious, marked by a large pile of excavated dirt; there are also a half-dozen or so inconspicuous entrances ("funk holes" for quick escapes) nearby in the squirrel's small territory. The nesting chamber is lined with grass and seed hulls. There may also be seed-storage rooms, although not usually, for Richardson's hibernates from mid-August until the first warm weather of late March or early April. The extra food may help the squirrels get through the first unpredictable weeks of spring, when snow can arrive suddenly and cover the sparse spring vegetation for several days. Richardson's also eats insects and carrion, including its own dead.

Breeding occurs right after hibernation; one litter a year of 5-11 is born about the end of April (gestation: 22-23 days). The young come above ground in late June and reach sexual maturity in time for next spring's mating.

Late summer of its first year is the toughest time in a ground-squirrel's life. That is when the current crop of juveniles disperse, engaging in a deadly serious game of musical chairs in which too many squirrels compete for too few territories. Most of the youngsters get gobbled by coyotes and hawks (especially by red-taileds).

In the spring, Richardson's ground squirrels are famous for flaunting themselves before that most wasteful of predators, the automobile. Ravens sit along the fencelines and wait for supper to be served. Driving west from Calgary or Lethbridge in spring, you may see dozens of squirrels along the highway shoulders, inching jerkily out into traffic and sitting upright in the middle of the road as the cars bear down. ("Hmmm . . . the ground's hard out here, but what the heck, it's unclaimed territory.") Any squirrel setting up shop in the middle of the TransCanada is doomed, of course, although it may survive a few encounters by coolly letting the monsters pass over.

Ranchers and farmers shoot, trap and poison Richardson's ground squirrel because it eats their grain and hurts their livestock (which can break their legs by stumbling in its holes). But these same folks also do in the coyotes that would otherwise gladly keep the ground-squirrel population under control.

Columbian ground squirrel
(spermophile du Columbia)
Spermophilus columbianus
(squirrel family, Sciuridae)
Spring to late summer or early fall

Common in meadows at all elevations from Pine Pass south, except where replaced at low elevations by Richardson's ground squirrel (previous entry). Length 35 cm (tail 10 cm), weight 400-1000 g.

This may be an illusion, but it seems to me that the higher the elevation, the larger these squirrels become.

In alpine meadows the squirrels are often mistaken for marmots (next entry). This is understandable, for the salt-and-pepper back coloration of the two species is similar. But the Columbian ground squirrel is much smaller, burnt-orange or reddish on the nose, chin, belly, legs and feet, while the hoary marmot is bigger and drably colored all over, except for some tawniness under the legs and in the tail. Its feet are black.

Columbian ground squirrels behave rather like Richardson's, active only in the daytime and living in small colonies in which each member has its own burrow. They graze nearby, eating the roots, stems and leaves of a great variety of wildflowers and shrubs. Like Richardson's, Columbians sit upright at their burrow entrances and dodge in when alarmed. They say "tweep" sharply and repeatedly, such that I have been fooled into thinking that I was hearing the alarm note of a robin—but where is the bird? Hikers on tundra trails will set off whole meadowfuls of these squirrels.

The burrow is wonderfully engineered. A main entrance with dirt mound angles downward for about a metre, then levels off and leads into a large central chamber about 75 cm across that contains bedding of grass or plant down. Radiating off are 3-20 m of tunnels that underlie the feeding area; placed along them are hidden entrances for quick dives underground. Disrespectful of this technology, grizzlies rip up the workings to gobble the workers.

In August the squirrel digs a special tunnel an additional metre downward to its solitary hibernation chamber, which it lines thickly with dried grass. To drain away any water that might percolate down, just off the chamber there is a sump tunnel that goes a half-metre deeper. Entering the winter den in late August (early October in the high country), the squirrel plugs the entrance of its chamber with soil and curls up tightly. In spring, it doesn't simply push out the plug and proceed through the house to the front door; it digs directly upward to the surface. Emergence is in early April down in the valleys, as late as mid-June above timberline.

Then it is mating time, with lots of fighting among the males, who have been up and about for ten days already, and chasing of the females. The children arrive about 24 days later, one litter of four (range 2-7) each year. They are weaned after a month, at which time you see them above ground for the first time; maturity and reproduction don't occur until the following spring (at low elevations—in the second spring higher up). This species does not seem as keen on playing in traffic as Richardson's is.

A couple of recent bubonic-plague cases in the mountains show that Columbian ground squirrels carry fleas that harbor the disease. Don't handle these squirrels or allow them to climb on you.

Hoary marmot (marmotte des rocheuses)
Marmota caligata
(squirrel family, Sciuridae)
Summer and fall

Common in alpine meadows from Bow River north, less common to the south. Length 72 cm (tail 21 cm), weight up to 5.8 kg.

"Hoary" refers to the long, coarse, white-tipped coat. A dark patch on the light forehead continues as two smudgy lines over the ears and down the neck. There is a black line across the nose, and the feet are all quite black. The lower back and rump are brownish, and the short, bushy tail is often streaky tawny/black. Underneath, the animal is gray, usually tawny on the inside of the legs.

Some people confuse the marmot with the Columbian ground squirrel (previous entry), despite their differences in size and coloration. One need only look at the paws: if they are black, it is a marmot.

Marmots whistle (well, vocalize) a loud, long note. Folk names include "whistler" and "whistle-pig." No matter what you call it, the marmot is a close relative of the **woodchuck/groundhog** *(Marmota monax)*, which comes close to the Rockies from Rocky Mountain House north, but doesn't quite make it into the foothills. Woodchucks also live in the Columbia Mountains (next range west of the Rockies), and they cross the Rocky Mountain Trench occasionally, turning up in the Radium area and in Mt. Robson Provincial Park.

The Whistlers, a mountain overlooking Jasper, is named for its marmots. Hundreds of people are taken nearly to the top every day of summer on a tramway. Thoroughly jaded, the marmots up there often lie stretched out indolently on the boulders as the admirers gather.

Marmots have an enviable life. They seem to have little to do in the summer except roll about in lush alpine meadows, eating anything green (and in so doing practically denuding the ground around their dens). Their only natural enemies are grizzlies, who must dig up their burrows to get them, and golden eagles, who pick them off from the air.

A marmot burrow is short and simple, dug among boulders with a grass-lined chamber at the end. Like other ground squirrels, marmots are loosely colonial, nesting near one another; families sometimes share digs. They end hibernation in late April or early May, digging their way out through the lingering high-country snow-cover and probably living on stored food for awhile until the snow melts in June. Four or five little marmots poke their noses above ground in July, and everyone goes back to bed in September.

Northern pocket gopher
(gaufre gris)
Thomomys talpoides
(pocket-gopher family, Geomyidae)
Active year-round, but unseen

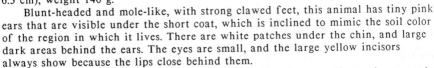

Common in Waterton/Glacier and the southern Rocky Mountain Trench, at low elevations in moist meadows with deep, fine soil. Fossorial (living underground) and thus seldom seen. Length 23 cm (tail 6.5 cm), weight 140 g.

Blunt-headed and mole-like, with strong clawed feet, this animal has tiny pink ears that are visible under the short coat, which is inclined to mimic the soil color of the region in which it lives. There are white patches under the chin, and large dark areas behind the ears. The eyes are small, and the large yellow incisors always show because the lips close behind them.

This is the only true gopher in the Canadian Rockies; the other rodents people call "gophers" here are actually ground squirrels.

Pocket gophers are so named because they have external cheek pouches: fur-lined pockets on the sides of their faces, extending from cheek to shoulder, opening toward the back and not connected through to the mouth. The gophers use their front feet to stuff these pockets with cut plant stems and roots, emptying them later underground.

The species is solitary and subterranean, emerging seldom and then only at night, but you can easily find its sign: low piles of soil pushed up from underground and scattered, with no hole to be seen. The gopher digs its burrow by loosening soil with its front feet and kicking it back; after awhile it turns and bulldozes the lot out to the surface.

Water voles (page 686) also push up soil from underground, but in lines directly above their tunnels. Pocket gophers don't make these ridges, although they burrow in the base of the snowpack like many other rodents, lining their snow runs with soil that remains for a while after the snow has gone.

Main foods: grasses and forbs (wildflowers), eaten mostly while burrowing. The incisors nip off roots, and whole plants are pulled down from underground. The shallow feeding tunnels branch off from a deeper system dug below the frostline (1-3 m down, depending on elevation). There are storage rooms for laying in winter supplies of greenery and roots (the animals don't hibernate) and a chamber for the grassy nest.

Breeding is in May and June; the young are born in late June or early July. There is usually just one litter of four (range 1-8). Gestation period: 19 days. The young are on their own after 6-8 weeks and must leave mum's burrow, resulting in a fall gopher-feast for predators. The average lifespan of those youngsters that get safely underground is 3-4 years; sexual maturity comes at 11-12 months.

IN THE TREES:
SQUIRRELS AND THE OCCASIONAL PORCUPINE
See also the marten, page 706

Red squirrel (écureuil roux)
Tamiasciurus hudsonicus
(squirrel family, Sciuridae)
Year-round

Very common in montane coniferous forest, less common in subalpine forest. Length 31 cm (tail 12.5 cm), weight 190 g.

Despite its name, the red squirrel is not particularly red in the Canadian Rockies. The summer coat is olive brown with pale buff or gray underparts; in winter the coat is thicker, finer and redder. The tail, though, is usually reddish above and grizzled black/gray below, with a dark tip. There is always a white ring (two crescents, really) around the eye.

Ubiquitous, mostly diurnal and not at all shy, this is probably our most commonly seen wild mammal—although the voles and mice outnumber it many times over. It is also the only tree squirrel in the Canadian Rockies that one is *likely* to see; the northern flying squirrel (next entry) is nocturnal and much less common.

Red squirrels are quite vocal, chattering loudly at passersby. They sound rather like a kid's pull-toy noisemaker that is dragged quickly at first, then slower and slower as the puller tires.

This species is mostly arboreal, but in the Canadian Rockies it nearly always nests in the ground, not in trees. Although summer nests of twigs are reported here, I have never identified one. People commonly confuse witches' brooms in spruce, which are parts of the tree perverted in growth by a fungal parasite (see page 298), with squirrel nests.

Each squirrel maintains a territory of 0.5-1.5 ha (1-3 acres) that includes a large trash heap called a **midden**. The burrow lies in and under it; there are several entrances.

These animals are cone-shuckers. They eat the seeds, discarding the scales in the midden, which can be 10 m across and a metre deep. It is the home of just one squirrel (or a female and her babies).

Most middens are large and deep, with many years of rot evident in the lower layers. Inspecting these heaps, which are made up mostly of cone scales, shows that the favorite cone species in the Rockies seem to be white spruce and black spruce. Lodgepole pine cones are less popular, which stands to reason because they are quite hard. For some reason the animals ignore Douglas-fir cones. I haven't seen the cones of subalpine fir in the middens, but such cones are stuck firmly to the trees and the squirrels may shuck the scales in place.

I often find lodgepole galls (branch swellings; see page 293) on the middens, their bark gnawed away. I could find no reports on this, but the squirrels may chew the galls because the cambium layer just under the bark is full of sugar and plant proteins created in the rapid growth of the gall.

Besides conifer seeds, red squirrels eat many other things: buds, bark, catkins and plant fruits, mushrooms (which they hang in the crooks of branches to dry), subterranean fungi, insects, birds' eggs, nestlings, baby rodents and carrion.

In exchange, lots of things eat squirrels. Their main predators are tree-climbing martens (page 706) and tree-raiding hawks such as Cooper's (page 601), with coyotes, wolves and lynx taking them on the ground. Forest fire is an obvious threat, although squirrels in the Canadian Rockies burrow among their middens and may survive minor fires in this way.

Red squirrels don't hibernate, but neither do they spend much of the winter in the trees. In fall they collect cones, piling them according to species on the midden. when the snow comes the piles are covered, and the squirrel connects them to its midden tunnels with short snow-runs. It stays below during very cold weather, drowsing the days away, but comes out on the warmer afternoons to patrol its territory.

Red-squirrel behavior around humans is puzzling. Sometimes a squirrel that is busy on the ground will let me pass closely by little interest, while at other times a squirrel 10 m up a tree and 10 m away will go shrieking farther up the trunk, scolding me until I'm out of earshot.

Breeding occurs in either early spring or early summer, at which time the males chase the females noisily up and down tree trunks and from tree to tree. After gestation of about 35 days there is a litter of five or so, born naked and helpless. They quickly get furry and stay with mum for about 18 weeks. Then each must locate a new territory.

Since the life span of an established adult can reach ten years, it is certain that the surviving proportion of each generation is quite small—or the mountains would be overrun with red squirrels. (Population explosions do occur from time to time).

Northern flying squirrel
(grand polatouche)
Glaucomys sabrinus
(squirrel family, Sciuridae) Spring to fall

Common in montane coniferous woods, yet seldom seen because the species is strictly nocturnal. Length 30 cm (tail 14.5 cm), weight 50 g. Easily identified in flight (in *glide,* really; they don't actually fly) by the thin furry membrane that stretches from the front paws to the back. It is gray, buff at the edges. The rest of the critter is grizzled brown. The eyes are quite large, and there is no eye-ring as in the red squirrel (previous entry).

Becoming active well after dark, flying squirrels scramble about the conifers and jump from tree to tree in search of lichens, buds, seeds and fruits. They are not nearly as dependent on cones as red squirrels are, and they spend more time in shrubs. Occasionally they produce a chirping call.

In winter the squirrels remain in their nests, which they build in hollow trees or large woodpecker cavities. They fight the cold with lots of nesting material and stock other cavities with cached food. They don't go underground or use snow runs as the red squirrel does.

Winter or summer, flying squirrels live in family groups, male and female sharing the nest with the young. Breeding occurs in early spring, with one litter of three born each year in May. That is a low reproduction rate for the squirrel family; the chances of survival must be pretty good. Gestation period is probably about 40 days; weaning is at about 65 days and climbing/gliding ability is not well developed until 90 days—a long apprenticeship in the rodent world.

Porcupine

(porc-épic d'Amérique)
Erethizon dorsatum
(New World porcupine family,
Erethizontidae)
Year-round

Fairly common in coniferous woods;
usually seen at subalpine elevations.
Mostly nocturnal, but also seen
frequently in the daytime. Length 77 cm
(tail 21 cm), weight 6.5 kg or more.

Our second-largest rodent (beaver is
the biggest), the porcupine is easily
identified by its long yellow-and-black
quills. The little blunt black face shows
at the front of this peculiar armor; the
short flat tail drags along behind. It may
assist in climbing.

Porkies are well-protected by some 30,000 sharp, stiff, hollow, barbed spines
that are modified hairs. Native peoples throughout North America have sewn short
sections of these quills onto apparel as decoration, sometimes dyeing them other
colors.

Besides the face, the only un-quilled parts of a porcupine are the legs and
belly; under attack the animal protects these places by turning its back on the
assailant, when possible with its head pressed into a shelter of some kind (between
two rocks, against a log, etc.). It seldom curls up. The quills fluff out, covering the
feet, and the tail flops back and forth—an effective weapon, for it swipes quickly
and the quills detach easily. Successful enemies (mainly the lynx, wolverine, wolf
and fisher) manage to reach under the animal and flip it over, biting the
underside. Any would-be porky predator risks blinding, starvation (from a mouth
full of quills) or a punctured gut (from eating quills).

If stupid Spot gets quilled-up, veterinarians recommend that you bring him in
as soon as possible, for the quills work their way in deeper and deeper until
removed. If you must do the job yourself, it may help to cut the end off each to
relieve air pressure built up inside its hollow length. This is supposed to relax the
barb somewhat—although one vet I spoke with says that this is untrue and a waste
of time. Grab the pliers, get a firm grip on the dog, and start pulling. Deep quills
may have to be pushed out the other side of a pinched-up skin flap, which is not
as painful as it sounds. Quills in the cheeks and lips can be pushed through rather
easily (somebody wearing heavy gloves must keep the mouth open). Any spines
embedded around the nose are particularly painful to remove because they must
be pulled, not pushed.

So keep your pets tied up in porcupine country. Occasionally an unwatchful
parent will let a toddler play with a porcupine, an early and unforgettable lesson
that nature can be nasty.

Porcupines are not as arboreal as many people think. They strip coniferous
bark, all right, but mostly in the winter when their preferred food—the leaves of
many kinds of plants—is unavailable. They seldom climb very high (usually only a
few metres), but they often kill a tree by removing the bark all the way around.
Porkies don't eat the bark; they gnaw the sugary cambium layer just beneath.

And they crave salt. This leads them to gnaw outhouse seats to get the salty
dried urine. Wooden-handled tools are also appealing. The animals have a taste for
painted or varnished signs, which they edit randomly, e.g.

Danger! Hikers are warned that the . . .
. . . in this area. Parks Canada.

Porcupines chew up plywood and cardboard to get the glue, and they love to gnaw rubber, including the tires and brake lines of vehicles parked overnight in the woods. Some people fence their cars with chicken wire to prevent this.

Porkies don't burrow. They use natural shelters such as boulder piles and jackstrawed timber. Predators along highways have learned to look for porcupines curled up in culverts. One night a porcupine simply walked right into my tiny one-man tent, stepping on me in my sleeping bag until I twitched out of my sleep. Then it turned around somehow (whew!) and walked back out. Now I keep my porcupine netting zipped. In winter the animals spend more time in their shelters, but they don't hibernate.

Breeding occurs in October and November in our area. Question: how do they do it? Answer: carefully. (This is the oldest joke in biology.)

Really, now: how *do* porcupines mate? The male follows the female around for days, grunting and humming sweet nothings. She squeals in reply. Later they cuff each other around and dance together on their hind feet (really!) until she decides that it's time. Then she flips her tail up over her back (the underside of the tail has no quills) and he gets his reward.

Seven months later she produces only one baby, in May or June. It is born with fur and quills (relax; they are soft) and it is able to see right away. This is all unusual: most rodents produce large litters of tiny, blind, naked babies after short gestations. Young porcupines are weaned in only a couple of weeks, but they follow mum around until sexual maturity in their second year.

Another tree-dweller: the marten, page 706.

IN THE WATER: BEAVERS, MUSKRATS AND SOMETIMES AN OTTER
See also the northern water shrew (page 680), Richardson's water vole (page 686) and mink (page 707).

Beaver (castor)
Castor canadensis (beaver family, Castoridae)
Active year-round, but not seen in winter

Fairly common in montane marsh ponds of its own creation, also in natural ponds and slow-moving streams. Length 105 cm (tail 44 cm), weight 20 kg. This is our largest rodent. Beavers are blunt-bodied and brown, with small eyes and ears, and a large flat hairless tail that is gray to dark-brown and appears scaly. It is used as a prop while standing up to gnaw and for whacking the water as an alarm before diving.

That is just the start of an astounding list of adaptations: a dense undercoat of fur for insulation in the water; lips that close behind the incisors for underwater chewing; self-stopping ears and nostrils for diving; large back feet with webbed toes for swimming; two serrated claws on each hind foot for combing oil through the coat from large oil glands located by the anus; other glands that discharge musky **castor oil** for scent-marking; small, well-coordinated front fingers for delicate handling of objects—and behavior that seems too advanced for a rodent.

Essentially nocturnal, beavers are also active in the early morning and the early evening, when there is enough light to watch them swimming slowly and smoothly about their ponds. As they make their way through marshes and along the shores, they squirt musky-smelling castor oil onto mud-pie scent posts and scratch the mud with their claws. This seems to be more than simple territory-marking; some biologists think that the communications are meant for group-members, all of whom do a lot of sniffing and squirting ("Gone for willows. Back in five minutes. - Al.") Females are dominant in beaver society.

Beavers are bark-eaters like porcupines, going for the nutritious cambium layer in willows, birch, balsam poplar, cottonwood and aspen (their favorite). They also eat leaves and twigs, and the seeds of some water plants. Conifers are the last resort. It takes an acre of medium-sized aspen to support one beaver for a year, so don't be surprised to walk into your favorite pond-side glade and find it gone. A beaver can bring down an aspen 25 cm in diameter in only a few minutes. Occasionally the tree-faller gets squashed in so doing.

Beavers are well-known dam-builders. Locating a narrowing in a gentle, marshy stream, a family of beavers builds up layers of sticks, logs, roots and stones, plastered together with mud and sod to dam the flow. As the water level rises the dam is extended to the sides and upward, until there is a sizable pond 1-3 m deep. The object seems to be to provide a safe medium for travel to and from the feeding grounds, which become more accessible as the pond grows. A network of canals is dug through water too shallow for swimming.

When the pond reaches its limit a large house is built (a **lodge**). (Prior to lodge construction the animals live in bank burrows; these are maintained after the lodge is done and used for emergencies.) The family builds its lodge on a small island or on a platform of sticks and mud in shallow water or against the shore. Placing heavy sticks and logs against a core of lighter vegetation, the animals construct a dome some 2-3 m tall and 3-6 m in diameter; the core is removed from the inside, the walls are heavily plastered with mud (except near the top, which allows ventilation between the sticks) and a couple of tunnels are dug down and out into the water at a level below the thickest winter ice. Inside there is a chamber about 150 cm wide and 75 cm high—dry quarters for the family.

Constructing a pond and lodge is a lot of work; why is it necessary when the simple bank burrows would seem to suffice? No one knows for sure—but then why do little kids dam up the streams, or their fathers the Grand Canyon? River-dwelling beavers, who don't build dams, don't seem to build lodges either.

Existing ponds are given up when the food supply runs low, a cyclic occurrence; I know of at least one case in which the beavers apparently drained the pond when they left.

The animals are especially busy in fall, when they are cutting a great deal of vegetation and towing it out into deep water near the lodge. By sticking the ends of saplings and branches into the bottom mud (or simply by stacking from the bottom up) this **raft** reaches from the surface to the bottom and provides food all winter under the ice.

Beavers don't hibernate. When the pond freezes thickly, their predators (grizzlies, wolves, coyotes, lynx and wolverines) can walk right over to the lodge, but by then it is a concrete-like mass of frozen mud and sticks. Should a foe persist in chewing its way in, bank burrows may provide emergency shelter. River otters (page 701) are not stopped by this arrangement, and they are thought to pick off the occasional young or feeble beaver in its den. Humans cut holes in the ice and stake traps on the bottom, drowning their prey to obtain its fur coat (and sometimes to eat the tail).

Beavers breed in January or February; the gestation time is 3.5 months, which is long for a critter this size. There is one litter every year of about four "kits" (range 1-8) born in late spring. Papa is banished to a bank burrow while they are nursing. Upbringing is also long by rodent standards: the young aren not put to work until their second summer. You can recognize the juveniles as they swim about: they have white noses.

In summer there are normally three generations in a beaver pond: mum and dad, last year's kits and this year's kits, for a total of 6-8 residents. The following spring the yearlings are chucked out before the next litter arrives.

Dispossessed, the juveniles of a family often travel together to a new location that may be up to 200 km away downstream, although it is usually much closer—about 10 km on the average, sometimes across a height of land to a different watershed. Lifespan in the wild: up to 12 years.

Muskrat/water rat (rat musqué)
Ondatra zibethicus (New World mice/rats family, Cricetidae) Spring to fall

Common in wetland ponds and lakes with marshy shores, sometimes in slow-moving streams with good cover along the banks. Length 57 cm (tail 25 cm), weight 1 kg.

Muskrats and beavers (above) are sometimes hard for people to differentiate in the water. They have a similar build: chunky and blunt-headed, with small eyes and ears. Both are brown. But muskrats are half the size of beavers, with round, rat-like tails, while beavers have very wide, flat tails. This leads to a difference in swimming style: the muskrat tail whips back and forth, visible in the churning wake, while the beaver tail lies out flat, leaving a smoother wake.

Muskrats are essentially large water-dwelling voles. Well-adapted to their amphibious lives, they have been known to stay underwater for 17 minutes at a time. Their back feet are partly webbed for swimming. Their lips close behind the incisors for underwater gnawing and cutting.

In the Canadian Rockies, muskrats eat mainly cattails, bulrushes, tubers, sedges, water milfoil and bladderwort; they have a taste for freshwater clams and take the odd frog or salamander. Having snipped, dug or caught its food, a muskrat takes it to a feeding platform made of mud and plant leaves surrounded by water. After eating it cleans the platform and grooms itself.

Like beavers, muskrats are house-builders. They also burrow in muddy banks and dig canals in marshes, which are other beaver-type activities. But they don't build dams. The animals maintain territories about 60 m in diameter, fighting savagely among themselves when challenged.

Muskrat houses appear in fall, just before freeze-up. They are usually located on an emergent bit of land (sometimes a tussock or a log) next to water that is too deep to freeze to the bottom. A dome about a metre high is built up from layers of marsh vegetation and mud; the structure quickly freezes and becomes very strong. Tunnels out the bottom lead into the water. Muskrats also build **push-ups**: holes in the ice covered with vegetation brought up from the bottom. Push-ups are essentially air pockets that allow extended foraging trips under the ice to beds of submerged plants that provide winter food. Muskrats don't hibernate, nor do they store food as beavers do.

Breeding begins in spring. The males become extremely aggressive, occasionally battling each other to the death (which is rare in nature) and even attacking human observers. The females, too, get quite nasty as they compete for bank-burrow dens. During April and May it seems that everybody is fighting and bloody, coats and ears torn. Eventually the sexes pair off and stay together for the summer and following winter, producing two litters of 3-7 young (more in the north, fewer in the south). Gestation is 25-30 days; the young are weaned in a month, ready to breed by the following spring. Lifespan of those reaching adulthood is about three years, up to ten years in captivity. The water rat is trapped, drowned and shot for its lovely soft coat.

See also Richardson's water vole, page 686.

River otter (loutre de rivière)
Lontra canadensis (weasel family, Mustelidae) Year-round

Occasional in lakes and the larger rivers, in clear (not silty or polluted) water; rare south of Banff. Length 110 cm (tail 42 cm), weight 7.5 kg. Otters are about the size of beavers and likewise dark brown, but they are easily differentiated by their swimming style: fast and undulating, alternately breaking the surface and going under. (Beavers swim slowly and smoothly, head out flat.) The tail of the otter is long, thick and pointed; the cheeks are very whiskery, and the throat is often pale or silvery. The toes are webbed.

Like the much-smaller mink (page 707), the otter is a water weasel. It lives in little family groups of 4-6. The species is mainly nocturnal, although sometimes active on cloudy mornings or afternoons, and quite shy of man, its major predator.

River otters eat mainly fish, with smaller catches of muskrats, small rodents, amphibians and insects; like sea otters they often float on their backs while dining. But they also spend a lot of time on land, loping about after meadow voles.

Otters are famous for their love of *sliding*. It seems to be part locomotion and part play. They like to enter the water by flopping down well-used muddy runs, and they play on grassy banks or muddy slopes, tobogganing over and over. These slides give their presence away. In winter the animals have a unique way of traveling on snow: they alternately run a few steps and then slide 6-8 m on their tummies. They have been clocked doing this at 25 km/h.

Otters don't hibernate, but they do hole up in their dens (usually borrowed bank-beaver burrows or abandoned lodges) during cold snaps.

Reproduction: right after one batch of young are born, otters start another. This occurs variably in late winter or early spring, but the embryo doesn't implant in the womb for many months, resulting in a gestation period of up to a year. The single annual litter is small (1-4, usually 2-3). Momma kicks poppa out while the kids are little; he returns in six months, by which time they are weaned and out of the nest, hunting and playing. Growing up takes a long time for an animal this size: females are not ready to breed for two years, males not until they are six or seven. Otter families are close, a rarity in the lonely, blood-and-guts world of the weasels.

HARES AND ROCK-RABBITS, BUT NO TRUE RABBITS
Order Lagomorpha

Snowshoe hare/varying hare (lièvre d'Amérique)
Lepus americanus
(rabbit/hare family, Leporidae)
Year-round

Common in the woods, but mostly nocturnal. Length 48 cm (tail only 5 cm), weight 1.5 kg. "Snowshoe" from the large furry feet. In the summer and fall, snowshoe hares are brown or grayish with white tummies; in the winter and spring they are white with black-tipped ears. The color change comes when the summer set of outer hairs ("guard" hairs) falls out and the winter set grows in. Underneath, the fur is silky gray/buff year-round. Moulting animals are mottled.

This is the only bunny you are likely to see in the mountains, although the **white-tailed jackrabbit** (lievre de Townsend, *Lepus townsendii*) is reported occasionally in the southern foothills. It is larger, with very long, jackrabbit-style ears. Those of the snowshoe hare are shorter (10-12 cm).

By day this species sleeps fitfully in its "form": a beaten-down spot under the drooping, thickly needled lower branches of a spruce, sometimes in dense brush or long grass, or under a log in a tangle of fallen timber.

At twilight the bunnies emerge to patrol their run-laced ranges of 6-7 ha (15-17 acres), often coming out early on a dim December afternoon. At night they stand transfixed in one's headlights and are just as likely to run right under the car as off into the bushes. Richard Adams, who wrote a great children's novel about rabbits called *Watership Down*, would say that they are "tharn."

Summer foods: grasses, wildflowers (especially pea-family plants and clover) and new leaves of aspen, willow and birch. In winter they eat the leaves of plants that stay green (kinnikinnik, wintergreen) and the twig-ends and buds of shrubs. At any time of year they eat their own special fecal pellets, green and made of partly digested food. When the hares are many and starving, they strip bark and eat their own dead.

Breeding begins in mid-March and continues until mid-summer. The males **(bucks)** chase the females **(does)** about with very little fighting among rivals; after a gestation period of 37 days the first litter of 3-4 young **(leverets)** comes along in May. There is usually one more litter that summer, sometimes two. Baby rabbits are born blind and naked, but newborn hares are furry and precocious—a major difference between these two groups.

Hares are out of the nest and starting on solid food after only a week. This gets them off the blocks quickly in a race with death that is soon over for most; even among adults, the yearly survival rate is only 10-50 percent, depending on the stage of the population cycle. Principal eaters of our bunnies are owls, lynx, martens (and other weasels), cougars, foxes, coyotes, wolves and man.

But the reproductive rate in snowshoe hares is so high that there are never enough predators to gobble up the population explosions typical of this species. Surges can send the concentration to 1300 individuals per square kilometre. These booms end in horrible busts: mass die-offs from starvation and disease. At such times the animals harbor many parasites and carry diseases such as tularemia, a bacterial infection that is serious in humans. Don't handle wild hares.

Pika/concy/rock-rabbit
(pica d'Amérique)
Ochotona princeps
(pika family, Ochotonidae) Spring to fall

Common from Jasper south, occasional north to Pine Pass, in alpine talus slopes and boulderfields with nearby vegetation; occasionally at lower elevations in slide heaps. Length 19 cm (no tail), weight 19 g. "Pika" is usually pronounced "PIE-ka," although the word is native Siberian and they pronounce it "PEE-ka," in imitation of the call.

The pika looks like a guinea pig but is not closely related; it is a lagomorph like the hares and rabbits (not a rodent, as is the guinea pig), with two sets of incisors and its testicles ahead of its penis. Such are the vagaries of taxonomy.

This is a creature that you hear first and see later. Something in the boulders gives forth a nasal "eek." What was that?

Not until the pika moves do you see it: a little gray beast with large round ears and no tail. The animal may be sitting on a rock only 5 m away, but it holds very still and the ventriloquisitic voice could have come from anywhere.

Pikas eat grasses, sedges, lichens, many kinds of alpine wildflowers and the emerging leaves of alpine willows and dwarf birch. In late August I have often seen piles of vegetation gathered by pikas and put out to dry on flat boulders; later in fall the animals take their hay indoors, down into their runs among the jumbled rocks. They also stash it under boulders that can be reached through snow burrows.

A lot of supplies must be laid in, for winters are long in the Canadian high country and the pika does not hibernate. Like rabbits and hares, pikas **refect,** meaning that they eat their own dung. This sounds disgusting, but only special pellets are eaten, soft and green, made of partly digested food. Normal droppings are not eaten.

Pikas live in loose colonies; each animal has its own territory, perhaps 50 m by 50 m in size. Those members of the group not otherwise occupied act as sentries, moving about from one vantage point to the next and warning everyone of approaching enemies: golden eagles, marsh hawks, weasels, wolverines and lynx. The most dangerous is the ermine (page 704), which is able to enter pika runs.

A study in southwestern Alberta has shown that pikas there produce 3-5 babies in May. Often another batch arrives in July, but few of the second litter survive. The young are precocious, born furry and active; they are weaned in only 12 days and are nearly grown in a couple of months, although they are not sexually active for at least a year. Lifespan is about 3-4 years.

VARIOUS WEASELS, AND THE RACCOON

Order Carnivora (carnivores), families Mustelidae (weasels) and Procyonidae (raccoon)

From the least (45 g) to the most (wolverine). Plus the raccoon, which isn't a weasel but sort of belongs in this section, and minus the otter, which is a weasel but has been grouped with the muskrat and beaver (see page 701) because it lives in the water.

Ermine/short-tailed weasel/stoat
(hermine)
Mustela erminea (weasel family)
Year-round

Ermine are common in subalpine meadows and surrounding forest; less common lower and higher. Like most weasels they are primarily nocturnal and thus seen less frequently than their numbers warrant. Males are about 20-30 percent larger than females; average length for both sexes is 27 cm (tail 7.5 cm), weight 80 g.

The ermine, our most common weasel, is long and skinny, with large black eyes, a pointed whiskery face with a pink nose, and a fairly short, fuzzy, club-shaped tail. From April to October this species is brown on top and white underneath, with black-tipped tail and white feet; in the snowy months (November to March) it is all white, except for the black tail-tip. Like the other weasels it has anal scent glands, which stain the fur yellowish under the tail.

The quintessential weasels, ermine are perfectly adapted to slip down rodent burrows after their prey and to spread terror through the network of winter runs that small mammals make at the base of the snowpack. They are voracious night-time hunters, knocking off mostly voles and mice but also killing ground squirrels their own size and even young snowshoe hares. Ermine climb to take tree squirrels and birds, and they swim readily, sometimes to catch fish but usually just to cross streams or to escape their own enemies: owls, larger weasel-family members, coyotes and foxes.

Ermine kill like other weasels, by quickly biting their prey through the neck vertebrae. Rather than eating the catch on the spot, an ermine usually carries it home to its burrow—which in most cases originally belonged to one of its victims—or to a storage burrow nearby. In winter the animals keep a few carcasses in the cooler for lean weeks.

Breeding begins in June and continues until August. Most females are impregnated in early summer. But the young aren't born until the following spring (April or May), because the tiny embryo doesn't implant in the uterus and begin growing until March, for a total gestation that lasts up to ten months. There are usually six in a litter (range of 4-9). The females grow up quickly: they are ready to reproduce in only 2-3 months. But the males are not sexually active until the next spring mating period, so the current crop of weasel maidens go with older guys.

Ermine are tied to the boom-and-bust cycles that afflict their prey. When the woods are full of mice there are also a lot of ermine.

Like their cousin the marten (page 706), ermine are very good at getting into unattended human dwellings and making off with goodies. They are not fearful of man, nor are they very smart about traps, which means that in Canada some 30,000-40,000 of them become furs each year.

Least weasel (belette pygmée)
Mustela nivalis (weasel family)
Year-round

Occasional from Columbia Icefield north,
rare to the south, where it has been
reported on the eastern slope in the
foothills. Lives in meadows and mixed
woods; active only at night. The smallest
weasel: adult males are only 20 cm in
length (tail 3.5 cm) and weigh only 45 g;
females are 10 percent smaller.

The least weasel closely resembles the ermine (previous entry) but is a third
shorter, with smaller ears and the shortest tail in the weasel tribe. In summer the
coat is dark brown above and white below; the feet are white (furry even on the
soles), and there are often buffy patches on the cheeks. The winter coat is the
whitest of any weasel, entirely so except for a bit of black at the tip of the tail.
Habits are like those of the ermine.

The smaller the animal, the more it seems to eat for its size. This one goes
through about half its body weight in small rodents every day; main prey is the
meadow vole. Least weasels also eat insects and amphibians. Burrows are taken in
the usual weasel fashion, from their victims, and lined with fur from carcasses,
something the ermine does also.

Breeding begins in February and continues until December, with a gestation
period of 35-37 days (no delayed implantation in this species); least weasels can be
born any time between March and January. They are weaned at 24 days, but their
eyes don't open until day 30. Sexual maturity comes at four months, when they
leave home.

Long-tailed weasel
(belette à longue queue)
Mustela frenata (weasel family)
Year-round

Occasional in open country, from
low-elevation meadows in the foothills to
the alpine tundra. Nocturnal. Length of
adult males 40.5 cm (tail 13.5 cm), weight
225 g; females are about 20 percent
smaller.

This species looks very much like the
ermine (page 704), but it's quite a bit
larger, with a noticeably longer tail. The
summer coat (April to October) is
cinnamon brown above and white below,
with a black tip on the tail; in winter
the animal is all white except for the
black tail-tip. Its diet and habits are like
that of the ermine, but it is inclined to
take somewhat larger prey and to eat
more birds. Reproduction is also
ermine-like, with delayed implantation
and litters of six (range 3-9).

The long-tailed weasel is seldom seen
in the Canadian Rockies, in part because
it's not common and in part because it is
quite wary of people. You may have to
wait for winter tracks to tell whether or
not this species is around.

American marten/American sable (martre d'Amérique)
Martes americana (weasel family) Year-round

Common in montane and lower subalpine forest; primarily nocturnal. Length 60 cm (tail 18 cm), weight 1 kg. Females 15 percent smaller. Typical weasel build, although not as long-bodied as the others and rather easily differentiated by the large ears and pale coloration. In the Rockies the coat is often reddish brown, with charcoal smudges on the legs and on the very bushy tail. The throat and chest of Canadian Rockies martens are often pale or orangey; the underside is light brown. There is no drastic color change in the winter.

Most of the weasel family are occasional tree-climbers, but especially so the marten—not so much in looking for prey (it does hunt arboreally for squirrels and sleeping birds), but mostly for safe snoozing quarters after night-time hunts that take place largely on the ground. The animal doesn't use burrows. Besides the standard rodent-rich weasel diet, martens eat a good many grouse, bugs and berries. They don't pass up carrion, either. And they seem to venture deep into caves, perhaps searching for bats. I have found three marten skeletons in Cadomin Cave, all farther in than 1 km.

Not many predators will take on a marten, for they are quite nasty in the clinch. But fishers, lynx and great horned owls will.

Reproduction: martens breed in July and August. Implantation of the blastocyst (early embryo) is delayed until at least the following February, though, so the young are not born until March or April. Thus there is just one litter a year, of 2-3 (range 1-4). Development is slow: the eyes don't open until day 39 and weaning isn't until six weeks. It usually takes two years for martens to reach sexual maturity; owing to the timing of the breeding season most young adults don't mate until they are over two years old.

Martens are not very sociable, and when several converge on the same booty there is bound to be a scene. At Mosquito Creek Hostel a very bold marten came down the chimney one early morning in February when I was there. It rattled around in the cold firebox of the wood-burning kitchen stove. The hostelers, snug in their sleeping bags, thought that someone had got up to start the fire, but no crackling ensued, so I investigated. Here was the marten trying to make off with half a chicken we had left out on the table the night before.

Quickly it dragged the bird off the table, across the floor and under the woodbox, where I could hear it crunching away, growling. This annoyed me: there went the chicken sandwiches. So I poked at it with a broom handle—and out it came, snarling. Yikes!

A couple of other people had got up to enjoy the growing fiasco, and I yelled at one of them to open the front door, intending to lob the marten out with a flick of the broom. But the marten was way ahead of me. It quickly dashed back to the woodbox, grabbed the chicken and was out the door with it before I could deliver a swat.

There is more. Other martens arrived, surrounding the one with the chicken. His problems, it appeared, were just beginning. In the ensuing noisy fight (martens yowl and hiss at one another) the chicken changed hands, I mean mouths, several times, until it was in so many pieces that everybody must have got some.

Here is the woodsy-lore part. Do you know how the martens did their battling? By backing up to each other and *kicking with their hind feet!* The jaws of these beasts are deadly weapons, full of sharp teeth, and if the animals habitually bit one another the species would probably be in trouble. So they have adopted this relatively harmless kick-boxing instead.

American mink (vison d'Amérique)
Mustela vison (weasel family)
Year-round

Fairly common along streams and lakeshores and in wetlands; seldom alpine. Nocturnal. Length of adult males 55 cm (tail 18 cm), weight 1.5 kg. Females are a little shorter and a good deal slimmer. Mink are about the same size as martens, but stockier and darker-brown, with shorter ears and blunter faces. Like martens, they don't change color in the winter.

Like otters (page 701), mink spend a good deal of time in streams and ponds, mostly at night, catching small fish, muskrats, water voles, water shrews, frogs and salamanders. They also venture well away from the wet, into grassy places full of sleeping meadow voles.

In winter the mink make use of a peculiar transport corridor: the space between water and ice that opens when stream levels drop after freeze-up. Mink usually live in bank burrows strong-armed from beavers or muskrats (which must not be easy, considering how tough these rodents are) but sometimes dig their own.

Breeding: mink mate promiscuously in late winter or early spring, then go their separate ways. Implantation of the embryo is delayed such that all the babies, called "kits," arrive at about the same time in any particular region (usually late April or early May). The kits, five or so (range 2-10) in the annual litter, are born deaf and blind, not opening their eyes for three weeks. A few days later they are weaned. They follow their mother around until fall comes, when they go on their own. It takes the females a year to mature sexually, the males 18 months.

Despite the growth of mink-ranching, a lot of mink meet nasty ends in traps. (Not that mink-ranching is particularly laudable.) Fortunately much mink habitat in the Canadian Rockies is either off-limits to trappers or inaccessible for their purposes, and most of the annual mink-kill, known to decimate populations, occurs elsewhere.

Fisher (pékan)
Martes pennanti (weasel family) Year-round

Occasional from Crowsnest Pass north, rare in Waterton/Glacier, in subalpine forest, usually near water. Length of males 95 cm (tail 35 cm), weight about 3.7 kg (but variable, as in other weasel species); females 15 percent smaller.

The fisher is the most sombre-colored weasel, ranging from chocolate brown to black. It is darkest underneath (the other weasels are lighter underneath), lightest on the head and shoulders. Seen in the twilight or dawn dimness, a fisher looks a lot like a big black cat.

This creature is misnamed; it seldom catches fish, if at all. Some sources suggest that the name was really meant for the mink, which fishes a lot.

Fishers are solitary hunters, active at any time of day or night. This is unusual for a weasel, most of which are nocturnal. Fishers hunt primarily on the ground, often running along the fallen logs that litter the subalpine forest floor. Prey: red-backed voles and snowshoe hares, grouse, deer mice and other small rodents, tree squirrels and porcupines, which they kill by flipping over on their backs and biting in the unprotected belly. Fishers are also fond of blueberries and grouseberries, which are common in the upper subalpine woods. The species has only one major predator: man, who traps it for its fur.

Like the wolverine (page 710), the fisher is nomadic, patrolling a territory some 15 km across. Along the way it curls up in simple but regularly used shelters among fallen timber or rocks. Females settle down for longer periods to raise the young. After breeding in March or April, implantation of the tiny blastocysts is delayed for about ten months. After a further two months in the womb, the young are born the following spring, between late March and late April, nearly a year after they were conceived (total gestation 338-358 days, the longest of any mammal in the Canadian Rockies). Litters are small by weasel standards (1-4, average 2-3); the helpless young don't even open their eyes for seven weeks. It is usually two years before the young animals breed.

In many years of tramping through fisher habitat I have seen two; this demonstrates the need to protect this sparsely distributed animal from trapping, which has wiped it out over much of North America.

See also the river otter, page 701.

Striped skunk
(moufette rayée)
Mephitis mephitis
(weasel family)
Late winter to fall

Fairly common south of Crowsnest Pass,
becoming scarce farther north, in grassy
or shrubby places at low elevations.
Mostly nocturnal. Length of males 57 cm
(tail 22.5 cm), weight 2.5 kg. Females
slightly smaller.

Skunks are the only boldly marked
members of the weasel tribe, readily
identifiable, and with good reason: that
black-and-white pattern tells everyone in
the woods to stand aside or suffer the
consequences.

All weasels squirt musk to mark territory, but the skunk has turned the trait
to defense. A pair of large musk glands empty into the anus through small spray
nipples. When a skunk is threatened it raises its tail, everts the anus to expose the
nipples and delivers a blast of oily greenish fluid that reaches out 5-6 m, misting
as it goes. Mercaptans (sulphur compounds) give the stuff such a strong and
revolting odor that a predator must be very hungry to continue the attack. A
squirt in the face causes momentary blindness, and a skunk can aim quite well by
twisting its rump around. Contrary to popular belief, picking up the animal by the
tail doesn't prevent it from squirting. Fortunately, skunks are loathe to use their
repellent in any but life-threatening situations.

Skunks waddle about with impunity, sometimes in daylight and often at dusk,
eating nearly anything: grasses, leaves, buds, fruits and berries, insects (especially
grasshoppers and grubs), small rodents, birds' eggs, fish, snails, amphibians, snakes
and carrion. And garbage out of cans in the alley. They are a natural reservoir for
rabies.

Skunks live in borrowed burrows when they can, sometimes digging their own
or simply sheltering in fallen timber or under buildings. They hibernate (skunks
and badgers are the only weasels in the Canadian Rockies that do) from early
December to March. Often several females and youngsters will curl up together in
a grass-lined nest. The males are less sociable and hibernate individually; they
arise early, in late February and March, and go searching for females. These they
awaken and pester for sex. Thus, for a couple of weeks the woods at night seem
full of horny, heedless skunks. At this time the eggs of the great horned owl are
hatching, and the owlets are fed largely on male skunk.

Gestation in skunks is about 62 days; the young are born black-and-white, for
cradle-to-grave protection, and they learn the fine art of musk-blasting by seven
weeks. They follow mom about at night, staying with her through the ensuing
hibernation and leaving in spring to find highways to cross. The rest you know.

American badger (blaireau d'Amérique)
Taxidea taxus (weasel family)
Spring to fall

Occasional from Valemount south on the
western slope and from Bow River south
on the eastern slope, at low elevations in
open grassy places. Length 70 cm (tail
14 cm), weight 7 kg. Unmistakable: a fat
and flattened-looking animal with a
grizzled buff/black back,

black-and-white face and black feet with long white claws. Badgers are grassland animals, uncommon in the mountains but reported a few times every summer, mainly south of Crowsnest Pass. They hunt mostly at night, digging out ground squirrels, pocket gophers and other small rodents, but they also emerge from their burrows in the morning to lie in the sun before the day gets too hot. Like skunks (previous entry), badgers hibernate in winter. After an August or September mating, there is one litter a year of four (range 2-5) young in April or May, the long gestation caused by delayed implantation of the embryo, as is the norm in the weasel family.

Wolverine (carcajou)
Gulo gulo (weasel family) Year-round

Occasional at subalpine or alpine elevations, in nearly any habitat. Length 100 cm (tail 23 cm), weight 15 kg. Females about 10 percent smaller. If you see something that is large, dark and too small-headed to be a bear, then it is either a wolverine or somebody's very ugly dog. This beast is thickly furred, mostly dark brown, but with a light band across the forehead and a broad light stripe along each side, extending into the tail.

Wolverines are fierce and aloof, each male patrolling a territory that may cover 2000 km^2 (females range through 500-1000 km^2). One winter I followed one for four days, covering 60 km before it out-distanced me. The species doesn't see well, but follows its nose from carrion-heap to carrion-heap, cracking bones and crunching cartilage between powerful jaws whose dentition resembles that of the African hyena.

Wolverines hunt, too, readily taking any small mammal—including muskrats and beavers, which are renowned fighters—and they do in the odd porcupine, sometimes dying when ingested quills perforate their stomachs. In winter they go for bigger game, bringing down mountain goats, caribou or even moose in weakened condition. They are very protective of their kills, supposedly standing their ground even against grizzly bears. When threatened (or doing the threatening), wolverines are quite vocal, snarling, hissing and yowling.

These animals are constantly on the move. They visit simple shelters along their routes as fishers do (page 708), the females digging in among boulders or heavy fallen timber for the natal lair. The breeding season runs from April to early September. One male tends several mates and keeps other males away. Whether the males fight one another is unknown.

Implantation of the embryo doesn't occur until January, delaying birth of the annual litter (2-5) until late February to mid-April. Development is quick; the young leave the den in a few weeks, after that following mum on her rounds through their first winter and going on their own about a year after birth. Age at mating seems to be about 15 months for females and 2-3 years for males; longevity and many other aspects of wolverine life history are unknown.

This amazing animal has only one enemy: man. Humans trap it for its fur, which has very long guard hairs that resist frosting up—just the thing for trimming parka hoods.

The wolverine is large enough and fierce enough to get even with us, but it doesn't attack people. Instead it attacks human dwellings while no one is home, breaking in and savaging the interiors. The Indians called this animal the "skunk bear," and with good reason: wolverines mark their kills and their carrion with foul-smelling musk. If your cabin has had a visit from a wolverine, you will probably find that everything edible has either been gobbled up ("Gulo gulo," the Latin name for wolverine, means "Glutton glutton") or squirted with Eau d'Unbearable. Bedding and mattresses are often ripped up and doused as well.

Mountain huts are sometimes hit by wolverines. A fibreglass igloo at Balfour Pass in Banff park was trashed repeatedly by a wolverine that was said to have simply chewed its way in (although I have since heard that it gained entry through a broken floor). Perhaps fearing a headline reading "Wolverine eats mountain hut!", Parks Canada replaced the structure with a cedar-log job that has proved less appealing. But please, fellow climbers and skiers, latch the door well when you leave your high-country haven, or a wolverine may come in and turn it into a skunk-works.

Raccoon (raton laveur)
Procyon lotor
(raccoon family, Procyonidae)
Year-round

Rare in the Canadian Rockies, reported occasionally from Glacier park but possible anywhere in the foothills from Peace River south, at low elevations along streamcourses. Length 85 cm (tail 25 cm), weight 8.6 kg. Females slightly smaller than males.

Raccoons are brownish grizzled gray, easily identified by the black mask around the large eyes, the mouse-like pale ears and the ringed tail. "Cute" is the word that comes to mind, although raccoons sometimes carry rabies and should not be handled or approached closely.

Sometimes singly, sometimes in family groups, raccoons move along streambanks at night, grabbing fish, frogs and insect larvae out of the water, taking small rodents in the grass, catching insects on the ground and eating berries. They spend their days well up in big poplars and cottonwoods, often in large natural tree holes; in winter they confiscate the dens of skunks or other largish burrowers, going dormant during cold snaps but otherwise remaining active.

Mating can occur anytime between February and June, with peak activity in March; there is one litter a year of 3-4, born March or later. The little coons follow their mother around and stay with her until the following spring, when sexual maturity rends raccoon families just as it does any others.

CATS
Order Carnivora, family Felidae (cat family)

This section is written in memory of Orval Pall, a wildlife biologist who studied cougars in the foothills and front ranges southwest of Calgary. Orv contributed much to scientific understanding and public appreciation of the big cats in the Canadian Rockies. His specialty was mapping the travels of cougars by capturing them, putting radio collars on them and then tracking them from aircraft. In June of 1986 he was killed in a plane crash on Mt. Galatea, in the Kananaskis area.

Lynx (loup-cervier)
Felis lynx (cat family) Year-round

Fairly common in deep subalpine forest in summer, sometimes seen above timberline, moving to lower elevations in winter. Nocturnal. Length of male 90 cm (tail 10 cm), weight 11 kg; females up to a third smaller.

A long-legged cat with big feet and a very short tail. Lynx are grizzled gray, buffy underneath, with black-trimmed ears that have long black tufts sticking up from the ends. The tail is black-tipped. Bobcats (next entry) are similar in size and build, but the legs are a little shorter, the feet are smaller and the tail is a little longer. Differentiate mainly by the browner coat of the bobcat, which is vaguely spotted. Bobcat also has small black smudges on the legs and more black on the tail; the ear tufts are shorter.

You seldom see a lynx. They prefer dense forest and brush, become active at dark and head home an hour or so before sunrise, hunting alone through a territory of 12-50 km^2 (up to 240 km^2) and usually keeping clear of settled places and highways. Often they lie in wait for their dinner to come to them.

Snowshoe hares are the favorite item on the menu; a single lynx may eat 200 of them each year. So lynx populations follow the ups and downs of the hare cycle (see page 702). Other foods: grouse and perching birds, ducks, rodents (mice, voles and ground squirrels/tree squirrels), sometimes young hoofed mammals. Like other cats, lynx hunt more with their eyes and ears than they do with their noses; they are good climbers, dropping on their prey occasionally from trees or ledges. Their own enemies are cougars and wolves, which kill them (particularly the kittens, which are vulnerable) perhaps as unwanted competition rather than as prey. Owls, foxes and coyotes pick off the kittens, too.

Lynx are not afraid of water and readily cross rivers. They mark their territories and leave messages for one another by scratching up the ground and urinating on it. Lynx are seldom vocal, although they yowl and cry like other cats. They need little shelter; a rough scrape under an overhang, among fallen timber or under the drooping lower branches of a big spruce will do—even for rearing offspring.

Little is known of this animal's life history beyond the essential facts. It mates in early spring (March to May). An annual litter of two or three (range 1-5) young are born about nine weeks later, from mid-May to mid-June, and they are tended by the female for about 12 weeks. The kittens are furry and playful; their eyes open at 12-17 days. They remain with the mother for the first 10 months, but the date of maturity is unknown. Few lynx live more than five years in the wild. In Canada up to 54,000 lynx have died every year so that people can look fashionable in their skins.

The lynx needs extensive forest and is thus losing ground steadily as agricultural land-clearing continues in North America. Further, it seems intolerant of humans. Orval Pall, an Alberta government biologist known for his cat-family studies, found only 12 lynx in 800 km^2 of suitable habitat in the foothills and mountains southwest of Calgary—a region of increasing human presence.

Bobcat/wildcat (lynx roux)
Felis rufus (cat family) Year-round

Occasional on the western slope from Peace River south and in the southern foothills. Length of male 83 cm (tail 18 cm), weight 10 kg; females about 30 percent smaller.

Bobcats look very much like lynx (previous entry) but they are much less common in the Canadian Rockies. Distinguish by the color (tawnier overall, with faint brown spotting and black smudges on the legs), tail (longer in the bobcat and white underneath for entire length, black-barred at the end rather than just black-tipped), and ears (outlined in black like those of the lynx but with shorter tufts).

Lynx behavior and bobcat behavior are fairly similar; both are hunters of small mammals. The differences seem mainly in the bobcat's vocalizations (louder and more frequent) and ability to live in open spaces, which the lynx cannot; thus, the bobcat survives longer after man has arrived and cleared the land. Population fluctuations among bobcats are less extreme than those in lynx.

The habits of the bobcat are better known than those of the lynx. Bobcats mate in early spring in the Rockies; gestation is 50-60 days. The young are weaned at two months, after which the father helps to supply food. In January, eight months after they are born, the young are on their own. Bobcats have lived 12 years in the wild, 25 years in captivity. Their fur is not as popular as that of the lynx, so in Canada we lose only 3200 a year to trappers.

Cougar/mountain lion/puma (couguar)
Felis concolor (cat family) Year-round

Occasional at montane and subalpine elevations. Length of males 230 cm (tail 75), weight 70 kg. Females are 25-30 percent smaller.

Readily identified: a great big cat with a fairly short brownish/grayish coat that is essentially unpatterned. The belly is buff; chest, throat, chin and whiskers are white; the ears are black on the back (but not tufted like the lynx or bobcat), and there is a dark vertical smudge above each eye. Tip of the tail is black.

When you see this animal you know it. But it is so shy that you may never see it. (There are notable exceptions to this. Not many years ago an aging female cougar moved in under a trailer in Jasper townsite and had her kittens there.)

Cougars are solitary, hunting from dusk to dawn (sometimes in the daytime) through territories of about 100km^2 for females and up to 300 km^2 for males. Their main prey in the Canadian Rockies is the mule deer (77 percent of stomach contents in one study), which they must surprise at close range for a successful attack, for the cougar tires quickly in a chase. It kills usually by leaping onto a deer's shoulders and biting through the neckbones, meanwhile pulling the neck back to break it and often slashing the throat with its claws. The canine teeth are long. The teeth farther back are massive and very sharp; placed near the hinge line, they work like powerful shears.

Cougars bring down elk, bighorn sheep (but seldom mountain goats) and even adult moose; they occasionally take the odd item of domestic livestock. Smaller prey include snowshoe hares, porcupines and beavers. Cats like their meat fresh and will often leave a kill half-eaten if there is an abundance of game. But cougars make a point of covering kills with leaves or forest duff in case they want to return to them. This tends to mask the scent.

Like other cats, cougars scratch up spots in their territories and mark them with urine. They groom themselves often, licking their coats, and they purr loudly. As shelter they prefer natural dens among boulders, but they will make do temporarily with a dry spot in dense cover under an overhang. They keep their dens clean, not leaving bones and other litter about as wolves do.

Unlike most other animals in the mountains, a female mountain lion can go into heat in any season; in Canada she often does so between March and June. She gets interested only every other year, normally, and goes searching for a male, often attracting other suitors who fight among one another for her as only cats can. After mating, the male leaves. Gestation is 90-96 days, with a litter of two to four (range 1-6) born between June and October.

The kittens are spotted and striped, quite unlike the adults. Weaning is gradual, usually complete at eight weeks. At six months the little lions become plain brown. During their first year they are fed on momma's kills. Initially she brings parts home; later the cubs follow her to the sites. They stay with their mother for at least a year, sometimes two. First mating is at about 2.5 years for both sexes. Longevity in the wild reaches 10-12 years; in captivity cougars have lived 18 years.

Is the mountain lion a dangerous beast? It can be—there have been five fatal attacks recorded in North America—but over the years we have been far more dangerous to it, taking after the species with dogs and guns. Having lost much of their North American habitat to human occupation, and persecuted by bounty hunting until the 1960s, cougars are now protected in eastern parts of Canada and the United States. But hunting cougars for sport continues in the Canadian Rockies.

The big cats seem reluctant to hunt us back, nor is the species known to attack people who have blundered on its babies. But in four documented cases starving cougars have killed children for food. It's something to think about when you're eight years old and sitting around the campfire with Uncle Al, who has been telling these really great cougar stories, but now you've got to go to the bathroom, and the outhouse is way over there, in the dark.

DOGS
Coyotes, wolves and foxes (order Carnivora, family Canidae)

Coyote (coyote)
Canis latrans (dog family) Year-round

Common in any montane setting, especially grassy places and open woods; sometimes in subalpine forest and occasional above timberline. Frequently seen around towns, picnic sites and campgrounds. Length of males 120 cm (tail 35 cm), weight 13 kg. Females a little smaller.

Coyotes are grizzled gray on top, buffy brown down the sides and pale underneath. There are patches of cinnamon on the nose, behind the ears and on the legs. Distinguish from the wolf (next entry) by size (coyotes are one-third smaller), tail (proportionately longer and bushier on the coyote, carried low when running, while wolves carry their tails straight out when running) and face (coyote is foxier-looking, with larger ears and a sharper muzzle). Canadian Rockies wolves are highly variable in coloration, while coyotes are not.

When people report seeing a wolf, it is usually a coyote. Wolves are much less numerous and quite a bit more wary of humans. Anyone spending a few days in the Canadian Rockies is likely to see at least one coyote, particularly around Banff or Jasper, where the animals regularly patrol the townsite outskirts, the picnic spots and the campgrounds. In summer I see them in ones and twos, sometimes in families of 3-6; in winter they are inclined to run in packs of 3-8.

Coyotes are out and about in any season and at any time of day or night. They are most active at dusk and dawn, when one hears them yipping, yapping and howling. They eat mainly small rodents (especially meadow voles), carrion and showshoe hares. During spring they take many newborn deer. They seldom kill livestock, but in agricultural areas have come to depend on carcasses in winter.

In summer, coyotes spend much of their time mousing in meadows. You may see a coyote snuffing about, then suddenly pouncing on a meadow vole, catching it between the front paws and gobbling it up. In badger country (southern foothills), a coyote will hang around while a badger digs into a ground-squirrel colony. Squirrels running out of their holes are snagged by the coyote. In winter, coyotes subsist mainly on carrion, occasionally working together in groups of 2-8 to bring down a deer, sheep or elk struggling in deep snow. Sometimes the tables are turned and the prey species will be seen chasing the predator. Part of the coyote diet is vegetarian.

Hearing and especially sense of smell are keen in coyotes, but they don't see at a distance as well as humans, and they are colorblind.

While history has shown that human fears about wolves are unjustified, coyotes are another matter. In the national parks they approach humans quite closely—sometimes with nasty results. There were four coyote attacks in Jasper park during the summer of 1985, all involving young children. In three cases the coyotes had been or were being fed; they nipped and bit when no further food was offered. Such incidents show the wisdom of the strict anti-feeding laws in the mountain parks.

Another incident that summer was more serious. A two-year-old child playing in her yard was attacked by a coyote that may have wanted to eat her. The child's mother came to the rescue as the coyote was dragging the toddler into the woods, but the child was badly bitten and required hospitalization. The coyote was killed and found to have a glove caught in its gut, which may have caused the desperate behavior. Keep an eye on the kids if there are coyotes about; toddlers should always be watched very closely when outdoors in the wildlife-rich areas.

A few years ago, a coyote on the Banff Springs Hotel golf course bit a player trying to retrieve her ball, which the coyote had stolen. No one knows why coyotes pick up the balls on the Banff and Jasper courses—maybe they look like edible eggs—but it is a fairly common occurrence. Coyotes sometimes sit by park highways, waiting for cars to stop. They approach the windows, hoping for a handout, and may chase the car, yapping and snapping at the wheels as it pulls away.

Wolves and cougars often kill coyotes, perhaps as competitors. Coyotes depend on big-game kills for food in winter. They drift over to a kill when the larger carnivores have eaten their fill and have flopped down for a nap.

Coyotes often mate for several years at a time; for life in some cases. The female comes into heat for just a few days sometime between late January and late March; after gestation of 60-63 days a litter of six pups (range 1-19) is born most often in late April or early May. The female digs the den, usually located in silty soil at the base of a rise near water. A tunnel 2-3 m long leads to a chamber at the end.

Coyote pups are dark tawny brown and look just like domestic-dog pups, their eyes opening at nine days. At three weeks they are venturing outside; at 5-8 weeks they are weaned. Like wolf pups, they are fed by both parents on vomit (doggy baby food) for a while. At one year they are fully grown, but most don't mate until they are almost two. Maximum age in captivity: 18 years. A *coydog* is the hybrid offspring of a coyote/domestic-dog mating. It is fertile, as are coywolves.

Coyotes are trapped in Canada at the rate of 48,000 a year. Fearing for their calves and lambs, ranchers often kill coyotes. Grain farmers are inclined to be more tolerant, for coyotes are effective predators of crop-eating mice and voles. Whatever one's view of this animal, the records show that it is increasing in numbers throughout western North America.

Gray wolf (loup)
Canis lupus (dog family) Year-round

Fairly common in nearly any natural environment, but in the Canadian Rockies seen most often in summer in grassy montane woods and in winter on montane or subalpine frozen lakes. Length 175 cm (tail 45 cm), height at the shoulder 1 m, weight 50 kg. Females are slightly smaller.

Unlike coyotes (previous entry), wolves vary a great deal in color; I have seen black ones and white ones in the same pack. They are inclined to be browner in summer, from molting. In the Canadian Rockies common colorings are often either a malamute-like black-on-pale-gray or dark brown with buffy trim. The eyes are always yellow.

Differentiate wolves from coyotes by size (wolves are about one-third larger), tail (relatively shorter and less fluffy on the wolf, carried straight out when running rather than letting it droop as coyotes do) and face (blockier on the wolf, the ears shorter and the muzzle blunter). But even with all these differences, people still confuse wolves and coyotes. It is usually the coyotes that are reported; even inside the national and provincial parks, where wolves are protected, it may be some time before you see one.

Wolves eat big game—especially in winter, when many of the smaller mammals are harder to get under the snow or in hibernation. Wolf menu for the Canadian Rockies, in order of amount consumed: elk, moose, deer, bighorn sheep, caribou, snowshoe hares, ground squirrels, beavers, muskrats, marmots and mice/voles. A single wolf can kill a deer rather easily by slashing its throat or belly; sometimes by strangulation (jaws clamped on the windpipe or nose). Lone wolves have been known to kill elk and moose, but the species routinely hunts in organized packs to bring down the larger prey. When attacking a herd or flock, the usual strategy is to separate one animal from the group and get it out in the open, where it can be chased to exhaustion. When it cannot run anymore, the wolves close in, nipping and biting until they either cut a major artery or inflict so many wounds that the victim dies from blood loss. The wolves then tear the prey to pieces, snapping and snarling.

Seeing this sort of thing makes one shudder; it's no wonder that people are afraid of wolves. But we needn't be. There have been only three documented wolf attacks in Canada, and only one resulted in injury (a badly-bitten arm).

Wolves are curious, and they will sometimes approach people quite closely. Perhaps they wish to see us clearly and catch our scent; once they do, they leave quickly. But they are also surprisingly tolerant of non-threatening humans in their territories, as students of wolves have learned.

Wolves live in packs of 4-7 (up to 14 members), which are essentially extended families. The largest, toughest, smartest male is the leader, a position that is occasionally challenged by a younger dog and is defended if need be by vicious fighting. The pack leader carries his tail high, while the others carry theirs lower. The leader usually mates for life, and these two often are the only breeding pair in the group; they try to prevent the rest of the pack from mating.

Given suitable habitat, a pack's territory in the Canadian Rockies might cover 100-200 km^2. The pack members move freely about this area, individually or together, the males constantly marking selected spots in the familiar lifted-leg manner. Packs avoid each other; if they should meet accidentally there are aggressive displays and occasional fighting.

Each pack has a home site with two or more dens; in the Canadian Rockies these dens are often old beaver bank-burrows beside a small lake or marsh, the burrows now above water level because the dam has been breached and abandoned. Bone fragments and white, bony scats show who has been living there.

The leader and his mate den-up after late-winter breeding (estrous occurs over a few days between late February and mid-March) to raise the pups. The other family members may hang around or they may drift away for much of the spring and summer, living mainly on the small game that is plentiful at this time.

There is normally a litter of five pups (range 1-11) born in late April or early May after a gestation period of 60-65 days. The pups are dark gray. Their eyes open at 5-9 days and they venture out of the den at three or four weeks, tussling about in typical doggy fashion. They are weaned at 6-8 weeks and fed for awhile on regurgitated meals bummed from any adult in the pack. A pup gets fed by licking and nipping his relatives around the mouth.

At about two months the female often carries the pups by the scruff of the neck to another den nearby, for reasons only she knows. It may be because the original den has become too dirty and buggy.

By late summer the pups are big enough to start hunting, and it is *rendezvous* time. Any pack members who have been away arrive at a particular meadow or lake to get organized for the winter. There is a lot of evening howling at this time, and if you know where a pack is located you can go out and howl to them; they will often howl back. Crisp moonlit nights from September on are best, around midnight. You need not howl convincingly; wolves will reply to anything from a moan to a noisy car radio. Once you have got them going, they often keep it up for several minutes at a time. Then maybe you will hear a bunch go off on the other side of the valley—which is what this must be all about: "We're the Pyramid Lake Pack. Who are you-oooooo?"

Humans are taught to fear and hate wolves, having grown up on *Little Red Riding Hood, The Three Little Pigs* and *Peter and the Wolf*. We learn that wolves are Bambi-killers, despicable savages that kill just for the fun of killing. Actually, wolves seldom kill more than they need, and their occasional killing sprees feed a host of scavengers on the remains. Unlike man, who hunts as trophies the strongest, healthiest animals in a herd, the wolf kills the old, the sick and the less-fit. This actually improves the viability of the herd.

Provincial wildlife agencies "manage wolf populations," meaning that they kill wolves. This is done at the request of ranchers who don't like wolves on their lands, and under pressure from hunter's organizations who would rather have Bambi for themselves. Studies suggest that wolves in Alberta may kill more deer and elk than hunters do, which fish-and-game associations find upsetting.

In protected, hunter-free situations, the wolf population is known to control itself. When the number of hoofed animals is steady, so is the number of wolves. When there are too many wolves their fertility drops naturally and so do their numbers.

Unlike the coyote, the wolf does not laugh at its tormentors and prosper anyway; *Canis lupus* has lost most of his former range in North America. Here in the Canadian Rockies we still have a lot of wolves, thanks in part to their protection in the national and provincial parks. But in the northern half of the range the only protection wolves have is the isolation of the wilderness—scant refuge from incidental killing by fly-in hunting parties that are mainly after other game. In 1984 there was a government-backed airborne wolf kill in British Columbia. The loud public outcry against it showed growing appreciation of the world's greatest dog. I can sometimes hear him singing from the hills above Jasper—the dog without a master, the dog who is free.

Red fox (renard roux)
Vulpes vulpes (dog family) Year-round

Occasional in grassy places and open woods; nocturnal, shy and seldom reported. Length 1 m (tail 40 cm), weight 5 kg. If it looks rather like a coyote (page 715), but it is smaller and the tail is nearly half the body length, than it may be a fox.

Like the black bear (page 720), the red fox has "phases": different coat colors that are genetically determined and always present in the same proportions in any population.

The most common phase (50-75 percent of individuals) is **red**: brown or cinnamon above, white below, with black-backed ears, black on the fronts of the legs and a white tip on the tail. The **cross phase** (a quarter to a third of the population) is mottled buff and dark brown, rather like a tortoise-shell housecat. A line of black down the back meets a line of black across the shoulders, which forms a cross-shaped figure. It, too, has a white tip on the tail. The other phase is rarer (no more than 17 percent of the population): the **silver fox**. Silver foxes are essentially black, but with white-tipped guard hairs on the head, back and tail that give them a grizzled silvery look. The ears and legs are black, the muzzle is dark, and there are black circles around the eyes, golden as in all foxes but especially striking in this one. And there is the ever-present white tip on the tail.

Red foxes are solitary during late fall and winter, living without dens in territories of 3.5-8.5 km^2. At this time the main foods are small rodents dug out from under the snow, birds and snowshoe hares. Foxes don't seem to eat much carrion.

When the female comes into heat, sometime between mid-January and mid-March, she chooses a mate from several suitors and the pair den up, usually in last-year's burrow. If it is unavailable, then they search for an abandoned beaver bank-burrow or dig a new one themselves. The **whelps** (sometimes called "kits") are born anytime from March to May, after gestating for 51 to 53 days. The usual litter is five (range 1-10).

Whelps are puppy-like; their eyes open in the second week and they are weaned at one month, by this time coming out of the den and feeding on fresh meat brought by both parents, who are themselves eating a lot of insects, vegetation and ground squirrels as summer rolls in. By 14-16 weeks the whelps are ready to leave home for good; they are sexually mature at 10 months—a short time for the dog family.

These facts may be of little use, for few people ever see a fox in this region. That is partly because they are mainly nocturnal, prowling nervously about from dusk to dawn, sometimes active in the early morning or late afternoon on dark days. They are also quite shy—although surprisingly bold on occasion. One family lived under a building at Rampart Creek Hostel in 1979, the adults coming and going when people were around.

The species is large enough that it would be reported more frequently if there were many foxes around. Inescapable conclusion: there aren't many around. The probable reason can be found in the large number of coyotes in the Canadian Rockies. The two species don't coexist very well.

BEARS
Bear family
(order Carnivora, family Ursidae)

Black bear (ours noir)
Ursus americanus (bear family)
Late April to early November

Fairly common in nearly any habitat below treeline, although most common in montane woods. Average length of males **(boars)** is 168 cm (tail 10 cm), height at shoulder 95 cm, weight 170 kg; females **(sows)** are about one-third smaller.

Black bears are not always black. There are two common color phases in the Canadian Rockies: black, often with a white spot on the chest, and light reddish brown (the **cinnamon bear**). Both types are usually tan on the sides of the muzzle. Like the phases of the red fox (previous page), black-bear phases are present throughout the population; black and cinnamon offspring **(cubs)** can be born in the same litter. Blacks outnumber cinnamons in the Grande Prairie area (just east of the Rockies) by 2.5 to 1; around Jasper I see brown-phase bears less frequently than this figure suggests.

To differentiate black bears from grizzly bears (next entry), go by size (grizzlies are usually larger), shape (black bears are short and round, with long faces and larger ears; grizzlies are rangier, with a prominent hump on the shoulder, flatter forehead and smaller ears), and color (black bears are usually evenly colored; grizzlies are usually multi-toned, in streaks and patches). The front claws of grizzlies are very long, for the digging this bear does; they are easily visible. Those of black bears are shorter, seldom seen.

Black bears are far more tolerant of humans than grizzly gears are; black bears are often seen beside highways, along trails, hanging around campsites, campgrounds and cabins, and in the alleys of national-park towns. They are mainly active at night, but may be about at any hour, shuffling along, nose to the ground, always looking for food. They don't see well; their well-developed sense of smell leads them to their meals. When a bear is trying to locate the source of a smell or sound, it often stands up on its hind legs. It turns from side to side, sniffing and grunting in what may appear to be a posture of attack but is actually not (real attacks are made on all four feet, usually low to the ground); perhaps in standing, the bear brings its nose up from the interference of odors near the ground.

Despite the inability of bears to digest cellulose (as hoofed animals can), the black bear diet is about 75 percent vegetarian. In spring and summer the animals prefer sprouting plants and the buds or inner bark of shrubs and trees, all of which are high in sugar and protein; in the fall they eat fruits and berries. In midsummer you may see black bears eating flowers; they are very fond of dandelions. They dig for roots and tubers, but not as much as grizzlies do. Carrion accounts for 10-15 percent of their diet, insects 5-10 percent and small mammals and fish less than one percent. Black bears occasionally take young deer, elk or moose. As explained on page 726, they have been known to prey on humans.

Tree-climbing is the black bear's main defence against the grizzly, which is its only natural enemy (probable reason: competition for food). A black bear cub runs quickly up the trunk by hugging it, cat-style, when it feels threatened; adult females climb as well, but the large boars seldom do. Aspens are often used as getaway trees (although any tree will do); look in aspen groves for black-scarred scratches on the trees caused by bears. Horizontal or slanting scratches that go well up the trunk are caused by ascents; vertical ones a metre or two above the ground are thought to represent territorial marking.

Black bears are generally solitary, except for females with cubs (siblings may remain together for a few months after leaving their mother's care). Male black-bear territories are overlapping, covering about 200 km^2 each in the mountains (but this figure can vary a lot, depending on a bear's sex, age and the population density). The boars are inclined to fight when they meet. Sow territories are smaller and usually non-overlapping.

Black bears are usually silent, but become vocal when agitated. They grunt and growl; the cubs cry to their mothers like human babies, and they make a humming/purring sound when contented. Normally there are 2-3 cubs per litter (range 1-5) born every other year. Breeding takes place between June 20 and July 10, but the cubs don't arrive until mid-January or early February. This long gestation (about 220 days) is caused by delayed implantation of the embryo, as in the weasel family. The embryo floats free in the womb, not attaching to the uterine wall and starting to grow until October or November. The cubs are born during the mother's dormant period. She may wake up during birth, but then becomes dormant after.

The cubs are inordinately small, about the size of puppies. They nurse and crawl about as the mother sleeps. Their eyes open at six weeks, but they are not weaned until five or six months old. They follow the sow around for the remainder of that summer, den with her the following winter, and finally leave in their second spring, just before mating time.

In late summer, black bears experience a powerful hunger that drives them to become grossly fat. They take in 4.7 kJ (20,000 calories) of food per day at this time; that compares with a normal human intake in Canada of about 0.5 kj (2000-3000 calories). When cold weather hits in early November, they move up the slopes to subalpine elevations, where the snow will be deepest (low-elevation denning occurs occasionally). Snow is good insulation, sufficient to keep the den temperature only a few degrees below freezing in the coldest weather. Each bear digs out a simple shelter, often among boulders, under an overhanging bank or among the roots of a wind-thrown tree. If the soil is hard-frozen, the bear may pile up brush or fallen trees and hibernate underneath. In the mountains the animals seldom burrow in more than a metre or two, and I have never seen a bear (or any bear sign) in a cave—a true cave, deeper than a few metres—in winter or in summer. In the Canadian Rockies, black bears emerge in late winter or early spring (usually in April in the central Rockies).

Bear-dormancy is a biochemical marvel. If the definition of "hibernation" includes a low body temperature, then bears are not true hibernators, for their body temperatures don't drop much. They decrease from the normal 38 °C to 34-31 °C.

The animals go through about 1 kJ of energy per day during dormancy, which is nearly as much as they require normally. How can they keep up that high metabolic rate for over five months without eating or drinking? No one knows, but recent work has shown that bears convert their own urea, a byproduct of metabolism that mammals normally unload as urine, into proteins. This makes all the difference during dormancy, preventing toxic buildups of urea while maintaining muscle mass until spring. There is a remaining mystery, though: how do the females manage to nurse their cubs during dormancy? The sows don't drink. Where does the water come from to produce enough milk? Perhaps from the breaking-down of fat, which releases water.

Grizzly bear (ours brun)
Ursus arctos (bear family) Late
March to early November

Occasional in any mountain environment;
usually found at low elevations in spring
and above timberline in summer. Length
190 cm (tail 80 cm), height at the
shoulder 130 cm; in the Canadian
Rockies males weigh 250-320 kg, females
200 kg or less.

A large bear, with a prominent shoulder hump. Most of our grizzlies are,
indeed, grizzled: white-tipped hairs give them a hoary look, especially over the
shoulders and down the back. But there is a lot of color variation, from black to
tawny. Unlike the black bear (previous entry), which can also be black or tawny,
the grizzly's color is not uniform: it is lighter here, darker there, often streaky.
Other obvious differences between the two species include size (grizzly is larger),
shape (grizzly is rangier, with big shoulders) and face (grizzly is more
teddy-bear-like, with a flatter face (dished around the bridge of the nose) and a
more pointed muzzle. Grizzly claws are longer than those of black bears.

In discussing the grizzly, I have often heard it said that this animal was
driven into the mountains from the Interior Plains, where it lived before
extermination there. While it is true that grizzlies once lived as far east as Lake
Winnipeg, the notion of them being "driven into the mountains" is false. Grizzlies
have always lived throughout the Canadian Rockies and west to the coast.

The grizzly's habits are rather like those of the black bear (previous entry),
but grizzlies are more active in daylight and they do a lot of digging for roots and
tubers; a favorite is sweetvetch (page 379). Sometimes grizzlies try to dig out
marmots and ground squirrels, tearing up alpine meadows. This is a lot of work
for very little reward, meal-wise; the bears may crave ground squirrels for their
high fat content.

Grizzlies eat astonishing quantities of buffaloberries (page 312)—often 200,000
per day—and leave characteristic red, seedy droppings along trails in late July and
early August (see sketch on page 674). The bears savor the fatty, nut-like seeds of
whitebark pine. They eat more fish than black bears, piling on the calories during
the late-summer salmon run up the Fraser River to Mt. Robson and the kokanee
run along McDonald Creek in Glacier National Park (see page 540). Grizzlies are
carnivorous, too, picking off weak or very young hoofed animals. Sometimes they
kill cattle or horses, which has not endeared them to ranchers. Despite this taste
for fresh meat, grizzlies almost never attack humans to eat them (the attacks are
for other reasons, as discussed in the next section). Their only predator is man.

Grizzlies cache their meat, covering a kill with scratched-up plant material
and soil. If they arrive at a kill made by another animal, they take it over. If you
find a lot of bones scattered around a fair-sized excavation, then you know what
did it. Don't hang around; some of the kill may still be buried and the bear may
be near.

Except when the females have cubs, grizzlies are solitary, moving about in
territories of at least 200 km^2. They travel long distances, crossing high passes and
traversing glaciers. A friend of mine saw one going over Abbot Pass, a glacial col
between Mt. Victoria and Mt. Lefroy above Lake Louise. Grizzlies have been
reported well out on the Columbia Icefield. They swim well, crossing swollen
glacial rivers with ease. These animals know where they are going.

Like black bears, grizzly females mate every other year (sometimes every
three years), in early summer (late June to early July). Gestation is 229-266 days,
with implantation delayed as in black bears. A pair of cubs (litters range from one
to four) are born between mid-January and early March, while the mother is
dormant. They are weaned at four or five months, but stay with mum through the
following winter, sharing her den, then leave in the spring as she prepares to mate

again. (There have been many reports of two-year-old cubs still with their mothers.) Like black bears, the cubs may den with each other in their third winter. They become sexually active at five or six years.

A grizzly sow is very protective while the cubs are with her, because a boar is inclined to kill them if he can. Although grizzly cubs will climb trees to escape, the species is often above timberline, where there are no trees to climb. The cubs must count on mum to stand up for them—which she does, sometimes leading to nasty encounters with people. When the people have guns, the mother often gets shot; later, the cubs die, too.

Grizzlies are winter-dormant in the manner of black bears, although grizzly dormancy is not as well-studied as black-bear dormancy (biologists have entered black-bear dens in winter, drugged the animals and done physiological measurements, but I know of no such data on grizzlies). They retire at the onset of cold weather (usually in late November or early December), preferring denning sites on rather steep slopes (25-45°) in high-subalpine meadows. They dig in more deeply than do black bears. In the Rockies they seem to emerge earlier, often in March, when the snow is still deep in the high country. Moving to lower elevations, they must live on their remaining fat reserve until the ground thaws and plants begin to sprout—unless they find carrion or manage to kill winter-weakened hoofed animals, which may be one reason for the early emergence.

PEOPLE AND BEARS IN THE ROCKIES

Bears and humans have never got along very well. Bears eat our unattended apple pies and make a mess of the garbage. They tear open our hives and eat the honey. They come into our campsites, intimidate us and steal our food. They are big enough to hurt us and sometimes do.

This last, especially, is not acceptable, so we have hunted bears to extinction in much of the world. But not in the Canadian Rockies, where our two species of bears currently have enough wilderness in the north and enough legal protection in the south at least to survive, if not to flourish. When one is on foot in these mountains one knows that the grizzly is also out there, neither well-intentioned nor malicious, just out there. Just around the corner, maybe.

This adds a dash of fear to a mountain outing. A lot of people never venture into the woods because of the bears. Never mind that they are more likely to be hit by lightning than hurt by a bear, or that the German shepherd tied up in the next campsite is probably more dangerous to one's toddler than a bear is.

I will take the bear. In 25 years on foot and unarmed in the mountains I have never been attacked by a bear, but I have been attacked by several dogs. All the bears I have met on the trail, including grizzlies, have either run away or watched me curiously until I passed by.

To those readers who worry about bears, the message in the next few pages is to relax. Bears? Respect them, yes, for they are amazing creatures. Be wary of them, yes, for they do unpredictable things. Avoid them if you can, yes. But don't *worry* about them. This is unnecessary and spoils an outing.

My bear worries are for *their* health and safety, not mine. Consider the hypothetical (but typical) chain of events outlined below.

A wild black bear follows its nose to a campground. There, left out on a table, is a loaf of bread. The bear eats, plastic wrapper and all. Ooo, that was good. Any more around? Yes! Over there. Can't see too well . . . smells like *meat!* Gotta have it. Uh, oh; something big coming. Noisy, but not grizzly. Got the meat. Run away now. Back tomorrow night.

The bear *does* come back the next night, to the same campsite at the same time. Bears have good memories that way. There is more booty; more easy pickings.

Night after night this happens. The bear becomes bolder and bolder. The campers are half-delighted, half-afraid; this is going to be memorable. Some of them feed the bear. Others throw things at it. Someone has a big dog; turns it loose on the bear. It runs up and bites the bear. Hah! Great show!

Whap! Take that, stupid wolf! And the dog is dying, ripped open. The owner runs for the wardens. The wardens come and shoot the bear.

The next night there is another bear . . .

The lesson here is that letting a bear get into human food (or human garbage) is much the same as killing that bear.* Eventually, whether it is shot by the authorities or hit by a car or strangled from the inside by a plastic bag snarled in its gut, that bear will probably die an unnatural death.

And rarely, very rarely, it may take a human with it.

I would rather that human not be me, as I'm sure you would rather it not be you. And I would like to continue seeing bears in the mountains. They are interesting to watch and not actually much of a threat. The only way to satisfy both these wishes is to leave the bears alone, never, ever, feeding them—or allowing them to get their first potato chip.

That means no garbage left around. No food left out on the picnic table. No fish guts dumped beside the stream (fishermen stand a greater-than-average chance of running into bears hanging around their fishing holes).

On the trail it means putting every bit of your food, including such bear-foods as toothpaste, soap and cosmetics, at least 4 m off the ground at night, slung between two trees on a rope, or up on the special poles erected just for this purpose in many back-country campsites. Eat up everything you cook, thereby avoiding the problem of garbage disposal.

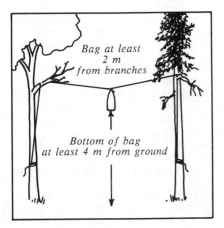

Bag at least
2 m
from branches

Bottom of bag
at least 4 m from ground

SLINGING FOOD BETWEEN TREES TO PROTECT IT FROM BEARS

Required: about 30 m of light nylon cord. There is no need to climb the trees; you can tie a weight to the cord and throw it over the limbs.

Try to pick dead (but sturdy) trees or limbs. Pulling the cord damages the bark of the tree.

---

*While this is true in the Canadian Rockies, a case has been made by the Craighead brothers, world-renowned grizzly experts, for allowing bears to eat garbage in Yellowstone National Park. Yellowstone can no longer sustain the bear population it used to, say the Craigheads, because of human settlement around it and heavy human presence in the park. Officials there closed the dumps to bears without realizing that the dumps were essential food sources; the bears became desperate, resulting in many destructive incidents and the killing of most bears in the park. The Craigheads warn that if grizzlies are to remain in Yellowstone, and more than a handful of black bears, they must be *fed*. Such is not the case here, where populations seem to be self-sustaining, but the time may come.

Polar bears are attracted to used tampons and black/grizzly bears may be as well. Although attacks on menstruating women have been reported, menstruation has *not* been shown to cause such attacks. Still, on an overnight hike, women in their periods are advised to change protection frequently and wash before going to bed. Put used tampons down outhouses, burn them or bury them deeply; don't carry them with you. And do not simply discard them in the woods, either. You may be long gone, but another person may happen by while a bear is investigating. The same can be said for disposable diapers.

For the sake of both bears and humans, I inform people whom I see breaking these rules. There is no need to be pedantic or authoritarian; if I see someone feeding a bear from the car window, I just say something like, "Hello. I noticed you feeding that bear, and I thought you should know that if the wardens see you doing that it's a $500 fine. Ooops—I think I see one turning around! 'Bye!"

What to do in an encounter with a bear

Here is a summary of expert advice on what to do if you and a bear find yourselves sharing the same patch of the mountains. Much of the following is distilled from *Bear Attacks: Their Causes and Avoidance* (Herrero, 1985), which is recommended reading for any outdoorsperson.

If you see the bear at a distance of more than 10 or 20 m, just stop walking (which is automatic, right? Wow! A bear!). Have a quick look around to see if there are any cubs, then walk away quietly without coming between mom and the kids. Black bears are fairly tolerant of people around their cubs, but grizzlies are not. Loop widely around the whole scene (a kilometre or more if it is a female grizzly with cubs) and continue your hike. The bear(s) will likely do the same. End of a typical encounter.

If the way is narrow and you are going to have to pass closely by the bear—i.e. you would like it to move out of your way—then stand beside a suitable escape tree and make some noise so that the bear realizes that you are there. It probably doesn't, or it would be gone by now. Chances are, it will now take off.

What if the bear doesn't run? If it just watches you, give it a wide berth as you go on. You may have to backtrack to get by.

What if it comes toward you? Possibly it's a garbage-addicted campground bear, used to people, not afraid of you and figuring to either beg or extort a handout. Or maybe there is a carcass nearby, and the bear is thinking that it may have to defend it from you. Either way, you need to leave. Walk quickly away, keeping an eye on the bear—but not staring it in the eye, for reasons coming up soon. Seldom will it follow.

What if it *does* follow? What if it starts to chase you? You are in trouble. Climb a tree.

Pick a sturdy one (bears have been known to bite off aspens 15 cm thick) and *climb up high:* grizzlies will climb partway up after you if they are really intent, but not over 5 m in reported incidents. Black bears are tree-climbers, but they climb primarily for escape, not for attack, and will seldom follow a person up a tree (although sometimes they have).

If you have a pack on, drop it as soon as you decide to climb; the pack will slow down the bear, which will probably stop to check it, and climbing the tree will be easier without the pack. (If the tree-climbing is strictly cautionary, meaning that you have plenty of time, you may want to take your pack up with you, to keep it from being damaged by the bear.)

Getting up the tree does not end the encounter. There you are, up in the tree, and there is the bear, down there. It may just *stay* down there, perhaps for hours and hours. However, if there is no carcass nearby that the bear is defending, it will probably amble away in less than half an hour. Watch the departure and be sure the coast is clear before descending.

Suppose you come face to face with a bear—a surprise encounter for both parties. We are getting into a very low-probability situation, here, but just suppose.

In a confrontation like this the instincts of both the bear and the person are to jump back and run. Again, end of encounter. But if it's a grizzly female with cubs, or either sex at a kill, then the bear may hold its ground, considering a charge. This has never happened to me, so I will have to provide the experience of others. Steve Herrero's excellent book covers the possibilities in detail.

The following can be applied just as well to a situation in which an aggressive bear has approached you above timberline, where there are no trees to climb.

If the bear snorts, makes other loud sounds and slaps the ground, then probably it is about to charge. There are three schools of thought on what to do next, each with statistical evidence of success.

One school suggests *running like hell.* That is a natural thing to do, and probably is what a charging grizzly is hoping that you will do. The usual reason for a charge is to drive away an intruder, and when you run, the bear may see that as submissive behavior not requiring further action. Thus, it may be wise to oblige. Most grizzly charges break off short of contact, when the bear decides that you have been sufficiently intimidated. However, a grizzly bear can easily catch a running human, going uphill or down; thus, if it wants to catch you, it will. Further, running may stimulate a curious bear to chase you as prey.

Assuming that the bear pursues and there are no trees, it seems wise to head for the nearest rocks or water. People have escaped attacks by jumping in lakes and climbing up cliffs. Or climbing *down* cliffs. But don't believe that story about running quickly downhill, so that the bear will trip over its short front legs and stumble. This is nonsense; bears can run downhill faster than humans can.

You may want to dump your pack, hoping to distract the bear and increase your speed. But a pack offers some protection from injury to the back and can be used as a shield in a fight.

School-of-thought number two suggests that you *back off slowly and quietly, avoiding eye contact with the bear.* This may tell the bear something important: that you are a powerful predator. Among mammals, the larger solitary predators are inclined to leave one another alone in chance encounters. Humans behave as if we were in this category, something that gives us uncanny protection in the wilds. Statistically, it is often a good plan to show little interest when blundering into a bear. You recognize the bear's presence but show no alarm. Avoid eye contact, which can be construed as threatening, and move slowly away.

The third approach is to *intimidate the bear.* It is a normal human reflex to become noisy when threatened, and most people automatically shout at the bear, waving their arms, snarling, showing their teeth, picking up something heavy—looking dangerous in typical primate fashion. Fortunately this, too, seems to work, especially on young bears.

But suppose the bear charges. Usually this is a bluff; it stops short (2-3 m away). Even at this point it is inclined not to take you on. It must overcome its fear to approach you at all. Your instinct is the same, and during a charge you will probably be projecting universal fear signs at the bear, which will tell it that you are not threatening, that you are just scared. Both parties can then back shakily away, ending the incident.

Given a charge that isn't a bluff, it is time to be sure of the species of bear and take action accordingly as it makes contact. If it's a black bear, *fight back.* If it's a grizzly, *play dead.*

Consider the black bear situation first. Black bears are less likely to charge humans than grizzlies are, and their charges are much more likely to be false. But if a black-bear continues the attack, then it may be trying to kill and eat you.

Black bears are actually more predatory on man than grizzlies are. I know this sounds strange, but Herrero has shown conclusively that while grizzlies are more likely to hurt humans than black bears, black bears are more likely to prey on humans for food than grizzlies are. Yet black bears are considerably less ferocious in the clinch.

This is not to say that black bears commonly prey on humans. Such attacks are extremely rare.

But the possibility has important implications for your actions during an attack. If it is a black bear, then experience has shown that you should fight. Use whatever comes to hand—a stick, your pack, a rock, a knife, your teeth. Kick and strike, struggle hard. Black bears are not as persistent in their attacks as grizzlies, and showing determined resistance will often drive the bear away.

Playing dead in a black-bear attack is *not* a good idea, for in many cases the bear begins to eat, often ripping the flesh from the apparently incapacitated victim's arms and legs or disemboweling him.

Clues to predatory behavior in black bears: the bear keeps approaching despite an absence of food, moving closer as if stalking. It approaches quietly, without slapping the ground, and tries to get in behind you, then runs suddenly toward you, trying to knock you down. The animals sometimes kill expertly, by biting the neck and shaking the victim until the neck breaks.

Grizzlies are more aggressive than black bears, yet they seldom kill humans in order to eat them. They seem to injure us as enemies, not as prey. When victims of grizzly attacks have lain very still, the attacks have nearly always ended. If a victim begins to move while the bear is still around, the bear often attacks again. So if it is a grizzly, play dead immediately on contact, and play dead well. In many cases a bear has given a motionless human a few nuzzles and walked away.

Of course, there is a slim chance that you are being attacked by a grizzly as prey—something that will become apparent if the bear drags you some distance and starts to pull away flesh. Better fight back; you have nothing to lose at this point, and grizzlies have been successfully denied human meals. In one case near Banff a few years back, a six-year-old was dragged into the bushes by a grizzly. The boy's parents, an English couple who had never been in the Rockies, took their shoes off and flung them at the bear. Confronted by the characteristic valor of the British, the bear dropped the lad and ran off.

Protective posture in a grizzly attack: the bear is inclined to bite your head, neck and shoulders. Curl up, knees drawn close to the chest and hands clasped over the neck. If possible, get your pack over your neck as well. Lying flat on the ground, again protecting the neck with the hands, also seems to be a good position.

To avoid bear trouble, avoid bears

Keep your eyes open in the back-country. Look ahead and to the side for bears and bear sign: tracks and scats, evidence of digging, flipped-over rocks and ripped-up logs or stumps, tipped-over garbage cans. Are the signs fresh? Is the odor of rotten meat on the wind, or are there many ravens and magpies in the area? There could be a kill nearby.

Avoid places where bears are likely to be feeding: berry patches, stream banks rich in cow parsnip (page 344) and horsetail (page 426), brushy areas.

Hike with a group, or ride a horse. Avoid hiking at night. Pitch your camp off the trail, for bears use trails at night. Sleep in a tent, not out in the open; bears often investigate people in sleeping bags, but seldom enter tents—unless they smell food in there. Before bed, search your clothing (and anything else going into the tent with you) for forgotten goodies. Check children's clothing and gear especially well.

Choose camping food that has little smell (dried, canned) and store it out of reach of bears, as shown on page 724. Take out only the food needed for the meal in preparation, leaving the rest safely stored. Cook at least 50 m downwind of your camp. Clean up well after, putting slops down an outhouse, burning them or burying them. Try not to have leftovers; cook the right amount of food and eat it all. Any leftovers should go back into your food cache. Burying garbage is not a good idea; it will be dug up. Burn cans to remove odors and pack all non-combustibles out.

Camping above timberline poses special problems: no trees to use in caching food, no trees for escape and no fuel for a fire. So whenever possible, camp below timberline. If you must camp above timberline, you can cache food and garbage on the ground in sealed bags (several layers of plastic garbage bags) hidden under bushes or among rocks. Containers made of PVC pipe with screw-on caps have been found to be bear-proof.

Regardless of where you are camped, if a bear arrives, pack up and leave immediately. It will hang around until it gets what it wants.

Making noise

If you let the bears know that you are coming along the trail, then the chance of an encounter is quite small, for wild bears nearly always do their utmost to clear out of your way.

Mind you, everything else in the woods will clear out, too, which means that one doesn't see much wildlife when clanging, whistling or shouting along. I'm a naturalist, and my job is to see things in the woods, so I usually go quietly, thus far without ill effect (knock on wood).

But there are times when all signs point to the necessity of making noise. When I'm moving along a noisy stream, or walking quickly along a winding trail in late summer (berry season), among head-high brush that blocks the view, with the wind coming toward me, then I contact the bears every minute or two, bellowing something like, "HOO-HOO-HOOOO! Hello, bears! This is a human being, and I'm coming through! No harm intended; would you mind letting me by?" They are always polite and quick to oblige.

Wearing a small bell on your pack, by the way, won't do the job. What the sporting goods shops sell as "bear bells" are not nearly loud enough. They serve only as talismans. If you want to use a bell, better get one off a locomotive—or use a cowbell at the very least.

Wildlife workers who spend time along streams during salmon spawning take the greatest risk of any group. They have found that frequent blasts from a gas-cartridge air horn eliminate bear encounters, even though many grizzlies are in the area.

Repellents and guns

One hears of putting moth balls around one's campsite to deter foraging bears at night, or of carrying squirt guns loaded with ammonia. Herrero reports that **anti-dog sprays** of the sort carried by mailmen are effective repellents, although they must be used at very short range and the tests have not included grizzly attacks in the wild. Repellents specifically against bears are rumored to be available soon. Ask at a sporting goods shop.

Loud noises—really loud noises, such as the sounds of firecrackers or guns—have successfully repelled charging bears. They have also failed. Pen-sized flare guns available in safety supply shops are often carried by people working in the wilderness, apparently with some success. But these flares can also start forest fires.

Should a person carry a gun in bear country? In most of the Rockies area this is allowed, although not in the national and provincial parks. Certainly firearms have saved human lives in bear attacks. But toting a gun on the trail is inclined to make a person overly bold and under-attentive—a bad combination. Twitchy fingers on the trigger have been the death of many, many bears during false charges.

Biologists who study grizzlies in the field seldom carry firearms; in fact, most recommend against doing so. An adequate rifle (minimum .30-06 with heavy slugs) is a tiresome burden, and a large-calibre pistol (illegal for most people to possess in Canada) is woefully inaccurate.

Aiming properly to kill a grizzly is difficult as it lunges forward. The shooter must be experienced with the weapon and the weapon must be ready. If you shoot a bear that is attacking someone else, you risk killing that person by mistake. My conclusion: firearms are dangerous, much more likely to hurt someone than a bear is. So I don't carry a gun in the mountains.

Being realistic

Despite the unpleasant nature of the foregoing, I hope that it has shown how unlikely it is that you will be injured by a bear in the Canadian Rockies. Herrero could document only 53 injuries by grizzlies reported in the national parks up to 1979, and 24 of those attacks were in Glacier Park, Montana, a small area of prime grizzly habitat that is heavily visited by people. For black bear attacks, Herrero found only 23 documented fatalities in all of Canada and the United States from 1900 through 1980.

Will the number of bear-inflicted injuries increase in the Canadian Rockies in the years ahead? Back-country use has not grown as quickly as once seemed certain, although in the long run the number of people in bear country is bound to increase, with more frequent encounters and thus more frequent injuries. One way to interpret the unusually high injury rate in Glacier is to conclude that the back-country there is saturated with people, from the bears' point of view, which induces a constant bear/human tension found nowhere else in the Canadian Rockies area. If this is the case, then perhaps the problem at Glacier may spread to other parts of the Rockies as similar heavy back-country travel occurs. But bear-carrying capacity varies greatly from place to place, and it would be folly to predict that what has happened in Glacier will happen everywhere. What is needed is continued, careful monitoring of the bears-and-man situation over the years. Hasty judgments by park managers, often made under pressure from a fearful public, have resulted in actions against wildlife that were regretted later.

Why we need the grizzly

Grizzlies have their place in the mountain ecosystem, but the great bear also represents something that we Canadians hold dear: our wildlands.

Let me illustrate this with a scenario I have seen often in Jasper National Park. A busload of visitors is cruising along the Icefields Parkway when someone shouts "A bear!"

There it is: a big, furry, brown-and-buff bear, turning over stones and licking up the bugs only 100 m from the highway. The bus driver stops. Everyone rushes to the windows and the Instamatics start popping. Other cars pull over; people are getting out of them and setting up cameras with long lenses. The driver at first refuses to open the door, but he can't hold back his passengers.

The bolder ones are easing outside just as a park warden shows up. He is surprisingly relaxed; tells people to keep well back but gives them to know that it is okay to watch and to take pictures. He is more concerned about an accident on the highway here than he is about a bear attack. To him it is a "bear jam," quite routine.

And the bear? It just keeps on with its bearish business (eat! eat!), ripping open rotting logs, rolling over boulders, ambling along from one scent to the next. Its coat ripples in the sun; it is the strongest wild thing in North America. It has little interest in the spectators along the highway. Just part of living in a national park, eh?

Indeed, this *is* part of the national-park experience, worthwhile and fine. Never mind the touristy aspect. *The bear is there, and it's not in a zoo.* If there were no bears here, if all the grizzlies were gone . . . then it would be like back home in Toronto. Or New Jersey, or Frankfurt, or Tokyo. It is the bear that awakens us to the fact that this is *not* any of those places. This is the **Canadian Rockies**, where bears run free in the wilderness.

CLOVEN-HOOFED CREW
Order Artiodactyla, including the deer family (Cervidae) and the Bovidae (sheep/goats/bison) in the Rockies

An obvious difference between the deer family and the bovids is that deer, elk, moose and caribou grow antlers that are shed each year, while the bovids have proper horns, which grow throughout their lives.

Deer

All members of the deer family lack upper front teeth (in caribou they do not develop enough to stick out through the gum) but have lower ones; rather than biting off their feed, they pinch it between the lower incisors and the palate and tear it off. Deer-family species have glands on their legs and built into their hoofs that spread scent wherever they go (moose and elk lack the hoof glands); the males also have scent glands at the bases of their antlers.

Mule deer (cerf mulet)
Odocoileus hemionus (deer family)
Year-round

Common in montane woods and brushy meadows from Peace River south; occasional farther north. Length 180 cm (tail 20 cm), height at shoulder 100 cm, weight 100 kg.

The smallest deer in the Rockies, much smaller than elk (page 732), with a smaller rack of antlers. Mule deer are reddish-brown in summer and gray in winter, always with a white rump patch, black-tipped white tail, white chin and white throat; the ears are white inside, rimmed with black.

To differentiate mule deer from the rather similar white-tailed deer (next entry), check the tail (narrow and white with black tip on mule deer; wide and brown on white-tailed, fringed with white, showing all-white only when it is flipped up), the ears (long on mule deer, shorter on white-tailed) and the eyes (large on mule deer, smaller on white-tailed).

Mule deer are active both day and night, napping every now and again; you see them most often at dusk and dawn. They move timidly about the woods, bounding away in stiff-legged jumps when approached—except in the national parks, where they have been protected for many generations and are thus a good deal less shy. I often see them along the highways, in campgrounds and walking down the alleys of Jasper townsite. They come into my yard to nibble the grass and the shrubbery, often staying the night and leaving gifts of fertilizer.

Female mule deer (called **does**) usually stay at low elevations year-round, seldom venturing far from a home range about 15 ha in size. Each doe keeps her immature young of both sexes with her. Mom and the kids talk softly to one another, making little plaintive bleats. The adult males (called **bucks**) are usually solitary, moving up to subalpine elevations in summer and returning to the valley floors in winter.

In spring and summer deer eat mainly grasses and wildflowers, favoring leaves at summer's end; in winter they are browsers, nibbling the twigs and late-winter buds of shrubs, aspens, poplars and evergreens. They are beset with heavy-duty predators: mountain lions, wolves, coyotes, grizzly bears, lynx and bobcats.

Breeding behavior starts in early fall, when the bucks get a big dose of testosterone. This period is called the **rut**. The necks of the bucks swell; they roll on urine-impregnated ground and follow females, curling their upper lips in the manner of most ungulates. They also become quite aggressive at this time and should not be approached. People have actually been killed by rutting deer.

The latest set of antlers has been growing since early spring, not long after the last set dropped off. The "velvet" (blood-rich tissue depositing the bony antler material) dries in early September, and the bucks rake their new sets through the brush and against small trees to strip it off. When the velvet is gone, the animals rub the bark off willows and small aspens, leaving scent on the injured stems from glands at the antler bases.

Mule deer don't bugle as elk do, but the bucks spar with each other, placing their antlers together and shoving back and forth. The object is to force an opponent's head to the ground, at which point he is bested and backs off.

This is not, as I once thought, a standard prelude to mating with a group of does, as it is among elk. Study has shown that mule-deer society is more complicated than that, and much of this sparring has to do with in-group and out-group rivalries. Fights over females do occur, of course, but mule deer do not gather harems as elk do; mule deer herds are small and most bucks have a chance to mate each year.

A successful buck will impregnate several does between mid-November and early December. After a gestation period of about 210 days, the fawns are born in early June (sometimes as early as March or as late as November, for deer will come into heat several times in order to get pregnant). A doe's first breeding usually gives her just one fawn; after that she normally has twins.

The fawns are spotted and odorless; they hide in the brush or under conifers for their first month, nursing. Later they follow the doe about, staying with her until the following spring. When separated from mum for a moment, the young bleat plaintively, saying "baaa" in a high-pitched voice. Fawns lose their Bambi suits in late summer; going gray for the winter. Sexual maturity comes at about 18 months, and mule deer have lived in captivity for 20 years.

Approaching and feeding deer is risky. Even though some deer seem tame, they are still wild animals and easily spooked. If this happens in close proximity to a human they often strike out with their front hooves, which are hard and sharp, inflicting bruises, cuts and even broken ribs. Deer fed by hand can become obnoxious and dangerous; they impatiently paw their providers, sometimes striking out.

White-tailed deer (cerf de Virginie)
Odocoileus virginianus (deer family)
Year-round

Fairly common in montane open woods, on the western slope from Fraser River south and on both slopes in Waterton/Glacier; occasional in the Athabasca and Bow River valleys, but scarce elsewhere on the eastern slope. Length 190 cm (tail 20 cm), height at shoulder 100 cm, weight 90 kg.

Reddish-brown in summer and grizzled gray in winter like the mule deer, the white-tailed deer doesn't seem at first sight to have a white tail; the outside surface of the tail is brown, with a narrow white edge. But when the deer is about to run away, it flips up the tail and, sure enough, it is white underneath. So is the exposed rump. The look-alike mule deer (previous entry) has a much narrower tail that is white on both surfaces, with a black tip. The white patch on a mulie's rump is bigger, and so are the ears.

The habits, food preferences and enemies of the white-tailed deer are similar to those of the mule deer, so check the previous listing for details. Some differences: while the female mule deer seldom moves out of its 15-ha montane territory, the white-tailed deer moves up the mountains in summer, from its winter range in the open montane woods, through the heavy subalpine forest (where there is little in the way of deer food) to the alpine meadows above. White-tailed deer do more browsing (shrub-eating) than mule deer do.

In this species the antlers of the bucks begin to grow in May, requiring about 140 days to reach full size in September. Older males drop their antlers in December, immediately after the fall rut; the younger ones keep theirs until early February.

What happens to all those antlers that deer-family animals grow and discard every year? By this time one would think the woods would be full of them. They do break down naturally, but the rodent tribe helps the process along considerably by gnawing them for the minerals (especially the phosphates) they contain.

White-tailed deer mate from mid-November through late December. The does usually drop their fawns in late May and early June, after gestation of 205-210 days. This means that most are impregnated in mid-November. The fawns, usually one in the first year and two thereafter, are reddish-brown with white spots, looking like dapples of sunlight on the conifer-needle duff of the forest floor. They lie very still. The mother caches each fawn separately, often under the covering lower boughs of spruce trees up to 100 m apart. The doe nurses first one, then the other. Deer-family newborns are odorless, so predators often walk right on by—although enough kills are made to eliminate about half the yearly production.

The fawns follow their doe around after three weeks and are weaned at four months. The bucks grow their first set of antlers in their second winter. Those reaching adulthood may live for ten years in the wild, up to 20 years in captivity.

Elk/wapiti (wapiti)
Cervus elaphus (deer family) Year-round

Common on the eastern slope from Grande Cache south, in grassy places; on the western slope from Golden south. Occasional farther north. Length of adult males 230 cm (tail 14 cm), height at shoulder 140 cm, weight 315 kg. Females are about ten percent smaller.

"Wapiti" is a Shawnee Indian word meaning "white rump," a fitting name for this animal. Using "wapiti" also straightens out a mistake that won't go away: "elk" is the European name for the moose. I guess we are stuck with "elk," though; when I use "wapiti" no one knows what I'm talking about. Early British visitors to the Canadian west called the animals "red deer," because a similar species occurs in the British Isles, in other parts of Europe and across mid-latitude Asia.

Whatever you call them, elk are easily identifiable: large, with a long head on a long neck. The neck and head are dark brown, as are the legs and a halo around the buffy rump patch, which has the shape of a light bulb. The tail is small, the same color as the patch. The rest of the animal is light-brown to buff, lightest in its coarse winter coat, at which time there is a shaggy mane on the neck. Hairy scent glands are present on the legs, but not in the hoofs; there is an extra pair of scent glands at the base of the tail.

Elk are grazing and herding animals, able to live in either forest or prairie habitats. In the Rockies the adult males head to the high country together in early June, leaving the females with the immatures of both sexes down below. In fall the males return to lower elevations, but in Banff and Jasper parks they seldom join the females to form the large herds noted in the American Rockies. Female/immature herds around here number about 10-50 animals; the males are usually either alone or in groups of fewer than 20. Winter and summer, the females prefer meadows and open woods; in winter the males are often in heavier timber.

If the snow-cover is thin, which it usually is in the montane valleys, the animals continue to paw through it to reach the grass that is their staple food; they also browse on montane shrubbery, aspen seedlings and lodgepole pine needles. When these foods are scarce, elk strip the bark off aspen trees—which is the main reason that aspen are often black-scarred to about head-height (scratches, which look different, are often made by bears).

Elk are preyed upon by wolves, men, mountain lions and grizzlies (roughly in order of number taken). In the late nineteenth and early twentieth centuries the elk of the Canadian Rockies were almost wiped out by hunters, who not only shot them for meat but also for their canine teeth, sold for up to 75 dollars a pair to members of the Elks Club, and for their antlers, which were made into knife handles. Small populations in the Tuchodi Lakes and Muskwa River areas of the northern Rockies survived.

Reintroduction in this century has been quite successful on the eastern slopes of Alberta, but in British Columbia the populations are growing more slowly. In BC, elk have become solidly reestablished only in the southeastern corner of the province.

The notion that elk are plains creatures, foreign to the mountains, is false; remains show that the species lived throughout the Canadian Rockies until the recent near-extermination.

Antler growth begins in April, not long after last-year's set has dropped off in February or March. Young males, who herd with the females for a couple of years, grow peculiar-looking antlers at first. They are small and upright, like two-tined pitchforks. The second set has three or four points and the third has four or five. The fourth set has the normal six tines, so beyond the third year the antlers give no obvious indication of age. The rack of a stag in its prime is magnificent: often 150 cm long, reaching well down the back and weighing perhaps 20 kg.

Why would an animal grow and then lose these heavy structures *each year?* There is a good evolutionary reason for doing so. Antlers are frills, growing large when an animal is strong and healthy, smaller when it is not. The bigger males, which usually have the largest antlers, are the ones that impregnate the females. Such animals are evolutionary successes, and their genes strengthen succeeding generations.

Rutting begins in late August, when the stags (not "bulls," as so many people say) thrash the velvet off their antlers against bushes and small pines. The necks of the stags swell up; they eat very little for the next several months, losing a lot of weight; they urinate in the mud, then roll in it, and they "bugle": make a strange call that starts with a low "unnh," goes up the scale in a series of whistles and finishes with grunts and coughs.

All of this is most attractive to the hinds (pronounced like "rinds"; the popular term "cows" is actually not correct). Each picks a favorite stag and hangs around him as part of a **harem.** Other stags challenge for possession of the harem. Rival stags lower their heads to bring their antlers together, then push and shove each other around. A successful stag might have up to 30 hinds in his harem; somehow, he manages to impregnate them all.

But the other stags are not denied entirely. While the dominant stag is dozing or busy, the bolder rivals mount the hinds.

In the national parks, elk rut along the highway shoulders and up and down the streets of Banff and Jasper. This is a bonus for fall visitors, but they must be careful not to smash into heedless elk along the roads at night. Elk don't run across the road suddenly, like deer do; they just walk majestically out into traffic.

Elk-watchers on foot are warned to be wary of the stags: the big animals, which stand taller than a man, consider any other creature that is not a hind to be an adversary. If you get too close to a rutting stag (10 m or so), it will come toward you, throwing those enormous antlers up and down and pawing the ground. Time to get back in the car.

The central meadow in Whistlers Campground, at Jasper, is the site of a 600-seat outdoor theatre where park naturalists present evening programs. In late August of most years that clearing also holds a stag and his harem. On some evenings the campers approach the theatre, carrying their blankets and flashlights, only to be driven back by the stag, who thinks they are after his females. But people are smarter than elk, so while the stag is threatening those campers coming from one side of the meadow, others sneak in from the opposite direction. Eventually everyone gets seated and the program begins.

Ah, but the stag is now patrolling the periphery of the theatre. Having resisted the intrusion into his meadow, he is not going to let anyone *leave*. The naturalist has a captive audience; if someone is overly bored, too bad. By the time the show ends, though, it is dark and the stag has settled down for the night. The campers go to their sites with a story to tell.

Each female elk usually bears one calf (fawn, really) each year, in late May or early June after gestation of 249-262 days). It is white-spotted, but rather than lying in the brush for three weeks like a mule-deer fawn it is up and following its mother immediately. Baby elk are often born on an island in a lake or river; they must swim to shore with their mothers only a few hours after birth. Weaning is in September, when the spots disappear. Maturity comes at 16 months (the second fall), but the females normally don't breed until their third year, and the males are not strong enough to gather a harem until they are four or five years old.

It is inadvisable to hand-feed elk, for the same reason that one shouldn't hand-feed deer (see page 731).

Moose (orignal)
Alces alces (deer family) Year-round

Fairly common in subalpine meadows and marshes, sometimes higher or lower. Length 257 cm (tail 17 cm), height at the shoulder 181 cm, weight 450 kg. Females are about ten percent smaller.

The moose is the second-largest naturally occurring land animal in North America (the bison, page 737, is even bigger; horses are imports). It is dark-brown on top, lighter underneath, with no white rump patch as other deer-family members have. There are scent glands on the legs and at the bases of the antlers, but not in the hoofs.

So ugly it is beautiful, the moose is hard to mistake for any other animal. This creature is a product of the Pleistocene, well-designed for an ice-age existence in cold, snowy, marshy country. It survives low temperatures and deep snow, simply cruising through on its long legs. Those same legs are useful in summer, for wading out into bogs and reaching down under the water with that enormously long muzzle to pull up swamp vegetation. Despite the ungainly look, moose are quite agile, able to run at 50 km/h through the woods. Moose swim well, as do other deer, but moose also dive beneath the surface in lakes to reach bottom-growing vegetation as deep as 5 m.

The antlers of the bulls have palm-like blades with tines along the edges. Hanging under the chin of bull moose there is a long skin flap (the **bell**) whose function is unknown. It follows antler size: if the antlers are large, so is the bell—unless the bell has frozen off, as sometimes happens.

"Moose" means "twig-eater" in Algonkian—an apt name, for the animal does a lot of that very thing. Its favorite browse species are willows, red-osier dogwood and shrub-size aspen and poplar. These are winter staples; in summer moose spend much of their time belly-deep in marshes, gobbling water plants.

Moose are loners, sharing overlapping ranges of a few square kilometres. You seldom see more than one at a time, except for a cow with her calf. Outside the rutting season they are quite shy, moving well away when humans are around. If you hold very still they seem to forget that you are there. They are active at any time, but mainly at dusk and at dawn.

In winter, when the other ungulates are down in the montane valley bottoms escaping the snow, the moose tend to stay at somewhat higher elevations, stepping through metre-deep drifts along shrubby streamcourses. They are inclined to stand in the middle of the road in winter, perhaps enjoying a respite from the constant post-holing, so watch out for them if you are driving at dusk. Their drab coloration makes them hard to see, even though they are huge.

The main predators of moose in the Canadian Rockies are packs of wolves and men. A grizzly is strong enough to take a weakened adult, as is a cougar.

Moose antlers begin to grow in April. The velvet dies and dries in late August; by early September the hormones are flowing freely and both sexes are completely wacko. They lose their shyness, the cows bleating and thrashing in the brush to attract the bulls, who produce very sexy coughs and bellows.

Contests between bulls are largely bluffing matches: they posture and shake their antlers menacingly at each other, mentally comparing size and shape. Rather than getting down to rude pushing and shoving, one party will often decide that, golly, the other's rack is just too wonderful, and bow out.

On the other hand, moose can fight viciously, jabbing with their hoofs and raking with their antlers. People are simply other suitors as far as the bulls are concerned, and one is well advised to keep clear in rutting season. There have been serious injuries and deaths from bull-moose attacks.

Valerius Geist, a well-known mammalogist from the University of Calgary, once attracted the wrath of a bull while filming it in the fall. The bull paid little attention to Val and his co-worker at first, so the two men decided to imitate another bull in order to get some action. Val rolled up his sleeves, exposing his white arms—white like antlers. He spread his arms out, tilting them as a moose does. This ploy was a little too successful; it provoked a charge. Fortunately the moose caught the human scent before making contact and veered away.

In light of that story, imagine some poor hiker in a teeshirt crossing a log or a beaver dam, arms out to keep his balance . . .

The females (cows) are impregnated between mid-September and late November. After gestating for 240-246 days, the cow bears one calf or twins (usually just one in the Canadian Rockies) in late May or early June. It is on its feet right away, depending on its mother for defense rather than on protective coloration and concealment.

A cow moose is quite protective (and thus dangerous to approach) when her calf is less than a month old. After that she kind of loses interest, expecting the calf to follow her across raging rivers and into deep lakes, wherein it sometimes drowns. Weaning is at about three months, but the calf follows doggedly throughout its first year. The young moose stays with its mother until the birth of the next offspring, when mum chases the yearling away. For a few weeks it seems

Deer family

rather lost, an easy target for the wolves. If it survives this crisis, it might live for another 20 years.

Caribou/reindeer (caribou)
Rangifer tarandus (deer family) Year-round

Fairly common on alpine tundra (summer) and subalpine forest (winter) between Pine Pass and the North Saskatchewan River (one group reported south of the North Saskatchewan, in the Siffleur Wilderness). Also present in the northern region, from Kwadacha Park north. Length of adult bucks 190 cm (tail 15 cm), height at the shoulder 100 cm, weight 120 kg. Does are noticeably smaller (about 25 percent). The name comes from the French pronunciation of "xalibu," an Algonquin word meaning "the one that paws or scratches."

Caribou are about the size of mule deer but more heavily built, with thick necks, long, moose-like heads and big feet. Both males and females have distinctive antlers: large and curved, with a palm-like section on one antler (seldom on both) that juts forward over the muzzle. The antlers become rubbery after they drop off, and their former owners are inclined to chew them up.

Our caribou are dingy brown in summer, with uneven patches of white on the rump, belly, backs of the legs and tip of the nose; there are bands of white just above the hoofs, like spats. There is a mane of long white hair on the neck, hanging down underneath and especially noticeable in winter, when the animals are generally lighter-colored in their long winter coats.

Caribou are creatures of the arctic tundra, remnants of what must have been huge herds in the Rockies at the end of the last big glacial interval (circa 12,000 years ago), when timberline was lower and much of the Canadian Rockies was above treeline.

In summer you have to get up above timberline to see caribou. In Jasper park there are some reasonably short routes to caribou country: the tramway up The Whistlers (one must walk to the summit of the peak and into the meadows on the other side) and the trail to Cavell Meadows, which starts at the end of the road to Mt. Edith Cavell. In winter caribou are often seen along the Icefields Parkway between the Jonas Creek Campground and Beauty Creek Hostel, and along Maligne Road not far from Maligne Lake; in spring they show up on the alluvial fan at the head of Medicine Lake, where horsetails and sedges come up early.

Main summer caribou foods are ground-growing lichens such as *Cladina* (page 437), grasses, sedges and horsetails; in winter they move down into the subalpine forest to get the tree-growing lichens that are abundant there (but eaten by few other species) and the twig-ends of shrubs. This puts the animals into deep-snow country, but nature has provided snowshoes: caribou hoofs grow large and splay out in winter, with a thick growth of stiff hair underneath and around the sides. Like moose, caribou will stand around on a plowed road, just enjoying the feel of solid ground.

Mountain caribou have few predators. Wolf packs seldom go above timberline, but grizzlies and mountain lions get a few. The animals stay in small herds; they are easily spooked and it is hard to get close in the treeless open. They run like horses, prancing along with their necks out straight. Tendons snapping over bones in their feet produce a unique clicking sound. Not very vocal, caribou snort when surprised and occasionally grunt to each other.

Antler growth on bucks starts in May; the velvet dries up in September, ready for the short fall rut, and the antlers drop off right afterward, when the annual descent into the trees begins. Female antlers are out of phase with male ones; they grow from June to September and stay on through April or May, dropping when the fawns are born. So in winter it is the females that have antlers, while the males do not. In summer it is possible to determine sex by antler size: mature males have larger ones.

Rutting begins in early October and ends in early November. The stronger bucks try to gather harems of does, as elk do; in the mountains the herds are small and so are the harems (fewer than a dozen animals). Gestation is long (7-8 months), and one calf is born between mid-May and July. The spotted fawn is up within 30 minutes and able to outrun a human by the next day, when it falls in with the herd. For the first month it lives on milk, then begins to eat vegetation, but it suckles occasionally throughout its first winter. Antlers appear in the first fall; females are sexually mature at 16 months and males later, as is typical of the deer family. Average longevity of caribou in the wild is 4.5 years, the record 13 years.

Bovids: one (1) wild bison, flocks of sheep and the goat that isn't a goat
Family Bovidae

Bison/buffalo (bison)
Bison bison (bovid family) Year-round

Not free-ranging in our area (but see discussion below); main herds found in paddocks near Banff and Waterton townsites; a few small herds and individuals kept as livestock on ranches.

Properly speaking it is *bison*, not buffalo; buffalo are creatures of Africa and Asia (as in water buffalo).

This is the largest land animal in North America: length of bulls 350 cm, height 170 cm, weight 700 kg. Females about 25 percent smaller. Easily identified: dark brown all over, shaggy from very large head to prominent shoulder hump but shorter-haired elsewhere, upturned black horns on both sexes.

Bison once lived in montane meadows and open woods throughout much of the eastern slopes of the Canadian Rockies, and on the western slope from Golden south, but they were hunted to extinction throughout the region by the 1880s. After the species was reintroduced in Canada in 1906, from a small herd kept in Montana, a few of the animals wound up in paddocks at Banff and Waterton, where they have remained ever since. Parks Canada is thinking of releasing the Banff bison herd by simply knocking down the fence, hoping that they will stay on in the park. One bull is in the habit of escaping, then returning during the rut to visit the cows. At time of writing he is back in the paddock.

Jasper National Park may have the best natural bison range in the Rockies, and in 1973 a small herd was helicoptered from the main Canadian preserve at Wainwright, Alberta to the remote northeast corner of the park. But nearly all the animals quickly moved out of the park and into the foothills to the northeast. Records of sightings there have not been kept, but it seems that all the runaways are now lost.

Two bulls stayed on in the park, moving south to the grassy meadows around the old Jasper House site along the Athabasca River. Too bad the animals had not been a cow/bull pair! One disappeared soon after, and the other was last seen in the fall of 1984.

However, at time of writing (1986) there is still at least one free-roaming bison in the Canadian Rockies: a female that entered eastern Jasper park in 1978 or 1979 via Mystery Pass, one of seven or eight escapees from a bison ranch near Hinton. The others in the group seem to have died, mostly in train/bison encounters, but this one hangs on.

Bison feed mostly on grasses and wildflowers. The sexes herd separately, coming together in July for rutting. The bulls charge each other, knocking heads (not horns) to achieve dominance of a harem. Gestation is 270-285 days, with birth (usually one calf) in May. It follows its mother right away; she protects it from intruders by charging, and the bulls can be ornery, too, so stay out of bison paddocks. The calf nurses for up to seven months; is sexually mature in 2-3 years (in the wild; sooner in captivity).

Bighorn sheep/mountain sheep (mouflon d'Amérique)
Ovis canadensis (bovid family) Year-round

Fairly common on the eastern slope from Pine Pass south and on the western slope from Golden south, on dry, rocky slopes with grass at any elevation. Length of adult males **(rams)** is 172 cm (tail 12 cm), height at the shoulder 97 cm, weight 125 kg. Females **(ewes)** are about 20 percent smaller and much lighter, averaging 72 kg. Both sexes have horns, and there is a scent gland at the base of each. Other scent glands are found in the hooves.

Shorter than a mule deer but stockier, the bighorn is mostly brown (grizzled gray in winter), with a large white rump patch, small dark-brown tail, white muzzle-tip and white line down the back of each leg. There are scent glands on the legs and between the two parts of the hoof. Dall's sheep (next entry) is quite similar, but lives north of Peace River. The two ranges do not overlap.

Many visitors to the Rockies have trouble telling bighorn sheep from mountain goats (page 741), especially when comparing females. But the two species really look quite different. The goats are completely white, rather than brown and white like bighorns. The goats' horns are shiny black, straighter and more slender than the gray-brown, rough-surfaced, well-curved horns of the sheep. The difference is most obvious in the rams, which have much longer, much heavier horns than the ewes do. Ram horns often spiral nearly 360°..

We are speaking here of true horns, which grow continuously from birth and are not shed and regrown annually as the antlers of the deer family are. Seasonal growth fluctuations in bighorns produce alternate grooves and swellings along the horn; counting the major ones, which are annual, gives an animal's age.

In June the thick winter coat is shed. It often comes off in tattered hunks that give the animals a diseased look. While the animals may indeed be diseased (most wild creatures have lots of parasites), the raggedness is quite normal at this time of year.

Bighorns eat mostly grasses (60 percent of their diet in summer), wildflowers and foliage. In winter they seek out windblown slopes where the grass is exposed, nibbling the shrubbery when grass is scarce or covered with snow. Bighorns are sociable, living in flocks of about 10-50 animals. They graze together on and near steep, rocky slopes—almost as precipitous as mountain goat terrain—and run to ledges when predators approach. Wolves, mountain lions and grizzlies kill adult sheep; lynx and possibly golden eagles are able to take lambs.

This species prefers to be in the open and seldom travels more than a few hundred metres through the woods. Fire prevention in the past 100 years has greatly increased the forest cover of the Rockies, such that suitable bighorn habitat is gradually shrinking. At the same time, the flocks are becoming isolated from one another. This may be just as well; bighorns are susceptible to fatal lungworm infestations (culprit: *Protostrongylus*) picked up from domestic sheep, and the disease spreads less easily when the flocks are well separated. But as the range decreases so does the total number of individuals it can support.

In summer the rams separate from the ewes and immatures, moving above timberline where possible; the rest often remain at lower elevations. In fall the sexes reconvene. When the herd isn't around you can tell where it has been by the dusty bedding-down spots littered with black pellet-like droppings.

Bighorns are best known for butting contests. Both rams and ewes engage in petty pushing and head-bumping to maintain the pecking order, but in the fall rut (November and December) the rams spend much of their time one-upping each other in displays of machismo that often lead to combat.

Like other ungulates, the necks of the rams swell. They follow the ewes about, curling their upper lips, heads raised and cocked to the side. When two rams court the same ewe, this posturing usually intimidates the one with smaller horns, but if neither backs down the script moves on to the strange and violent ritual for which these beasts are famous. The animals back off 10-15 m and rear up on their hind legs, snorting loudly. They lower their heads as they charge forward, front legs pawing the air. The horns collide with an echoing crack; the combatants stagger away for a moment, shaking their heads. When the bells quit ringing they back off and do it again, over and over (reportedly for up to 20 hours at a stretch), until one or the other gives up his right to mate with the ewes.

Bighorns hardly ever charge humans, thank heavens, but the species gets touchy during the rut, and it is wise to keep well out of the way.

The toughest ram impregnates most of the ewes, maintaining the genetic strength of the flock. But the strength of that particular ram may be at a low ebb after beating his head for weeks, during which time he seldom eats. The coldest part of winter is just ahead, and the wolves are waiting for the least sign of weakness. He who most recently walked the halls of power may soon lie mangled in the snow. Among bighorns the position of chief stud changes every couple of seasons. Only the true herd leader, always an old ewe, abides.

Bovid family: bison, sheep, mountain goat

The new lambs arrive in late May and early June (gestation 175 days). Births are usually single. Each lamb lies hidden for its first week, then quickly learns to follow its mother on the precipitous terrain this species uses to evade its predators. Mum says "baa" to her lamb when it bleats. Weaned at five or six months, the young mature sexually at two to three years and may live for 14 years in the wild.

Despite gradually declining populations of bighorns in the Rockies, the provincial governments allow the rams to be killed by people who wish to possess sheep-heads. The animals are quite shy in places where they are hunted, but in the national parks they have been protected for many generations; they are frequently seen close beside the highway (or right in the middle of it) and are readily approachable. Poachers in Jasper park have been known to simply walk up to tame bighorns licking salt off the road and shoot them point blank. The wardens will go to any length, including long investigations in cooperation with the police forces of other countries, to catch the people who do this. The penalties used to be trivial, but by the time you read this new legislation will have raised the fine to $30,000, plus a prison term, for any animal poached in the parks.

Its craving for salt costs the bighorn dearly. The animals do not get out of the way when a car comes; sometimes a fast-moving truck kills several at once. Rather than refusing to salt the highways in the national parks, which would result in the deaths of equally inattentive drivers, Parks Canada has tried to get the sheep off the road by using foul-tasting highway salt, placing salt blocks for cattle well off the shoulders and even trying intimidation. Nothing works, and some visitors still feed the sheep out the car window—a criminal thing to do under the circumstances (and punishable by a hefty fine). In Banff park the TransCanada Highway, scene of horrifying sheep slaughter, is being fenced off. This may be the only way to keep the animals from committing suicide.

If you want to see bighorn sheep, the following places offer a good chance. Please be cautious as you drive by; the sheep can run out in the road suddenly.

- At Appekunny Creek along the Many Glacier Road in Glacier park.

- Near the trail to Crandell Lake, along the Akamina (Cameron Lake) Road in Waterton park.

- Along the road to Red Rock Canyon in Waterton.

- In Sinclair Canyon, along Highway 93 near Radium Hot Springs.

- In the first few kilometres west of the Mt. Norquay/Banff intersection on the TransCanada Highway. Vermilion Lakes Drive passes through the same area.

- At the Mt.-Kitchener and Tangle-Falls viewpoints along the Icefields Parkway in southern Jasper park, just north of the Columbia Icefield.

- Along Highway 16 east of Jasper. Good locations: at the junction with the Maligne Road, at Cold Sulphur Spring (20 km east of the townsite), at Cinquefoil Bluff (west end of Talbot Lake) and at Disaster Point, where there is a mineral lick frequented by mountain goats.

- At Miette Hot Springs in eastern Jasper park.

Dall's sheep/Stone's sheep (mouflon de Dall)
Ovis dalli (bovid family) Year-round

Fairly common from Peace River north, in steep, rocky places with grass. Length 160 cm (tail 10 cm), height at shoulder 95 cm, weight 90 kg. Females are about 15 percent smaller.

Dall's sheep are very similar to bighorns (previous entry) but a little smaller and less ruggedly built, with pointier faces and smaller horns. In our area we have the race known as Stone's sheep (*O. dalli stonei*, named for their discoverer). Unlike the better-known pure-white race *(O. dalli dalli)*, which lives in most of the Yukon, Stone's sheep is mostly dark-brown to black, with a gray head. The rest is bighorn-like: white rump with black tail, white muzzle, white stripes down the

Bovid family: bison, sheep, mountain goat

backs of the legs. Habits are practically identical to those of the bighorn, including ignorance of predatory cars and trucks. The sheep are frequently out on the Alaska Highway around Summit Lake in Stone Mountain Provincial Park; please watch out for them.

Mountain goat (chèvre de montagne)
Oreamnos americanus (bovid family)
Year-round

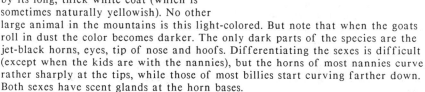

Fairly common on very steep, cliffy terrain, usually at high elevations. Unreported between Pine Pass and Peace River. Males **(billies)** average 180 cm long (tail 12 cm), stand 106 cm at the shoulder and weight 85 kg. Females **(nannies)** are about 30 percent smaller.

A mountain goat is easily identified by its long, thick white coat (which is sometimes naturally yellowish). No other large animal in the mountains is this light-colored. But note that when the goats roll in dust the color becomes darker. The only dark parts of the species are the jet-black horns, eyes, tip of nose and hoofs. Differentiating the sexes is difficult (except when the kids are with the nannies), but the horns of most nannies curve rather sharply at the tips, while those of most billies start curving farther down. Both sexes have scent glands at the horn bases.

Rumors that this creature is not really a goat are true: it is related most closely to the **scrow** and **goral** *(Capricornis* and *Naemorhedus),* which are mountain antelopes of Asia. A more distant relative is the chamois of Europe *(Rupicapra).* The pronghorn antelope of the prairies, often compared with the mountain goat, is not even in the same family.

Mountain goats are loosely social. Typically one sees them as a half-dozen white dots scattered over the gray limestone slabs of a front-range peak. They are present in the main ranges as well; the foothills belt is generally too low in elevation to support mountain goats.

These animals use communal shelters under big overhangs; I have often come across the dusty bedding spots amid accumulations of pellet-like droppings, which look just like sheep scats. While grazing, nannies with kids tend to stay near other females, but the billies prefer solitude. Despite this sociability the nannies do not tolerate the close approach of other nannies; like the billies, they use their horns to intimidate one another.

Any rockclimber knows that viewers looking up from below see nothing but the cliffs, while the climber or the goat, looking down from on high, sees the ledges. This kind of terrain keeps the goats safe from most predators. Mountain lions take a few, golden eagles may kill the odd kid, and humans get the most.

Some goats are killed in falls despite their incredible climbing ability, but the main hazard to this species turns out to be avalanches. In winter the fierce high-country wind keeps grassy west-facing slopes clear of snow, and the goats, warm in their shaggy coats, prefer to stay up high while all the other ungulates are heading down to the valley floors. Steep gullies are routinely crossed, and sometimes the snow lets go. Several times I have come across the bodies of goats melting out of avalanche debris.

What do they find to eat up there in the barren rocks? Mostly grass (about 75 percent of the diet in summer), growing luxuriously on ledges. The windiness of this habitat tends to expose feed in winter, but the goats must sometimes depend upon subalpine fir needles and twigs.

Mountain goats molt in June, when bushes along goat-paths become adorned with fluffy white hair. Their coats look just as ragged and terrible as those of shedding bighorns. The goats also crave salt at this time of year, which brings them down from the heights to the valley floors to lick at salt-rich outcrops of

Bovid family: bison, sheep, mountain goat 741

black shale and sulphate-rich deposits of glacial silt. (I have never seen one licking the highway as sheep do.)

The animals are not very shy at these licks, and if you have a telephoto lens on your camera you can get superb pictures. The goats are unknowingly (and busily) passing parasites around, from mouth to ground and back to mouth, so don't do any licking yourself.

Jasper park is fortunate in having two licks that are right next to the road. There is parking at both. One, the Goats-and-Glaciers Viewpoint, is 38 km south of Jasper on the Icefields Parkway; the other is at Disaster Point, 29 km east of Jasper along Highway 16.

Another well-known goat lick is on the southern boundary of Glacier National Park, along Highway 2 about five kilometres east of the Walton Ranger Station.

Glacier, by the way, has the greatest concentration of mountain goats in the Rockies. Anyone walking in the high country there is likely to see a few. The peaks, steep but ledgy, afford excellent goat habitat.

Mating among mountain goats takes place in November. One looks for bizarre behavior in ungulates during the rut, and the goats don't disappoint. The billies coat themselves well in urine-soaked dust. They thrash vegetation with their horns, which are encircled with scent glands at the base, and they strike heroic poses before the nannies. Competing billies circle each other, hunching their backs and throwing the heads up and down. They lie next to each other in dust wallows, pawing the ground with a foreleg. In fights, the billies spar with their horns, sometimes inflicting serious injuries or even killing each other. Harem-building often occurs.

A billy approaches his mate-to-be from behind, actually or ritually sneaking up until he can kick her sharply in the side in what must be construed as a sign of affection. There is usually one kid, sometimes twins, born in late May or mid-June after gestation of 178 days. The little goats are endearing: lively and playful, nursing on bended front knees with tiny wriggling tails, tripping after the nannies wherever they go, up and down the cliffs. The kids are usually present at the licks described above. They are weaned at six weeks and on their own by the following spring, although they stay in the parents' neighborhood until sexual maturity (27 months for nannies, 39 months for billies). Mountain goats may live 12 years in the wild.

PRIMATES
Order Primates, Family Hominidae

Man (homme)
Homo sapiens (hominid family)
Year-round

Photo courtesy Jasper National Park

Common in townsites and other inhabited places, fairly common on highways, occasional on trails, seldom seen in untracked places. Average length of adult males **(men)** 170 cm (no tail), height at the shoulder 145 cm, weight 75 kg. Females **(women)** are somewhat smaller. Easily identified: our only mammal that habitually walks on its hind legs.

This animal is sparsely haired over most of its body, but grows visible patches on the head, groin and under the front legs. Coat color varies considerably from individual to individual. Males and females are difficult to tell apart, for the species is inclined to cover the diagnostic features—even in hot weather and when swimming. Men have hairy faces and women don't, but many males disguise their sex by shaving their facial hair. Human vocalizations are incredibly varied.

Humans are predominantly migratory, arriving in the Canadian Rockies in June and July (biggest influx: July 1) and leaving in early September. The summer visitors live in densely colonial campgrounds, staying in family groups in a bewildering variety of mobile temporary shelters (popular forms: tents, towed hutches and motorized cottages). A few humans remain in the mountains year-round, building large heated dens for winter use and stocking them with food, television sets, etc.

H. sapiens is omnivorous, consuming everything from raw fish and grains to foods that apparently have no nutritive value whatever. Eschewing naturally occurring foods, humans carry imported delicacies for use during their summer migrations. A favorite seems to be beef cooked over an open fire until covered with ashes, then placed on stale bread and washed down with alcoholic beverages. Warning: the species is unpredictable and dangerous when intoxicated.

Reproduction: human females are sexually receptive in any season but rarely produce young—an average of only three or four in a lifetime. Gestation is about 280 days. The babies are born helpless, although not blind or deaf as among the rodents. Weaning is at six months to a year, followed by hand-feeding for about another year; sexual maturity is reached at age 13 or 14, but successful mating is usually delayed for several more years. Man cannot survive for long in the wild, but has been known to live well over 100 years in captivity.

SUGGESTED REFERENCE BOOKS ON MAMMALS

There are any number of good publications available. Items in the short list below are representative and easily obtainable at time of writing. Some are specific to the Canadian Rockies.

Alberta Fish and Wildlife (undated) *Cloven-hoofed Animals of Alberta* and *Large Carnivores of Alberta* Alberta Energy and Natural Resources, Edmonton. Free pamphlet/posters, in color, with good illustrations and accompanying texts.

Banfield, A. (1974) *The Mammals of Canada* University of Toronto Press/National Museum. The standard book, available in French, but getting old; with illustrations, range maps and index; 438 pages.

Burt, W. and P. Grossenheider (1964) *A Field Guide to the Mammals* Houghton Mifflin, Boston. Peterson-series field guide, with good painted illustrations in color, rough range maps, skull photos and a few tracks; 284 pages.

Carbin, L., ed. (1983) *Wolves in Canada and Alaska* Canadian Wildlife Service Report Series, Number 45; Canadian Government Publishing Centre, Ottawa. Collection of pivotal papers, with photos, maps and other graphics; 135 pages.

Cowan, I. and C. Guiguet (1956) *The Mammals of British Columbia* BC Provincial Museum, Handbook 11. Now under revision; wait for the new edition.

Glacier National Park (undated) *About Bears* Glacier National Park; West Glacier, Montana. Short pamphlet on bears; some misinformation but not bad.

Glacier Natural History Association/National Park Service (1978) *Glacier National Park Mammals, Field Checklist* Glacier National Park; West Glacier, Montana. Pocket checklist, good for entire Canadian Rockies region if you add dusky shrew, pygmy shrew, Richardson's ground squirrel, caribou, bison and Stone's sheep.

Herrero, S. (1985) *Bear Attacks: Their Causes and Avoidance* New Century; Piscataway, New Jersey. The authoritative work on problems with grizzlies and black bears; completely referenced, quite readable, illustrated, indexed; 287 pages.

Murie, O. (1954) *A Field Guide to Animal Tracks* Houghton Mifflin, Boston. Peterson-series guide, comprehensive and well illustrated (line drawings), including scats. Enjoyable text with lots of anecdotes; 374 pages.

Nelson, D. and S. Nelson (1978) *Easy Field Guide to Mammals of Glacier National Park* Tecolote Press; Glenwood, New Mexico, or pick up in Glacier park. Inexpensive pamphlet with basic information on 30 common species; good line drawings.

Parks Canada (1974) *Wapiti* and *Bighorn Sheep* Parks Canada, Calgary. Short pamphlets, in French and English.

Province of British Columbia (1978) *Some Mammals of Interior Parks* Ministry of Recreation and Conservation; Victoria, BC. Pamphlet on 13 western-slope mammals.

Savage, Arthur and Candace (1981) *Wild Mammals of Western Canada* Western Producer Prairie Books, Saskatoon. Coffee-table book on 70 species. Interesting text, excellent photo illustrations in color, index and bibliography; 209 pages.

Soper, J. (1965) *The Mammals of Alberta* Hamly Press, Edmonton. Standard reference for the eastern slope, due for updating; 402 pages.

Government libraries in the various national parks have hard-to-find reports on mammals. Many of the Parks Canada reports are also available at the Western Regional Office in Calgary.

History outline
Briefly please: who did what and when?

Most of the readily available historical literature about the Canadian Rockies concerns events in the Canadian national parks, a bias reflected in this outline. But I have tried to include some essential information about other parts of the region, including Glacier National Park, Montana. Events of interest to naturalists and recreationists have been emphasized.

The current population of the region is given in the table on page 766.

11,500 BP (years before the present)

First datable evidence of human activity in the region. A radiocarbon-dated site at **Vermilion Lake** (on the southern slope of Mt. Cory, west of Banff) has yielded stone spear points, choppers and knives, along with many bones of butchered animals (mostly bighorn sheep). Possible evidence of a house, if verified, would make it the oldest known structure in the Rockies.

Major eastern-slope valleys seem to have been occupied, at least in summer, since the end of the late Wisconsinan glacial period (20,000-11,000 BP). However, man had journeyed to North America by way of Alaska some 20,000 years earlier, and may have seen the Canadian Rockies soon thereafter, during the period of ice retreat between the early and late Wisconsinan advances (64,000-20,000 BP). Even during the late Wisconsinan, the Rockies formed the western wall of an **ice-free corridor** (page 193) between mountain glaciers and a great ice sheet covering the prairies. The ice-free corridor connected unglaciated regions to the north (in the western Yukon and Alaska) with the southern limit of ice in Montana. It is quite possible that men passed through the corridor during most of the late Wisconsinan ice advance; the corridor was closed by glaciers for perhaps only a few thousand years, if at all. (It was probably closed during much of early Wisconsinan glaciation: 75,000-64,000 BP.)

In addition to the Vermilion Lakes bonanza, other major prehistoric sites in the Rockies include chert (flint) quarries near Crowsnest Pass and in Top of the World Provincial Park, pictographs in the Canmore area and camps in Waterton Lakes National Park.

Just before European contact

North of the Athabasca River, the **Déné** (Athapaskan-speaking Indians)probably occupied both sides of the Rockies, although in small numbers. Main tribes: **Sarcee** between Jasper and Prince George, **Beaver** from there north to Peace River and **Sekani** (a branch of the Slave group) in the northern Rockies.

South of the Athabasca* River, the game-rich **Ya-Ha-Tinda** area (name means "Meadow in the Mountains") along the mountain front north of Bow River was particularly attractive, winter and summer, to prehistoric peoples. Artifacts from there and from elsewhere in southern Alberta show the most successful of these were the **Kootenay** Indians (American spelling

---

*"Athabasca," also spelled "Athabaska," is a Cree word meaning "the place where there are reeds." It refers to the delta of the Athabasca River at Lake Athabasca in northeastern Alberta.

"Kootenai"), who were linguistically and culturally unrelated to surrounding groups. The language of the Kootenays resembled the Uto-Aztecan tongues of Mexico; perhaps the Kootenays stayed in Canada while other Indians moved on to settle Central America.

Proper mountain Indians, the Kootenays occupied both the eastern and western slopes of the Canadian Rockies from the North Saskatchewan River south. In the southern foothills their easterly neighbors were the **Blackfoot** branch of the Plains Indians and, on the south, the **Shoshoni** (sometimes called "Snakes"). On the west they met the **Shuswaps** (Interior Salish branch of the Plateau peoples, sometimes called "Carriers"), for both groups fished the lakes and rivers of the Rocky Mountain Trench.

Relations among the various tribes were cordial, with constant trade and little conflict. Shuswap-style pit houses on have been found on the Banff Springs Hotel golf course, suggesting that Shuswaps overwintered occasionally on the eastern slope, and there is evidence of Shuswap occupation in eastern Jasper park, near the site of Jasper House.

Early 1700s

Pushed westward by white conquest of eastern North America, eastern Indians displaced a tribe of the Sioux group: the **Stoneys** (spelled with an *e*), named for their method of cooking by boiling with hot stones; also called "Assiniboines," "Nakodas" and "Dakotas." The Stoneys came from Lake of the Woods on the Canadian Shield.

Desperately fleeing smallpox and fighting other tribes along the way, bands of Stoneys moved west along the North Saskatchewan to the western edge of the prairies, where dwelled the **Blackfoot, Blood and Peigan** tribes of the Blackfoot Confederacy. (Peigan is spelled "Piegan" in the USA.) The Stoneys were tough, but so were the Blackfoot (American name "Blackfeet"); conflicts often resulted in killings, so they came to be resolved ritually, in the form of games. If not welcomed, the Stoneys were tolerated.

The Stoneys preferred the mountains and foothills, home of the Kootenays—whom they attacked. About this time the Kootenays, Stoneys and Peigans acquired **horses,** brought to the New World in the 1500s by Spain and traded north.

Mid-1700s

Guns came into use among the western Indians, increasing the bloodshed. Horse-mounted, gun-toting Stoney and Peigan warriors pushed the Kootenays off the eastern slope and back to their safer western-slope lands. Fear of smallpox kept them there.

At about this time the Sarcees were moving south, pushed by the Cree: a James Bay tribe who had spread through much of northern Canada as middlemen and trappers working for whites. The Sarcees reached the Bow River in the early 1800s; they survived along the western plains margin in uneasy coexistence with the Stoneys, who had become the dominant tribe in the central Rockies.

1754 **Anthony Henday,** scouting for the fur-trading **Hudson's Bay Company,** saw the Rockies from near a location near modern-day Innisfail (between Calgary and Edmonton). But he didn't reach the mountain front.

1780s **Smallpox** killed three-fifths of the western Indians. The fur trade arrived not long after, bringing more disease and more guns. There was now continuous warfare among displaced tribes.

1793 Scottish fur-trader **Alexander Mackenzie,** a partner in the **North West Company,** which competed with the Hudson's Bay Company in the fur trade, followed Peace River to the Rockies from Fort Chipewyan (on Lake Athabasca in northeastern Alberta). He reported that the Beaver Indians had been displaced by the Cree. By this time there were also scattered

Stoney Indians Samson Beaver, his wife Leah and daughter Frances Louise at a camp on the Kootenay Plains (near today's Two-O'Clock Creek Campground along Alberta 11) in August of 1907. Photo by Mary Schäffer reproduced courtesy Whyte Musuem of the Canadian Rockies, Banff.

Mollie Adams, Mary Schäffer, Billy Warren and Joe Barker at a back-country camp. Photographer unknown; photo reproduced courtesy Whyte Museum of the Canadian Rockies, Banff. See entry for 1908, page 760.

bands of **Iroquois, Algonquin** and **Nipissing** Indians in the area, remnants of eastern tribes trying to keep ahead of white settlement while working in the fur trade. Bloodthirsty by reputation, the Iroquois were hated by most western Indians, who killed them at every opportunity (see the death of Pierre Bostonais, 1820 entry).

Mackenzie followed the Rocky Mountain Trench up the Parsnip River to the Fraser, traveled south on it for a while, then was warned by his Indian guides of watery perils ahead and turned west, reaching the Pacific via the Bella Coola River. His was the first known overland trip across western Canada.

1797 or 1798

John Finlay, another partner in the North West Company, founded **Fort St. John** just east of the Rockies along Peace River.

1799

Farther south, **Duncan McGillivray** established **Rocky Mountain House,** a North West Company post, just east of the foothills on the North Saskatchewan River.

1800

English-born **David Thompson,** a trader with the North West Company at Rocky Mountain House, sent his scouts **La Gassi** and **Le Blanc** across the Rockies with a band of Kootenay Indians to set up trade on the fur-rich western slope. That same year, Thompson and McGillivray traveled south to Highwood River and scouted Bow River as far west as the mountain front. Lacking Indian guidance—the local Peigans were uncooperative—they turned back. McGillivray explored north along the front ranges, reaching Brazeau Lake and continuing to the Sunwapta River. But no suitable pass was found.

Also in 1800

The Nor'westers built **Fort Nelson** near the site of the modern community. It soon fell into disuse, but was revitalized by the Hudson's Bay Company in 1865.

1805

Simon Fraser, another partner in the North West Company, built a fur-trade post at **Hudson's Hope,** where the Peace leaves the mountains. That community still exists; it is the oldest in the Canadian Rockies.

The following year Fraser followed the Peace through the northern Rockies and took the Rocky Mountain Trench south to found **Fort George** (now Prince George) in 1807. In 1808 he followed the Fraser to the Pacific and confirmed that it was too dangerous for regular travel. David Thompson named the Fraser River for its explorer, who had already named the Thompson River, a tributary from the Columbia Mountains, for his friend David (who didn't travel it).

Also in 1805

Merriwether Lewis approached the Montana Rockies on the outbound, westward leg of the Lewis and Clark Expedition. He explored 50 km of the Marias* River, naming it after his cousin Maria Woods, but decided to cross the mountains farther south, along the route of today's Interstate 90. On the 1806 return trip, after crossing the Rockies from the west, Lewis again followed Marias River northward, hoping to establish an easy connection with the Saskatchewan River system of Canada. He took the Cutbank Creek branch and came within 15 km of what is now the eastern boundary of Glacier park. The Lewis Range and Clark Range are named for that expedition.

---

*The geographic pronunciation is "ma-RYE-us."

1806 **Pine Pass** (between Jasper and Peace River) was crossed by a couple of unnamed deserters from Simon Fraser's trip up the Peace.

1807 Guided by Kootenays, Thompson followed the North Saskatchewan valley to **Howse Pass,** crossing it to reach the Columbia. He continued upstream and built **Kootenae House** (sic) at the Columbia headwaters near present-day Invermere. Having recruited the Kootenays as trappers, Thompson returned, but was harassed at Rocky Mountain House by the Peigans, who feared he would arm the Kootenays. He *did* arm the Kootenays.

1810 The Peigans had closed Howse Pass to David Thompson, so he looked farther north for an alternative. **Thomas,** an Iroquois, led Thompson's group over **Athabasca Pass** in January of 1811 and down the Wood River to the Columbia. They wintered uncomfortably at **Boat Encampment** on the Big Bend of the Columbia (historic site now under Kinbasket Lake), then went up the Columbia in the spring to Kootenae House, down the Kootenay River to its junction with the Columbia and so reached the west coast in July, claiming Oregon (at that time a vast territory that also included modern Washington state) for Britain and the North West Company.

However, American fur-traders (the **Astorians**) had arrived first. This didn't faze Thompson; he had been told of a deal between the two companies. Little did he know that the deal had fallen through. After many years of legal haggling, dirty tricks and the occasional act of violence, the Americans got Oregon and the Brits got "British" Columbia.

Also in **1810**

Three of David Thompson's scouts made the first recorded crossing of **Marias Pass,** the southern boundary of Glacier park. **Finan McDonald, Michael Bordeaux** and **Baptiste Buché** were taken across from west to east by Kootenay guides. Ambushed in the pass by primitively armed Blackfoot warriors, the whites used guns against them, chasing the attackers east over the top.

1811 While Thompson was away exploring the Columbia basin, a few of his men were left behind to build **Henry House** on the Athabasca River opposite the site of modern Jasper. The earliest permanent structure built by non-natives in the Canadian mountain national parks, Henry House (named for **William Henry,** head of the construction crew) has since disappeared—perhaps under Jasper Park Lodge. If so, then the site has been the location of first one kind of hotel, then another. The fur-trade posts of the Rockies were mostly for sheltering company employees on the trail and for keeping their horses, not mainly for trading.

Thompson paddled back up the Columbia to Boat Encampment that same year, proving the Columbia navigable to the west coast. He recrossed Athabasca Pass to Henry House in October and thus set the main route of trans-Rockies travel for the next 50 years.

A cartographer as well as a fur-trader, Thompson drew the first accurate map of the west (he had used sextant readings to determine locations) upon his return to Montreal. He never went back to the Rockies. By now a partner in the North West Company, he became rich as well as famous. But he invested his money badly and died poor in 1857.

The once-a-year fur brigades, composed mainly of French-speaking **voyageurs** ("voy-ah-ZHOORS," meaning "travelers"), were a romantic part of Canada's history. Starting in the spring from Ft. William on Lake Superior, the voyageurs paddled and portaged northwest across the lakes and rivers of the Canadian Shield to the North Saskatchewan River. At Edmonton they portaged north to the Athabasca and followed it to the mountain front, where they quit paddling and took to horses, following the Athabasca valley to a large, snowy mountain they called **la montagne de la**

grande traverse: "the mountain of the great crossing." Today it is called Mt. Edith Cavell (see 1916 entry for the reason). Turning west up Whirlpool River, the eastern brigade met a brigade from the Columbia River at the pass summit. The western group exchanged its furs for trade goods from the east and each party headed back the way it came.

In 1821 the Hudson's Bay Company and the North West Company merged. Instead of going all the way to Lake Superior, the voyageurs took the furs to the HBC port of York Factory, on Hudson Bay.

Many voyageur names survive in the Jasper area, the best known being **Roche Miette,** a landmark in the east end of Jasper park. Long thought to be a person's name, "Miette" ("mee-YET") is more likely a French corruption of "myatuck," Cree for "bighorn sheep." Bighorns are quite common now at Roche Miette, just as they were in the fur-trade era.*

1813   The North West Company built another "Rocky Mountain House" along the shore of Brûlé Lake (a widening in the Athabasca at the mountain front). The structure soon became known as "Jasper's House," named for **Jasper Hawes,** the company's man there. This is the place at which the voyageurs became horse-riders for the upper-Athabasca part of the trip.

In 1829 the post was moved farther upstream, to near the junction of the Snake Indian River and the Athabasca. The name "Jasper" settled over the whole district. "Jasper's House" became **Jasper House.**

1820   First reference to **Pierre Bostonais** ("boss-tun-AE"),** a fair-haired Iroquois trapper and fur-company guide more commonly known as **Tête Jaune** ("tet zhawn"), French for **Yellowhead.** Bostonais operated out of **Tête Jaune Cache,** in the Rocky Mountain Trench at the western approach to **Yellowhead Pass.** Yellowhead Pass didn't get much fur-trade use, for it connected with the surly Fraser River, not with the placid Columbia. However, shipments of leather goods through it to the Prince George district between 1826 and 1828 gave it the temporary name **Leather Pass.**

Like many other eastern Indians trying to survive in the west, Bostonais and his family were killed by local natives, in this case by a band of Beavers in late 1827 or 1828.

1824   Scot **Sir George Simpson,** a higher-up in the Hudson's Bay Company, crossed Athabasca Pass. At the summit he toasted other HBC officers at a small lake he named the **Committee's Punch Bowl.** Simpson continued to the Columbia and on to the coast.

In 1841, now governor of the entire company, Simpson passed through the Bow valley on his way west, crossing **Simpson Pass** (near today's Sunshine ski area) to the Vermilion River, then down the Kootenay until turning west, crossing Sinclair Pass (see entry for 1841) and emerging in the Rocky Mountain Trench near **Radium Hot Springs.** This was the first recorded pleasure trip in the Canadian Rockies, it would seem; the gentleman continued west, right around the globe and back to England.

1825   **Thomas Drummond,** a Scottish botanist, was the first naturalist to visit the Canadian Rockies. He traveled from Edmonton up the Athabasca to Jasper House, then up the Snake Indian River and along the front ranges to the **Grande Cache** area. Drummond wintered in the Rockies, visited Boat Encampment and returned to Edmonton in 1826 with 2000 specimens of plants, mammals and birds in his collection—including a number of species

---

*Jim MacGregor makes a convincing case for this view (MacGregor, 1975, page 66).

**David Smith (1984) has shown that Yellowhead's last name was not Hatsinaton, as historians had believed previously.

new to science that bear his latinized name *(drummondii)* after the genus designation.

1826   **David Douglas,** another Scottish botanist, traveled up the Athabasca. His discoveries included the Douglas-fir and Douglas maple (now more commonly known as Rocky Mountain maple).

   Douglas crossed Athabasca Pass and climbed Mt. Brown, the western pass buttress, giving its height and that of Mt. Hooker, the eastern buttress, as 16,000-17,000 feet (4800-5100 m). This would have made them by far the highest peaks in the Rockies. His report attracted climber/explorers for the next 70 years, looking for the monstrous peaks (see page 755).

   Douglas's climb was notable in being the first recorded ascent of a major peak on the continental divide in the Canadian Rockies. In 1835 Douglas died nastily in Hawaii, trampled to death in a pit used to catch wild cattle.

1830   Twenty-four of 37 Shuswap Indians camped near Jasper House (known locally as "Snakes" or "Snaring" Indians) were killed by Stoneys at the mouth of Snake Indian River. One of the survivors was a 17-year-old girl (name not recorded) who lived alone for 18 months in the foothills east of Grande Cache before she was taken in by the Iroquois Metis community there. A domestic job at Jasper House led to reunion with a group of her people five or six years after the massacre.

1835   **Colin Fraser** was placed in charge of Jasper House. Beginning his fur-trade career as Alexander Mackenzie's bag-piper, this Fraser (no relation to Simon Fraser) was well known in the Jasper area for 15 years; the **Colin Range** is named after him.

1841   **James Sinclair** took a group of 200 Metis, including many families, from Manitoba across the Rockies via **Kananaskis, White Man and Sinclair** passes to settle Oregon and thus to support Britain's claim to it. The group survived the trip, but Oregon became American territory anyway. Sinclair was killed there by Indians in 1856.

1845   **Father Pierre Jean de Smet,** a Jesuit missionary from Belgium, crossed the Rockies from the west, via White Man Pass, to make peace among the Indians and to convert them to Christianity. In 1846 he returned over Athabasca Pass. He was well received on his journeys, a jovial fat man who gave away white shirts (including the one off his back when he ran out of the gift supply).

   De Smet kept a witty journal. In it the name **Maligne** ("muh-LEEN," French for "wicked") first appears, used to describe a tricky crossing of an Athabasca tributary near Jasper. The name was applied to that river, and later to the now-famous valley and lake upstream.

   De Smet was the first to record the presence of **coal** in the Rockies, in 1845 noting exposures along Elk River in the Fernie/Crowsnest area.

Also in 1845

   British soldiers **James Warre** and **Mervin Vavasour** crossed White Man Pass on their way to Oregon to spy on the Americans. They posed as traveling gentlemen; Warre painted views of the Rockies, including a picture of Jasper House done on the return trip over Athabasca Pass.

1846   **Paul Kane,** a well-known painter (and genuine traveling gentleman), ventured through Athabasca Pass with a fur brigade. Later, he published the first printed illustrations of the Canadian Rockies in his popular 1859 travelogue. The educated world noticed the mountains of Canada.

1847   **Robert Rundle,** a Wesleyan (Methodist) missionary, held Sunday service with a small congregation of Stoneys near the site of modern Banff. The Rockies' most-photographed mountain was later named for him.

About 1850

The Hudson's Bay Company decided to ship furs to its beaver-hat factories from the west coast rather than by the overland route, and thus the fur-brigade days ended. Athabasca Pass was seldom crossed in the years ahead and Jasper House was staffed less often; in the 1860s it was abandoned.

1858 **John Palliser,** who was Irish, organized a joint British/Canadian exploratory trip across the Canadian west to see whether the land there could be settled. The **Palliser Expedition** traveled up Bow River into the Rockies and split into three groups.

Captain Palliser took a group over **North Kananaskis Pass** (in modern Kananaskis Country) to the Palliser River, then recrossed eastward just south of the Crowsnest area through **North Kootenay Pass.** Lieutenant **Thomas Blakiston** led a group to the **Waterton** area. **Dr. James Hector,** a physician and geologist, lead a third group up the Bow valley and west over **Vermilion Pass** (along the route of modern Highway 93) to the Kootenay River.

Hector's crew did the most exploring in the Rockies. A series of misadventures with a confused Stoney guide took them up the Kootenay, down the Beaverfoot, up the Kicking Horse (where Hector was the one kicked) to **Kicking Horse Pass;** then up the Bow, down the Mistaya, back west nearly to Howse Pass and finally east to Edmonton in late fall.

Hector was soon off again, this time journeying up the Athabasca in January of 1859 with **Tekarra,** an Iroquois guide, to Whirlpool River (Hector's name, by the way, for what the voyageurs thought was the upper Athabasca) and the entrance to Athabasca Pass. Next spring, Hector ventured up the Bow again, this time reaching Howse Pass and crossing it to the Columbia.

Another member of Palliser's expedition was **Eugène Bourgeau,** a respected Swiss botanist. Part of Hector's party but hopelessly incompetent on horseback, he remained in the Banff area to collect plants while Hector and the others continued their explorations, meeting later at Fort Edmonton.

1859 **James Carnegie, Earl of Southesk,** went hunting in the front ranges between Athabasca and Bow rivers, crossing **Pipestone Pass** among others. An interesting and light-hearted account of his adventures was published, somewhat excusing the amount of killing he indulged in.

1862 Gold was discovered on the western slope of the Cariboo Mountains south of Prince George. A group of 100 would-be miners from eastern Canada (the **Overlanders,** all men except for one woman) crossed the Rockies by way of Yellowhead Pass. They suffered mightily, and several drowned in the Grand Canyon of the Fraser River upstream from Prince George (still called "Fort George" at that time). The trip was a bust—the gold strike was overrated—but many of the Overlanders stayed in the west to become pioneers.

1863 **Lord Milton** and **Dr. Cheadle,** two wealthy Britishers, found Canadian Rockies accommodations and travel arrangements in 1863 to be rather more primitive than expected. Along with a wimpy, unwelcome companion named **Mr. O'Byrne,** they barely survived to write a popular book about their adventures.

1868 **John "Kootenai" Brown** was the first non-native settler in the Waterton area. Hearing of Yellowstone park in the USA (founded 1872), he petitioned Ottawa for a national park in his area and became the first superintendent of Waterton park when it was created in 1895.

1871 British Columbia joined the Canadian confederation.

1872 **Walter Moberly** surveyed Yellowhead Pass as the Rockies crossing for the **Canadian Pacific Railway**. This easy grade was intended to be coupled with equally easy Albreda Pass through the Columbia Mountains to the west.

But the proposed route was not used. In 1881 Kicking Horse Pass was chosen for the CPR instead, to keep the tracks close to the international boundary to prevent American railways from siphoning off business on branch lines up from the south.

To mark the site for an important 1872 meeting with **Sir Sanford Fleming**, who was directing the survey, a Douglas-fir along the Athabasca just east of modern Jasper was stripped of all branches except those near the top. In the lingo of that era, the tree was a **lobstick**. In 1986 the tree is long-dead but still standing.

Under Fleming's direction, Irish botanist **John Macoun** crossed the Rockies via Peace River in 1872 and 1875, cataloging hundreds of species (including Macoun's buttercup, page 360). Farther south, Macoun collected plants and animals for the Canadian government along the CPR route between 1879 and 1904. His daughter married A.O. Wheeler (page 760) in 1888.

Between 1871 and 1875, **Alfred Selwyn,** English director of the Geological Survey of Canada, mapped the rocks along the proposed CPR route. In Albreda Pass, west of Tête Jaune Cache, Selwyn's horse ate his field book.

1873 **Crowsnest Pass** had somehow escaped non-native attention until now, when **Michael Phillipps** and **John Collins** blundered through it looking for new trapping territory. An easy route over the Rockies, Crowsnest had been avoided by the Indians, perhaps because of legends surrounding Turtle Mountain (see the Frank Slide, 1903 entry) but the pass was used by migrating bison.

1875 **Henry McLeod**, a CPR surveyor, explored Maligne River as a possible rail shortcut southeast through the Rockies. He reached a big lake at the end of the valley, named it "Sore-foot Lake" (recalling the difficult trip up the rockslide-strewn streamcourse) and dismisses the idea. This was the first written reference to **Maligne Lake.**

Also in 1875

Peter Younge and **Benjamin Pease** received directions from Stoney Indians to hot springs on Sulphur Mountain in the Bow Valley. Although the Indians knew of these springs long before, the two American hunter/trappers were the first non-natives to record a visit to what would become **Banff Hot Springs**. Younge built a shack at the Cave and Basin, but lacked the money to register a claim and abandoned the springs the following year.

Frank McCabe and the brothers **William and Tom McCardell** rediscovered the Cave and Basin hot springs in 1883. The three young men applied unsuccessfully for a homestead permit (of all things) and were also denied a mineral lease.

Interlopers soon arrived at the springs, bringing on legal (and not-so-legal) maneuvering. When the steam finally cleared in 1885, (a) the three lads had been bought out for a pittance and (b) the government had set aside a federal reserve around the springs, later expanded to become today's **Banff National Park**. (This is the third national park in the world, following Yellowstone, USA and Royal National Park, Australia.)

1879 The **Dewdney Trail**, a wagon road built across southern British Columbia to the Rocky Mountain Trench in 1860, was extended to Crowsnest Pass. The 1.2-m-wide road connected BC with established routes east to become the first improved route across the Canadian Rocky Mountains. Today's

Historical outline 753

Highway 3 follows the Dewdney route; the first auto road over the pass dates to the early 1920s.

1881-1884

Geologist **George Dawson** and his assistant, **Richard McConnell,** mapped the topography and rocks of the southern and central Canadian Rockies for the fledgling Geological Survey of Canada. This despite Dawson's handicaps (he was hunch-backed and very small).

1882 Town of **Golden** founded.

Also in 1882

Tom Wilson, who horse-packed supplies for the CPR construction crews, is taken up into a cirque fronting the Bow River to see the "Lake of Little Fishes" by a Stoney named **Edwin Hunter, the Gold Seeker.** Wilson named it "Emerald Lake," but George Dawson renamed it **Lake Louise** after visiting it with Wilson in 1884. The construction camp down the hill was named "Laggan"; it later became Lake Louise station on the CPR.

In 1884 Wilson started an outfitting (horseback trip) business in Banff, attracting such notable trail guides as the colorful **Bill Peyto,** (for whom **Peyto Lake** is named) and **Jimmy Simpson,** who built lovely **Num-ti-jah Lodge** (Stoney term for the pine marten) at Bow Lake in 1923.

1883 The CPR reached **Banff,** then called "Siding 29." Carelessness in camping and construction set fires that swept the Bow Valley.

1884 The CPR crossed Kicking Horse Pass and headed down the steep, avalanche-prone western slope to the Rocky Mountain Trench. The last spike was driven at Craigellachie in the Columbia Mountains in 1885. In 1909, the **Spiral Tunnels** were drilled under the western lip of Kicking Horse Pass to lessen the grade and render obsolete some long, scary trestles.

1886 **Banff townsite** was laid out. The name came from Banffshire, a district in Scotland in which George Stephen, a principal in the CPR, was born.

This funny-sounding word is properly pronounced somewhere between "bamph" and "BAN-fuh," but it is often mispronounced "BAN-iff."

Also in 1886

Steamboat service began between Golden, British Columbia, and Libby, Montana along the lakes and rivers of the southern Rocky Mountain Trench. The boats ran until 1914, when the crews went off to war. In 1921 a railway line up the trench ended the business permanently.

Further, in 1886

Coal-mining began in the Rockies at **Canmore** and **Anthracite,** east of Banff along the CPR. The federal government actually encouraged mining in Banff park because it brought royalty payments; **Bankhead,** a large mine with a company town, sprang up in 1905 along the road between Banff and Lake Minnewanka.

Over the next 20 years collieries opened in the **Crowsnest Pass** area, in the **Nordegg** region (foothills along the North Saskatchewan River), in the **Coal Branch** (foothills south of Hinton), at **Pocahontas** in Jasper park and in the foothills along Peace River. The First World War created a coal-mining boom as the Allies bought all the Rockies coal they could get to fuel troop ships crossing the Atlantic. Reason: it was semi-anthracite and burned without making smoke. After the war, a depressed market closed most of the mines, many of them permanently.

There was a resurgence in coal-mining in the 1960s, when Japan started to buy Rockies coal for use in making steel. **Strip mining,** despite its heavy environmental damage, was by now the usual mining method; it had been practiced sporadically in our area since the 1950s, but major new pits were opened in the Crowsnest area (where the new town of **Sparwood** was created), in the Coal Branch and at **Coal Valley** (near Brazeau River). By this time coal-mining had been banned in the national parks (1930).

In 1969 a large combination underground/strip mine started up in the foothills along Smoky River. The Alberta government built a town here, not far from the old Metis community of **Grande Cache.** Like other coal towns, Grande Cache went through periods of boom and bust, leading the locals to give it the nickname "Grande Crash."

The most recent Rockies coal town is **Tumbler Ridge,** built in the foothills southeast of Pine Pass by the BC government in 1982. Critics warned that the development was uneconomic; by 1985 they had been proven correct, as the BC government wrote off 300 million dollars in loans to the companies there. But some mining continues, and the town survives.

Yet one more event in 1886
Yoho National Park was established.

1887   R.G. McConnell, of the Geological Survey, traveled Liard River, mapping the strata of the remote north end of the Rockies. This was no mean feat, for the Liard runs in a deep, dangerous canyon.

1888   The CPR opened the original, log-frame **Banff Springs Hotel. William Cornelius Van Horne,** head of the CPR, visited during construction and discovered that the hotel was being built facing the wrong way (the wonderful view to the east was going to be enjoyed by the kitchen staff rather than by the guests). He quickly designed a viewing pavilion on the kitchen side.

Between 1904 and 1928 (helped along by a fire in 1927), the hotel was entirely rebuilt in its present form. It is much larger than the original, made of concrete instead of wood and covered with Spray River siltstone from nearby outcrops. And it faces the right way.

Also in 1888
In Yoho park, the **Monarch** and **Kicking Horse mines** (lead/silver/zinc) opened along the Kicking Horse River near Field, producing 826,000 t of ore until closure in 1952—the last mining operation in the mountain-parks block. These were the only sizable metal-ore mines in the Canadian Rockies.

At the time the mines opened there were many other prospecting sites in Yoho park, perhaps related to a nearby igneous intrusion (see the Ice River Complex, page 150). Small deposits of low-grade copper ore were found in the Castle Mountain/Copper Mountain area of Banff park. But the mines at Field were the only ones developed. Today, the entrances to the Kicking Horse Mine are plainly visible from the TransCanada Highway at the turn-off for Takakkaw Falls. Look north, on the cliffs of Mt. Field. Those of the Monarch Mine are on the south side of the valley, in Mt. Stephen.

More in 1888
A.P. Coleman and **Frank Stover** followed the Columbia River from Golden to Boat Encampment, intending to climb two peaks flanking Athabasca Pass: Mt. Brown and Mt. Hooker, which had been reported by David Douglas (see the entry on 1826, page 751) as being about 5000 m high. But lacking a guide or outfitter, geology-professor Coleman and his friend got no farther than Kinbasket Lake (the original lake in the area, from which the modern reservoir takes its name) before illness and lack of food forced them back.

Thus began an interesting story, typical of its time.

In 1892 Coleman tried again, this time with his brother L.Q. and a stronger party. They followed the mountain front from Bow River to Brazeau River, then over **Poboktan Pass** to the Sunwapta, which they thought was the Athabasca. They came to the junction with the real

Athabasca, which they assumed to be Whirlpool River, and followed it to a lake that they took to be the Committee's Punchbowl in Athabasca Pass. But they noted that this lake was much too big to be the Committee's Punchbowl and realized that they were not in Athabasca Pass at all. Instead, they were lost. They climbed the adjacent peaks, saw no sign of the giants they sought, and went home—having discovered **Fortress Lake.**

Undeterred, the Coleman brothers returned the following summer for one more try, this time following the North Saskatchewan and Cline rivers to Pinto Lake in the north end of Banff park and thence to the Sunwapta and the Athabasca. Yet again they missed Athabasca Pass, this time by overshooting it and mistakenly following Miette River toward Yellowhead Pass. But the group soon backtracked south, finally reached the pass—and where were the two great mountains? Not knowing that Douglas had erred in his measurements, the Coleman party climbed what they thought was a minor peak buttressing the pass (it was actually the fabled Mt. Brown) and headed home terminally mystified.

Next up at the wicket: **Walter Wilcox,** in 1896. A climber from Washington, D.C., Wilcox made the first recorded trip from Banff to the Athabasca River along the route of today's Icefields Parkway (Highway 93). But like the others he could not find the huge peaks.

The saga continued. In 1898 British peak-hunters **Herman Woolley** and **Norman Collie** failed to reach Athabasca Pass, but along the way they climbed **Mt. Athabasca.** From the top they beheld the **Columbia Icefield,** the first recorded non-native view.

Our story ends back in England, when chemistry-professor Collie read David Douglas's journal carefully and discovered a discrepancy. How could Douglas have climbed a 5000-m peak from a 1700-m pass in only *five hours,* as he stated? A fit mountaineer would have taken at least 10 hours to climb 3300 m—probably more, considering the altitude. The lad's altimeter must have been off, Collie decided.

He was right: Mt. Brown's elevation was later determined to be 2799 m; that of Mt. Hooker, 3286 m.

1889 Noting that the Kootenay River came within 2.5 km of Columbia Lake, which is the headwaters of the Columbia River in the Rocky Mountain Trench, **William Baillie-Grohman** built a **canal** between the two, intending to divert Kootenay water down the Columbia and thereby end annual floods at the inlet of Kootenay Lake (farther west in BC), an area that he hoped to develop as farmland.

This scheme was scuttled by the CPR, who feared flooding along the Columbia and convinced Ottawa to install a government-controlled lock in the canal.

Never put to its original purpose, the canal was used once to move a steamboat from Columbia Lake to the Kootenay River. An attempt to move a second boat through damaged the lock and the canal was permanently closed. Legacy of this fiasco: **Canal Flats,** the logging town.

Also in 1889
Montana became a state.

1890 The CPR built a log chalet at Lake Louise, the forerunner of **Chateau Lake Louise,** which grew steadily larger as the years passed. In 1912-1913 the present concrete structure was built as a wing of 350 rooms. In 1924 the rest of the place burned.

1893 **Lewis Swift,** an American who didn't talk much about his past, built a cabin under the **Palisade** (a big cliff just east of Jasper) to ranch, to trade with the Metis living in the valley (mostly members of the **Cardinal** and **Moberly** families) and to wait for the inevitable railway line that would buy him out and make him rich. But when the railway land agent finally showed up Swift received only a pittance for a small piece of his spread.

In 1910 a government representative arrived who wanted to clear settlers out of then-new Jasper National Park. The Metis accepted cash and deeds to land outside the park, mostly in the foothills around Hinton and Grande Cache. But Swift hung on, not selling out until the thirties, when a dude-ranch operator purchased Swift's ranch. The dude-rancher finally turned the property over to the government (for a hefty price) in 1962. This was the last privately held land in Jasper park. In Banff and Yoho, CPR and other private holdings remain to this day.

Swift's ranch eventually became a training centre for Parks Canada employees. Cabins of Ewan (who pronounced it "EE-wun") and John Moberly remain in their abandoned state in eastern Jasper park.

Also in 1893

Walter Wilcox looked into the **Valley of the Ten Peaks,** near Lake Louise. In 1899 he explored it, discovering **Moraine Lake.** His friend, **Samuel Allen,** gave the ten peaks Indian names for the numbers one to ten in Stoney; these have since been replaced by the names of people, except for peaks nine and ten, which still bear the Stoney-language names **Neptuak** and **Wenkchemna.** What the Indians themselves called them, if anything, is unknown.

Yet more in 1893

The **Great Northern Railway** crossed Marias Pass. The pass had been explored as a railway route by engineer/surveyor **John Stevens** in December of 1889. Stevens achieved fame in 1905, when he became chief engineer of the American Panama Canal project.

1894-1913

This was the **golden age of mountaineering** in the Canadian Rockies, in which nearly all the major peaks were climbed, starting with Mt. Temple in 1894 and ending with Mt. Robson in 1913. American and British climbers made most of the first ascents, climbing with **Swiss guides** brought to Lake Louise by the CPR in 1899.

1896 Sidney Abbot fell from Mt. Lefroy, above Lake Louise, and thus became the first known mountaineering fatality in the mountain parks.

1897 A party of Mounties headed by Inspector **J.D. Moodie** crossed the Rockies north of Peace River, bound for the Yukon goldfields to uphold law and order. Following a guide known only as "Dick," they traveled up Halfway River and Cypress Creek, over **Laurier Pass** to the Ospika River, down the Ospika and west over **Herchmer Pass** to a Hudson's Bay Company post on the Finlay River known as **Fort Grahame** (site now under Williston Lake). The following year the party continued up the northern Rocky Mountain Trench to **Lower Post** and on to Dawson City.

Most of the gold-rushers reached the Klondike from the west coast, an easier route, but some came from the east, up Liard River.

Also in 1897

Fernie was founded, named after **William Fernie,** a coal-mining developer.

1898 The CPR lay track across Crowsnest Pass, linking the main line at Medicine Hat with a line across southern British Columbia. Objective: to develop coal-mining in the area and to get the jump on American branch lines from Montana, Idaho and Washington. **Blairmore** was the first of ten communities to appear along a 20-km stretch through the pass at the turn of the century (see also the entry on coal-mining, 1886).

Left to right: Conrad Kain, Albert MacCarthy and William Foster after the first verifiable ascent of Mt. Robson, made on July 31, 1913. Photo by Byron Harmon reproduced courtesy Whyte Museum of the Canadian Rockies, Banff.

The Champion Forest Products pulp mill at Hinton in December of 1985.

Historical outline

1900   **Bill and Jim Brewster** started an outfitting service in Banff to compete
        with Tom Wilson's. Brothers **Fred and Jack** set up shop in Jasper soon
        thereafter, and by the twenties the family had come to dominate tourist
        transport throughout the mountain-park block—until 1965, when the
        Brewsters sold out to Greyhound.

1901   **James Outram**, a British climber, ascended **Mt. Assiniboine** on his first try.
        Walter Wilcox had failed on the peak several times and was annoyed, as
        was Edward Whymper, the conqueror of the Matterhorn, who ostensibly
        came to try Assiniboine but was now too old (62) and apparently too
        alcoholic to attempt it. Outram was an upstart companion of Whymper's.

1902   The first **oil well** in the Rockies was drilled along Cameron Creek in
        Waterton park, near seeps known since 1886. Other wells were drilled in
        Glacier park area, along Swiftcurrent Creek and on the western slope at
        Kintla Lake. The oil had moved up through the thin Lewis Thrust Sheet
        (page 27) from oil-bearing Cretaceous rock below. Insufficient flow from
        these shallow wells caused abandonment a few years later.
            But in 1913 oil in quantity was discovered in the foothills at **Turner
        Valley**, southwest of Calgary. Alberta has never been the same.
            Deeper drilling in the years ahead showed that the Rocky Mountain
        foothills held a great deal of **natural gas.** The foothills were gradually
        crisscrossed by straight **seismic lines** cut out of the forest by exploration
        crews using dynamite shock waves to map the folds and faults below.
        Foothills gas was loaded with stinky, poisonous hydrogen sulphide, so
        processing plants popped up throughout the foothills to remove it from the
        gas headed for market. People living downwind of these plants discovered
        that Alberta was becoming industrial. Clean-air court battles in the Pincher
        Creek area and elsewhere are still unresolved at time of writing.
            Meanwhile, **clear-cut logging** on the western slope had been turning the
        forests of the Rocky Mountain Trench into patchwork since the arrival of
        the CPR, and the atmosphere there had become smoky from sawdust
        burners. It still is. The Alberta side saw little activity at first—the lumber
        industry considered eastern-slope timber too short and scrubby—until the
        late 1950s, when the paper-making industry built large **pulp mills** at Hinton
        and Grande Prairie. Loggers, coal miners and seismic crews found
        themselves in competition to get government permits and tax concessions
        for carving up a particularly exploitable part of the foothills: the section
        between Highway 16 and the North Saskatchewan River.
            Today, the pulp mill at Hinton spreads rotten-egg odors up and down
        the Athabasca valley; Hintonites depend on the mill for jobs and accept the
        air pollution. Occasionally the fumes reach Jasper, 70 km away, where the
        locals are forcibly reminded of what is happening to the Rockies outside
        the national parks.

Also in 1902
        An underground explosion in a coal mine near Fernie killed 128 miners. In
        1914 another explosion killed 189 at **Hillcrest**—Canada's worst underground
        accident. This and other mining accidents have taken over 500 lives in the
        Crowsnest area.

1903   Photographer **Byron Harmon** arrived in Banff. His photos, films and
        postcards publicized the Canadian Rockies worldwide.
            At about this time, **Bill Oliver** set up a photo and film business in
        Calgary. Ottawa was a steady client, and Oliver produced a string of
        educational films about the mountain parks.

Also in 1903
        The **Frank slide** killed at least 76 people in the Crowsnest Pass area. In the
        slide, some 36.5 million cubic metres of rock fell from Turtle Mountain—a

peak known to the Kootenay Indians as "the mountain that moves"—and smashed part of the town of Frank, established just two years before. The CPR line through the pass was temporarily blocked.

1904 The first automobile entered Banff park, along the railway tracks. Thought to scare the animals (and certain to interfere with the Brewsters' livery service) cars were immediately banned. A road reached the park gates from Calgary in 1909, but visitors were not permitted to drive into the park until 1915, when the future was seen by both the park and the tour company, and the ban was lifted.

One-lane wagon tracks were widened in the teens for tough Brewster touring cars to follow from Banff to Lake Minnewanka and from Lake Louise to CPR "bungalow camps" (groups of cabins; the first motels) at Moraine Lake and Wapta Lake. The government completed a road from Banff to Lake Louise in 1921 (the section to Castle Junction had existed since 1914), extended it to Field in 1926 and to Golden in 1928. Side roads led to bungalow camps at Lake O'Hara, Takakkaw Falls and Emerald Lake. In Yoho park, west of the divide in very British BC, cars had be driven on the *left* side of the road for a few years.

In 1923 a road between Banff and Radium (then known as the **Banff-Windermere Highway,** now part of today's Highway 93) opened as a link in the first public highway across the Canadian Rockies. It used Vermilion Pass, connecting with routes from the United States on the west and from Calgary on the east to form part of something the Americans called the "Grand Circle Tour," which included Yellowstone and the Grand Canyon. Motorized tourism had been invented.

Construction of the modern **TransCanada Highway** over Kicking Horse Pass began in 1956; the highway opened officially in 1962.

Also in 1904
Sixty-year-old butterfly-collector Mary de la Beach Nichol (British in spite of the name) engaged outfitter Jimmy Simpson in a collecting expedition that saw the famous big-game hunter running about the meadows of Yoho park with a butterfly net. It was so much fun that Simpson worked for her again in 1907, this time in northern Banff park.

1905 Alberta, previously part of the North West Territories, became a province.

1906 **A.O. Wheeler,** Irish-born topographic surveyor, formed the **Alpine Club of Canada.** Annual ACC camps drew climbers from all over the world, and a string of mountain huts was established. At the camps, A.O. lined up the climbers and shook their hands as they left to make official club ascents.

1907 **Jasper National Park** was created.

1908 **Mary Schäffer,** a middle-aged Quaker widow from Philadelphia, followed the directions of Stoney **Samson Beaver** to a lake in Jasper park the Indian called "Chaba Imne," meaning "Great Beaver Lake." There were no beaver at the lake (and probably had never been); the name may have come from the shape of the lake, or from the Beaver Indians, or from Samson Beaver himself. At any rate, the name is now **Maligne Lake.**

Schäffer spent her summers exploring the Rockies with her friends **Mollie Adams** and **Mary Vaux** (pronounced "VOX," in the American manner, not the French "VOE"), guided by single males **Sidney Unwin** and **Billy Warren.**

Schäffer painted wildflowers, took photos and kept a journal. In 1911 she published an illustrated book about her adventures called *Old Indian Trails of the Canadian Rockies.* It was a hit; she wrote humorously and well about roughing it in the remote Canadian mountains. Reprinted recently under the title *A Hunter of Peace,* the book captures the feeling of that age: ladies and gentlemen enjoying the Rockies area for its wildness and beauty. Schäffer's work helped to establish the value of the region as a place for wilderness journeys and scientific study—right in line with the objectives of the growing national park system.

Mary Schäffer moved to Banff in 1912 and married Billy Warren in 1915, dying there in 1939.

The Vaux family included Mary's brothers **George and William Vaux,** who became enthusiastic amateur glaciologists in the Rockies and Selkirks. In 1914 Mary Vaux married **Charles Walcott,** the paleontologist famous for his work on the Burgess Shale fossils in Yoho park (page 98).

1909   **Curly Phillips,** an Ontario trapper and canoe guide, arrived in Jasper to start an outfitting business. He was hired that summer by **Rev. George Kinney,** who needed help in making the first ascent of Mt. Robson, highest peak in the Canadian Rockies (3954 m). Kinney was experienced, but Phillips had never climbed a mountain in his life. Still, the two very nearly reached the summit.

Kinney insisted that they actually *did* reach it. Doubtful of his story, A.O. Wheeler organized further attempts, leading to undisputed success in 1913 by Austrian **Conrad Kain,** the region's most famous alpine guide, and two ACC members: **Albert MacCarthy** (an American ranching in southeastern BC) and **William Foster** (BC's deputy minister of public works).

Curly Phillips went on to become Jasper's premier back-country guide. He was killed in an avalanche near Jasper in 1938.

1910   **Glacier National Park, USA** was established. In 1913, Glacier Park Lodge opened in East Glacier, Montana, and the tourist business began there.

1911   The **Grand Trunk Pacific Railway** reached the mountain front from the east. The remains of an old log structure near the mouth of the Snake Indian River were dismantled by railway surveyors needing a raft to cross the Athabasca—and thus did Jasper House meet its end. Tracks were laid all the way to Yellowhead Pass in that same year; "Fitzhugh" was established, renamed **Jasper** in 1913.

A second transcontinental railway was built through Yellowhead Pass in 1913: the **Canadian Northern,** headed for Vancouver (the GTP line went to Prince Rupert). One line would have done the job as far as Yellowhead Pass; the government assumed control during the First World War and sent some redundant track to France. Both lines went broke after the war, so in 1922 Ottawa picked up the pieces and created the **Canadian National Railways** system.

1912   The CPR installed a narrow-gauge railway from Lake Louise station to the chateau at the lake. It ran until 1930, replaced by an improved auto road. Lot-leasing by the government in the years ahead allowed more hotels, restaurants and other commercial operations to open at the lake, creating a textbook example of wilderness despoilment. See the entry for 1971, page 763.

1913   **Mount Robson Provincial Park** was established.

1916   In a burst of patriotic indignation, Canada named the great white peak south of Jasper **Mount Edith Cavell,** after a British nursing instructor who stayed behind in fallen Brussels to treat wounded soldiers. She was executed by the Germans for helping Allied prisoners of war to escape.

1917   Elk, hunted to extinction in the southern and central Rockies by the turn of the century, were reintroduced in Banff park. Jasper park received a herd in 1920. The animals have prospered.

1920   **Kootenay National Park** was established.

1922   Having begun as "Tent City" in 1915, **Jasper Park Lodge** was opened by the Grand Trunk Pacific Railway. A set of cabins surrounded a central dining hall, ballroom and lounge housed in what was billed as the largest log structure in the world. The lodge burned in 1952, to be replaced by a fireproof building in a style resembling that of Frank Lloyd Wright, the great American architect.

Also in 1922

The first auto to reach Jasper from Edmonton used abandoned railway grades; the trip took six days. An all-weather road (Highway 16) was not built until 1951. Much of it followed the railway route, which accounts for the wide curves and gentle grades.

Although motorists could drive through Yellowhead Pass to Valemount and McBride on a narrow dirt road built during the Second World War, there was no paved road west of Jasper until the **Yellowhead Highway** opened in 1970.

1925   **Mt. Alberta,** most difficult of the major Rockies peaks, was climbed by a Japanese party employing Swiss guides from Jasper Park Lodge. Rumor had it that the group left a silver ice axe on the summit, but an ice axe found on a later climb was of the ordinary sort.

1930   Parliament passed the **National Parks Act,** establishing the current park boundaries, current names and current philosophy of Parks Canada.

1931   As make-work during the Great Depression, construction began on the **Icefields Parkway** (Highway 93, then called the "Banff-Jasper Road"). Total heavy equipment: one medium-sized farm tractor and two smaller ones. The road was completed in 1939; it opened in 1940 as a single-lane dirt track and was upgraded in the 50s and 60s to the current all-weather standard.

1933   The **Going-to-the-Sun Road,** another depression-era project, was opened over Logan Pass in Glacier park. A road over Marias Pass (now Highway 2) had been completed in 1930.

1939   **Mona Matheson and Agnes Truxler** of Jasper park became the Rockies' first and second licenced female outfitters (guides for horse trips).

Second World War

Prisoner-of-war camps were set up in Banff and Jasper parks, and in the Kananaskis area, as were concentration camps for Canadian civilians of Japanese ancestry and for conscientious objectors to conscription. The internees were put to work building park roads. After the war some of the camp buildings were moved to locations along the Icefields Parkway to become youth hostels (see page 805 for more on these hostels).

1942   The **Alaska Highway** was completed. The northern tip of the Rockies was now accessible, but little development occurred in the years ahead and the northern Rockies today remain largely the preserve of a few hunting outfitters.

1952   A pipeline was built through Yellowhead Pass, carrying oil from Alberta to Vancouver.

1952   The **Hart Highway** (Highway 97) crossed Pine Pass. In 1958 the **Pacific Great Eastern Railway** (now part of the British Columbia Railway) used Pine Pass to link Prince George with Grande Prairie and the east. The line was completed to Fort Nelson in 1971.

1959   **Willmore Wilderness Park** was created as the largest provincial park in the Rockies. It was named in 1965 for Alberta minister of lands and forests Norman Willmore.

1962   The **TransCanada Highway** opened, making travel over Kicking Horse Pass
        much easier. But the new highway is hard on park animals, prompting
        park-warden poet Sid Marty to refer to it as "the Meatmaker" (Marty, 1978,
        page 192).

1967   **Bennett Dam** on the Peace River near Hudson's Hope backed up **Williston
        Lake,** the largest reservoir in the world, submerging a 360-km stretch of the
        northern Rocky Mountain Trench and upsetting the ecology of the Peace
        River delta downstream at Lake Athabasca (home of the whooping cranes).
        But there was now lots of electricity for northern British Columbia.

1971   Following an American lead, Parks Canada planned new roads and other
        developments for the mountain parks, but reaction at public hearings was
        so negative that the plans were scrapped. This was an early skirmish in
        today's ongoing struggle between developers and environmentalists. The
        next fight was in 1972, over plans for a large development at Lake Louise.
        The preservationist faction appeared to win, but a toned-down development
        proceeded in the 1980s. On the positive side, some of the problems noted
        there have been solved.

        By 1976 Parks Canada no longer held public hearings on its plans,
        preferring instead to have something it called "open houses" for "public
        input." In this atmosphere a bitterly contested plan for enlarging Sunshine
        ski area went ahead (despite a protest march in Banff), as did piecemeal
        developments at the other ski areas within the national parks over the next
        ten years.

1973   **Mica Dam,** along the Columbia River upstream from Revelstoke, backed up
        Kinbasket Lake (called "McNaughton Lake" for a few years), which flooded
        the Rocky Mountain Trench from Golden to Valemount.

1977   **Kananaskis Country** was formed in the foothills and front ranges between
        the TransCanada Highway and Highwood River. It became the largest
        provincial recreation area in Alberta, enclosing the older Kananaskis and
        Bow Valley provincial parks.

        This new mountain playground pleased those who liked motorized
        recreation, with upgraded roads and more accommodation. In an attempt to
        control and concentrate previously uncontrolled and widespread land abuse
        by motorcyclists and snowmobilers, large blocks were set aside for these
        activities. Golfers got a 36-hole course and lodge; downhill skiers got a new
        ski area built on Mt. Allan for the 1988 winter Olympics, complete with
        lodge. Environmentalists got hopping mad: most of these projects were hard
        on the land, and all were paid for with public funds.

Also in 1977

        The Alberta government presented its landmark **Eastern Slopes Policy,**
        which protected much of the foothills and mountains outside the national
        parks from development. Several new provincial wilderness areas were also
        declared in the 1970s.

        But in 1984 the policy was revised to make it easier for development to
        occur, and in 1985 the government announced that some public lands would
        be sold off to their current lease-holders.

1986   Parks Canada presented a long-term "management framework" for the
        mountain-park block (Parks Canada, 1986). Public response sought
        throughout the project had been strongly anti-development, and the plans
        called for less development than had been feared by the preservationist
        faction.

        *See page 829 for some thoughts about the accelerating pace of
        wilderness erosion and environmental damage in the Canadian
        Rockies.*

FURTHER READING

There is a voluminous historical literature on the Canadian Rockies. For this list, I have chosen only those publications that bear directly (and mainly) on the area and are still current. Some historic reprints have been included, along with a few spot references from the history outline.

Akrigg, G.P.V. and Helen (1986) *British Columbia Place Names* Sono Nis Press, Victoria. Long-awaited update to the Akrigg's 1969 *1001 British Columbia Place Names.* 346 pages.

Anderson, Frank and Elsie Turnbull (1984) *Tragedies of the Crowsnest Pass Frontier,* Calgary. Accounts of the Frank slide and Hillcrest mine explosion; 96 pages, not referenced.

Brewster, Pat (1977) *Weathered Wood* Altitude, Banff. Memoirs of the nephew of Banff's Brewster brothers. 64 pages.

—— (1979) *They Came West* Altitude, Banff. More reminiscences as above. 63 pages.

—— (1982) *Wild Cards* F.O. Brewster, Banff. Yet more vintage Brewster. 64 pages.

Carnegie, James; Earl of Southesk (1969) *Saskatchewan and the Rocky Mountains* Hurtig, Edmonton. Reprint of Carnegie's 1875 travelogue.

Cavell, Edward, editor (1980) *A Delicate Wilderness: the Photography of Elliott Barnes, 1905--1913* Altitude/Whyte Foundation, Banff. Scenes from early Banff park and east along the Bow Valley, with a biography; 32 pages.

—— (1984) *Legacy in Ice: the Vaux Family in the Rockies* Altitude, Banff. Excellent photo collection, with biographies and amusing diary entries; 100 pages, no index.

—— and Jon Whyte, editors (1982) *Rocky Mountain Madness, a Bittersweet Romance* Altitude, Banff. Selection of whimsical historical photos and texts; 127 pages.

Dixon, Ann (1985) *Silent Partners: Wives of National Park Wardens* Dixon and Dixon, Box 1893, Pincher Creek, AB. Biographies of women in the mountain parks, with many anecdotes; 205 pages, not referenced.

Dowling, Phil (1979) *The Mountaineers: Famous Climbers of Canada* Hurtig, Edmonton. Covers many exploits in the Rockies; 258 pages, 15 photos, glossary of climber's terms.

Fraser, Esther (1969) *The Canadian Rockies: Early Travels and Explorations* Hurtig, Edmonton. Best historical summary on the region available; 252 pages.

Fryer, Harold (1982) *Ghost Towns of Southern Alberta* Heritage House, Surrey, BC. Short items on Bankhead, Antrhacite, Silver City and other extinct Alberta communities south of Bow River. Well-illustrated, but no index or references; 62 pages.

Hallworth, Beryl (1985) *Pioneer Naturalists of the Rocky Mountains and the Selkirks* Calgary Field Naturalists' Society. Biographies of John Macoun, Arthur Wheeler, Eugène Bourgeau, James Hector, Norman Sanson, Mary Schäffer, the Vaux family and Mary de la Beach-Nichol; a few photos and maps, no index; 39 pages.

Harmon, Carole, editor (1978) *Great days in the Rockies* Oxford University Press, Toronto. Selected photos of Byron Harmon, with a biography by Bart Robinson and afterword by Jon Whyte; 110 pages, no index.

Hart, E.J. (1979) *Diamond Hitch: the Early Outfitters and Guides of Banff and Jasper* Summerthought, Banff. 160 pages.

—— (1981) *The Brewster Story* EJH Enterprises, Banff. Detailed account of the major tourist-transport business in the mountain parks; 161 pages.

—— (1983) *The Selling of Canada: the CPR and the Beginnings of Canadian Tourism* Altitude, Banff. Exactly as stated; 180 pages, unreferenced.

Houk, Rose; Pat O'Hara and Danny On (1984) *Going-to-the-Sun: the Story of the Highway across Glacier National Park* Woodlands Press, Del Mar, CA.

Kane, Paul (1859) *Wanderings of an Artist* Hurtig, Edmonton. Reprint (1968) of Paul Kane's famous travelogue; 329 pages.

Liddell, Ken (1981) *Exploring Southern Alberta's Chinook Country* Frontier Books, Calgary. Historical and other features from the TransCanada south to the international boundary; 62 pages, unreferenced, no index.

Lothian, W.F. (1976) *A History of Canada's National Parks, Volume I* Parks Canada, Ottawa. The official account; 123 pages, not illustrated, no index. Three other volumes present more detail.

MacGregor, J.G. (1974) *Overland by the Yellowhead* Western Producer, Saskatoon. History of the area traversed by Highway 16, from Edmonton to the Rocky Mountain Trench; good coverage of Jasper park; 270 pages, 38 photos, not referenced.

Marty, Sid (1978) *Men for the Mountains* McClelland & Stewart, Toronto. Reminiscences from Marty's years as a Parks Canada warden; 270 pages, not illustrated or indexed.

—— (1984) *A Grand and Fabulous Notion: the First Century of Canada's Parks* NC Press, Toronto. History of Banff National Park; 156 pages, not referenced.

Parks Canada (1986) *In Trust for Tomorrow: a Management Framework for Four Mountain Parks* Parks Canada, Ottawa. Policy statements for Banff, Jasper, Kootenay and Yoho parks; illustrated, 80 pages.

Pringle, Heather (1986) "Vision quest" *Equinox* 26, pages 73--85. Good summary of current developments in Rockies archaeology, with photos.

Robinson, Bart (1973) *Banff Springs: the Story of a Hotel* Summerthought, Banff.

Scace, Bob (1973) *Banff, Jasper, Kootenay and Yoho: an Initial Bibliography of the Contiguous Rocky Mountains National Parks* Parks Canada, Ottawa. Not a public document, but can be seen in park libraries or at the western regional office in Calgary.

Schäffer, Mary (1980) *A Hunter of Peace* Whyte Foundation, Banff. Mary Schäffer's 1911 *Old Indian Trails of the Canadian Rockies* reprinted with color separations of her hand-tinted lantern slides, plus the previously unpublished account of her 1911 trip to Maligne Lake and a biography by Ted Hart; 153 pages.

Smith, Cyndi (1985) *Jasper Park Lodge, in the Heart of the Canadian Rockies* Cyndi Smith, Jasper. History of the CNR hotel; 87 pages, footnoted.

Smyth, David (1984) "Tête Jaune" *Alberta History* 32/1

Spry, Irene (1963) *The Palliser Expedition* Macmillan, Toronto.

Strom, Erling (1977) *Pioneers on Skis*, Smith Clove, Central Valley, NY. Autobiographical account of early ski-touring in Banff, Jasper, Assiniboine and Glacier parks; 239 pages, photos, no index.

Taylor, William (1973) *The Snows of Yesteryear: J. Norman Collie, Mountaineer* Holt, Rinehart and Winston, New York. Biography emphasizes climbing in the Rockies; 186 pages, no index.

—— (1984) *Tracks across My Trail: Donald "Curly" Phillips, Guide and Outfitter* Jasper-Yellowhead Historical Society. Biographical; 146 pages.

Whyte, Jon (1982) *Lake Louise: a Diamond in the Wilderness* Altitude, Banff. Early history of the Lake Louise area, with much about climbing; 128 pages, unreferenced, no index.

Wilson, Tom (1972) *Trail Blazer of the Canadian Rockies* Glenbow Alberta Institute, Calgary. Wilson's memoirs, as told to W.E. Round and edited by Hugh Dempsey; 54 pages.

POPULATION OF THE CANADIAN ROCKIES
Based on provincial and state government estimates current in 1985

ALBERTA

Banff & Lake Louise (I.D. 9)	6949	Grande Cache to Brazeau River	
Black Diamond	1450	(I.D. 14)*	500
Bow R to Red Deer R. (I.D. 8)	1158	Jasper	3970
Bragg Creek and area (M.D. 44)*	1000	Kananaskis area (I.D. 5)	122
Canmore	4012	Longview	292
Cardston	3546	Nanton to Ft. Macleod (M.D. 26)*	1000
Cardston area (M.D. 6)*	2000	Pincher Creek	3712
Crowsnest Pass	7577	Pincher Creek area (M.D. 9)*	1500
North and south		Sundre	1750
of Crowsnest Pass (I.D.6)	119	Turner Valley	1298
Calgary to Nanton (M.D. 31)*	5000	Waterton Park	176
Glenwood	297		
Grande Cache	4624		
Hinton	8904	**Total Alberta**	**60,956**

BRITISH COLUMBIA

Chetwynd and area	2800	McBride and area	650
Elkford and area	4000	Sparwood and area	4950
Fernie	7500	Tumbler Ridge and area	3300
Golden	3460	Valemount and area	1150
Hudson's Hope area	2000		
Invermere and area	1969		
Mackenzie and area	4800	**Total BC**	**36,579**

MONTANA

Browning	1226	Martin City	500
Columbia Falls	3112	West Glacier	250
Coram	300	Whitefish	3703
East Glacier	500	Estimated rural*	10000
Eureka	1119		
Hungry Horse	900	**Total Montana**	**21,610**

GRAND TOTAL 119,145

---

*Regions that extend east of the foothills into more densely populated areas. Mountain and foothills populations in such areas are estimated roughly.

M.D. = Municipal District. I.D. = Improvement District.

SOURCES

Municipal Statistics, 1983 (1985) British Columbia Ministry of Municipal Affairs, Victoria

Alberta Municipal Affairs Population List, 1985 (1985) Alberta Municipal Affairs, Edmonton

Census of Population and Housing, 1980 (1981) Summary Tape File 1A, Fiche 15--19 and 22, United States Census Bureau, Washington, D.C. (latest available at time of writing)

Enjoying the Rockies
Beside the highway, along the trail, over the snow and up the peaks

Herewith some information about **auto-touring, hiking, mountaineering, cross-country skiing and bicycling** in the Canadian Rockies, condensed from many years of personal experience. There are recreational guidebooks available that hold far more detail than I can give here. See page 811 for a list.

I have done too little canoeing or kayaking to offer good advice about these sports, popular and appropriate in the Canadian Rockies though they be. In another category, you will find little here for devotees of fishing, hunting, off-road motorcycling or back-country dynamiting—activities in which I will probably never gain much expertise.

THE MUST-SEE LIST

Auto-accessible highlights of the region are listed below, each offering a whopping view right out the car window.

In your glove compartment you may want a copy of Brian Patton's excellent *Parkways of the Canadian Rockies.* It covers all the scenic stuff in the four-mountain-parks block (Banff, Jasper, Kootenay and Yoho).

- **Logan Pass and the Going-to-the-Sun Road** in Glacier National Park: high point of the Going-to-the-Sun Road is Logan Pass (2031 m, just at timberline), with interpretive centre and a short hike to nearby Hidden Lake Overlook (4.1 km return). See castle-like peaks cut in colorful Purcell Group rock, marmots, ptarmigan and other high-country dwellers going about their business among hordes of people.

  The road itself is narrow and winding, very slow in afternoon traffic—but a marvel, etched along the steep valley walls and lovingly built during the Great Depression, with stone guard-railings and many viewpoints. Closed in winter.

- **Highway 5 between Cardston and Waterton Lakes National Park:** the grassy foothills south of Crowsnest Pass. The rangeland carries on right to the mountain front, a unique situation, for the inner foothills are normally forested. Interesting glacial features between the park gate and the townsite.

- **The Wilmer Wildlife Sanctuary north of Invermere:** a fine spot to see flora and fauna typical of the southern Rocky Mountain Trench. Dry terraces, complete with juniper trees and the only cactus in the Canadian Rockies (page 367), slope down to the marshy trench floor, which is usually quacking with water birds. Hoodoos (page 200) in the terrace edges display Quaternary sediments. From Invermere, go north to the little community of Wilmer. Continue north until you see the wildlife sanctuary sign; park there and stroll down toward the water on sandy trails.

- **Southern Alberta foothills and front ranges scenic drive:** a one-day field trip that can easily be stretched into a week of puttering. Highway 3 west of Pincher Creek follows the Oldman River across foothills hogbacks set with gnarled Douglas-firs and limber pines. Turn north on Highway 22, following it between Livingstone Ridge and the Porcupine Hills to just past Chain Lakes, where Highway 532 takes you through the aspen-covered inner foothills and over the gray limestone of the mountain front to Highway 940.

Looking northwest from Logan Pass along Going-to-the-Sun Road in Glacier National Park, Montana.

Moraine Lake and Valley of the Ten Peaks in Banff National Park. Photo courtesy Banff National Park.

Must-see list

Following 940 north, it becomes Highway 40, running over Highwood Pass and among the cockscomb ridges of Kananaskis Country. Watch for the great fold on Mt. Kidd, which marks the end of the Lewis Thrust (page 185). The route finishes across Morley Flats, where it meets the TransCanada Highway.

- **The view west of Calgary** from the TransCanada Highway just east of the Highway 22 junction, or from nearby Highway 1A atop the hill overlooking Cochrane: a grand perspective of the foothills and front ranges of the central Rockies. Stop on the shoulder, near the crest of the hill. There is no viewpoint pull-off here, but there ought to be; wooded ridges and meadowy dales roll up to the mountain wall in a scene that is weepy-beautiful. I hope it stays this way.

- **The Ten Peaks** above Moraine Lake, near Lake Louise in Banff National Park: the main ranges at their best. This may be the greatest of all cliffs in the Rockies, if you are figuring by height and length combined: 15 km long between hikable passes and mostly over 1000 m tall from base to ridgeline. Wow! No wonder this scene is on Canada's $20 bill. See also the Larch Valley trail, page 773.

- **Lake Louise** in Banff park: the cliche capital of the Canadian Rockies. Enjoy with the multitudes. Or leave them behind by walking to Lake Agnes nearby (page 773). The color of the water? Rock flour from the glaciers feeding the lake. See page 234 for the whole story.

- **Kinbasket Lake** between Valemount and Golden on the western slope: included here as the second-best example of human folly in the Rockies. The best example is **Williston Lake,** another big reservoir in the Rocky Mountain Trench farther north. Purpose of both: to generate electricity so that people can watch television in their British Columbia cabins. Same sort of thinking that drowned parts of the Grand Canyon to supply power to the Las Vegas casinos.

- **Takakkaw Falls** in Yoho National Park at the end of the Yoho Valley Road: 380 m tall, one of the higher falls in Canada. Icefield-fed, the falls are slim in the wee hours, swelling with gray meltwater in the afternoon. Stentorian. Every now and again one hears the crack of a water-flung boulder.

- **The Icefields Parkway** in Banff and Jasper parks: the most beautiful road in the world, I am told by well-traveled people who ought to know. Highlights: **Crowfoot Glacier Viewpoint** (closest auto approach to an ice cliff in the region), **Bow Lake** (graceful in its subalpine bowl, with views of the Wapta Icefield to the west), **Bow Summit** (interpretive trail leads to a view of **Peyto Lake,** turquoise-like in the valley below), the **Weeping Wall** (filmy waterfalls over a big cliff of Palliser limestone; wonderful ice drapery in winter) and **Athabasca Glacier** (friendliest glacier in the Rockies; lets you walk right up and pet it).

- **The Maligne Valley** near Jasper: three wonders within an hour of one another on the same road.

  At 50 m deep and so narrow in places that the squirrels jump across, **Maligne Canyon** is the most impressive of the car-accessible limestone gorges in the Rockies (list of others on page 219). To see it best, walk from Fifth Bridge up the canyon to the main parking area at the top (2.7 km one way).

  Medicine Lake is next, with its disappearing water and strange annual cycle (page 224). Interpretive signs at the north-end viewpoint explain. Peaks made of huge limestone slabs flank the road.

  At road's end, **Maligne Lake** spreads serenely down the rest of the valley. At 22.3 km from end to end, this is the longest natural lake in the Rockies. Parks Canada has held fast under constant pressure to develop the shore, allowing only a day-use chalet, some parking lots and a cruise-boat concession. Thanks to that good stewardship, the place remains beautiful. A short walk down the **Mary Schäffer Trail** leads past picnic tables to interpretive signs about the lady explorer from Philadelphia (more on page 760) and a fine view of the lake. See also the Bald Hills Trail, page 775.

- **Mount Robson,** 80 km west of Jasper on Highway 16: not the highest, but the *biggest* peak in the entire Rockies, Canadian and American. With the summit at 3954 m above sea level and the base at 853 m, Robson presents 3100 m of mountain mass—800 m more than Pikes Peak, biggest of the Colorado Rockies peaks (although again not the highest) with relief of 2300 m (summit elevation 4300 m, base elevation 2000 m). Highest peak in the entire Rockies chain is Mt. Elbert in central Colorado (4399 m). Stop in at the provincial park visitors' centre at the Robson viewpoint. (Climbers: see page 793.)

- **Swift Creek and Rearguard Falls** during the **chinook salmon run** (late August to mid-September): two places to witness this impressive event. Swift Creek is on the northern outskirts of Valemount; there is a viewing bridge and interpretive display right beside Highway 5. The big red fish are practically close enough to touch in the clear water as they spawn and die.

  At Rearguard Falls, between the Mt. Robson viewpoint and Tête Jaune Cache on Highway 16, a short trail leads to excellent viewpoints from which to watch the salmon trying to jump a step in the Fraser River. Few manage it. For more on the salmon run, see page 539.

- **Pine Pass** on Highway 97 (the Hart Highway) between McLeod Lake and Chetwynd: lowest road-or-rail pass in the Rocky Mountains (869 m). Timberline is low this far north, so even at such a low elevation the pass is in the subalpine zone. Stop at the Lake Azouzetta overlook for good views of the long whaleback ridges typical of the northern Rockies.

- **Trutch Viewpoint** on the Alaska Highway: a perch on the edge of the Interior Plains escarpment. View is west across the shale valley that fronts the northern Rockies, toward the rolling foothills and the mountain backbone sticking up beyond. This is the best spot on the highway to appreciate these features, so different from the mountain-front view west of Calgary.

- **The northern foothills at Tetsa River** on the Alaska Highway: the glacially gravelled valley floor winds between rounded ridges, with subalpine forest on the south side of the road and montane forest on the north side (see page 265 for the reason). The central and southern foothills are very different from the northern ones.

- **Summit Lake** on the Alaska Highway: best views of the north end of the Rockies. From just west of the restaurant, a rough road, ungated in 1984, leads up to a microwave station above timberline. Not recommended for passenger cars. But it is a walk of only a few kilometres through high-subalpine woods and tundra with rewarding views of the lake, of Mt. St. Paul and the Stone Range to the north, MacDonald Creek to the west, with its colorful peaks of ancient rock (page 77) and the slopes of Mt. St. George near at hand.

- **Liard Hot Springs Provincial Park** along the Alaska Highway: my favorite thermal springs in the Rockies (well, not quite *in* the Rockies, for they are on the far side of Liard River, which is the northern boundary). Extensive marshes between the parking lot and the springs are quite interesting, traversed via boardwalk. Schools of little warmth-tolerant lake chub swim under the walkway, while mew gulls screech in for mock attacks on half-dressed people coming and going from the pools. No charge to use the springs; there is a small changing building at poolside. These are the most natural of the popular springs in the region—and the hottest!

Lake Azouzetta,
along Highway 97 in Pine Pass.
Pine Pass (935 m) is the most northerly
rail pass in the Rocky Mountains,
as well as the lowest.

Mt. Robson (3954 m), highest peak in the Canadian Rockies. This mountain has the
greatest vertical rise (3100 m) of any peak in the entire Rockies chain.
Photo courtesy Jasper National Park.

Aerial tramways are quick and dirty routes to the high country. There are trams at Banff (Sulphur Mountain Gondola Lift, operating April 1 to November 15; Mount Norquay Scenic Lift, June 16 to September 3 and Sunshine Village Gondola, June 29 to September 3), Lake Louise (Lake Louise Gondola Lift, June 7 to September 2) and Jasper (Jasper Tramway, April 1 to Thanksgiving). These operating seasons may vary from year to year.

HIKING

Season: early April to about the end of October at lower elevations in the southern and central sections (Glacier to Jasper), the season somewhat longer on the western slope and somewhat shorter north of Peace River (where there aren't many hiking trails anyway). For hikes that reach timberline, expect to cross patches of snow before mid-July; late-summer snowfalls begin in the middle of August, but normally melt away in a day or two until mid-September, when the stuff starts to pile up.

Between early May and mid-August, the days are so long in the Canadian Rockies that one can cover amazing distances between dawn and dusk. By about 4 a.m. there is enough light to see, and it doesn't become too dim for comfortable walking until about 11 p.m. Around the summer solstice (June 21 or 22), it never gets really dark, so you could walk around the clock if you wanted to. People traveling light and moving steadily walk/jog the entire Skyline Trail (44 km, see page 781) in one go—although I wouldn't recommend it unless you are in shape and experienced at such things.

Recommended clothing and equipment for day hikes

The new ultra-light boots of fabric and leather are excellent, as long as hikers from drier climes realize that the trails here can be boggy and these boots will get wet. A coat of wax waterproofing (Sno-seal or some such) put on hot over both the leather and fabric parts helps in repelling the wet and hastening drying. Dribble it right over those flashy Cordura or Goretex panels, which will leak otherwise.

Short-pants hiking weather here runs only from early July to mid-August, which gives you an idea of typical daytime temperatures. I always have a jacket in my pack, plus a sweater, knit cap and light gloves if I'm going above timberline (where the wind is cold).

There is usually water along trails in the Canadian Rockies, but it may be contaminated with *Giardia lamblia* (see page 824). If you don't want to risk a run-in with this pest, then it is a good idea to carry water from a safe source. Except on the hotter days, a litre will do for most people.

Small items always with me on hikes: dark glasses, small pocketknife (with scissors and tweezers), bug repellent, sunburn cream, bandaids, aspirin, lighter or waterproof matches, moleskin, handkerchief, small flashlight, small binoculars, equally small camera, maps (often one that covers a large area, so I can identify peaks in the distance, plus the appropriate 1:50,000 topo), compass (seldom used, but useful for bushwhacking when no landmarks are in sight or settling arguments about which mountain in the distance is which) and assorted nature guides (lucky you; all you need is this book). Yikes; almost forgot the toilet paper. Again.

Representative day-hikes

The hikes listed below are my favorites among the popular, easy-to-follow routes. I have chosen ones in the national parks, where the trails are kept up and unpleasant surprises are rare. In unprotected places last years' trail can become this year's road, the forest can be logged off and the destination can change from wilderness meadow to coal-mine pit or oil-company wellsite.

- **Avalanche Lake** in Glacier National Park (4.5 km one way, 3-4 hr return): a moderate climb from the Lake McDonald rainforest to the lower subalpine ecology of Avalanche Lake, with its spectacular backdrop of cliffs and waterfalls.

The first kilometre is along the **Trail of the Cedars**: a stroll through classic Columbian forest. A well-made boardwalk keeps you out of the mire; a free interpretive pamphlet at the trailhead keys to signs along the way. This place contrasts wonderfully with the windy barrens of Logan Pass, an hour away on the same road.

- **Siyeh Pass** in Glacier National Park (13.8 km total, 6-8 hr): classic Glacier-park hike. Steep climb from the Going-to-the-Sun Highway takes you up into a hanging valley at timberline (Preston Park) and over the rocky alpine pass at 2362 m, then steeply down to Baring Creek, for a touristy finish at Sunrift Gorge.

- **The Carthew Trail** in Waterton Lakes National Park (20.1 km total, 7-9 hr): from Cameron Lake up a well-graded woodsy trail to fields of bear grass and the alpine zone at Carthew Summit (2410), then down past three lakes (alpine, subalpine, upper montane) to Waterton townsite at Cameron Falls. A long day, but it hits every life zone in the region.

- **Ink Pots** in Banff National Park (5.8 km one way, 3-4 hr return): lots of variety. Start on the Johnston Canyon trail, joining the throngs along the metal walkway, then leaving them as you take the stairs up and out of the canyon near the end. Steady climb through the woods ends with a steep (but short) descent to lower subalpine meadows and the Ink Pots: several interesting karst springs (for more on karst, see page 221). Impressive views there of Mt. Ishbel and other slabby front-range peaks.

- **Lake Agnes** in Banff park (3.4 km one way, 2-3 hr total, or loop trip by Plain of Six Glaciers trail, 18 km 6-7 hrs): steady climb up to a textbook tarn lake (glacially-carved basin), with teahouse treats recalling the ladies-and-gentlemen days of the pre-war Rockies (see photo on next page). From Chateau Lake Louise, follow the lakeshore trail northwest and branch off at the Lake Agnes sign. Fairly steep climb finishes up wooden stairs to the tarn and teahouse (open July 1 to Labour Day). Pay princely sum for freshly baked goodies and start back, or, fueled by teahouse caffeine, continue up rougher trail over the Beehive at timberline (2268 m) and down to yet another teahouse in the next valley to the south (the **Plain of Six Glaciers**). Complete the loop downhill to Lake Louise. Glacial geology and best views of Canada's postcard-image paradise.

- **Larch Valley and Paradise Valley via Sentinel Pass** (16.9 km, 6-8 hr): another classic of the Lake Louise area. Begin at Moraine Lake. Terrific views of the great Ten Peaks wall (photo on page 768) enliven the steady climb to Larch Valley (3 km). The grade eases through high-subalpine larch woods and tundra ponds. Either return (2-3 hrs total) or continue through Sentinel Pass (2611 m) and down a steep, bouldery section into Paradise Valley, with Mt. Hungabee lurking at the end. Gentler trail leads past the waterfalls of the Giant Steps and back to the Moraine Lake Road. Hitching back to the car usually doesn't take too long.

- **Opabin Plateau** in Yoho National Park (5.1 km loop; 2-3 hr): take the bus to Lake O'Hara (only way to get in unless you walk; mountain bicycles are not allowed). Info from Brewster Transport in Calgary, Banff or Lake Louise). Opabin Plateau is a hanging valley at timberline, with larch trees among heathery meadows and reflecting ponds. All trails beginning at Lake O'Hara are terrific; the place offers the best selection of day-hikes on the western slope of the Rockies.

- **Chephren Lake and Cirque Lake** in Banff park (4.0 km one way to Chephren, 2-3 hrs; add 5.8 km and another 2 hrs to include Cirque Lake): moderate climb through subalpine forest opening suddenly on the lakes, set against immense cliffs. Pronunciation: "KEFF-ren" is correct, for the name is indeed Egyptian

Lake Agnes, a small tarn reached in a walk of 1-2 hours from Lake Louise. There is still a little ice on the lake in July. Teahouse is visible in centre of photo; Lookout Point beyond. The Lake Louise area is famous for its spectacular day-hiking trails.

(Mt. Chephren was originally named Pyramid Mountain, then renamed for Chephren, builder of pyramids, to avoid confusion with the Pyramid Mountain located near Jasper).

- **Parker Ridge** in Banff Park (2.4 km one way, 2-3 hr): a popular alpine-zone hike. Steady grade through upper subalpine woods and tree islands to timberline, then over a broad ridge to views of Saskatchewan Glacier and Columbia Icefield on the other side. Fossils enroute (white corals in black Mt. Hawk limestone, page 135) and good variety of alpine flowers mid-July to early August.

- **Cavell Meadows/Path of the Glacier** in Jasper park (9 km total, 3-4 hrs): from the Mt. Edith Cavell parking lot, through Little Ice Age moraines into subalpine forest and alpine meadows above, famous for wildflowers. Postcard views of the north face of the mountain and Angel Glacier. On your way back, branch left when you hit the paved part of the trail to take in the short Path of the Glacier interpretive loop, which finishes at the parking lot.

- **The trail network surrounding Jasper townsite:** for those who like short walks in easy terrain, the Jasper trails are ideal. Be aware, though, that as this book goes to press the network is incompletely signed, so it can be confusing. It is wise not to get in too deeply at first. If you get lost, remember that most of the well-used trails eventually cross a road or reach an overlook where you can get your bearings. As well, the trails are popular and you are likely to run into other hikers.

- **Valley of the Five Lakes** in Jasper National Park (2.3 km one way, 2-3 hrs, or continue to Old Fort Point (see next entry; 18.5 km 5-7 hr): perhaps the best of the Jasper valley-floor hikes. The monotonous lodgepole-pine forest of the upper Athabasca valley hides a surprisingly varied landscape of small hills and dales cut in the interesting rock of the Miette Group (page 77). This hike has it all: small lakes, grassy meadows, cool woods and birdy marshes. Continuation to Old Fort Point recommended; keep right at the major trail junction just north of the only stream crossing beyond the lakes.

- **Old Fort Point** in Jasper park (4.0 km total, 1-2 hrs): a glacially carved bedrock hill in the middle of the Athabasca Valley near Jasper townsite. Superb views in all directions from the top. Pleasant after supper, when the weather is inclined to clear and a fine sunset is often on the way. Turn south onto Highway 93A off the Highway 16 bypass around Jasper and follow the signs to a parking lot just beyond the old metal bridge over Athabasca River. Don't take the stairs south of the lot; follow the trail east along the cliffy north side of Old Fort Point, keeping right at junctions as you climb through woods, emerging into open sections and getting the surprise view from the top. Backtrack 50 m from the summit to find the trail continuation running along the south side and thence west, quickly back to the lot (finishing down the stairs).

- **Bald Hills** in Jasper park (5.2 km one way, 2-5 hr return): a moderate approach to lush alpine country on a wide, well-graded trail that was once the road to a fire lookout (nothing left now but the foundation). The lookout site offers a fine view of Maligne Lake (better than the one from the **Opal Hills** trail on the other side of the valley, also recommended but steeper). Several easy summits south and west are as little as one hour farther—but keep an eye on the weather and the time.

- **Overlander Trail** in Jasper park (15 km, 4-5 hr): takes the wilderness side of Athabasca River from the Sixth Bridge picnic site on Maligne River to the Cold Sulphur Spring viewpoint on Highway 16. Easy walking, with good views and a variety of forest and meadow; good birding for hawks near the northeastern end. Passes by the photogenic ruins of John Moberly's ranch (see page 757).

Start by heading left from the far side of Sixth Bridge over Maligne River. Follow the bankside trail to the Athabasca confluence, then continue along the path downstream, which will take you dry-footed through marshes beyond, at the end of which the trail broadens as the connection to the warden's corrals comes in. Keep left, heading down the valley. At Moberly Meadows the trail disappears; just wander across to the far end of the meadow, where it picks up again.

BACKPACKING

This is where the national-park block really shines, with its enormous back-country open to everyone for overnight and multi-day walks. The deeper rivers are bridged (although you may have to wade the odd stream), primitive campsites are provided and frequent warden patrols add to safety. Many people walk these mountains alone, knowing that they will probably meet others on the way should they get into trouble. Still, it is wise to have at least one companion on any hike in the wilds.

For essential information on weather and other matters, read the introductory material on hiking (page 772).

Suggested equipment, clothing and food

Besides the day-hiking items suggested on page 772, you might want to consider the following for longer walks. They have worked well for me.

- **Frame pack.** My nice old external-frame pack gathers dust these days, used only when I am packing very heavy loads. My new internal-frame pack is light, comfortable, holds lots, and doesn't catch in the trees as I walk. Further, it goes small for day use from a back-country campsite and rides low for overnight ski trips.

- **Light self-supporting tent.** The kind you can pick up and move after you discover The Lump. Look for one that pops up in a trice, requires as few stakes as possible and weighs less than 2 kg. The more you pay, the better off you will be when the weather gets nasty.

  Guyed, staked-out tents are harder to set up on stony ground—next to impossible on the horrible gravel tent pads one finds more and more these days. (Aside to park administrators: if you are going to demand that campers use established pads, please make them from a mixture of sand and loam, or sand and expanded mica, or sand and wood chips—anything but gravel. Gravel is just too coarse for pegging, no matter what you mix it with. Coarse sand will do, if you mix it well with the filler.)

  With a light tent, you can afford the small extra weight of a light tarp that provides head-high shelter for cooking and eating under in bad weather—or for just waiting out a thunderstorm. Make your own 3-m by 3-m tarp from the lightest coated nylon you can buy (hem the edges, then add nylon-tape ties at each corner and halfway along each side). Slung over a cord strung between trees, a tarp makes a big difference on a rainy day.

- **Long foam pad.** The ground is always cool in the Canadian Rockies, and any part of you that touches it through your sleeping bag will be, too. A thin, featherlight foamy is fine for summer; you will sleep warmer if it reaches from head to toe.

- **Down sleeping bag.** My summer bag weighs only 1 kg and stuffs into a small sack that forms the bottom layer in my pack. If the weather is cool and rainy, though, the down gets damp overnight and I have to dry the bag every couple of days to keep it cozy. The synthetic-fill bags don't have this disadvantage, and they are half the price, but they weigh nearly twice as much for equivalent warmth and don't pack as small.

Near Assiniboine Pass on the trail to Mt. Assiniboine.

- **Gasoline or butane cooker.** An evening fire is always pleasant, but it is seldom necessary and is always hard on the surrounding vegetation—especially if you are in an upper-subalpine area, where every stick of wood has a purpose, even the dead snags, and should be left alone. I use the lightest, hottest white-gas stove on the market and spare the forest. Implements: fuel bottle, eyedropper for priming, pot with lid, edge-gripping lifter, insulated plastic cup and nylon spoon.

- **Incidentals:** light line for stringing up food sack at night, more film than I carry on day hikes, more toilet paper, more complete first-aid kit (see page 825 for suggested contents), extra glasses, extra flashlight batteries.

- **Clothing:** in addition to the usual day-hike stuff, I always pack a pair of long pants, a change of socks and underwear, a tuque (rhymes with "Luke," Americans; it's the Canadian knit cap) and light gloves. In spring and fall a light down jacket takes the chill off in the morning and evening. Good anytime that your only sweater gets wet. For wading streams, a pair of light plastic sandals or moccasins will protect your feet from the stones; you can also wear them in camp while drying your boots out.

- **Food.** Freeze-dried stuff for supper and breakfast on trips of three days or more. Minimal breakfast: instant porridge and dried fruit. (My favorite breakfast: chili.) Good at lunch: cream cheese and devilled ham on crackers, dry salami, cheese, sardines (messy; you have to pack out the can), dried fruit, cookies, candy bars. Good anytime: GORP (acronym for Good Old Raisins and Peanuts). To bloat up supper, try Japanese instant noodles mixed with Swiss instant soup—made thick. Hot drinks: tea, cocoa (with a touch of peppermint schnapps), hot Jello (don't knock it 'til you've tried it). Cold drinks: plain water, usually, because drink mixes don't quench the thirst as well.

    With four days of food, my pack comes to about 12-13 kg when I am going alone; a couple of kilos less when I'm with someone else and sharing the weight of tent and cooking stuff.

Representative backpacking trips

As in the case of the day hikes listed earlier, these are all within national or provincial parks, and for the same reasons: reliable trail maintenance and ongoing land protection. They require back-country permits—a small inconvenience, considering the value of the national-park turf one tramps.

- **Gunsight Pass** in Glacier National Park (35.3 km, overnight): an east-west traverse through the heart of the park, from St. Mary Lake to Lake McDonald. Enroute are two high passes (Gunsight and Lincoln, Gunsight reputedly the best place in the park to see mountain goats) and two high lakes (Gunsight and Ellen Wilson). On the eastern approach to Gunsight Pass the trail has been blasted out of the cliff in classic Glacier park style. There is a shelter (not for camping) in the pass. Usual campsites: at either Gunsight Lake or Ellen Wilson Lake, depending on whether you make it over the pass on the first day.

- **North and South Kananaskis passes** in Kananaskis Country (40 km total, three days): perhaps the best K-Country loop trip, set among the great folds and flatirons of the front ranges. Routes in the region are becoming easier to follow as the province improves the trails, but this one has an unmaintained section on the B.C. side of the divide, so expect a few problems there, made easier if you have a copy of the *Kananaskis Country Trail Guide* along.

    Hike to Three Isle Lake (trailhead is on the north side of Upper Kananaskis Lake), climbing into the meadows of South Kananaskis Pass and then crossing the divide for a night at Beatty Lake, with the impressive Royal Group to the west. Next day, drop precipitously down the Beatty Creek drainage until possible to head north across the slopes of the peak west of Mt. Beatty and bushwhack down into the valley of Leroy Creek, where a good trail on the north side heads toward North Kananaskis Pass. Once over, there is camping downstream from Maude Lake, near the amazing Turbine Canyon. Finish by way of Lawson Lake, along the high-line trail past Mt. Putnik and beside Upper Kananaskis River to close the loop.

- **Mt. Assiniboine** in Banff National Park and Mount Assiniboine Provincial Park (47.2 km, three days): pilgrimage to the Matterhorn of the Canadian Rockies. If the weather is poor, go in via Bryant Creek (take the Smith-Dorrien Road from Canmore past Spray Lake to a marked turnoff and side road to the trailhead) and over Assiniboine Pass in one long day to Magog Lake under the peak; this route stays in the valleys. If the day is pleasant, go from the opposite direction by way of Sunshine Meadows (drive to Sunshine ski area west of Banff and take the gondola up to the trailhead). The Sunshine route is at or above timberline to Citadel Pass, then descends steeply to Simpson River and the last water for 13 km. It is a very long day to Magog Lake in this approach (27 km), so you may want to camp along the river and enjoy the strange Valley of the Rocks on the morrow. This route joins the Bryant Creek route a few kilometres before Magog Lake.

  Going in one way and out the other is the best, of course, but you may want two cars; hitch-hiking between can take all day. A popular plan is to go in from Sunshine and out over Wonder Pass, a variation of the Bryant Creek route that offers views of Assiniboine's enormous east face hulking over Marvel Lake.

- **Nigel Pass, Jonas Shoulder, Poboktan Creek** in Jasper park (55 km; three days): a straightforward and scenic hike through the front ranges east of the Columbia Icefield. Good trail all the way. It is 6.7 km from the southern trailhead near Parker Ridge to Nigel Pass, with its interesting orange dolomite lumps. Then steeply down to the headwaters of Brazeau River (picturesque ponds) and a campsite near the Four Point warden cabin (15 km on the first day). Up Four Point Creek to the high country next morning, with rusty-colored, glacier-spotted peaks of Gog quartzite (page 88) on the west side of the valley. Keep right for the high pass over Jonas Shoulder (which forms the eastern side of the valley) to Poboktan Creek on the other side—a long day (19.3 km) and mostly uphill. The last day is even longer (21.7 km), but it is all downhill along Poboktan Creek to the Sunwapta Warden Station.

- **Tonquin Valley loop** in Jasper park (43 km, two or three days): the grandest place in the park and perhaps in the entire Canadian Rockies. Do this one with two cars, if possible, leaving one at the Portal Creek trailhead on the access road to Marmot Basin Ski Area (south of Jasper on the Icefields Parkway and Highway 93A) and continuing in the other to Mt. Edith Cavell (farther south on 93A). Trailhead is near the end of the Cavell Road, opposite Cavell Hostel.

  A wide trail contours the southern side of the Astoria River valley, crossing the river and switchbacking up the north side to verdant high-subalpine country characteristic of the main ranges in Jasper park (a nearby pass is named "Verdant," in fact). Suddenly one sees the tops of mountains peeking up, then more and more of them: the sensational Ramparts. On a good day they reflect in Amethyst Lakes. No wonder this scene is known worldwide.

  So are the bugs and the mud here. The Tonquin Valley is mosquito-plagued all summer, the fly capital of the park in August, and outfitter country, too (there are two groups of horse-supplied commercial cabins at the lakes). The Parks Canada trail crews can't seem to keep ahead of the wear and tear.

  Camping at the lakes makes for a long day of 23 km; you may want to camp sooner and stretch the hike to three days. At any rate, continue the loop north, being careful at Maccarib Creek to catch the hikers' trail, which high-lines the north bank, rather than the valley-bottom horse trail. Beyond Maccarib Pass it is mostly downhill along Portal Creek.

Wading Poboktan Creek on the way to Jonas Shoulder in Jasper National Park.

- **The Skyline Trail** in Jasper park (44.1 km, two or three days): the best hike in the Rockies, I think. It runs from Maligne Lake to Maligne Canyon, and over half of it is above timberline (which means that in bad weather it is the *worst* hike in the Rockies). There are three high passes, one of which tops out and then stays high, following the crest of the Maligne Range for about 5 km. No other established trail that I know of stays so high for so long. Supreme views of the Maligne Lake peaks, the gray waves of the front ranges, the Athabasca River far below and the glacier-draped main ranges to the west. You can see everything from the Columbia Icefield to Mt. Robson.

  Park at the second lot at Maligne Lake (the one past the bridge over the outlet stream) and choose the righthand of two trailheads there. For a two-day trip, a good campsite is the one below Curator Lake; three-day hikers often camp in the Snowbowl and at Tekarra Lake.

- **Berg Lake** in Mount Robson Provincial Park (17.4 km one way, two or three days): the best view of the biggest mountain in the Rockies—if the weather allows you to see it at all. The trailhead is at the end of a short road leading to Robson River from the Mt. Robson viewpoint and park information centre, 80 km west of Jasper along Highway 16. A busy trail follows the river 4.5 km uphill through cedar forest to Kinney Lake, then up and down along the shore to the far end and a warden cabin beyond. Things get serious at 11.3 km, where the trail begins a steep ascent to the lip of the hanging valley on the north side of Robson. This is a tough pull with a heavy pack, so keep it light. Waterfalls along the way are distractions from the toil, especially Emperor Falls, the sight of which means that you are nearly up the hill.

  But not at your objective, yet, because the campsites lie 6 km farther, across bleak gravel flats and along Berg Lake. The provincial park has lately been charging people money to stay at these sites, which is not standard practice in the back-country; if you continue past Berg Lake to Adolphus Lake (only 3 km farther and flat going), you can stay just inside Jasper park for free—but the view of Robson is accordingly cheapskate, and you must get a camping permit in Jasper beforehand.

Long walks in the mountain parks

These are possibly unique in North America. I can't think of anyplace else on the continent where it is possible to go hiking for two weeks in the wilderness, never crossing a road, yet traveling on maintained trails with bridged rivers. (Well, *mostly* bridged rivers.) But that is what you can do in the Canadian Rockies. There isn't room here to describe these hikes in detail, so use one of the trail guides listed on page 811.

The **North Boundary Trail** in Jasper and Mt. Robson parks (173.4 km, typically ten days) starts at the end of the Celestine Road in eastern Jasper park, curves through the northern part of the park and comes out by way of Berg Lake to Highway 16 at Mt. Robson. A trip of this duration makes for a heavy pack until you have made a dent in your food supply, and much of the North Boundary Trail is in boring valley bottoms, but it's great for woodsy wildlife, long subalpine meadows over gentle passes and the knowledge that you are a long way from the nearest used car lot. There are seldom-visited side valleys to explore enroute.

The **South Boundary Trail** in Jasper park (176 km) is more serious than the North Boundary (above), with longer high-country stretches, trickier route-finding, a couple of over-the-knees stream fords and few easy escape routes. Reward: better scenery, more sense of adventure. Starting from Medicine Lake (arbitrarily; these long trips go equal well from either direction), the route runs past Beaver Lake and Jacques Lake to the Rocky River; up the Rocky and the Medicine Tent to Southesk Pass, down Cairn River to the Southesk, across a low height of land in the foothills to the Brazeau, then up the Brazeau to Nigel Pass and down Nigel Creek to the Icefields Parkway near Sunwapta Pass.

The **Sawback Trail** in Banff and Jasper parks (149 km, 10-14 days) lies entirely within the front ranges and mostly in Banff park. Very scenic, with five passes. Starts at the lowest parking lot near the end of the Norquay Road near Banff. Route: Forty-Mile Creek, Mystic Pass, Johnston Creek, Pulsatilla Pass, Baker Creek, Baker Lake, Red Deer Lakes (either via upper Red Deer River, which is shorter, or via Deception Pass and Skoki, which are more scenic), Little Pipestone Creek, Pipestone River (over-the-knees ford), Pipestone Pass, Siffleur River (fords at Dolomite Creek and Porcupine Creek) to the North Saskatchewan River (bridged along old road) and Highway 11.

This route is about as difficult as the South Boundary Trail, perhaps tougher beyond Red Deer Lakes because of the fords. Shortly after Dolomite Creek you cross out of the park and into the provincial Siffleur Wilderness, wherein trail maintenance is spotty and the way not as clearly indicated. If you want to stay in the park, double back at Dolomite Creek and follow it over Dolomite Pass to the Icefields Parkway at the Crowfoot Glacier Viewpoint. For a shorter trip (8-10 days), take the trail west to Fish Lakes from Pipestone River beyond Cataract Peak, continuing over North Molar Pass to Mosquito Creek and out the Icefields Parkway at Mosquito Creek Campground.

The Great Divide Trail

The **Great Divide Trail** is a wonderful idea that has not quite been scribed onto the land yet. At the Maligne Canyon end of the Skyline Trail in Jasper park a sign reads "Northern terminus, Great Divide Trail," and scattered signs on various trails southward through the mountain national parks indicate that you are on the route. But overall there is little marking. On provincial lands there is even less; coupled with the unreliable maintenance one finds there, especially on the British Columbia side of the divide, a hike from Jasper to Waterton/Glacier would be considerably more difficult than, say, an equivalent stretch of the Appalachian Trail.

This journey has almost certainly been done, although I can't name anyone who has succeeded. This leaves two great challenges, neither of which seems to have been accomplished yet.

One is to hike the entire Canadian Rockies, from Marias Pass to Liard River, a distance of 1450 km as the raven flies. North of Willmore Wilderness Park there are few trails. No roads cross the Rockies between Peace River and the Alaska Highway, so resupplying yourself would be difficult (maybe arrangements could be made with the outfitters who have camps in this section). It seems possible to do the whole hike in a summer.

The grandest hike of all would be one covering the Rocky Mountains from end to end: from Sante Fe, New Mexico to Liard River, near the B.C./Yukon boundary. That would add another 1550 km, for a total of 3000 km. Increase the figure by 50 percent for the approximate trail distance, and you are really looking at a walk of 4500 km. Good luck.

BACK-COUNTRY ACCOMMODATION

Here are the commonly known off-road shelters, huts and lodges in the Canadian Rockies. There are many other back-country structures, of course: private cabins, wardens' and rangers' patrol cabins, ranch buildings, fire lookouts, abandoned structures and so on. But these are the ones legally available to recreationists and popularly used. Most are primitive, variously with or without stoves, foamies and cooking facilities. As such, they provide little more than a dry place to sleep, but use is either free of charge or inexpensive.

Some of these are climbers' and icefield-skiers' huts, requiring proper skills and equipment to reach safely. Persons unfamiliar with off-trail and glacier travel in the Canadian Rockies should stick to the trail-accessible shelters.

Most of the simple huts are in the national parks, administered by Parks Canada and requiring a permit but no fee; others are privately operated (or run by clubs) and a fee must be paid. Some are uncontrolled (i.e. no fee, reservation or permit required).

There are also a few commercial operations in the back-country, most of which offer meals and bedding (even hot showers in some cases). Prices are similar to those charged at hotels.

To book space in national-park shelters, telephone Parks Canada in Banff (403-762-3324), Lake Louise (403-522-3866) or Jasper (403-852-6661). Addresses and telephone numbers for making reservations at other huts are given in the list entries.

If you are planning to visit mountain huts, you may wish to carry a copy of Murray Toft's detailed guidebook (Toft, 1984), which provides complete directions, capacities and other useful information. Much of the information below is compiled from Murray's book. I have included his grid coordinates and map numbers for Canadian huts; coordinates are not available for huts in Glacier National Park, Montana. Distances are given when the approach is by established trail.

- **Sperry Chalet** is at 1980 m near head of Sprague Creek in Glacier park, 10.7 km from Lake McDonald on Gunsight Pass Trail. Operated July to September under park concession; reserve through Belton Chalets, Box 188, West Glacier, MT 59936 406-888-5511.

- **Granite Park Chalet** is at 2039 m west of Swiftcurrent Pass, in the Granite Park area of Glacier park, 6.4 km from Going-to-the-Sun Road along Granite Park Trail. Park concession open July to September; reserve as per Sperry Chalet (previous entry).

- **Goat Haunt Trail Shelter** is at south end of Upper Waterton Lake in Glacier park, along shore 300 m east of ranger station. Access via motor launch or Goat Haunt Trail from Waterton Park (14 km). Four small shelters sleep four each; contact Glacier National Park, West Glacier, MT 59936 406-888-5441.

- **Fish Lake Cabin** is at Fish Lake in Top of the World Provincial Park (119227, 83G/14). 6 km by trail from Lussier River Road. Sleeps 20-30; uncontrolled.

- **Elk Pass Cabin** is in the Kananaskis area, 1 km east of Lower Elk Lake (368015, 82J/11). 11 km by trail from Lower Kananaskis Lake via Elk Pass, or up Elk River Road (last 30 km four-wheel-drive). Sleeps six; uncontrolled and unmaintained.

- **Archie Simpson Hut** is at the mountain front west of Calgary, in the next valley north of Yamnuska Mountain (324669, 82O/3). Via unmaintained path from quarry below Yamnuska mentioned on page 180. Sleeps ten; uncontrolled.

- **Bryant Creek Shelter** is in the Assiniboine area of southern Banff park, south of junction of Bryant Creek and Marvel Lake trails (041394, 82J/13). 14.2 km on Watridge Lake and Bryant Creek trails from Smith-Dorrien Road in Kananaskis Country. Sleeps 18; free permit from Parks Canada required.

- **Naiset Cabins and Mt. Assiniboine Lodge** are at Lake Magog in Mt. Assiniboine Provincial Park (973404, 82J/13). Various approaches; popular ones are via Sunshine Meadows and Bryant Creek, about 27 km each, or by helicopter. Naiset Cabins: four cabins, sleeping 28 in total. Custodian, fee. Reserve for winter use from BC Provincial Parks, Box 118, Wasa, BC V0B 2K0 604-422-3212. Lodge: several cabins and lodge, modern conveniences; reserve Box 1527, Canmore, AB T0L 0M0 403-678-2883.

- **Bob Hind Hut** is a climber's hut at 2710 m below Mt. Assiniboine (946373, 82J/13). Up obvious snow gully (ice axes) in headwall at southwest end of Lake Magog, or, later in season, up exposed ledges to right (northwest) of gully. Sleeps 16; uncontrolled.

- **Mitchell River Cabin** is along the western approach to Mt. Assiniboine, in the provincial park (875382, 82J/13). 3.5 km west of Ferro Pass Junction along Mitchell River Trail. Small cabin sleeps four; uncontrolled.

- **Surprise Creek Cabin** is at junction of Surprise Creek and Simpson River in Mt. Assiniboine park (826468, 82J/13). 11 km via Simpson River Trail from Kootenay park. Sleeps eight; uncontrolled.

- **Police Meadows Cabins** are on upper Simpson River, along Sunshine route to Mt. Assiniboine (907484, 82J/13). 14 km from Sunshine Ski Area; can be tricky to find. Two cabins; space for ten in total. Uncontrolled hunting guide's cabin, closed to public during fall hunting season.

- **Egypt Lake Shelter** is near Egypt Lake in central Banff park (772621, 82O/4). 12.5 km via Healy Pass Trail from Sunshine Ski Area parking lot. Sleeps 18; obtain free permit from Parks Canada (the cabin at nearby Shadow Lake is held by Canadian Pacific and not open to the public).

- **Castle Bivouac Hut** is a climbers' hut at 2390 m on the big ledge halfway up Castle Mountain in Banff park (743836, 82O/5). Scramble up steep gully from Castle Fire Lookout (reached via 5-km trail from Highway 1A). Sleeps four; obtain free permit from Parks Canada.

- **Fay Hut** is at 2108 m above Tokumm Creek in northern Kootenay Park (553791, 82N/8). Rough path leads up from Tokumm Creek Trail, 12 km from Marble Canyon on Highway 93. Sleeps 18; obtain free permit from Parks Canada.

- **Neil Colgan Hut** is a climbers' hut at 2940 m on the Ten Peaks ridge above Moraine Lake in Banff park (568830, 82N/8). All routes require mountaineering skills and equipment. Sleeps 24; obtain free permit from Parks Canada.

- **Abbot Pass Hut** is at 2925 m in Abbot Pass, above Lake Louise in Banff park (495903, 82N/8). Mountaineering approach via Lower Victoria Glacier, or gully-scramble in late season from Lake Oesa (O'Hara area). Sleeps 32; obtain free permit from Parks Canada.

- **Skoki Lodge** is 13 km northeast of Lake Louise, north of Deception Pass beside Skoki Mountain in Banff park (643081, 82N/9). 14.4 km via Boulder Pass Trail from Louise Ski area. Operated by Skiing Louise Ltd., Box 5, Lake Louise, AB T0L 1E0 403-522-3555.

- **Elizabeth Parker Hut** is in the subalpine meadow 500 m west of Lake O'Hara in Yoho park (457893, 82N/8). A short walk from the end of the Lake O'Hara Fire Road, which is traveled in summer by scheduled bus from Wapta Lake along the TransCanada Highway west of Lake Louise or from hotels in Lake Louise area (inquire 604-343-6418). In winter, ski 13 km up the fire road from Wapta Lake. Two cabins sleep total of 24; custodian and fee; reserve from Alpine Club of Canada, Box 1026, Banff, AB T0L 0C0 403-762-4481.

- **Lake O'Hara Lodge** is at the end of the fire road mentioned in the previous entry, so it is accessible by bus in summer, but it's run as a back-country lodge in winter, when it must be reached on skis (location 463895, 82N/8). The route is the same as that for the Elizabeth Parker Hut (see previous entry). Several cabins and a lodge building; reservations from Box 1677, Banff, AB T0L 0C0 403-762-2118.

- **Stanley Mitchell Hut** is at 2055 m in Little Yoho Valley, western branch of Yoho Valley in Yoho park (303083, 82N/10). About 9 km via Yoho Valley and Yoho Skyline trails. Winter approach is 13 km longer because road to Takakkaw Falls is closed. Sleeps 24; fee; reserve through Alpine Club at Banff (see previous entry).

The Bob Hind Hut at Mt. Assiniboine.

Abbot Hut, in Abbot Pass above Lake Louise.

- **Twin Falls Chalet** is near the foot of the falls in upper Yoho Valley, Yoho park (323104, 82N/10). 8.5 km along the Yoho Valley Trail. Operated July 1 to Labor day by Fran Drummond, Suite 11, 230 21st Ave. SW, Calgary T2S 0G6 403-228-7079.

- **Balfour Hut** is at 2500 m near Balfour Pass, above Hector Lake in Banff park (365162, 82N/9). A skiers' and climbers' hut reached from Bow Lake via Wapta Icefield (icefield skiing experience required in winter; glacier-travel approach in summer). Sleeps 12; obtain free permit from Parks Canada.

- **Bow Hut** is at 2500 m southwest of Bow Lake, in Banff park (350205, 82N/9 and 82N/10). A skiers'/climbers' hut reached from Bow Lake via complicated, off-trail, separate winter and summer routes (both with hazards). Sleeps 18; obtain free permit from Parks Canada.

- **Peter and Catherine Whyte Hut** is at 2503 m on southeast side of Peyto Glacier in Banff park (314237, 82N/10). A skiers'/climbers' hut reached by trail from Peyto Lake Overlook and glacier route (mountaineering skills and equipment required), in winter by ski from along Icefields Parkway 2.5 km north of Bow Summit (icefield skiing). Also commonly gained from Bow Hut (previous entry). Sleeps 24; obtain free permit from Parks Canada.

- **Lloyd Mackay Hut** is at 2100 m off Freshfield Icefield in northern Banff park (057347, 82N/15). A climbers'/skiers' hut reached via Howse Pass Trail, Freshfield Creek and glacier (mountaineering equipment and skills required). Sleeps 24; obtain free permit from Parks Canada.

- **Lawrence Grassi Hut** is at 2100 m on Cummins Ridge, near Cummins Glacier 10 km SW of Mt. Clemenceau, in BC northwest of Columbia Icefield (320813, 83C/4). A climbers'/skiers' hut normally reached by helicopter from Golden or Valemount; otherwise by multi-day icefield trip beginning at Athabasca Glacier. Sleeps 20; fee; reserve from Alpine Club of Canada, Banff (see Elizabeth Parker Hut for address and telephone number).

- **Mt. Alberta Hut** is at 2720 m just off glacier on north end of Little Alberta, local name for peak 1.5 km SW of Mt. Woolley in southern Jasper park (702926, 83C/6). A climbers' hut reached via strenuous off-trail route across Sunwapta River (ford), up Woolley Creek, over Woolley Shoulder and across glacier. Sleeps six; obtain free permit from Parks Canada.

- **Sydney Vallance Hut** is along upper Fryatt Creek in central Jasper park (403174, 83C/12). At end of Fryatt Creek Trail, 22 km from Geraldine Lakes Road (off Highway 93A near Athabasca Falls), atop the headwall and falls. Trip is 6 km shorter in winter, when it is possible to cross Athabasca River near Fryatt Creek confluence. Sleeps 16; obtain free permit from Parks Canada.

- **Mt. Colin Centennial Hut** is at 2020 m below Mt. Colin in central Jasper park (333724, 83C/13). A climbers' hut reached along faint trail branching up Garonne Creek from Overlander Trail, which follows east (roadless) side of Athabasca River between Maligne River confluence and highway bridge 20 km northeast of Jasper. Sleeps four; obtain free permit from Parks Canada.

- **Shangri-la** is in the Maligne Valley area of Jasper park (479448, 83C/13). Skiers' cabin open December to April only, reached via Jeffery Creek (about 8 km) from Maligne Road. Sleeps six; fee to Maligne Lake Ski Club; reserve from Bette Jeffery-Weir, Box 325, Jasper T0E 1E0.

- **Wates-Gibson Hut** is at 1900 m, 3 km south of Amethyst Lakes in the Tonquin area of Jasper park (152353, 83D/9). 18 km via Astoria River and Chrome Lake trails. Sleeps 40; fee; reserve from Alpine Club of Canada in Banff (see Elizabeth Parker Hut).

- **Tonquin Valley outfitter's camps** are at either end of Amethyst Lakes in Jasper park (Olson's Tonquin Valley Lodge: 148389, Dixon's Chalets: 132413, both on 83D/9). Reached by Astoria River trail from Mt. Edith Cavell (19 km to Olson's) or Maccarib Pass Trail (22 km to Dixon's). Information: Wald & Lavone Olson, Brule, AB T0E 0C0 (403-866-3946); Gordon Dixon: Box 550, Jasper, AB T0E 1E0 (852-3909). Dixon is open in winter.

- **Ralph Forster Hut** is at 2470 m on Mt. Robson in Mt. Robson Provincial Park (559843, 83E/3). A climbers' hut with a very steep, complicated scrambling approach off Berg Lake Trail above Kinney Lake. Sleeps eight; uncontrolled (although an overnight trail permit is required, with fee) and busy in summer. Bring a tent if unsure of number staying in hut.

MOUNTAINEERING

This information is mainly for climbers with enough experience to take the lead on fairly difficult rock, snow and ice. If you are a beginner, or if you haven't climbed but would like to learn, then please get some good instruction before attempting to do any of the routes listed here. To be blunt: without training in this sport you stand a good chance of getting killed. Here are several organizations that teach climbing in the Canadian Rockies at the time of writing. Some of them offer **mountain-guide service** as well.

Alpine Club of Canada, Box 1026, Banff T0L 0C0 (403) 762-4881
Association of Canadian Mountain Guides, Box 1537, Banff T0L 0C0
Banff Alpine Guides, Box 1025, Banff T0L 0C0 (403) 762-2791
Blue Lake Centre, Box 850, Hinton T0E 1B0 (403) 865-4741
Canadian School of Mountaineering, Box 723, Canmore T0L 0M0
    (403) 678-4134
Hans Schwarz, Mountain Guide, Box 452, Jasper T0E 1E0 (403) 852-3964
Lac Des Arcs Climbing School, 1116 19th Avenue NW, Calgary T2M 0Z9
    (403) 289-6795
Yamnuska Mountain School, Box 7500, Canmore T0L 0M0 (403) 678-4164

For information on instruction and guiding in Glacier Park, contact the Glacier Mountaineering Society, Box 291, Whitefish, MT 59937 (406) 862-2884.

For locations of climbers' huts, see the list of back-country accommodation on previous pages.

Climbing season

Rockclimbing begins in late April here, when south-facing cliffs at low elevations become clear of snow and the rock warms up. The most popular spring practice crag in the area is **Wasootch Slabs** in Kananaskis Country, an hour's drive west of Calgary. Turn south on Alberta 40 and follow it for 24 km to the access road to Wasootch Creek, parking at the end. A five-minute walk up the gravelly valley floor takes you to the limestone slabs, which offer some 50 one-pitch routes at all levels of difficulty. My 1980 guidebook to Wasootch is out of print, but John Martin has included the area in his recent, comprehensive *Sloping Climbs*. See the complete guidebook listing on page 811.

After doing mostly rock climbs in the front ranges during spring, many Canadian Rockies climbers turn to the glacier-hung main ranges for mountaineering during July and August. Here, one finds classic alpine-style climbs of 1000-2000 m on snow and ice. The higher peaks are usually at their driest and warmest in the first week of August. Many one-day climbs can be done from the Icefields Parkway, although in the same area it is possible to walk in the wilderness for a couple of days to a back-country peak and do a climb in splendid isolation.

Winter snow (November to May) provides ski-mountaineering ascents. The peaks between Kicking Horse Pass and Bow Summit are the most popular for this;

The last pitch of Brewer's Buttress on Castle Mountain.

they are reached from Bow Hut and Balfour Hut, on the Wapta Icefield. From November to April, frozen waterfalls also attract climbers.

The following sections include recommended routes on rock, snow and ice for competent climbers. These are not the hardest climbs; they show what the region has to offer—and they are all favorites of mine. The guidebooks offer more detail on some.

Rockclimbing

Rockclimbing in the Canadian Rockies is mostly on steep limestone of the Eldon and Palliser formations (see pages 100 and 138 for geology), with discontinuous crack systems and less-than-trustworthy rock. A typical route takes you up a series of short faces and inside corners on small, square-cut holds. Overhangs are common, and stemming is probably the most-used technique.

This is all rather different from jamming the long, solid cracks found in granite. Climbers not used to limestone often find that they must lower their standard for a few days until they catch on. Limestone offers one advantage: it is less slippery when wet than other kinds of rock.

The usual granite gear-rack also works on limestone, but be aware that limestone is harder to protect than granite, for the rock is softer, splittier, and the crack systems are less continuous. Limestone cracks often take keystone-shaped nuts (Stoppers ands Rocks) better than they take Hexentrics. **Friends** are terrific in the shallow cracks and holes you often find in this rock; they are perhaps an even greater leap forward in protecting limestone than they are in protecting granite. Most climbers carry a few small pitons on routes they are unsure of (although pegging in limestone quickly damages the rock and should be avoided wherever possible). Rather than packing a hammer, I use a nut hook with a small hammer head on one end.

There is also some very good climbing on **quartzite** in the main ranges of the Canadian Rockies, especially in the Jasper area, where quartzite faces of 1300 m are climbed on Mt. Edith Cavell, in the Ramparts and elsewhere. These routes are moderate in difficulty (many are graded 5.5 to 5.7), but the length and objective dangers make them serious climbs (alpine grade III-VI). Lately there has been a trend to doing short, difficult routes on quartzite—similar to climbs at Eldorado Springs, Colorado, or in the Shawangunks of New York state. Rock jocks from these areas will enjoy the cliffs at the end of Lake Louise and Lake O'Hara, and the east face of Sorrow Peak (beside Mt. Edith Cavell).

Four fine rock routes

The most popular cliff in the region is called **Yamnuska**, the Stoney Indian name for what is marked on the map as "Mt. Laurie" at the mountain front west of Calgary. Approach via the TransCanada Highway, turn right (north) on Highway 1X across the valley to Highway 1A, and turn right again on 1A. Follow for two kilometres at the foot of the mountain to the dirt access road on the left (there is no sign; take the first obvious left). There are many routes up the two-kilometre-long cliff face, with easy hiking descents on the back side. The current guidebook is by Urs Kallen (see page 811).

- **Red Shirt** on Yamnuska (eight pitches, II, 5.6): best introduction to limestone climbing in the Canadian Rockies, steep and sustained but at a moderate grade and on excellent rock. However, it is easy to get off-route on traverse pitches; follow the guidebook carefully or (better) go with someone who knows the climb.

- **Direttissima** on Yamnuska (ten pitches, III, 5.7, A1): the classic Yamnuska climb, directly to the summit. Route-finding is fairly straightforward; beyond the second pitch there are several alternative sections in what is essentially a great inside corner, all coming together for the difficult exit pitch over a big overhang at the top (free at 5.8/5.9, but most often done by grabbing a couple of fixed pegs).

- **Reprobate** on EEOR (13 pitches, III, 5.9, or 5.7 and A1): a long and fairly serious climb offering the best limestone in the Bow Valley corridor. Get Greg Spohr's guidebook *Selected Climbs in the Canmore Area* for this and other routes in the area. "EEOR" is short for "East End of Rundle," the cliff marking the southeast end of Mt. Rundle above Canmore. Approach is via the road to Spray Lakes, scrambling from the gap between EEOR and the next peak to the south (Chinaman's Peak, which has excellent climbs on it, too). Reprobate takes a fairly direct line between the big left buttress and two prominent cracks to the right. Three easy pitches up a rottenish pillar lead to excellent rock—and a two-grade jump in difficulty. Getting into the huge inside corner above goes free at 5.9 (or use etriers), then things ease somewhat from there to the top. Easy ridge-walking descent.

- **Tower of Babel** at Moraine Lake, in the Valley of the Ten Peaks near Lake Louise (10 pitches, II, 5.5): a moderate quartzite climb with a spectacular finish. The tower is the obvious buttress southeast of Moraine Lake; note the big ledge two-thirds of the way up (the Ski Jump). Starting near the centre of the base, work up and right for two pitches to the right edge, then more easily up and left into a big corner that ends at the Ski Jump. The excellent rock above goes most easily from just right of centre, straight up, then slightly left to a belay ledge below the last pitch. Off the right end of the ledge, angle right into a crack and follow it to the top. Descent is south along the crest of the buttress, then down the steep gully along the tower's right (west) side. Watch out for rolling rocks in the gully.

Summer snow and ice

We are speaking now of the big main-range peaks of the central Rockies. A word of warning: these peaks are for climbers experienced in glacier travel, use of crampons, ice axe, ice screws and so on. Hikers should stay off glaciers (see page 214).

A party of three (a climber at each end and in the middle of the rope) is good for snow and ice climbs: this group size offers safety on crevassed glaciers and is ideal for climbing ice faces quickly by using **running protection**: the leader puts in an ice screw every 20-25 m, the party moving together until the leader runs out of screws, whereupon he waits for the tail end to transfer them.

Popular equipment for main-range mountaineering: light climbing rope (9-mm single rope, 45 m long), helmet, seat harness (and a chest sling, for the glacier travel involved), metal-shafted ice axe, ice hammer in holster, ice screws, two or three snow flukes if a knife-edged snow ridge or avalanche-prone slope is in the plan, a half-dozen carabiners and slings, a few nuts or pitons if it is a mixed climb (rock sections on ice peaks are inclined to be terribly rotten), rappel gadget if required, warm single boots or double boots (the new plastic double boots are quite popular), waterproofed gloves and/or mitts with boiled-wool liners, longies, wool or Goretex knickers or climbing pants, gaiters, sweater, Goretex jacket, tuque, dark glasses.

Those used to climbing in the sunny Colorado Rockies or California Sierras will find greater objective danger here: crevasses, summer avalanches of wet snow and ice, more rockfall, poorer holds, colder and more frequent storms, whiteouts on glaciers. But the altitude is lower—summits are typically 3000-3500 m above sea level rather than the 4300 m elevations of the southern Rockies—and there is less lightning.

Crevasses claim a mountaineer every now and again in the Canadian Rockies; it is surprising how few climbers practice or even understand crevasse rescue. The Swiss method still seems the best to me: it's quick and the victim need do nothing to help himself (see diagram on page 792). Keep in mind that this method requires two climbers on the surface, making a party of three essential.

Climbing Mt. Robson (Kain route). Photo by Greg Spohr.

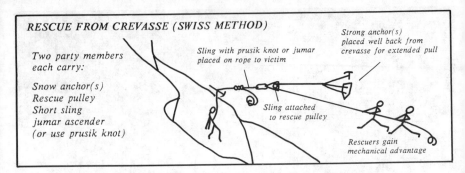

RESCUE FROM CREVASSE (SWISS METHOD)

Two party members
each carry:

Snow anchor(s)
Rescue pulley
Short sling
jumar ascender
(or use prusik knot)

Sling with prusik knot or jumar
placed on rope to victim

Sling attached
to rescue pulley

Strong anchor(s)
placed well back from
crevasse for extended pull

Rescuers gain
mechanical advantage

The most dangerous part of a glacier in summer is the **firn line**: first snow you come to as you walk up. Snow bridges over crevasses are thinnest here. Most accidents happen on the way down, when the snow is soft in the late afternoon, the footfalls heavier (one is going downhill) and the views limited by the stair-step character of most crevasse fields (going down-glacier, one often cannot see a crevasse until right on the lip).

Four fine peaks

- **Mount Victoria** above Lake Louise: a two-day ascent, with an elegant ridge traverse. Take the trail from the lake to Plain of Six Glaciers, passing the teahouse and getting onto the Lower Victoria Glacier at the point at which the trail begins to fade (scramble down a steep moraine to the ice). Follow the glacier to Abbot's Pass (some danger of avalanche from above on the narrow approach) and stay overnight in the Abbot Hut. No charge, but you must register with Parks Canada at the information office in Lake Louise townsite. Bring sleeping bag, fuel and food; stove and foamies are in the hut. Start at dawn the next morning, scrambling up rocks west of the hut, over a short snow/ice patch and on to the south summit. Follow the ridge north, belaying the narrow spots, to the centre summit (4-6 hr from hut). Avoid straying out on the east face, which is avalanche-prone. Most parties return to the hut and descend the glacier to Lake Louise the same day.

- **Mt. Athabasca** in the Columbia Icefield area: most popular snow-and-ice peak in the Canadian Rockies. Approach to most routes is from the first major stream along the Athabasca glacier-ride road (a little beyond the first kilometre). The road is open only to shuttle buses most of the day, but climbers may drive up to the small parking spot beside the stream if they do so before 7 a.m. A trail along the right (west) moraine leads through a rubbly gully in the cliff and up to the glacier well right of centre. Gain the ice easily (a little steep at the start), then angle up and left toward the base of the ice-clad Silverhorn.

  From there the regular route (Saddle Route) traverses right across fairly steep slopes to the long col right of the horn. Head south across a flat section to the rocky west ridge of the peak and follow it east to the top of the Silverhorn. It is only a short way from there to the summit along a narrow and very beautiful snow/ice ridge. Descend same way, or, if you are good at self-arrest with your ice axe, consider dropping down long snow gullies from the saddle into the next cirque west—a quick descent in bad weather. Keep to the east side of the cirque, scrambling down ledges at the lip to the snowmobile concession and the road.

  Silverhorn Route: from the base of the horn, climb left a hundred metres to the entrance of the north cirque, then right up the Silverhorn (mixed snow and ice at 35-40°) to the summit ridge.

  North-face Route: cross the north cirque and take to the face at about the middle, heading for a snow/ice gully through the rock band just below the summit. Climb a short, steep section of water ice or rotten rock to get into the gully. Ice is at 50° most of the way up; 10 rope-lengths in all.

- **Mt. Edith Cavell** near Jasper, east-ridge route (III, 5.3): a moderate mixed climb on quartzite, usually in good condition after mid-July. Leave Jasper a half-hour before first light, taking the Cavell road to the end and following the trail to Cavell Meadows for 20 minutes or so, until it switchbacks away from the mountain. A faint climber's trail leads southeast just inside the moraine to the snow/ice patch that takes you to the col at the foot of the east ridge. Scramble up the ledgy first buttress (class three); the alternatives gradually diminish as the buttress narrows and you are forced over to a steep, narrow snow/ice gully on your left. Crossing it there avoids a longer ice patch higher up.

  Beyond the flat spot in the ridge the grade goes up to lower fifth class in spots; most parties belay from there to the summit (bring a dozen nuts up to 5 cm). Occasional bits of ice/snow usually require crampons, but not screws.

  Descent: back down the ridge, or continue over the summit and down the normal route on the west side (much longer, but offering a scenic hike). To descend the normal, follow the summit ridge west, working right (north) onto the wide col between Cavell and Sorrow Peak. From the centre, head down over scree, talus and ledges, angling gradually right; cliffs near the bottom will force you northwest into a through-going gully down to the meadows at Verdant Pass. Angle right to a stream, where you should pick up the trail at timberline; it stays on the east side of the creek, well above it. Joining the Astoria River Trail, turn right and head east to the parking lot. In late summer most parties finish in the dark.

- **Mt. Robson** west of Jasper, Kain route (V): 3000 m to the top; a mini-expedition for experienced climbers. Plan to spend a week on the mountain. ("Kain" refers to Conrad Kain, leader of the first-ascent party in 1913. See page 758 for photo.)

  Day one: to Berg Lake from Highway 16. A hard grind, but get as close to Robson Pass (beyond the east end of the lake) as you can. Camping at Adolphus Lake, just inside Jasper park, will save the provincial park fee.

  Day two: up the Robson Glacier, following a rough trail along the moraine on the left (east side) for the first kilometre and gaining the glacier where it peters out. At the icefall, move left off the glacier and up rock benches, passing in front of Extinguisher Tower and then easily back onto the glacier. Higher up, the glacier steepens toward the Robson-Resplendent Col (big crevasses here to end-run), but there is a flat pocket under the col suitable for a camp. Or, if you are traveling fast and have six hours of climbing time left, do the next day's work.

  Day three: if there is lots of snow, the icefall on the south side of the Dome may be an easier route than the Robson-Resplendent Ridge, which is very narrow and often double-corniced early in the summer. But if the icefall looks nasty and the snowmelt season is well on, then the ridge will probably be easier because the snow along it will have melted back on the south side, exposing a ledge for walking. There is still a 20-m pitch of fourth-class rock (nasty if iced-up) to do on the ridge. The Dome is flat on top, a good spot to camp.

  Day four: take the Kain Face (angle is 52°) on either side of the central ice bulge for 10-12 rope-lengths to the ridge. Left is shorter than right. Follow the ridge up the Roof, staying on the right side of the face but moving left if need be among the cauliflower-ice formations there, and thence along the short summit ridge. Descend same way. Climbing time is quite variable (12-20 hr), depending on weather, snow conditions and stamina. Be prepared to wait awhile atop the Kain Face if it has softened into avalanche soup.

  Retreat: it is usually possible to go from the Dome to Berg Lake in one day, then out the next, for a total of five or six days on the mountain. But count on losing at least one day to the weather.

The key to this ascent is to go lightly and quickly. Too many parties labor up the peak under 30-kg loads, burning themselves out. Try for 15-16 kg. Gear considerations: you will need a strong tent, bags good to -15°C, two or three snow flukes for belaying the Robson-Resplendent Ridge and 10-15 ice screws for doing the Kain Face with running protection (see page 790). No rock gear required. Most parties carry a dozen-or-so wands to mark important points on the route beyond the Dome, for it often whites out and new snow can fill tracks.

Frozen waterfalls

The season for winter ice-climbing begins in November in most years and lasts until early May (even later at high elevations, when you can climb waterfall ice in June or even July).

This sport is so specialized that it is pointless to offer advice. But here are some tidbits applicable in the Canadian Rockies. The weather is usually very cold from late December to early February. Still, waterfall-climbers here happily whack and stab the hard, brittle ice of January at temperatures of -30°C. Screws go in more easily than hammered anchors in such conditions. Double boots (or overboots with thick liners that surround the boot) and thick mitts are essential. The days are short—only eight hours of light sufficient for climbing at Christmas—so it is wise to pack a headlamp on even a short climb.

Four popular waterfall climbs

- **Cascade Falls** in Banff park (grade 3): the central waterfall on Cascade Mountain near Banff. Long (300 m), but can be soloed from tier to tier until roping for the top section, two pitches of moderate ice. Avalanche danger.

- **Louise Falls** (grade 4) in Banff park: beside the trail at the far end of Lake Louise. Three pitches, including an intimidating vertical section. Climbers who back off lose face before an audience of cross-country skiers watching from the popular trail below.

- **Carlsberg Column** (grade 5) in Yoho park: 1.5 km west of Field along a road on the opposite side of the river from the TransCanada Highway. Four pitches, the first two of which are on a vertical column 60 m tall. This is an attractive climbing spot, with other falls nearby. Temperatures are often higher on this side of the divide than they are on the eastern slope. But there is avalanche danger.

- **The Weeping Wall** in Banff park (grades 4-6): near the north end of the park, beside the Icefields Parkway. Three routes on this wide and beautiful curtain of ice: left side (grade 4), centre (grade 5, some vertical ice) and right side (grade 5, more vertical ice). These routes are 100-125 m long, ending at the big tree-covered ledge halfway up the cliff. The main waterfall above the ledge is called **Teardrop** and is grade 6 (155 m).

For more information, including details of descent routes, get Albi Sole's guidebook to the area, *Waterfall Ice* (list of guidebooks on page 811).

Peaks in the Canadian Rockies over 3500 m (11,500 feet) in elevation			
Mt. Robson	3954	Mt. Alberta	3619
Mt. Columbia	3747	Mt. Assiniboine	3618
North Twin	3718	Mt. Forbes	3609
Mt. Clemenceau	3657	South Twin	3566
Twins Tower*	3627	Mt. Goodsir, S.	3562
		Mt. Temple	3544
*If counted separately		Mt. Goodsir	3524
from North Twin		Mt. Bryce	3507

Climbing the Weeping Wall in northern Banff National Park. Photo by Will Gadd.

SKI-TOURING

Many summer trails in the Canadian Rockies make terrific winter ski routes. The season is long (six months at subalpine elevations) and the variety is endless.

By mid-November there is usually enough snow on the ground to ski the easier trails, dodging the rocks. Around Christmas the skiing improves dramatically: a couple of Pacific storms have often deepened the accumulation and in the subalpine zone the snowpack is becoming solid enough to support one's weight off the packed trails.

January is often quite cold (daytime temperatures seldom rise above -15°C), but by mid-February the weather is warmer and the days are longer. Late February to early March is perhaps the prime period: plenty of snow-cover, good base, small accumulations at night and sunny days.

The latter half of March is frequently stormy, with poor visibility at high elevations. This is also the beginning of climax-avalanche season on the western slope; by mid-April the avalanche danger is general. Further, the snow is becoming wet near the surface, although deeper down it is still cold and dry—a combination that is difficult to wax for. A wax sticky enough to hold properly going uphill will clog (clumps of snow will adhere to the ski bottoms) in shady places and when breaking trail. This is when I put the skis away for the season.

In about one year out of four the skiing is generally poor in the Canadian Rockies—more often from the Columbia Icefield north. This is because the Rockies are drier and colder than other ranges in western Canada, climatic factors that tend to produce **depth hoar**: loose, sugary-textured snow created at the base of the snowpack by recrystallization of normal flakes. When there is a thick layer of depth hoar, the snow cannot support a skier's weight. One step off the packed trail and one is floundering. In such conditions the avalanche hazard is usually extreme, too. See page 816 for more on avalanches and depth hoar.

Skiing on steep mountain trails is more difficult than skiing on groomed tracks in gentler terrain. While it is quite possible to learn this game on your own, some good instruction will help. The groups listed below offer training and/or organized outings in the Rockies at time of writing.

Banff Alpine Guides, Box 1025, Banff T0L 0C0 (403) 762-2791
Blue Lake Centre, Box 850, Hinton T0E 1B0 (403) 865-4741
Canadian Hostelling Association, 1414 Kensington Road NW, Calgary T2N 3P9
    (403) 283-5551
Nordic Ski Institute, Box 1050, Canmore T0L 0M0 (403) 678-4102
Yamnuska Mountain School, Box 7500, Canmore T0L 0M0 (403) 678-4164

Equipment

Fifteen years of ski-touring in the Canadian Rockies have taught me a few things about the gear required to enjoy it best. The key words are *light, strong* and *warm.*

Skis: I use shorter skis than those preferred by most Nordic skiers. Mine are just a little over head-high. Such skis turn more easily on steep, switchbacking trails than longer ones do, yet they still provide enough flotation for powder skiing. When the base is poor, though, and my pack is heavy, I tend to break through more easily than people wearing longer skis.

For eight seasons now I have used the same pair of **foam-cored light-touring** skis. These are versatile and amazingly strong, good even for icefield trips. They are also wonderfully light—something my legs appreciate in the last hour or two of a long day on the trail. These skis are 65 mm wide at the tip, with lots of sidecut (about 10 mm). Yet they are not too wide to slide smoothly in tracks made by narrower skis. The camber is soft, which gives good uphill grip, and the tips are floppy, which means that the skis turn easily in powder and tend to stay up on crusty snow rather than digging in.

Double-cambered skis (ones with a stiff arch in the centre) are faster for racing on set tracks through gentle terrain, where the skier kicks (slams down the stiff, stickily waxed centre) on each step and glides (slides on the very slippery

Skiing near Maccarib Pass in Jasper National Park.

waxed tip and tail as the centre pops back up). But on mountain trails this kind of skiing is rare. A typical mountain trail runs steadily uphill from the valley floor to a timberline pass, lake or summit, followed by lunch and a long downhill run. There is little kick-and-glide on such trips; the idea is to get up with minimal backslipping and get down with the fewest falls. A short, soft ski seems ideal.

I have tried **metal-edged skis** but found them to be of little use except when crossing ice or skiing with the downhillers. Besides making a ski heavier, metal edges tend to stiffen it; the tip cuts into the crust and the centre section must be waxed quite stickily to hold properly on the steeper uphill grades. Perhaps a light, flexible design with metal edges will show up on the market soon.

Bindings: a combination **three-pin/cable binding** made of light alloy seems ideal. Going uphill, across the flats or gently downhill, I leave the cable off to get lots of heel lift; atop a difficult run I snap on the cable to get more control. The cable is also a big help when I am forced to sidestep uphill in deep powder; it lets me pop the tail of the ski up, making the sidestepping easier.

Boots: single for day trips in reasonable temperatures, double for longer tours, icefield trips or very cold days. The higher the boot-tops, the better the control on downhill runs. The sole should resist twisting but should bend fairly easily at the toe. When buying single boots, I get them big enough to fit two pairs of heavy wool socks *and* an insulating insole (which greatly increases the warmth). Long and narrow is the ticket here, so that you have plenty of toe room and adequate width when the laces are loose, but foot-huggers when the laces are tightened up for better control on the hills. I wear my socks inside out, with the smooth side against the skin to delay the blisters.

Gaiters: waterproof around the boot, breathable higher up. The fattest zippers last the longest.

Poles: mine are fibreglass, light and strong, with large baskets for planting in the powder. Length: just reaching my armpit when I'm standing in socks. This is somewhat shorter than nordic skiers recommend, and admittedly a bit too short for elegant kick-and-glide skiing, but with short poles I don't reach as high on each step, which my arms appreciate after a long day, and short poles are not as awkward on the sideslope. They are also better for doing unweighted turns and telemark turns, two popular techniques these days.

Clothing: layers work well in winter, for they can be donned and shed as the weather changes. A popular combination: turtleneck shirt (for a warmer neck on downhill runs and in icy winds), flannel or wool shirt and a sweater.

When needed for wind or snowfall, slip on a *breathable* (i.e. not waterproof) shell parka or anorak. It should be long enough to reach over your rear and cut large enough to fit over a down jacket. The front should zip up to your nose, and there should be a deep hood that can be closed with a drawstring. I use a single-layer uncoated ripstop anorak with those features; it is extremely lightweight and packs to a handful, yet has proved adequate in the worst conditions. All it has to do is stop the wind from penetrating the underlying insulating layers while letting the sweat out. For some reason this kind of shell is hard to find. Cheap shells of coated nylon with inferior hoods and flimsy zippers are plentiful, but a *proper* one is a prize; buy two. Mountain Equipment Co-op (stores in Calgary, Vancouver and Toronto) carry them at time of writing.

On very cold days, a light down jacket over the sweater and under the shell has always sufficed for me. Heavy down jackets are good for only two things: climbing K2 or waiting for the bus in Edmonton in January.

Concerning Goretex jackets: this material, wonderful in the rain, is inclined to ice-up inside at low temperatures.

For my hands, I like long-wearing leather work gloves soaked with wax boot waterproofing and large enough to hold knit liners. These are warm enough for most days, but I carry leather mitts with **boiled-wool liners** for really cold conditions. Down-filled mitts are light and warm (as long as they don't get wet), but much more expensive to lose. They wear out rather quickly, too.

Headwear: anything that keeps one's ears warm. A billed cap with earflaps will keep the sun out of your eyes. Some knit caps (tuques) also have bills on them.

Pack: a **fanny pack** is great for day trips. Low centre of gravity and no shoulder straps to hinder poling—but a down jacket won't go in. However, I seldom carry my downie on day trips, and my sweater can be tied round my waist when not needed. When I must carry more, a **teardrop-shaped day pack** with a waistbelt (done up during downhill runs to stop balance-disturbing flopping) also keeps the weight low. For longer trips, an internal-frame backpack offers plenty of room and, again, keeps the weight low.

Items always in the pack: wax bag, spare tip (even though I haven't broken a ski in years—but if it ever happens it will occur 10 km from the highway), lunch, water bottle (tightly capped, wrapped up in clothing to delay freezing and carried upside down so the bottom freezes first rather than the lid), dark glasses, compass (necessary if you are going above timberline, into white-out country; see page 826 for compass-using essentials), map and guidebook, matches, tiny first-aid kit (it goes into a 35-mm film can: moleskin for blisters, a couple of bandaids and some pain pills), toilet paper (in winter used paper is not easily buried; I burn mine in the snow or pack it out); a headlamp (not a flashlight; you need both hands for skiing) with a lithium battery (maintains power at low temperatures and lasts a long time) and an avalanche beacon on trips with slide hazard.

Although rarely needed, a **balaclava** (knit head-sock with holes for eyes and mouth) prevents facial frostbite in extreme conditions.

In the **wax bag:** fewer waxes every season. These days I seldom use anything but **gold** (the colder wax in a two-wax all-purpose pair) and **purple.** Either the waxes are getting better or I'm getting less fussy.

On a typical tour, morning temperatures will be -10°C to -20°C; in such conditions gold or blue works well for the usual uphill grind. There'll be less slipping if you wax from tip to tail. Rubbing-in seems to make little difference in either speed or wearability going uphill. If it's rather warm or really steep, some purple crayoned onto the middle third of the ski usually ends backslipping. That amount of purple wax wears off in three or four hours, which is often enough time to reach the top of the day's climb.

For long, steep climbs in untracked snow (such as you find on most icefield trips), **skins** made for skinny skis are just the thing. There are times when wax simply will not work, but skins will see you through.

Also in the wax bag: a putty-knife scraper (sharpened to a bevel edge), cork for smoothing wax, roll of filament tape for mending poles, an extra binding screw and a neat pair of pliers that has a little adjustable wrench on one handle and a screwdriver tip on the other. This tool fixes everything: broken bindings, broken stoves in mountain huts, cars that won't start when they have been parked at the trailhead all day, etc. If the bail from your binding (movable wire or plate that tightens down on the boot) is of the type that can come loose and be lost, bring a spare. If you have plain cable bindings be sure to bring an extra cable.

For trips requiring camping you will need a winter sleeping bag (or an overbag for your three-season bag, or a slim summer-weight bag to slip inside a three-season bag, which is the combination I use). Important: you will probably still be cold unless you have a **long foam pad:** one long enough to keep your whole sleeping bag off the tent floor. These are seldom available, but you can lengthen a shorter one by sticking on a piece from another pad. Cloth-cored duct tape works well for joining the two. Be sure to get the type of foamie that doesn't crack in the cold. Most parties carry a collapsible snow shovel.

Technique

For skiing packed trails, mastering the simple **snowplow turn** on those narrow, unstable skis will get you down alive. The best way to learn it is at your local ski area (in disguise, if you like). Instructions:

Get your weight back on the skis a little and push your heels out so that you are sliding along in a sort of VEE, the tips close together and the tails far apart. Now turn your ankles in a little, so the inside edges of the skis dig in and slow you down. Oops! Too much edging; the skis crossed in front and you fell on your face, ha ha. But you get the idea. To turn, just do the VEE thing, but put all your weight on the left ski (if you want to turn right) or on the right ski (if you want to turn left). This will magically swing you around. Keep the ski on the inside of the turn flat, and let it slide around, too. So much for the snowplow turn.

Next step: *pick up the inside ski* as you go around the corner and turn it to match the outside ski (which is doing all the work). Now you've got the cross-country version of the **christie**. Try holding the turn until you swing right around and stop. Neat, eh? If you can get some weight onto the *outside edge of the inside ski* as it comes around, then the christie turn becomes pretty snappy.

Most skiers discover the **omigod powder turn** by accident, when confronted by some frightening obstacle. Lacking the time to stop by falling, they instinctively lean hard to left or right—and then fall, having mysteriously missed the boulder, the tree or whatever. There is no mystery, here; your skis will turn in powder if you simply lean in the direction you want to go. On a gentle slope, you can make lovely gradual curves by leaning left and right. To tighten them up, lean more. The trick, of course, is to straighten up after the turn. Try sticking your pole in and pushing yourself back up.

With pole-use comes the **unweighted turn,** which is so fast that you can stop sideways on a narrow trail when you have to. This turn works great for mogul-bashing with the downhillers, as long as there aren't any icy patches. The how-to:

Crouch a bit, then *plant the pole* on the side you are going to turn toward and *rise up suddenly,* swinging both skis in the direction of the turn. When the skis have come around, which will happen quickly because you have taken your weight off them, bend your legs again and prepare to plant the other pole, for a rise-up and turn in the other direction. Keep your body more or less straight down the fall line as you do one quick turn after another. As usual, keep most of your weight on the outside ski.

This technique is good for both packed and untracked snow. The Powder People use it on downhill skis to make those rhythmic, wiggly tracks. The steeper the hill, the quicker the skis snap around and thus the better the unweighted turn works. There is no need to turn very sharply in the powder. Just turn more often, which will kill off the speed.

The more competent you are at this turn, the more parallel (and closer together) your skis will be.

Finally, we come to the ancient but effective **telemark turn**. The important thing in what the glossy magazines call "telemarking" is to look right. You need special telemark skis, telemark boots, telemark bindings, telemark poles, telemark ski suit, telemark gloves, telemark sunglasses, telemark tuque, telemark lip balm and tanning cream . . .

Doing telemarks is sort of like doing that Russian dance that wrecks your knees. You crouch a bit, thrusting one foot forward, knee bent, the foot *angling inward*. Keep the other ski—the one inside the turn—well back, trailing along, the *tip riding against the inside of your ankle*. Thus, the inside ski has to follow along and you carve a turn on bended knee.

The telemark turn is slower to get into and out of than the unweighted parallel turn, and the radius is wider, so it is not as good on packed trails. But it's the best way to beat your way down through crusty snow. If you like to ski above timberline, you may want to add the telemark to your repertoire.

Safety considerations

The cold, the sloping snow, the sun and your own headlong speed can all hurt you in ski-touring. Here are some tips on avoiding trouble in the Canadian Rockies.

It is surprising how warm even a pair of skimpy racing boots can be, but the warmth lasts only as long as you are moving. A felt insole will help a lot in keeping January's icy maw from nibbling your toes; overboots provide more protection, double boots the most. Gaiters not only keep the snow from wetting your socks and getting down your boots; they help keep your lower legs and feet warm.

Children need warmer boots and gloves than adults. When my kids were little I made sure that they had ski boots big enough to hold felt liners of the type that insulate bush boots or snowmobile boots. Large, puffy mitts are essential for kids, and the cuffs of their jackets should not be so tight that circulation to their hands is impaired.

A vigorous start in warm clothing fights the tendency to get cold hands and feet during the first hour of a tour. Stoking the metabolic furnace with strenuous activity warms the whole body; this is preferable to stopping and waving one's arms about or stamping one's feet. Just go hard until you are warm all over. Be patient; a lot of morning coldness is just the delay between the time you turn up your body's thermostat and the time the heat comes on.

If a quick start in cold air makes it hard for you to breathe—especially on the exhale and after you have stopped for a moment—then you may suffer from mild exercise-induced **asthma**. Many skiers have this condition; untreated, it takes the fun out of winter sports. See your doctor if you suspect that you may have this easily treated problem.

As continued exercise warms you, peel off layers of clothing before you soak them with sweat and destroy their insulating ability. When you stop to eat, put a layer or two back on to hold onto your body's heat; eating is inclined to make you colder than just resting will.

If your toes or fingers just won't warm up, turn around and go home; you are risking frostbite. For more on that unpleasant subject, including how to avoid it, turn to page 822.

Avalanches are a major hazard in mountain ski-touring. They are discussed in detail on page 816, in the safety section.

Snowblindness is seldom a problem in the Canadian Rockies, for the sun is not as bright in winter here as it is in, say, the Colorado Rockies. But even on overcast days there is a great deal of ultraviolet filtering through. Snowblindness can incapacitate you for several days, so always bring sunglasses and put them on whenever the scene gets uncomfortably bright. If you see pink or red when closing your eyes, then it is definitely time for sunglasses; if things have a pinkish cast when your eyes are open, then you should have put them on sooner; you can expect your eyes to feel grainy and light-sensitive that evening.

April is the worst month for **skier's sunburn**. People are inclined to spend long days outdoors, often without a hat, and the sun is strong in early spring. Sunburn is seldom a problem during the dark months of December and January, but at high elevations it can get you nonetheless. If you are fair-skinned and haven't been out enough to acquire a winter tan, beware the ides of March.

Finally, it pays to ski cautiously until there is enough snow on the ground to cover the stumps and cushion the falls.

Places to ski

The Canadian Rockies are most heavily skied in Banff, Jasper and Peter Lougheed parks. These are all eastern-slope areas offering excellent snow: dry and even for easy waxing. South of Kananaskis Country on the eastern slope, frequent chinooks and lighter snowfalls tend to cause uneven conditions, while north of Jasper the depth-hoar buildup in most winters is great enough to cause breakable crust. The problem gets worse the farther north you go.

The entire western slope of the Canadian Rockies is generally warmer and wetter in winter than the eastern slope. There is more snow there, but it's harder to wax for. The valleys are deeper, with correspondingly bigger and more numerous avalanches. Outside the national parks, auto access is not as easy on the western slope and there are fewer trails. Popular places include Yoho park, Kootenay park (between Vermilion Pass and Floe Lake) and western Glacier park.

This is not to say that you can't find good skiing in other parts of the western slope, or north of Jasper or south of Kananaskis country on the eastern slope. Frequently you can. You just have to look a little harder.

Some popular day tours

The ratings are:

Easy: suitable for skiers without much experience.

Intermediate: enjoyable for competent skiers, who can turn easily and can control their speed on hills.

Difficult: for experienced skiers only, who can handle tight turns, narrow, steep sections and powder snow. Beginners are likely to fall often, risking equipment breakage or personal injury.

For figuring times, an average for reasonably fit skiers is about 4 km/hr, uphill and back.

- Prepared trails in Peter Lougheed Provincial Park west of Calgary: those heading at Pocaterra Creek are mostly easy with intermediate sections; the Boulton Creek area offers intermediate trails with some difficult sections. A good loop for intermediate skiers takes in the Boulton Creek, Elk Pass, Tyrwhitt and Whiskey Jack trails (16 km total). Pick up a map at the information office as you enter the park.

- Boom Lake in Kootenay National Park (4 km one way): wide most of the way, and easy with intermediate sections. Skiable early in the season and quite popular; expect a lot of company in the afternoon. Trailhead is 7 km west of the Highway 93-TransCanada junction, just over Vermilion Pass.

- Stanley Glacier in Kootenay park (4.4 km one way): passes through the Vermilion Pass burn of 1968; see how the forest is regenerating. Intermediate in the lower parts, with fairly steep grades and switchbacks; easier higher up, with some gentle powder slopes at timberline that are good for learning telemark or unweighted parallel turns. Avalanche danger increases quickly if you go farther.

- The Ink Pots in Banff National Park (6 km one way): an intermediate trip, with one difficult section. Begins at Johnston Canyon, which is lovely in winter. You can start immediately north of cabins, where the fire road begins, or see the canyon first by carrying your skis along the walkways, then climbing out of the canyon up the stairway and steep path at the end to join the main ski trail. The trail climbs steadily through the trees to its high point, then drops very steeply to the Ink Pots (see page 773 for a description), which sit in meadows surrounded by superb scenery.

- Plain of the Six Glaciers, in Banff park (7 km one way): takes you around Lake Louise to the west end and on to timberline. Excellent scenery in good weather and a variety of skiing: easy around the lake, intermediate in the forest and difficult in the powder higher up. Do this one from February on, when there is usually enough snow to ski Louise Creek rather than the avalanche-prone route of the summer trail.

- Lake O'Hara Fire Road in Yoho National Park (13 km one way): an easy trip with rewarding scenery at the end, although it makes for a long day. The summer road from Wapta Lake (near Kicking Horse Pass) to Lake O'Hara is not plowed in winter; it is wide, with moderate grades—ideal for beginners with stamina, who will learn a lot in skiing it. Many skiers use the road to get to the Elizabeth Parker Hut near Lake O'Hara, a centre for many fine day trips in this famous area.

- **Bald Hills,** above Maligne Lake in Jasper National Park (5 km one way): a quick route to the high country, with a good intermediate run down. From the second parking lot at Maligne Lake, follow the old fire-lookout road steadily up to the lookout site (nothing left but the foundation) to get fine views of the Maligne area. There is good powder skiing to the south, on leeward sides of the Bald Hills (avalanche danger on the steeper slopes). The run down the fire road is fast and continuous. A more difficult alternative is to follow the first broad gully south of the lookout, skiing down from clearing to clearing in the gradually thickening forest and joining the fire road at about the 3-km mark.

- **Trackset trails at Maligne Lake** in Jasper park: short loops in the deep subalpine snow. Pick up a copy of the ski-trails map at the Parks Canada information centre in Jasper; the wooded loops at the lake range from easy to intermediate with the odd difficult bit. Recommended: the **Lorraine Lake** loop, with moose-tracked meadows and occasional views. Take the Bald Hills Trail at the start if you want an intermediate run down a bit of the Skyline Trail at the end, or go the other way (up the Skyline first) for a rating of easy. Kids and novices will enjoy the **Mary Schäffer** loop, which runs from the first parking lot to a good viewpoint along the lakeshore and then back to the lot through the trees. The Maligne Lake Chalet may be open for treats, but don't count on it.

Overnight trips with hut accommodation

Don't try these until you are able to handle intermediate trails while wearing a fairly heavy pack. More endurance is required than that needed for the average day trip.

A three-season sleeping bag is usually sufficient, even if the hut is unheated. You must sign out in advance to do the ones listed below; check at the time to see whether you need to pack a foamie and/or a cooker.

For exact locations of mountain huts, see the back-country accommodation guide beginning on page 783.

- **Healy Pass and Redearth Creek** in Banff park (34 km total): varied skiing with good views throughout and a high pass to cross.

    Start at the Sunshine ski area parking lot, taking the ski-out trail at the southwest end of the lot for a few hundred metres then turning right onto the Healy Creek Trail. The trail climbs gradually at first, then quite steeply to the high subalpine meadows below a long whaleback ridge called The Rampart (not the Ramparts southwest of Jasper). Cross this long ridge at timberline on its northern end. On the other side is a north-angling intermediate run through scattered larch into heavier woods and the exquisite setting of the Egypt Lake Hut.

    This hut can be hard to find. It sits on the west side of Pharoah Creek, out of sight from the creek bed that most skiers descend to and follow when they have lost the regular trail in new snow. If you come to the warden cabin, you went by the hut. Backtrack south along the west side of the creek for about half a kilometre.

    The following day, head north down Pharoah Creek to its junction with Redearth Creek and a long kick-and-glide run (one of the few like it in the Rockies) to the TransCanada Highway.

    Strong skiers often do this loop in a day, starting at dawn, lunching at the hut and finishing at dusk. You may want two cars for this one because the trip doesn't end where it began. Hitching back to the Sunshine lot can take a long time, especially after the ski area closes.

Ski-touring

- **Wapta and Waputik icefields** in Banff and Yoho parks (35 km total): also called the "Bow-Lake-to-Wapta-Lake traverse," this is the classic icefield ski trip in the Canadian Rockies. The route goes from Bow Lake on the Icefields Parkway to the Bow Hut (visible from the highway below St. Nicholas Peak), then over the Wapta Icefield, through the Nicholas-Olive Col and down the Vulture Glacier to Balfour Pass and a hut there. Then along the eastern slopes of Mt. Balfour to a very high pass over the continental divide, across the Waputik Icefield on the other side, through the col between Mt. Niles and Mt. Daly and down to Sherbrooke Lake and the TransCanada Highway at Wapta Lake.

  If you are going to try this trip without someone who has done it before, I strongly recommend that you carry *Ski Trails in the Canadian Rockies,* the excellent guide by Rick Kunelius and Dave Biederman, which gives complete directions—and good advice about staying alive on an icefield in winter.

  Most parties take two or three days to do this trip, although I have spent up to a week at it, enjoying ski ascents of the peaks along the way and waiting out bad weather. For many skiers an overnight visit to Bow Hut is a good introduction to icefield skiing.

  Permits are required for using these huts, and advance reservations are recommended. Call Banff National Park, 403-762-3324 or 762-4506.

Crossing the Wapta Icefield in Yoho National Park.

BICYCLING

Main roads in the Canadian Rockies are good, often with shoulders wide enough for comfortable cycling. There are large national and provincial parks with plenty of campsites. Hostels (cheap overnight accommodations) are found along the major routes. Thus, the region is just *made* for bicycle tours.

Cycling is a fine way to see new country: slow enough to take in the passing scene in detail; fast enough to cover a lot of ground in a day.

A few must-do tours are presented here. For many other good routes in the Rockies, pick up a copy of *Bicycle Alberta,* a guidebook by Gail Helgason and John Dodd.

Season, weather

In most years, cycling becomes practical at low elevations in the Canadian Rockies in late April, when daytime temperatures are above freezing—but cyclists here must watch for ice patches until mid-May, when it is more likely to rain than to snow. The higher passes are still chilly until July, and near-freezing temperatures are possible anywhere in the mountains throughout the summer, so bring long pants, a jacket, warm gloves and a knit cap to keep your ears warm on any multi-day ride in the Rockies.

After the usual early-September nasty spell, there is often lovely fall cycling until late October, when the roads are becoming icy and most cyclists pack it in for the season.

How tough are the Canadian Rockies?

The Canadian Rockies are very rugged, but the highway grades are not as long or steep as one might think because glaciation has carved deep passes through the mountains. But be prepared to go a long way between towns and food stores. And keep your supplies hung up at campgrounds, for there are bears here. They don't seem to have a taste for cyclists (although a cyclist was killed by a bear on the Alaska Highway a few years ago). If you see a bear along the road, approach cautiously. If it pays you no attention, just cruise on by. My wife was once delayed along the Icefields Parkway by an aggressive moose that would not let her pass. She had to sneak through beside a slow-moving auto.

Accommodations for cyclists

Campgrounds abound in the southern and central Rockies. Provincial road maps and Parks Canada brochures show campground locations. However, many cyclists prefer to use the **Canadian Hostelling Association cabins** in the region.

Nonmembers pay a little more than members. Bring your own sleeping bag and food; all else is available, including cooking and eating implements. You have to do your own cooking and cleanup, and the hostel manager (who used to be called a "houseparent") will ask that you help out with one small chore or another.

At time of writing, hostel rates are $4-6/night for members; $2-3 more for nonmembers. Most hostels close between 9 a.m. and 5 p.m. daily; as well, many close one day a week in the winter months (October to May). These days are changeable, so it is wise to check with the Edmonton or Calgary offices before setting out. You can also get reservations at these offices—a good idea in July and August, when the hostels are sometimes full. Addresses and telephone numbers are given on page 807.

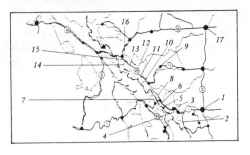

HOSTELS IN AND NEAR THE CANADIAN ROCKIES

Operated by the Canadian Hostelling Assoc.

1. **Calgary:** 540 7th Avenue SE, Calgary T2G 0J6, 403-269-8239. 114 beds, closed 10--5 daily. Showers, laundry, snacks, bike workshop.
2. **Ribbon Creek:** in Kananaskis Country, 24 km south of TransCanada on Alberta 40, 403-591-7333. 40 beds, closed 10--4 daily and Tuesdays in winter. Showers, family rooms.
3. **Banff:** 3 km from Banff on Tunnel Mountain Road. Box 1358, Banff T0L 0C0, 403-762-4122. 154 beds, closed 10--4 daily. Showers, family rooms, laundry, cafeteria, bike and ski workshop.
4. **Spray River:** 3.5 km south of Banff Springs Hotel on Spray River Fire Road (no motor vehicles). 47 beds, closed Thursdays in winter. Groceries, bike/ski rentals.
5. **Castle Mountain:** between Banff and Lake Louise, 1.5 km south of Castle Junction on Highway 1A (Bow Valley Parkway), 403-762-2367. 40 beds, closed Wednesdays in winter. Groceries.
6. **Corral Creek:** 1.5 km south of Lake Louise on Highway 1A. 50 beds, closed Mondays in winter. Groceries.
7. **Whiskey Jack:** near Takakkaw Falls, 13 km north of Field in Yoho park. 27 beds, open June to Labor Day. Showers, groceries.
8. **Mosquito Creek:** 26 km north of Lake Louise on Icefields Parkway. 30 beds, closed Tuesdays in winter. Groceries.
9. **Shunda Creek:** near Nordegg, 3 km north of Highway 11 on road to Shunda Creek Recreation Area, 403-721-2140. 44 beds, closed Tuesdays and Wednesdays year-round. Showers, family rooms.
10. **Rampart Creek:** 20 km north of Saskatchewan Crossing on Icefields Parkway.30 beds, closed Wednesdays in winter. Groceries.
11. **Hilda Creek:** near Columbia Icefield, 8.5 km south of Icefield Centre on Icefields Parkway. 21 beds, closed Thursdays in winter. Groceries.
12. **Beauty Creek:** 86.5 km south of Jasper on Icefields Parkway. Box 387, Jasper T0E 1E0. 20 beds, open May to September, closed Thursdays.
13. **Athabasca Falls:** 32 km south of Jasper on Icefields Parkway. Box 387, Jasper T0E 1E0. 40 beds, closed Tuesdays year-round. Propane heat.
14. **Mt. Edith Cavell:** Near end of Cavell Road, 13 km from Highway 93A junction south of Jasper. Box 387, Jasper T0E 1E0. 30 beds, closed Wednesdays year-round. Access in winter is by ski (13 km).
15. **Whistlers:** along road to Jasper Tramway off Icefields Parkway, 7 km from Jasper. Box 87, Jasper T0E 1E0, 403-852-3215. 50 beds, closed 9--5. Showers, groceries.
16. **Maligne Canyon:** 15 km east of Jasper on Maligne Road. Box 387, Jasper T0E 1E0, 403-852-3584. 24 beds, closed Wednesdays year-round. Propane heat.
17. **Edmonton:** 10422 91 St. 403-429-0140. Mail and reservations: 10926 88 Ave., Edmonton T6G 0Z1, 439-3089. 35 beds, closed 9--5. Showers, family rooms, laundry, snacks, rentals.

Hostels with showers have automatic heat and hot running water. Except as noted, others have wood heat and water must be carried; some of these have outdoor showers and/or saunas.

To make reservations at hostels without telephones or mailing addresses, use the Canadian Hostelling Association addresses given on the next page.

Addresses of interest to cyclists:

Bikecentennial, Box 8303, Missoula, Montana 59807 (406) 721-1776
Rocky Mountain Cycle Tours, Box 895, Banff T0L 0C0 (403) 762-3477

Canadian Hostelling Association:

Hostels from Calgary to Columbia Icefield: Southern Alberta Hostelling Assoc., Room 203, 1414 Kensington Road NW, Calgary T2N 3P9 (403) 283-5551.

Hostels from Columbia Icefield to Jasper: Northern Alberta District, CHA: 10926 88 Avenue, Edmonton T6G 0Z1 (403) 439-3089

Cycling the Icefields Parkway

The ride between Jasper and Banff is generally considered to be the finest short bicycle tour in the world. I am not exaggerating; this route is internationally famous, attracting thousands of cyclists from all over the globe each summer. It follows the valleys of the Athabasca, North Saskatchewan, Mistaya and Bow rivers, paralleling the continental divide through the heart of the Canadian Rockies.

Total distance: 287 km. Most cyclists take four or five days for the trip, doing 60-70 km per day, but fast riders do it in a couple of days. Starting from Banff means easier grades on the two passes easier than starting from Jasper. But you are more likely to get headwinds if you start from Banff. Take your pick. I usually go from Jasper, getting the hills done in strenuous but short climbs and enjoying the long downhill grades beyond, often with a tail wind. So the tour is described here from Jasper to Banff.

Getting to the start: if you can't arrange for two cars, a bus runs between Calgary and Jasper daily (May to October), passing through Banff and Lake Louise. You can fly into Calgary with your bike and catch this bus right at the airport. Call Brewster Transport in Calgary, Banff or Jasper for details. There is VIA passenger train service to Banff from Calgary and Vancouver, and VIA serves Jasper from Edmonton and Vancouver (there is no air service into Jasper or Banff). The bike goes for free on the train, and boxing is not required, but to avoid damage VIA recommends a box and supplies a nice big one for $5 at the station (you have to remove pedals and handlebars to fit). The bus lines and airlines demand that bikes be boxed; VIA boxes are suitable.

If you would rather not ship your bike at all, touring bikes may be rented in Banff (Spoke 'n Edge, 315 Banff Avenue, Banff T0L 0C0) or in Jasper (Mountain Air Sports, 622 Connaught Drive, Jasper T0E 1E0 or Freewheel Cycle, Box 2541, in back at Miette and Patricia).

Day one: Jasper to Athabasca Falls Hostel. A short day (31 km), but recommended if your behind hasn't put in many warm-up kilometres before starting the tour. The next hostel is at Beauty Creek, 55 km farther, if you feel like doing more distance the first day and taking a shorter ride on the second, which will provide time for a hike in the Columbia Icefield area before supper on the second day.

Day two: reach Hilda Creek Hostel, just over Sunwapta Pass and close to timberline (81 km from Athabasca Falls; 26 km from Beauty Creek Hostel). The day starts with a couple of moderate hills, then things get serious as you tackle Sunwapta Pass, the steepest, longest hill on the route. But for diversion there are often bighorn sheep along here, mingling with the tourists at the viewpoints. If you arrive at Hilda with a couple of hours of daylight left (and any energy), take the walk up to the alpine zone on Parker Ridge, well known for wildflowers and fossils (illegal to grab either in the national park) and views of the glaciers and peaks roundabout.

Day three (94 km): blast down the long grade south of Sunwapta Pass, stopping on the high bridge to admire Nigel Falls (missed by motorists, because it is practically right under the bridge). There is another hostel at Rampart Creek,

*Along the Icefields Parkway
(on the unpaved access road
to Hilda Creek Hostel)
in northern Banff National Park.*

*Taking a break after climbing the long hill to the Athabasca Glacier along the
Icefields Parkway.*

only 30 km from Hilda Creek and often used by cyclists going from the Beauty Creek hostel through the Icefield area without stopping at Hilda. Copious carbohydrate-pigging at the Saskatchewan Crossing restaurant will stoke the fires for the long climb up the Mistaya River valley, past Waterfowl Lakes and over Bow Summit, the second (and last) pass on the route. Reach Mosquito Creek Hostel 16 km beyond.

Day four (83 km): Cruise the last of the Icefields Parkway, joining the TransCanada Highway near Lake Louise. It is a strenuous side trip up to the lake, but if you start early that morning you can see the Gem of the Rockies **and** the scene featured on Canada's twenty-dollar bill: Valley of the Ten Peaks at Moraine Lake. This adds 34 km to the day's ride.

Most of the TransCanada between Lake Louise and Banff is two lanes wide and traffic is often very heavy, but just past Lake Louise you can turn off on the old highway (1A), which is at time of writing being reconstructed as a slow-speed road dubbed the **Bow Valley Parkway.** It will have many pull-offs, interpretive exhibits and such. Enquire at Lake Louise about the status of the road; it is complete at least between Castle Junction and Banff and great for cycling—although the shoulders are rather narrow and there are a couple of hills here that you miss if you stay on the TransCanada.

All traffic must follow the TransCanada the last few kilometres to Banff, but for bicyclists there is a secret escape route: Vermilion Lakes Drive, an old-road remnant now serving as a dead-end scenic drive from Banff. Past the Highway 1/1A junction, keep an eye out on your right for the old road at the base of the hill, running along the lakeshore. Just push your bike down to it for a pleasant back-door approach to the townsite.

Continuation from Banff to Calgary is a ride of 122 km, usually done in one day. The grades are very easy and you often get a whopping tailwind through the foothills—in the afternoon. In the morning there are likely to be headwinds, especially out on the prairie.

Going-to-the-Sun Road in Glacier park (85 km)

Shorter than the Icefields Parkway, but offering scenery nearly as grand, the route over Logan Pass is steep and narrow, with so much traffic that cyclists are banned on certain sections between 11 a.m. and 4 p.m., June 15 to Labor Day.

Check at the park gates for advice on cycling this road. It is possible to do it all in one day, by starting early and going partway in the morning, then taking a hike or a snooze during the hours of moto-madness, leaving the afternoon to finish up. The days are long in late June and July, so there is plenty of daylight. Accommodation: campgrounds along St. Mary Lake and at Avalanche Creek, east of Lake McDonald. No hostels. A paved trail runs between West Glacier and Apgar.

Cycling in Kananaskis Country

Kananaskis Country is a large provincial recreation area in the mountains west of Calgary; the roads in it make very good cycling trips. There is also something unique in the Canadian Rockies here: paved trails designed with bicycling (and ski-touring) in mind.

Riding from the TransCanada Highway to Kananaskis Lakes (56 km one way along Alberta 40) is a fine way to see the front ranges. There is hostel accommodation at Ribbon Creek (23 km), camping at Eau Claire (41 km) and at Kananaskis Lakes in Peter Lougheed Provincial Park. Groceries can be bought at the Fortress Mountain Ski Area exit (48 km) and at Boulton Campground in the park.

For a longer tour with a 2206-m pass, keep going past the park entrance for 17 km to reach Highwood Pass (74 km from the TransCanada). The pavement continues over the pass (to Highwood Junction, where the road east to Longview (Alberta 541) is now paved. This allows a wonderful loop trip from Calgary south on highways 2 and 22 to Longview, then west on 541 to Kananaskis Country, north through the mountains to the TransCanada and back to Calgary.

Hardy types on mountain bikes continue south of Highwood Junction, traveling the gravelled road through the front ranges all the way to Crowsnest Pass (112 km). Another good trip for folks with fat tires is the Smith-Dorrien Road between Kananaskis Lakes and Canmore, by way of Spray Lakes (75 km). This road may be paved by the time you read this, providing a two/three day loop if you travel the TransCanada Highway between Canmore and the Kananaskis Country turnoff. The TransCanada is not particularly dangerous in this section; it is a four-lane divided highway.

Paved trails suitable for touring bicycles connect the visitor centre near the entrance to Kananaskis Lakes park with Upper Kananaskis Lake, passing the Elkwood and Boulton parking lots along the way. Total distance one way: 29 km. Another bike trail runs for 8 km between Ribbon Creek and Wedge Lake, north of the park within Kananaskis Country.

Trail bicycling

A new breed of bicycle has appeared: the mountain bicycle. With its fat tires and low gears, a mountain bike can carry you over a trail at two or three times the speed of hikers and backpackers—whose territory, already shared with trail-destroying, polluting horse parties, is now being invaded by people on wheels. Reaction is mixed. Horse outfitters hate the idea. Most hikers I have talked with about it don't particularly like cyclists zooming by: "I walked all day to get here and those jerks got here in two hours!"

Unlike many of its critics, I have actually tried trail bicycling (starting in 1980, for mapping the trails around Jasper) and have found it to be a quick, although strenuous way to get around in places where I would otherwise have to walk. Trail damage does occur: the tires leave ruts in muddy spots, locking the brakes on steep downhill sections causes scuff marks, and some cyclists are inclined to cut switchbacks. But the human engine lacks the power to damage trails as motorcycles do. Trail wear and tear caused by bicycles is heavier than that caused by hikers, but lighter than that caused by horses. Safety problems include breakdowns in the back-country by ill-prepared cyclists (who might then have to be rescued), high-speed accidents and close encounters of the worst kind with bears. These incidents must be rare, for I haven't heard of any.

On the plus side, trail bicycling is good exercise and a lot of fun. It's easier on the back, knees and feet than hiking, especially if the hiker is wearing a heavy pack. Cycling is more enjoyable than walking on long, wooded, dull stretches of such back-country routes as the North Boundary Trail. By passing through the back-country more quickly than hikers, mountain cyclists go more lightly on the land: they camp, build fires and excrete fewer times on a given route than hikers do. Bicycles are self-propelled and non-polluting, meeting two of the criteria normally applied in finding a particular sport acceptable in a national park.

All the national and provincial parks in the Canadian Rockies allow trail bicycling, although not on all trails. Jasper park is currently the most liberal (all trails open except the Skyline, those leading to Tonquin Valley, the one along Maligne Canyon and the paved wheelchair path around Lake Annette); Waterton is the most restrictive (all trails closed except part of Snowshoe and Akamina Pass routes). Regulations vary from park to park, and they are subject to change as various studies are completed, so I am hesitant to recommend good trails for off-pavement cycling. Enquire locally.

Wherever you go, though, please ride politely or you will give the sport a bad name. When approaching horses and hikers from the rear, do so cautiously, by slowing down and asking to go through. When approaching horses head-on, stop and move off the trail (below it if on a slope) to let them go by. Skidding down steep sections and around corners causes trail damage. Riding off the trail is not allowed in the parks—although it is so much work that few mountain cyclists care to do it anyway.

RECREATIONAL GUIDEBOOKS

Ambrosi, Joey (1984) *Hiking Alberta's Southwest* Douglas and McIntyre, Vancouver. Much-needed guide to the eastern slope south of Kananaskis Country. Photos, maps, trail profiles; 166 pages.

Beers, Don (1981) *The Magic of Lake O'Hara* Rocky Mountain Books, Calgary. Excellent guide to trails in the Lake O'Hara area of Yoho park.

Boles, Glen; Robert Kruszyna and William Putnam (1979) *The Rocky Mountains of Canada, South* Standard climber's guide to the Rockies between Waterton and the North Saskatchewan River. Illustrations, maps; 473 pages.

Breeze, Ray (1981) *Selected Whitewater in the Canadian Rockies* Ray Breeze. The author's favorite runs between Oldman and Maligne rivers. Maps; 28 pages.

Daffern, Tony and Gillean (1985) *Kananaskis Country Trail Guide* Rocky Mountain Books, Calgary. Photos, maps; 158 pages.

Dodd, J. and G. Helgason (1985) *The Canadian Rockies Access Guide* Lone Pine, Edmonton. An interesting compendium of things do, from touristy stuff to back-country adventures, in Banff and Jasper national parks. Day hikes, mostly, with condensed information on wildlife, fishing, boating, cycling, cross-country skiing, trail-running and something the authors define as "rock-scrambling." Illustrated, 335 pages.

Edwards, Barry and Ken Uyeda (1983) *Banff Naturguide* Blackbird Naturgraphics, Calgary. Folded sheet summarizing natural and cultural features in and near Banff townsite. Maps, diagrams, drawings, text.

Edwards, J. Gordon (1976) *A Climber's Guide to Glacier National Park* Mountain Press, Missoula. Maps, drawings; 188 pages.

Helgason, Gail and John Dodd (1984) *Bicycle Alberta* Lone Pine Publishing, Edmonton. Careful descriptions of 69 tours in the province, including many in the Rockies. Advice for cyclists, list of clubs, tour organizers, shops; 240 pages.

Kallen, Urs (1977) *A Climber's Guide to Yamnuska* Urs Kallen, Calgary. 43 routes on the most popular cliff in the Canadian Rockies; 44 pages, illustrated.

Kunelius, Rick and Dave Biederman (1981) *Ski Trails in the Canadian Rockies* Summerthought, Banff. The definitive guide for skiing the trails of the Banff, Jasper, Kootenay and Yoho national parks, with good information in the front on equipment and safety. Illustrated, maps, 183 pages.

MacDonald, Janice (1985) *Canoeing Alberta* Lone Pine, Edmonton. Covers the eastern slope between Waterton and Grande Cache; includes whitewater runs. Photos, maps, hydrographic charts; 240 pages.

Martin, John (1985) *Sloping Climbs* John Martin, Calgary. Rockclimbs on tilted limestone slabs between Ribbon Creek in Kananaskis Country and Canmore. Maps, climbing topos; 23 pages.

Nelson, Bob (1982) *The Prince George and District Trail Guide* Caledonia Ramblers. Popular hikes on the western slope between Valemount and Pine Pass. Maps; 56 pages.

Nelson, Dick and Sharon (1978) *Short Hikes and Strolls in Glacier National Park* Tecolote Press, Glenwood, New Mexico. Photos, maps; 47 pages.

Norheim, B. (1982) *Prince George and District Cross-Country Ski Trails* Sons of Norway Skitouring Club, Prince George. Popular trails on the western slope between Valemount and Smithers (the Rockies between Valemount and Pine Pass). Maps, survival information, 25 pages.

Oltmann, Ruth (1978) *The Kananaskis Valley Hikers' and X-C Skiers' Guide* Ribbon Creek Publishing, Seebe, AB. Popular routes near the Ribbon Creek Hostel, which Ruth Oltmann looked after for many years. Maps, photos, index, 68 pages.

Parks Canada (1983) *Cross-country Skiing: Nordic Trails in Banff National Park* Environment Canada. Routes recommended by Parks Canada, with maps; 32 pages.

Patton, Brian (1975) *Parkways of the Canadian Rockies: an Interpretive Guide to Roads in the Mountain Parks* Summerthought, Banff. Descriptions of roadside features in Banff, Jasper, Yoho and Kootenay parks. Roadlogs, maps, photos; 192 pages.

—— and Bart Robinson (1986) *The Canadian Rockies Trail Guide* Summerthought, Banff. Covers Waterton, Banff, Jasper, Kootenay, Yoho, Mt. Assiniboine and Mt. Robson parks. The original and best, newly revised; photos, maps, index; 363 pages.

Perry, Chris (1980) *Ghost River Rockclimbs* Chris Perry, Calgary. Guidebook to the mountain-front cliffs north of Yamnuska Mountain, between Orient Point and Devil's Head. Annotated drawings; 20 pages.

Putnam, William; Robert Kruszyna and Chris Jones (1974) *Climber's Guide to the Rocky Mountains of Canada—North* American Alpine Club/Alpine Club of Canada. Covers the Rockies north of North Saskatchewan River. Photos, maps; 259 pages.

Reese, Rick (1981) *Montana Mountain Ranges* Montana Magazine, Helena. Non-technical description of Montana ranges, including Glacier National Park and the Whitefish Range. Photos (including a satellite photo of Montana); 96 pages.

Root, John, et al. (1981) *Rocky Mountain Landmarks* Hosford, Edmonton. Two-page descriptions of selected natural features and topics in Banff, Jasper, Yoho and Kootenay parks. Photos, maps, diagrams; 128 pages.

Ruhle, George (1976) *Roads and Trails of Waterton-Glacier National Parks* John Forney, Minneapolis. The two parks in great detail. Photos, maps, peak-finder diagrams; 164 pages.

Savage, Brian and Margaret Barry (1985) *Ski Alberta* Lone Pine, Edmonton. Includes some areas not covered in *Ski Trails of the Canadian Rockies*: Waterton and the area south of Crowsnest Pass, Kananaskis Country and Switzer Provincial Park (near Hinton). Emphasis on short, easy tours. The park-maintained loops in Banff and Jasper are also covered, as are Alberta downhill ski areas. Illustrated, maps, 239 pages.

Seibel, Roberta and Barbara Blair (1979) *Motorist's Guide to Glacier National Park* Glacier Natural History Association. Road logs, photos; 49 pages.

Sole, Albi (1980) *Waterfall Ice* Rocky Mountain Books, Calgary. Illustrated guide to 90 routes in the Canadian Rockies between Waterton and Grande Cache.

Spohr, Greg (1976) *Selected Climbs in the Canmore Area* Alpine Club of Canada. 40 routes, mostly rockclimbing, along the TransCanada Highway between the mountain front and Banff, centred on the Alpine Club's Canmore clubhouse.

Spring, Vicky and Gordon King (1982) *95 Hikes in the Canadian Rockies* Douglas and McIntyre, Vancouver. Covers Banff, Kootenay and Mt. Assiniboine parks. Photos, good route diagrams; 224 pages.

Toft, Murray (1981) *Banff Rock Climbs* Murray Toft, University of Calgary. 45 routes in the Banff area, with photos and topo diagrams; 97 pages.

—— (1984) *High and Dry: Alpine Huts of the Canadian Rockies* Druid Mountain Enterprises, Calgary. Names most mountain huts in the Rockies between Crowsnest Pass and Mt. Robson and gives directions to them. Photos, maps and diagrams; 84 pages.

Urbick, Dee and Vicky Spring (1983) *94 Hikes in the Northern Canadian Rockies* Douglas and McIntyre, Vancouver. Covers Yoho, Jasper, Mt. Robson and Willmore Wilderness parks. Photos, good route diagrams; 223 pages.

Yandell, Michael (1974) *National Parkways Photographic and Comprehensive Guide to Glacier & Waterton Lakes National Parks* World-wide Research and Pubiishing, Casper, Wyoming. Not comprehensive, but with large full-color photos accompanying naturalist's information and road logs.

Keeping yourself together
Mountain dangers, mountain safety, first aid and navigation

Every Canadian has the right to become sunburned, blistered, bug-chewed, frostbitten, lightning-struck, bear-mauled and killed in his or her national park. (We extend this right to visitors from other countries.) So if you are intent on coming to grief in the Canadian Rockies, no one is going to stop you. But if you would like to walk this country in safety and comfort, then read on.

The main message: *think as you go.*

We humans live by our wits. Physically unimpressive, we can still survive nearly anywhere by figuring out what to eat, what to wear, where to find shelter and—equally important—what *not* to do. Success in the Canadian Rockies is no different. If you keep your brain in gear, you are going to be okay.

For example, outwitting a great big icy mountain is not particularly difficult. We are a lot smarter than it is. So if we wish to climb it we give the matter some thought, find out what others who have climbed it recommend, prepare our bodies for the task and gather the necessary gear. Clever and cautious, we practice on small mountains first. Then, when we know what we're doing, we go for the big one. We tread carefully up, protecting ourselves with rope in places where a fall would break our fragile bodies. We insulate our nakedness with layers of feathers and animal hair and plastic as we climb higher, to the land where the wind sticks its cold fingers under our shirts even in summer. We stand on the summit and smile, magically saving the scene in our cameras, then tread carefully back down again, unscathed, to our horribly dangerous automobiles.

AVOIDING TROUBLE IN THE MOUNTAINS

1. Approach new places and new activities cautiously.

   Accidents often happen to people who are new to the mountains and get carried away with what the Rockies offer—"Wow! I'm going up there, Wilma!"—such that they literally get carried away later. If you are a novice at mountain travel, it is wise to limit yourself at first to well-traveled trails not far from civilization. These are the safer places. Later, when you understand the lay of the land, you will be competent enough to travel off the beaten track safely.

2. When you are headed off on something potentially risky—a hike off established trails, for example—go with other people, not alone, and be sure that the organizer/leader is someone whom you *know* to be able and experienced.

   If you don't know the group leader, then do some checking beforehand. Who is this person? Is he reliable? Or does he have a reputation for generating fiascos? Most of the nasty experiences I have had in the mountains were the result of relying on poor judgment and bad advice. Trips put on by large clubs and schools are particularly subject to screw-ups of this sort, for the participants seldom know the people with whom they entrust their lives.

   The best approach to learning your way around the mountains is to join a small, experienced group with a good reputation. Go with them on several outings. If you do well, you will soon become one of the gang. The next-best approach is to book trips with respected organizations or guides and pay for competent leadership. Outdoor-skills courses offered by several organizations in the Rockies area are good training; there is a list on page 787.

3. Carry enough creature comforts and technological goodies to beat the weather, to take care of thirst and hunger, to keep from getting lost, and to deal with minor injuries or make temporary repairs to equipment.

Avoiding trouble   813

A couple may intend to walk for an hour, carrying no jackets, no water, no lunch, no sunburn cream, no insect repellent, no map and no matches. Yet, because they are having fun, they push on and on. Eventually they find themselves 10 km from the car, above timberline, drenched in a cold and frightening thunderstorm.

This is unpleasant but seldom fatal; a common experience hereabouts. Lots of people who stride unprepared into these hills are quickly humbled, having discovered that the Canadian Rockies are tougher than they look. Next time these folks come prepared, more knowledgeable and better-equipped—and they enjoy themselves, snug in their warm jackets, eating their lunches in comfort as they wait out the storm under the big overhang that the guidebook mentioned.

Things get serious when the unpleasantness gets out of hand: the blisters become more painful and the steps slower, there is nothing in the pack left to eat, there is nothing to drink, the body is running out of fuel, the rain turns to snow, the slope steepens, lightning hits close by, the mind panics, the body starts to run, the ankle twists . . . and they read about you in the papers.

IF AN ACCIDENT SHOULD OCCUR . . .

Remember: keep cool, assess the situation before acting, reassure the victim, and above all don't endanger yourself. Congratulate yourself on having taken a first-aid course recently (readers who haven't should do so).

IF YOU HAVE TO GO FOR HELP . . .

Always remember the following:

1. Determine exactly where the victim will be found. Look around, identify the landmarks, and describe the place to yourself so you can describe it to the rescuers. You may not be able to go back with them.

2. Stay long enough to determine as fully as possible the nature of the injured person's condition. This will help in mounting the rescue. If possible, write these things down and carry the note with you.

3. Be careful on your way out. Hurrying can cause another mishap.

STORMS AND LIGHTNING

A warm rain is unheard-of in the Canadian Rockies; the stuff comes down cold, quickly chilling unprepared people caught outdoors. So carry a waterproof rain jacket in the summer, even if the weather looks good. And a sweater if you are going above timberline. Alpine-zone squalls are windy, carrying rain mixed with snow—a nasty combination that can sweep in quite suddenly, catching hikers off guard. For the results, read the section on hypothermia (page 820). In spring and fall, alpine-style weather reaches down to the valley bottoms.

The **thunderstorm** season here is July and (especially) August. Lightning is most common over the front ranges and least common over the main-range icefields. Occasionally we get thunderstorms from the east, but only a few times in a summer.

The usual situation is to come over the crest of a ridge from the east to find a squall line moving in quickly from the west. Down, boy! It pays to keep an eye on the clouds north and south of you; even though it may be clear overhead, evidence of a general buildup elsewhere means that there is probably something nasty bearing down that you can't see—yet. There is one sure way of telling whether the clouds starting to stream over are tugging in an electrical horror: carry a pocket radio and tune it between stations. Popping and crackling will be caused by you-know-what.

Lightning is so common in the mountains that you would think climbers and hikers would come to ignore it, but not so. Most of us have lived through several close calls, during which we have felt like flies about to be swatted, and thus we try to avoid future encounters.

So when wispy strands of rain are starting to hang down from the cumulus clouds, or you can see a blue-black wall of cloud approaching, it is prudent to head back down to timberline. Caught in the open, get at least a hundred metres down from the crest of a ridge or the top of a mountain.

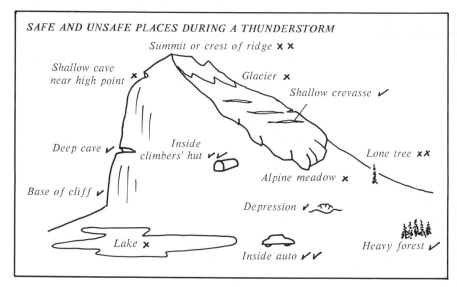

SAFE AND UNSAFE PLACES DURING A THUNDERSTORM

Summit or crest of ridge ✗ ✗

Shallow cave near high point ✗

Glacier ✗

Shallow crevasse ✔

Deep cave ✔

Inside climbers' hut ✔✔

Lone tree ✗✗

Base of cliff ✔

Alpine meadow ✗

Depression ✔

Lake ✗

Inside auto ✔✔

Heavy forest ✔

There are two kinds of relatively safe places in the high country: low spots or depressions without tall rocks or trees nearby, and the bases of cliffs. Squat in such places, keeping your contact with the ground small so as to get the minimal dose of ground currents, which spread out within a 30-m radius of a strike. At a cliff base, you should move out a few metres from the rock to avoid currents traveling over the surface in a close blast; like a lightning rod, which protects a cone-shaped area under it, the cliff above will take the stroke.

Places to avoid: stands of trees in open, flat or gently sloping places (sheltering under a lone tree is statistically quite stupid) and shallow concavities in cliffs (where current running through the rock can take a shortcut through your body).

Metal alone does not attract lightning, so theoretically it is not necessary to place your ice axe, pack frame and so on at a distance—but touching these items during a close strike can give you burns, as can coins and a knife in your pants pockets, or metal watches and jewelry. Caught in a risky spot during an electrical storm, I get metal items off my body.

Deep woods, with many trees, are statistically safe (unless you are standing under the tallest tree in the woods), as are rock shelters deep enough to keep you well out of the rain. Stay a metre away from the walls. Climber's huts above timberline are protected from lightning by metal cables running over their roofs or by the metal skin of some such huts. You are safe inside, protected by the **Faraday-cage effect:** electricity will pass through the metal rather than the air within the structure. Same with a metal-roofed automobile.

Should someone in your party receive a jolt, be sure that this person is breathing properly afterward and has a steady heartbeat. If knocked unconscious, the victim will probably need mouth-to-mouth resuscitation (page 818).

AVALANCHES

Avalanches are slides of snow. Some people refer to rockslides as "avalanches," but this isn't correct. In the Canadian Rockies a few people die each winter in avalanches, along with a fair bit of wildlife (mountain goats are especially endangered by avalanches). Human losses have been mounting lately in the Columbia Mountains, just west of the Rockies, where helicopter-assisted skiing is putting the powder-hounds into steep-and-deep country that has killed up to a dozen at a time.

It is easy to avoid avalanches: don't go to the mountains. But for oromaniacs like me, life is inordinately dull elsewhere, so we have had to learn something about staying alive in avalanche country. Herewith some advice, intended mostly for cross-country skiers.

Even a moderate ski trail in the Canadian Rockies seems always to cross one or two **avalanche tracks.** Usually, these are pretty obvious: you break out of the woods into a bare strip that reaches well up the mountain, often into a gully capped by a **cornice:** an overhanging mass of wind-driven snow built out from the leeward side of a ridge. Often there will be small, bent-over and stripped-looking trees in the track, and if an avalanche has come down already that winter the lumpy, over-deep snow remains as evidence.

Rule: only one person should cross an avalanche track at a time. On wide ones, where solo crossings would use up too much time, the party should space themselves well apart. If the track is steep (over 20°), consider the avalanche warning signs given next before crossing it at all.

The most dangerous time is the 24 hours following a heavy snowfall (20 cm or more), before the stuff has settled. Early-winter snowfalls are quite dangerous in this way, especially at high-subalpine levels—where the best skiing is, of course. November and December storms often dump copiously on grassy slopes that avalanche easily. Beware of Parker Ridge and Bow Summit, popular early-season skiing spots along the Icefields Parkway. There have been fatalities here on innocent-looking slopes.

Signs that the snow is unstable: the settling sound (a dull "whoomph" spreading from under your skis), and cracks on the downhill side of boulders and groups of trees, where the snow is pulling away. Poke your ski pole down, basket first. If you encounter increasing resistance all the way, and the other signs are good, then probably the snow is stable. If your basket passes through zones of sudden give, weak layers exist that can form sliding planes. On a slope I'm unsure of, I test the snow with my pole every few metres.

Places to avoid in unstable conditions: any slope of over 30°, especially leeward slopes that are convex (avalanches frequently start from such bulges) and any spot threatened by a cornice.

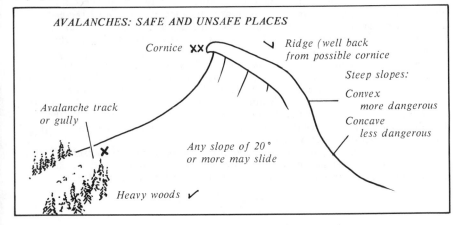

AVALANCHES: SAFE AND UNSAFE PLACES

Cornice **xx**

Ridge (well back from possible cornice

Steep slopes:

Convex
    more dangerous
Concave
    less dangerous

Avalanche track
or gully

Any slope of 20°
or more may slide

Heavy woods ✔

Ridgecrests offer avalanche-free routes in poor conditions, but they present another danger: you may be walking on a cornice, treading over thin air. Cornices are seldom obvious from the upwind side and they can break off anytime—or you can simply fall through. A friend of mine was killed this way, by falling unroped through a cornice on the summit of Mt. Assiniboine. I make it a habit to keep at least 10 m back from ridgelines if I can't see both sides.

On one trip a cornice let go above us. It seemed a safe distance away, but the avalanche that resulted ended at our ski tips. On another trip, a helicopter passed low overhead while I was crossing a steep gully. The vibration knocked off a cornice at the top. The gully avalanched, but there was a flattening in it just above our crossing point that stopped the slide. Whew.

On the eastern slope, **depth-hoar buildups** are frequent causes of avalanche accidents. Depth hoar is a layer of loose grains at the base of the snowpack. Other terms are more descriptive: "sugar snow" and "rotten snow."

This is snow that has recrystallized from the ground up. The greater the temperature difference between the soil and the air, the faster it develops and the thicker the depth-hoar layer gets. A long stretch of cold, clear weather can rot the entire snowpack, which is bad news for skiers. There is no firmness (no "base"), so skiing off the trails or outside the ski areas means constantly breaking through to your knees. Depth hoar also slides quite easily and makes any slope at an angle greater than 20° avalanche-prone.

In 1973, while skiing up the trail to Stanley Glacier (near Vermilion Pass), a friend and I noted depth hoar over a metre deep, and settling all around us. But it lay deceptively under a solid layer that supported our weight. As we approached timberline, a long sighing sound indicated that a big depth-hoar avalanche had let go on the steep slope just ahead (most avalanches crack or rumble; depth-hoar avalanches swish along almost silently). Emerging from the trees, we saw the last movements of a slide a kilometre wide and a kilometre long. On that slope there had been a party of four inexperienced skiers. Unaware, they had ventured out in the face of terrible danger. Two of them died.

With the beginning of April, skiers must be wary of **climax avalanches,** especially on the western slope, where the valleys are deep and the avalanche chutes are long. A climax avalanche is the main one of the year in any particular chute. It involves the whole thickness of the snow, right down to the ground (or to the ice on a steep glacier). Such slides can come earlier in the proper conditions, and they continue through June and into July at higher elevations, but after April most cross-country skiers quit for the season anyway because the snow becomes wet and hard to wax for.

Park wardens and ski patrollers seem obsessed with avalanches—as well they might, for they are the ones who have to recover the twisted, suffocated victims. Parks Canada wardens assess the avalanche hazard regularly through the winter by digging pits in the snow and doing various measurements and tests, the details of which are beyond the scope of this book. The experts know of what they speak; before heading into the high country in winter, get the latest avalanche forecast and heed the warnings.

IN CASE OF AVALANCHE . . .

If someone is buried, and the party on the surface is small (two or three), all should stay and search for a while. Consider the possibility that another slide may come down while you are absorbed in the rescue. Keep an eye on what is above, and if the situation looks very dangerous, leave the area before you, too, become a victim.

If the group was carrying avalanche beacons, *be sure* you switch yours to receive. Forgetting to switch over to receive is common during the tension of an emergency.

There isn't space here to describe how to track down the transmitting victim, so be sure to practice the technique. Wear that wonderful gadget *close* to your body, not slung over your clothes or carried in your pack.

If a victim was not wearing a beacon, note where he was last seen and search below that point for the victim's hat, ski poles, skis, pack or anything else that might have come off. *If you find something, don't touch it. Leave it there, and mark the location with a ski or a pole.*

Check very carefully downhill from anything you find, probing suspected spots with ski poles (pull the baskets off) in hope of finding the buried person(s) quickly.

If a half-hour search turns up no sign, then it is time to send one person for help (two if the party is larger). Send out fast, strong skiers, for chances of survival under the snow fade quickly after a half-hour.

Those remaining on the scene should continue the search. Thoroughly check the whole slide downhill from where the tracks entered it, then begin probing systematically. Stand shoulder to shoulder and probe uphill, one short step at a time, starting at the toe of the slide directly below the last-seen point and working uphill.

- Don't probe systematically going downhill (your steps will be too long).

- Don't piss in the slide, or drop cigarette butts, food wrappers or anything else human into the snow nearby. These things tend to confuse a rescue dog, as will touching an item of a victim's.

- When the victim is found, uncover the head first. If he is unconscious, check for breathing. If there is no apparent breathing (chest does not rise and fall, pair of glasses held over mouth does not fog), begin mouth-to-mouth resuscitation (see below) immediately, while the others free the victim's chest. Check for injuries. Hypothermia is likely (see page 820).

MOUTH-TO-MOUTH RESUSCITATION

Tilt the head gently back to open the airway. Clear the mouth and upper throat of any obstructions (snow, food). Pinch the victim's nostrils closed and place your mouth over the victim's mouth.

Breathe out vigorously one time, filling the victim's lungs enough to see the chest rise. If something is blocking the airflow, check the airway again and clear it. If the chest rises, remove your mouth and let the air expel naturally. If it doesn't, press the chest down to force the air out.

Repeat about 12 times per minute. For children, the rate is 20 times per minute and the breaths should be shallower to prevent damage to a child's small lungs. For infants, breathe in small puffs. On a small face, cover both the nose and the mouth with your mouth.

While you are doing the resuscitation, get someone to check for heartbeat (listen to the chest). As long as a heartbeat is detected, no matter how faint, continue with resuscitation. It may be an hour or more before the victim can breathe on her/his own. To detect a faint heartbeat, remove the victim's shirt and press your ear onto the bare chest, just left—victim's left—of centre.

If the heart has stopped, and someone in the group is practiced at CPR (cardio-pulmonary resuscitation), then try this. But be *sure* that there is no heartbeat, and that the person doing CPR is well-practiced, for improperly applied CPR can be damaging.

STOPPING HEAVY BLEEDING

This is caused by a cut artery. First, try putting pressure directly on the wound. Don't wait to dig a bandage out of the first-aid kit; use anything handy: a handkerchief, a glove—even your bare hand. This will usually stop the bleeding in a few minutes, at which point you can tape a sterile compress over the wound, putting it on fairly tightly (but not so tightly as to cut off downstream circulation).

If pressure from a compress doesn't stop the bleeding, then a major artery has been cut. The victim may die quickly from loss of blood. Apply strong pressure with the fingers, searching for the spot that stops the flow. When you find it, *keep the pressure on,* trading off with someone else when your hand tires. If there are just two of you, the victim may be able to help. Once the flow is under control, search the wound for the end of the artery. If you can find it, and there is enough sticking out to tie it closed with something (some thread from your repair kit, a pair of tweezers clamped on and tied shut, a twist tie from a plastic bag) you may save the victim's arm or leg.

If gushing cannot be stopped or reduced to a trickle with direct pressure and/or tying off the artery, then find a wide strap or cord (a belt will do) and a stick to make a **tourniquet** (see diagram). You must leave the tourniquet on until the victim reaches hospital, loosening it just a little from time to time to see if enough clotting has occurred to stop the bleeding. While it is tight, the tourniquet stops all circulation in the limb, killing it in time and necessitating amputation later. So use a tourniquet only as a last resort, to prevent bleeding to death.

TOURNIQUET

Use only if direct pressure fails to control bleeding.

Wrap belt or rolled-up shirt twice around injured limb above the wound.

Tie half a knot, place a stick on the knot and tie a square knot snugly above the stick. Twist to tighten the strap until blood flow stops. Tie end of stick to limb to keep tourniquet tight.

Heavy bleeding causes **shock**: the effect of blood loss on the heart and brain. Shock produces paleness, cool skin, thirst and a weak pulse, followed if blood loss is great by confusion, stupor, coma and death. A person who has lost more than a litre of blood will probably show signs of shock. Treatment: the victim should lie down, with head slightly lower than hips and legs raised 25-30 cm to allow blood in extremities to reach major organs more easily. Keep the victim warm, giving him hot drinks and warming him externally (as per hypothermia, page 820) if shock is severe. It is okay to give painkillers; the relaxing effect is beneficial. But nothing alcoholic.

HEAD INJURIES

A knock on the head hard enough to cause unconsciousness often creates a **concussion**: the tearing of small blood vessels on the surface of the brain. A pool of blood forms between the brain and the skull, usually (but not always) at the point of impact, putting pressure on the brain and causing the following symptoms:

- Confusion. Victim asks same question over and over.

- Upset stomach, often with vomiting.

- Unequally dilated pupils.

- Return of unconsciousness, a sign the concussion is worsening and that the victim may not survive.

There is no field treatment for concussion. Since it comes on gradually, watch anyone who has suffered a head injury for symptoms and head for the hospital at the first sign.

MOUNTAIN SICKNESS

Symptoms: nausea, headache and weakness caused by an inadequate supply of oxygen to the brain.

Although the proportion of oxygen in the atmosphere (20 percent) is nearly the same from sea level to 8000 m (height of the Himalayas), the low pressure of the atmosphere at high elevations makes it difficult for the body to extract enough oxygen from the air. Some people can function atop Mt. Everest without breathing bottled oxygen (although humans cannot live higher than 6000 m above sea level without steady deterioration), while others may feel queasy at 2500 m. Mountain sickness symptoms often start at 3000-3500 m, elevations typical for summits in our area—so mountain sickness is a climber's problem here, not a hiker's.

General rule: as long as you are not feeling sick to your stomach you can go higher, but cautiously; once you are nauseous the only thing to do is to go back down, or probably you will soon be sitting in the snow throwing up. Keep moving down, even though you won't want to walk, until you feel better. Losing only a couple of hundred metres in elevation can bring a big improvement.

If you find that you are susceptible to mountain sickness, then the thing to do is **acclimate** yourself: increase the concentration of red blood cells in your body and increase the efficiency of your heart and lungs by spending as much time as possible at elevations just below those that make you sick. Research on Mt. Rainier has shown that drinking plenty of water helps (several litres over the course of the day, with copious pee production), and there is some evidence that taking antacid tablets helps, too.

HYPOTHERMIA

Definition: failure of the body to produce enough heat to keep the inner organs at the proper temperature.

This used to be known as "exposure," as in "He died of exposure." The usual cause is fatigue and hunger coupled with inadequate insulation (wet clothing, not wearing enough clothing) and sometimes complicated by drinking alcohol, which accelerates heat loss. Skinny people are more susceptible to hypothermia than fat people are. The condition often strikes near the end of a long, wet day at higher elevations, when everyone is tired and soaked and the temperature is near freezing. Surprisingly, it's just as common in summer as it is in winter—perhaps more so. In winter, people dress warmly; in summer they often dress lightly and don't carry enough extra clothing.

When you are very tired and/or hungry and thirsty, your metabolic furnace is not burning as hot as usual. In warm surroundings this is not a serious condition; you eat, drink, sleep and feel better. But when the surroundings are cold—and they needn't be very cold, for hypothermia can occur at temperatures well above freezing—and when there is no rest in sight and no food in the tummy, then the body cannot produce enough heat to overcome the steady loss and hypothermia results.

The body's first defense is to slow the circulation in the hands and feet. This decreases heat flow from the extremities, which helps to maintain the temperature of the internal organs—the body core. If you know you are tired, and your hands and feet are getting cold, then put on your jacket, pull up your hood—do whatever you can to avoid further chilling. Moving more quickly will generate more heat and get you back home sooner. Shivering is a sign of incipient hypothermia. The result of millions of years of mammal evolution, this response gives the furnace a vigorous stoke; it is intended to get you through the episode before the fire flickers out.

Normal body-core temperature is 37 °C. At 37-35 °C shivering starts. At 35-34 °C there is obvious uncoordination (sluggish pace, apathy). At 34-32 °C there is stumbling and inability to use the hands. At 32-30 °C severe hypothermia sets in. Shivering stops; the victim can no longer walk. He is confused, irrational, helpless. At 30-28 °C death is close: victim is barely conscious, with dilated pupils; is barely breathing; has practically no heartbeat. At 28 °C the heartbeat stops.

Obviously, the idea is to keep the situation from going beyond the shivering stage.

If someone in your group is cold and tired, watch him for these symptoms: a fatigued look and irritability, followed by shivering, dullness and inattentiveness. Be alert for signs of hypothermia and do something about it *before* you note poor coordination (fumbling with pack straps, staggering). If the shivering stops but the victim doesn't brighten up, he is in big trouble.

At the first sign of hypothermia, consider how far it is to the car, the cabin or the tent. If it is only an hour or two at the most, call a short halt. Be sure that any victim is wearing the warmest, driest clothing available. A soaked sweater, for example, might be replaced by a dry one or by a warm jacket if there is an extra available. Cover the victim's head. Make the victim eat *and drink* something (dehydration is a contributor to hypothermia) and then *get him moving as quickly as possible toward home.* He may not be very cooperative, saying something like "I'm okay; leave me alone." But that person is *not* okay and needs help.

If the victim cannot walk any farther and you have no camping gear, find a sheltered spot and *build a fire* for warmth. Use the brown needles of evergreens as tinder; they burn explosively when dry and can even be coaxed into flaming when wet. Add small twigs at first, gradually building the fire up until it is large and throwing off plenty of heat. Get the victim to stand beside it, removing layers of clothing and thus allowing the heat to penetrate. Use the fire to dry out the clothing.

If you haven't brought matches, or your fire fails, make an all-out effort to reach civilization. The victim's life probably depends on it. If he comes to a halt and cannot be cajoled or shouted into continuing, and you are still in good condition, it might be best to go for help. Most people can take several hours of severe hypothermia before they die.

Suppose the worst: going for help is not possible, there just isn't enough clothing to keep warm and you can't build a fire. You still have a chance. Break off evergreen boughs (the driest ones are those near the ground) and quickly build a nest in a sheltered spot, perhaps under another evergreen. Put down a thick layer of boughs, for insulation against the cold ground, and another thick layer over you and victim. Open your clothing to get skin-to-skin contact. Huddle and rest, eating any food you have.

If you are hiking or skiing in the back-country and have camping gear with you, *get a tent up when you notice an attack of hypothermia*—assuming that other measures have failed (changing into dry clothing, eating, moving faster). Get the victim inside, undressed and into a sleeping bag (wet clothing will only delay the recovery). Prepare a hot, sugary drink.* Give this to the person and note the response. If he brightens up, the emergency is over. Feed the grateful victim and allow enough rest before moving on. It is often wise to simply camp on the spot.

But if a cup of hot chocolate taken while in a dry sleeping bag doesn't do the trick, then the victim cannot generate enough heat on his own. Someone will have to *strip down and get in the sleeping bag with the victim,* warming him by skin-to-skin contact. This works very well. Never mind the social taboos.

A word of warning: do not try to rewarm a victim of severe hypothermia *rapidly.* For example, a comatose person dragged into a mountain hut should not be stripped and laid out in front of the stove. This can kill him, for cold, acidic,

---

*Non-alcoholic drinks only. Alcohol worsens hypothermia.

poorly oxygenated blood in the extremities will move into the heart, causing fibrillation (random twitching of the heart muscle) and death. Instead, it is better to put that person in a sleeping bag and surround him with more insulation, then try to get him to drink warm liquids (be careful not to choke him) so the body temperature rises internally. Be gentle in handling the victim; jolts can bring on fibrillation. At the same time, someone should go for the helicopter. The victim will probably get no worse than he already is, and once in hospital he can be rewarmed internally by using a heart-lung machine.

Apparently dead victims have recovered from severe hypothermia, even when the heart has stopped for several hours. As it says in *Medicine for Mountaineering,* "No one should be considered cold and dead until he has been warm and dead." (Wilkerson, 1985)

In the Canadian Rockies we frequently have a rash of hypothermia cases during the week-long summer drizzles that are caused by upslope weather (see page 253). The sun doesn't shine and the air is very cool—often just above freezing for days on end. Hikers in the back-country find themselves in trouble when all their clothing is wet and they can't dry it. In really miserable conditions above timberline it is not even possible to start a fire to warm up and dry out.

Prevention: bring several plastic garbage bags to keep your sleeping bag, spare clothing and whatnot out of the wet. A good, leak-proof tent and a cooker that can be fired up inside it (ignoring in this case the reasons for not running a cooker in a tent) can get you out of a jam. Make sure the tent door is partly open, for adequate ventilation.

FROSTBITE

Frostbite is the killing of cells caused by the freezing of body fluids. You *cannot* become frostbitten at temperatures above freezing, and you *can* develop frostbite without showing signs of hypothermia. Noses, faces and ears are seldom badly damaged by frostbite, but fingers and toes often are.

Once frostbitten, always susceptible, for the circulation is permanently impaired. So the idea is to *avoid that first encounter*. Wear boots, gloves and clothing warm enough for the lowest temperatures you are likely to encounter. When it is very cold, don't wear metal earrings. Metal-framed glasses can cause frostbite where they touch the skin. The skin of light-colored people becomes quite pink when threatened by frostbite; skin of any color goes pale as it freezes. Amazingly, the face feels little pain when it is being frostbitten. Keep an eye on your companions"s noses, ears and cheeks, looking for telltale white patches.

Feet and hands complain bitterly as they cool. The feet are the most difficult parts to keep warm—and the most awkward for someone else to have to warm for you out of doors—so choose your footwear carefully. For walking or working in the cold, I have found **bush boots** (also called "shoe pacs") to be the best. They have rubber bottoms, leather tops, and thick felt liners that surround the foot. Unlike fabric-topped snowmobile boots or military arctic boots, bush boots can get wet without wetting the insulation within. This is good to know if you have broken through the ice into the creek.

Double-layer mountaineering boots (climbing boots with removable inner boots) are fairly good, but the insulation is not as thick as the average felt liner and the toes don't bend, so they won't keep you as warm as bush boots will. Single-layer mountaineering boots are cold—a factor in the high incidence of frostbite among climbers.

For cross-country skiing at low temperatures, **double ski boots** or loose-fitting single boots with insoles and overboots are usually adequate. Double boots are best for multi-day trips; their outer surfaces are not warmed by body heat and thus these boots don't get wet from snow melting on them.

The toes of cross-country boots bend easily with every step; as long as you keep moving, your feet stay warm at surprisingly low temperatures—even in light, low-cut boots. But when you stop, light boots cool rapidly. I don't recommend them for anything other than short jaunts, not far from the car. See page 798 for more on selecting ski boots for mountain touring.

If your feet are getting cold, *loosen your boots and pick up the pace.* Put on your hat if it isn't on already. Some skiers carry a pair of extra-large wool socks to pull over their boots. These add more comfort than one might imagine.

Always carry a very warm pair of mitts to put on if your hands get cold under the gloves or light mitts that most people wear. Don't take your mitts off and blow on your fingers; this will just make them colder more quickly. Flinging your arms round and round may warm the arm muscles and thus the hands. The best thing for cold hands is the same as for cold feet: ski or walk faster, causing the whole body to heat up.

Many people—especially kids and women—tend to get cold feet and hands at the beginning of a trip. Then their extremities warm up comfortably as they continue to exercise. If your feet or hands have gone numb, be patient. They will most likely warm up soon—although you can expect some pain as they do. If there is no further pain once feeling and warmth have returned, then you haven't been frostbitten.

But if your hands or feet just aren't warming up after an hour or so, *turn around and go home.* You will probably make it back before frostbite occurs.

If you can't do that (it is too far to go, say, or you have been injured), then *take off your gloves or boots and quickly stick your hands or feet under a companion's shirt,* warming your fingers or toes on his bare abdomen.

This feels awfully chilly for the person offering the belly, of course, but it has a wonderfully positive effect on children. You simply take off a kid's mitts and stick his cold hands up under your sweater and onto a large, warm, grown-up tummy. There is some psychology at work, here: the sniveling youngster, his hands becoming more and more painful, realizes that the adults aren't going to let him die after all. Once the pain of warming stops, he feels much better and usually has warm hands for the rest of the day.

I have been on trips in which my feet were miserably cold for days, yet no frostbite resulted. As long as you can feel your toes wiggling, you are okay, no matter how uncomfortable you are.*

But if sensation is lost for many hours, and the pain at rewarming is strong and continues, then you probably have frostbite. Frostbitten flesh is hard and white when frozen; it blisters the day after rewarming and often discolors. As the days go by, the skin peels. Badly frostbitten toes and fingers often become infected and gangrenous if untreated. Frostbite can kill you.

Treatment: warming in a carefully controlled sequence in hospital, where medications can be used to improve circulation and prevent infection. In this way, fingers and toes are seldom lost as they used to be 20 years ago.

So don't attempt to treat frostbite out of doors, or in a mountain hut. Get the victim to hospital. Warming the injured parts above body temperature will damage them further, as will rubbing them. Put the victim in a sleeping bag and keep the frostbitten parts protected from heat.

It is quite possible to ski for days on frozen feet, but often impractical once they thaw (the pain is too severe). So if your toes are really frozen (the skin is hard and white, with no sensitivity, and you can't wiggle the toes), get to civilization before you are disabled. If your feet thaw enroute and you are unable to continue, stay in a protected place (in your sleeping bag, in a tent or cabin) while others go for help; you may be tough enough to walk or ski in spite of the pain, but you will damage the tissues further if you do—and you may get frostbitten all over again, worsening the injury considerably.

---

*Up to a point. Cold feet, especially cold *wet* feet, can be injured by constant blood-vessel constriction and accompanying oxygen deprivation—a condition known mainly in the military, where it is called **trench-foot.**

GIARDIASIS
Folk name: "beaver fever"

Any surface water in the Canadian Rockies is possibly contaminated by *Giardia lamblia*, a protozoan parasite that attaches inside the small intestine and sometimes the gall bladder. It affects most mammals, including humans. It enters streams and lakes as cysts in the feces of a carrier.

Studies in Montana have shown that beavers do indeed carry the parasite there, and the increase in Rocky Mountain beaver populations has been accompanied by an increase in giardiasis. But let us not blame the beaver only. Human population growth in the Canadian Rockies area and the boom in wilderness hiking have sent a great number of people into the back-country. They have also brought their dogs, and man's best friend is a well-known carrier of *Giardia lamblia*.

The organism is not killed by municipal chlorination. Giardiasis outbreaks in Banff and Jasper have prompted these high-profile tourist centres to change from surface water supplies to wells, for *G. lamblia* cysts are naturally filtered out of groundwater. In the late 1970s, between discovery of the problem in Banff and completion of the well system there, sales of beer, wine and soft drinks took a dramatic rise as restaurants stopped serving water with meals.

If you have drunk water contaminated with *Giardia* (or in rarer cases eaten infested food or touched the unclean hands/paws/underwear/bottom of a carrier), the symptoms begin in about 15 days. They include diarrhoea, abdominal cramps, lack of appetite and weakness.

These cover a multitude of illnesses, but giardiasis often shows a couple of additional symptoms that are more diagnostic: soft, yellowish, greasy-looking and very foul feces (caused by a reduced ability to process dairy fats); gas and a bloated feeling in the belly; more-frequent but less-productive trips to the toilet. When a giardia attack is at its height there is often localized pain in the lower abdomen, sharp when stepping down stairs or walking down a steep trail.

It is this kind of abdominal pain that frequently sends a victim to the doctor for treatment of what feels rather like a bladder infection. A stool sample is necessary for firm diagnosis.

Annoying but seldom incapacitating, giardiasis is so common in third-world countries that it is rarely treated there. Some people carry the parasite and hardly notice it. Others (like me) can become miserable with it. Kids are hit harder than adults. In most untreated cases the victim kicks the parasite or develops a tolerance that keeps the symptoms at low levels for years, with occasional flare-ups.

A ten-day course of the anti-protozoan drug *Flagyl* rids the body of *G. lamblia*, but the treatment is tough on the bowels generally. Better to avoid ingestion in the first place.

Prevention: boil for *five minutes* all mountain water used for drinking and washing, or put it through a portable ceramic water-purifying filter (these are now available at many outdoor equipment shops). Treating water with tablets will not kill the cysts; they are resistant to iodine and halizone as well as chlorine.

Further, keep your hands clean in the mountains. Wash them after handling your pets. To slow the spread of the parasite, defecate at least 100 m from any stream or lake and bury your poop.

TREATING MINOR INJURIES

- **Blisters:** prevention is the key to these, the most common injuries in the mountains. As soon as you feel a hot spot, stop and put on a piece of moleskin, Spenco or adhesive tape large enough to cover it well. Too many people keep walking until the hot spot has become a blister, at which point there is little you can do to get relief.

If it is too late, cover the blister with a bandaid to minimize further damage. Taking your sock off when you are not walking will help to dry the loose skin and thus speed callous formation. If you are going to prick a fluid-filled blister, wash it first, flame a needle to reduce the risk of infection and open the blister at the edge.

- **Scrapes and cuts:** for minor ones, with little bleeding and nothing foreign stuck in the injury, just put on a bandaid. For deeper ones, which have bled freely, any bits of dirt or whatever should be picked out, and the wound cleaned with water that has been boiled (but allowed to cool, of course). Cover the injury with a bandage. Antiseptics (iodine, etc.) do more harm than good.

- **Burns:** quickly head for the creek (or nearest cold water) and stick the burned place in for several minutes. This will reduce the degree of injury. Burns infect rather easily, so keep a burn clean. Minor ones heal best if kept exposed to the air. Don't use creams or other ointments on them.

- **Sunburn:** suffer stoically, use a spray-on painkiller or pop some pills. File away under "Lessons learned." There is little you can do for a sunburn, although drinking lots of water will prevent the accompanying dehydration. Prevention is quite easy: wear a hat, put on sunglasses and use a sun-blocking (not sun*tanning*) cream. Go by the PABA number on the container: the larger the number, the better the protection.

  The higher you go up the mountain, the stronger the ultraviolet solar radiation you receive and the faster you burn. Glaciers provide the worst burns; they reflect the light up at you, under your hat, to attack the undersides of your lips, your chin, your ears. Even people with dark tans are usually sunburned after a bright day on a glacier.

  Following a typically dim, soggy spring in the Rockies, the equally typical early-July burst of summer brings with it terrible cases of sunburn. Untanned hikers wander the high country in shorts and no shirt; untanned climbers get up on the glaciers and broil their faces in the first two hours of the day. Bear this in mind: recent study suggests that a common cause of skin cancer is a bad sunburn many years earlier.

- **Insect bites and stings:** see page 466 (mosquito bites), page 475 (bee stings) or page 481 (ticks).

FIRST-AID KIT

My first-aid kit is small, but it has everything I have ever needed in an emergency. Note that many of the items are for repairing broken equipment, which seems to need first aid more often than people do.

- **Moleskin:** several large pieces.

- **Bandaids:** three regular ones, three small ones, a couple of large ones for big scrapes and a butterfly type for a deep cut. Sometimes I carry a large sterile bandage, but it won't fit in the kit and thus often gets left at home. For larger wounds, a pocket handkerchief used only for wiping glasses (not for blowing your nose) will work as a compress—and I have used it that way on a couple of occasions.

- **Adhesive tape,** supposedly for holding on bandages, but used mostly for fixing broken equipment.

- **Some twist ties,** for closing plastic bags or making repairs.

- **Q-tip,** for getting something out of someone's eye, or cleaning grit out of a camera.

- **Aspirin** (or some other painkiller). I pack a dozen Tylenol 3 tablets.

First-aid kit

- **Can opener** (one of those little flat ones) in case someone brought a can of something to eat and forgot an opener.

- **Butane lighter,** in case the one in my pocket quits working, or I forget it.

- **Pack of waterproof matches,** in case the lighter fails.

- **Needle and thread:** heavy needle and dental floss, which makes extra-strong thread. Dental floss can also be used for its intended purpose.

- A couple of **safety pins,** half a metre of **wire** and some **rubber bands,** all for fixing things.

- A piece of **stick-on ripstop-nylon repair material,** to cover holes in down sleeping bags and jackets.

- **Coleman mantles,** for making a hut lamp work. All guests will praise you.

- **A pamphlet on first aid,** for looking up things one might not remember in the crunch. (How can you tell whether a person is in a diabetic coma? What do you do for a person with a broken neck?)

- **Pencil and a couple of filing cards,** for leaving notes or whatever.

- **Money:** a ten-dollar bill and a couple of quarters for making phone calls.

- Not in the kit, but always with me: **pocket knife with scissors and tweezers** on it. My wife packs a tiny knife like this right in her first-aid kit. Some people carry little folding scissors and tweezers.

All these items fit into a small polyethylene freezer container (12 cm by 13 cm by 5 cm). On backpacking trips, I often add an **elastic bandage** (Tensor bandage) for wrapping up a sprained ankle.

Rick Kunelius, who is a Banff park warden, mountain-rescuer and the author of *Ski Trails in the Canadian Rockies,* recommends carrying a couple of external-type sanitary napkins to use as dressings for large wounds, and a pair of pantyhose to use in holding a compress in place (you cut a section from the hose to slip over arm, leg, tummy, head or whatever, holding the compress against the wound). Chic hikers and skiers could wear the pantyhose at formal parties in mountain huts.

HOW TO USE A COMPASS

Be sure to carry a compass on any ski trip that will take you above timberline, or on any mountaineering route that may put you out on a glacier in a whiteout. The clouds can roll in, leaving you a choice of (a) relying on your sense of direction (in my case always a mistake), (b) waiting until the fog lifts (often a reasonable plan, for whiteouts in the Canadian Rockies seldom last more than an hour—although the clouds can sock in for several days at a time on an icefield or (c) following your compass. Many hikers and skiers carry compasses, but few can actually use them, intimidated as they are by maps, declinations and other navigational witchcraft.

Yet following a compass is quite easy. In most situations no numbers are involved, and you don't even need a map. The method explained below can also be applied when bushwhacking through dense forest.

1. Get the compass out *before the fog rolls in* (or before you enter the woods), while you can still see the place you are headed for.

2. Point the compass at your objective, holding the instrument flat so that the needle is free to swivel, not jammed up against the glass.

3. Keeping the compass pointed in the direction you want to go, turn the bezel (the movable ring surrounding the needle) so that the red arrow on it (or the two marks on the bezel in some models) lines up with the compass needle.

4. Check your setting. When you point at your objective with the compass, the needle should line up with the red arrow (or it should lie between the two marks).

5. And away you go, keeping the needle aligned but following the compass, not the needle.

Nine times out of ten, that is all there is to using a compass. There is no need to figure declinations or to get out the map. Just point, turn the bezel, check the setting and stride confidently into the unknown. Keep an eye on what you are walking over, though; you don't want to stride confidently over a cliff or into a crevasse.

The method described above is okay for rough orienteering, but there are times when you may need greater accuracy in following your course. People are inclined to drift off course when holding a compass and trying to go in a straight line. After a couple of kilometres, that drift adds up. So here is how to pass through a whiteout with very little error. One person acts as the **compass-reader,** while another person acts as the **leader:**

- Send the leader forward in the direction of travel. When he reaches the limit of visibility, ask him to stop.

- Sight at the leader with the compass. Is he left or right of the true line? Ask the leader to step left or right to come back onto the true line. Sight again, just to be sure.

- When the leader is on the line, then the compass-reader and the rest of the party ski/walk up to the leader and the process repeats.

This procedure is amazingly accurate. On one trip, we crossed a 4-km stretch of icefield by compass, aiming to hit the gap between two peaks. A couple of hours later we came up against a rocky slope in the fog. The col was snowy, so we figured that we must have erred to right or left. Suddenly the clouds broke and we found that we were on a small nipple of rock sticking up exactly in the centre of the gap!

If **you cannot see your objective,** you must use a topographic map (preferably a 1:50,000-series map) to set a compass course. For this, carry a small protractor and a straight-edge. There is a protractor printed on the inside back cover of this book (poke a small hole in the cover, right where the protractor lines converge, to use it). One edge of the cover can be used for a straight-edge. Some compasses can be used as protractors.

- You don't have to orient the map; just set it on a flat surface. Draw a line on the map between you and the point you want to reach. If you haven't got a pencil, hold the straight-edge on the line during the next step.

- Now use the protractor to measure the angle between the line and true north on the map. Be sure to read the angle in the direction that you will be going, rather than the other way around, or your compass will point from the goal to you rather than from you to the goal (and you could take off in exactly the wrong direction).

   Note: the blue grid-lines on the Canadian government topo maps usually don't align exactly north/south and east/west. That is because they are based on UTM zones, which align with the true directions only on maps that happen to cover the centre of a zone. So you can't rely on the grid to align the protractor for measuring. But sometimes the grid lines are fairly close. You can see *how* close by noting how they converge with the map edges, which are usually true. If the grid is way out, then line up the protractor with something on the map that *is* properly oriented, such as a map edge, a township line, a line of latitude or longitude, or a north-south boundary of some kind.

- Having got the angle of your proposed route, set the bezel on the compass to that angle. But don't start off yet, because you are not quite finished.

- Add or subtract the **magnetic declination** of the compass needle: the number of degrees east or west of true north that the needle points. Magnetic north is not in the same spot on the globe that true north is.

  The declination angle is shown on all Canadian government topo maps. In the central Rockies it is about **25° east.** So you *add* 25° to the setting you just made. Examples: if the angle on the map is 75°, or roughly northeast, then set the compass to 100°. If it is 212°, or roughly southwest, set the compass to 237°. If it is 348°, set it to 13° (having gone round past 360).

- Follow the compass, using the leader/compass-reader method of travel discussed above.

FURTHER READING

Daffern, Tony (1983) *Avalanche Safety for Skiers and Climbers* Rocky Mountain Books, Calgary. The definitive treatment.

Gross, H. et al. (undated) *Mountaineering First Aid and Accident Response* The Mountaineers, Seattle. Pocket-size first-aid manual, small enough to go into a first-aid kit.

LaChapelle, E.R. (1978) *The ABC of Avalanche Safety* The Mountaineers, Seattle. Excellent pocket guide.

Wilkerson, J.A. (1985) *Medicine for Mountaineering* The Mountaineers, Seattle. The standard work on mountain first aid, recently updated.

Four things that people have actually done to pass the time in a small tent on a rainy day:

- *Sat at opposite ends of the tent and talked to each other as if they were using walkie-talkies.*

- *Grabbed the noses of mosquitoes when they stuck them through the netting and held onto them while they buzzed.*

- *Torn pages out of a book, making tiny paper airplanes and flying them in the tent.*

- *Played worms by crawling into their sleeping bags head-first and wiggling around.*

Afterword
Tell them what you've told them

Three hundred thousand words after starting this book, I have learned something about the Canadian Rockies:

> This place is special, unlike any other place on earth.
> So we have to protect it, keep it *wild*.

Most outdoorspeople are now familiar with wilderness ethics—if you packed it in you can pack it out; take only pictures, leave only footprints, etc.—but have you heard the latest argument for preserving wildlands? It is wonderfully convincing: *wilderness pays.*

Forget for a moment the oft-used argument that wildlands are essential islands in a sea of humanity (true though that argument is, and I'll get back to it). This is age of the bottom line, and studies have shown that mountain wilderness is worth far more to the economy as a place for nondestructive forms of recreation than it is as a place for tough-on-the-land activities such as logging, mining, drilling for oil and gas, building roads and so on.

We are speaking of dollars here; income and jobs. You add up the value of everything that can be dragged off or ripped out of a given chunk of real estate, then compare that with what the public would spend over the years to enjoy that chunk in its original state. Surprise! Hands down, it is worth more as wilderness. People put an amazing amount of money into such things as bird books, binoculars, backpacks . . . and especially *vacations,* which are often taken in pretty parts of the outdoors.

Once the loggers and miners and oilmen are allowed in, these places are not very pretty anymore. Hunters and trappers destroy wilderness, too, for they do to the wildlife what the industrialist does to the land. Farmers and ranchers alter the landscape and its natural biota to their own ends. Resort developers take over prime pieces of wildlands and make the rest of us pay to enjoy it, turning mountain meadows into golf courses and forested slopes into ski areas.

The Canadian Rockies haven't much to interest the hard-rock miner (yet), but there are people who want the coal, the natural gas, the trees, the water and the big game. They want more roads, more towns, more hotels, more dams—more of everything human and thus less of everything natural.

But these incredible mountains are *ours.* Most of the Rockies is crown land, belonging to all Canadians. We shouldn't give it away to people who want bits and pieces for themselves. If we do, the Canadian Rockies will look like the American Rockies: full of mines and mills and fences and cows and ski areas and condominiums and roads and jeeps and garbage dumps. Missing: much of the forest, most of the native animals, all of the views that stretch from horizon to horizon without anything manmade for the eye to trip over. Why do so many American visitors show up in the Canadian Rockies each year? They envy what we have, and they ache for what they have lost.

Despite their perennial problems, the *national parks* still have the best record of wilderness protection in Canada. That is because the parks exist for preservation, education and enjoyment, not for that sneaky euphemism "multiple use." Outside the parks, developers find a sympathetic ear at the provincial level, where multiple use is accepted and practiced by the governments of Alberta and British Columbia. What those governments allow in wild parts of their jurisdictions—what they *promote*—is senseless, unconscionable, outrageous. They do not understand.

My conclusion: we Canadians need to get more of our Rockies—far more—under federal control, i.e. inside national-park boundaries.

Currently about 24,000 km^2 are protected, which is only 13 percent of the total. Worse, the zone of protection, which is patchy, ends less than halfway to the north end of the Rockies.

Yet the large-scale *integrity* of the Canadian Rockies is perhaps the region's most striking feature. Nearly 1500 km long, this mountain range has a characteristic style that is consistent from end to end (see page 1). Preserving only a bit here and a bit there, while letting the rest fall to human encroachment, will destroy that integrity. With it will go the marvelous ecosystems that depend on it. Our islands of wilderness must be *large;* large enough to give the big animals enough range; large enough to give the big fish unpolluted water and the big birds an uncluttered sky.

To protect the northern Rockies properly we need large national parks there, and we need them soon. We have perhaps twenty years left before the human tide will have engulfed this place, changing it forever.

My parting message, then, dear Canadian reader, is this. The next time the opportunity presents itself, please take your Member of Parliament aside and whisper in his or her ear the magic phrase "I will vote for you if you will get me some more national parks in the Rockies." I'm sure that a whole lot of mountain goats and wolverines and wildflowers would appreciate it.

Ben Gadd, Naturalist

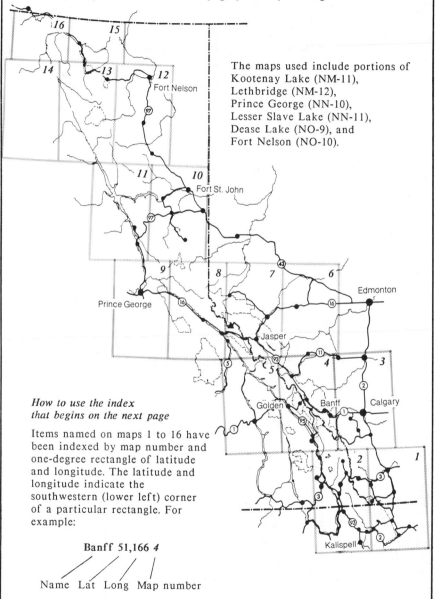

TOPOGRAPHIC MAPS OF THE CANADIAN ROCKIES

Reproduced from the International Map of the World series, 1971, with the permission of Energy, Mines and Resources Canada.

This map shows how the 16 topographic maps fit together.

The maps used include portions of Kootenay Lake (NM-11), Lethbridge (NM-12), Prince George (NN-10), Lesser Slave Lake (NN-11), Dease Lake (NO-9), and Fort Nelson (NO-10).

How to use the index
that begins on the next page

Items named on maps 1 to 16 have been indexed by map number and one-degree rectangle of latitude and longitude. The latitude and longitude indicate the southwestern (lower left) corner of a particular rectangle. For example:

Banff 51,166 *4*

Name Lat Long Map number

Scale bar and key to the hypsometric tint are shown on Map 1.

INDEX TO MAPS

Abraham Lake 52,117 *4*
Akie R. 57,125 *13*
Albreda 52,120 *7*
Aldersyde 50,114 *3*
Alexo 52,116 *6*
Aleza Lake 54,123 *9*
Angusmac 54,123 *11*
Anzac 54,123 *10*
Apgar 48,114 *1*
Arras 55,121 *10*
Assiniboine, Mt. (3618 m)
　50,116 *4*
Athabasca Falls 52,118 *7*
Athabasca R. 52,118 *7*
Attachie 56,122 *10*
Averil, Mt. (1311 m)
　54,123 *9*
Aylmer, Mt. 51,116 *4*

Babb 48,114 *1*
Baldonnel 56,121 *10*
Banff 51,116 *4*
Banff Nat. Park 51,117 *4*
Baptiste R. 52,116 *6*
Barons 49,114 *1*
Bear Flat 56,122 *10*
Beatton Prov Park
　56,121 *10*
Beaver Mines 49,115 *2*
Beaver R. 51,118 *5*
Beavermouth 51,118 *5*
Beazer 49,114 *1*
Belcourt Ck. 54,121 *8*
Belly R. 49,114 *1*
Berland R. 53,118 *7*
Besa R. 57,124 *12*
Big Bend Res. 52,116 *6*
Bigfork 48,115 *2*
Birch Ck. 48,113 *1*
Black Diamond 50,115 *3*
Blackfeet Indian Res.
　48,112 *1*
Blackfoot 48,113 *1*
Blackie 50,114 *3*
Blackstone R. 52,117 *6*
Blairmore 49,115 *2*
Blueberry R. 56,122 *10*
Bond 55,122 *10*
Bottrel 51,115 *3*
Bow Pass (2068 m)
　51,117 *4*
Bow Valley Prov. Park
　51,116 *4*
Bragg Creek 50,115 *3*
Brant 50,114 *3*
Brazeau R. 52,116 *6*
Brazeau, Mt. (3410)
　52,118 *7*
Brisco 50,117 *4*
Brocket 49,114 *1*
Browning 48,114 *1*
Brûle L. 53,118 *7*
Bryce, Mt. (3507 m)
　52,118 *5*
Bull R. 49,116 *2*
Burden, Mt. 56,124 *11*
Burmis 49,115 *2*
Burnt R. 55,123 *10*

Cadomin 53,118 *7*
Calgary 51,115 *3*
Canal Flats 50,116 *2*
Canmore 51,116 *4*
Carbon R. 55,123 *11*
Cardinal R. 52,117 *6*
Cardston 49,114 *1*
Carmangay 50,114 *1*
Castle Ck. 53,121 *8*

Castle Mountain 51,116 *4*
Cataract Mtn 48,114 *1*
Cayley 50,114 *3*
Cecil Lake 56,121 *10*
Champion 50,114 *3*
Chapman, Mt. (3075 m)
　51,119 *5*
Charlie Lake 56,121 *10*
Chetwynd 55,122 *10*
Chin 49,113 *1*
Chown, Mt. (3331 m)
　53,120 *8*
Churchill Pk. 58,126 *13*
Claresholm 50,114 *1*
Clearwater R. 51,116 *4*
Cleveland, Mt. (3194 m)
　48,114 *1*
Cline R. 52,117 *4*
Coal Creek 49,115 *2*
Coal R. 59,128 *16*
Coal River 59,127 *16*
Coaldale 49,113 *1*
Coalhurst 49,113 *1*
Coalspur 53,117 *6*
Cochrane 51,115 *3*
Coleman 49,115 *2*
Columbia Falls 48,115 *2*
Columbia L. 50,116 *4*
Columbia R. 52,119 *5*
Columbia, Mt. (3747 m)
　52,118 *5*
Conrad 48,112 *1*
Copton Ck. 54,120 *8*
Corbin 49,115 *2*
Coutts 49,112 *1*
Cow L. 52,115 *3*
Cowley 49,115 *2*
Cranbrook 49,116 *2*
Cremona 51,115 *3*
Crescent Spur 53,121 *8*
Creston 48,115 *2*
Crimson Lake Prov. Park
　52,116 *6*
Cristina Falls 56,124 *11*
Crooked R. 54,123 *11*
Crooked River
　Prov. Park 54,123 *9*
Crowsnest 49,115 *2*
Crysdale, Mt. (2420 m)
　55,124 *11*
Cut Bank 48,113 *1*
Cut Bank Ck. 48,113 *1*
Cutbank R. 54,119 *7*

Davie 54,123 *9*
Davie L. 54,123 *9*
Dawson Creek 55,121 *10*
Dawson, Mt. (3390 m)
　51,118 *5*
De Winton 50,115 *3*
Del Bonita 49,112 *1*
Deserters, Pk. (2275 m)
　56,125 *13*
Diamond City 49,113 *1*
Dogpound 51,115 *3*
Dome Creek 53,122 *8*
Donald 51,118 *4*
Dunedin, R. 59,125 *15*
Dunster 53,120 *8*
Dupuyero 48,113 *1*

East Glacier Park
　48,114 *1*
East Pine 55,122 *10*
Eddy 53,121 *8*
Edgewater 50,117 *4*
Edith Cavell, Mt.
　(3363 m) 52,119 *7*
Edson 53,117 *6*
Elbow River 50,115 *3*
Elk R. 49,115 *2*

Elko 49,116 *2*
Elkton 51,115 *3*
Embarras R. 53,117 *6*
Ensign 50,114 *3*
Entrance 53,118 *7*
Erith R. 53,117 *6*
Essex 48,114 *1*
Ethridge 48,113 *1*
Eureka 48,116 *2*
Exshaw 51,116 *4*

Fairmont Hot Springs
　50,116 *4*
Farmington 55,121 *10*
Farnham, Mt. (3468 m)
　50,117 *4*
Farrell Ck. 56,122 *10*
Fellers Heights 55,121 *10*
Ferndale 53,123 *9*
Fernie 49,116 *2*
Field 51,117 *4*
Finlay R. 57,126 *13*
Fisher, Mt. (2846 m)
　49,116 *2*
Flathead L. 48,115 *2*
Flathead Nat. For.
　48,114 *1*
Flathead Nat. For.
　48,115 *2*
Flathead Range 48,114 *1*
Flathead River 48,115 *2*
Foothills 53,117 *6*
Forbes, Mt. (3612 m)
　51,117 *4*
Fort Macleod 49,114 *1*
Fort Nelson 58,123 *12*
Fort St. John 56,121 *10*
Fort Steele 49,116 *2*
Fortress L. 52,118 *5*
Fox R. 57,126 *13*
Frances L. 48,113 *1*
Frank L. 50,114 *3*
Fraser R. 53,120 *8*
Frog R. 58,128 *14*
Fryatt, Mt. (3361 m)
　52,118 *7*

Gable Mtn. 54,122 *8*
Gallup City 48,113 *1*
Gataga R. 58,126 *13*
Gething, Mt. (1823 m)
　56,123 *10*
Giscome 54,123 *9*
Glacier Nat. Park, BC
　51,118 *5*
Glacier Nat. Park, MT
　48,114 *1*
Glenwood 49,114 *1*
Goat Mountain 48,114 *1*
Goat R. 53,121 *8*
Golden 51,117 *4*
Goodsir, Mt. 51,117 *4*
Graham R. 56,124 *11*
Grand Haven 56,121 *10*
Grande Cache 53,120 *7*
Granum 49,114 *1*
Grasmere 49,116 *2*
Grayling R. 59,126 *15*
Groundbirch 55,121 *10*

Halfway R. 56,123 *12*
Hallam Pk. (3219 m)
　52,119 *5*
Hamber Prov. Park
　52,118 *5*
Hansard 54,122 *9*
Harrogate 50,117 *4*
Hartell 50,115 *3*
Haworth Falls 57,126 *13*
Head, Mt. (2782 m)
　50,115 *3*
Heart Butte 48,113 *1*

Hector, Mt. (3394 m)
　51,117 *4*
Henri, Mt. 56,125 *11*
Herrick Ck. 54,122 *8*
High River 50,114 *3*
Hill Crest 49,115 *2*
Hill Spring 49,114 *1*
Hinton 53,118 *7*
Holmes R. 53,120 *8*
Hominka R. 54,122 *10*
Hornbeck 53,117 *6*
Hosmer 49,115 *2*
Hudson's Hope 56,122 *10*
Hungry Horse 48,115 *2*
Hungry Horse Res.
　48,114 *1*

Ingenika R. 56,126 *13*
Invermere 50,117 *4*
IR (Indian Reserve)
　1 49,116 *2*
IR　2, AB 49,116 *2*
IR　2, BC 56,125 *13*
IR　3 50,116 *4*
IR　3, Shuswap 50,117 *4*
IR 142, Stony 51,116 *4*
IR 142B 51,115 *3*
IR 143, Stony 51,116 *4*
IR 144, Stony 51,116 *4*
IR 144A 52,117 *4*
IR 145 50,115 *3*
IR 147, Peigan 49,114 *1*
IR 147B 49,114 *1*
IR 148, Blood 49,114 *1*
IR 148A 49,114 *1*
IR 168 55,122 *10*
IR 168 56,122 *10*
IR 169 55,122 *10*
IR 202 52,116 *6*
IR 203 52,116 *6*
IR 204 56,121 *10*
IR 205 56,122 *10*
IR 216 50,115 *3*
IR 4839 57,126 *13*
Iron Springs 49,113 *1*

Jackpine R. 53,120 *8*
Jaffray 49,116 *2*
Jasper 52,119 *7*
Jasper Nat. Park 52,118 *7*
Jefferson 49,114 *1*
Joffre, Mt. (3449 m)
　50,116 *4*

Kakwa R. 54,119 *7*
Kalispell 48,115 *2*
Kaska Ck. 59,129 *16*
Kechika R. 59,128 *16*
Keho L. 49,114 *1*
Kennedy 55,123 *11*
Kevin 48,113 *1*
Kicking Horse Pass
　51,117 *4*
Kila 48,115 *2*
Kilkerran 55,121 *10*
Kimberley 49,116 *2*
Kinbasket L. 51,119 *5*
Kintla Pk. (3082 m)
　48,115 *2*
Kiowa 48,114 *1*
Kirkcaldy 50,114 *3*
Kiskatinaw R. 55,121 *10*
Klua Lks. 58,123 *12*
Koocanusa, L. 49,116 *2*
Kootenay Nat. For.
　48,115 *2*
Kootenay Nat. Park
　51,117 *4*
Kootenay R. 50,116 *4*
Kwadacha R. 57,126 *13*
Kwadacha Wilderness
　Prov. Park 57,126 *13*

832

Lake Louise 51,117 *4*
Lake McDonald 48,114 *1*
Lamming Hills 53,121 *8*
Laurier, Mt. (2358 m)
 56,124 *11*
Leavitt 49,114 *1*
Lemoray 55,123 *11*
Lethbridge 49,113 *1*
Lewis and Clark
 Nat. For. 48,114 *1*
Liard R. 59,126 *15*
Liard River 59,127 *15*
Liard River Hot Springs
 Prov. Park 59,127 *15*
Little Bow River
 50,114 *1*
Little Red Deer R.
 51,115 *3*
Logan Pass 48,114 *1*
Lone Prairie 55,122 *10*
Longview 50,115 *3*
Longworth 53,122 *8*
Lovettville 53,117 *6*
Lower Post 59,129 *16*
Lower St. Mary L.
 48,114 *1*
Lucerne 52,119 *7* ,
Lundbreck 49,115 *2*
Luscar 53,118 *7*

Mackenzie 55,124 *11*
Magrath 49,113 *1*
Maligne L. 52,118 *7*
Marias Pass 48,114 *1*
Marion 48,115 *2*
Marlboro 53,117 *6*
Marysville 49,116 *2*
Mason Ck. 57,123 *12*
McBride 53,121 *8*
McDonald, L. 48,114 *1*
McGregor R. 54,122 *8*
McLeod L. 54,123 *11*
McLeod Lake 54,124 *11*
Mcleod R. 53,117 *6*
Mercoal 53,118 *7*
Middle Fork Flathead R.
 48,114 *1*
Midnapore 50,115 *3*
Miette Hotsprings
 53,118 *7*
Miette R. 52,119 *7*
Milk R. 49,113 *1*
Milk River 49,113 *1*
Milk River Ridge
 49,113 *1*
Milk River Ridge Res.
 49,113 *1*
Minnewanka, L. 51,116 *4*
Moberly L. 55,122 *10*
Moberly Lake 55,122 *10*
Monarch 49,114 *1*
Monkman Pass 54,122 *8*
Monteith, Mt. (2089 m)
 55,123 *11*
Montney 56,121 *10*
Morkill R. 53,121 *8*
Morley 51,115 *3*
Mount Assiniboine
 Prov. Park 50,116 *4*
Mount Robson Prov. Park
 52,119 *7*
Mountain Park 52,118 *7*
Mountain View 49,114 *1*
Moyie R. 49,116 *2*
Muncho Lake 58,126 *13*
Muncho Lake Prov. Park
 58,126 *13*
Murray 55,123 *11*
Murray R. 54,122 *10*
Muskeg R. 53,119 *7*
Muskwa R. 58,124 *12*

Nanton 50,114 *3*
Narraway R. 54,121 *8*
Natal 49,115 *2*
Netson L. 58,127 *13*
New Dayton 49,113 *1*
Newgate 49,116 *2*
Newlands 54,123 *9*
Nobleford 49,114 *1*
Nordegg 52,117 *6*
Nordegg R. 52,116 *6*
North Pine 56,121 *10*
North Ram R. 52,117 *4*
North Saskatchewan R.
 52,117 *4*
North Star Mtn. (2515 m)
 53,121 *8*
North Thompson R.
 52,120 *5*
Nose Ck. 54,120 *8*

Obed 53,118 *7*
Obo R. 57,127 *13*
Obstruction Mtn.
 (3168 m) 52,117 *4*
Okotoks 50,114 *3*
Oldman R. 49,115 *2*
Olney 48,115 *2*
Ospika R. 56,125 *12*
Ozada 51,115 *3*

Pack R. 55,124 *11*
Parkland 50,114 *3*
Parsnip R. 54,123 *10*
Parson 51,117 *4*
Patrick Gass, Mt.
 (2655 m) 48,113 *1*
Peace R. 56,121 *10*
Pearce 49,114 *1*
Pendroy 48,113 *1*
Penny 53,122 *8*
Picture Butte 49,113 *1*
Pincher 49,114 *1*
Pincher Creek 49,114 *1*
Pine R. 56,121 *10*
Pine Valley 55,123 *10*
Pineview 53,123 *9*
Pink Mountain 57,123 *12*
Pink Mtn. (1787 m)
 57,123 *12*
Polebridge 48,115 *2*
Porcupine Hills 49,114 *1*
Pouce Coupe 55,121 *10*
Prairie Ck. 52,116 *4*
Priddis 50,115 *3*
Prince George 53,123 *9*
Progress 55,121 *10*
Prophet R. 58,123 *12*
Prophet River 58,123 *12*
Purden L. 53,122 *9*

Quentin L. 57,126 *13*

Rabbit R. 59,127 *16*
Racing R. 58,126 *13*
Radium Hot Springs
 50,117 *4*
Rae, Mt. (3225 m)
 50,115 *3*
Rajah, The (3018 m)
 53,119 *7*
Ram R. 52,116 *4*
Raush R. 53,120 *8*
Raven R. 52,115 *3*
Raymond 49,113 *1*
Red Deer R. 51,116 *4*
Red Eagle 48,114 *1*
Red Pass 52,120 *7*
Redwillow R. 54,121 *10*
Ricinus 52,115 *3*
Rider 53,121 *8*
Robb 53,117 *6*

Robert, Mt. 55,122 *10*
Robson, Mt. (3954 m)
 53,120 *7*
Rocky Mountain House
 52,115 *3*
Rocky R. 52,118 *7*
Rogers 51,118 *5*
Rogers Pass 51,118 *5*
Rolla 55,121 *10*
Roosville 49,116 *2*
Rose Prairie 56,121 *10*
Russel, Mt 57,126 *13*

Saint Mary 48,114 *1*
Salmon Valley 54,123 *9*
Santa Rita 48,113 *1*
Saunders 52,116 *6*
Sentinel Pk. 54,122 *10*
Sheep Ck. 53,120 *8*
Shelley 54,123 *9*
Shepard 50,114 *3*
Sifton Pass 57,127 *13*
Sikanni Chief 57,123 *12*
Sikanni Chief R.
 57,123 *12*
Sinclair Mills 54,122 *8*
Sinclair Pass 50,116 *4*
Sir Alexander, Mt.
 (3277 m) 53,121 *8*
Sir Douglas, Mt. (3406 m)
 50,116 *4*
Sir Sandford, Mt.
 (3522 m) 51,118 *5*
Sir Wilfrid Laurier, Mt.
 (3505 m) 52,120 *8*
Skookumchuk 49,116 *2*
Slim Ck. 53,122 *8*
Slocomb, Mt. 57,127 *13*
Smith R. 59,127 *15*
Smith River 59,127 *15*
Smoky R. 53,120 *7*
Snake Indian Falls
 53,119 *7*
Snake Indian R. 53,119 *7*
Snaring 53,119 *7*
Snaring R. 53,119 *7*
Somers 48,115 *2*
Sorcerer Mtn (3168 m)
 51,118 *5*
Spillimacheen 50,117 *4*
Spillimacheen R. 51,117 *4*
Spring Coulee 49,114 *1*
St. Bride, Mt. (3312 m)
 51,116 *4*
St. Mary L. 48,114 *1*
St. Mary Res. 49,114 *1*
Stand Off 49,114 *1*
Stanley Falls 52,118 *5*
Stavely 50,114 *1*
Steamboat 58,124 *12*
Sterco 53,117 *6*
Stillwater R. 48,115 *2*
Stimson, Mt. (3103 m)
 48,114 *1*
Stirling 49,113 *1*
Stone Mountain
 Prov. Park 58,125 *13*
Stryker 48,115 *2*
Sukunka R. 55,122 *10*
Sulphur R. 53,119 *7*
Summit 48,114 *1*
Summit Lake 58,125 *13*
Summit Lake, 54,123 *9*
Sunburst 48,112 *1*
Sundre 51,115 *3*
Sunrise Valley 55,121 *10*
Sunset Prairie 55,121 *10*
Sunwapta Falls 52,118 *7*
Sunwapta Pass (2035 m)
 52,118 *5*
Sunwapta R. 52,118 *5, 7*

Sweetgrass 48,112 *1*
Sweetwater 55,121 *10*
Switzer Prov. Park
 53,118 *7*
Sylvia, Mt. (2942 m)
 58,125 *13*

Taylor 56,121 *10*
Tête Jaune Cache 52,120 *8*
Toad R. 58,126 *13*
Toad River 58,126 *13*
Toby Ck. 50,117 *4*
Tommy Lks. 56,122 *12*
Tornado Mtn (3099 m)
 49,115 *2*
Trailcreek 48,115 *2*
Trepanier Ck. 59,129 *16*
Trout R. 59,126 *15*
Trutch 57,123 *12*
Tuchodi L. 58,125 *13*
Tuchodi R. 58,125 *13*
Tumbler Ridge 55,121 *10*
Turner Valley 50,115 *3*
Twidwell Bend 55,122 *10*
Two Medicine R. 48,113 *1*

Upper Cutbank 55,121 *10*
Upper Fraser 54,122 *9*

Valemount 52,120 *7*
Valier 48,113 *1*
Valley View 56,121 *10*
Verdigris L. 49,113 *1*
Vermilion Pass (1639 m)
 51,117 *4*
Victoria Pk. (2579 m)
 49,115 *2*
Vulcan 50,114 *3*

Wapiti R. 54,121 *10*
Wardner 49,116 *2*
Ware 57,125 *13*
Wasa 49,116 *2*
Water Valley 51,115 *3*
Waterton Lakes 49,114 *1*
Waterton Lakes
 Nat. Park 49,114 *1*
Waterton Park 49,114 *1*
Waterton R. 49,114 *1*
Wellingo 49,113 *1*
Wells Gray Prov. Park
 52,120 *8*
West Glacier 48,114 *1*
West Kiskatinaw R.
 55,121 *10*
Whiskey Gap 49,114 *1*
White River 50,116 *2*
Whitefish 48,115 *2*
Wildhay R. 53,118 *7*
Williams 48,113 *1*
Williston L. 55,124 *11*
Willmore Wilderness
 Prov. Park 53,119 *7*
Willow Ck. 50,115 *3*
Willow River 54,123 *9*
Willow Valley 55,121 *10*
Willowbrook 55,121 *10*
Windermere 50,116 *4*
Windermere L. 50,116 *4*
Wolverine R. 55,122 *10*
Wonowon 56,122 *10*
Wood R. 52,119 *5*
Woodhouse 49,114 *1*
Woolford 49,114 *1*
Wrentham 49,113 *1*
Wycliffe 49,116 *2*

Yellowhead Pass
 (1131 m) 52,119 *7*
Yoho Nat. Park 51,117 *4*

833

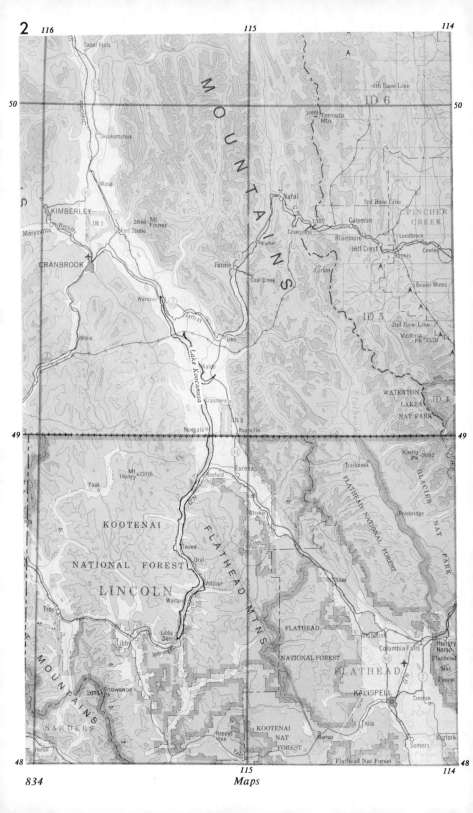

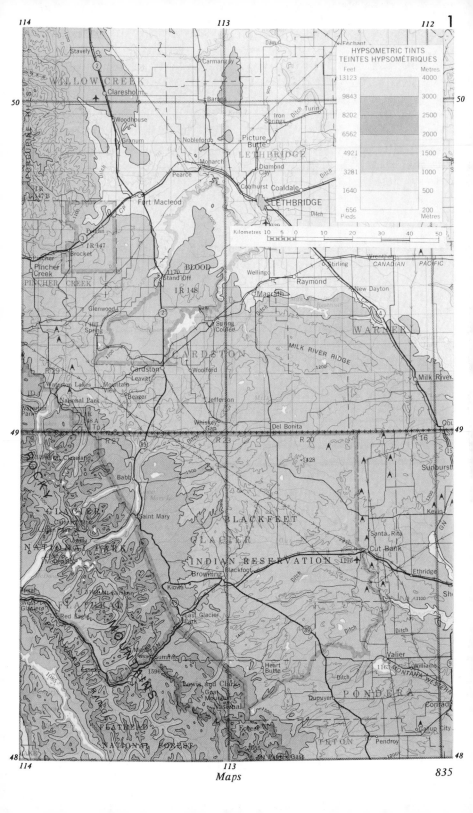

HYPSOMETRIC TINTS
TEINTES HYPSOMÉTRIQUES

Feet		Metres
13123		4000
9843		3000
8202		2500
6562		2000
4921		1500
3281		1000
1640		500
656 Pieds		200 Métres

Kilometres 10 5 0 10 20 30 40 50

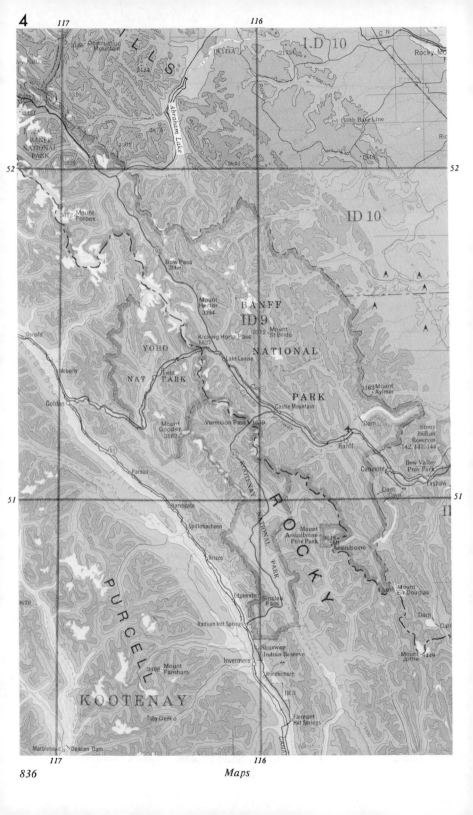

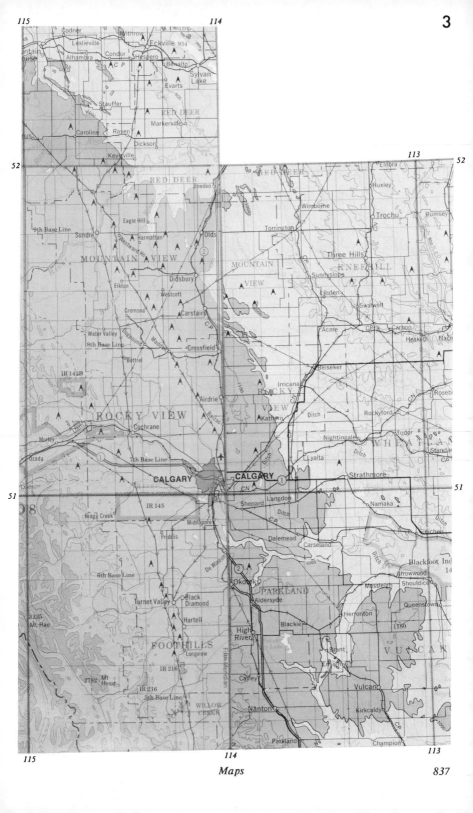

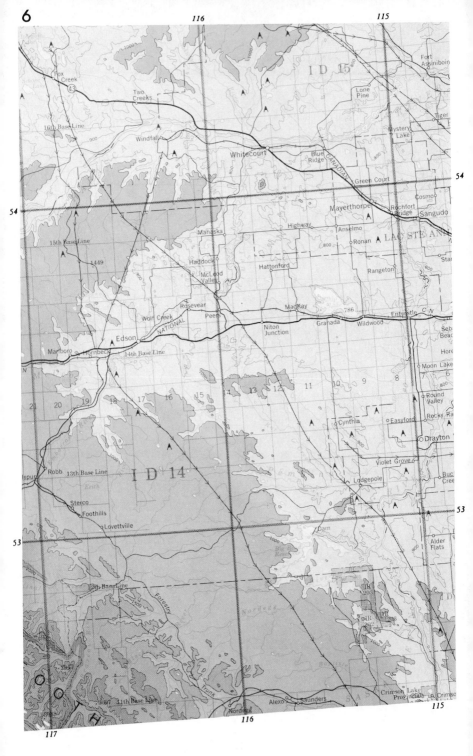

3

Maps

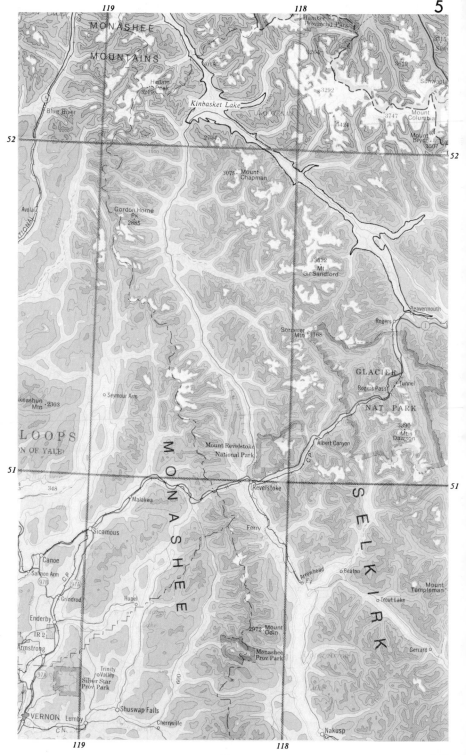

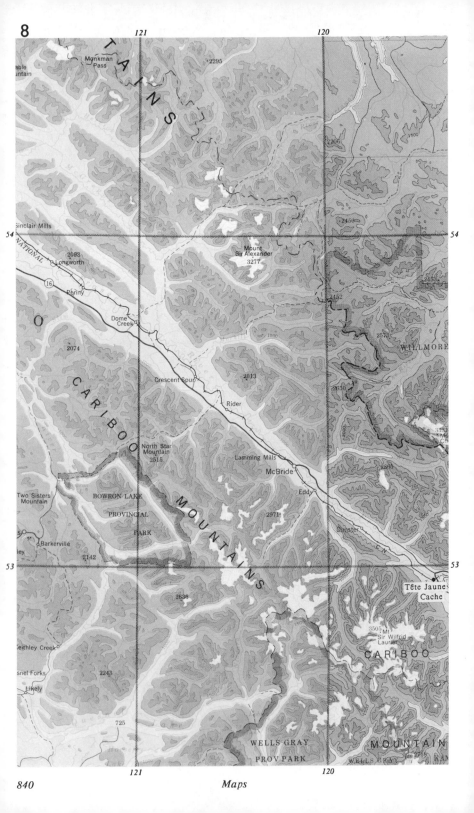

Maps

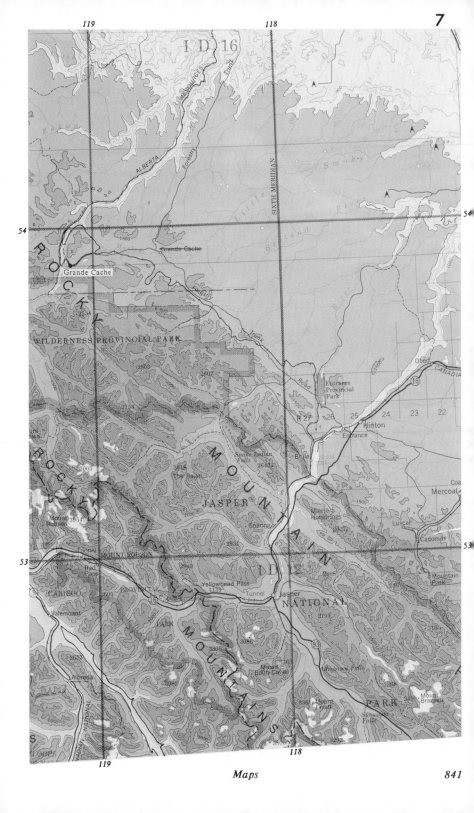

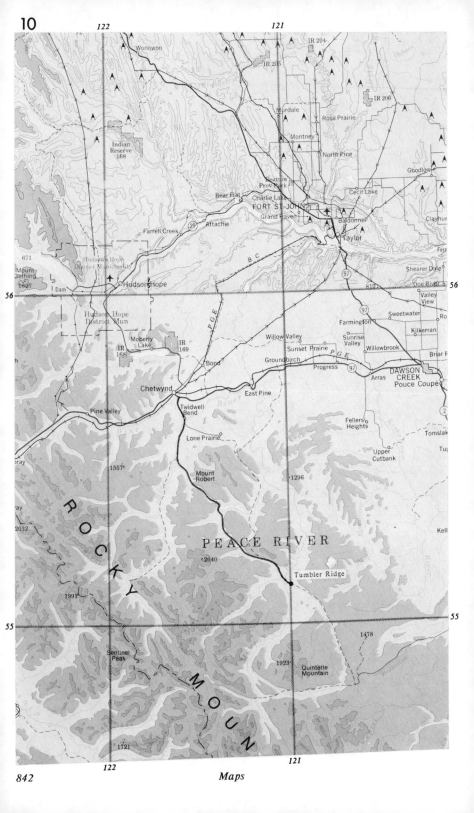

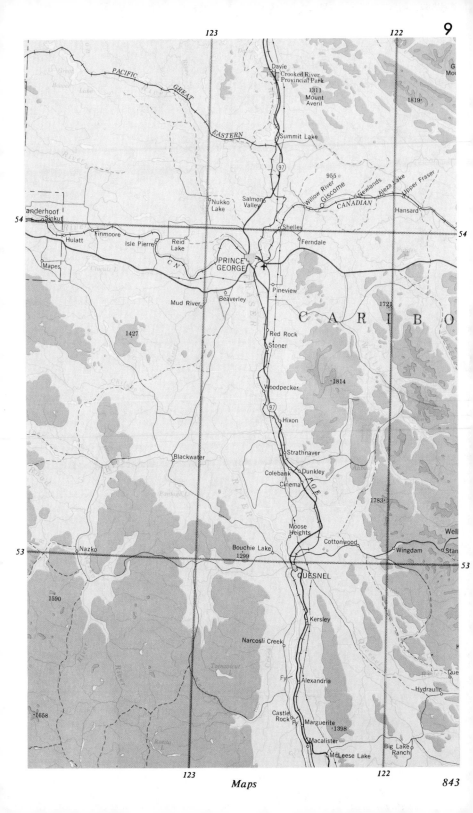

123   122

PACIFIC   GREAT

Davie
Crooked River
Provincial Park
1311
Mount
Averil
1819·

EASTERN   Summit Lake

97

955
Willow River   Giscome   Newlands   Aleza Lake   Upper Fraser
CANADIAN   Hansard

anderhoof   Nukko   Salmon
Sinkut   Lake   Valley
54   Shelley   54

Hulatt   Finmoore   Isle Pierre   Reid   Ferndale
Lake
Mapes   PRINCE
GEORGE
C N   Pineview
Mud River   Beaverley
C A R I B O
1427   1721·

Red Rock
Stoner

·1814
Woodpecker

97   Hixon

Strathnaver
Blackwater   Colebank   Dunkley
Cinema
1783·

Moose
Heights
Well
53   Nazko   Bouchie Lake   Cottonwood   Wingdam   Stan   53
1299
QUESNEL
1590

Kersley

Narcosli Creek   Que

Fy   Alexandria
Hydraulic
Castle
Rock   Fy   Marguerite
·1658   ·1398
Macalister
Big Lake
Ranch
McLeese Lake

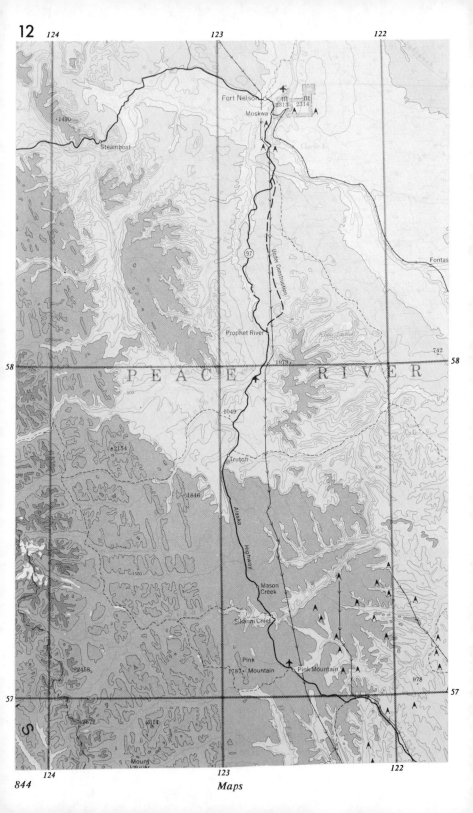

Maps

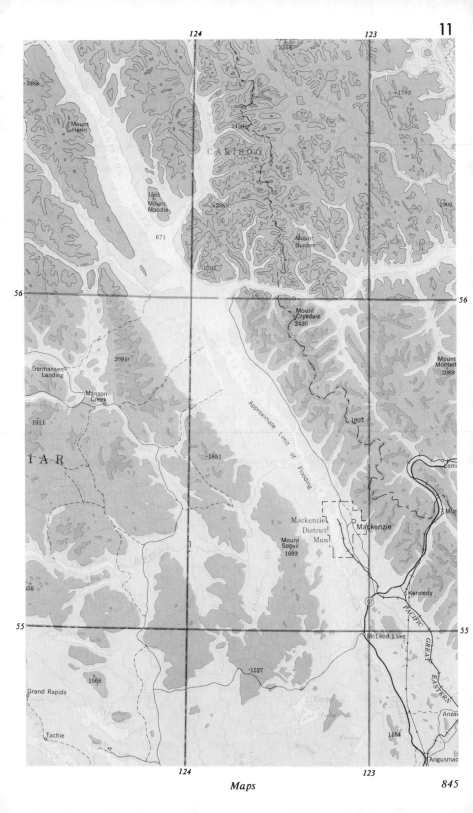

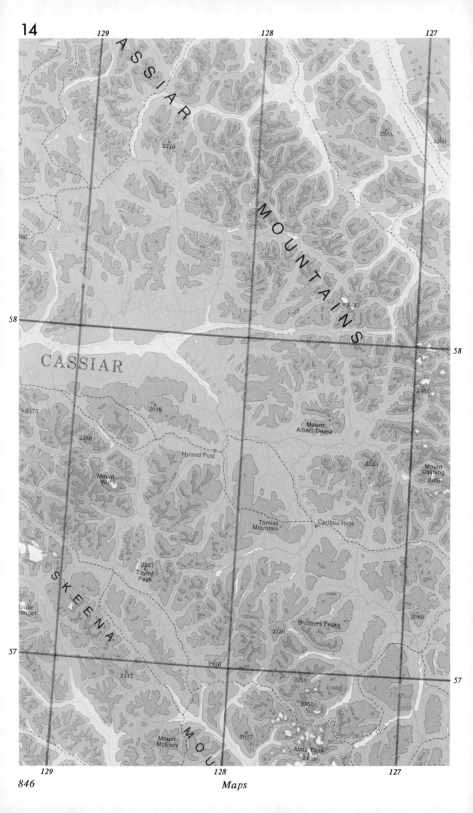

14

Maps

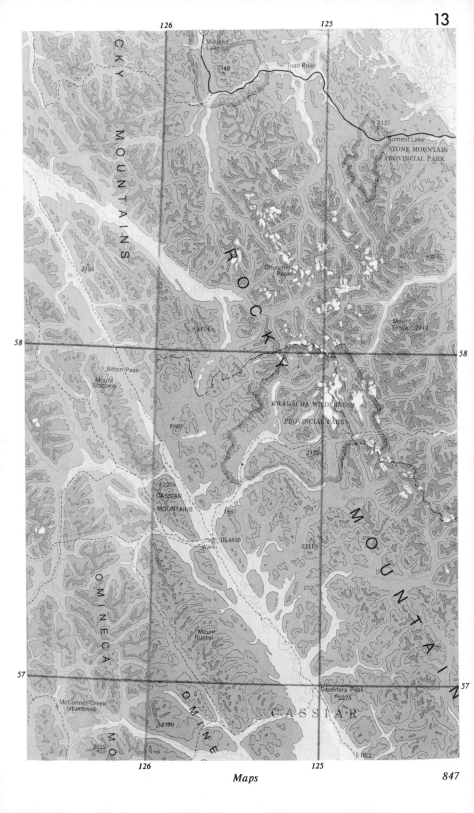

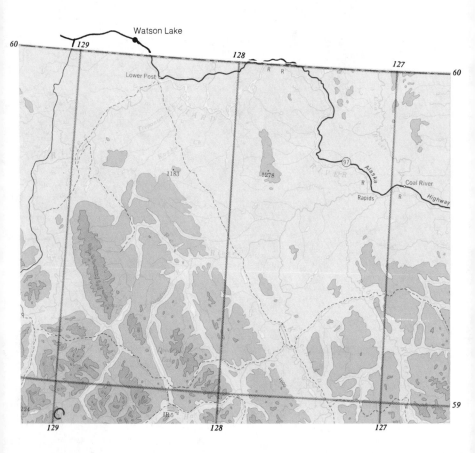

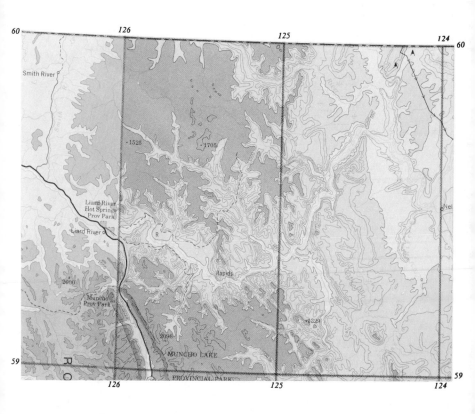

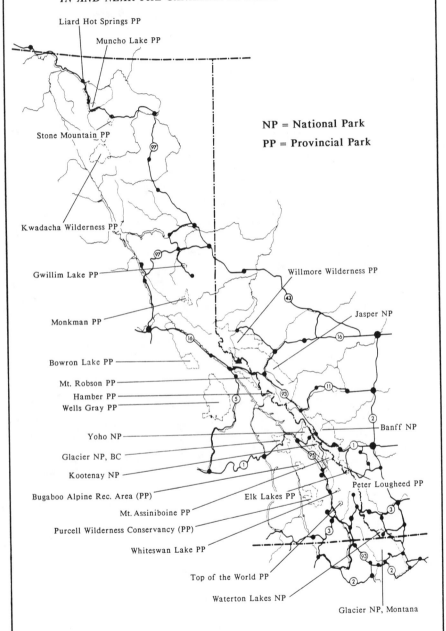

NATIONAL PARKS AND MAJOR PROVINCIAL PARKS IN AND NEAR THE CANADIAN ROCKIES

Liard Hot Springs PP

Muncho Lake PP

NP = National Park

PP = Provincial Park

Stone Mountain PP

Kwadacha Wilderness PP

Gwillim Lake PP

Willmore Wilderness PP

Monkman PP

Jasper NP

Bowron Lake PP

Mt. Robson PP

Hamber PP

Wells Gray PP

Yoho NP

Banff NP

Glacier NP, BC

Kootenay NP

Bugaboo Alpine Rec. Area (PP)

Peter Lougheed PP

Mt. Assiniboine PP

Elk Lakes PP

Purcell Wilderness Conservancy (PP)

Whiteswan Lake PP

Top of the World PP

Waterton Lakes NP

Glacier NP, Montana

(For names of map features see base map opposite page 1)

Abbot
  Pass 784, 785p
  Hut 784, 785p
  Sidney 757
Abdomen, of insects 468
Abies lasiocarpa 298
Ablation, zone of 212
Absolute ages of rocks 70
Accidents 814
Accipiter
  cooperii 601
  gentilis 601
  striatus 600
Acclimation 820
Accommodation
  for cyclists 805
  back-country 782
Accretion (geology) 170,
  172d
Accumulation, zone of 212
Acer
  glabrum 314
  negundo 306
Achaearanea tepidariorum
  483
Achillea millefolium 344
Acid-testing carbonate
  rocks 98
Acinophyllum 132
Acipenser transmontanus
  546
Acipenseridae 546
Acknowledgments *vi*
Acmon blue 508
Aconite 386
Aconitum delphinifolium
  386
Acraea
  moth 525
  caterpillar 528
Acrididae 479
Actaea rubra 344
Actitis macularia 590
Adalia
  bipunctata 477
  frigida 477
Adams, Mollie 760, 747p
Addresses and telephone
  numbers of national
  parks (see National
  parks)
Aechmophorus occidentalis
  573
Aedes
  communis 467
  vexans 467
Aegolius
  acadicus 608
  funereus 608
Aerial tramways 770
Aeschnidae 493
Agaric
  fly 445
  panther 446
Agaricus
  augustus 448
  campestris 447

haemorrhoidarius 448
Agaricus, bleeding 448
Age
  of rock, methods of
    determining 70
  of rockslides in
    Canadian Rockies 218
  of the Rockies compared
    to other ranges 3
Agelaius phoeniceus 645
Aglais milberti 495
Agnes, Lake 774p
Agoseris
  aurantiaca 354
  glauca 354
Agriades franklinii 508
Agrostis scabra 419
Aida Formation 77
Aitken, Jim 103
Aix sponsa 584
Akie River 210
Alaska Highway
  construction of 762
  highest point on 34
  physiography seen along
    31
Alberta
  arctic 518
  fritillary 515
  Group 165
  Mt., first ascent 762
  province of 760
Albertan till 195
Albertella 95, 98
Alces alces 734
Alcohol inky 450
Alder 313
  flycatcher 635
Alderleaf buckthorn 314
Alectoria 435
Alexander Creek 158
Alfalfa
  looper 527
  purple 386
  yellow 364
Algae 409
  attached 409
  in hot springs 227
  in snow 532
  red 409
Algal mounds 108
Algonquin 746
Aliens 436
Alisma plantago-aquatica
  413
Alistostromes 93
Alkaline rock 150
Allan
  J.A. 24, 101
  Mt. 160, 763
Allanaria 131
Allen, Samuel 757
Allium
  cernuum 378
  schoenoprasum 378
Alnus
  crispa 313
  tenuifolia 313
Alopecurus
  aequalis 417
  alpinus 417
Alpine
  anemone 392
  arnica 399
  bluegrass 419

buttercup 399
campion 398
checkered skipper 521
cinquefoil 399
Club of Canada 760
coltsfoot 396
columbine 406
dandelion 399
early yellow locoweed
  401
everlasting 396
fir 298
fleabane 395
forget-me-not 404
goldenrod 402
grass-of-Parnassus 392
grasshopper 480
harebell 404
hawksbeard 400
laurel 403
lousewort 403
marsh marigold 393
meadow or tundra,
  ecology of 283p
milk-vetch 406
mosses 432
potentilla 399
purple wallflower 405
pyrola 394
rock cress 404
speedwell 404
spring beauty 393
starwort 393
veronica 404
wildflowers 391
willow 308
willow-herb 375
wormwood 397
yellow paintbrush 402
Alpine zone 4, 268
Alpines (butterflies)
  arctic 519
  common 519
  red-disked 519
  spruce-bog 519
Alsike clover 369
Altitude, effect of 820
Altricial birds 572
Altyn
  Formation 73
  locality of 76
Alveolites 131, 132
Amanita
  muscaria 442, 445
  pantherina 442, 446
  virosa 442
Amblyscirtes vialis 524
Ambystoma
  macrodactylum 559
  tigrinum 558
Amecephalus 95
Amelanchier alnifolia 324
American
  avocet 590
  badger 709
  bittern 588
  coot 586
  copper 509
  crow 623
  dipper 598
  golden-plover 663
  goldfinch 664
  house spider 483

kestrel 599
larch 303
marten 706
mink 707
redstart 642
robin 627
sable 706
toad 559
tree sparrow 664
vetch 378
white pelican 663
wigeon 576
American Rockies 174
  comparison with
    Canadian Rockies 12
Amethyst Lakes 779
Ammodramus
  bairdii 664
  caudacutus 664
  leconteii 660
Ammonite, giant 160
Ammonites 152, 165
Ammonoid cephalopods 158
Ammophila 475
Amphibians and reptiles
  558
Amphipods 486
Amphipora 131, 132
Amygdaloidal basalt 76
Anadromous life cycle 537
Anagymnotoceras 158
Anas
  acuta 578
  americana 576
  clypeata 575
  crecca 576
  cyanoptera 577
  discors 577
  penelope 663
  platyrynchos 575
  strepera 578
Ancestral Rockies 14
Ancient Wall Reef 130, 132
Andes 170
Androsace 332
Androsace
  chamaejasme 332
  septentrionalis 332
Anemone
  alpine 392
  Drummond's 334, 392
  northern 392
  western 391
Anemone
  drummondii 334, 392
  multifida 334
  occidentalis 391
  parviflora 392
  patens 377
Angel wings 457
Angelica arguta 344
Angelica, white 344
Angle of sun, effect on
  climate 251
Anglewings 503
  faunus 503
  satyr 503
Angular unconformity 122
Anhydrite 123
Anicia checkerspot 510
Anise swallowtail 502
  caterpillar 530
Anise-scented clitocybe 448
Annette, Lake 8, 570
Annual moraine 212

Anopheles earlei 467
Anostracads 486
Antelope
  bush 320
  pronghorn 741
Antenna plant 343
Antennaria
  alpina 396
  anaphaloides 339
  microphylla 338, 370
  racemosa 339
  rosea 370
Anthocharis sara 499
Anthracite 754
Anthus
  spragueii 663
  spinoletta 595
Anticline, defined 184
Antler Orogeny 128
Antlers 730
Ants 475
  giant carpenter 476
  red 475
Apatite 149
Aphanitic texture in rocks
  115
Aphelaspis 108
Aphididae 476
Aphids 476
Aphrodite fritillary 512
Apidae 471
Apis mellifera 471
Apocynum
  androsaemifolium 325
Appalachians 32
Appekunny Formation 73
Apricot jelly 453
Aquila chrysaetos 605
Aquilegia
  brevistyla 385
  coerulea 385
  flavescens 361
  formosa 373
  jonesii 406
Arabis
  drummondii 382
  lemmonii 404
  lyalli 404
Aragonite 72, 96
Aralia nudicaulis 349
Arceuthobium
  americanum 294
  douglasii 300
Archaeocyathids 86, 91
Archie Simpson Hut 783
Archilochus colubris 663
Arcs Member 132
Arctic
  alpine (butterfly) 519
  grayling 544
  poppies 398
  raspberry 374
  skipper 523
Arctics (butterflies)
  Alberta 518
  Canada 518
  chryxus 517
  jutta 517
  melissa 518
  polixenes 518
  Uhler's 517
  white-veined 517
Arctiidae 525
Arctomys
  Cave 223
  Formation 105p
  Peak 105
Arctostaphylos
  alpina 337

rubra 337
uva-ursi 337
Ardea herodias 587
Area of Canadian Rockies
  1
Arenaria 333
  interpres 663
Argillite 72
Arizona ponderosa 295
Armillariella mellea 449
Arnica 356, 399
Arnica
  alpina 399
  cordifolia 356
  fulgens 356
  latifolia 356
  louiseana 356
  parryi 356
Arrow-grass 413
Arrowhead
  balsam root 356
  blue 506
Artemisia
  dracunculus 389
  frigida 361
  ludoviciana 389
  norvegica 397
  tridentata 319
Artogeia
  napi 497
  rapae 497, 530
Arum, water 414
Aruncus sylvester 317
Arvicola richardsoni 686
Ascaphus truei 561
Asclepias speciosa 375
Ash, volcanic 205
Asio
  flammeus 663
  otus 663
Aspen
  grove, ecology of 275p
  parkland 269
  trembling 303
Asphodel, false 343
Assiniboine, Mt. 95
  hiking to 777p, 779
  hut on 785p
Assiniboines 746
Astarte fritillary 515
Aster
  conspicuus 387
  hesperius 347
Aster
  blue/purple species 387
  golden 357
  western willow 347
Asthma 801
Astoria River 779
Astorians 749
Astraeus hygrometricus 461
Astragalus 340
  alpinus 406
Atan Group 91
Athabasca
  Falls 219
  Hostel 807
  Glacier 210, 213d, 255,
    769, 808p
  Mt. 756, 792
  Pass 749
Athabasca Valley Erratics
  Train 200
Athene cunicularia 663
Athyris 131
Athyrium filix-femina 424
Atlantic Ocean, origin of
  168
Atlantis fritillary 513

Atom bomb and Franco
  Rasetti 103
Atrypa 131, 135
Attached algae 409
Audubon's warbler 640
Augite 75, 150
Auricularia auricula 459
Auto-accessible highlights
  767
Autographa californica 527
Automobile 760
Autumn willow 308
Avalanche 816
  Lake 772
  lily 352
  track 816
  track, ecology of 284p
Avalanches
  climax 817
  erosion by 209
  response to 817
  safe and unsafe routes
    816d
Avens
  three-flowered 370
  white mountain 393
  yellow 360
  yellow mountain 361
Aves 567
Avocet, American 590
Awnless brome 418
Aythya
  affinis 580
  americana 579
  collaris 580
  valisineria 579
Azalea, false 327
Azouzetta, Lake 770
Azure, spring 507

Bacidia 440
Back-country 7p, 780p
  accommodation 782
Backpacking 6, 776, 780p
  trips 778
Backswimmer 489
Bacteria in hot springs 227
Badger, American 709
Baillie-Grohman, William
  756
Baird's
  sandpiper 592
  sparrow 664
Baked-apple 322
Baker Creek, Lake 782
Bald
  eagle 605
  Hills 775, 803
Bald-faced hornet 473
Baldonnel Formation 158
Balfour Hut 711, 786
Balsam poplar 304
Balsamorhiza sagittata 356
Band-tailed pigeon 663
Banded woollybear 527
Baneberry 344
Banff 7p, 140, 157, 276, 754
  Formation 140, 141p
  Hot Springs, discovery
    of 753
  National Park, origin of
    753
Banff Springs Hotel 157,
  755
Banff-Jasper Road 762
Banff-Windermere
  Highway 760
Banffshire 754
Bank swallow 615

Bankhead 21, 161, 754
Barbarea vulgaris 362
Barbilophozia
  lycopodioides 430
Barclay's willow 308
Baril Member 144
Baring Creek 773
Barite 127
Barn swallow 613
Barnaby Rudge 544
Barometer earthstar 461
Barratt's willow 308
Barred owl 607
Barrow's goldeneye 581
Bartramia longicauda 663
Basalt 75, 86
  amygdaloidal 76
Base map *xvi*
Basement (geology) 122
  rock at the surface 122
Basin (geology) 123
  and Range geological
    province 103
Bats 675
  big brown 676
  hoary 678
  little brown 676
  long-legged 677
  silver-haired 677
Bay-breasted warbler 663
Beadlily 329
Beaked hazelnut 313
Bears 720
  attacks on people,
    numbers of 729
  black 720
  cinnamon 720
  encounters 725
  grizzly 722
  relationship with man
    723
  repellents 728
Bearberry 337
Beard-tongue
  blue/purple species 380
  Lyall's 372
  yellow 354
Beargrass 343
Bearpaw
  Formation 167
  Sea 157
Beattie Peaks Formation
  161
Beatty Creek 778
Beauty
  Creek 231
  Creek Hostel 807
  Flats 231
Beauvert, Lac 234, 236
Beaver 698, 745
  fever 824
  Lake 136, 781
  Mines 162
  Mines Formation 162
Beaver, Samson 747p, 760
Beaverfoot
  Formation, Range 114
  River 150
Bebb's willow 307
Bed load of stream 209
Bedson Ridge fold 139, 184
Bedstraw, northern 345
Bee hawk-moth 526
Beehive, The 773
Beeplant, purple 407
Bees, wasps, hornets and
  their mimics 471
Beetles 477
  black ground 477

black pine sawyer 478
diving 491
engraver 478
giant water scavenger 491
ladybird/ladybug 477
water 489
whirlygig 490
Belcourt Formation 150
Belemnites 160
Bell, moose 735
Belly River 167
Formation 180
Belostomidae 490
Belt Supergroup 71
Belted kingfisher 598
Bennett Dam 164, 763
Berberis
nervosa 358
repens 358
Berg Lake 781
Bergamot, wild 369
Berland River 128
Besa River 134
Formation 134
Betula
glandulosa 319
occidentalis 314
papyrifera 305
Bibliography, selected
amphibians and reptiles 565
birds 665
botany 462
ecology 270
fishes 557
geology/geography 237
human history 764
insects and spiders 531
mammals 744
naturalist's guides 9
recreation 811
safety and first aid 828
weather and climate 263
Bickford Formation 161
Bicknell's geranium 381
Bicycling 8, 805, 808p
the Icefields Parkway 807
on trails 810
Big
Bend of the Columbia 749
brown bat 676
poplar sphinx 526
red-stem 430
Rock 203p, 204
Springs 225
Bighorn
Dam 165
sheep 666p, 738
Bighornia 115
Bilberry 323
Bioherm 130
Biologically induced erosion 210
Biology summary 4
Biostrome 130, 131, 135
Bioturbation 138
Birch
bracket-fungus 457
leaf miner 529
polypore 457
dwarf 319
water 314
white 305
Birds 567
abundance of 571
altricial 572

attracting 567
breeding in 571
calls/songs 571
checklists 665
diving 597
eggs and nestlings of 572
families, names of 664
fastest 600
fledging of 572
flight speeds of 572
flocking in 571
foods of 571
habitats of 571
identifying 567
incubation period in 572
largest 587
lifespans of 572
listings, order of and use 570
little gray (LGBs) 634
nesting records of 571
names of 570
nests of 572
places for birding 568
precocial 572
ranges of 572
raptorial 599
rare list 663
recorded songs of 567
red or pink 647
swamp-dwelling 587
times of occurrence 571
yellow 638
Bird-beak pattern 518
Bird's-eye
primrose 374
texture in rock 144
Bird's-nest fungi 459
Biscuit root 366
Bishop's-cap 349
Bison 737
Creek 108
Creek Formation 108
Bison bison 737
Bistort 396
Bitter cherry 316
Bittern, American 588
Bitterroot 375
Bjerkandera adusta 458
Black
bear 720
cottonwood 305
flies 471
fly larvae 488
ground beetles 477
hawthorn 316
henbane 390
morel 454
pine sawyer beetle 478
spruce 297
swift 616
tern 598
twinberry 325
Black-and-white warbler 663
Black-and-yellow mud dauber 474
Black-backed woodpecker 620
Black-bear attacks 727
Black-bellied plover 663
Black-billed magpie 623
Black-capped chickadee 649
Black-headed grosbeak 664
Black-throated
gray warbler 663
green warbler 663
Blackbird
Brewer's 645

red-winged 645
rusty 645
yellow-headed 644
Blackfoot Indians 746
Blackman Creek 79
Blackpoll warbler 641
Blackstone Formation 165
Bladder
campion 398
fern 424
locoweed 406
Bladderwort 411
Blaeberry River 108
Blairmore 162, 757
Group 162, 163p
Blakiston, Lt. Thomas 752
Mt. 76
Bleeding 818
agaricus 448
Blisters 824
Block
diagrams of geological history 45
faulting 177
Blood Indians 746
Bloodworms 488
Bloom, algal 409
Blooming season 290
Blowdown, ecology of 285p
Blue
bottle flies 469
butterflies 505
camas 378
clematis 377
copper 506
grouse 610
jay 625
wildflowers 377, 404
Blues (butterflies) 505
acmon 508
arrowhead 506
common 506
greenish 505
high-mountain 508
northern 507
orange-bordered 507
western tailed 506
Blue-berry elder 316
Blue-bottle gentian 407
Blue-bur 382
Blue-eyed grass 377
Blue-winged teal 577
Bluebell 383, 384
Blueberries 323
Blueberry sulphur 499
Bluebird
eastern 663
mountain 630
western 663
Bluegrass 418
Bluegreen willow 308
Bluejoint reedgrass 418
Blues (butterflies) 505
Bluets 493
Boa, rubber 564
Boat Encampment 749
Bob Hind Hut 783, 785p
Bobcat 713
Bobolink 663
Bog
fritillary 514
lemming, northern 687
orchids 341
Bohemian waxwing 633
Boldly patterned
butterflies 495
Boletus
admirable 443
king 443

rough-stemmed 443
Boletus
edulis 443
mirabilis 443
Boloria
bellona 524
napaea 515
polaris 524
Bombus fervidus 472
Bombycilla
cedrorum 633
garrulus 633
Bonaparte's gull 597
Bonasa umbellus 609
Bonner Formation 76
Bones (see Skulls)
Boom Lake 802
Bordeaux, Michael 749
Boreal
chickadee 650
foothills 269
owl 608
toad 559
Boreidae 534
Boreus 534
Borsato Formation 132
Bostonais, Pierre 750
Botany 264
listings, how to use 289
Botaurus lentiginosus 588
Botrychium
lunaria 423
virginianum 423
Boulder, Colorado 13
Boulton Creek 802
Boundaries 11
Bourgeau, Eugène 752
Bovidae 730
Bovids 737
Bow
Falls 156p, 157
Hut 786
Lake 210, 754, 769
Pass/Bow Summit 210, 281, 570, 769
Peak 78
River 156p, 218
Bow Valley
birding along 568
glaciation in 197
Parkway 275, 809
Provincial Park 763
Box elder 306
BP, defined 189
Brachiopods 140, 141p
Bracken 424
Bracket fungi 456
Bracted
honeysuckle 325
lousewort 365
Braided stream 231
Branch-tip spiders 483
Brant 663
Branta canadensis 586, 663
Brazeau
Formation 165, 166p
Icefield 212
Mt. 19
River 91, 160, 779
Breccia 82p, 83, 138
Breeding (see individual species)
Brewer Buttress 788p
Brewer's
blackbird 645
sparrow 658
Brewster brothers 757
Brickellia 339
Brickellia grandiflora 339

Bridge
  natural 219
  River tephra 205
Briscoia 109
Bristlecone pines of
    California 292
British Columbia 752
    Railway 762
British geologic names vs.
    American 113
Brittle cactus 367
Broad-leaved
    water-plantain 413
    willow-herb 373
Broad-winged hawk 663
Broadcast Hill 187, 188p
Brocket, tills at 194p
Brome 418
Bromus inermis 418
Bronze bells 350
Brook
  lobelia 385
  stickleback 555
  trout 543
Broomrape
  clustered 381
  one-flowered 381
Broom (on tree) 294p, 300p
Broomweed 357
Brown
  butterflies 504
  creeper 654
  elfin 504
  lemming 687
  John ("Kootenai") 752
  Mt. 755
  trout 542
Brown-eyed Susan 357
Brown-headed cowbird 646
Brûlé Lake 750
Bryant Creek 779
  cabin on 783
Bryophytes 429
Bryoria 436
Bryozoans 135
Bryum 432
Bubnoff 210
Bubo virginianus 606
Bubonic plague 690
Bucephala
  albeola 583
  clangula 581
  islandica 581
Buchanan, Mt. 127
Buché, Baptiste 749
Buchia 161
Buckbean 414
Buckbrush 324
Buckthorn 314
Buckwheat, wild 366
Buellia 440
Buff-breasted sandpiper
    663
Buffalo 737
  bean 364
Buffaloberry 312
Bufflehead 583
Bufo
  americanus 559
  boreas 559
Bugs, water 489
Bull
  thistle 388
  trout 544
Bulldog Creek 79
Bullhead Group, Mtn. 164
Bullsnake 563
Bulrush, common great 412
Bumble bee, golden

northern 472
Bunchberry 336
Bungalow camps 760
Bunting
  lark 664
  lazuli 630
  snow 658
Bur-reed, giant 412
Burbot 547
Burgess Shale 98, 99d, 103
Buried valleys 192, 193
Buried-stalk puffball 461
Burls 293
Burnais Formation 128
Burned areas, ecology of
    284p
Burns, treatment of 825
Burrowing owl 663
Bush boots 822
Bushy pondweed 557
Bushy-tailed wood rat 682
Buteo
  jamaicensis 602
  lagopus 603
  platypterus 663
  regalis 663
  swainsoni 603
Butorides striatus 663
Butter-and-eggs 365
Buttercups 360
  alpine 399
  snow 399
Butterflies 494
  blue 505
  boldly patterned 495
  brown 504
  checkered 510
  copper-colored 508
  orange-and-black 511
  rare list 524
  watching 494
  white 497
  with eyespots on their
      wings 516
  with irregular wing
      edges 503
  with large tails on their
      wings 502
  yellow 499
Butterwort 385
Buttery collybia 451
Byng Formation, Pass 85
Bynumiella 109

Cabbage white 497
  caterpillar 530
Cactus 367
Caddisfly larvae 489
Cadomin 162, 164
  Formation 162, 163p
Cairn
  Formation 132, 133p,
      781
  River 132
Calamagrostis
  canadensis 418
  purpurascens 418
Calamospiza melanocorys
    664
Calcarius ornatus 664
Calcite 72
Calcium carbonate 72
Calgary-Golden
    physiographic tour 16
Calidris
  alba 663
  alpina 663
  bairdii 592
  himantopus 593

mauri 663
  melanotos 592
  minutilla 591
  pusilla 592
California gull 596
Calla palustris 414
Calla, wild 414
Calliope hummingbird 626
Calliphora
  cadaverina 469
  vomitoria 469
Calliphoridae 469
Callippe fritillary 512
Callophrys
  sheridanii 504
  siva 524
Calls of birds 571
Calochortus
  apiculatus 329
  macrocarpus 377
Caloplaca 439
Caltha leptosepala 393
Calvatia booniana 460
Calypso bulbosa 371
Calypso orchid 371
Calyptra 433
Camarotechia 139
Camas
  blue 378
  white 331
Camassia quamash 378
Cameron
  Creek 759
  Falls 72
  Lake Road 73
Campanula
  lasiocarpa 404
  rotundifolia 383
Campbell, J.W. 292
Campion
  bladder/alpine 398
  moss 402
Camponotus herculeanus
    476
Canada
  arctic 518
  goose 586
  thistle 388
  warbler 663
Canadian
  buffaloberry 312
  Cordillera 11, 168, 172d,
      178
  Dominion Mining 162
  Hostelling Association
      cabins 805, 806mt
  National Railways,
      origin of 761
  Northern Railway 761
  Pacific Railway 753
  Shield 11, 89, 168, 192
  toad 559
Canadian Rockies
  area of 1
  auto-accessible
      highlights of 767
  bicycling in 805
  biology of 4
  boundaries of 11
  building of 168, 172d,
      175d
  climate of 248t
  comparison with
      American Rockies 12
  creation, summary of
      178, 179
  cross-sections of 50d
  date of appearance 153
  day-length in 252t

definition of 1
  ecology of 265m, 266,
      273-288p
  endurance of 210
  erosional processes in
      209
  geography and geology
      of 3, 10
  geologic map of 47m
  highest point in 1
  human history of 8
  Ice Age in 189
  icefields in 211m
  impact of humanity on 6
  integrity of 830
  landscape features of
      209
  length of 1
  length of day in 252t
  lowest point in 1
  major characteristics of
      1
  mountaineering in 787
  national parks, percent
      protected in 830
  physiography of 15
  population of 6, 766t
  recreation in 6
  safety in 813
  ski-touring in 796
  structure of 180
  style of 1
  temperature in 250m
  typical animals of 4
  unprotected area of 8
  value of 829
  vegetation pattern in
      265
  weather and climate of
      4
  width of 1
Canadiphyllum 145
Canal Flats 251, 269, 756
Cancer-root 381
Canidae 715
Canis
  latrans 715
  lupus 717
Canmore 161, 218, 754
Cantharellus cibarius 452
Canvasback 579
Canyons (gorges) 219
  ecology of 280p
  origin and age of 221
Cape May warbler 663
Capniidae 533
Capricornis 741
Carabidae 477
Carbon-isotope dating 197
Carbonate rocks, definition
    of 37
Carbonatite 87, 150
Carbondale River 76, 132,
    138
Cardinal family (historical)
    756
Cardium Formation 165
Carduelis
  flammea 649
  hornemanni 649
  tristis 664
Carex
  atrosquama 421
  geyeri 421
  nigricans 421
  rostrata 421
  scirpoidea 421
  scopulorum 421
Cariboo Mountains, gold in
    752

Caribou 736
Carlsberg Column 794
Carnarvon Member 144
Carnegie, James 752
Carnivora 704
Carpet pink 402
Carpodacus
  cassinii 664
  mexicanus 664
  pupureus 648
Carpophore 441
Carterocephalus palaemon 523
Carthew Trail 773
Cascade
  Falls 794
  Mtn. 19, 140
  River 231
Casmerodius albus 663
Cassiar Mountains 12, 171, 177
Cassin's finch 664
Cassiope
  mertensiana 396
  tetragona 396
Castilleja
  lutescens 365
  miniata 368
  occidentalis 402
  raupii 368
  rhexifolia 368
Castle
  Bivouac Hut 784
  Junction 760
  Mtn. 22, 23p, 93, 94p, 788p
Castleguard
  Cave 222p, 223, 225
  Mtn. 87
  Mtn., dykes on 87p
Castor canadensis 698
Castor oil 699
Castoridae 698
Catabatic winds 255
Catbird, gray 663
Caterpillars 528
  acraea moth 528
  anise swallowtail 530
  cabbage white 530
  common blue 530
  creamy marblewing 530
  eastern tiger swallowtail 530
  forest tent 528
  mourning cloak 529
  phoebus parnassian 529
  white-marked tussock moth 529
  woollybear 528
Cathartes
  aura 663
  fuscescens 629
  guttatus 628
  minimus 663
  ustulatus 628
Cathedral
  Escarpment 101, 102d
  Formation 95
  Mtn. 95
Catkins 290
Catostomidae 548
Catostomus
  catostomus 548
  commersoni 548
  macrocheilus 549
  platyrhynchus 549
Cats 712
Cattail, common 411
Cauliflower

fungus 456
  Tree 300p
Cavell (see also Edith Cavell, Mt.)
  Advance, 205
  Edith 761
  Meadows 775
Caves 221, 222p
  age of 221
  ecology of 287p
  glacier 214
  in Skoki Formation 113
  Ordovician 223
Ceanothus velutinus 314
Cedar
  waxwing 633
  western red 301
Cedared Creek, Formation 127
Cedaria 106, 117
Cedarina 106
Celastrina ladon 507
Celestine Road 781
Cellulose 161, 431
Centaurea maculosa 389
Central Canadian Rockies 15
  eastern main ranges of 22
  foothills of 16
  front ranges of 16
  highest point in 26
  physiography of 16
  summary of features 26
  timberline elevation in 26
  western main ranges of 24
Cephalodia 438
Cephalopods 152d
  ammonoid 158
  ammonite 152
Cerambycidae 478
Cerastium 333, 393
Cercariae 535
Cerci 489
Cercyonis
  oetus 516
  pegala 516
Cerisy's sphinx 526
Certhia americana 654
Cervidae 730
Cervus elaphus 732
Ceryle alcyon 598
Cetraria
  cucullata 438
  nivalis 438
  pinastri 436
  tilesii 438
Chaba
  Icefield 212
  Imne 760
Chaetura vauxi 616
Chain Lakes 767
Chalceria
  cupreus 509
  heteronea 506
Chalice flower 391
Chamois 741
Chamomile, scentless 358
Chancellor
  Formation 116, 119p
  Peak 116
Chanterelles and lookalikes 452
Chanterelle
  floccosus 452
  subalbidus 452
Chaoborus 488

Char, speckled 543
Charadrius
  semipalmatus 590
  vociferous 589
Charidryas
  damoetas 510
  palla 510
Charina bottae 564
Charlie Lake Formation 158
Charts, correlation 42, 143, 191
Chatanooga Formation 139
Chateau Lake Louise 756
Cheadle, Dr. 752
Checkerspot
  Anicia 510
  Edith's 511
  Gillette's 511
  northern 510
  rockslide 510
Checklists, bird 665
Chen caerulescens 587
Chephren Lake 773
Cherry 315
Chert 146, 147p
  origin of 148
Chestnut-collared longspur 664
Chetang-Tatei Formation 96
Chetwynd 164
Chickadee
  black-capped 649
  boreal 650
  mountain 650
Chicken mushroom 457
Chickweed 333, 393
Chief Mtn. 28, 29p
Chimaphila umbellata 370
Chinaman's Peak 790
Chinese lantern 398
Chinook
  arch 258p
  salmon 549
Chinooks (weather) 257, 258p
Chionea 534
Chipmunks 688
  least 688
  red-tailed 689
  yellow pine 689
Chipping sparrow 656
Chischa Formation 77
Chitin 118
Chive, wild 378
Chlamydomonas nivalis 532
Chlidonias niger 598
Chloramphenicol 482
Chlorite 73, 83, 164
Chlorophyllum molybdites 445
Choke cherry 315
Cholla cactus 367
Chondroceras 160
Chordeiles minor 617
Chorus frog 561
Chown, Mt. 88
Christie turn 800
Christmas fern 425
Chrysanthemum leucanthemum 347
Chrysemys picta belli 564
Chrysomyxa arctostaphyli 294, 299
Chrysops 470
Chrysopsis villosa 357
Chrysothamnus nauseosus 320

Chryxus arctic 517
Chub
  flathead 550
  lake 551
  peamouth 550
Chungo Member 165
Chushina Formation 110
Cicadas 480
Cicadidae 480
Cichlasoma nigrofasciatum 556
Cichlid, convict 556
Cicuta maculata 415
Cinclus mexicanus 598
Cinnamon
  bear 720
  teal 577
Cinquefoil 358
  alpine 399
  shrubby 318
Circus cyaneus 602
Cirque Lake 773
Cirrus Mountain 134
  Campground 113
Cirsium
  arvense 388
  vulgare 388
Cistothorus palustris 663
Citadel Pass 779
Cladina
  mitis 438
  rangiferina 438
  stellaris 437
Cladonia
  chlorophaea 437
  coccifera 437
  cornuta 437
  gracilis 437
  pyxidata 437
Clams
  fingernail 535
  fossil 164
Clangula hyemalis 579
Clark's nutcracker 296, 624
Clastic rock, origin of 88
Clavaria 455
Clavariadelphus
  pistillaris 455
  truncatus 455
Clay-colored sparrow 658
Claytonia
  lanceolata 332
  megarrhiza 393
Clearing trend, mid-day 254
Clearwing,
  thetis/snowberry 526
Cleavage 78, 79d
Clematis
  columbiana 377
  ligusticifolia 331
Clematis
  blue 377
  western 331
Clemenceau
  Icefield 212
  Mt. 210
Clethrionomys
  gapperi 684
  rutilus 684
Cleveland, Mt. 30
Cliff
  swallow 613
  woodsia 425
Cliffside Cave 222p
Climate 4, 247
  change, recent 260
  data 248t

definition of 247
effect of continental divide on 257
effect of sun angle on 251
effects of latitude and slope angle 251
influence of Pacific Ocean 251
influence of prairie on 253
summary of 247
table 248
Climax avalanche 817
Climbing
  guides 787, 788p, 791p, 795p
  routes 789, 792, 794
  season 787
Cline River
  Bridge 134
  Canyon 139
Clintonia 329
Clintonia uniflora 329
Clitocybe
  aurantiaca 452
  dealbata 451
  gigantea 446
  nuda 449
  odora 448
Clitocybe
  anise-scented 448
  giant 446
Cloaca (birds) 571
Clossiana
  alberta 515
  astarte 515
  freija 514
  frigga 514
  improba 515
  selene 515
  titania 514
Clothing
  backpacking 778
  day-hiking 772
  ski-touring 798
Cloudberry 322
Clouds, lenticular 258p, 259
Cloudywing, northern 523
Clover
  alsike 369
  red 368
  white 340
  white sweet 340
  yellow sweet 364
Club-like fungi 455
Clubmoss, stiff 428
Clubtails 493
Clustered broomrape 381
Coal 152, 161, 163p, 176
  Branch 754
  first noted in Rockies 751
  in Blairmore Group 163p, 164
  in Coalspur Formation 165
  River 86
  Valley 754
Coal-mining 21, 161, 163p, 754
Coalspur Formation 165
Coast Mountains 4, 174
Coccinella
  novemnotata 477
  trifasciata 477
Coccinellidae 477
Coccothraustes vespertinus 643

Codfish 547
Coenagrionidae 493
Coenonympha tullia 516
Colaptes auratus 617
Cold Sulphur Spring 110, 132, 140, 226p
Coleman, A.P. and L.Q. 755
Colias
  alexandra 501
  eurytheme 524
  gigantea 501
  hecla 500
  interior 500
  meadii 500
  nastes 500
  palaeno 500
  pelidne 499
  philodice 501
Colin Range 136, 139, 751
Collembola, Mt. 533
Collembolans 533
Collie, Norman 756
Collins, John 753
Collomia 374
Collomia grandiflora 374
  linearis 374
Colluvium 187
Collybia butyracea 451
Collybia, buttery 451
Color of lakes, ice 234
Coltsfoot 339
  alpine 396
Columba
  fasciata 663
  livia 631
Columbia
  Icefield 210, 213p, 223, 532, 756
  Lake 756
  lily 352
  Mountains 4, 12, 171
Columbian
  forest 269, 274p
  ground squirrel 692
  hawthorn 306
  Orogeny 171
Columbine
  alpine 406
  northern blue 385
  red 373
  yellow 361
Committee's Punch Bowl 750
Common
  alpine 519
  banded skipper 520
  blue 506
  blue caterpillar 530
  cattail 411
  checkered skipper 522
  fireweed 373
  fleabane 346
  flicker 617
  garter snake 563
  goldeneye 581
  grackle 663
  great bulrush 412
  horsetail 426
  juniper 328
  merganser 584
  nighthawk 617
  raven 622
  redpoll 649
  saxifrage 334
  sheep moth 527
  snipe 589
  sulphur 501
  tern 597
  yellowthroat 639

Comparing the Canadian and American Rockies 12, 13d
Compass use 826, inside back cover
Compression of Canadian Rockies 171, 175d
Conaspis 109
Concussion 819
Coney 703
Conglomerate 89
  Cadomin 162, 163p
Conifer false morel 454
Conodonts 127
Conscientious-objector camps 762
Contents, table of x
Continental
  crust 168
  divide 22, 257
  drift 168, 169d
  shelf, western 174
Contopus
  borealis 636
  sordidulus 636
Contorted lousewort 395
Coversion table, metric to American units: inside front cover
Cook, Don 101
Cooking in the backcountry 776
Cooley spruce gall aphid 299
Cooper's hawk 601
Coosella 106
Coot, American 586
Copepods 486
Copper
  Mtn. 111
  ore 76
  sulphate 234
Coppers (butterflies) 508
  American 509
  blue 506
  dorcas 509
  lustrous 509
  mariposa 509
Coprinus
  atramentarius 450
  comatus 444
Coral
  fungi 455
  hairstreak 504
Coral fungus
  flat-topped 455
  pestle-shaped 455
Coral-root
  northern 353
  spotted 354
  striped 354
Corallorhiza
  maculata 354
  striata 354
  trifida 353
Corals (sea) 145p
Corbula munda 160
Cordulia shurtleffi 493
Corduliidae 493
Coregonus clupeaformis 545
Corixidae 490
Cormorant, double-crested 663
Cornice 816
Cornus
  canadensis 336
  nuttallii 336
  stolonifera 313

Correlation charts
  formations and groups 42
  glacial deposits 191
  Rundle Group 143
Cort, silvery violet 446
Cortinarius alboviolaceus 446
Cortinarius, silvery 446
Corvus
  brachyrynchos 623
  corax 622
Cory, Mt. 745
Corydalis 365
Corydalis aurea 365
Corylus cornuta 313
Costigan Member, Mt. 138
Cottidae 554
Cotton grass 421
Cottonwood
  Black 305
  plains 305
  Slough 278, 570
Cottus
  cognatus 554
  ricei 555
Coturnicops novabonracensis 663
Couesius plumbeus 551
Cougar 714
Cow parsnip 344
Cow-berry 369
Cowbird, brown-headed 646
Coydog 716
Coyote 715
Cracker Flats 76
Craighead brothers 724
Cranberry
  high-bush 315
  low-bush 326
  mountain 369
  small bog 372
Cranbrook 160
Crane fly 468
  snow 534
Crane's-bill 381
Crane, sandhill 588, 663
Crataegus
  columbiana 306
  douglasii 306
Cratoneuron 432
Creamy marblewing 498
  caterpillar 530
Creeper, brown 654
Creeping
  juniper 328
  mahonia 358
  snowberry 338
  wintergreen 338
Crep, jelly 457
Crepicephalus 108
Crepidotus mollis 457
Crepis nana 400
Crescentspot
  field 512
  pearly 511
Cretaceous seaway 155, 156m
Crevasse 214, 215p, 792
  rescue 792d
Cricetidae 680
Cricket, field 480
Crinoids 109, 142
Crocus, prairie 377
Cronartium ribicola 296
Cross fox 719
Cross-bedding 89
Cross-sections

of Rockies 50d
of western Canadian
Cordillera 172d
Crossbill, red 648
white-winged 647
Crossing Rockies without
crossing thrust faults
182, 183d
Crow, American 623
Crowberry 408
Crowfoot
Advance 205
Dyke 86
Glacier Viewpoint 86,
769
Crowfoot, water 414
Crowsnest
Formation 155, 162
Mtn. 28
Pass 27, 753, 757
volcanics 162
Crowsnest Pass,
Municipality of 162
Crucibulum 459
Crustaceans 486
Crustose lichens 439, 440
Cryptogamic soil 275
Cryptogramma
crispa 424
stelleri 423
Cudonia 455
Cudonia circinans 455
Cudweed sagewort 389
Cuesta 31
Culaea inconstans 555
Culex tarsalis 467
Culicidae 466
Cup fungi 458
Cup, eyelash 459
Curlew
eskimo 663
long-billed 663
Currie, K.L. 151
Cut-away views of
Canadian Rockies 50d
Cutbank Creek 748
Cutthroat trout 541
Cyanocitta
cristata 625
stelleri 625
Cyathus 459
Cyclic sediments 103
Cyclomedusa 85
Cygnus columbianus 587
Cypress Creek 757
Cyprinidae 549
Cypripedium
calceolus 353
montanum 341
passerinum 341
Cypseloides niger 616
Cyrtospirifer 135
Cystopteris fragilis 424

Dabbling (ducks) 567
Dace
finescale 553
leopard 552
longnose 552
northern redbelly 553
pearl 551
Dacrymyces palmatus 459
Dactylina arctica 437
Daddy-long-legs 485
Daisy
fleabane 346
ox-eye 347
Dakotas 746
Dall's sheep 740

Daly, Mt. 804
Dam
Bennett 763
Grand Coulee 539
Mica 763
Damselfly naiad 489
Dandelion 354
alpine 399
Dandelions, false 354
Danthonia californica 420
Dark wood-nymph 516
Dark-eyed junco 655
Darners 493
Dating geological events
using lichens 207
Dawson, George 148, 160,
754
Day length 251, 252d
Day-hikes, recommended
772
de Smet, Father Pierre Jean
751
Dead-man's fingers 455
Deadman Flats 139
Death camas 331
Debris flows, Devonian 130
Deception Pass 782
Declination, magnetic 828
Deepest
cave 223
lake 234
Deer 730
brush 314
flies 470
mouse 680
mule 730
white-tailed 731
DEET 466
Definition of "Canadian
Rockies" 1
Delicious lactarius 453
Delphinium 385
Delphinium
bicolor 385
glaucum 385
menziesii 386
Delta 234
Den
bear 721
wolf 718
Dendragapus
canadensis 610
obscurus 610
Dendroctonus ponderosae
478
Dendroica
castanea 663
coronata 640
magnolia 641
nigrescens 663
palmarum 663
petechia 638
striata 641
tigrina 663
townsendi 639
virens 663
Déné 745
Dennis, Mt. 101
Dentinum repandum 444
Denver, Colorado 13
Deposition in Mesozoic 153
Deposits in Rocky
Mountain Trench 186
Depth hoar 796, 817
Dermacentor andersoni 481
Descurania sophia 363
Desquamatia 128
Development in national
parks 763

effect of 829
Devil's-club 317
Devonian
geography, maps of 124
reefs 128, 129d
Devonoproductus 135
Dewberry 374
Dewdney Trail 753
Diabase 75, 86
Diamictite 86
Diamonds 87
Diatoms 486
Diatremes 87
Dick (Indian guide) 757
Dickcissel 664
Dickens, Charles 544
Dicranum 430
Dictyna 483
Didymograptus 110
Differential erosion of
mountain front 19
Digger wasp 475
Dikelocephalus 109
Dingy arctic fritillary 515
Dinorthis 115
Dinosaurs 167
Dip (geology) 19
slope 19
Dipodidae 683
Dipper, American 598
Direttissima 789
Disaster Point 131, 285
Discharge of rivers
seasonal and daily
variation in 231
table 232
Disconformity 122
Discotropites 158
Disk-flowers 346
Disporum trachycarpum
331
Dissolved load of stream
209
Distance of shortening in
Rockies 174
Distichum capillaceum 433
Ditrichum flexicaule 433
Diving beetles 491
Dock 389
Docking (geology) 171
Dodecatheon
conjugens 372
pulchellum 372
Dog violet 384
Dog-ear lichen 438
Dog-hair forest 293
Dogbane 325
Dogs 715
Dogtooth violet 352
Dogwood
dwarf 336
red-osier 313
Dolichonyx oryzivorus 663
Dolly Varden 544
Dolomite 96, 97p
Creek 782
mottling 97
Dolomitization 96
Dorag dolomitization 97
Dorcas copper 509
Double bladder-pod 401
Double-crested cormorant
663
Douglas
David 751
maple 314
Douglas-fir 299
broomed 300p
oldest in Alberta 300p

woods, ecology of 277p
Dove
mourning 632
rock 631
Dowitcher
long-billed 594
short-billed 663
Downy woodpecker 619
Drab wildflowers 389, 397
Draba
white 333
yellow 362
Draba 333
aurea 362
incerta 362
Draco skipper 520
Dragon sagewort 389
Dragonflies and
damselflies 492
Dragonfly naiads 488
Dreamy duskywing 522
Drepanocladus 409, 431
Drosera
anglica 341
linearis 341
rotundifolia 341
Drumlins 197
Drumming
in grouse 609
in woodpeckers 571
Drummond, Thomas 750
Drummond's
anemone 334, 392
willow 308
Dryas flats, ecology of
279p
Dryas
integrifolia 393
drummondii 361
octopetala 393
Dryas
white 393
yellow 361
Dryocopus pileatus 618
Duck
harlequin 583
ring-necked 580
ruddy 583
wood 584
Ducks and duck-like water
birds 572
Duckweed 410
Dumetella carolinensis 663
Dunedin Formation 127
Dunes 235p, 236
Dung fly 469
Dung-loving psilocybe 451
Dunlin 593
Dunvegan Formation 164
Dusky
flycatcher 635
shrew 679
Duskywing
dreamy 522
Persius 522
Dust, volcanic 174
Dutch clover 340
Dwarf
birch 319
epilobium 375
false asphodel 343
raspberry 374
willow-herb 375
Dykes (geology) 36, 75, 77,
86, 87p, 115
Dytiscidae 488
Dytiscus 491
Eagle
bald 605

golden 605
Eared grebe 574
Earl of Southesk 752
Early
  blue violet 384
  Pleistocene 192
  yellow locoweed 364
  yellow locoweed, alpine 401
Earthquake 177, 210, 227
Earthstar, barometer 461
East
  Glacier 761
  Kootenays 160
Eastern
  bluebird 663
  kingbird 634
  main ranges of central Rockies 22
  phoebe 663
  Slopes Policy 763
  tiger swallowtail 502
  tiger swallowtail caterpillar 530
Echinoderms 142
Ecological
  communities 273
  divisions 264m, 267
Ecoregions 266
Edibility of mushrooms 441
Edith Cavell 761
  Mt. 88, 92p, 761, 793
  Mt., glacial recession at 206p, 207
Edith's checkerspot 511
Edith, Lake 570
Edwards' fritillary 512
EEOR 790
Eggs of birds 572
Egret, great 663
Egypt Lake Shelter 784
Ekvasophyllum 145
Elaeagnus commutata 312
Elbert, Mt. 770
Elderberry 316
Eldon and Palliser formations, differentiating 138
Eldon
  Formation 97p, 100, 103, 138, 180
  siding 100
Elephant-head 371
Elevation, effect on climate 254
Elfin
  brown 504
  hoary 505
  western pine 505
Elizabeth Parker Hut 784
Elk 5p, 732, 761
  Formation 160
  Pass Cabin 783
  River 112, 187
Elko 136
  Formation 96
Ellen Wilson Lake 778
Ellesmerian Orogeny 128
Elvinia 108, 109
Elymus glaucus 418
Elytra 477
Emerald Lake 754
Emeralds 493
Emergencies 813, 814
Emetic russula 447
Emperor Falls 781
Empetrum nigrum 408
Empidonax
  alnorum 635

difficilis 636
  flaviventris 663
  hammondii 635
  minimus 634
  oberholseri 635
  trailli 635
Empire Formation 74
Encalypta 433
Encounters with bears 725
Encrinurus 115
Endless Chain Ridge 88
Endocronartium harknessii 294
Endogone 681
Endymion nonscriptum 383
Engelmann spruce 297, 328
Engraver beetles 478
Entosphenus tridentatus 547
Epargyreus clarus 524
Epidemia
  dorcas 509
  mariposa 509
Epilobium, dwarf 375
Epilobium
  alpinum 375
  angustifolium 373
  latifolium 373
Epiphyte 435
Epiphyton 101
Eptesicus fuscus 676
Equisetum
  arvense 426
  fluviatile 427
  hyemale 427
  laevigatum 427
  palustre 426
  pratense 426
  scirpoides 427
  sylvaticum 426
  variegatum 427
Erebia
  disa 519
  discoidalis 519
  epipsodea 519
  magdalena 524
  rossii 519
  theano 524
Eremophila alpestris 612
Erethizon dorsatum 697
Erethizontidae 697
Erigeron
  aureus 400
  caespitosus 346
  compositus 346
  lanatus 395
  pallens 395
  peregrinus 387
Eriogonum
  flavum 366
  ovalifolium 401
  umbellatum 366
Eriophorum chamissonis 421
Ermine 704
Erosion 19, 210, 221
  processes, list of 209
Erratics 195, 196p, 202, 203p
Erynnis
  icelus 522
  pacuvius 524
  persius 522
Erysimum
  inconspicuum 363
  pallasii 405
Erythronium grandiflorum 352
Eskers 197, 199d

Eskimo curlew 663
Esocidae 546
Esox lucius 546
Estigmene acraea 525, 528
Etherington Creek, Formation, Mt. 145
Euchloe
  ausonides 498, 530
  creusa 498
  hyantis 524
Eumeces skiltonianus 565
Euomphalus 139
Euphagus
  carolinus 645
  cyanocephalus 645
Euptoieta claudia 524
Eurasian water-milfoil 410
European
  starling 631
  wigeon 663
Eutamias
  amoenus 689
  minimus 688
  ruficaudus 689
Evaporation of snow (sublimation) 212
Evaporative reflux 97
Evaporites 105, 144
Evening grosbeak 643
Everes amyntula 506
Evergreen
  conifers 292
  violet 352
Everlasting
  alpine 396
  pearly 339
  rosy 370
  small-flowered 338
Eversmann's parnassian 499
Exfoliation 209
Expansion and contraction of rock 209
Explorer's gentian 406
Exposure, injury by 820
Exshaw Formation, community 139
Extinguisher Tower 793
Eyed hawk-moth 526
Eyelash cup 459
Faberophyllum 145
Facies change 101
Fairholme Group, Range 128
  Reef Complex 132
Fairy
  bells 331
  candelabra 332
  rings 451
  shrimp 486
  upchuck 439
Fairy's-slipper 371
Fairy-ring mushroom 451
Falco
  columbarius 599
  mexicanus 600
  peregrinus 599
  rusticolus 663
  sparverius 599
Falcon
  peregrine 599
  prairie 600
Fall color, time for 291
Falls
  Overlander 539
  Punchbowl 163p
  Rearguard 539
  Takakkaw 219, 769
False
  asphodel 343

azalea 327
chanterelle 452
dandelions 354
hellebore 350
huckleberry 327
leather-leaved saxifrage 335
lupine 364
mitrewort 345
morel, conifer 454
morel, saddle-shaped 454
Solomon's-seal 330
tarragon 389
Families of birds 664
Fammenian 131
Fanglomerate 187
Fantasque Formation 149
Faraday-cage effect 815
Fastest bird 600
Fathead minnow 554
Faulting
  recent 178, 187
  strike, slip 176
Faults
  along bedding planes 184, 185d
  following layering 180
  normal (see normal faults)
  tear (see tear faults)
  thrust (see thrust faults)
Faunus anglewing 503
Fawn mushroom 449
Fay Hut 784
Feather mosses 429p
Feldspar 150
Felidae 712
Felis
  concolor 714
  lynx 712
  rufus 713
Felwort 388
Fenland Trail 278, 568
Fenster 28
Fern
  grape 423
  holly/Christmas 425
  lady 424
  oak 425
  parsley 424
Fern-like, but not ferns 425
Fernie 27, 757
  Basin 152
  Formation 152, 158, 174
  William 757
Ferns 423
Ferruginous hawk 663
Fescue 418
Festuca
  saximontana 418
  scabrella 418
Fever, tick 482
Fiddle River 135
Fiddlehead 423
Field 24, 257
  crescentspot 512
  cricket 480
  geology 180
Filbert 313
Finch
  Cassin's 664
  gray-crowned rosy 648
  house 664
  purple 648
  rosy 648
Finescale dace 553
Fingernail clams 535
Finlay River 757
Finlay, John 748

Fir, alpine/subalpine 298
Fire (see forest fire)
Fireside 86
Fireweed 373
Firn line 792
First aid 818, 824
  kit 825
Fishes 536
Fish
  during Ice Age 536
  fossils 123
  ladder 539
  Lake Cabin 783
  Lakes 782
  reproduction 537
Fish-hawk 604
Fisher 708
Fitzhugh 761
Fitzwilliam, Mt. 85
Flag trees 328
Flash floods 22
Flat-topped coral 455
Flathead
  chub 550
  Fault 30, 178, 186
  Formation 88
  River 11
  Road 186
  Valley 11
Flatirons (Boulder,
  Colorado) 13
Flatworms 486
Flax, wild blue 384
Fleabane 346
  alpine 395
  common 346
  golden 400
  showy 387
  woolly 395
Fledging (birds) 572
Fleming, Sir Sanford 753
Flexural-slip folding 184,
  185d
Flicker
  common 617
  gilded 617
  red-shafted 617
  yellow-shafted 617
Flight speed of birds 572
Flint 148
Flixweed 363
Flocking, in birds 571
Floe Lake 107p
Flowering season 290
Flume Creek, Formation
  131
Fluted white helvella 454
Fly
  agaric 445
  black 471
  blue bottle 469
  crane 468
  deer 470
  dung 469
  green bottle 469
  horse 470
  house 468
  hover 473
Flycatcher
  dusky 635
  Hammond's 635
  least 634
  olive-sided 636
  Traill's 635
  western 636
  yellow-bellied 663
Flying squirrel, northern
  696
Foam flower 345

Foehn (wind) 257
  wall 259
Folded-wing skippers 520
Fold in Mt. Kidd 184, 185p
Folding
  flexural slip 184, 185d
  Mtn. 140, 142
Folds
  effect of on hard and
    soft layers 184
  overturned 25
  shape of in front ranges
    184
Foliose lichens 439
Food for backpacking 778
Fool's gold (iron pyrite) 90
Foothills
  of central Rockies 16,
    18p
  of northern Rockies 32,
    33p
  of southern Rockies 28
  southern, ecology of 269,
    274p
Foothills Erratics Train
  202, 203d
Foraminifera 132
Forb, definition of 289
Foredeep 154d, 174
Forest
  feather-moss 277p
  fires in Bow Valley 754
  lower subalpine 280p
  montane 276p
  tent caterpillar 525, 528
  upper subalpine 281p
Forewings 494
Forget-me-not, alpine 404
Formation (geology) 39
Formations
  and groups, chart of 42
  out of order due to
    faulting 180
Formic acid 476
Formica 475
Formicidae 475
Forster's tern 663
Fort
  Chipewyan 746
  George 748
  Grahame 757
  Nelson 748
  St. John 164, 748
  St. John Group 164
  William 749
Fortress
  Lake 756
  Mountain ski area 184
Forty-Mile Creek 782
Fossil
  fish plates 123
  marine plants 128
  Mtn. 112
  plants 164, 187
  pollen 187
  snails 167
  soft-bodied creatures 98
Fossils
  earliest known of
    animals 85
  microscopic 149
  illustrations of 67
Foster, William 761, 758p
Four
  great layers of the
    Rockies 37
  Point Creek and cabin
    779
Four-parted gentian 407

Four-spot skimmer 493
Fox
  cross 719
  red 719
  silver 719
  sparrow 661
Foxtail 417
  barley 419
Fragaria virginiana 337
Frank Slide 216, 217p, 759
Franklin's gull 597, 663
Fraser River, Grand
  Canyon of 752
Fraser
  Colin 751
  Simon 748
Frasnian 131
Freeze-and-thaw 209
Freshfield Icefield 87, 212
Freya's fritillary 514
Frigga fritillary 514
Fringe-cup 334
Fringed
  gentian 388
  grass-of-parnassus 335
Fritillaries 511
Fritillary
  Alberta 515
  aphrodite 512
  astarte 515
  Atlantis 513
  bog 514
  callippe 512
  dingy arctic 515
  Edwards' 512
  Freya's 514
  frigga 514
  great spangled 513
  hydaspe 513
  Mormon 513
  napaea 515
  silver-bordered 515
  Titania's 514
  zerene 512
Fritz, Bill 103
Frog
  chorus 561
  northern leopard 560
  spotted 561
  tailed 561
  wood 560
Front ranges of central
  Rockies 16
  date of appearance 155
Frost
  cankers 304
  hollows 255
  pockets 221
Frost-wedging 209
Frostbite 822
Fry, fish 549
Fulica americana 586
Fungal rust 382
Fungi
  bird's-nest 459
  bracket 456
  club-like 455
  coral 455
  cup 458
  jelly 459
  mushrooms 441
  mycorrhizal 441
  shelf 456
Fungus, cauliflower 456
Fur trade 746-752
Furcula 533
Fuzzy foot 450
Gadidae 547
Gadwall 578

Gaillardia aristata 357
Galatea, Mt. 712
Galerina 452
Galium boreale 345
Gaillardia, wild 357
Gallinago gallinago 589
Galls 293
  eaten by squirrels 695
  on willows 307
Galton Range 12
Gambusia affinis 556
Gapper's red-backed vole
  684
Garbitt, Mt. 88
Garnets 79
Garter snakes 562, 563
Gas, natural 142, 152, 759
Gasterosteidae 555
Gastroplites 164
Gastrotrichs 486
Gataga Formation 77
Gates Formation 164
Gateway Formation 76
Gaultheria
  hispidula 338
  procumbens 370
  humifusa 338
Gavia
  arctica 663
  immer 572
  stellata 663
Geese and swans 586
Geikie siding 87
Gem-studded puffball 460
Gemmae 429
Gentians 388, 406
  blue-bottle/smooth
    alpine 407
  four-parted 407
  fringed 388
  moss 407
  mountain/explorer's 406
  northern 388
Gentiana
  amarella 388
  calycosa 406
  detonsa 388
  glauca 407
  propinqua 407
  prostrata 407
Geocaulon livida 348
Geologic
  column for Rockies 38d,
    40
  cross-sections of Rockies
    50d
  history, block diagrams
    of 45d
  map of Canadian
    Rockies 47m
  maps list 244
  periods 42t
  symbols and
    abbreviations 40
  views, labeled sketches
    of 51d
Geological Survey of
  Canada, address in
  Calgary 237
Geology, roadside (sketches
  of) 51-66
Geomyidae 694
George Formation 77
Geothlypis trichas 639
Geranium
  bicknellii 381
  richardsonii 332
  viscosissimum 381

Geranium
  sticky/Bicknell's 381
  wild white 332
Gerridae 491
Gething Formation, Mt. 164
Geum
  aleppicum 360
  macrophyllum 361
  triflorum 370
Ghost River 110
Giant bur-reed 412
Giant
  carpenter ant 476
  clitocybe 446
  dandelion 355
  Steps 773
  water bug 490
  water scavenger beetle 491
Giardia lamblia 824
Giardiasis 824
Gilia aggregata 374
Gillette's checkerspot 511
Glacial
  advance and retreat, reasons for 212
  budget 212
  chronology, table of 189
  deposits, correlation chart of 191
  deposits in northern Rockies 210p
  drumlins 197, 198p
  eskers 197, 199d
  flow, rate of 212
  front 212
  kame terraces 197, 198d, 199d
  kames 197, 199d
  moraines 189, 190p, 201p, 212
  periods, table of 189t
  recession 206p
  recession areas, ecology of 287p
  silt (see rock flour)
  till 189, 190p, 194p, 200
  winds 255
  zones of ablation and accumulation 212
Glaciation 189
  as erosional process 209
  in Bow Valley area 197
  early Pleistocene 192
  effect of on Rockies 190d
  future 207
  Gunz 192
  Holocene 204, 205
  Illinoian 192
  in Jasper area 200
  Kansan 192
  Mindel 192
  modern 210
  Nebraskan 192
  north of Athabasca River 34, 202
  pre-Pleistocene 189
  Riss 192
  in Waterton/Glacier area 197
  western slope 202
  Wisconsinan 196
  Würm 192
Glacier
  caves 214, 215p
  Lake 106
  lily 352
  National Park 761

National Park, bear attacks in 729
  Peak tephra 205
Glaciers
  features of (at Athabasca) 199d
  firn line on 792
  rock 216
  speed of 212
Gladstone Formation, Mt. 162
Glaucidium gnoma 608
Glaucomys sabrinus 696
Glaucopsyche piasus 506
Glenmore Reservoir 16
Glenogle
  Creek 118
  Shales 117, 119p
Globeflower 391
Glossopleura 98
Glycyrrhiza lepidota 350
Gnats (midges) 468
Gneiss 3, 79, 80p, 171
Goat Haunt Trail Shelter 783
Goat's-beard 317, 355
Goat, mountain 741
Godwit, marbled 663
Goethite 90, 227
Gog
  Group 88, 92p
  Lake 88
  erratics 195, 196p, 203p
Going-to-the-Sun Road 76, 281, 282, 767, 768p
  construction of 762
  bicycling on 809
  geology seen from 28
Gold Creek 187
Golden age
  of Canadian Rockies geology 40
  of mountaineering 757
Golden
  aster 357
  corydalis 365
  eagle 605
  Embayment 127
  fleabane 400
  northern bumble bee 472
  town of 754
  trout 542
Golden-crowned
  kinglet 651
  sparrow 657
Golden-mantled ground squirrel 689
Golden-plover, lesser 663
Goldeneye
  Barrow's 581
  common 581
Goldenrod
  alpine 402
  mountain 364
  spider 484
Goldenweed, Lyall's 400
Goldeye 555
Goldfinch, American 664
Gomphidae 493
Goodsir, Mt. 108
Goodyera oblongifolia 342
Goose
  Canada 586
  snow 587
Gooseberry 322
Gopher
  snake 563
  northern pocket 694
Goral 741

Gordon Formation 95
Gorges 219, 221
Gorget 626
Gorman Creek Formation 161
Goshawk, northern 601
Graben 177, 186
Grackle, common 663
Graded bedding 84
Graminoid, definition of 289
Grand
  Circle Tour 760
  Coulee Dam 539
  Trunk Pacific Railway 761
Grande
  Cache 161, 162, 164, 750, 755
  Prairie 759
Granite 3, 81, 171
  Park 76, 783
  Park Chalet 783
Grape fern 423
Graptolites 118p
Grass, description of 416
Grass-of-parnassus 335
  alpine 392
Grasses and grass-like plants 416
Grasshopper
  alpine 480
  pallid-winged 479
  sparrow 664
Grasshoppers and crickets 479
Gray
  catbird 663
  hairstreak 504
  jay 566p, 624
  partridge 663
  wolf 717
Gray-cheeked thrush 663
Gray-crowned rosy finch 648
Grayling
  arctic 544
  Formation 158
Greasewood 320
Great
  blue heron 587
  Divide Trail 782
  egret 663
  Glaciation 192
  gray owl 606
  horned owl 606
  Northern Railway 757
  northern sulphur 501
  Plains 11
  Salt Lake, Utah 97
  Snowy Mountain 210
  spangled fritillary 513
Greater yellowlegs 593
Grebe
  eared 574
  horned 574
  pied-billed 574
  red-necked 573
  western 573
Green
  alder 313
  bottle fly 469
  heather 397
  heron 663
  wildflowers 348, 397
  mudstone, origin of color in 73
  pyrola 348
Green-banded mariposa 377

Green-spored lepiota 445
Green-winged teal 576
Greenhouse effect 260
Greenish blue (butterfly) 505
Greenland sulphur 500
Greenock, Mt. 150
Greyson Formation 73
Grillidae 480
Grimmia 433
Grindelia squarrosa 357
Grinnell
  Formation 74
  Point 76
Gritstone 77, 83
Grizzly bear 722, 729
  attacks by 727
Grosbeak
  black-headed 664
  evening 643
  pine 647
  rose-breasted 664
Grotto
  Member 132
  Mtn., quarrying on 218
Ground
  birch 314
  moraine 197
Ground squirrel
  Columbian 692
  golden-mantled 689
  Richardson's 691
  thirteen-lined 690
Ground squirrels as carriers of plague 690
Ground-cedar 428
Groundhog 693
Groundsel 363
Group (geology) 71
Grouse 609
  blue 610
  ruffed 609
  sharp-tailed 663
  spruce 610
Grouseberry 369
Grus canadensis 588, 663
Grylloblatta
  campodeiformis 534
Gryllus pennsylvanicus 480
Gryphaea 160
Guidebooks
  general naturalist's 9
  recreational 811
Guides, mountain 787
Gulls 595
  Bonaparte's 597
  California 596
  Franklin's 597, 663
  herring 596
  mew 596
  ring-billed 595
  Sabine's 663
  Thayer's 663
Gulo gulo 710
Gumweed 357
Gunsight Lake, Pass 778
Gunz glaciation 192
Guppy 556
Gutierrezia sarothrae 357
Gymnocarpium dryopteris 425
Gypidula 135
Gypsum 225
Gyrfalcon 663
Gyrinidae 490
Gyrinus 490
Gyromitra
  esculenta 454
  infula 454

Gyromitra, hooded 454

Habenaria
　dilitata 342
　hyperborea 342
　obtusata 342
　unalascensis 342
　viridis 342
Habitats of birds 571
Hail, erosion by 209
Hair lichens 436
Hairgrass 419
Hairstreak
　coral 504
　gray 504
　white-lined green 504
Hairy woodpecker 618
Hairy-cap mosses 434
Half-graben 177
Halfway River 757
Haliaeetus leucocephalus
　605
Hammond's flycatcher 635
Hanging valleys 219
Hanington Formation 149
Haplopappus lyallii 400
Hard-rock mining 755
Hardest rock in the
　Rockies 88
Hare, snowshoe/varying
　702
Harebell 383
　alpine 404
Harem, elk 733
Harkenclenus titus 504
Harlequin duck 583
Harmon, Byron 759
Harrier, northern 602
Harris' sparrow 664
Harrogate Formation 127
Hart Highway 762
Hartley Creek 158
Harvestmen 485
Hatsinaton, Pierre 750
Hawes, Jasper 750
Hawk Mtn. 135
Hawks 599
　broad-winged 663
　Cooper's 601
　ferruginous 663
　marsh 602
　pigeon 599
　red-tailed 602
　rough-legged 603
　sharp-shinned 600
　sparrow 599
　Swainson's 603
Hawk-moth
　bee 526
　eyed 526
Hawk-owl, northern 607
Hawksbeard, alpine/dwarf
　400
Hawkweed 355
　narrow-leaved 355
　prairie 355
　slender 355
Hawthorn 306
Hazelnut 313
Head injuries 819
Head-shaped lousewort 401
Heal-all 386
Healy Pass, skiing to 803
Heart-leaved twayblade 371
Heather vole 685
Heather
　green/yellow 397
　pink 403
　white 396

Hebeloma crustuliniforme
　448
Hector
　Dr. James 752
　Lake 210
Hedgehog mushroom 444
Hedysarum
　alpinum 368
　boreale 379
Hedysarum
　Mackenzie's 379
　pale 368
Helen Creek 86
Helena Formation 74
Heliotropium 345
Hellebore, false 350
Helleborus 350
Helmet Mtn. 158
Helvella crispa 454
Helvella, fluted white 454
Hemaris
　diffinis 526
　thysbe 527
Hematite 90
Hemi-penis 563
Hemichromis bimaculatus
　557
Hemileuca eglanterina 527
Hemlock
　water 415
　western (tree) 301
Henbane, black 390
Henday, Anthony 746
Henderson, G.G. 114
Henry
　Creek Formation 77
　House 749
　William 749
Heracleum lanatum 344
Herb, definition of 289
Herchmer Pass 757
Hermit thrush 628
Heron
　great blue 587
　green 663
Herrero, Steve 725
Herring gull 596
Hesperia
　comma 520
　nevada 521
Hesperiidae 520
Heteroscelus incanus 663
Heuchera
　cylindrica 362
　parvifolia 335, 362
Hibernation (dormancy) in
　bears 721
Hidden Lake Overlook 767
Hieracium
　cynoglossoides 355
　triste 355
　umbellatum 355
Hierochloe odorata 419
High-bush cranberry 315
High-mountain blue 508
Higher peaks (over
　3500 m), list of 794
Highest point in Canadian
　Rockies 1
　in central region 26
　in northern region 36
　in southern region 30
Highwood
　Pass 216, 282
　Range 145
Hiking 6, 7p, 772, 777p
Hilda Creek Hostel 807
Hill-topping 465
Hillcrest Disaster 759

Himalayas 170
Himavatites 158
Hind Hut 785p
Hindwings 494
Hinton 759
　pulp mill at 785p
Hiodon alosoides 555
Hiodontidae 555
Hippodamia convergens
　477
Hippuris
　montana 410
　vulgaris 410
Hirundo
　pyrrhonota 613
　rustica 613
History 8
　outline of 745
Histrionicus histrionicus
　583
Hoary
　bat 678
　elfin 505
　marmot 693
　redpoll 649
　willow 308
Hogback ridge 18p
Hollebeke Formation 132
Holly fern 425
Hollyhock 375
Holocene Epoch 204
Holodiscus discolor 317
Holroyd, Geoff 616
Hominidae 742
Homo sapiens 742
Honey
　bee 471
　mushroom 449
Honeydew (aphid) 475
Honeysuckle
　bracted 325
　orange 317
　twining 326
　Utah 325
Hooded
　gyromitra 454
　ladies' tresses 342
　merganser 585
Hoodoos 200, 201p
Hook Lake 138
Hooker
　Icefield 212
　Mt. 755
Hordeum jubatum 419
Horn corals 145
Horned
　grebe 574
　lark 612
Hornet, bald-faced 473
Horntail, smoky 474
Horse flies 470
Horsemint 369
Horsetail 426
　common 426
　sedge-like 427
Horsethief Creek Group 81
Host plants, of butterflies
　494
Hostels 805, 806m,t
Hot springs and mineral
　springs 225, 226d
　data table for 228t
　organisms in 227, 556
House
　finch 664
　fly 468
　mosquitoes 467
　mouse 681
　sparrow 654
　wren 653

Hover flies 473
Howse Pass, 749
Huckleberry 323
　false 327
Hudson's
　Bay Company 746
　Hope 164, 748
Hugh Allan Creek 78, 79
Human affairs in Canadian
　Rockies, summary of
　6
Hummingbird
　calliope 626
　moth 527
　ruby-throated 663
　rufous 626
Hungabee, Mt. 101
Hunter, Edwin ("The Gold
　Seeker") 754
Hurd, Mt. 24
Huts 782, 785p
Hybomitra 470
Hybopsis gracilis 550
Hydaspe fritillary 513
Hydnum imbricatum 444
Hydrocarbons, dried 132
Hydrogen sulphide 225
Hydrophilidae 491
Hydrophilus triangularis
　491
Hydrozoans 486
Hygrohypnum luridum 432
Hygrophorus
　oliveaceoalbus 450
Hyla regilla 562
Hylocomnium splendens
　430
Hyoscyamus niger 390
Hyphae 441
Hypnum
　revolutum 434
　vaucheri 434
Hypodryas gillettii 511
Hypogymnia physodes 436
Hypothermia 820
Hypsithermal 204

Icaricia
　acmon 508
　icarioides 506, 530
Ice
　Age (Pleistocene Epoch)
　189
　cap in British Columbia
　192
　insects 534
　River, alkaline complex
　150, 151d
　worms 533
　color of 234
　flowage of 212
Ice-climbing 794, 795p
Ice-cored moraine 214
Ice-free corridor 193, 194d,
　745
Icefall Brook 87
Icefield 210
　Campground 110
　Centre 255
　Columbia 213p
　skiing 804
Icefields
　and glaciers 210
　locations of 211m
Icefields Parkway 210, 762,
　769
　bicycling on 807
Ichneumon, western giant
　474

Ichneumonidae 474
Ichnofossils 90
Icmadophila ericetorum 438
Icterus galbula 663
Ijolite 150
Iliamna rivularis 375
Illinoian glaciation 192
Imbricated thrusts 180
Impacts
  erosion by 209
  extraterrestrial 131
Incisalia
  augustus 504
  eryphon 505
  mossii 524
  polios 505
Incubation period in birds
  572
Index fossils 70
Indian pipe 341
Indians
  Algonquin 746
  Beaver 745
  Blackfoot 746
  Blood 746
  Iroquois 746
  Kootenay 227, 745
  Nipissing 746
  Peigan 746
  Sarcee 745
  Sekani 745
  Shoshoni 746
  Shuswap 746
  Snake 746
  Stoney 227, 746
Ingenika River 186
Injuries, minor 824
Ink Pots 773, 802
Inky cap 450
Inland ocean, Cretaceous
  157
Innisfail 746
Inoceramus 160, 164, 165
Inocybe umbratica 451
Insects and spiders 465
Insect
  awards 465
  bites and stings 475, 825
  ice 534
  larvae, aquatic 486
  repellents 466
  stings 475
Insular Terrane 155, 170
Interfemoral membrane 675
Interior Plains 11
  margin of, northern
    Rockies 31
Intermontane Terrane 153,
  170
Internment camps 762
Intoxicating mushrooms
  442
Introduction 1
Intrusions 87p, 151p
Involucral bracts 346
Ips 478
Iridium 167
Iron pyrite 90
Iron-plant, Lyall's 400
Iroquois Indians 746
Irridinitus 85
Ishbel Group 149
Isia isabella 527, 528
Island arcs 170
Isotopic dating of rocks 70,
  197
Ixoreus naevius 627

Jack pine 294
Jackfish 546
Jackpine River 100, 104
Jackrabbit, white-tailed
  702
Jacob's ladder 383
Jacques Lake 781
Jacupirangite 150
Jade 151
Jaeger
  long-tailed 663
  parasitic 663
Japanese internment 762
Jarvis Lakes 138
Jasper 276, 761
  birding at 570
  House 750
  Lake 236
  Lake, dunes at 235p
  National Park 760
  Park Lodge 749, 761
  trails 775
  Tramway 283
Jasper-Hinton Airport 165
Jay
  blue 625
  Canada 624
  gray 624, 566p
  Steller's 625
Jelly
  apricot (fungus) 453
  crep 457
  fungi 459
Jesus bugs 492
Jewelfish 557
John McKay Creek 117
John Stevens Canyon 25
Johnston
  Canyon 149, 219, 568,
    773
  Canyon Formation 149
  Creek 782
Jonas
  Creek rockslide 216
  Shoulder 779
Joyce, James 179
Jubilee Formation 94
Jumping mouse
  meadow 683
  western 683
Jumping Pound Creek 165,
  568
Jumping spiders 485
Junco hyemalis 655
Junco
  dark-eyed 655
  Oregon 655
  slate-colored 655
Juncus
  balticus 422
  bufonius 422
  mertensianus 422
Juneberry 324
Junegrass 418
Juniper
  common/prickly 328
  creeping 328
  Rocky
    Mountain/scopulorum
    318
Juniperus
  communis 328
  horizontalis 328
  scopulorum 318
Jutta arctic 517

Kain
  Conrad 758p, 761
  Face 793

Kakwa Lake 112, 161
Kalispell 257
Kalmia
  microphylla 403
  polifolia 373
Kame terraces 197, 198d,
  199d
Kames 197, 199d
Kananaskis Country 763
  bicycling in 809
Kananaskis
  Dam 165
  Formation 149
  Pass 751, 778
  Provincial Park (Peter
    Lougheed Provincial
    Park) 763
Kane, Paul 751
Kansan glaciation 192
Karst 218, 223, 224p
  Spring 225
Kaufmann Peaks 93
Kaza Group 81
Kechika Group 115
Kentucky bluegrass 419
Kerkeslin, Mt. 91
Kern River 542
Kestrel, American 599
Kettles (geology) 197, 199d
Kicking Horse
  Canyon 25
  Mine 755
  Pass 22, 95, 752, 753,
    754, 760
  Rim 103, 117
  River 23p, 755
Kidd, Mt. 27, 184, 185p
Killdeer 589
Kimberley 160
Kinbasket Lake 755, 763,
  769
Kindle Formation 150
King boletus 443
Kingbird
  eastern 634
  western 663
Kingfisher, belted 598
Kinglet
  golden-crowned 651
  ruby-crowned 651
Kinney
  Lake 781
  Rev. George 761
Kinnikinnik 337
Kintla
  Formation 76
  Lake 759
Kiowa/Skull Creek Sea 157
Kirkidium 123
Kishenehn Formation 186
Kitchener, Mt. 212
  rockslide at 216
Klippe 28, 29d,p
Klotz, Otto 98
Knapweed, spotted 389
Knight's-plume 430
Knotweed, water 413
Koeleria macrantha 418
Koeppen classification 247
Kokanee 540
Kootenae House 749
Kootenay
  Crossing 231
  Group 21, 153, 159p, 160
  Indians 745
  National Park 761
  Plains 255, 570
  River 231
Kormagnostus 106

Krummholz 268, 282p, 328
Kucera, Richard 214
Kuijt, Job 420
Kwadacha Lakes
    Provincial Park 210

La Gassi 748
Labechid stromatoporoids
  139
Labrador
  sulphur 500
  tea 319
Labuma till 195
Lac
  Beauvert 234, 236
  des Arcs 132, 139, 568
Lace flower 345
Lactarius delicosus 453
Lactarius, delicious 453
Ladies' tresses, hooded 342
Lady fern 424
Lady's-slipper
  mountain 341
  northern 341
  yellow 353
Ladybird/ladybug 477
Laetiporus sulphureus 457
Lagopus
  lagopus 612
  leucurus 611
Lake
  Agnes 773, 774p
  Annette 8
  chub 551
  Koocanusa 11
  Louise 184, 236 (color
    of), 754, 763, 769
  McDonald 30, 274
  Minnewanka 138
  O'Hara Fire Road 802
  O'Hara Lodge 784
  of the Woods 746
  trout 543
  whitefish 545
Lakes
  colors of 234
  ecology of 278p
  ice-dammed (proglacial)
    193, 194d, 536
Lamprey, Pacific 547
Landslides 209
  underwater 83
Lanius
  excubitor 604
  ludovicianus 604
Lantern, Chinese 398
Lapland
  longspur 662
  rosebay 405
Lappula echinata 382
Laramide Orogeny 14, 174
Larch (see also tamarack)
  American 303
  grove, ecology of 282p
  Lyall's 302
  subalpine 302
  Valley 773
  western 302
Large
  purple aster 387
  wood nymph 516
Largescale sucker 549
Larix
  laricina 303
  lyallii 302
  occidentalis 302
Lark
  bunting 664
  horned 612

Larkspur 385
Larus
  argentatus 596
  californicus 596
  canus 596
  delawarensis 595
  philadelphia 597
  pipixcan 597, 663
  thayeri 663
Larvae
  black fly 488
  caddisfly 489
  damselfly 489
  diving beetle 488
  dragonfly 488
  mayfly 489
  midge 486
  mosquito 486
  stonefly 488
Lasiocampidae 525
Lasionycteris noctivagans
  677
Lasiurus cinereus 678
Lathyrus ochroleucus 340
Latitude
  and slope angle, effects
    on climate 251
  effect on day length
    252t
Laurel
  alpine 403
  mountain 373
Laurier Pass 757
Lava 162
Lawrence Grassi Hut 786
Lawson Lake 779
Lazuli bunting 630
Le Blanc 748
Leaf miner, birch 529
Leafy trees 303
Least
  chipmunk 688
  flycatcher 634
  sandpiper 591
  weasel 705
Leather Pass 750
Leather-leaved saxifrage
  334
Lecanor 440
Leccinum scabrum 443
Lecidea 440
LeConte's sparrow 660
Leduc 131
Ledum
  glandulosum 319
  groenlandicum 319
  palustre 319
Leeches 535
Leiobunum 485
Lemming
  brown 687
  northern bog 687
Lemmus sibiricus 687
Lemna
  minor 410
  trisulca 410
Lemonweed 358
Length
  of Canadian Rockies 1
  of day 251, 252t
Lenticels 315
Lenticular clouds 258p, 259
Lentil (geological term) 71
Leopard dace 552
Leopiota, green-spored 445
Lepista nuda 449
Leporidae 702
Leptarrhena pyrolifolia 334

Lepus
  americanus 702
  townsendii 702
Leroy Creek 778
Lesser
  scaup 580
  wintergreen 394
  yellowlegs 593
Lestidae 493
Letharia vulpina 436
Lethocerus americanus 490
Lettuce, white 339
Leucorrhinia 493
Leucosticte arctoa 648
Leverets 702
Lewis
  and Clark Expedition,
    Range 748
  Thrust 12, 27, 186
Lewis's woodpecker 621
Lewisia
  pygmaea 376
  rediviva 375
LGBs 634
Liard
  Formation 158
  Grand Canyon of the 36
  Hot Springs 18p, 36, 570,
    770
  Plain 12
  Plateau 12
  River 12, 36, 231, 251,
    755
Libellula quadrimaculata
  493
Libellulidae 493
Lichen
  dog-ear 438
  map 440
  wolf 436
Lichen-dating 207
Lichens 435
  age of 435
  crustose 439, 440
  foliose 439
  hair 436
  on rocks 439
  on the ground 437
  on trees 435
  photos of 435-440
  reindeer 437
  slippery 440
  used in dating moraines
    440
Licks, animal 741
Licorice, wild 350
Life
  zones 266
  in the snow 532
Lifespan
  of birds 572
  of mammals 667
Lightning 814, 815d
Lilium
  columbianum 352
  philadelphicum 352
  tigrinum 352
Lily
  Columbia/tiger 352
  glacier 352
  mariposa 329
  western wood 352
Limber pine 296
Limenites
  archippus 524
  arthemis 495
  lorquini 496
Limestone
  Cathedral 95

Eldon 100
  nodular 111p
  origin of 72
  Ottertail/Lyell 106
  Rundle 142
  Palliser 138
  weathered 196p
Limnodromus
  griseus 663
  scolopaceus 594
Limosa fedoa 663
Linaria vulgaris 365
Lincoln Pass 778
Lincoln's sparrow 660
Ling 547
Lingonberry 369
Lingula 140
Linnaea borealis 338
Linum lewisii 384
Lion, mountain 714
Listera cordata 371
Listric shape of Rockies
  thrust faults 182
Lithophragma
  parviflora 334
  ruderale 358
Little
  brown bat 676
  brown mushrooms
    (LBMs) 451
  elephants 371
  Fishes, Lake of 754
  gray birds (LGBs) 634
  green mosses (LGMs) 429
  Ice Age 204, 206p
  Pipestone Creek 782
Liverworts 434
Livingstone
  Formation 142
  Range 27, 142
  Ridge 767
Lloyd
  George Icefield 210
  Mackay Hut 786
Load of stream 209
Lobaria pulmonaria 436
Lobelia kalmii 385
Lobelia, brook 385
Lobstick 753
Locoweed
  alpine early yellow 401
  bladder 406
  early yellow 364
  showy 379
Lodge, beaver 699
Lodgepole pine 293
  broom on 294p
Loess 236
Logan Pass 76, 282, 283,
  762, 767, 768p
Loggerhead shrike 604
Logging 479, 759
Lomatium 366
Long dash 520
Long-billed
  curlew 663
  dowitcher 594
Long-eared
  bat 677
  owl 663
Long-jawed orb weaver 484
Long-legged bat 677
Long-tailed
  jaeger 663
  vole 686
  weasel 705
Long-toed salamander 559

Longspur
  Lapland 662
  chestnut-collared 664
Longstem greencaps 397
Lonicera
  ciliosa 317
  dioica 326
  involucrata 325
  utahensis 325
Lontra canadensis 701
Loomis Member 144
Loon
  arctic 663
  common 572
  red-throated 663
Looper, alfalfa 527
Lophodytes cucullatus 585
Lophophore 140
Lorquin's admiral 496
Lorraine Lake 803
Lota lota 547
Louis, Mt. 139
Louise Falls 794
Lousewort
  alpine 403
  contorted 395
  head-shaped 401
  western/bracted 365
Low-bush cranberry 326
Lower
  Fairholme Group 131
  Miette Group 81
  Post 757
  subalpine forest, ecology
    of 280p
Lowest point in Canadian
  Rockies 1
Loxia
  curvirostra 648
  leucoptera 647
Lucerne (plant) 386
Lucilia illustris 469
Luetkea 395
Luetkea pectinata 395
Lungworm 739
Lungwort 384
Lupine 379
  false 364
Lupinus
  arcticus 379
  nootkatensis 379
  sericeus 379
Luscar Group, mine 163p,
  164
Lusk Creek Road 162
Lustrous copper 509
Luzula parviflora 422
Lyall's
  beard-tongue 372
  goldenweed 400
  iron-plant 400
  larch 302
  saxifrage 394
Lycaeides
  argyrognomon 507
  melissa 507
Lycaena
  hyllus 524
  phlaeas 509
  xanthoides 524
Lycaenidae 504
Lychnis apetala 398
Lycoperdon perlatum 460
Lycopodium
  annotinum 428
  complanatum 428
Lyell
  Formation 106, 107p
  Icefield 212
  Mt. 106

Lymantriidae 526
Lymnaea 535
Lynx 712
   Group 110
   Mtn. 110
Lyonetia saliciella 529
Lyonetiidae 529
Lysichitum americanum 412

Maccarib
   Creek 779
   Pass 797p
MacCarthy, Albert 758p, 761
MacDonald
   Platform 123
   Range 12
MacGillivray's warbler 639
MacGregor, Jim 750
Mackenzie
   Mountains 12
   Alexander 746
Mackenzie's hedysarum 379
Maclurites 112
Macoun, John 753
Macrolepiota rhacodes 445
Madison Formation 142
Magnesium 96
Magnetic declination 828
   significance of in rocks 170
Magnetite 150
Magnolia warbler 641
Magog Lake 779
Magpie, black-billed 623
Mahonia, creeping 358
Mahto Formation 91
Main ranges of central Rockies 22
   date of appearance 153
Main/front ranges in northern Rockies 34
Malacosoma spp. 525, 528
Malaria mosquito 467
Malayites 158
Malenoplus alpinus 480
Maligne
   cave system 223
   origin of name 751
   River 750
   Road, geology along 146, 147p, 186p, 206p
   Valley 769
   rockslides 218
Maligne Canyon 219, 220p, 280, 769
   Formation 131
   mosses in 432
   springs at 223, 225, 236
Maligne Lake 212, 235p, 246p, 753, 769
   algal bloom in 409
   birding at 570
   color of 236
   discovery of 760
   fish-stocking in 536
   rockslide dam at 218
   skiing at 803
Mallard 575
Malton
   Gneiss 80p, 81
   Range 81
Mammals 667
   body measurements and weights of 667
   lifespans of 667
Man 742
Managanese Mtn. 150

Manitoba maple 306
Mantle (geologic term) 168
Manyglacier Hotel 76
Map lichen 207, 440
Maps
   Cretaceous Seaway 156
   Devonian geography 124
   ecological divisions of Rockies 264
   Foothills Erratics Train 203
   geology of Canadian Rockies 47
   icefield locations 211
   list of geologic 244
   list of topographic 245
   national and provincial parks 850
   temperature in Rockies 250
   topographic 834 (index to, 832)
Maple
   manitoba 306
   Rocky Mountain 314
Marasmius
   cystidosius 451
   oreades 451
Marble 76
   Canyon 221
Marbled godwit 663
Marblewing
   creamy 498
   northern 498
Marchantia polymorpha 434
Mare's-tail 410
Marias Pass 12, 257, 749, 757, 762
   River 748
Marine invasion, mid-Cretaceous 157
Marine plant fossils 128
Mariposa
   copper 509
   lily 329
   sagebrush/green-banded 377
Marjumia 104
Marmot Basin 254
Marmota
   caligata 693
   monax 693
Marmot, hoary 693
Marsh
   ecology of 278p
   hawk 602
   marigold, alpine 393
   reedgrass 418
   wren 663
Marston Member 144
Marten, American 706
Martes
   americana 706
   pennanti 708
Marvel Lake 779
Mary Schäffer Trail 769
Marty, Sid 763
Masked shrew 679
Maskinonge Lake, birding at 568
Mass extinction events 131, 167
Matheson, Mona 762
Matricaria
   matricarioides 365
   perforata 358
   recutita 358
Mattson Formation 146

Maude Lake 779
Maunsell till 195
Mauve mitrewort 382
Maycroft till 195
Mayflies 492
Mayfly naiad 489
Mazama, Mt., tephra from 205, 206p
McBride 177
McCabe, Frank 753
McCardell, William and Tom 753
McConnell
   Richard 754
   Thrust 16, 180, 181p
McDonald
   Creek 77, 127, 540
   Finan 749
   Lake 292, 537, 540, 568
McGillivray, Duncan 748
McKay Group 117
McLeod, Henry 753
McNamara Formation 76
McNaughton
   Formation 91
   Lake 763
Mead's sulphur 500
Meadow
   jumping mouse 683
   montane, ecology of 276p
   mushroom 447
   spirea 395
   subalpine, ecology of 255, 281p
   vole 685
Meadow-rue 348
Meadowhawks 493
Meadowlark, western 644
Meal moth 525
Mealy primrose 374
Meatmaker, The 763
Medicago sativa 386
Medicine Lake 136, 184, 769
   annual cycle of 223, 224p
   rockslide dam at 218
   slickensides at 215p
Medicine Tent River 781
Meeting of eastern and western ice sheets 193
Megarhyssa nortoni 474
Melanerpes lewis 621
Melanitta
   fusca 582
   perspicillata 582
Melilotus
   alba 340
   officinalis 364
Melissa arctic 518
Melospiza
   georgiana 664
   lincolnii 660
   melodia 660
Meltwater stream 214
Member (geology) 71
Membrane, interfemoral 675
Mentha arvensis 386
Menyanthes trifoliata 414
Menziesia 327
Menziesia ferruginea 327
Mephitis mephitis 709
Merganser
   common 584
   hooded 585
   red-breasted 585

Mergus
   merganser 584
   serrator 585
Merlin 599
Mertensia 384
Mertensia
   longiflora 384
   paniculata 384
Mesenchytraeus 533
Mesozoic 152
   Episode I 153
   Episode II 155
   Episode III 155
Metamorphic sequence 81, 78
Metric to American conversion table: *inside front cover*
Mew gull 596
Mica 87
   Dam 763
Microseris
   nutans 354, 355
   hoyi 679
Microtus longicaudus 686
   pennsylvanicus 685
Mid-day clearing trend 254
Mid-oceanic ridges 168
Midden, squirrel 695
Middle
   Cambrian sandwich 93, 94p
   carbonate unit 37, 136
Midges 468
   larvae 486
Miette
   erratics 81
   grits 82p, 83
   Group 77
   Hot Springs 131, 161
   Reef 130, 132, 136
   River 78, 756
   schist 80p
   slate 80p
Milbert's tortoiseshell 495
Mildred Lake, birding at 570
Milfoil 344
Milk-vetch 340
   alpine 406
Milkweed, showy 375
Mill Creek Formation 162
Milt 537
Milton and Cheadle 752
Mimulus
   guttatus 353
   lewisii 371
Mimus polyglottos 663
Mindel glaciation 192
Miner's candlestick 366
Mineral
   licks 741
   springs 226pd, 227
Mines (names of, locations of)
   Altyn 76
   Anthracite 754
   Bankhead 21, 161, 754
   Canmore 161, 754
   Coal Branch 754
   Coal Valley 755
   Crowsnest Pass area 161
   Fernie 757
   Field 755
   Grande Cache 161, 164, 755
   Hinton 161
   Hillcrest 759

Kicking Horse 755
Monarch 755
Luscar 164
Nordegg 164, 754
Pocahontas 164, 754
Sparwood 754
Tumbler Ridge 164, 755
Mink, American 707
Minnes Group, Mt. 161
Minnow, fathead 554
Minnows 549
Minor intrusives 86
Mint, wild 386
Misinchinka Group 86
Miss Devonian's sandwich 136
Missoula Group 76
Mist Mountain Formation 160
Mistaya 109
Canyon 219
Formation 109
River 109
Mistletoe, pine dwarf 294
Misty Formation 149
Misumena vatia 484
Mitchell River Cabin 783
Mitella
nuda 349
pentandra 349
trifida 382
Mitoura spinetorum 524
Mitrewort 349
false 345
mauve/three-tooth 382
Mniotilta varia 663
Moberly
family 756
Meadows 776
John 775
Walter 753
Moccasin flower 353
Mock orange 327
Mockingbird, northern 663
Modocia 104
Molecule plant 339
Molly, sailfin 556
Molothrus ater 646
Monach Formation 161
Monarch
butterfly 518
Mine 755
Monarda fistulosa 369
Monashee Mountains 81
Monger, Jim 170
Monkey-flower, red 371
yellow 353
Monkman
Pass 112
Quartzite 112
Monkshood 386
Monochamus oregonensis 478
Monocraterion 90
Monotis 158
Monotropa uniflora 341
Mons Icefield 212
Montagne de la grande traverse 749
Montana becomes a state 756
Montane
and subalpine river communities, ecology of 279p
feather-moss forest, ecology of 277p
meadow, ecology of 276p
or subalpine canyon, ecology of 280p

or subalpine wetland, ecology of 278p
Montane forest 269
eastern-slope 269
ecology of 276p
in Rocky Mountain Trench 269
western-slope 269
Monte Cristo Mtn. 85
Monteith Formation 161
Moodie, Insp. J.D. 757
Moonwort 423
Moose 734
Mtn. 140, 142
Moosebar Formation 164
Moraine Lake 286, 757, 768p
rockslide at 216
Moraines 189, 190p, 201p, 212
Morchella
angusticeps/elata 454
esculenta 453
Morels 453
black/narrow-capped 454
conifer false 454
saddle-shaped false 454
yellow 453
Morley Flats 16, 18p
Mormon fritillary 513
Morrissey Formation, siding 160
Morro
Member 138
Peak 138
Mosquito Creek 782
Hostel 809
Mosquitoes 466
larvae 486
malaria 467
snow 467
house 467
Mosquitofish 556
Moss
big red-stem 430
campion 402
gentian 407
goose-neck 430
knight's-plume 430
phlox 336
Spanish 435
stairstep 430
Mosses 429
along streams and at springs 432
feather 429
hairy-cap 434
in swamps 431
on cliffs 432
on the forest floor 429
swamp/peat 431
water 409
Moth
acraea 525
forest tent caterpillar 525
hummingbird 527
meal 525
Moths 525
Moult (mammals) 667
Mount (see also mountains listed by second part of name; e.g. "Assiniboine, Mt." The entries below are *named for* mountains)
Alberta Hut 786
Assiniboine Lodge 783

Colin Centennial Hut 786
Edith Cavell Road 280
Forster Formation 127
Head Formation 142, 144, 145p
Hawk Formation 135
Robson Provincial Park 761
Shields Formation 76
Whyte Formation 95
Wilson Quartzite 113, 114p
Mountain
alder 313
ash 316
bicycles 810
bluebird 630
chickadee 650
cranberry 369
dryas 393
fireweed 373
front 19, 16, 28, 32
gentian 406
goat 741
goldenrod 364
guides 787
hollyhock 375
lady's-slipper 341
laurel 373
lion 714
pine beetle 478
sandwort 333
sheep 738
sickness 820
sorrel 398
spray 317
sucker 549
whitefish 545
Mountain-building 168, 169d, 172d, 179
Mountaineering 8, 787
routes 792
Mourning
cloak 495, 529
dove 632
Mouse
deer 680
house 681
meadow jumping 683
western jumping 683
Mouth-to-mouth resuscitation 818
Mowitch Formation 150
Mt. (see Mount)
Mud dauber, black and yellow 474
Mudflows 187, 209
Mudstone 72
Mule deer 730
Mullein 366
Muncho Lake 36, 93, 123
Muncho-McConnell Formation 123
Mural formation 91, 223
Murchison, Mt. 140
Muridae 680
Murray, Mt. 88
Mus musculus 681
Musca domestica 468
Muscidae 468
Mushroom
chicken 457
fairy-ring 451
fawn 449
honey 449
meadow 447
oyster 456

Mushrooms 441
edibility of 441
identifying 442
ordinary capped 443
poisonous/intoxicatin 442
Muskeg 431
Muskrat 700
Muskwa
Assemblage 32, 77
Muskwa River 32
Mustard family plants, common 362
Mustela
erminea 704
frenata 705
nivalis 705
vison 707
Mustelidae 701
Myadestes townsendi 629
Myatuck 750
Mycelium 441
Mycorrhizal fungi 441
Mylocheilus caurinus 550
Myosotis alpestris 404
Myotis
evotis 677
lucifugus 676
volans 677
Myriophyllum spicatum 410
Myrtle warbler 640
Mystic Pass 782

Naemorhedus 741
Naiad
damselfly 489
dragonfly 488
mayfly 489
stonefly 488
Naiset
Cabins 783
Formation 95
Najas microdon 557
Nakodas 746
Names
confusion in 14
of bird families 664
of birds 570
of geological periods, mnemonic for remembering 70
of plant families 271
Nancy-over-the-ground 345
Napaea fritillary 515
Narrow-capped morel 454
Nashville warbler 663
National parks 8, 763
Addresses and telephone numbers

Banff National Park
Box 900, Banff, AB
T0L 0C0
403-762-3324

Glacier National Park
West Glacier, MT 59936
406-888-5441

Jasper National Park
Box 10, Jasper, AB
T0E 1E0
403-852-6161

Kootenay National Park
Radium Hot Springs, BC
V0A 1M0
604-347-9615

Yoho National Park
Box 99, Field, BC
V0A 1G0
604-343-6324

Index (d-diagram, m-map, p-photo, t-table)

Waterton Lakes National Park
Waterton Park, AB T0K 0M0 403-859-2262
legislation 762
map of locations 850
wilderness protection in 829
Natural
  bridge 219
  gas 142, 152, 759
Nausea 820
Navigation by compass 826
Nebraskan glaciation 192
Needle-and-thread 419
Neil Colgan Hut 784
Nelson Formation 76
Neoglacial 204
Neominois ridingsii 524
Neophasia menapia 524
Neotoma cinerea 682
Nepheline 151
  syenite 150
Neptuak Peak 757
Nesting records of birds 571
Nests and nestlings of birds 572
Nettle, stinging 351
Nevada skipper 521
Ney, Charles 103
Nichol, Mary de la Beach 760
Nidula 459
Nigel
  Creek 781
  Falls 131, 807
  Pass 779
Nighthawk, common 617
Nikanassin Formation, Range 161
Niles, Mt. 804
Ninebark 316
Nipissing Indians 746
Noctonectide 489
Noctuidae 527
Nodding
  onion 378
  pink 398
  saxifrage 394
Nodular
  chert 147p, 148
  limestone 111d
Nonconformity 122
Nonda Formation 116
Nonmarine rock 38
  Mesozoic 153
Nordegg 164, 754
Normal faults 177, 182, 181d
North
  American Plate 16, 81, 93, 168
  Boundary Trail 781
  Kananaskis Pass 752
  Kootenay Pass 76, 132, 138, 752
  Kootenay Pass 752
  Molar Pass 782
  Saskatchewan Canyon 219
  Saskatchewan River 782
  Saskatchewan River, erosion in 210
  West Company 746
North, F.K. 114

Northern
  anemone 392
  bastard toadflax 348
  bedstraw 345
  blue 507
  blue columbine 385
  bog lemming 687
  brome 418
  checkerspot 510
  cloudywing 523
  coral-root orchid 353
  false toadflax 348
  flying squirrel 696
  gentian 388
  goshawk 601
  harrier 602
  hawk-owl 607
  lady's-slipper 341
  leopard frog 560
  marblewing 498
  mockingbird 663
  oriole 663
  pike 546
  pintail 578
  pocket gopher 694
  pygmy owl 608
  red-backed vole 684
  redbelly dace 553
  Rocky Mountain Trench Fault 177
  rough-winged swallow 615
  saw-whet owl 608
  shoveler 575
  shrike 604
  squawfish 550
  water shrew 680
  waterthrush 642
Northern Rockies 31
  foothills 32, 33p
  of USA 14
  comparison with central and southern Rockies 31
  eastern margin of 31
  glaciation in 34
  highest point in 36
  main/front ranges of 34, 35p
  mountain front in 32
  physiography of 31
  summary of features 36
  timberline elevation in 36
  western slope of 34
Northwestern woodsia 424
Nose Hill 187
Notropis hudsonius 553
Noturus flavus 547
Nucifraga columbiana 624
Nuclear energy and plate tectonics 168
Nudirostra 135

Old-man's beard 435
Old-man's whiskers 370
Old-world swallowtail 503
Older-over-younger rule 180
Oldman River 767
  tills exposed near Brocket 194p
Oldsquaw 579
Ole Creek Window 28
Olive-sided flycatcher 636
Oliver
  Bill 759
  Mt. 19
Ollenelus 91

Olor columbianus 587
Omineca Mountains 171
Onchocephalus 95
Oncolites 95, 98, 112
Oncorhynchus
  nerka 540
  tshawytscha 539
Ondatra zibethicus 700
One Ten Creek 135
One-flowered
  broomrape 381
  clintonia 329
  wintergreen 335
One-sided wintergreen 348
Onion, nodding 378
Oolites 91, 98, 108, 144
Opabin Plateau 773
Opal 148
  Hills 148, 218, 775
  Member 145
  Range 143p
Ophiogomphus severis 493
Ophionidae 474
Oplopanax horridum 317
Oporornis tolmiei 639
Opuntia fragilis 367
Orange
  clitocybe 452
  honeysuckle 317
  wildflowers 352, 398
Orange-and-black butterflies 511
Orange-bordered blue 507
Orange-crowned warbler 640
Orange-latex milky 453
Orangetip, sara 499
Orb weaver, long-jawed 484
Orchid
  bog/rein 341
  calypso 371
  northern coral-root 353
  round-leaved/spotted 343
  sparrows's-egg 341
Orchis rotundifolia 343
Oreamnos americanus 741
Oregon
  grape 358
  junco 655
Orgyia leucostigmata 526, 529
Orienting by compass 826
Oriole, northern 663
Orobanche
  fasiculata 381
  uniflora 381
Orogeny 171
Orographic
  lifting 253
  weather 253
Orthocarpus
  luteus 365
  tenuifolius 368
Orthotrichum 433
Oryzopsis asperifolia 420
Osmorhiza
  depauperata 343
  occidentalis 349
Ospika River 757
Osprey 604
Ostracods 149, 164, 486
Otidea leporina 458
Otter, river 701
Ottertail
  Formation 106, 107p
  River 108
Otus kennicottii 663

Our Lady 478
Outram Formation 111p
Outram
  James 111, 759
  Mt. 111
Ouzel, water 598
Oval-leaf alumroot 362
Ovenbird 663
Overlander
  Falls 539
  Trail 140, 775
Overlanders, The 752
Overturned rock 25
Ovipositor 480
Ovis
  canadensis 738
  dalli 738
Owen Creek, Formation 113
Owls 606
  barred 607
  boreal 608
  burrowing 663
  great gray 606
  great horned 606
  long-eared 663
  northern pygmy 608
  northern saw-whet 608
  short-eared 663
  snowy 663
  western screech 663
Owl-clover 365
  thin-leaved 368
Ox-eye daisy 347
Oxyria digyna 398
Oxytoma 160
Oxytropis
  campestris 364
  podocarpa 406
  sericea 364, 401
  splendens 379
Oxyura jamaicensis 583
Oyster
  mushroom 456
  plant 355

Pachysphinx modesta 526
Pacific
  Great Eastern Railway 762
  influence on climate of Rockies 251
  lamprey 547
  ponderosa 295
  treefrog 562
  willow 307
  yew 318
Packs 776, 799
Pack rat 682
Packhorse Peak 186
Paint Pots 227
  red 368
  yellow 365
Painted
  lady 496
  turtle, western 564
Palaeno sulphur 500
Pale
  coral-root orchid 353
  hedysarum 368
  sweetvetch 368
Paleofavosites 115
Paleomagnetism 170
Palisade, The 756
Pall, Orval 712
Pallid-winged grasshopper 479
Palliser
  and Eldon formations, differentiating 138

Index (d-diagram, m-map, p-photo, t-table)

Capt. John 752
  Expedition 752
  Formation 138
  Range 138
  River 112, 752
Palliseria 112
Palm warbler 663
Pandion haliaetus 604
Panther agaric 446
Papaver
  kluanensis 398
  pygmaeum 398
Paper birch 305
Papilio
  machaon 503
  zelicaon 502, 530
Papilionidae 497, 502
Paradise Valley 773
Parallel ridges and valleys
  21
Parasites 535
Parasitic jaeger 663
Paratrachyceras 158
Pardonet Formation 158
Pardosa 484
Parker Ridge 134, 281, 570,
  775
Parks Canada
  planning 763
  addresses (see National
  parks)
Parks, national and
  provincial 8, 850
Parmelia sulcata 436
Parmeliopsis ambigua 436
Parnassia
  kotzebuei 335, 392
  palustris 335
Parnassian
  Eversmann's 499
  phoebus 498
Parnassius
  eversmanni 499
  phoebus 498, 529
Parsley fern 424
Parsnip, water 415
Partridge, gray 663
Partridge-foot 395
Parus
  atricapillus 649
  gambeli 650
  hudsonicus 650
Paskapoo Formation 166p,
  167
Pasque flower 377
Passage Beds 160, 174
Passer domesticus 654
Passerculus sandwichensis
  659
Passerina amoena 630
Pasture sage/wormwood
  361
Path of the Glacier Trail
  775
Pathfinder 345
Pea, wild sweet 340
Peace River 231
  Arch 120, 128
  Embayment 146
  gap 192, 257
Peacock 372
Peamouth chub 550
Pearl dace 551
Pearly
  crescentspot 511
  everlasting 339
Pease, Benjamin 753

Peat 431
Peck, Mt. 112
Pectinations 610
Pectoral sandpiper 592
Pedicel 475
Pedicularis
  arctica 403
  bracteosa 365
  capitata 401
  contorta 395
  groenlandica 371
Pediment 162, 187
Pedley Pass 115
Peechee Member 132
Pegmatite boulders 87
Peigans 746
Pekisko Formation 144
Pelecanus erythrorynchos
  663
Peltigera
  aphthosa 438
  canina 438
Pemmican 337
Penstemon
  confertus 354
  ellipticus 380
  eriantherus 380
  gracilis 380
  lyallii 372
  nitidus 380
  procerus 380
Penstemon
  blue/purple species 380
  yellow 354
People and bears 723
Peppergrass 349
Percopsidae 556
Percopsis omiscomaycus
  556
Perdix perdix 663
Perdrix Formation 134,
  135p
Peregrine falcon 599
Perigynium 420
Perisoreus canadensis 624
Permafrost 209
Permeability, defined 225
Peromyscus maniculatus
  680
Persius duskywing 522
Pestle-shaped coral 455
Petasites
  frigidus 339, 396
  sagittatus 339
Peter
  and Catherine Whyte
  Hut 786
  Lougheed Provincial
  Park (Kananaskis
  Park) 802
Petromyzontidae 547
Peyto
  Formation 91
  Glacier 210
  Lake 210, 754, 769
  Bill 754
Phacelia
  lyallii 407
  sericea 407
Phacelia, silky 407
Phalacrocorax penicillatus
  663
Phalangium 485
Phalarope
  red 663
  red-necked 594
  Wilson's 594
Phalaropus
  fulicarius 663

lobatus 594
  tricolor 594
Phantom midges 488
Pharoah Creek 803
Phasianus colchicus 663
Pheasant, ring-necked 663
Phenacomys intermedius
  685
Pheucticus
  ludovicianus 664
  melanocephalus 664
Phidippus 485
Philadelphia vireo 663
Philadelphus lewisii 327
Phillipps, Michael 753
Phillips
  Curly 761
  Formation 76
  Peak 138
Phleum
  commutatum 417
  pratense 417
Phlogiotis hellevoides 453
Phlox
  alyssifolia 336
  diffusa 402
  hoodii 336
  multiflora 336
Phlox
  moss 336
  spreading 402
Phoebe
  eastern 663
  Say's 663
Phoebus parnassian 498
  caterpillar 529
Phosphate, phosphorite 149
Phosphoria Formation 149
Phoxinus
  eos 553
  neogaeus 553
Phragmites communis 412
Phyciodes
  campestris 512
  selenis 511
Phyllite 25, 79
Phyllodoce
  empetriformis 403
  glanduliflora 397
Phyllograptus 110
Physaria didymocarpa 401
Physiographic map 10
Physiography 15
  of central Rockies 16
  of northern Rockies 31
  of southern Rockies 27
Physocarpus malvaceus 316
Pica pica 623
Picea
  glauca 297
  engelmannii 297
  mariana 297
Picoides
  arcticus 620
  pubescens 619
  tridactylus 619
  villosus 618
Pictures of ecological
  communities 273-288
Pied-billed grebe 574
Pieridae 497
Pigeon 631
  hawk 599
  milk 632
  band-tailed 663
  Pika 703
  Formation 104
  Peak 104
Pike, northern 546

Pileated woodpecker 618
Pillow lava 76
Pimephales promelas 554
Pin cherry 315
Pine
  and spruce engraver
  beetles 478
  dwarf mistletoe 294
  grosbeak 647
  siskin 662
  Pass 34, 748, 762, 770,
  771p
Pines
  jack 294
  limber 296
  lodgepole 293
  ponderosa 295
  western white 295
  whitebark 296
Pineapple weed 358
Pinguicula vulgaris 385
Pinicola enucleator 647
Pink
  heather 403
  pussytoes 370
  spirea 326
  wildflowers 368, 402
  wintergreen 370
Pink-edged sulphur 500
Pintail, northern 578
Pinto Lake 756
Pinus
  albicaulis 296
  banksiana 294
  contorta 293
  flexilis 296
  monticola 295
  ponderosa 295
Pipeline, oil 762
Pipestone
  Pass 752, 782
  River 782
Pipilo erythrophthalmus
  664
Pipit, Sprague's 663
  water 595
Pipsissewa 370
Piptoporus betulinus 457
Piranga ludoviciana 643
Pisoliths 85
Pituophis melanoleucus 563
Pixie cups 437
Placenticeras 167
Plagioclase feldspar 75
Plagiura 95
Plague, bubonic 690
Plain of Six Glaciers 6,
  773, 802
Plains cottonwood 305
Plankton 131, 409, 486
Planolites 85, 90
Plant
  families, scientific
  names of 271
  listings 289
Plantain, rattlesnake 342
Plate
  tectonics 168, 169d
  North American (see
  North American
  Plate)
Platform (geology) 123
Platypedia 480
Plebejus
  optilete 524
  saepiolus 505
  shasta 524
Plectrophenax nivalis 658

Pleistocene 189
  deposits, correlation
    chart of 191
Pleurocybella porrigens 457
Pleurotus sapidus 456
Pleurozium schreberi 430
Plover
  black-bellied 663
  semipalmated 590
Pluteus cervinus 449
Pluvialis
  dominica 663
  squatarola 663
Poa
  alpina 419
  pratensis 419
Poboktan
  Creek 113, 779, 780p
  Pass 755
Pocahontas 164, 184, 754
  marshes, birding at 570
Pocaterra Creek 568, 802
Pocket gopher, northern
    694
Podalonia 475
Podetia 437
Podiceps
  auritus 574
  grisegana 573
  nigricolli 574
Podilymbus podiceps 574
Poecilia
  latipinna 557
  reticulata 556
Pogonatum alpinum 434
Pohlia 432
Poison
  ivy/oak 325
  pie 448
Poisonous mushrooms 442
Polemonium
  acutiflorum 383
  pulcherrimum 383
  viscosum 406
Police Meadows Cabins 784
Polites
  coras 524
  draco 520
  mystic 520
  themistocles 524
Polixenes arctic 518
Pollen, fossil 160, 221
Polygonatum 330
Polygonia
  faunus 503
  gracilis 524
  progne 524
  satyrus 503
  zephyrus 524
Polygonum
  amphibium 413
  viviparum 396
Polypore
  birch 457
  smoky 458
  violet toothed 458
  white spongy 457
Polystichum lonchitis 425
Polytrichum
  commune 431
  juniperinum 434
  piliferum 434
Pond lily, yellow 414
Pond-skaters 492
Ponderosa pine 295
  Arizona 295
  Pacific 295
  Rocky Mountain 295
Pondweed 413, 557

Pontia
  occidentalis 498
  sisymbrii 498
Pooecetes gramineus 659
Poplar, balsam 304
Poppies, arctic 398
Population 6, 766t
Populus
  balsamifera 304
  tremuloides 303
  trichocarpa 305
Porcupine 697
  Creek 782
  Hills 167, 193, 767
  Hills Formation 167
Portulaca oleracea 361
Porzana carolina 588
Posidonia 164
Post-orogenic deposits 186
Potamogeton richardsonii
    414
Potentilla 358
  alpine 399
  early 359
  montane 359
  shrubby 318
  subalpine 359
Potentilla
  anserina 359
  concinna 359
  diversifolia 359
  fruticosa 318
  glandulosa 359
  gracilis 359
  ledebourniana 399
  nivea 399
Potholes 219
Prairie
  crocus 377
  falcon 600
  influence on climate 253
  parsley 366
  ringlet 516
  sagewort 389
  smoke 370
Pre-glacial deposits 186,
    187, 188p
Pre-Pleistocene glaciation
    189
Precipitation 248t, 254
Precocial birds 572
Predaceous diving beetle
    larvae (water tigers)
    488
Prenanthes sagittata 339
Presqu'ile Barrier Reef 127
Pressure gradient 260
Pressure-melting at glacial
    sole 214
Preston Park 773
Price, Ray 170
Prickly
  currant 322
  juniper 328
  saxifrage 334
Primates 742
Primrose
  bird's-eye 374
  mealy 374
Primula
  incana 374
  mistassinica 374
Prince of Wales Hotel 198p
Prince's pine 370
Prince, the 448
Prionolubus 158
Prisoner-of-war camps 762
Proclossiana eunomia 514
Procyon lotor 711

Procyonidae 711
Productid brachiopods 140
Proglacial lakes 193, 194d,
    536
Prolegs 528
Proleus 528
Prophet
  Formation 146
  River 32
Prosaukia 109
Prosopium
  coulteri 545
  williamsoni 545
Protostrongylus 739
Protrachyceras 158
Provincial parks 8
  locations of major 850m
Prunella vulgaris 386
Prunus
  emarginata 316
  pennsylvanica 315
  virginiana 315
Pseudacris triseriata 561
Pseudotsuga menziesii 299
Psidium 535
Psilocybe 442
  coprophila 451
Psilocybe, dung-loving 451
Ptarmigan
  white-tailed 611
  willow 612
Pteridium aquilinum 424
Pterobranchs 118
Pterourus
  eurymedon 524
  glaucus 502, 530
  multicaudatus 502
  rutulus 502
Ptilium crista-castrensis
    430
Ptychaspis 109
Ptychocheilus oregonensis
    550
Puccoon, yellow 358
Puffballs 460
  buried-stalk 461
  gem-studded 460
  giant western 460
Pulp mills 758p, 759
Pulsatilla Pass 782
Puma 714
Punchbowl Falls 162, 163p,
    164
Puns, geological 81
Purcell
  dykes 75
  Landmass 120, 128, 136,
    138
  Lava 75
  Mountains 71, 78
  Sill 75
  Supergroup 71
Purcell-type sediments 37
Purple
  alfalfa 386
  bee-plant 407
  finch 648
  reedgrass 418
  saxifrage 405
  wildflowers 377, 404
Purshia tridentata 320
Purslane 361
Push-up, muskrat 700
Pussy willow 307
Pussytoes 338, 370
Putnik, Mt. 779
Putty shales 110
Pygmy
  flower 332
  nuthatch 663

shrew 679
  whitefish 545
Pyralidae 525
Pyralis farinalis 525
Pyramid
  Lake Road 275
  Mtn. 88
  Mtn. (in Banff park) 773
Pyrgus
  centaureae 521
  communis 522
  ruralis 522
Pyrite 225
  in Besa River and
    Perdrix shales 134
  in Exshaw shale 139
  in Sassenach Formation
    136
Pyrola
  asarifolia 370
  chlorantha 348
  minor 394
  secunda 348
  uniflora 335
Pyrola
  alpine 394
  green 348
  pink 370

Quartz veins 83
Quartz, microcrystalline
    146
Quartzite 89, 90p
  erratics 195
  Flathead 88
  Gog 88
  Monkman, Tipperary
    112
  Mt. Wilson 113, 114p
  origin of 89
Quaternary
  geology 189
  Period 204
Queen
  Alexandra's sulphur 501
  cup 329
Questionable stropharia
    449
Quiscalus quiscula 663

Rabbit ears, yellow 458
Rabbitbrush 320
Rabies 675
Raccoon 711
Radioactive-decay heat 168
Radiocarbon dating 197
Radiolaria 148
Radiometric dating of
    rocks 70
Radium Hot Springs 750
Raft, beaver 699
Ragwort 363
Rail
  Virginia 663
  yellow 663
Railways
  British Columbia 762
  Canadian National 761
  Canadian Northern 761
  Canadian Pacific 753
  Grand Trunk Pacific
    761
  Great Northern 757
  narrow gauge at Lake
    Louise 761
  Pacific Great Eastern
    762
Rain shadow 255
Rainbow trout 540

Raindrops, erosion by 209
Ralph Forster Hut 787
Ralus limicola 663
Ramaria 455
Rampart
  Creek 807
  The (Banff Park) 803
Ramparts, The (Jasper
  park) 779
Rana
  pipiens 560
  pretiosa 561
  sylvatica 560
Ranger Canyon Formation
  147p, 148
Ranges of birds 572
Rangifer tarandus 736
Ranunculus
  acris 360
  aquatilis 415
  circinatus 414
  cymbalaria 415
  eschscholtzii 399
  flammula 415
  gmelinii 414
  macounii 360
  occidentalis 360
  uncinatus 360
  verecundus 399
Raptorial birds 599
Rare lists
  birds 663
  butterflies and skippers
    524
Rasetti, Franco 103
Raspberry 321
  dwarf 374
  trailing 337
Rat, bushy-tailed
  wood/packrat 682
  water 700
Rate
  of closure of terranes
    with North America
    170
  of deposition in Rocky
    Mountain Trough 153
  of slippage along major
    strike-slip faults 177
  of subduction 174
Rattlesnake plantain 342
Raven, common 191p, 622
Ray-flowers 346
Rearguard Falls 539, 770
Recent climatic change 260
Recolonization by fish 536
Records for Canadian
  Rockies
  Deepest cave: Arctomys,
    522 m, page 223
  Deepest lake: Upper
    Waterton, 148 m, 234
  Earliest fossils: algae,
    600 million years, 85
  (earliest signs of life:
    stromatolites, 1.5
    billion years, 74)
  Fastest animal: golden
    eagle, 320 km/h, 605
  First non-native
    community: Hudson's
    Hope, 1805, 748
  First oil well: Cameron
    Creek, 1902, 759
  Hardest rock: Gog
    quartzite, 88
  Highest point: Mt.
    Robson, 3954 m, 26

Largest bird: tundra
  swan, wings 200 cm,
  587
Largest fish: white
  sturgeon, 1.5-2 m, 546
Largest measured spring:
  Big Spring, 225
Largest native animal:
  bison, 700 kg, 737
Largest rockslide:
  Sinking Ship, 218
Longest cave:
  Castleguard, 20 km,
  221
Longest lake: Maligne,
  22.3 km, 234
Longest-lived bird: bald
  eagle, 40-50 years, 605
Lowest point: Liard
  River, 305 m, 1
Oldest living plants:
  lichens, 435
Oldest reef: ca. 600
  million years, 85
Oldest rock: North
  American Plate, 1.8
  billion years, 123
Oldest sedimentary rock:
  Waterton Formation,
  1.5 billion years, 71
Oldest tree: whitebark
  pine, 750 years, 292
Smallest bird: calliope
  hummingbird, 7 cm,
  626
Smallest mammal: pygmy
  shrew, 3 g, 679
Tallest tree (likely):
  black cottonwood, 292
Weirdest rock: 146
Recreational section 767
Recurvirostra americana
  590
Recycling of sediments
  during creation of
  Rockies 155
Red
  admiral 496
  ants 475
  clover 368
  columbine 373
  crossbill 648
  Deer Lakes 782
  Deer River 782
  elderberry 316
  fox 719
  monkey-flower 371
  paintbrush 368
  phalarope 663
  Shirt 789
  squirrel 695
  twinberry 325
  wildflowers 368, 402
Red-belt 259, 294
Red-breasted
  merganser 585
  nuthatch 652
Red-disked alpine 519
Red-eyed vireo 637
Red-necked
  grebe 573
  phalarope 594
Red-osier dogwood 313
Red-tailed
  chipmunk 689
  hawk 602
Red-throated loon 663
Red-winged blackbird 645
Redd 539

Redearth Creek, skiing
  along 803
Redhead 579
Redpoll
  common 649
  hoary 649
Redside shiner 552
Redstart, American 642
Redwall
  Fault 182
  Limestone 142
Reedgrass 418
Reef Icefield 212
Reefs
  Cambrian 101
  Devonian 46d, 126m,
    128, 129d
  Hadrynian 85
  oldest known 85
  rock in 133p
Refection 703
Refugia, fish 536
Regulus
  calendula 651
  satrapa 651
Rein orchids 341
Reindeer 736
  lichens 437
Relative ages of rocks 70
Rendezvous, wolf 718
Repellents
  bear 728
  insect 466
Reprobate 790
Reptiles 562
Rescue from crevasse 792p
Resthaven Icefield 212
Resuscitation, mouth to
  mouth 818
Revegetation of strip mines
  161
Reynolds Creek 186
Rhabdosome 118
Rhamnus alnifolia 314
Rhinichthys
  cataractae 552
  falcatus 552
Rhizines 438
Rhizocarpon geographicum
  88, 207, 440
Rhizopods 486
Rhododendron 327
Rhododendron
  albiflorum 327
  lapponicum 405
Rhus radicans 325
Rhytidiadelphus triquetrus
  430
Ribbon Creek 160
Ribes
  inerme 322
  lacustre 322
  oxyacanthoides 322
  viscosissimum 322
Ricegrass 420
Richardson's
  ground squirrel 691
  water vole 686
Richardsonius balteatus
  552
Rickettsia rickettsii 482
Rifting 45d, 78, 93, 168
Rillenkarren 218, 223
Ring-billed gull 595
Ring-necked
  duck 580
  pheasant 663
Ringlet, ochre/prairie 516
Riparia riparia 615

Riser 301
Rising Sun Campground 28
Riss glaciation 192
River
  alder 313
  beauty 373
  ecology 279p
  otter 701
  Rock 139
Rivers 231
  discharge of 232t
  ecology of 279p
  seasonal and daily
    variation in flow 231
Robin, American 627
Robson
  Glacier 793
  River 781
  Mt. 26, 757, 761, 770,
    771p, 791p, 793
Roche
  à Perdrix 134
  Miette 131, 139, 195, 750
  Miette, erratics on 196p
  noire *front cover*
  Ronde 136
Rock
  brake, Steller's 423
  cress 381
  cress, alpine 404
  dove 631
  flour 214, 231
  glaciers 216
  rose 375
  structures in the Rockies
    180
  willow 308
  wren 653
Rock-jasmine 332
Rock-rabbit 703
Rockclimbing 788p, 789
Rockslide checkerspot 510
Rockslides 208p, 216, 217p
  age of 218
  boulders 147p
  ecology of 286p
  erosion by 209
Rockwall, The 107p, 108
Rocky
  River 781
  slope or cliff, ecology of
    285p
Rocky Mountain
  House 748
  juniper 318
  maple 314
  ponderosa 295
  rhododendron 327
  spotted fever 482
  wood tick 464p, 481
Rocky Mountain Trench
  11, 153, 167
  deposits in 186
  origin of 176
Rocky Mountain Trough
  153, 154d, 167, 176
  as seaway 155
  rate of deposition in 153
  thickness of deposits in
    153
Rocky Mountains, southern
  and northern ends of
  31
Roemeripora spelaeana 127
Romanzoffia 394
Romanzoffia sitchensis 395
Ronde Formation 135
Roosterhead 372
Roosville Formation 76

Rosa
  acicularis 321
  arkansana 321
  gymnocarpa 321
  nutkana 321
  woodsii 320
Rose-breasted grosbeak 664
Rose-root 403
Rosebay, Lapland 405
Roses, wild 320
Ross
  Creek Formation 149
  Lake Member 98
Rosy
  everlasting 370
  finch 648
Rotifers 486
Rough-legged hawk 603
Rough-stemmed boletus 443
Round-leaved orchid 343
Roundworms 486
Rowia 104
Rubber boa 564
Rubicapra 741
Rubus
  chamaemorus 322
  idaeus 321
  parviflorus 321
  pedatus 337, 374
Ruby-crowned kinglet 651
Ruby-throated
    hummingbird 663
Rudbeckia 357
Ruddy
  duck 583
  turnstone 663
Ruffed grouse 609
Rufous hummingbird 626
Rufous-sided towhee 664
Rumex 389
Rundle
  Group and related rocks
    142, 145p, 147p
  Mt. 19, 20p, 136, 137p,
    140, 142, 256p
  Rev. Robert 751
Running water, erosion by
    209
Rushes 416, 422
  toad 422
  wire 422
Rusophycus 90
Russet-scaly trich 445
Russian thistle 351
Russula
  aeriginea 447
  emetica 447
  xerampelina 447
Russula
  emetic 447
  shellfish/woodland 447
  tacky green 447
Rust, on wildflowers 382
Rusty blackbird 645
Rut, in deer 730
Rutter, Nat 189
Ryegrass 418
Rynchonellid brachiopods
    140
Rynchotrema 115

Sabine's gull 663
Sable, American 706
Saddle-shaped false morel
    454
Safety 801, 813
Sage, pasture 361
Sagebrush 319
  mariposa lily 377

Sagewort, cudweed/dragon
    389
Sailfin molly 556
Sailing at Maligne Lake
    246p
Saint
  Eugene Formation 187,
    188p
  George, Mt. 201p, 770
  Helens, Mt. 162, 227
  Helens, Mt., tephra from
    205
  Mary Lake 28, 29p, 73
  Mary River 167, 187
  Paul, Mt. 127, 770
Salamander
  blotched tiger 558
  eastern long-toed 559
Salix
  amygdaloides 307
  arctica 308
  barclayi 308
  barrattiana 308
  bebbiana 307
  brachycarpa 308
  candida 308
  caudata 308
  commutata 307
  discolor 307
  drummondiana 308
  exigua 308
  farriae 308
  glauca 308
  lasiandra 307
  maccalliana 307
  monticola 307
  myrtillifolia 308
  nivalis 308
  planifolia 307
  rigida 307
  scouleriana 307
  serissima 308
  vestita 308
Salmo
  aguabonita 542
  clarki 541
  gairdneri 540
  trutta 542
Salmon
  and trout 537
  run 539
  chinook/spring 539
  sockeye 537
Salmonberry 321
Salmonidae 537
Salpinctes obsoletus 653
Salsola kali 351
Salt-crystal casts 105p
Salter Member 144
Salvage logging 479
Salvelinus
  confluentus 544
  fontinalis 543
  malma 544
  namaycush 543
Sambucus
  cerulea 316
  racemosa 316
San Andreas Fault 176
Sand
  dunes 235p, 236
  wasp 475
Sandbar willow 308
Sanderling 663
Sandhill crane 588, 663
Sandpipers and other
    shorebirds 589
  Baird's 592
  buff-breasted 663

least 591
  pectoral 592
  semipalmated 592
  solitary 591
  spotted 590
  stilt 593
  upland 663
  western 663
Sandstone 89
  Blairmore Group 162,
    163p
  Brazeau Formation 165,
    166p
  Paskapoo Formation 165,
    166p
Sandwort, mountain 333
Sapsucker
  Williamson's 621
  yellow-bellied 620
Sara orangetip 499
Sarbach, Mt. 93
Sarcee 745
Sarsaparilla, wild 349
Saskatchewan Glacier 257,
    775
Saskatoon 324
Sassenach Formation 136
Satellite photos 2, 245
Saturniidae 527
Satyr anglewing 503
Satyridae 516
Satyrium
  acadica 524
  fulginosum 524
Satyrs 516
Saukia 109
Saussurea 408
Saussurea nuda 408
Savannah sparrow 659
Saw wort 408
Sawback Trail 781
Saxifraga
  bronchialis 334
  cernua 394
  hyperborea 394
  lyallii 394
  occidentalis 335
  oppositifolia 405
  tricuspidata 394
Saxifrage
  leather-leaved 334
  Lyall's 394
  nodding 394
  prickly/common/spotted
    334
  purple 405
  three-point 394
  western/false
    leather-leaved 335
Say's phoebe 663
Sayornis
  phoebe 663
  saya 663
Scaly tooth 444
Scaphites 165
Scathophaga stercoraria
    469
Scathophagidae 469
Scaup, lesser 580
Scats, pictures of 673
Sceliphron caementarium
    474
Scentless chamomile 358
Schäffer, Mary 148, 747p,
    760
Schist 79, 80p
Schist and gneiss erratics
    81
Schistosoma 535

Scirpus
  caespitosus 412
  validus 412
Sciuridae 688
Scleroderma citrinum 460
Scolytidae 478
Scopulorum juniper 318
Scorpionfly, snow 534
Scorpionweed 407
Scoter
  surf 582
  white-winged 582
Scottish thistle 388
Scouler's willow 307
Scouleria aquatica 432
Scouring-rushes 427
Scrapes and cuts 825
Scree slope, ecology of
    286p
Scuds 486
Sculpin
  slimy 554
  spoonhead 555
Scutellinia scutellata 459
Sea lilies 142
Sea-level fluctuations,
    Cretaceous 155
Seagulls 595
Season, blooming 290
Seaway, Cretaceous 155
Sedges 416, 420
Sedge-like horsetail 427
Sedum 362
Sedum
  roseum 403
  stenopetalum 362
Sego lily 329
Seismic lines 759
Seiurus
  aurocapillus 663
  novaboracensis 642
Sekani Indians 745
Selaginella densa 428
Selasphorus rufus 626
Self-heal 386
Selkirk Mountains 81
Selwyn
  Alfred 753
  Range 78, 81
Semi-anthracite coal 161
Semipalmated
  plover 590
  sandpiper 592
Semotilus margarita 551
Senecio
  canus 363
  triangularis 363
Sentinel
  Mtn. 195
  Pass 773
Serotonin 259
Serow 741
Serviceberry 324
Seton watching 567
Seton, Ernest Thompson
    567
Setophaga ruticilla 642
Shading, effect on local
    climate 251
Shaggy
  mane 444
  parasol 445
Shale 89
  basins 130
  belt 116
  Besa River/Perdrix 134,
    135p
  Burgess 98
  Exshaw 139

Fernie 158, 159p
  Glenogle 117, 119p
  Sullivan 106
  Stephen 98
Shangri-la 786
Shark Bay, Australia 74
Sharp-shinned hawk 600
Sharp-tailed
  grouse 663
  sparrow 664
Sheep
  moth, common 527
  bighorn 666p, 738
  Dall's (Stone's) 740
Shelf fungi 456
Shellfish russula 447
Shepherdia canadensis 312
Sheppard Formation 76
Sherbrooke Lake 804
Shiner
  redside 552
  spottail 553
Shingle-top 444
Shock from blood loss 819
Shooting star 372
Shorebirds 589
Short-billed dowitcher 663
Short-eared owl 663
Short-tailed weasel 704
Shortening across Rockies,
  amount of 174, 175d
Shoshoni 746
Shoveler, northern 575
Showy
  aster 387
  fleabane 387
  locoweed 379
  milkweed 375
Shrews 678
  dusky 679
  masked 679
  northern water 680
  pygmy 679
  vagrant 679
Shrike
  loggerhead 604
  northern 604
Shrimp, freshwater 486
Shrubs 289, 307
Shrubby
  potentilla/cinquefoil
    318
Shunda Formation 144
Shuswap
  Indians 746
  Metamorphic Complex
    81
Sialia
  currucoides 630
  mexicana 663
  sialis 663
Sibbaldia 400
Sibbaldia procumbens 400
Sickness, mountain 820
Sideswimmers 486
Siding 29 754
Siffleur River, Wilderness
  782
Sifton
  Formation 178, 186
  Pass 186
Sign (mammal) 667
Sikanni Chief 161
  River 164
Silene acaulis 402
Silica 148
Silky phacelia 407
Sills (geology) 75, 87, 151
Silt, glacial (see rock flour)

Siltstone 89, 157
  Nikanassin Formation
    161
  Sulphur Mtn. Formation
    156p, 157
Silver
  fox 719
  plant 401
Silver-bordered fritillary
  515
Silver-haired bat 677
Silverberry 312
Silverhorn 792
Silverweed 359
Silvery cortinarius 446
Silvery-violet cort 446
Simla
  Formation 135
  Mt. 136
Simpson
  Jimmy 754
  Pass 750
  Pass Thrust 22
  River 779
  Sir George 750
Simuliidae 471
Simulium 471, 488
Sinclair
  Canyon 25, 221
  James 751
  Pass 751
Single delight 335
Singleshot Mtn. 73
Sinking Ship, The 218
Sir
  Alexander, Mt. 91
  Douglas, Mt. 112
Siricidae 474
Siskin, pine 662
Sisyrinchium montanum
  377
Sitta
  canadensis 652
  carolinensis 663
  pygmaea 663
Sium suave 415
Siyeh
  Formation 74
  Pass, hike over 773
  Mt. 76
Ski area expansion 763
Ski-touring 8, 796, 797p
  equipment 796
  on Wapta Icefield 804p
  safety 801, 816
  technique for mountain
    trails 800
  trails, ratings of
    difficulty of 802
  trips 802
Skimmer, four-spot 493
Skink, western 565
Skins (skiing) 799
Skippers 520
  alpine checkered 521
  arctic 523
  common banded 520
  common checkered 522
  Draco 520
  Nevada 521
  two-banded checkered
    522
  woodland 521
Skoki
  Formation 112
  Lodge 784
  Mtn. 112
Skolithos 90
Skookumchuck 11, 27, 177

Skulls, mammal 668
Skunk
  bear 711
  striped 709
Skunkcabbage, yellow 412
Skunkweed 406
Sky pilot 406
Skyline Trail 781
Slate 25, 78, 80p
Slate-colored junco 655
Slaty cleavage 78
Sleet, erosion by 209
Slickensides 184, 185p
Slides of soft material 209
Slimy sculpin 554
Slimy-sheathed waxy cap
  450
Slippage along major
  strike-slip faults, rate
  of 177
Slumps 209
Small
  bog cranberry 372
  River 199
  winter stoneflies 533
Small-flowered
  everlasting 338
  rocket 363
  woodrush 422
Smallest mammal 679
Smallpox 746
Smartweed, water 413
Smerinthus cerisyi 526
Smilacina
  racemosa 330
  stellata 330
  trifolia 330
Smoky
  Group 165
  horntail 474
  polypore 458
Smooth
  alpine gentian 407
  brome 418
  ryegrass 418
Smythe, Mt. 36
Snails 535
  fossil 112, 164, 167
Snakes
  garter 563
  gopher 563
  western terrestrial
    garter/wandering
    garter 562
Snake Indian
  Formation 96
  River 184
  River 750
Snake Indians 746
Snakeweed 357
Snaring
  Indians 751
  karst 224p
Snipe, common 589
Snow
  avalanches 209, 817
  blowing over ridges
    256p
  bunting 658
  buttercup 399
  cranefly 534
  depth hoar 796, 817
  Dome 212
  firn line 792
  fleas 533
  goose 587
  lily/ 352
  maximum depth of 254
  mosquito 467

  organisms in 532
  rotten 817
  scorpionfly 534
  sublimation of 212
  sugar 817
  watermelon 532
  willow 308
  worms 533
Snowbank, ecology of 288p
Snowberry 324
  clearwing 526
  creeping 338
Snowblindness 801
Snowbowl 781
Snowbrush 314
Snowflakes, erosion by 209
Snowplow turn 800
Snowshoe hare 702
Snowslip Formation 76
Snowy owl 663
Soapberry 312
Sockeye 537
Sodalite 151
  Creek 150
Soil
  creep 209
  cryptogamic 275
  slumps 209
Solidago
  gigantea 364
  missouriensis 364
  multiradiata 402
  spathulata 364
Solifluction 209
Solitaire, Townsend's 629
Solitary sandpiper 591
Solomon's-seal 330
  false 330
Solorina crocea 438
Somatochlora 493
Sonar, in bats 675
Sonchus arvensis 356
Song sparrow 660
Songs of birds 571
Soopolallie 312
Sora 588
Sorbus
  scopulina 316
  sitchensis 316
Soredia 436
Sorefoot Lake 753
Sorex
  cinereus 679
  monticolus 679
  palustris 680
  vagrans 679
Soricidae 678
Sorrel, mountain 398
South Boundary Trail 781
Southern red-backed vole
  684
Southern Rockies
  foothills of 28
  highest point in 30
  mountain front in 28
  physiography of 27
  summary of features 30
  timberline elevation in
    30
Southern Rocky Mountain
  Trench floor, ecology
  of 273p
Southern-foothills meadow
  or grassland, ecology
  of 274p
Southesk
  Earl of 752
  Formation 132

Pass 781
Reef 134
River 132, 781
Sow thistle 356
Spalling 209
Spanish moss 435
Sparassis radicata 456
Sparganium angustifolium 412
Sparrow's-egg orchid 341
Sparrows 654
  American tree 664
  Baird's 664
  Brewer's 658
  chipping 656
  clay-colored 658
  fox 661
  golden-crowned 657
  grasshopper 664
  Harris' 664
  house 654
  LeConte's 660
  Lincoln's 660
  savannah 659
  sharp-tailed 664
  song 660
  swamp 664
  vesper 659
  white-crowned 656
  white-throated 657
Sparrowhawk 599
Spawning 537
Spear grass 419
Speckled
  alder 313
  char 543
Speculum 575
Speedwell 382
  alpine 404
Spermophilus
  columbianus 692
  lateralis 689
  richardsonii 691
  tridecemlineatus 690
Sperry Chalet 783
Speyeria
  aphrodite 512
  atlantis 513
  callippe 512
  cybele 513
  edwardsii 512
  hydaspe 513
  mormonia 513
  zerene 512
Sphagnum 431
Sphecidae 474
Sphingidae 526
Sphinx moth
  Cerisy's 526
  big poplar 526
Sphragis 499
Sphyrapicus
  thyroideus 621
  varius 620
Spicules 148
Spiculite 146
Spiders 483
  American house 483
  branch-tip 483
  goldenrod 484
  jumping 485
  wolf 484
Spike trisetum 417
Spikemoss 428
Spiraea
  betulifolia 326
  densiflora 326
Spiral Tunnels 754
Spiranthes romanzoffiana 342

Spirea
  meadow 395
  pink 326
  white 326
Spirifer rowleyi 140
Spiriferid brachiopods 140
Spirodela polyrhiza 410
Spiza americana 664
Spizella
  arborea 664
  breweri 658
  pallida 658
  passerina 656
Splake 544
Spokane Formation 74
Sponge
  mushroom 453
  spicules 148
Sponges 146
Spongiporus leucospongia 457
Spoonhead sculpin 555
Spore print 442
Spores, fossilized 160
Sporophyte 429
Spottail shiner 553
Spotted
  coral-root 354
  frog 561
  frog 561
  orchid 343
  sandpiper 590
  saxifrage 334
Sprague Creek 783
Sprague's pipit 663
Spray
  Lake 112
  Lakes Group 149
  River 157
  River Group 156p, 157
Spread-winged skippers 521
Spreading
  dogbane 325
  phlox 402
Spreadwings 493
Spring
  azure 507
  beauty, alpine 393
  beauty, western 332
  largest measured 225
  salmon 539
  sunflower 356
  white 498
Springs, hot (see hot springs)
Springtails 533
Spruce
  brooms on 298p
  grouse 610
  black 297
  Engelmann 297
  white 297
Spruce-bog alpine 519
Squashberry 326
Squawfish, northern 550
Squirrel
  midden 695
  northern flying 696
  red 695
St. (see Saint)
Stairstep moss 430
Stanley
  Glacier Trail, 802, 817
  Mitchell Hut 784
Star-flowered Solomon's-seal 330
Starfish 142
Starlight Member 158
Starling, European 631

Starwort 333
  alpine 393
Steamboats in Rocky Mountain Trench 754
Steelhead 540
Stelgidopteryx serripennis 615
Stellaria 333
  monantha 393
Steller's
  jay 625
  rock brake 423
Stellula calliope 626
Stemmatoceras 160
Stenanthium occidentale 350
Stenanthium, western 350
Stephen
  Formation 98, 101
  George 754
  Mt. 98, 101
Stephen-Dennis Fault 101
Sterco 165
Stercorarius
  longicaudus 663
  parasiticus 663
Stereocaulon
  paschale 438
  tomentosum 438
Sterna
  forsteri 663
  hirundo 597
Stevens, John 757
Stickleback, brook 555
Stickseed 382
Sticky
  currant 322
  geranium 381
Stiff clubmoss 428
Stilt sandpiper 593
Stinging nettle 351
Stings of bees, wasps and hornets 475
Stipa comata 419
Stoat 704
Stoddart Group 146
Stone
  Formation, Mtn. 127
  Range 770
Stone's sheep 740
Stonecat 547
Stonecrop 362
Stoneflies, small winter 533
Stonefly naiad 488
Stoney Indians 746, 747p
Storelk Formation 149
Storms and lightning 814
Stover, Frank 755
Stratigraphy
  basic concepts of 39
  of the Rockies 37
Strawberry, wild 337
Streams
  erosion caused by 209
  sub-glacial 214
Streptopus amplexifolius 350
Stridulating 480
Strike-slip faults 176
Strip-mining for coal 161, 163p, 754
Striped
  coral-root 354
  skunk 709
Strix
  nebulosa 606
  varia 607
Stromatolites 74, 75d
Stromatoporoids 128

in Nonda Formation 116
  labechid 139
Stropharia
  ambigua 449
  coronilla 450
Stropharia, questionable 449
Structural
  control 108
  geology in Canadian Rockies 180
Strymon melinus 504
Sturgeon, white 546
Sturnella neglecta 644
Sturnus vulgaris 631
Style of Canadian Rockies 1
Sub-Devonian unconformity 120, 121d
Sub-glacial streams 199d, 214
Subalpine
  fir 298
  forest, lower 280p
  larch 302
  meadow 255, 281
  woods, upper 281p
  zone 268
Subduction 168, 174
Sublimation 212
Subsidence of continental margin, reason for 71
Substrate 265
Succulent plants 362
Suckers 548
  largescale 549
  longnose 548
  mountain 549
  white 548
Suctorians 486
Suillus 444
Suillus tomentosus 444
Sukunka River 140
Sullivan Formation, Peak 106
Sulphides 227
Sulphur
  in hot springs water 227
  Mtn. Formation 156p, 157
  Mtn. 157, 753
  plant 366
  shelf 457
Sulphurs (butterflies) 499
  blueberry 499
  common 501
  great northern 501
  greenland 500
  Labrador 500
  Mead's 500
  palaeno 500
  pink-edged 500
  Queen Alexandra's 501
Summary of
  creation of Canadian Rockies 179
  climate 247
  geography and geology 3
  mountain-building sequence 178
  central Rockies features 26
  southern Rockies features 30
  northern Rockies features 36
Summit
  Lake (northern Rockies) 32, 34

Index (d-diagram, m-map, p-photo, t-table)

Lake (Waterton) 770
Mtn. 28
regions, ecology of 283p
Sun angle, effect on
climate 251
Sunburn 825
Sundew 340
Sundogs 253
Sunrift Gorge 773
Sunshine (place) 281
Meadows 779
Ski Area expansion 763
Sunwapta
Falls 219
Pass 95, 255, 281, 807
River 216, 231
Warden Station 113
Supergroup (geology) 71
Surf scoter 582
Surnia ulula 607
Surprise Creek Cabin 784
Survey Formation, Peak
110
Suspended load of stream
209
Swainson's
hawk 603
thrush 628
Swallow
bank 615
barn 613
cliff 613
northern rough-winged
615
tree 614
violet-green 614
Swallowtails 502
anise 502
eastern tiger 502
Old-World 503
two-tailed tiger 502
western tiger 502
Swamp
birds 587
gas 431
laurel 373
mosses 431
sparrow 664
Swan, tundra 587
Sweet
cicely 343
cicely, western 349
clover, yellow 364
pea, wild 340
Sweet-flowered androsace
332
Sweetgrass 419
Sweetvetch 379
pale 368
Swift
Creek 539, 770
black 616
Jonathan 486
Lewis 756
Vaux's 616
Swiftcurrent
Creek 539, 759
Icefield 212
Swimmer's itch 535
Switzer Provincial Park
570
Swordtail 556
Sydney Vallance Hut 786
Symbiosis 435
Sympetrum 493
Symphoricarpos
albus 324
occidentalis 324
Synaptomys borealis 687

Syncline 184
Syringa 327
Syringopora 132
Syrphidae 473

Tabanidae 470
Tables
climate data 248
conversion, metric to
American units:
inside front cover
day length 252
formations and groups
(geology) 42
glacial periods 189
hot springs data 228
population data 766
Tachycineta
bicolor 614
thalassina 614
Tacky green russula 447
Taiga 649
Tailed frog 561
Takakkaw Falls 219, 769
Talbot Lake, birding at 570
Tall
delphinium 385
larkspur 385
lungwort 384
Tallest tree species in
Canadian Rockies 292
Talus or rockslide, ecology
of 286p
Tamiasciurus hudsonicus
695
Tamarack 303
Tanager, western 643
Tangle Ridge 106, 111
Tansy 344
Tape grass 557
Taraxacum 399
officinale 354
Tardigrades 486
Tarragon, false 389
Tattler, wandering 663
Taxidea taxus 709
Taxus brevifolia 318
Teal
bluewinged 577
cinnamon 577
green-winged 576
Tear faults 182, 183d
Teardrop 794
Technique for ski-touring
800
Tectonics
plate 168, 169d
Miocene 187
recent 186
Tegart Formation, Mt. 115
Tekarra (Indian guide) 752
Lake 781
Telemark turn 800
Telephone numbers for
national parks (see
National parks)
Telesonix 405
Telesonix heucheriformis
405
Telford Formation 149
Temperature
data for the Rockies
248t
increase with depth
underground 225
inversion 254, 255
in Canadian Rockies
250m
Temple, Mt. 757

Ten Peaks, Valley of the
88, 768p, 769
Tennessee warbler 641
Tent City 761
Tents for backpacking 776
Tentaculites 134
Tephra 205, 206p, 227
Terminal Range 115
Tern
black 598
common 597
Forster's 663
Terraces, kame 198p, 199d
Terranes 46d, 170, 176
Terrestrial sediments 153
Tertiary deposits 188p
Testing carbonate rocks
with acid 98
Tête Jaune 750
Cache 750
Tetracycline 482
Tetragnatha 484
Tetsa
Formation 77
River 32, 33p, 770
Thalictrum
occidentale 348
venulosum 348
Thamnolia vermicularis
437
Thamnophis
elegans 562
sirtalis 563
Thamnopora 131, 132
Thayer's gull 663
Thermopsis rhombifolia
364
Thetis clearwing 526
Thickness
of deposits in Rocky
Mountain Trough 153
of rock in the Rockies 3
Thimbleberry 321
Thin-leaved owl-clover 368
Thinleaf alder 313
Thirteen-lined ground
squirrel 690
Thistle
bull/Scottish 388
Canada 388
Russian 351
sow 356
Thomas (Indian guide) 749
Thomomys talpoides 694
Thompson, David 748
Thorax, of insects 468
Thorybes pylades 523
Three Isle Lake 778
Three Sisters 139
Three-flowered avens 370
Three-leaved Solomon's-seal
330
Three-point saxifrage 394
Three-toed woodpecker 619
Three-tooth mitrewort 382
Thrombolites 108, 110
Thrushes 627
gray-cheeked 663
hermit 628
Swainson's 628
varied 627
Thrust
Lewis 12, 27, 186
McConnell 16, 180, 181p
Simpson Pass 22
Thrust faulting 16
amount of shortening
accomplished by 174
of young rock over older
(apparent) 180

sequence 176
Thrust faults 16, 17d, 175d,
181pd, 183d
cutting up-section 182
low-angle 180
relationship to folds
181d, 182
Thuidium abietinum 433
Thuja plicata 301
Thunderstorms 814
and flash floods 22
safe and unsafe places
during 815d
Thymallus arcticus 544
Tiarella unifoliata 345
Tick
fever 482
Rocky Mountain wood
464p, 481
Ticklegrass 419
Tiger
lily 352
salamander 558
trout 543
Till (glacial) 189, 190p,
194p, 200
Tillandsia usneoides 435
Tillite 189
Timber oatgrass 420
Timberline elevation
in central Rockies 26
in northern Rockies 36
in southern Rockies 30
Timberline trees 282p, 328
Time of year for flowers
290
Times of occurrence, birds
571
Timing of events in
forming Canadian
Rockies 179
Timothy 417
Tintina Trench 11
Tipperary Lake, Quartzite
112
Tipula 468
Tipulidae 468, 534
Titanaugite 150
Titania's fritillary 514
Titanites occidentalis 160
Titanium 150
Titkana Formation 104
Toad
American/Canadian 559
Formation 158
River 36
rush 422
western/boreal 559
Toadflax
bastard 348
yellow 365
Tobermory Formation 149
Toe-biter 490
Tofieldia
glutinosa 343
pusilla 343
Tomenthypnum 409
nitens 431
Tonquin Valley
hiking to 779
outfitter's camps 786
Top of the World
Provincial Park 783
Topographic maps 245
Topographic relief
in central Rockies 19
in northern Rockies 32
in southern Rockies 28
Tortoiseshell, Milbert's 495

Index (d-diagram, m-map, p-photo, t-table)   873

Tortula ruralis 433
Tourists 6
Tourniquet 819d
Tower of Babel 790
Towhee, rufous-sided 664
Townsend's
    solitaire 629
    warbler 639
Townsendia 376
Townsendia
    hookeri 376
    parryi 376
Trachyte 162
Tracks
    Animal 673
    Fossil 67
Tragopogon
    dubius 355
    pratensis 355
Trail
    Avalanche Lake 772
    Bald Hills 775, 802
    Berg Lake 779
    bicycling 810
    Boom Lake 802
    Carthew 773
    Cavell Meadows 775
    of the Cedars 773
    Cephren Lake and
        Cirque Lake 773
    Creek 27, 138
    Fenland 568
    Great Divide 782
    Gunsight Pass 778
    Healy Pass 803
    Ink Pots 773, 802
    Jonas Shoulder 779
    Kananaskis passes 778
    Lake Agnes 773, 774p
    Larch Valley 773
    Mt. Assiniboine 777p,
        779
    network at Jasper 775
    Nigel Pass 779
    Old Fort Point 775
    Opabin Plateau 773
    Overlander 775
    Paradise Valley 24
    Parker Ridge 775
    Path of the Glacier 775
    Plain of Six Glaciers
        773, 802
    plant 345
    Poboktan Creek 779,
        780p
    Redearth Creek 803
    Sawback 782
    Sentinel Pass 773
    Siyeh Pass 773
    Skyline 781
    Stanley Glacier 802
    Tonquin Valley 779
    Valley of the Five Lakes
        775
Trailing raspberry 337
Traill's flycatcher 635
Trametes versicolor 458
Tramways 770
TransCanada Highway 760,
    762
    physiography seen along
        16
Trapper's tea 319
Traveler's joy 331
Tree swallow, American
    614
Trees 292
    at timberline 328
    definition of 289

oldest 292
shortest 292
stunted 328
tallest species 292
Tree-ear 459
Treefrog, Pacific 562
Trellis drainage 21
Trembling aspen 303
Tremeila mesenterica 459
Trench-foot 823
Trich, russet-scaly 445
Trichapum biformis 458
Tricholoma vaccinum 445
Trifolium
    hybridum 369
    repens 340
    pratense 368
Triglochin maritima 413
Trillium 329
Trillium ovatum 329
Trimerotropis pallidipennis
    479
Tringa
    flavipes 593
    melanoleuca 593
    solitaria 591
Trinity Lakes Member 98
Trisetum spicatum 417
Troglodytes
    aedon 653
    troglodytes 652
Trollius albiflorus 391
Tropical fish at the Banff
    Hot Springs 556
Trout
    brook 543
    brown 542
    bull 544
    cutthroat 541
    Dolly Varden 544
    golden 542
    lake 543
    rainbow 540
    River 36
    tiger 543
Trout-perch 556
Trutch Viewpoint 770
Truxler, Agnes 762
Tryngites subruficollis 663
Tsuga heterophylla 301
Tuchodi Formation 77
Tufa 227
Tuff 227
Tule 412
Tulostoma simulans 461
Tumbler Ridge 161, 164,
    755
Tumbleweed 351
Tundra swan 587
Turbidites 83, 84d
    in Chancellor Formation
        117
    in Prophet Formation
        146
Turbidity currents 83
Turbine Canyon 779
Turdus migratorius 627
Turkey
    tail 458
    vulture 663
Turner Valley 759
    Formation 144
Turnstone, ruddy 663
Turtle Mountain 216, 759
Turtle, painted 564
Tussock moth,
    white-marked 526
Twayblade 371
Twenty-dollar bill, scene
    on 809

Twin Falls Chalet 784
Twinberry, black 325
    red 325
Twinflower 338
Twining honeysuckle 326
Twisted stalk 350
Two O'clock Creek
    Campground 570
Two-banded checkered
    skipper 522
Two-tailed tiger
    swallowtail 502
Tympanuchus phasianellus
    663
Type section (geology) 109
Typha latifolia 411
Tyrannus
    tyrannus 634
    verticalis 663
Tyrwhitt Formation 149

Uhler's arctic 517
Ulysses, Mt. 36
Umbilicaria
    krascheninnikovii 440
Umbrella plant 366
Unconformities 120, 121d
Underground temperature
    225
Underwater landslides 83
Unglaciated places 193
United States Geological
    Survey 28
Unweighted turn 800
Unwin, Sidney 760
Up-piling as main cause of
    Rockies 174
Upchuck, fairy 439
Upland sandpiper 663
Uplift
    at end of Devonian 138
    Devonian 128
    Early Cretaceous 155
    Late Cretaceous and
        Early Tertiary 155
    Late Permian or Early
        Triassic 152
    Middle Jurassic 153
    Miocene 187
    of the Galton Range 178
    Permian 145
Upper
    Kananaskis Lake 112
    subalpine woods, ecology
        of 281p
    Waterton Lake 198p
Upslope weather 253
Urocerus 474
Ursidae 720
Ursus
    americanus 720
    arctos 722
Urtica dioica 351
Urtite 150
Using the
    bird listings 570
    botany listings 289
    geological listings 70
Usnea 435
Utah honeysuckle 325
Utopia Mountain 132
Utricularia vulgaris 411

Vaccinium
    caespitosum 323
    membranaceum 323
    myrtillus 323
    occidentale 323
    scoparium 369
    vitis-idaea 369

Vagrant shrew 679
Valenciennes Creek 87
Valerian 345
Valeriana
    dioica 345
    sitchensis 345
Valley
    of the Five Lakes 775
    of the Rocks 779
    of the Ten Peaks 88,
        757, 768p, 769
Valley-depth difference
    between eastern and
        western slope 24
Valleys, hanging 219
Vallisneria spirilis 557
Van Horne, William
    Cornelius 755
Vanessa
    anabella 524
    atalanta 496
    cardui 496
Varied thrush 627
Vaux's swift 616
Vaux, George and William
    761
    Mary 24, 760
    Mt. 24
Vavasour, Mervin 751
Veery 629
Vegetation, map of 264m
Veined white 497
Veins of quartz 83
Velvet, antler 731
Vent (in snakes) 558
Venus's-slipper 371
Veratrum viride 350
Verbascum thapsus 366
Verdant Pass 779
Vermilion
    Lakes 278, 568, 745
    Pass 284, 752
Vermilion Pass burn 570
Vermivora
    celata 640
    peregrina 641
    ruficapilla 663
Veronica 382
    alpine 404
Veronica
    americana 382
    catenata 382
    peregrina 382
    wormskjoldii 404
Vesper sparrow 659
Vespertilionidae 675
Vespidae 472
Vespula 472
    maculata 473
Vetch, wild 378
Vetchling 340
Viburnum
    edule 326
    trilobum 315
Vicia americana 378
Victoria
    Cross Range 88
    Mt. 100, 792
Viola
    adunca 384
    canadensis 336
    glabella 352
    nuttallii 353
    orbiculata 352
Violet
    toothed polypore 458
    early blue 384
    western Canada 336
    yellow mountain 352
    yellow prairie 353

Violet-green swallow 614
Vireo
  gilvus 637
  olivaceous 637
  philadelphicus 663
  solitarius 637
Vireo
  Philadelphia 663
  red-eyed 637
  solitary 637
  warbling 637
Virginia rail 663
Visitor activities 6
Voices of birds 571
Volcanic
  dust/ash/tephra 174, 205, 206p
  eruption, effect on weather 227
  mountains 170
  pipes 87
  rock 162
Volcanoes 87, 151, 155, 162
Vole
  heather 685
  long-tailed 686
  meadow 685
  northern red-backed 684
  Richardson's water 686
  southern red-backed/Gapper's 684
Voyageurs 749
Vulpes vulpes 719
Vulture
  Glacier 804
  Glacier, cave in 215p
  turkey 663

Wake-robin 329
Walcott, Charles 98, 761
Wallflower 363
  alpine purple 405
Wandering tattler 663
Wapiabi Formation 165
Wapiti 732
  Formation 165
Wapta
  Icefield 24, 210, 804
  Lake 22
Waputik Icefield 24, 210, 804
Warbler
  Audubon's 640
  bay-breasted 663
  black-and-white 663
  black-throated gray 663
  black-throated green 663
  blackpoll 641
  Canada 663
  Cape May 663
  MacGillivray's 639
  magnolia 641
  myrtle 640
  Nashville 663
  orange-crowned 640
  palm 663
  Tennessee 641
  Townsend's 639
  Wilson's 638
  yellow 638
  yellow-rumped 640
Warbling vireo 637
Warre, James 751
Warren, Billy 747p, 760
Wasatchites 158
Wasooth Creek, Slabs 787
Wasp, sand/digger 475

Water
  arum 414
  beetles 489
  birch 314
  boatmen 490
  bugs 489, 490
  crowfoot 414
  fleas 486
  hemlock 415
  insects 486
  knotweed 413
  lily 414
  mosses 409
  parsnip 415
  pipit 595
  plants 409
  rat 700
  shrew, northern 680
  smartweed 413
  striders 491
  vole, Richardson's 686
Water-milfoil, Eurasian 410
Water-plantain, broad-leaved 413
Waterfalls 163p, 220p, 219
  climbing frozen 794, 795p
Waterfowl (section includes duck-like birds as well as ducks, geese and swans) 572
  Formation 106
  Lakes 106
Watermelon snow 532
Waterthrush, northern 642
Waterfalls 163p, 219, 220p, 769
Waterton
  area, exploration of 752
  Formation 72
  glacial features of 199d
  Lakes National Park 752
  townsite 773
  windiness at 260
Waterton/Glacier area, physiography of 27
Wates-Gibson Hut 786
Watinoceras 165
Watridge Lake 225
Watt Mountain Break 128
Wave-lapping, erosion by 209
Waxwing
  bohemian 633
  cedar 633
Waxy cap, slimy-sheathed 450
Weasel
  least 705
  long-tailed 705
  short-tailed 704
Weather
  affected by volcanic eruptions 227
  and climate 4, 247, 248t
  effect of continental divide on 257
  in Colorado Rockies, comparison 253
  pattern, annual 260
  prediction 262
Weathering
  chemical 209
  mechanical 209
Wedge Lake 184
Weeping Wall 139, 769, 794, 795p
Weirdest rock in the Rockies 146

Wenkchemna Peak 757
Wenkchemnia 95
West Alberta Ridge 45d, 120, 128
Western
  anemone 391
  bluebird 663
  Canada violet 336
  clematis 331
  Cordillera 11
  flycatcher 636
  gall rust 294
  giant ichneumon 474
  giant puffball 460
  grebe 573
  hemlock 301
  Jacob's ladder 383
  jumping mouse 683
  kingbird 663
  larch 302
  lousewort 365
  main ranges 24
  meadowlark 644
  pine elfin 505
  ranges 25
  red cedar 301
  sandpiper 663
  saxifrage 335
  screech owl 663
  skink 565
  slope of northern Rockies 34
  Solomon's-seal 330
  spring beauty 332
  stenanthium 350
  sweet cicely 349
  tailed blue 506
  tanager 643
  terrestrial garter snake 562
  tiger swallowtail 502
  toad 559
  white 498
  white pine 295
  willow aster 347
  wood lily 352
  wood-peewee 636
  yellow-jacket 472
  yew 318
Wetlands
  Cottonwood Slough 570
  ecology of 278p
  Fenland trail 568
Wheeler, A.O. 760
Whelp 719
Whiplash willow 308
Whirlpool
  Point 91
  River 752
Whirlygig beetles 490
Whistler (marmot) 693
Whistlers, The 234, 283, 570, 693
White
  admiral 495
  angelica 344
  birch 305
  butterflies 497
  cabbage 497
  camas 331
  clover 340
  draba 333
  dryas 393
  heather 396
  lettuce 339
  Man Mtn. 106
  Man Pass 751
  mariposa lily 329
  meadowsweet 326

mountain avens 393
pelican, American 663
phlox 336
pussytoes 338
rhododendron 327
spirea 326
spongy polypore 457
spruce 297
sturgeon 546
sucker 548
sweet clover 340
water crowfoot 414
wildflowers 329, 391
Whyte, Mt. 95
Whites (butterflies) 497
  spring 498
  veined 497
  western 498
White-breasted nuthatch 663
White-crowned sparrow 656
White-lined green hairstreak 504
White-marked tussock moth 526
  caterpillar 529
White-spruce forest, ecology of 275p
White-tailed
  deer 731
  jackrabbit 702
  ptarmigan 611
White-throated sparrow 657
White-veined arctic 517
White-winged
  crossbill 647
  scoter 582
Whitebark pine 296
Whitefaces (dragonflies) 493
Whitefish
  lake (fish) 545
  mountain 545
  pygmy 545
  Range 12, 27, 138
Whitehorse
  Creek 158
  Formation 157
Whitlow-grass 333
  yellow 362
Whortleberry 323
Whymper, Edward 759
Width of Canadian Rockies 1
Wigeon
  American 576
  European 663
Wilcox
  Pass 108, 216
  Walter 756
Wild
  bergamot 369
  blue flax 384
  buckwheat 366
  calla 414
  chive 378
  choke cherry 315
  gaillardia 357
  gooseberry 322
  licorice 350
  lupine 379
  mint 386
  raspberry 321
  roses 320
  sarsaparilla 349
  strawberry 337
  sweet pea 340
  vetch 378
  white geranium 332

Index (d-diagram, m-map, p-photo, t-table)

Wildcat 713
Wilderness preservation 829
Wildflowers 329
above timberline
(alpine) 391
below timberline 329
blue or purple 377, 404
drab, odd colors 389, 397
greenish 348, 397
red or pink 368, 402
yellow or orange 352,
398
white 329, 391
Wileman Member 144
Williamson's sapsucker 621
Williston Lake 87, 177, 186,
270, 763, 769
Willmore
Wilderness Park 762
Norman 762
Willow
Creek Formation 167
flycatcher 635
ptarmigan 612
Willow-herb
broad-leaved 373
dwarf 375
Willows 307
Wilmer Wildlife Refuge
273, 568, 767
Wilson's
phalarope 594
warbler 638
Wilson
Mt. 108, 115p, 210
Tom 754
Wilsonia
canadensis 663
pusilla 638
Wind
catabatic 255
chinook 257
erosion by 209
direction, effect on
weather 255
glacial 255
Tower 139
Windermere Supergroup 78,
86
Windflower 334
Windiness at
Waterton/Glacier 260
Window (geology) 28
Windsor Mtn. Formation
94, 100
Windy Point 100, 104
Winnowing 589
Winter wren 652

Wintergreen
common pink 370
creeping 338
lesser 394
one-flowered 335
one-sided 348
Wire rush 422
Wisconsinan glaciation 196
Witch's
broom 294, 298p
butter 459
Wokkpash Creek,
Formation 123
Wolf
gray 717
lichen 436
spider 484
willow 312
Wolfberry 324
Wolverine 710
Wonah Formation 113
Wonder Pass 779
Wood
betony 365
duck 584
frog 560
rat, bushy tailed 682
River 11, 177
tick 481
Wood-nymph
dark 516
large 516
Wood-peewee, western 636
Woodchuck 693
Woodland
russula 447
skipper 521
Woodpeckers 517
black-backed 620
downy 619
hairy 618
Lewis's 621
pileated 618
three-toed 619
Woodrush, small-flowered
422
Woodsia
oregana 424
scopulina 425
Woodsia
cliff 425
northwestern 424
Woolley
fleabane 395
gromwell 358
Herman 756
Woollybear caterpillar 528
moth 527

World Heritage Site
(Burgess Shale) 98
Worm burrows, fossilized
90, 92p, 97, 160
Worms, snow/ice 533
Wormwood
alpine 397
pasture 361
Wren
house 653
marsh 663
rock 653
winter 652
Wrigglers 486
Würm glaciation 192

Xanthocephalus
xanthocephalus 644
Xanthoria elegans 439
Xema sabini 663
Xeromphalina campanella
450
Xerophyllum tenax 343
Xiphophorus helleri 556
Xylaria polymorpha 455

Ya-Ha-Tinda 745
Yahatinda Formation,
Ranch 127
Yamnuska Mtn. 16, 18p,
100, 165, 180, 789
fault at base of cliff
(McConnell Thrust)
181p
Yarrow 344
Yellow
alfalfa 364
avens 360
beard-tongue 354
butterflies 499
columbine 361
dryas 361
lady's-slipper 353
monkey-flower 353
morel 453
mountain avens 361
mountain violet 352
paintbrush 365
paintbrush, alpine 402
penstemon 354
pine chipmunk 689
pond lily 414
prairie violet 353
puccoon 358
rabbit ears 458
rail 663
rocket 362
salsify 355

skunkcabbage 412
sweet clover 364
toadflax 365
warbler 638
water crowfoot 414
wildflowers 352, 398
Yellow-bellied
flycatcher 663
sapsucker 620
Yellow-headed blackbird
644
Yellow-jacket, western 472
Yellow-rumped warbler 640
Yellowhead (Pierre
Bostonais) 750
Highway 762
Lake 79
Pass 750, 753, 761, 762
Yellowlegs
greater 593
lesser 593
Yellowstone National Park
753
bear problems in 724
Yellowthroat, common 639
Yew 318
Yoho
Blow 257
National Park 150, 755
River 24
Valley 24
York Factory 750
Young clastic unit 38, 152
Younge, Peter 753
Youth hostels 805, 806mt

Zacanthoides 98
Zapus
hudsonius 683
princeps 683
Zenaida macroura 632
Zerene fritillary 512
Zinc Mtn. 150
Zone
alpine 268
of ablation 212
of accumulation 212
subalpine 268
Zones, life 266
Zonotrichia
albicollis 657
atricapilla 657
leucophrys 656
querula 664
Zygadenus
elegans 331
venenosus 331

This book was written, edited and typeset on a TRS-80 Model 4P microcomputer, using the *Allwrite* word processing program and a Hewlett Packard LaserJet printer. The type is 11-point Times Roman reduced photographically to about nine points. The paper is 33-lb Century Opaque Litho. The cover is Kivar.

Notes

Notes

For making paper airplanes